Second Canadian Edition

HUMAN GEOGRAPHY

LANDSCAPES OF HUMAN ACTIVITIES

JEROME D. FELLMANN
University of Illinois, Urbana-Champaign

ARTHUR GETIS
San Diego State University

JUDITH GETIS

DAN SHRUBSOLE
University of Western Ontario

JEFF HOPKINS
University of Western Ontario

 **McGraw-Hill Ryerson**

Toronto   Montréal   Boston   Burr Ridge, IL   Dubuque, IA   Madison, WI   New York
San Francisco   St. Louis   Bangkok   Bogotá   Caracas   Kuala Lumpur   Lisbon   London
Madrid   Mexico City   Milan   New Delhi   Santiago   Seoul   Singapore   Sydney   Taipei

ISBN-13: 978-0-07-097005-2
ISBN-10: 0-07-097005-X

1 2 3 4 5 6 7 8 9 10 QPD 0 9

Printed and bound in the USA.

Care has been taken to trace ownership of copyright material contained in this text; however, the publisher will welcome any information that enables them to rectify any reference or credit for subsequent editions.

Vice-President and Editor-in-Chief: *Joanna Cotton*
Executive Sponsoring Editor: *Leanna MacLean*
Marketing Manager: *Mary Costello*
Developmental Editor: *Jennifer Oliver*
Editorial Associate: *Stephanie Hess*
Supervising Editor: *Jessica Barnoski*
Copy Editor: *Sarah Powell*
Team Lead, Production: *Jennifer Hall*
Permissions Editor/Photo Researcher: *My Editor Inc.*
Cover Design: *Dave Murphy*
Cover Image: *Darwin Wiggett*
Interior Design: *Dave Murphy*
Page Layout: *Laserwords Private Limited*
Printer: *Quebecor Printing Dubuque*

Library and Archives Canada Cataloguing in Publication

Human geography : landscapes of human activities / Jerome D. Fellmann . . . [et al.].–2nd Canadian ed.

Includes index.
ISBN 978-0-07-097005-2

1. Human geography–Textbooks. 2. Human geography–Canada–Textbooks. I. Fellmann, Jerome Donald, 1926-

GF41.H89 2009   304.2   C2008-907834-9

Brief Contents

Contents

Part One

Some Key Themes in the Study of Human Geography 29

Two

The World in Spatial Terms—Geographic Research and Maps 30

Three

Geographic Perspectives on Space 58

Part Three

Dynamic Spaces of Cities and Economies 247

Eight

Urban Systems and Urban Structures 248

Nine

Livelihood and Economy: Primary Activities 296

Part Four

Human–Environment Interactions 411

Twelve

Human Impacts on Natural Systems and Human Health 412

Online Chapter

Available at **www.mcgrawhill.ca/olc/fellmann**:
Geographies of Gender: Feminism and Masculinities

List of Boxes

List of Boxes *continued...*

Chapter 10

Chapter 11

Chapter 12

Preface

Human Geography: Landscapes of Human Activities, second Canadian edition, introduces readers to the scope and excitement of geography, and establishes its relevance in their daily lives and in their roles as informed citizens. We recognize that for many students, human geography may be the first and only contact with geography, and that this is their first and only textbook in the discipline. For those students particularly, we seek to convey the richness and breadth of human geography and to give insight into the nature and intellectual challenges of the field of geography itself. Our goals are to be inclusive in content, current in data, and relevant in interpretations. These goals are elusive. We therefore depend on feedback and a continuing partnership with classroom instructors to provide the currency of information and the interpretation of new patterns of human geographic substance that changing conditions demand.

Organization

This text can be easily read in a one-term course. The emphasis on human geographic current events and interpretation builds on our initial obligation to set the stage in the first three chapters. Chapter 1 briefly introduces students to the scope and background basics of geography as a discipline. The major traditions in geographic research are described, as are some of its major philosophies, and the development of the discipline in Europe and Canada. Examples of geographic questions related to a range of topical issues are also presented.

Part One, comprising Chapters 2 and 3, establishes a sense of how geographic research is conducted, and introduces the basic tools of geographic research, particularly maps. Chapter 2 offers a more detailed treatment of map characteristics, map projections and descriptions of GIS, remote sensing, and mental maps; and draws on the Census of Canada, an invaluable secondary source of data. Chapter 3 describes some of the major concepts that support geographic research with a focus on globalization, which is new for the second Canadian edition. Subsequent chapters refer back to portions of this chapter where appropriate.

Chapters 4 through 7 comprise Part Two and examine four traditional foci of geographic inquiry: population, culture, social, and political. Chapter 4 introduces various kinds of data, measurements, and models used by population geographers to identify and interpret population distributions, densities, and future projections. New to the second Canadian edition is the more detailed treatment of migration in this chapter. Chapter 5 explains the

many characteristics and processes inherent in the concepts of culture and landscape, and provides the basis for Chapters 6 and 7, which illustrate the many social identities, spaces, and boundaries created and practised by people.

Part Three consists of Chapters 8 through 11, and attends to economic forces that are shaping human societies and landscapes and urban settlements. Chapter 8 looks specifically at urban systems, patterns, and structures. Chapter 9 reviews primary economic activities (e.g., agriculture, fishing, forestry, and mining), while Chapter 10 delves into the secondary and tertiary economic sectors of manufacturing, service, and information. Chapter 11 examines issues related to globalization and development.

Part Four includes the twelfth and final chapter, which examines the impacts of human activities on the landscape and on human health.

An important emerging perspective that underpins many issues studied by geographers is gender. Since gender issues are so pervasive and significant, we have incorporated "Gender" boxes and significant portions of text to provide a gender perspective throughout the book. Further emphasis on the importance of this perspective is included in the supplementary chapter "Geographies of Gender: Feminism and Masculinities," available on the Online Learning Centre located at **www.mcgrawhill.ca/olc/ fellmann**.

We hope by means of these chapters and sequences to convey to students the logic and integration we recognize in the broad field of human geography. Since the preferred organization and continuity of topics may vary among instructors, we have designed each chapter to be reasonably self-contained, allowing instructors to teach in any sequence that satisfies their preferred arrangement.

New to the Second Canadian Edition

Several updates and changes have been made for the second Canadian edition, including the re-organization of material on drawing maps, migration, and hazards, which promotes a more coherent and logical flow throughout the text. Chapter-by-chapter content changes are as follows:

Chapter 1
- Incorporates the work of Harold Innis: staples theory and his heartland/hinterland theory.

- Provides additional Canadian content, including phrases used for directions.
- Expands coverage of geographic research questions.

Chapter 2
- Incorporates material on drawing maps, fomerly located in Appendix A.
- Includes a more extensive discussion of map projections and UTM systems.
- Contains an updated discussion of feminist research methods, including the use of GIS.
- Offers more information on Google Earth and other accessible forms of GIS.
- Expands material on mental maps.

Chapter 3
- Introduces Wallerstein's world systems theory to denote use of regional and historical perspectives in understanding globalization.
- Offers an expanded discussion of the core-periphery model.
- Includes more information about "place" as a geographic tradition.
- Provides additional Canadian content and examples of geographic perspectives on globalization.

Chapter 4
- Presents updated statistics using the 2006 Canadian Census and 2007 World Population Data.
- Includes an enhanced discussion of migration, based on the material formerly located in Chapter 3.

Chapter 5
- Discusses chapter themes with a greater focus on globalization.
- Offers an expanded definition of "culture."
- Includes a new discussion of environmental politics, which explains and illustrates political ecology.

Chapter 6
- Provides additional detail about the concentration and dispersal of French speakers in Canada.
- Presents a new boxed insert discussing the relationship between globalization and cultural homogeneity.

Chapter 7
- Includes a discussion of modern imperialism as a central element of contemporary geopolitics, which is linked to the core-periphery model described in Chapter 3.
- Offers updated information about international boundary disputes involving Canada, as well as additional Canadian content.

Chapter 8
- Includes a new discussion of urban sustainability and sustainable cities in Canada.
- Presents updated population data for Canadian and U.S. metropolitan areas.
- Offers additional information about the similarities and differences between Canadian and U.S. cities.

Chapter 9
- Introduces the relationship between food and energy consumption.
- Offers a new box about the history and challenges of the organic farming movement in Canada.
- Presents a map of commercial forest regions in Canada in order to illustrate Canada's position in relation to the rest of the world.

Chapter 10
- Introduces a new box discussing global employment trends for women.

Chapter 11
- Provides a brief and comparative treatment of development theories.
- Makes a linkage to world systems theory described in Chapter 3.

Chapter 12
- Is re-organized to increase flow and clarity of ideas.
- Includes a discussion of hazards, formerly located in Chapter 3.
- Places less emphasis on biophysical aspects of resource issues.

Features

- Each chapter opens with two features that outline and preview the content that follows. "Aims" describe key objectives that students should aim to achieve when reading and studying chapter material. "Some Specific Considerations for Review" alert students to the main themes of the chapter.

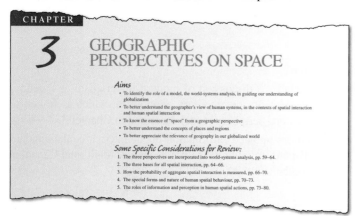

- Canadian and world maps help to identify key areas of topical coverage and discussion.

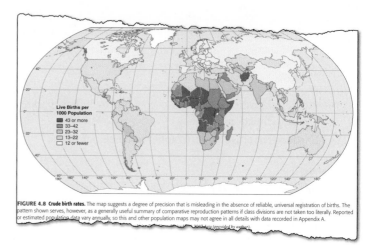

FIGURE 4.8 Crude birth rates. The map suggests a degree of precision that is misleading in the absence of reliable, universal registration of births. The pattern shown serves, however, as a generally useful summary of comparative reproduction patterns if class divisions are not taken too literally. Reported or estimated population data vary annually, so this and other population maps may not agree in all details with data recorded in Appendix A.

- "Geography and Public Policy" boxes introduce a discussion of a topic of current national or international interest and conclude with a set of questions designed to induce thought and class discussion of the topic viewed against the background of human geographic insights.

Geography and Public Policy

Reclamation of Mines in Canada's North

The mining of Canada's North has a long history, and its legacy is mixed. From the earliest explorations of what is now Nunavut for gold in the late 1500s by England's Martin Frobisher, through to the great Klondike gold rush of the Yukon in the late 1890s, to the extraction of uranium from the Northwest Territories (NWT) in the 1940s for the atomic bombs dropped on Japan, to the 1998 opening of Canada's first diamond mine 300 kilometres (185 miles) northeast of Yellowknife, mining has generated both economic prosperity and a host of political, legal, and environmental issues (Mining Watch Canada, 2002).

Obtaining mining rights is surprisingly simple in Canada, while the responsibility for regulating mines is a complex political and legal matter. Under the law of "free entry," individuals and companies alike may acquire exclusive rights from the government to mine virtually any portion of Crown-owned land—virtually all land in Canada—to an unlimited depth. These rights take privilege over private property rights, Aboriginal land claims, and resource management and land use plans. The costs to obtain a prospector's licence and to register a land claim should minerals be found and mining conducted are not entirely "free" per se and do vary across Canada, but the costs are minimal. In Ontario, for example, a prospector's licence costs about $25 and fees for registering a land claim vary with land size, roughly $20 to $65 (Campbell, 2004).

Who regulates the mines and their eventual closure and clean up is not so simple a process. The federal government manages mineral resources in the Yukon, NWT, and Nunavut, but does so through a variety of federal agencies. The Department of Indian Affairs and Northern Development (DIAND) is perhaps the most important of these agencies because it is responsible for Aboriginal peoples and the environmental protection of the North. Territorial and Aboriginal governments, however, are playing larger leadership roles due to their increasing political autonomy and as part of land ownership transfers as land claims are settled. Nevertheless, Canada has no national program to address abandoned and contaminated mine sites, although some provinces do hold mining companies legally responsible.

A geographical study of abandoned mining exploration sites in Nunavik, Northern Quebec, illustrates this point well (Duhaime, Bernard, and Comtois, 2005). Prior to 1976, mining companies were not obliged to clean up their excavation sites, and materials remain there today that pose dangers to the environment and human health. Entire mining sites were simply abandoned when mining ceased, leaving behind various chemical products, gasoline tanks, oil cans, entire buildings (tents, garages, laboratories, cabins), vehicles, machinery and assorted scrap (mattresses, debris, tools). There are some 595 known and documented abandoned mining sites with varying degrees of residual toxins and waste remaining in Nunavut today.

Who should clean up and restore such abandoned sites? Who should pay for this reclamation? And who should enforce these measures? Some argue that DIAND should legislate and enforce reclamation standards, and compel mining companies to contribute financially to the clean up of sites their industry has damaged while amassing huge profits. Still others maintain that the Canadian federal, provincial, and territorial governments must coordinate their positions and laws to ensure effective action is taken to clean up toxic mine sites from coast to coast. Clearly there is a policy gap in need of closure. Between the variety of governmental agencies and levels involved in overseeing mines and the mining industry, and the sweeping privileges granted through "free entry" law, the issue of mine abandonment has fallen through the cracks.

Questions to Consider

1. If the house you live in has minerals underneath the surface, someone else can register a claim and literally mine beneath your house. Should this be permissible? And if so, should you get a portion of the profits? Why or why not?

2. "Free entry" law is intrinsically tied to the "right to explore," which was a driving force in the economic development of what is now Canada by European interests and settlers of centuries past. Has such a law outlived its original intent, or would any modification to this law hinder the mining industry in Canada? First consider the point of view of a miner, and then consider the position of someone displaced by a mining operation.

3. Are toxic sites in the North simply the cost Canadian society must pay to enjoy the material and economic benefits accrued from mining? If so, does the fact that profits from mining public land go to private interests alter your initial position?

4. Who do *you* think should clean up and restore abandoned mine sites? Who do *you* think should pay for mine clean up and reclamation? And who do *you* think should enforce these measures? Why?

- Boxed inserts extend text material by expanding on chapter-related topics or introducing key examples related to those topics.

Canada's Technology Triangle

Anchored by the three cities of Kitchener, Cambridge, and Waterloo, "Canada's Technology Triangle" (CTT) is located in the Waterloo Region of southwestern Ontario, just west of Toronto. Herein lays a rapidly growing cluster of businesses and manufacturers on the cutting edge of research, development and production. Between 1996 and 2001, CTT grew by over 8.2%, with a gross domestic product larger than several Canadian provinces: $18.6 billion. In 2002 alone there were some 260,000 people employed, producing $10.8 billion in product exports shipped throughout the world.

The business base is diverse and may be categorized into seven key sectors: *high tech* includes more than 400 companies producing goods and services, including information technologies such as wireless and Internet hardware and software; *automotive* comprises more than 450 automotive-related companies, both car manufacturers and auto parts suppliers; *advanced manufacturing* consists of engineering and robotic designers and producers, which provide still other businesses and manufacturers with the latest means of accelerating their own methods of production; similarly the *business process*

outsourcing sector provides telecommunication and technical services; *business and financial services* are diverse and numerous, and include several large insurance companies; *biotech and life sciences* is an emerging cluster of research institutes producing medical and biological technologies; and finally, *other sectors* are comprised of such manufacturing and services as food processing, furniture manufacturing, transportation, and warehousing. There are also more than 150 research centres within the CTT, as well as The University of Waterloo, Wilfrid Laurier University, The University of Guelph, and Conestoga College Institute of Technology and Advanced Learning.

The businesses and services here are truly global in constitution and market. A 2005 survey of the CTT revealed that 247 of the firms are foreign-owned, meaning investment in this area extends outside of Canada and included much of the rest of the world: 68% were U.S., 26% were European—Germany, United Kingdom, France, The Netherlands, Ireland, Switzerland, Italy—others were Asian—China, Japan and Taiwan—and still others Brazilian and Australian. This is not by chance but design.

CTT is more than simply an organizing label designated to an economic region, it is a not-for-profit, private-public economic development organization formed to market, grow, and develop the Waterloo region. Its goals include the attraction and retention of investment and businesses from around the country and the world, and to create and sustain a highly skilled and educated workforce, with high incomes and low unemployment rates. The project is successful: Waterloo Region has become an important part of the postindustrial global, Canadian, and Ontarian economies.

- "Gender" boxes provide distinctive coverage of gender roles in society and culture.

Women and the Green Revolution

Women farmers grow at least half of the world's food and up to 80% in some African countries. They are responsible for an even larger share of food consumed by their own families: 80% in sub-Saharan Africa, 65% in Asia, and 45% in Latin America and the Caribbean. Further, women comprise between one-third and one-half of all agricultural labourers in developing countries. For example, African women perform about 90% of the work of processing food crops and 80% of the work of harvesting and marketing.

Women's agricultural dominance in developing states is increasing, in fact, as male family members continue to leave for cities in search of paid urban work. In Mozambique, for example, for every 100 men working in agriculture, there are 153 women. In nearly all other sub-Saharan countries the female component runs between 120 and 150 per 100 men. The departure of men for near or distant cities means, in addition, that women must assume effective management of their families' total farm operations.

Despite their fundamental role, however, women do not share equally with men in the rewards from agriculture, nor are they always beneficiaries of presumed improvements in agricultural technologies and practices. Often, they cannot own or inherit the land on which they work, and they frequently have difficulty in obtaining improved seeds or fertilizers available to male farmers.

As a rule, women farmers work longer hours and have lower incomes than do male farmers. This is not because they are less educated or competent. Rather, it is due to restricting cultural and economic factors. First, most women farmers are involved in subsistence farming and food production for the local market, which yields little cash return. Second, they have far less access than men to credit at bank or government-subsidized rates that would make it possible for them to acquire the Green Revolution technology, such as hybrid seeds and fertilizers. Third, in some cultures women cannot own land and so are excluded from agricultural improvement programs and projects aimed at landowners. For example, many African agricultural development programs are based on the conversion of communal land, to which women have access, to private holdings, from which they are excluded. In Asia, inheritance laws favour male over female heirs, and female-inherited land is managed by husbands; in Latin America, discrimination results from the more limited status held by women under the law.

At the same time, the Green Revolution and its greater commercialization of crops has generally required an increase in labour per hectare, particularly in tasks typically reserved for women, such as weeding, harvesting, and postharvest work. If women are provided no relief from their other daily tasks, the Green Revolution for them may be more burden than blessing. But when mechanization is added to the new farming system, women tend to be losers. Frequently, such predominantly female tasks as harvesting or dehusking and polishing of grain—all traditionally done by hand—are given over to machinery, displacing rather than employing women. Even the application of chemical fertilizers (a "man's task") instead of cow dung ("women's work") has reduced the female role in agricultural development programs. The loss of those traditional female wage jobs means that already poor rural women and their families have insufficient income to improve their diets even in the light of substantial increases in food availability through Green Revolution improvements.

If women are to benefit from the Green Revolution, new cultural norms—or culturally acceptable accommodations within traditional household, gender, and customary legal relations—will be required. These must permit or recognize women's landowning and other legal rights not now clearly theirs, access to credit at favourable rates, and admission on equal footing with males to government assistance programs. Recognition of those realities fostered the Food and Agriculture Organization of the United Nations' "FAO Plan of Action for Women in Development (1996–2001)" and its "Gender and Development Plan (2002–2007)." Both were aimed at stimulating and facilitating efforts to enhance the role of women as contributors and beneficiaries of economic, social, and political development. Objectives of the plan included promoting gender-based equity in access to, and control of, productive resources; enhancing women's participation in decision- and policy-making processes at all levels, local and national; and encouraging actions to reduce rural women's workload while enhancing their opportunities for paid employment and income.

- "Want to Learn More?" boxes at the end of each chapter suggest additional resources, which students can use to further explore key topics.

Want to Learn More?

High Technology and the Global Economy

Canada's Technology Triangle
Learn more about Canada's high-tech industries and kinds of businesses that comprise this growing sector of our economy.
http://www.techtriangle.com/

Markham, Ontario: Canada's High-Tech Capital?
The city of Markham promotes itself as Canada's "high-tech capital": find out why.
http://www.markham.ca/Markham/Departments/EDO/HiTech_Capital.htm

Canada in the Global Economy
New industries such as telecommunications equipment, lasers, pharmaceuticals, aerospace, and biotechnologies have become important sectors of Canada's place in the global economy. To learn more about Canada in the global economy, visit this website.
http://www.international.gc.ca/commerce/strategy-strategie/details.aspx

Globalization and Transnational Corporations
A global economy is premised upon global businesses. Learn what the United Nations says about transnational corporations.
http://www.hri.ca/fortherecord2001/vol1/globalization.htm

International Labour Organization
This United Nations agency seeks the promotion of social justice and internationally recognized human and labour rights. It generates numerous reports and data bases on employment issues around the world.
http://www.ilo.org/

Transportation Industries

Canadian Trucking Alliance
The Canadian trucking industry has a slogan: "if you got it, a truck brought it." Explore an industry crucial to keeping the Canadian economy operating.
http://www.cantruck.com/industry/profile.php

Rail Transport
Since 1836 Canada's rail industry has served industry and remains essential to the country's prosperity and economic growth. Learn more about the history and role of this vital form of transporting goods and people.
http://www.hrsdc.gc.ca/en/hip/hrp/sp/industry_profiles/railway_transport.shtml

International Shipping
International trade is largely dependent upon shipping to move freight around the globe. Learn more about international shipping at this website.
http://www.shipping-international.com/?google

Outsourcing and Offshoring

Outsourcing: Frequently Asked Questions
Explanations, advantages, and disadvantages of outsourcing are found here.
http://www.outsourcing-faq.com/

Offshoring: Frequently Asked Questions
Visit this website for answers about offshoring.
http://www.epinet.org/content.cfm/issueguide_offshoring_faq

- The "Summary" at the end of each chapter reiterates the main points of the chapter and provides a bridge to the chapter that follows.

Summary

Culture lies at the root of human geography. To study the diversity of ways people interact with the natural environments they occupy, and the plurality of built environments they create, is an immense and interesting challenge, particularly in light of increased globalization. As the subsequent chapters show, geographers have developed specialized subfields to address the many strands in the web of culture. In this chapter, the concept of *culture* itself has been discussed, with particular emphasis on the spatial and social processes through which culture is expressed, displayed, and changed over time in the landscape. Change is induced by innovations that spread outward from their origin points, carried by migrants through relocation diffusion or adopted by others through a variety of expansion diffusion and acculturation processes. Although diffusion barriers exist, most successful or advantageous innovations find adopters, and both cultural modification and cultural convergence of different societies result. *Traditional cultural geography* seeks to observe and describe the spread and impact of human activities, technologies, and beliefs of cultural groups over time—*cultural history*—to the natural environment—*cultural ecology*—as distributed over a particular space—*cultural area*—as manifest in a *cultural landscape*. It takes an historical approach to changes in a particular group's human–environment relationship. Contemporary or *new* cultural geography takes a political approach to explain the creation of culture and the social mechanisms of cultural and environmental change. The focus is upon culture as a *site of struggle* for identity—the meanings, values, and ideas people make for themselves and others—which requires examining who has the *power* to dominate other cultural groups, and which cultural groups are subordinate to others and why, be it a local or global scale. Physical, social, and lived *spaces* play a fundamental role in the exercise of power, through *exclusion*, *expulsion*, *containment*, and *inclusion*. *Class, "race," and gender* are among the primary markers of cultural identity and conflict. By understanding how social intolerance and inequality work in the production of cultural landscapes, cultural geography may assist in the intervention of such processes.

- New terms, as well as special usages of words and phrases, are indicated throughout the text using boldface or italic type. Boldface terms are included in the "Key Words" list at the end of each chapter and are defined in a cross-referenced glossary at the end of the text.

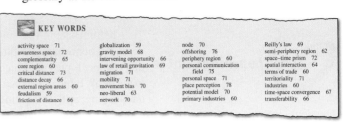

KEY WORDS

activity space 71
awareness space 72
complementarity 65
core region 60
critical distance 73
distance decay 66
external region areas 60
feudalism 59
friction of distance 66
globalization 59
gravity model 68
intervening opportunity 66
law of retail gravitation 69
migration 71
mobility 71
movement bias 70
neo-liberal 63
network 70
node 70
offshoring 76
periphery region 60
personal communication field 75
personal space 71
place perception 78
potential model 70
primary industries 60
Reilly's law 69
semi-periphery region 62
space–time prism 72
spatial interaction 64
terms of trade 60
territoriality 71
industries 60
time-space convergence 67
transferability 66

- "For Review" questions at the end of each chapter direct students' attention to important concepts developed in the chapter.

FOR REVIEW

1. How important an influence has history played in defining core and peripheral regions? How do core regions maintain control over the periphery?
2. Draw a mental map of the core and periphery regions in your university town?
3. What parts of your province would you consider core and periphery? Are there parts of the province which are semi-periphery?
4. What parts, if any, of your university town are "unique?" Explain. Are there elements of a globalization there? What parts, if any, of your university town would you consider to be "placeless." Explain.
5. What is meant by *spatial interaction*? What are the three fundamental conditions governing all forms of spatial interaction? What is the distinctive impact or importance of each of the conditions?
6. What variations in *distance decay* curves might you expect if you were to plot shipments of ready-mixed concrete, potato chips, and computer parts? What do these respective curves tell us about transferability?
7. What is *activity space*? What factors affect the areal extent of an individual's activity space?
8. On a piece of paper, plot your *space–time path* for your movements on a typical class day. What alterations in your established movement habits might be necessary (or become possible) if: (a) instead of walking, you rode a bike? (b) instead of biking, you drove a car? (c) instead of driving, you had to use the bus or go by bike or on foot?
9. What does the thought that transportation and communication are *space-adjusting* imply? In what ways has technology affected the "space adjustment" in commodity flows? In information flows?
10. Recall the places you have visited in the past week. In your movements, were the rules of *distance decay* and *critical distance* operative? What variables affect *your* critical distances?
11. Notice that the Yukon and Northwest Territories are high income areas (Figure 3.5). Do you think this map is "lying"? Why?

- "Focus Follow-up" questions conclude each chapter by posing one question about each major chapter concept, relating back to the themes listed in "Some Specific Considerations for Review."

FOCUS FOLLOW-UP

1. **How do we define development and explain the occurrence or persistence of underdevelopment?** pp.xxx–xxx.
   Development implies improvement in economic and quality-of-life aspects of a society. It presumably results from technology transfer from advanced to developing states and, through consequent cultural convergence, promises the full integration of the developing society into the larger modern world order. When that stage of advancement is reached, transition from the world economic and social "periphery" to its "core" has been achieved. Persistence of underdevelopment is usually attributed to failure of a culture or region to accumulate capital, develop skills, or achieve technology transfers to improve its prosperity or quality of life.
2. **What economic measures mark a country's stage of development or its progress from underdevelopment?** pp.xxx–xxx.
   Gross national income and purchasing power parity per capita, per capita commercial energy consumption, percentage of labour force in agriculture, and average daily caloric intake are common, accepted measures of development. Attempts to model the process of development have led to inconclusive and contrasting theories of inevitable "stages of growth," optimistic "Big Push" ideas of coordinated investment, and pessimistic "dependency theory" concepts of perpetual exploitation of underdeveloped regions.
3. **What are non-economic aspects of development, and how are they related to measures of economic growth?** pp.xxx–xxx.
   Education, sanitation, and health services are among many non-economic indices of development that are strongly related to income and national wealth. The higher a country's ranking on purely economic measures, the more it can and does spend on improvement of quality-of-life conditions for its citizens. Similarly, the higher those expenditures are, the lower on average are national rates of infant mortality, births and deaths, rates of natural increase, and the like. "Happiness" or satisfaction of such cultural wants as social support, aesthetic and sensory needs, creativity outlets, etc., also figure as importantly into well-being assessments as do gross domestic product or energy consumption.
4. **What conditions underlie the varying world pattern of women's roles, status, and rewards?** pp.xxx–xxx.
   The status of women is a cultural spatial variable reflecting gender relationships characteristic of different societies. The world pattern of gender-related institutional and economic role assignments and rewards appears strongly influenced by national levels of economic development and by the persistence of customary and religious restrictions on women. With few exceptions, women worldwide spend more hours per day working than do men; everywhere they are paid less for comparable work. A general world trend is toward greater equality for women in political and economic opportunities and status.

Supplements

For the Student

Human Geography *Online Learning Centre* at *www. mcgrawhill.ca/olc/fellmann.*

This helpful site gives students the opportunity to further explore topics presented in the book. Interactive chapter quizzing, critical thinking questions, internet resources, case studies, interactive maps, and videos are all available online.

Sights & Sounds CD-ROM (ISBN 978–0–07–312210–6)

This CD-ROM offers a unique opportunity in "seeing and hearing" the music and cultural perspectives of 10 regions:

*   North America: Appalachia
*   Central America: Oaxaca, Mexico
*   South America: Ecuador
*   Europe: British Isles
*   Africa South of the Sahara: Tanzania
*   South Asia: Nepal
*   Middle East
*   Insular Southeast Asia: Bali, Indonesia
*   East Asia: China
*   South Pacific: Samoa

For the Instructor

Human Geography *Online Learning Centre* at *www. mcgrawhill.ca/olc/fellmann.*

An Instructor's Manual, Computerized Test Bank, Image Bank, and Power-Point Presentations are available for download from the password-protected section of the Online Learning Centre.

*   The **Instructor's Manual** provides chapter summaries, expanded key word listings, and lecture and discussion topics.
*   The **Computerized Test Bank** contains over 550 multiple choice, true/false, and short answer questions. Available for Macintosh or Windows users, the computerized test bank using EZ Test—a flexible and easy-to-use electronic testing program—allows instructors to create tests from book-specific items. EZ Test accommodates a wide range of question types and allows instructors to add their own questions. Test items are also available in Word format (Rich text format). For secure online testing, exams created in EZ Test can be exported to WebCT, Blackboard, and EZ Test Online. EZ Test comes with a Quick Start Guide, and once the program is installed, users have access

to a User's Manual and Flash tutorials. Additional help is available online at www.mhhe.com/eztest.

*   The **Image Bank** contains all of the illustrations, photographs, and tables from the text for use in multimedia presentations. Instructors can use these resources to create their own lecture presentations.
*   **PowerPoint Presentations** outline the main concepts and themes in each chapter and offer brief teaching tips for each slide.

Teaching, Technology and Learning Conference Series

The educational environment has changed tremendously in recent years, and McGraw-Hill Ryerson continues to be committed to helping you acquire the skills you need to succeed in this new milieu. Our innovative Teaching, Technology & Learning Conference Series brings faculty together from across Canada with 3M Teaching Excellence award winners to share teaching and learn best practices in a collaborative and stimulating environment. Pre-conference workshops on general topics, such as teaching large classes and technology integration, are also offered. We will also work with you at your own institution to customize workshops that best suit the needs of your faculty at your institution.

Course Management

For the integrated instructor, we offer *Human Geography* content for complete online courses. Whatever your needs, you can customize the *Human Geography* Online Learning Centre content and author your own online course materials. It is entirely up to you! You can offer online discussion and message boards that will complement your office hours, and reduce the lines outside your door. Content cartridges are also available for course management systems, such as **WebCT** and **Blackboard**. Ask your *i*Learning Sales Specialist for details.

CourseSmart

CourseSmart brings together thousands of textbooks across hundreds of courses in an eTextbook format providing unique benefits to students and faculty. By purchasing an eTextbook, students can save up to 50 percent off the cost of a print textbook, reduce their impact on the environment, and gain access to powerful Web tools for learning including full text search, notes and highlighting, and e-mail tools for sharing notes between classmates. For faculty, CourseSmart provides instant access to review and compare textbooks and course materials in their discipline area without the time, cost, and environmental impact of mailing print examination copies. For further details contact your *i*Learning Sales Specialist or go to *www.coursesmart.com.*

Acknowledgements

A final note of thanks is reserved for the staff at McGraw-Hill Ryerson. It is a privilege to emphasize their efforts and helpful courtesy. Jennifer Oliver has been very good at providing support and direction for putting the final product together. Katherine Goodes and Jessica Barnoski have provided excellent support for selecting and drafting figures. Leanna MacLean was able to quarterback the endeavour and continues to assist in linking text content to the Web and popular media. We also thank Sarah Powell for her editorial suggestions. Finally, as noted in the first edition, behind every author there is a personal base of support—we wish to acknowledge the ongoing support of Connie, Evan, and Ethan at home, and our colleagues within the Department of Geography at Western.

We would also like to thank our reviewers for their guided feedback and contributions to this text:

Ken Brealey – *University of the Fraser Valley*
Alan Brunger – *Trent University*
Bill Burgess – *Kwantlen Polytechnic University*
Sean Doherty – *Wilfrid Laurier University*
Michael Fox – *Mount Allison University*
Charles Greenberg – *Capilano College*
Jocelyn Guindon – *Dawson College*
Bernard Henin – *Camosun College*
Linda Joan Paul – *University of Regina*
Julie Podmore – *John Abbott College*
Jeanne Maurer – *Ryerson University*
Colin Mills – *Langara College*
Derek Smith – *Carleton University*
Rosario Turvey – *Nipissing University*
Jon Unruh – *McGill University*
Tom Whillans – *Trent University*
Francis Yee – *Camosun College*

Meet the Authors

Jerome D. Fellmann

Jerome Fellmann received his B.S., M.S. and Ph.D. degrees from the University of Chicago. Except for visiting professorships at Wayne State University, the University of British Columbia, and California State University/Northridge, his professional career has been spent at the University of Illinois at Urbana-Champaign. His teaching and research interests have been concentrated in the areas of human geography in general and urban and economic geography in particular, in geographic bibliography, the geography of Russia and the CIS, and geographic education. His varied interests have been reflected in articles published in the *Annals of the Association of American Geographers*, *Professional Geographer*, *Journal of Geography*, the *Geographical Review*, and elsewhere. He is the co-author of McGraw-Hill's *Introduction to Geography*. In addition to teaching and research, he has held administrative appointments at the University of Illinois and served as a consultant to private corporations on matters of economic and community development.

Arthur Getis

Arthur Getis received his B.S. and M.S. degrees from Pennsylvania State University and his Ph.D. from the University of Washington. He is the co-author of several geography textbooks as well as two books dealing with map pattern analysis. He has also published widely in the areas of urban geography, spatial analysis, and geographical information systems. He is co-editor of *Journal of Geographical Systems* and for many years served on the editorial boards of *Geographical Analysis and Papers in Regional Science*. He has held administrative appointments at Rutgers University, the University of Illinois, and San Diego State University (SDSU), and currently holds the Birch Chair of Geographical Studies at SDSU. In 2002, he received the Association of American Geographers Distinguished Scholarship Award. Professor Getis is a member of many professional organizations and has served as an officer in, among others, the Western Regional Science Association and the University Consortium for Geographic Information Science.

Judith Getis

Judith Getis earned her B.A. and a teaching credential from the University of Michigan and her M.A. from Michigan State University. She has co-authored several geography textbooks and written the environmental handbook *You Can Make a Difference*. In addition to numerous articles in the fields of urban geography and geography education, she has written technical reports on topics such as solar power and coal gasification. She and her husband, Arthur Getis, were among the original unit authors of the High School Geography Project, sponsored by the National Science Foundation and the Association of American Geographers. In addition, Mrs. Getis was employed by the Urban Studies Center at Rutgers University; taught at Rutgers; was a social science examiner at Educational Testing Service, Princeton, NJ; developed educational materials for Edcom Systems, Princeton, NJ; and was a professional associate in the Office of Energy Research, University of Illinois.

Dan Shrubsole

Dan Shrubsole is currently a Professor and Chair of the Department of Geography at the University of Western Ontario. He has published many research papers on the institutional aspects of resource management, particularly water resource management in Canada. His perspectives have been published in *Eau Canada: The Future of Canada's Water* (2007, edited by K. Bakker), *Practicing Sustainable Water Management: Canadian and International Experiences* (1997), *Canadian Water Management: Visions for Sustainability* (1994), and *Every Drop Counts* (1994), along with many others. Dan has been a Visiting Research Fellow with Australia's Commonwealth Research and Scientific Organization (CSIRO) and participated in research concerning catchment management and environmental management in the sugar cane industry. Dan has been fortunate to have had three mentors who have taught him about the discipline, resource management on life—Dave Rees (Nipissing College), Jerry Hall (Wilfrid Laurier), and Bruce Mitchell (Waterloo). Also, since working at Western, Don Cartwright has helped his development as a practising academic. Dan dedicates this book to his mentors and hopes that this book helps students appreciate the value that geography provides to understanding and solving real-world problems and the career possibilities it can lead to.

Jeff Hopkins

Jeff Hopkins received his Ph.D. in cultural geography from McGill University, and his B.A. and M.A. from The University of Western Ontario. His research interests include symbolic landscapes (advertisements, film, place promotion), the creation of successful public places (indoor cities, shopping malls, public libraries), and the geography of gender, specifically the place and production of masculinity. He has taught numerous courses in cultural, social, gender, urban and philosophical geographies, ranging from the introductory to doctoral levels. He is a member of several professional geographical associations and has served as the President of the Canadian Association of Geographers, Ontario Division.

INTRODUCTION—GEOGRAPHY: ITS DEVELOPMENTS, RESEARCH THEMES, AND CONCEPTS

Aims

- To understand the terms "geography" and "human geography"
- To recognize the recent development of the discipline in Canada and the meaning of a geographic approach
- To appreciate some key geographic concepts

Some Specific Considerations for Review:

1. The nature of geography and the role of human geography, pp. 2–7.
2. The geographical standards (research themes), pp. 12–15.
3. The development of geography in Europe and Canada, pp. 7–12.
4. Seven fundamental geographic observations and the basic concepts that underlie them, pp. 13–22.
5. The regional concept and the characteristics of regions, pp. 22–25.

Some Geographical Issues:

- What is the pattern of human development globally? Although Canada is one of the most developed countries in the world, many of its people are poor. How can this occur? The pattern of poverty in Canada has been labelled "postal code poverty." Why?

- What is the future of suburbia? Rising transportation costs, increased awareness of the environmental impact of driving, and increased congestion are among many factors that may see people wanting to live closer to work and school. How will the planning of our cities change to meet these challenges?

- What has the impact of North American Free Trade Agreement on Canadian border towns? How has the response to terrorism in the United States affected the flow of people, goods and services across the world's longest undefended border?

- Despite the availability of technology and billions of dollars being spent over the last 10 years, over 1 million infants and children still die each year from water-borne diseases, and hundreds of millions people are debilitated by illness, pain, and discomfort.

- Coral reefs, tropical rainforests, and the boreal forest are among the many ecosystems that are threatened by human activities. What should and could be done to protect the environmental base which supports all life on the planet?

A key to understanding and answering these and other questions lies in geography. In a world that is becoming intimately more interconnected through the Internet, transportation networks, the global financial system, and the media, geography provides a deeper understanding of how and why differences exist, how people and goods move from place to place, and how people relate to each other and with their environment. Ozone depletion, droughts in western Canada and elsewhere, and the threat of global warming, poverty, urban blight, and international development are issues we see on the news almost daily. Very high demands are made on the environment by people who, increasingly, are living in urban areas. This concentration of people often has implications, which sometimes lead to tensions and conflicts. At the same time, resource projects located in remote and fragile environments, such as oil and gas drilling in Canada's north, are being proposed to meet peoples' demands for goods from far away. The relevance of geography to solving contemporary world problems was highlighted by the comments of Kofi Annan when he was United Nation's Secretary-General. He believed that the work of the United Nations and geographers shared a great deal in common because many of the problems facing humanity—climate change, population, consumption, poverty, and supporting the achievement of sustainable development for all people of the world—required attention be paid to the importance of people, borders, and science. This is an exciting time to be studying geography with many opportunities for employment (see "Careers in Geography").

Geography has a long history dating back to the Greek geographers who first gave structure to the discipline. Geography's name was reputedly coined by the Greek scientist Eratosthenes over 2200 years ago from the words *geo,* "the earth," and *graphein,* "to write." From the beginning, that writing focused both on the physical structure of the earth and on the nature and activities of the people who inhabited the different lands of the known world. To Strabo (*ca.* 64 B.C.E.–20 A.C.E.), the task of geography was to "describe the several parts of the inhabited world to write the assessment of the countries of the world [and] to treat the differences between countries." Even earlier, Herodotus (*ca.* 484–425 B.C.E.) had found it necessary to devote much of his book to the lands, peoples, economies, and customs of the various parts of the Persian Empire as necessary background to an understanding of the causes and course of the Persian wars.

Greek (and later, Roman) geographers measured the earth, devised the global grid of parallels and meridians (marking latitudes and longitudes—see Chapter 2), and drew upon that grid surprisingly sophisticated maps of their known world (Figure 1.1). They explored the apparent latitudinal variations in climate and described in numerous works the familiar Mediterranean basin and the more remote, partly rumoured lands of northern Europe, Asia, and equatorial Africa. Employing nearly modern concepts, they described river systems, explored causes of erosion and patterns of deposition, cited the dangers of deforestation, described areal variations in the natural landscape, and noted the consequences of environmental abuse. Against that physical backdrop, they focused their attention on what humans did in home and distant areas—how they lived; what their distinctive similarities and differences were in language, religion, and custom; and how they used, altered, and perhaps destroyed the lands they inhabited. Strabo, indeed, cautioned against the assumption that the nature and actions of humans were determined by the physical environment they inhabited. He observed that humans were the active elements in a human–environmental partnership.

These are enduring and universal interests. The ancient Chinese, for example, were deeply involved in geography as an explanatory viewpoint, though there was no exchange between them and Westerners. Further, as Christian Europe entered its Middle Ages between 500 A.C.E. and 1400 A.C.E., and lost its knowledge of Greek and Roman geographical work, Muslim scholars—who retained that knowledge—undertook to describe and analyze their known world in its physical, cultural, and regional variation. Aboriginal communities in Canada were also mapping their world and some shared this knowledge with European explorers and fur traders (Figure 1.2). In the last 100 years, we have gone from a period where mapping was a labour intensive exercise conducted by surveyors in the field, to the use of satellites, which can provide information on individual properties (Figure 1.3). Perhaps some of you have seen how accessible mapping technologies have now become in searching for maps on "Google Earth," "Map Quest," or using a global positioning system (GPS). Chapter 2 provides more information on mapping. For now, you have a sense that geographers study a wide range of issues, and are adept at using maps and related computer technologies.

In our globalized world, geography matters a great deal. On the one hand, international financing, improved transportation and communications, transnational corporations and internationalization of the labour force have promoted

Careers in Geography

Geographers are in demand by a wide range of employers because they are able to consider both human and physical aspects of problems, can think spatially, and are computer literate. In a general sense, geography can make us better informed citizens, more able to understand the important issues facing our communities, our country, and our world, and better prepared to contribute solutions. Modern geography is both a physical and social science, and fosters a wealth of technical skills. The employment possibilities it presents are as many and varied as are the agencies and enterprises dealing with the natural environment and human activities and with the acquisition and analysis of spatial data.

Many professional geographers work in non-profit, the private, or government sectors. Although many positions do not carry a geography title, physical geographers serve as water, mineral, and other natural resource analysts; weather and climate experts; soil scientists; and the like. There has been recent high demand for environmental managers and technicians. Geographers who have specialized in environmental studies find jobs assessing the impact of proposed development projects on such things as air and water quality and endangered species, as well as preparing the environmental impact statements required before projects can begin.

Human geographers work in many different roles in the public sector. Jobs include data acquisition and analysis in health care, transportation, population studies, economic development, and international development. Many geography graduates find positions as planners in local and provincial governmental agencies concerned with housing and community development, park and recreation planning, and urban and regional planning. They map and analyze land use plans and transportation systems, monitor urban land development, make informed recommendations about the location of public facilities, and engage in basic social science research.

Most of these same specializations are also found in the private sector. Geographic training is ideal for such tasks as business planning and market analysis; factory, store, and shopping-centre site selection; community and economic development programs for banks, public utilities, railroads, and similar applications. Publishers of maps, atlases, news and travel magazines, and the like employ geographers as writers, editors, and mapmakers. Teaching in elementary, high school, college, and university is a longstanding employment opportunity.

The breadth and depth of knowledge combined with the technical skills required in geographic research and analysis gives geography graduates a competitive edge in the labour market. These field-based skills include familiarity with geographic information systems (GIS), cartography and computer mapping, remote sensing and photogrammetry, and competence in data analysis and problem solving. In particular, students with expertise in GIS are finding that they have ready access to employment opportunities. The following table, based on the booklet "Careers in Geography,"[*] summarizes some of the professional opportunities open to students who have specialized in one (or more) of the various subfields of geography. Also, be sure to read the informative discussions under the "Careers in Geography" option on the home page of the Canadian Association of Geographers at **www.cag-acg.ca.** Additional links on the topic of geography careers can be found in the Online Learning Centre for this text. That connection may be found at the end of this chapter.

Geographic Field of Concentration	Employment Opportunities
Cartography and geographic information	Cartographer for federal government (agencies such as Environment Canada, National Resources Canada) or private sector (e.g., Environmental Systems Research Institute, ERDAS, or Intergraph); map librarian; GIS specialist for planners, land developers, real estate agencies, utility companies, local government; remote-sensing analyst; surveyor
Physical geography	Weather forecaster; outdoor guide; hydrologist; soil conservation/agricultural extension agent
Environmental studies	Environmental manager; forestry technician; park ranger; hazardous waste planner, park manager
Cultural geography	Community developer; social policy analyst, health care analyst
Economic geography	Site selection analyst for business and industry; market researcher; traffic/route delivery manager; real estate agent/broker/appraiser; economic development researcher
Urban and regional planning	Urban and community planner; transportation planner; housing, park, and recreation planner; health services planner
Regional geography	Regional specialist for federal government (e.g., Foreign Affairs); international business representative; travel agent; travel writer
Geographic education or general geography	Elementary/secondary school teacher; university or college professor; overseas teacher

[*]"Careers in Geography," modified from Richard G. Boehm. Washington, D.C.: National Geographic Society, 1996. Previously published by Peterson's Guides, Inc.

globalization—a phenomenon that has largely occurred during your lifespan—and has increased economic, cultural, social and political interaction among people and nations. Some people suggest that cultures, economies, and landscapes across the world are becoming the same (Figure 1.4). At the same time, many people resist the forces of globalization and/or wish to express their local cultures and return to more traditional economic systems and structures. Sometimes tensions between global forces and local

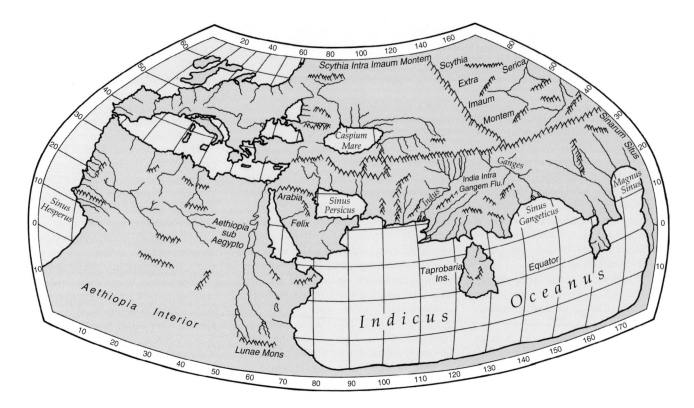

FIGURE 1.1 World map of the 2d-century A.C.E. Greco–Egyptian geographer-astronomer Ptolemy. Ptolemy (Claudius Ptolemaeus) adopted a previously developed map grid of latitude and longitude based on the division of the circle into 360°, permitting a precise mathematical location for every recorded place. Unfortunately, errors of assumption and measurement rendered both the map and its accompanying six-volume gazetteer inaccurate. Ptolemy's map, accepted in Europe as authoritative for nearly 1500 years, was published in many variants in the 15th and 16th centuries. The version shown here summarizes the extent and content of the original. Its underestimation of the earth's size convinced Columbus a short westward voyage would carry him to Asia.

interests have resulted in armed conflicts and terrorism. Geographers are concerned with the impact of this global trend on people—their culture, economy, social and political systems—the environment, and the landscape, and to balance the desire for local autonomy and tastes.

What is Geography and Human Geography?

Geographers devote themselves to answering a number of questions about biophysical and human systems: Where is something? Why is it there? How did it get there? How does it interact with other things? What alternative locations exist to situate this activity? What might be expected in the future? How can benefits arising from this activity be best distributed to people over space and time? Geography is often referred to as the *spatial* science, that is, the discipline concerned with the use of earth space. Geography might better be defined as the study of spatial variation, of how—and why—physical and cultural items differ from place to place. It is, further, the study of how observable spatial patterns evolved through time. If things were everywhere the same, if there were no spatial variation, the kind of human curiosity that we call "geographic" simply would not exist. For example, it matters a great deal that different languages are spoken in certain places. However, knowledge of the location of a specific

language group is not of itself particularly significant. Geographic study of language shows different characteristics in different locations and how the present distribution of its speakers came about. In the course of our study, we would logically discuss such concepts as migration, acculturation, the diffusion of innovation, the effect of physical barriers on communication, and the relationship of language to other aspects of culture. As geographers, we are interested in how things are interrelated in different regions over space and time, and provide evidence of the existence of "spatial systems."

You consciously or subconsciously display geographic awareness in your own daily life. You are where you are, doing what you are doing, because of locational choices you faced and spatial decisions you made. You cannot be here reading this book and simultaneously be somewhere else—working, perhaps, or at the gym. And should you now want to go to work or take an exercise break, the time involved in going from here to there (wherever "there" is) is time not available for other activities in other locations. Of course, the act of going implies knowing where you are now, where "there" is in relation to "here," and the paths or routes you can take to cover the distance. These are simple examples of the observation that "space matters" in a very personal way. Your understanding of your hometown, your neighbourhood, or your campus is essentially a geographic understanding. It is based on your awareness of where things are, of their spatial relationships,

Athapescon Lake
Lake Athabasca

Black Lake
Black Lake

ul ti ah wooz ze too ah, Jack Lake
good water B

Engemann Lake

Trout river very crooked
easy current - no rapids

Cree River strong current

Indian river very strong current and full of small ripples

Mr Dace 1803

Trout Lake
Weitzel Lake

3

Mr Huwatt 1803

Plenty of Trout & other kinds

5 Days in canoe full of Islands

Little Sandy Lake

In na too ah
Cree Lake

Indian Lake very large -

3 days

1803

3.5 mile good water

3 days walk short

3/4 mile good

1/2 very swampy and bad
1/4 mile good

the Jipowyans or Northern Indians

Little Sandy Lake
Solitude Lake

Deers River

Big sandy lake or
Thay ki too ah cho
Gwillam Lake

Mudjatik

3 Carrying places before first lake—
short. don't carry canoe - none beyond except
a hen shoal - very sandy and crooked - 12 days
from mouth to portage to leave the river

Thay ki too ah yazza
or small sandy lake
Loon Mud Lake

Mouth Deers River

FIGURE 1.2 An Early Map Of Canada—Cot aw ney yaz zah. This map drawn by a Chipewyan First Nations in 1810 provides information about canoe travel between the Churchill River and Lake Athabasca. The Historical Atlas of Canada notes that "it is typical for maps produced by natives to exaggerate the scale at important points, such as the major portage between Deers River (Mudjatik River) across the height of land between Hudson Bay and the Atlantic Ocean. The recommended route to Black Lake from Indian Lake (Cree Lake) is down the swiftly flowing Indian River (Cree River). The return route avoids this strong current and follows a double backway to Trout Lake (Weitzel Lake) and thence to Indian Lake."

Source: Plate 59 from Historical Atlas of Canada *(Vol. 1). University of Toronto Press. ISBN 0-8020-2495-5.*

and of the varying content of the different areas and places you frequent.

Geography is about space and the content of space in the past, at present, and in the future. This temporal element also makes the discipline a dynamic one. It straddles both natural sciences (physical geography) and social sciences/liberal arts (human geography). Geographers think of and respond to place from the standpoint not only of where they are, but rather more importantly, of what they contain or what we think they contain. Reference to a place or an area usually calls up images about what people do there and often suggests, without conscious thought, how those objects and human activities are related. "The Alps," "mountains," and "skiing" might be a simple example. Mention place names, such as Shanghai, Rome, Sydney, New York, or Calgary, or events like Mardi Gras, spring break, or winter carnival, and landscapes will be an important part of one's mental image. The key message from the discussion above is that the content of an area has physical and cultural aspects, and geography is always concerned with understanding both (Figure 1.5).

Over time, the discipline of geography has developed sub-specialties based on the subject matter being addressed. At its broadest level, the sub-specialties are divided between physical and human geography (Table 1.1). Physical geographers seek to understand environmental processes, such as climate patterns and change (climatology), the origin and evolution of various landforms (river basins, coasts, mountains—various forms of geomorphology), and the distribution of plants and animals (biogeography). Human geographers study various aspects of human phenomena—social, political, demographic, economic, cities—or the interaction between people and the natural environment best illustrated in resource and environmental management research. Within each one of these sub-specialty areas are further areas of specialization. To illustrate, in the area of resource and environmental management, one can focus attention on water, land, forests, hazards, and parks. Health geographers study a range of topics from access to health care facilities, to the determinants of health, and to environment–health interactions. Economic geographers can focus on location analysis, foreign direct investment, and the production, consumption, and/or movement of goods and services. In all areas of study, geographers provide a geographic approach—something that we will clarify later in this chapter and Part 1 of this book. This book focuses on human geography, and in particular, how human activities are reflected in the patterns that shape our landscapes.

Human geography focuses on people: where they are, what they are like, how they interact over space, and what kind of landscapes of human use they erect on the natural landscapes they occupy. It encompasses all those interests and topics of geography that are not directly controlled by the physical environment or, like cartography, are strictly technical in orientation. For example, economists are generally concerned with trends and patterns over time, not space, and psychology rarely considers the interaction between space and behaviour. At the same time, human geography draws on other social sciences in the analyses identified with its subfields, such as *political, economic,* or *social geography* (Table 1.1).

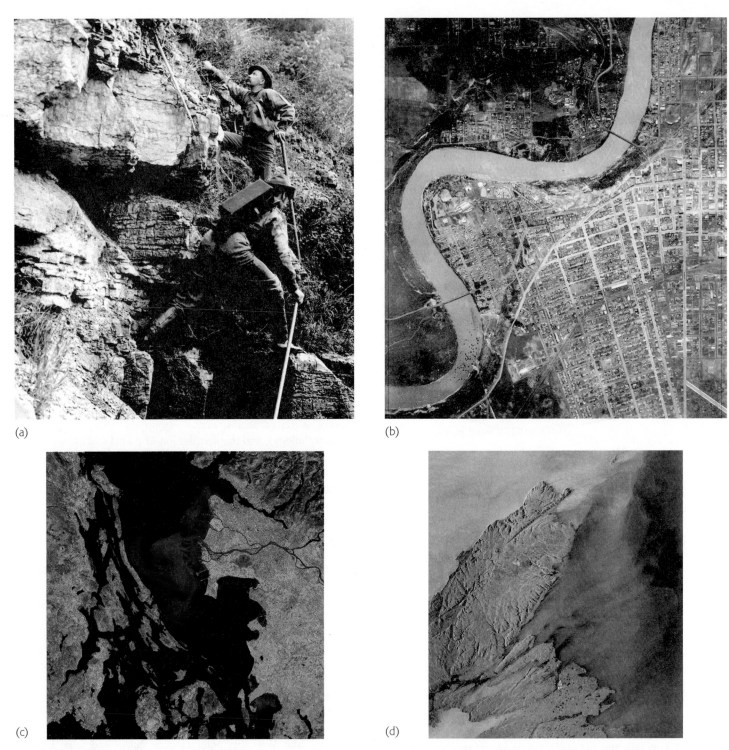

(a)

(b)

(c)

(d)

FIGURE 1.3 Changing mapping technologies. Many of the first reliable maps of Canada were completed by surveyors who traversed the country. In Figure 1.3(*a*), we see a topographer and his assistant inching their way along a rockface with their equipment in 1887. In Figure 1.3(*b*), we see an aerial photograph of Edmonton from 1924. The first Canadian aerial photograph was taken in 1923. By 1963, 97% of the country had been photographed in black and white. Aerial photographs, combined with surveying, were the main tools of cartography until the 1970s, when mapping from satellite imagery became feasible (Figure 1.3(*c*)). The first satellite designed specifically for remote sensing purposes was ERTS 1 (later named Landsat 1), launched in 1972. It was followed by Landsat 2 (1975), Landsat 3 (1978), Landsat 4 (1982), and Landsat 5 (1984). Since the Landsat images detect wavebands outside the visible spectrum of light, images are in false colour. In Figure 1.3(*c*), the plume from the Fraser River as it enters the waters between Vancouver and Victoria is the colour blue, while urban areas are purple. Radar is now being used more frequently to produce images as shown in Figure 1.3(*d*). This is an image of the Cape Breton Highlands in Nova Scotia and is one of the first images collected by RADARSAT, Canada's first earth observation satellite. This image was taken at 5:41 pm local time on November 28, 1995, through darkness, cloudy skies, rain, and strong winds.

FIGURE 1.4 A Sign of Our Global World. McDonald's illustrates the power and effect of globalization on landscapes. Who would have imagined that the golden arches would grow from a single restaurant built in 1953 in Phoenix, Arizona into a global business? In 2007, there were over 31,000 outlets in more than 119 countries on six continents. There are over 1,400 McDonald's restaurants in Canada. Since opening in Russia in 1990, McDonald's now operates 127 restaurants in that country. McDonald's in India has several vegetarian options, and given that cows are sacred to millions of people there, this makes sense.

Human geography helps us to understand the world we occupy and to appreciate the circumstances affecting peoples and countries other than our own. It clarifies the contrasts in societies and cultures, and in the human landscapes they have created in different regions of the earth. Its models and explanations of how things are interrelated in earth space give us a clearer understanding of the systems within which we live and operate. Its analyses of those spatial systems make us more aware of the realities and prospects of our own society in an increasingly connected and competitive world. To illustrate these comments and the value of human geography, let's focus attention of the work of Piers Blaikie, a British geographer who wrote a book in 1985 entitled *The Political Economy of Soil Erosion*. Most of us would initially think that erosion is a function of the land (soil type, slope), the weather (wind, rain intensity, amount and duration), land cover, and human use and management. Blaikie combined this traditional understanding of soil erosion with analysis of larger-scale economic and political processes. Based largely on his field work in south Asia, he suggested that erosion was not strictly a problem of managing the land. What made erosion much worse pertained to poor farmers who were forced off the good land into marginal regions—often with steeper slopes—by more powerful interests. Blaikie concluded that this form of poverty often magnified soil and other forms of environmental degradation. Blaikie's approach of combining our knowledge of physical processes with political and economic aspects eventually led to the interdisciplinary field of political ecology. Thus, a human geographer made an important and significant contribution to knowledge. For many of you, your contributions will be in the work place, possibly in applying some geographic concepts and skills.

The Evolution of Geography in Europe

Employers want graduating university and college students not only to "do things," such as be able to conduct survey research, draw a map, or manipulate a GIS, but to be critical thinkers as well. An important element in this aspect is gained by understanding some of the broader intellectual traditions that have developed over time in geography, particularly in Canada and those parts of the world that have influenced the development of geography in Canada.

The study of regions has long been a focus of geographical study. Alexander von Humboldt (1769–1859) and Carl Ritter (1779–1859) were German geographers who also focused their studies on interactions between humans and nature. In the 19th century, French geographers Élisé Reclus (1830–1905) and Paul Vidal de la Blanche (1845–1918) examined how communities existed within natural regions. Essentially, they argued that it was not possible to distinguish between natural and cultural boundaries—an idea that that forms an element of sustainability (Chapter 12).

During the Renaissance period (1350–1750), European exploration prompted governments to map their new territories. Map making (cartography) and the describing of these areas became dominant aspects of geography. Atlases were produced and governments created mapping divisions, in part, to support their claims to sovereignty and promote development in the new territories. During the 19th century, national censuses and trade statistics gave firmer foundation to human geographic investigation. During this time period, many influential individuals and government officials (predominately men) actively participated in many independent geographical societies that were located in major cities such as Paris, Berlin, London, St. Petersburg, and New York. These societies promoted exploration and held meetings to hear about far away places from guest speakers.

Modern geography, as Canadians know it, had its origins in the surge of scholarly inquiry that, beginning in the 17th century, gave rise to the traditional academic disciplines we know today. The growing importance of geography in the late 1800s was highlighted by the Prussian (now German) government's decision in 1874 to establish permanent chairs of geography at all its universities. This firmly established geography as an academic discipline. In Britain, the first personal chair of geography was established in 1833, and the first department of geography was established in 1900. The first department of geography in the United States was founded in 1903 at the University of Chicago.

FIGURE 1.5 The ski development at Whistler Mountain, British Columbia, Canada, clearly shows the interaction of physical environment and human activity. Climate and terrain have made specialized human use attractive and possible. Human exploitation has placed a cultural landscape on the natural environment, thereby altering it. This type of human activity can contribute to environmental degradation (e.g. soil erosion) and increase the local ecological footprint due to the influx of tourists.

TABLE 1.1

Geography and some of its sub-specialist areas of study

GEOGRAPHY

Physical Geography	Human Geography
Sub-specialty areas include:	*Sub-specialty areas include:*
Biogeography	Agricultural Geography
Climate Reconstruction	Cultural Geography
Climatology	Economic Geography
Coastal Geomorphology	Health Geography
Fluvial Geomorphology	Historical Geography
Paleo-environmental	International Development
Reconstruction	Political Geography
	Population Geography
	Resource and environmental
	management
	Rural Geography
	Social Geography
	Urban Geography

Canada had its first chair of a geography department in 1935. There are differences among nations about how geography should be practiced. British geographers were strongly committed to regional geography. However, relative to their counterparts in America, they were also actively engaged in physical geography while Americans did not share this level of interest. Johnston (1991: 48) attributed this difference in emphasis to the "excesses of environmental determinism (see "Environmental Determinism, Possibilism, and Probabilism"), and a subsequent desire to remove all traces of that connection and to see society as the formative agent of landscape patterns and change. . ."

Mainstream geography prior to the 1950s primarily sought to map and describe places and regions. While these are important objectives, a sense of disappointment emerged and grew among geographers in North America during the 1950s that reflected, in part, a realization that much of their work was becoming irrelevant and provided only superficial analysis. This sentiment was highlighted in a 1953 paper by Fred Schaefer (1904–1953), who challenged the discipline to adopt more scientific approaches. In Schaefer's view, geographers should be developing laws that explained location that might differentiate regions, rather than providing endless descriptions of the world. In response to this and other criticisms, systematic geography became much more popular in the 1960s, particularly in Britain, the United States, and Canada.

Systematic geographers studied the processes of systems—human (e.g., economic, transportation, political, cultural) and physical (e.g., water, geomorphic, climatic)—often operating within functional and administrative regions in order that problems could be understood and solutions provided. In the 1960s, data for systematic studies would often come from reliable published sources, such as the census or traffic records, as well as measurements from maps and air photographs. Statistical techniques, aided by emerging computer technologies, were also employed with increasing regularity. Simulation modelling, such as linear programming, was developed to forecast future conditions. Mainstream human geography in the 1960s was closely associated with urban and economic geography. A key focus of this

Between the mid-1800s to the mid-1900s, many geographers in Europe and North America, who studied how humans interacted with their environment, assumed that the environment largely determined human activities and landscapes. This perspective, referred to as **environmental determinism**, was held by many geographers including Friedrich Ratzel (1844–1904) in Germany, Ellen Churchill Semple (1863–1932) and Ellesworth Huntington (1876–1947) in the United States, and Griffith Taylor (1880–1963) in Australia and Canada. Ratzel's book, published in 1882, entitled *Anthropogeography, Outline of the Influences of the Geographical Environment upon History and Semple's Influences of the Geographic Environment* (1911) suggested how these and many other geographers perceived human–environment interactions at the time. More specifically, Semple made the following astonishing claims:

- living in a plains area is "stultifying to national life" because of its extreme monotony;
- those who live in mountain passes tend to be marauders and robbers; and
- "a cold climate puts a steadying hand on the human heart and brain" as opposed to warmer places where "national life and temperament have the buoyancy and thoughtlessness of childhood, its charm and weakness."

Huntington maintained that civilizations could best develop in regions of favourable climates (i.e., the mid-latitudes) and that the hot temperatures found in tropical latitudes precluded societies located there from achieving high levels of civilization and development. In another example, Griffith Taylor, an Australian who later became the first person to chair a geography department in Canada, opposed the Australian government's encouragement of immigration because it did not understand the limits imposed by the environment. It was these types of claims that contributed to the disrepute and decline of geography as an academic discipline in the United States, and the closing of the Geography Department at Harvard (Johnston and Sidaway, 2004). One positive aspect of environmental determinist research was the general desire by geographers to provide explanations of human settlement patterns. Previously, this emphasis had been often lacking. However, a major problem with environmental determinism was the inadequate evidence and limited attention to supporting theories and poor research design. Although environmental determinism has been discounted, remnants linger as we will see in later chapters (e.g. Chapter 11 and the Brandt Report).

A contrasting view to environmental determinism was provided by French historian Lucien Febvre (1878–1956). While **possibilism** did not deny that the environment placed some limits on human activities, it promoted that a more important factor to consider were the choices made by people in response to the opportunities and constraints provided by the environment. The possibilist approach was adopted by geographers Paul Vidal de la Blache (1845–1918) and Jean Brunhes (1869–1930) in France. Later, Isaiah Bowman (1878–1950) and Carl Sauer (1889–1975) were among its strongest proponents in the U.S. This doctrine became increasingly accepted and environmental determinism declined among the geographic community.

Probabilism is a third perspective of human–environment interactions, and lies between environmental determinism and possibilism. Probabilism suggests that based on the nature of the environment, humans will be more likely to make certain decisions over other ones. For instance, if forests are in relatively scarce supply, homes may be more frequently constructed from clay or stone rather than wood. In contrast, possibilism would identify the range of materials houses could be constructed from. In this example, probabilism attempts to measure which building material is most likely to be used in constructing houses.

research was on the measurement of direction, distance, and connectivity—important concepts of spatial interaction (Chapter 3). These geographical concepts, when combined with economic theories, provided for the development of location theories. This research was interested in establishing and explaining patterns and order in the distribution of economic activities across space. Economic geographers used mathematics, later supported by GIS, to describe and explain these spatial patterns.

In the late 1960s and early 1970s, this quantitative approach to geography was criticized because many of its theories provided for poor explanation and/or prediction of actual human use of and patterns on the landscape. The assumptions associated with location analysis assumed economic rationality–that people were motivated by economic gain–were being questioned. A view developed during this time that suggested geographic research should combine decision-making theories from psychology and sociology with geography's spatial concepts. As will be described in Chapter 3, perceptual data were obtained from people (i.e., decision makers), through such research tools as questionnaires and perceptual tests. Respondents were often grouped into

categories (e.g., floodplain resident, socio-economic status, level of experience with issue) and statistical analysis was commonly performed. Like the quantitative geographers, these researchers, called **behaviouralists**, desired to provide general explanations and to develop laws and theories such as explaining how humans adjust to hazards or the reasons for certain land use patterns in urban and agricultural areas. These outcomes are very different than those pursued by regional and quantitative geographers.

Since the 1970s, a number of philosophies and approaches have emerged as "significant" within the discipline. Two important influences—social and technological—can be identified as the drivers behind developments since the late 1960s. In the 1960s, the public's concern for a number of social issues—poverty in the Third World, civil rights, women's rights, Vietnam War, sexual freedom, concern for the environment—was rising. Development based on traditional measures, such as the accumulation of wealth or a rise in a nation's gross national product (GNP), was being questioned. Critics charged that locational analysis research had failed to adequately address the social and spatial inequities in economic development that were emerging at global and local scales. **Radical geographies**, which include the philosophies of **Marxism** and **structuralism**, adopted a progressive social agenda and provided two contributions to geography. First, as a body of knowledge, radical geographies promoted a greater understanding of why and how social problems were evident in space. For instance, in examining why people moved to specific houses, behaviouralists and logical positivists would focus attention on issues of choice, preference, and/or cost. A radical geographer would question the role of land developers and urban planners/managers in determining which sites were built upon, the style of housing available, access to facilities (e.g., police, fire), and location relative to undesirable land uses (e.g., dumps, highways, rail lines). Second, as a social movement, radical geographers wanted to redress many of the inequities that were present in societies, particularly those in many developing countries. The term "radical" was applied to these ideas because in most instances, some form of socialism was seen as the solution to problems emanating from market-driven (capitalist) economies. **Socialism** is a form of economic and social organization based on common ownership of means to produce and distribute products. It contrasts capitalism, based on private ownership of production, as the dominant form of economic and social organization in the world. Feminist geographies and post-modern geographies are more recent philosophies to be incorporated as part of the discipline (see "Feminist Geographies"). Some geographers are now adopting perspectives from **political ecology** in order to better understand how political and economic systems influence our use and perception of the natural environment. This is a significant departure from the earlier views of human–environment interactions that would have been adopted through environmental determinism. We now realize that political and economic systems can influence human impact on the environment. The significance of this discussion is the rise and fall of different philosophies within the discipline, which are often tied to changing social, political, cultural, and economic preferences.

Since the mid 1990s, geographers are seeing the value of merging economic processes with cultural, social and political factors. Rather than treating separately, cultural, social and institutional elements, this integrated approach can assist in our understanding of economies.

As an academic discipline, geography is quite strong in many developed nations. According to Moseley et al. (2007), geography is a popular subject area in the English speaking world—Canada, the United Kingdom, Australia, New Zealand and South Africa. Over the past 15 years, it has made a comeback, and geography has been reintroduced at Harvard in 2006. In the non-English speaking world, they report that several years of geography are required in the high school curricula of France, Germany, Russia, and Switzerland, and other European countries require at least one year for graduation. They also report that high school students in Japan, Korea, Taiwan, Singapore, and Malaysia are required to complete several years of geography. Li (2007) reports that student enrolment in Chinese geography programs is growing quickly.

Development of Geography in Canada

When European explorers arrived in Canada, some Aboriginal people shared their intimate knowledge of the land, even drawing maps for them (Figure 1.2) suggesting that mapping was conducted independently by societies throughout the world. What might be labelled the "exploration period," which was characterized by surveying and mapping of new lands, dominated geographic activity in Canada until about 1930.

One of the most important geographers in the history of North America was David Thompson (1770–1857) who surveyed almost 4.5 million square kilometres by foot, horseback, snowshoe, dogsled, and canoe. Like many geographers of the time, he produced maps (that covered over 20% of North America) and compiled 77 volumes of journals describing its physical features and people (Figure 1.6).

After Confederation in 1867, much of the attention of the newly created federal government departments was on mapping its natural (e.g., topography) and human (e.g., place names) aspects (see toponymy, Chapter 6). The importance of geography to the federal government was illustrated by the appointment of James White as "geographer" in 1899, and as his staff grew he became "Chief Geographer." In 1877, la Société de géographie de Québec was founded "to popularize geography, and study Québec and make it known." In 1929, the Canadian Geographical Society was formed by a few federal civil servants. It became the Royal Canadian Geographical Society in 1957. These organizations published the *Canadian Geographical Journal* (first in 1930), which later became *Canadian Geographic*.

The discipline of geography is a relatively new entrant onto the university scene in Canada. The first university department was established at the University of Toronto in 1935, headed by Griffith Taylor, an Australian geographer. He was a member of Scott's expedition to Antarctica (1910–1912). As mentioned earlier, he was an environmental determinist, who believed that the Australian government was irresponsible to suggest that the interior of that country could support 100 million people based on its dry and hot climate. Based on climatic factors, he suggested a reasonable limit was between 20 to 30 million. The Australian Government responded by banning some of his books. Shortly afterwards, Taylor left for the University of Chicago, and later formed the geography department at U of T. Other universities also formed departments of geography shortly after this time. In 1938, the University of Western Ontario hired Dr. Edward Pleva to its geology department and in 1948 he headed an independent department of geography. McMaster (1939), McGill (1945), British Columbia (1945), Manitoba (1949), and Queen's (1952) also hired geographers, who started new departments or were hired into other departments (often geology) that would lead to the later creation of new departments of geography.

Geographers often borrow the ideas of other disciplines to support their work. For example, the research findings of political economist Harold Innis played an influential role in thinking about the economic geography of Canada. He was a major contributor to **staples theory**, which suggests that the essence of Canada's culture, political history, and economy have been predominantly influenced by the exploitation and export of a series of "staples"—raw materials such as fish (cod in Atlantic Canada), timber (in Eastern and central Canada and British Columbia), fur (in central Canada), wheat (in the prairies), and fossil fuels (in western Canada and now Newfoundland). In Canada's development, fur was

Feminist Geographies

One of the most pervasive "radical" geographies to emerge in the last three decades has been "feminist geography." There are many variations on feminist theory, and hence many feminist geographies, but common to them all is the underlying premise that inequality exists between men and women, and that this inequality must be eradicated. Differences in the power, status, and resources of men and women are not biologically determined—this is considered **sexist**—but rather socially constructed through actions, attitudes, institutions, and policies that favour males over females. Male dominance is not the "natural" order of society, but a culture of **gender** dominance termed **patriarchy**: a learned way of doing and thinking that privileges men and certain forms of masculinity over women and specific types of femininity (e.g., "real" men are logical, independent, and heterosexual; "real" women are emotional, dependent, and sexually subdued). For feminist geographers—and these include both female and male geographers—human landscapes are seen as engendered with masculine and feminine characteristics, and sexist inequalities (e.g., sports bar as masculine; flower shop as feminine; higher wages for men than women). How does gender identity vary over space from one location, city, region, or country to another, and why? Which places in Canadian society are considered masculine, feminine, or gender neutral, and what processes create them? What is the geography of gender division in labour, and what are the economic, political, social, and spatial consequences? Is there gender bias in the methods social scientists use to conduct research? In the ways geographers themselves view landscapes? Feminist geographers maintain that answers to these questions will assist in achieving gender equality. Chapters 4–12 will highlight selected aspects of feminist geography and women's issues in order to provide you with greater appreciation of the contributions and perspectives of this geographic tradition.

(a)

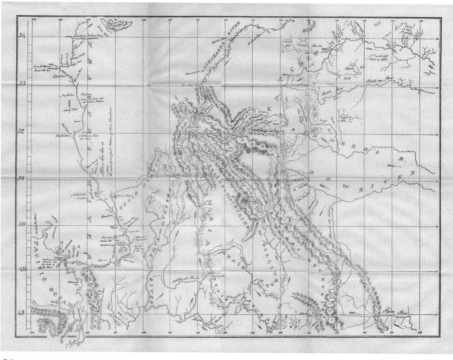

(b)

FIGURE 1.6 David Thompson—Map maker extraordinaire. David Thompson used a sextant such as the one above, as well as a watch, thermometer, and compass to survey the unexplored territories of North America. The sextant (Figure 1.6(*a*)) allowed him to locate positions by reading angles of the sun, moon, and selected stars. From these, he calculated latitude and longitude to fix the positions on his maps, such as the one provided in Figure 1.6(*b*), which is located in what is now southern B.C. and Alberta and the bordering United States of America.

the main staple and was exported to Europe. For many years, the fur trade was dominated by large firms—the North West Company and the Hudson's Bay Company. Innis suggested that the nature of trade and economic structure influenced Canada's subsequent development—a centralized, market-oriented economy reflected by the major centres of Montreal and Toronto. Innis went on to describe the economic relationship in Canada as heartland and hinterland (also see **core and periphery regions** (Chapter 3)). The hinterland was dominated by **primary industries**—those that make staples (or natural resources) available for use or further processing (see Chapters 9 and 10). The heartland dominated the hinterland and sought to manufacture goods from the staples provided from the hinterland. These and other theories have been used by geographers to describe the relationships within the global economy. Some studies of Canada's cultural, historical social characteristics, and rural and urban areas have been influenced by the ideas of historian Maurice Careless, who studies urban-rural relationships, the development of the Canadian city, and the impact of 'identity'—class, ethnicity, gender, and regionalism—in Ontario. Thus, geographers have sometimes borrowed ideas from other disciplines to conduct their research.

The Canadian Association of Geographers (CAG) was started in 1951 at a meeting in Montreal attended by 65 people. Its first honorary president was Griffith Taylor and the first president D.F. Putnam, both of whom were connected to the University of Toronto. The Canadian Association of Geographers Directory (2007) identified 45 departments of geography across the country, 26 of which had Ph.D. programs. *The Canadian Geographer* is the CAG's flagship journal and has a worldwide circulation.

In its early development, there was a strong relationship between the CAG and the public service, particularly the Geographical Branch and the Defence Research Board. Audrey Kobayashi (2001), herself a former CAG president, maintained that this relationship primarily focused on military geography, the development of Canada's north (particularly its socio-political, economic, and military aspects), and mapping and analyzing the spatial distribution of populations, cities, and economic activities. This orientation led D.F. Putman to suggest that the "duty of Canadian geographers to pursue [were] Canadian population, Canadian unity and Canadian outlook on the world" (as cited by Kobayashi, 2001). Canadian geography has focused on the large size of the country and the challenges it posed for transportation, communication, resource development, cultural diversity, and population distribution. Prior to the 1960s, geographers, who were primarily "white and male," mapped and described the spatial characteristics of the settlement of Canada from a eurocentric and male perspective.

The 1950s and 1960s saw increasing numbers of Canadian geographers using quantitative techniques, particularly to questions related to central place theory, location theory, and economic development. There was also an emphasis on describing the physical geography of the country and the impacts that human activity had upon the landscape. By the 1990s, the use of qualitative methods, which will be discussed in Chapter 2, were in vogue, and geographic research was informed by and contributed to ideas of "society, power, politics, gender, and class, ideology, culture, language and discourse" (Warf, 1995: 185). Between the 1960s and 1990s, the focus of research shifted from economic considerations to ones that were often informed by social theory and political economy. According to Wheeler (2002), the use of maps, which had been the traditional centrepiece of geographic analysis, had declined. This has been reflected in the broadening of the philosophical base of the discipline, which now includes behaviouralist, feminist, Marxist, structuralist, post-colonial, and postmodernist geographies. Human–environment relations have moved beyond environmental determinism, possiblism and probablism to include political ecology, international development,

sustainable development, environmental management, and issues related to human health. Some of these perspectives will be highlighted in forthcoming chapters.

A Geographic Approach

The basic tenets of a geographic approach may be defined as the six themes that were identified by the Canadian Council for Geographic Education (see "The Geographical Standards"). The first element in is "Physical Systems," which might be best renamed "biophysical systems" since many geographers study the plants and animals that inhabit the world with us. This, along with Human Geography, was identified as one of the main specialty area of the discipline (Table 1.1). Physical processes shape Earth's surface and interact with plant and animal life to create, sustain, and modify the cultural and natural environment. This text book does not devote much attention to this element. At the same time, the earth's surface reflects human activities, perhaps best illustrated by our urban centres. The second element noted by the Council is termed the "World in Spatial Terms," which refers to the use of maps and other geographic representations, tools, and technologies to acquire, process, and report information. In this way, the spatial variation and interrelationships among people, places, and environments are communicated. The remaining aspects essentially define how human geographers provide a spatial perspective to their studies. Integrating these elements has traditionally been viewed as leading to the third element, "Places and Regions." Geographers study regions: the physical and human systems, their spatial relationship, interactions between society and environment in specific locational settings. The study of "Human Systems" examines the spatial organization of society, which is a mosaic of population movements, settlement patterns, economic activity, transportation, communication, and political organizations. Finally, geography examines relationships between "Society and the Environment." For instance, early settlers cleared the land to plant crops and graze livestock. Biophysical factors, such as soil fertility, slope, weather, and climate, influenced these land use decisions. Today, the impacts arising from air and water pollution and the management of solid waste and hazardous materials are of concern to people. These specialized subfields suggest the diversity of the discipline but also its interrelatedness. The meaning and significance of place, as illustrated by differences between a "house" and a "home" must be understood. Finally, the Council suggested that students must understand the "Uses of Geography." Kofi Annan made reference to some of the geographic tools and technology that are required for some of the UN's initiatives. The earlier feature, "Careers in Geography," indicates the variety of opportunities for geographers to apply their craft daily.

Table 1.1 indicated some of the specialization within the discipline. If we now apply the Geographical Standards to the human geography elements of that table, we develop a matrix that can assist us in better understanding the discipline (Table 1.2). The matrix illustrates how geographers might approach their specialized research interests from a geographical perspective. Geographic research of many varieties is often supported through

The Geographical Standards

According to the Canadian Council for Geographic Education, the six standards listed below specify the essential subject matter, skills, and perspectives that students who have gone through the Canadian public school system should acquire and use. Although not all of the standards are relevant to our study of human geography, together they help frame the kinds of understanding we will seek in the following pages and suggest the purpose and benefit of further study of geography. The geographically informed person knows about the following:

Physical Systems

1. The physical processes that shape the patterns of Earth's surface.
2. The characteristics and spatial distribution of ecosystems on Earth's surface.

The World in Spatial Terms

3. How to use maps and other geographic tools and technologies to acquire, process, and report information from a spatial perspective.

4. How to use mental maps to organize information about people, places, and environments in a spatial context.
5. How to analyze the spatial organization of people, places, and environments on Earth's surface.

Places and Regions

6. The physical and human characteristics of places.
7. That people create regions to interpret Earth's complexity.
8. How culture and experience influence people's perceptions of places and regions.

Human Systems

9. The characteristics, distribution, and migration of human populations on Earth's surface.
10. The characteristics, distribution, and complexity of Earth's cultural mosaics.
11. The patterns and networks of economic interdependence on Earth's surface.

12. The processes, patterns, and functions of human settlement.
13. How the forces of cooperation and conflict among people influence the division and control of Earth's surface.

Society and the Environment

14. How human actions modify the physical environment.
15. How physical systems affect human systems.
16. The changes that occur in the meaning, use, distribution, and importance of resources.

The Uses of Geography

17. How to apply geography to interpret the past.
18. How to apply geography to interpret the present and plan for the future.

Source: Canadian National Standards for Geography: A Standards-Based Guide to K–12 Geography *2001. http://www.rcgs.org/ccge/english/Pro_development/docs/Canadian_Geography_Standards.doc.*

---

field work, maps, GIS, quantitative, or qualitative methods. These techniques reflect the "World in Spatial Terms" standard. These techniques provide the means for geographers to specialized issues from one of the three substantive standards—Places and Regions, Human Systems, and Society and the Environment. It is their perspective as well as their tools that distinguishes a social, economic or political geographer from a sociologist, economist or political scientist. Also be aware that geographers and others

academics will adopt a philosophical perspective—behaviouralist, radical, Marxist, political-ecology, structuralist, post-modern, post-colonial, and feminist are a few examples previously mentioned. Having an understanding of a geographer's perspective enhances the understanding of the remaining chapters that are focused on the major sub-specialty fields in human geography. Before turning attention to these matters, it is important to understand some basic concepts.

Some Background Basics

Core Geographic Concepts

The topics included in human geography are diverse, but that very diversity emphasizes the reality that all geographers are united by the similar questions they ask and the common set of basic concepts. They will often ask: What is it? Where is it? How did it come to be what and where it is? Where is it in relation to other things that affect it or are affected by it? How is it part of a functioning whole? How does its location affect people's lives and the content of the area in which it is found? These and similar questions are

rooted in geography's central concern with *space* and *place* and in the special meanings geographers attach to those terms.

For geographers, *space* implies areal extent and may be understood in both an absolute and a relative sense. *Absolute space* is objectively and physically real with measurable extent and definable boundaries. In that sense, space is fundamental to areal relationships between physical or cultural features on the earth's surface and is basic to such geographic interests as making maps, analyzing distributions, and conducting spatial analysis of locational patterns. *Relative space* is perceptual, not objective, and variable, not permanent, over time. In this relative sense, space can be seen as socially produced, reflecting activities and the interrelationships between activities. Since activities and relationships are constantly changing, relative space adjusts in size and form in response to developing socio-economic processes and the passage of time.

For human geographers, *place* is the companion concept to *space*. In common understanding, *place* is a synonym for *location*. In human geography, however, *place* refers to the attributes and values we individually associate with a location. Our home town and neighbourhood, the university we attend, a favourite downtown shopping area, and the like are all examples. Clearly, *our sense of place*—the attachments we have to specific locations and their complex of attributes—is unique to each of us, though we may share some aspects of our regard for a place with many others. And clearly, too, we can even have a favourable sense of place about locations we may never have personally experienced: Rome or Mecca or Jerusalem, for example, or—closer to home— the West Edmonton Mall or Yellowknife.

Our individual or group sense of place and attachments can, of course, set us off from others. Our home neighbourhood that we find familiar and view favourably may equally be seen as alien and, perhaps, dangerous by others. The attributes and culture of places shape the lives and outlooks of those who inhabit them in ways basic to the socio-economic patterning of the world. The viewpoints, normative behaviour, religious and cultural beliefs, and ways of life absorbed and expressed by a white, middle-class, suburban Canadian are undoubtedly vastly different from the understandings, cultural convictions, and life expectations of, for example, a young, unemployed male resident of Baghdad or the slums of Cairo. The implicit, ingrained, place-induced differences between the two help us understand the resistance to the globalization of Western social and economic values by those of vastly different cultural backgrounds and place identification.

The sense of place is reinforced by recognized local and regional distinctiveness. It may be diminished or lost and replaced by a feeling of *placelessness* as the uniformity of brand-name fast-food outlets (Figure 1.4), national retail store chains, uniform shopping malls, repetitive highway billboards, and the like, spread nationally and even internationally, reducing or eliminating the uniqueness of formerly separated locales and cultures. We'll examine some aspects of the sense of place and placelessness in Chapter 6.

Geographers use the word *spatial* as an essential modifier in framing their questions and forming their concepts. Geography, they say, is a *spatial* science. It is concerned with *spatial behaviour* of people, with the *spatial relationships* that are observed between places on the earth's surface, and with the *spatial processes* that create or maintain those behaviours and relationships. The word *spatial* comes, of course, from *space*, and to geographers, it always carries the idea of the way items are distributed, the way movements occur, and the way processes operate over the whole or a part of the surface of the earth. The geographer's space, then, is earth space, the surface area occupied or available to be occupied by humans. Spatial phenomena have locations on that surface, and spatial interactions occur among places, things,

and people within the earth area available to them. The need to understand those relationships, interactions, and processes helps frame the questions that geographers ask.

Additionally, those questions have their starting point in basic observations about the location and nature of places and about how places are similar to or different from one another. Such observations, though simply stated, are profoundly important to our comprehension of the world we occupy.

- Places have location, direction, and distance with respect to other places.
- A place has size; it may be large or small. Scale is important.
- A place has both physical structure and cultural content.
- The attributes of places develop and change over time.
- The elements of places interrelate with other places.
- The content of places is structured and explainable.
- Places may be generalized into regions of similarities and differences.

These are basic notions understandable to everyone. They also are the means by which geographers express fundamental observations about the earth spaces they examine and put those observations into a common framework of reference. Each of the concepts is worth further discussion, for they are not quite as simple as they at first seem.

Location, Direction, and Distance

Location, direction, and *distance* are everyday ways of assessing the space around us and identifying our position in relation to other items and places of interest. They are also essential in understanding the processes of spatial interaction that figure so importantly in the study of human geography.

Location

The location of places and objects is the starting point of all geographic study as well as of all our personal movements and spatial actions in everyday life. We think of and refer to location in at least two different senses, *absolute* and *relative*.

Absolute location is the identification of place by some precise and accepted system of coordinates; it therefore is sometimes called *mathematical location*. We have several such accepted systems of pinpointing positions. One of them is the global grid of parallels and meridians, which will be discussed in Chapter 2. With it, the absolute location of any point on the earth can be accurately described by reference to its degrees, minutes, and seconds of *latitude* and *longitude* (Figure 1.7).

Other coordinate systems are also in use. Survey systems such as the township, range, and section description of property in much of Canada (see "The Ethnic Landscape," Chapter 5) give mathematical locations on a regional level, while a street address precisely defines a building according to the reference system of an individual town. For convenience or special purposes, locational grid references may be superimposed on the basic global grid.

TABLE 1.2

Human Geography and the Geographic Standards

Human Geography Specializations	THE SUBSTANTIVE GEOGRAPHIC STANDARDS		
	Places and Regions	Human Systems	Society and the Environment
Agricultural Geography	Where is the wheat belt?	How is wheat transported from fields to the market? In terms of farming practices? What are the similarities and differences between male and female wheat farmers?	What is the ecological footprint of wheat farming?
Cultural Geography	Why do Montreal, Toronto and Vancouver all have 'Chinatowns'?	What social processes encourage or compel ethnic concentration within cities?	Has the ancient Chinese practice of landscape interpretation—*Feng Shui*—played a role in the design and development of Chinatowns?
Economic Geography	Why do rents and real estate prices vary within the same city?	What does the highest rents and prices tell us about location preferences?	Is there a direct relationship between low rents and prices and high rates of environmental pollution?
Health Geography	Which countries have the highest and lowest total cancer rates?	What are the similarities and differences between these two countries in terms of economic development, diet and lifestyle?	Which of the two countries has the higher level of air and water pollution? Which country uses more agricultural pesticides?
Historical Geography	Why is Ottawa the capital of Canada?	Who or what body ultimately made the final selection? What social factors favoured Ottawa over other potential locations?	How important was the Ottawa River and other physical features in the selection process?
International Development	How should we measure development and what is the pattern of underdevelopment in the world?	What are the causes of underdevelopment? What could/should be done to reduce poverty?	How does poverty contribute to environmental degradation?
Political Geography	How should disputed boundaries resolved and established?	How do land-locked states secure access to coastal areas?	How should freshwater systems that are shared by two or more countries be allocated?
Population Geography	Where do most immigrants to Canada come from?	Why do they come to Canada? Where do they settle and why? To what cities and portions of cities do they move? Why? How do they travel here?	What is the impact of human population on the environment?
Resource and Environmental Management	Where are the world's most threatened ecosystems?	What is the flow of pollutants through an ecosystem?	How should resource development decision making address environmental and social concerns?
Rural Geography	Why does the number of Canadian farmers continue to decline?	What is the role of economic globalization on farming rates in Canada?	What are the environmental costs of consuming imported food rather than locally grown?
Social Geography	Why does homelessness persist in Canada when we know how to build shelters?	What are the economic, social, political, and spatial barriers to solving this problem?	How do the changing seasons impact the immediate needs of those living on the street?
Urban Geography	How is an 'urban region' or 'city' defined? Is there a difference between these terms?	What is the movement of people within a city over the day? How do people move within the city?	What is the relationship between urban form and human health?

The World in Spatial Terms

* Field Work * Maps * GIS * Quantitative Methods * Qualitative Methods

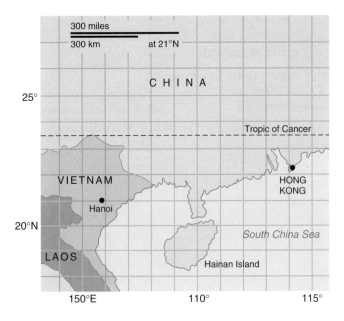

FIGURE 1.7 The latitude and longitude of Hong Kong is 22° 15′ N, 114° 10′ E (read as 22 degrees, 15 minutes north; 114 degrees, 10 minutes east). The circumference of the earth measures 360 degrees; each degree contains 60 minutes and each minute has 60 seconds of latitude or longitude. What are the coordinates of Hanoi?

FIGURE 1.8 The reality of *relative location* on the globe may be strikingly different from the impressions we form from flat maps. The position of Russia with respect to North America when viewed from a polar perspective emphasizes that relative location properly viewed is important to our understanding of spatial relationships and interactions between the two world areas.

The Universal Transverse Mercator (UTM) system (see Chapter 2) is widely used in geographic information system (GIS) applications and, with different notations, as a military grid reference system. Absolute location is unique to each described place, is independent of any other characteristic or observation about that place, and has obvious value in the legal description of places, in measuring the distance separating places, or in finding directions between places on the earth's surface.

When geographers—or real estate agents—remark that "location matters," however, their reference is usually not to absolute but to **relative location**—the position of a place in relation to that of other places or activities (Figure 1.8). Relative location expresses spatial interconnection and interdependence and may carry social (neighbourhood character) and economic (assessed valuations of vacant land) implications. On an immediate and personal level, we think of the location of the university library not in terms of its street address or room number but where it is relative to our residence, home faculty building, the student centre, or some other reference point. On the larger scene, relative location tells us that people, things, and places exist not in a spatial vacuum but in a world of physical and cultural characteristics that differ from place to place.

Montreal, for example, may be described in absolute terms as being located at (approximately) latitude 45° 28′ N and longitude 73° 45′ W. We gain a better understanding of the significance of its location, however, when reference is made to its spatial relationships: located near the Lachine Rapids on the St. Lawrence River, the furthest point ocean tankers can travel prior to entering the St. Lawrence Seaway; and along the major highway and railway systems connecting Atlantic Canada to the rest of Canada. Its location relative to Ottawa, Quebec City, eastern Canada,

and Toronto would amplify its situational characteristics. Within the City of Montreal, we gain understanding of the locational significance of Outremont, Mount Royal, Pointe Claire, and Westmount, not solely by reference to the street addresses or city blocks they occupy, but by their spatial and functional relationships to the total land use, activity, and population patterns of Montreal.

In view of these different ways of looking at location, geographers make a distinction between the site and the situation of a place. **Site,** an absolute location concept, refers to the physical and cultural characteristics and attributes of the place itself. It is more than mathematical location, for it tells us something about the internal features of that place. These would include the climate, soils, water sources, vegetation, elevation, latitude, and longitude. The site of Saskatoon, for example, is on the South Saskatchewan River, which divides the city into east and west (Figure 1.9). **Situation,** on the other hand, refers to the external relations of a locale and provides insight into the importance of a place. The situation of Saskatoon is reflected in its nickname "Hub City" because both of Canada's major rail operators, the Canadian Pacific Railway, and the Canadian National Railway have lines running to the city. Saskatoon also has 9 major highways meet in the city (Figure 1.10).

Direction

Direction is a second universal spatial concept. Like location, it has more than one meaning and can be expressed in absolute or relative terms. **Absolute direction** is based on the cardinal points of north, south, east, and west. These appear uniformly and independently

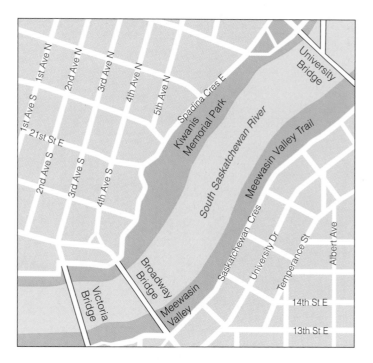

FIGURE 1.9 The site of Saskatoon.

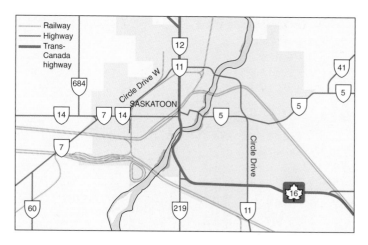

FIGURE 1.10 Road and Rail Lines in Saskatoon reflect, in part, the city's situation.

in all cultures, derived from the obvious "givens" of nature: the rising and setting of the sun for east and west, the sky location of the noontime sun and of certain fixed stars for north and south.

We also commonly use **relative** or *relational* **directions**. In Canada we go "down East," "out West," or "down South," and "up North." We refer to the "Near East" or economic competition from the "Far Eastern countries." These directional references are culturally based and locationally variable, despite their reference to cardinal compass points. The Near and the Far East locate parts of Asia from the European perspective; they are retained in the Canada by custom and usage, even though one would normally travel westward across the Pacific, for example, to reach the "Far East" from California, British Columbia, or Chile. For many Canadians, "out West" reflects the migration paths of earlier generations for whom home was in the eastern part of the country, to which they might look back. "Up North" and "down South" reflect our accepted custom of putting north at the top and south at the bottom of our maps. These relative directional references are also relative locational ones.

Distance

Distance joins location and direction as a commonly understood term that has dual meanings for geographers. Like its two companion spatial concepts, distance may be viewed in both an absolute and a relative sense.

Absolute distance refers to the spatial separation between two points on the earth's surface measured by some accepted standard unit such as miles or kilometres for widely separated locales, feet or metres for more closely spaced points. **Relative distance** transforms those linear measurements into other units more meaningful for the space relationship in question.

To know that two competing malls are about equidistant in kilometres from your residence is perhaps less important in planning your shopping trip than is knowing that because of street conditions or traffic congestion, one is 5 minutes and the other 15 minutes away. Most people, in fact, think of time distance rather than linear distance in their daily activities; downtown is 20 minutes by bus, the library is a 5-minute walk. In some instances, money rather than time may be the distance transformation. An urban destination might be estimated to be a $10 cab ride away, information that may affect either the decision to make the trip at all or the choice of travel mode to get there. Another common relative distance measure is the "block" (e.g., "I live five blocks from campus."). In rural Canada, a number of terms might be used. In Quebec, reference is made to the "rang." People in Ontario refer to "concessions," while residents west of Ontario refer to the "section." In coastal areas, reference is made to "the bay (e.g., "I live two bays down the coast.").

A *psychological* transformation of linear distance is also frequent. The solitary late-night walk back to the car through an unfamiliar or dangerous neighbourhood seems far longer than a daytime stroll of the same distance through familiar and friendly territory. A first-time trip to a new destination frequently seems much longer than the return trip over the same path. Distance relationships, their measurement, and their meaning for human spatial interaction are fundamental to our understanding of human geography. They are a subject of Chapter 3, and reference to them recurs throughout this book.

Size and Scale

When we say that a place may be large or small, we speak both of the nature of the place itself and of the generalizations that can be made about it. In either instance, geographers are concerned with **scale**, though we may use that term in different ways. We can, for example, study a problem—say, population or agriculture—at the local scale, the regional scale, or on a global scale. Here the reference is purely to the size of unit studied. In this context, scale is

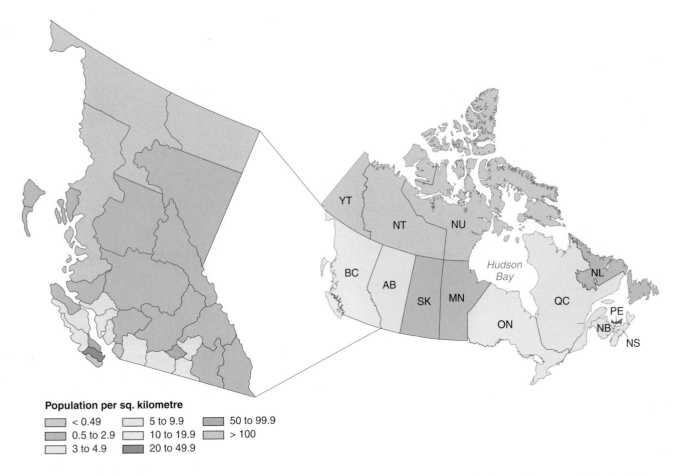

Population per sq. kilometre

- < 0.49
- 0.5 to 2.9
- 3 to 4.9
- 5 to 9.9
- 10 to 19.9
- 20 to 49.9
- 50 to 99.9
- > 100

FIGURE 1.11 Population Density and Map Scale. "Truth" depends on one's scale of inquiry. Map (a) reveals the maximum population density in Canada was no more than 50 people per square kilometre. The inset map of B.C. suggests that population densities exceed this by at least 5 times (>100 people per square kilometre). If we were to reduce our scale of inquiry even further, examining city blocks in Vancouver, we would find densities reaching 100s or more people per square kilometre. Scale matters!

Source: Statistics Canada, 2006 Census.

a human construct and operates on a continuum—from local to global. More technically, scale tells us the mathematical relationship between the size of an area on a map and the actual size of the mapped area on the surface of the earth (see Figure 1.11). In this sense, scale is a feature of every map and essential to recognizing the areal meaning of what is shown on that map.

In both senses of the word, scale implies the degree of generalization represented. Geographic inquiry may be broad or narrow; it occurs in many different size scales. Appreciating the scale of analysis is extremely important to a geographer because different insights can be made at different scales. The study of world agricultural patterns may refer to global climate regimes, cultural food preferences, levels of economic development, and patterns of world trade. These large-scale relationships are of little concern in a study of the crop patterns with the lower Fraser River valley of the Clay Belt in Ontario where topography, soil and drainage conditions, farm size, ownership and capitalization, or even personal management preferences may be a greater explanatory significance.

Physical and Cultural Attributes

All places have physical and cultural attributes that distinguish them from other places and give them character, potential, and meaning. Geographers are concerned with identifying and analyzing the details of those attributes and, particularly, with recognizing the interrelationship between the physical and cultural components of area: the human–environmental interface.

Physical characteristics refer to such natural aspects of a locale as its climate and soil, the presence or absence of water supplies and mineral resources, its terrain features, and the like. These **natural landscape** attributes provide the setting within which human action occurs. They help shape—but do not dictate—how people live. The resource base, for example, is physically determined, though how resources are perceived and utilized is culturally conditioned.

Environmental circumstances directly affect agricultural potential and reliability; indirectly they may influence such matters as employment patterns, trade flows, population distributions,

FIGURE 1.12 Sites (and sights) such as the filth-strewn water of Manila Bay, Philippines, are all-too-frequent reminders of the adverse environmental impacts of humans and their waste products. Many of those impacts are more subtle, hidden in the form of soil erosion, increased stream sedimentation, plant and animal extinctions, deforestation, and the like.

and national diets. The physical environment simultaneously presents advantages and drawbacks with which humans must deal.

FIGURE 1.13 This NASA image reveals contrasting cultural landscapes along the Mexico–California border. Move your eyes from the Salton Sea (the dark patch at the top of the image) southward to the agricultural land extending to the edge of the image. Notice how the regularity of the fields and the bright colours (representing growing vegetation) give way to a marked break, where irregularly shaped fields and less prosperous agriculture are evident. Above the break is the Imperial Valley of California; below the border is Mexico.

Thus, the danger of typhoons in central China or monsoonal floods in Bangladesh must be balanced against the agricultural bounty derived from the regions' favourable terrain, soil, and moisture conditions.

At the same time, by occupying a given place, people modify its environmental conditions. The existence of agencies such as Environment Canada (and its counterparts elsewhere) is a reminder that humans are the active and frequently harmful agents in the continuing interplay between the cultural and physical worlds (Figure 1.12). Virtually every human activity leaves its imprint on an area's soils, water, vegetation, animal life, and other resources and on the atmosphere common to all earth space. The impact of humans has been so universal and so long exerted that essentially no "natural landscape" any longer exists.

The visible expression of that human activity is the **cultural landscape**. It, too, exists at different scales and different levels of visibility. Differences in agricultural practices and land use between Mexico and southern California are evident in Figure 1.13, while the signs, structures, and people of, for instance, Vancouver's Chinatown leave a smaller, more confined imprint within the larger cultural landscape of the metropolitan area itself.

Although the focus of this book is on the human characteristics of places, geographers are ever aware that the physical content of an area is also important in understanding the activity patterns of people and the interconnections between people and the environments they occupy and modify. Those interconnections and modifications are not static or permanent, however, but are subject to continual change. For example, marshes and wetlands, when drained, may be transformed into productive, densely settled farmland, while the threat or occurrence of eruption of a long-dormant volcano may quickly and drastically alter established patterns of farming, housing, and transportation on or near its flanks.

The Changing Attributes of Place

The physical environment surrounding us seems eternal and unchanging but, of course, it is not. In the framework of geologic time, change is both continuous and pronounced. Islands form and disappear; mountains rise and are worn low to swampy plains; vast continental glaciers form, move, and melt away, and sea levels fall and rise in response. Geologic time is long, but the forces that give shape to the land are timeless and relentless.

Even within the short period of time since the most recent retreat of continental glaciers—some 11,000 or 12,000 years ago—the environments occupied by humans have been subject to change. Glacial retreat itself marked a period of climatic alteration, extending the area habitable by humans to include vast reaches of northern Eurasia and North America formerly covered by hundreds of metres of ice. With moderating climatic conditions came associated changes in vegetation and fauna. On the global scale, these were natural environmental changes; humans were as yet too few in numbers and too limited in technology to alter materially the course of physical events. On the regional scale, however, even early human societies exerted an impact on the environments they occupied. Fire was used to clear forest undergrowth, to maintain or extend grassland for grazing animals and to drive them in the hunt, and later to clear openings for rudimentary agriculture.

With the dawn of civilizations and the invention and spread of agricultural technologies, humans accelerated their management and alteration of the now no longer "natural" environment. Even the classical Greeks noted how the landscape they occupied differed—for the worse—from its former condition. With growing numbers of people and particularly with industrialization and the spread of European exploitative technologies throughout the world, the pace of change in the content of area accelerated. The built landscape—the product of human effort—increasingly replaced the natural landscape. Each new settlement or city, each agricultural assault on forests, each new mine, dam, or factory changed the content of regions and altered the temporarily established spatial interconnections between humans and the environment.

Characteristics of places today are the result of constantly changing past conditions. They are, as well, the forerunners of differing human–environmental balances yet to be struck. Geographers are concerned with places at given moments of time. But to understand fully the nature and development of places, to appreciate the significance of their relative locations, and to comprehend the interplay of their physical and cultural characteristics, geographers must view places as the present result of the past operation of distinctive physical and cultural processes (Figure 1.14).

FIGURE 1.14 The process of change in a cultural landscape. Before the development of the freeway in the 1970s, this portion of suburban Long Island, New York, was largely devoted to agriculture (top). The construction of the freeway and cloverleaf interchange ramps altered nearby land uses (bottom) to replace farming with housing developments and new commercial and light industrial activities.

FIGURE 1.15 Air Canada's Routes. An indication of one form of spatial interaction and connectivity is suggested by this map of Air Canada's air routes around the world.

Source: Reproduced with the permission of Air Canada.

You will recall that one of the questions geographers ask about a place or thing is "How did it come to be what and where it is?" This is an inquiry about process and about becoming. The forces and events shaping the physical and explaining the cultural environment of places today are an important focus of geography. They are, particularly in their human context, the subjects of most of the separate chapters of this book. To understand them is to appreciate more fully the changing human spatial order of our world.

Interrelations between Places

The concepts of relative location and distance that we earlier introduced lead directly to a fundamental spatial reality: Places interact with other places in structured and comprehensible ways. In describing the processes and patterns of that **spatial interaction**, geographers add *accessibility* and *connectivity* to the ideas of location and distance.

Tobler's First Law of Geography tells us that in a spatial sense everything is related to everything else but that relationships are stronger when items are near one another. Our observation, therefore, is that interaction between places diminishes in intensity and frequency as distance between them increases—a statement of the idea of *distance decay,* which we explore in Chapter 3. Think about it—are you more likely to go to a restaurant next door or to a nearly identical restaurant across town? Human decision making is unpredictable in many ways and decisions are frequently made for obscure reasons, but in this case you can see how you will probably frequent the nearer place more often.

Consideration of distance implies assessment of **accessibility**. How easy or difficult is it to overcome the "friction of distance?" That is, how easy or difficult is it to surmount the barrier of the time and space separation of places? Distance isolated North America from Europe until the development of ships (and aircraft) that reduced the effective distance between the continents. All parts of the ancient and medieval city were accessible by walking; they were "pedestrian cities," a status lost as cities expanded in area and population with industrialization. Accessibility between city districts could be maintained only by the development of public transit systems whose fixed lines of travel increased ease of movement between connected points and reduced it between areas not on the transit lines themselves.

Accessibility, therefore, suggests the idea of **connectivity**, a broader concept implying all the tangible and intangible ways in which places are connected: by physical telephone lines, street and road systems, airline routes, pipelines and sewers; by unrestrained walking across open countryside; by radio and TV broadcasts beamed outward uniformly from a central source (Figure 1.15). Where routes are fixed and flow is channelized, *networks*—the patterns of routes connecting sets of places—determine the efficiency of movement and the connectedness of points. Demand for universal instantaneous accessibility and connectivity is common and unquestioned in today's advanced societies. Technologies and devices to achieve it proliferate, as our own lifestyles show. Cell phones, e-mail, broadband wireless Internet access, instant messaging, and more have erased time and distance barriers formerly separating and isolating individuals and groups, and have reduced our dependence on physical movement and on networks fixed in the landscape. The realities of accessibility and connectivity clearly change over time.

There is, inevitably, interchange between connected places. **Spatial diffusion** is the process of dispersion of an idea or an item from a centre of origin to more distant points with which it is directly or indirectly connected. The rate and extent of that diffusion are affected by the distance separating the originating centre of, say, a new idea or technology and other places where it is eventually adopted. Diffusion rates are also affected by population densities, means of communication, obvious advantages of the innovation, and importance or prestige of the originating *node*. These ideas of diffusion are further explored in Chapter 5.

Geographers study the dynamics of spatial relationships. Movement, connection, and interaction are part of the social and economic processes that give character to places and regions. Geography's study of those relationships recognizes that spatial interaction is not just an awkward necessity but a fundamental organizing principle of human life on earth. That recognition has become universal, repeatedly expressed in the term *globalization*. **Globalization** implies the increasing interconnection of peoples and societies in all parts of the world as the full range of social, cultural, political, economic, and environmental processes becomes international in scale and effect. Promoted by continuing advances in worldwide accessibility and connectivity, globalization encompasses other core geographic concepts of spatial interaction, accessibility, connectivity, and diffusion. More detailed implications of globalization will be touched on in later chapters of this text.

The Structured Content of Place

A starting point for geographic inquiry is how objects are distributed in area—for example, the placement of schools or supermarkets within a town. That interest distinguishes geography from other sciences, physical or social, and underlies many of the questions geographers ask: Where is a thing located? How is that location related to other items? How did the location we observe come to exist? Such questions carry the conviction that the contents of an area are comprehensibly arranged or structured. The arrangement of items on the earth's surface is called **spatial distribution** and may be analyzed by the elements common to all spatial distributions: *density, dispersion,* and *pattern*.

Density

The measure of the number or quantity of anything within a defined unit of area is its **density**. It is therefore not simply a count of items but of items in relation to the space in which they are found. When the relationship is absolute, as in population per square kilometre, for example, or dwelling units per acre, we are defining *arithmetic density*. Sometimes it is more meaningful to relate item numbers to a specific kind of area. *Physiological density*, for example, is a measure of the number of persons per

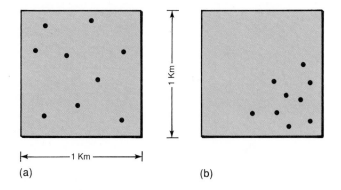

FIGURE 1.16 Density and dispersion each tell us something different about how items are distributed in an area. *Density* is simply the number of items or observations within a defined area; it remains the same no matter how the items are distributed. The density of houses per square kilometre, for example, is the same in both (*a*) and (*b*). *Dispersion* is a statement about nearness or separation. The houses in (*a*) are more *dispersed* than those shown *clustered* in (*b*).

unit area of arable land. Density defined in population terms is discussed in Chapter 4.

Dispersion

Dispersion (or its opposite, **concentration**) is a statement of the amount of *spread* of a phenomenon over an area. It tells us not how many or how much but how far things are spread out. If they are close together spatially, they are considered *clustered* or *agglomerated*. If they are spread out, they are *dispersed* or *scattered* (Figure 1.16).

If the entire population of a metropolitan county were all located within a confined central city, we might say the population was clustered. If, however, that same population redistributed itself, with many city residents moving to the suburbs and occupying a larger portion of the county's territory, it would become more dispersed. In both cases, the *density* of population (numbers in relation to area of the county) would be the same, but the distribution would have changed. Since dispersion deals with the separation of things one from another, a distribution that might be described as *clustered* (closely spaced) at one scale of reference might equally well be considered *dispersed* (widely spread) at another scale.

Pattern

The geometric arrangement of objects in space is called **pattern**. Like dispersion, pattern refers to distribution, but that reference emphasizes design rather than spacing (Figure 1.17). The distribution of towns along a railroad or houses along a street may be seen as *linear*. A *centralized* pattern may involve items concentrated around a single node. A *random* pattern may be the best description of an unstructured irregular distribution.

The rectangular system of land survey adopted in much of Canada creates a checkerboard rural pattern of "sections" and

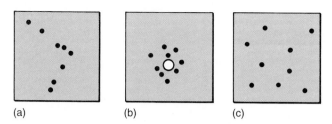

FIGURE 1.17 *Pattern* describes spatial arrangement and design. The *linear* pattern of towns in (*a*) perhaps traces the route of a road or railroad or the course of a river. The central city in (*b*) with its nearby suburbs represents a *centralized* pattern, while the dots in (*c*) are *randomly* distributed.

"quarter-sections" of farmland (see Figure 6.15). As a result, in most Canadian cities, streets display a *grid* or *rectilinear* pattern. The same is true of cities in Australia, New Zealand, the United States, and South Africa, which adopted similar geometric survey systems. The *hexagonal* pattern of service areas of farm towns is a mainstay of central place theory discussed in Chapter 10. These references to the geometry of distribution patterns help us visualize and describe the structured arrangement of items in space. They help us make informed comparisons between areas and use the patterns we discern to ask further questions about the interrelationship of things.

Place Similarity and Regions

The distinctive characteristics of places in content and structure immediately suggest two geographically important ideas. The first is that no two places on the surface of the earth can be *exactly* the same. Not only do they have different absolute locations, but—as in the features of the human face—the precise mix of physical and cultural characteristics of a place is never exactly duplicated.

Because geography is a spatial science, the inevitable uniqueness of place would seem to impose impossible problems of generalizing spatial information. That this is not the case results from the second important idea: The physical and cultural content of an area and the dynamic interconnections of people and places show patterns of spatial similarity. For example, a geographer doing fieldwork in France might find that all farmers in one area use a similar specialized technique to build fences around their fields. Often, such similarities are striking enough for us to conclude that spatial regularities exist. They permit us to recognize and define **regions**—earth areas that display significant elements of internal uniformity and external difference from surrounding territories. Places are, therefore, both unlike and like other places, creating patterns of areal differences and of coherent spatial similarity.

The problem of the historian and the geographer is similar. Each must generalize about items of study that are essentially unique. The historian creates arbitrary but meaningful and useful historical periods for reference and study. The "Roaring Twenties" and the "Victorian Era" are shorthand summary names for specific time spans, internally quite complex and varied but

significantly distinct from what went before or followed after. The region is the geographer's equivalent of the historian's era. It is a device of areal generalization that segregates into component parts the complex reality of the earth's surface. In both the time and the space need for generalization, attention is focused on key unifying elements or similarities of the era or area selected for study. In both the historical and geographical cases, the names assigned to those times and places serve to identify the time span or region and to convey between speaker and listener a complex set of interrelated attributes.

All of us have a general idea of the meaning of region, and all of us refer to regions in everyday speech and action. We visit "the old neighbourhood" or "go downtown"; or we speculate about the effects of weather conditions in the Prairies on next year's food prices. In each instance, we have mental images of the areas mentioned, and in each, we have engaged in an informal place classification to pass along quite complex spatial, organizational, or content ideas. We have applied the **regional concept** to bring order to the immense diversity of the earth's surface.

Regions are not "given" in nature any more than "eras" are given in the course of human events. Regions are devised; they are spatial summaries designed to bring order to the infinite diversity of the earth's surface. At their root, they are based on the recognition and mapping of *spatial distributions*—the territorial occurrence of environmental, human, or organizational features selected for study. For example, the location of Welsh speakers in Britain is a distribution that can be identified and mapped. As many spatial distributions exist as there are imaginable physical, cultural, or connectivity elements of area to examine. Since regions are mental constructs, different observers employing different criteria may bestow the same regional identity on differently bounded areal units (Figure 1.18). In each case, however, the key characteristics that are selected for study are those that contribute to the understanding of a specific topic or problem.

Types of Regions

Regions may be *formal, functional,* or *perceptual.* A **formal** or **uniform region** is one of essential uniformity in one or a limited combination of physical or cultural features. Your home province is a precisely bounded formal political region within which uniformity of law and administration is found. The "Bible Belt" in the United States suggests a region based on religious characteristics. Later in this book we will encounter formal (homogeneous) cultural regions in which standardized characteristics of language, religion, ethnicity, or economy exist. Figure 1.19a and the foldout maps of landform regions and country units show other formal regional patterns. Whatever the basis of its definition, the formal region is the largest area over which a valid generalization of attribute uniformity may be made. Whatever is stated about one part of it holds true for its remainder.

The **functional** or **nodal region**, in contrast, may be visualized as a spatial system. Its parts are interdependent, and throughout its extent the functional region operates as a dynamic, organizational unit. A functional region has unity not in the sense

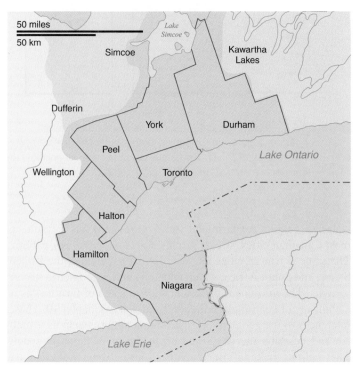

The Golden Horseshoe

FIGURE 1.18 The Golden Horseshoe. Agreement on the need to recognize spatial order and to define regional units does not imply unanimity in the selection of boundary criteria as illustrated above. All the sources above concur in the significance of the Golden Horseshoe as a regional entity in the spatial structure of Canada and agree on its core area. These sources differ, however, in their assessment of its limiting characteristics.

Source: Maps Courtesy: Mobile Business Communications, Ltd.

of static content but in the manner of its operational connectivity. It has a *core* area in which its characterizing features are most clearly defined; they lessen in prominence toward the region's margins or *periphery.* As the degree and extent of areal control and interaction change, the boundaries of a functional region change in response. Trade areas of towns, national "spheres of influence," and the territories subordinate to the financial, administrative, wholesaling, or retailing centrality exercised by regional centres are cases in point (Figure 1.19b).

Perceptual regions are less rigorously structured than the formal and functional regions geographers devise. They reflect feelings and images rather than objective data and because

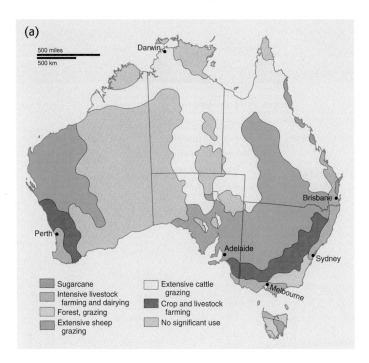

(a)

of that may be more meaningful in the lives and actions of those who recognize them than are the more abstract regions of geographers.

Ordinary people have a clear idea of spatial variation and employ the regional concept to distinguish between territorial entities. People individually and collectively agree on where they live. The *vernacular regions* they recognize have reality in their minds and are reflected in regionally based names employed in businesses, by sports teams, or in advertising slogans. The frequency of references to "Dixie" in the southeastern United States represents that kind of regional consensus and awareness. Such vernacular regions reflect the way people view space, assign their loyalties, and interpret their world. At a different scale, such urban ethnic enclaves (see Chapter 6) as "Little Italy" or "Chinatown" have comparable regional identity in the minds of their inhabitants. Less clearly perceived by outsiders but unmistakable to their inhabitants are the "turfs" of urban clubs or gangs. Their boundaries are sharp, and the perceived distinctions between them are paramount in the daily lives and activities of their occupants. What perceptual regions do you have clearly in mind?

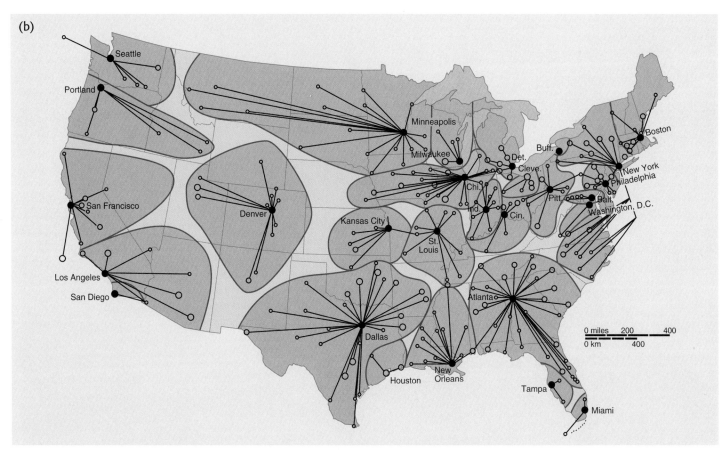

(b)

FIGURE 1.19 (*a*) This **generalized land use map of Australia** is composed of *formal regions* whose internal economic characteristics show essential uniformities, setting them off from adjacent territories of different conditions of use. (*b*) **Nodal Regions of Banks in the United States.** The functional (or nodal) regions shown on this map were based on linkages between large banks of major central cities and the "correspondent" banks they served in smaller towns in the 1970s, before the advent of electronic banking and bank consolidation. Note how the Canada–U.S. border affects the shape of the banking regions.

Source: (b) Redrawn by permission from Annals of the Association of American Geographers, *John R. Borchert, vol. 62, p. 358, Association of American Geographers, 1972.*

Want to Learn More?

Professional Associations

As noted in the Chapter, geographers have professional associations, which publish journals and books, organize conferences, and promote the discipline and offer scholarships and information about job prospects. In North America, these are the two premier geography associations:

Canadian Association of Geographers: www.cag-acg.ca/en/

American Association of Geographers: www.aag.org/

Geography on the Web

If you type "geography" into your search engine, hundreds of hits will result. Two popular sites that provide insight into geography from a layperson's perspective are:

Geography Homepage: http://geography.about.com

Geography Network: www.geographynetwork.com

Geographic Standards in Canada and the United States

To find out more about the Geographic Standards, go to either:

The Canadian Council for Geographic Education: www.ccge.org/ccge/english/programs/programs_geoStandards.htm

National Council for Geographic Education (US): www.ncge.org/publications

Jobs in Geography

"Geographer" is one of the many job profiles that is published on the Alberta Learning Information Service website. To find out what Alberta says geographers do, go to this site:

http://alis.alberta.ca/occinfo/Content/RequestAction.asp?aspAction=GetHTMLProfile&format=html&SNT_ID=25&occPro_ID=71002507

Summary

Geography is about earth space and its physical and cultural content. Throughout its long history, geography has remained consistent in its focus on human–environmental interactions, the interrelatedness of places, and the likenesses and differences in physical and cultural content of area that exist from place to place. The collective interests of geographers are summarized by the spatial and systems analytical questions they ask. The responses to those questions are interpreted through basic concepts of space and place, location, distance, direction, content evolution, spatial interaction, and regional organization.

In their study of the earth's surface as the occupied and altered space within which humans operate, geographers may concentrate on the integration of physical and cultural phenomena in a specific earth area (regional geography). They may, instead, emphasize systematic geography through study of the earth's physical systems of spatial and human concern or, as here, devote primary attention to people. This is a text in *human geography*. Its focus is on human interactions both with the physical environments people occupy and alter, and with the cultural environments they have created. We are concerned with the ways people perceive the landscapes and regions they occupy, act within and between them, make choices about them, and organize them according to the varying cultural, political, and economic interests of human societies. This is a text clearly within the social sciences, but like all geography, its background is the physical earth as the home of humans. As a human geography, its concern is with how that home has been altered by societies and cultures.

KEY WORDS

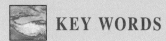 ## KEY WORDS

natural landscape 18	primary industries 11	relative location 16	spatial distribution 22
nodal region 23	probabilism 9	scale 17	spatial interaction 21
patriarchy 11	radical geographies 10	sexist 11	staples theory 10
pattern 22	region 23	site 16	structuralism 10
perceptual region 24	regional concept 23	situation 16	uniform region 23
political ecology 10	relative direction 17	Socialism 10	
possibilism 9	relative distance 17	spatial diffusion 22	

 ## FOR REVIEW

1. In what two meanings and for what different purposes do we refer to *location*?

2. Describe the *site* and the *situation* of the town where you live, work, or go to school.

3. What kinds of distance transformations are suggested by the term *relative distance*? How is the concept of *psychological distance* related to relative distance?

4. What are the common elements of *spatial distribution*? What different aspects of the spatial arrangement of things do they address?

5. What are the common characteristics of *regions*? How are *formal* and *functional* regions different in concept and definition? What is a *perceptual region*?

6. Describe the site and situation of hospitals in your college/university's city? Why are they sited and situated where they are? What might a better location(s) be, and why?

7. Describe your favourite place? As appropriate, describe its geographic elements (i.e., relative and absolute location, scale, physical structure and cultural content, its relationship with other places, its structured content, and its regional structure). Which are the elements that make this your favourite place?

8. What is meant by a "geographic approach"?

 ## FOCUS FOLLOW-UP

1. **What is the nature of geography and the role of human geography?** pp. 2–7.

Geography is a *spatial* science concerned with how the content of earth areas differs from place to place. It is the study of spatial variation in the world's physical and cultural (human) features. The emphasis of human geography is on the spatial variations in characteristics of peoples and cultures, on the way humans interact over space, and the ways they utilize and alter the natural landscapes they occupy.

2. **What are the geographical standards and why are they important?** pp. 12–15.

The geographical standards were established in 1974 by the National Council for Geographic Education and later endorsed by the Canadian Council for Geographic Education. The standards identify the six core areas of geography and can be used to determine "geographic literacy." The six standards identify the essential elements of geography that are based upon six essential elements of geography: (1) the world in spatial terms (location); (2) places and regions; (3) physical systems; (4) human systems; (5) society and the environment; and (6) the uses of geography.

3. **What was the development of geography in Canada?** pp. 7–12.

Geography is a spatial science that asks fundamental questions about where and why things occur in particular places. It offers the perspective of "space." Between the 14th and 17th centuries, European exploration prompted the need for governments to map their new territories. Modern Canadian geography has its roots in Europe in the 17th century. At this time, leading geographers provided systematic and clear descriptions of places and began to comment on the relationships between people and nature. Geography as an academic discipline at a university was first recognized in Prussia (now Germany). Since that time, there has been an explosion in the type of research conducted by geographers, reflecting the development of new

FOCUS FOLLOW-UP

technologies, and socio-economic and political factors. Computer technologies have allowed for the manipulation of large data sets, sometimes in real-time, and improved monitoring over larger geographic scales. Over the past two centuries the quantity of knowledge and the number of tools has exploded. There are strong links between geography and the sciences of geology and botany, as well as economics, sociology and demographics. In the West during the 20th century, the discipline of geography went through four major phases: environmental determinism, regional geography, the quantitative revolution, and critical geography.

4. **What are the seven fundamental geographic observations and their underlying concepts?** pp. 13–22.

Basic geographic observations all concern the characteristics, content, and interactions of places. Their underlying concepts involve such place specifics as location, direction, distance, size, scale, physical and cultural attributes, interrelationships, and regional similarities and differences.

5. **What are the regional concept and the generalized characteristics of regions?** pp. 22–25.

The regional concept tells us that physical and cultural features of the earth's surface are rationally arranged by understandable processes. All recognized regions are characterized by location, spatial extent, defined boundaries, and position within a hierarchy of regions. Regions may be "formal" (uniform) or "functional" (nodal) in nature.

ONLINE LEARNING CENTRE

The World Wide Web has a tremendous number and variety of sites pertaining to geography. To access Web sites, Internet exercises, self-quizzes, videos, and additional study tools relevant to this chapter's content, visit the *Human Geography* Online Learning Centre at **www.mcgrawhill.ca/olc/fellmann.**

The importance of site is illustrated in this photo. The land adjacent to the Red River was viewed as ideal for human occupation because it was flat, fertile, and adjacent to a major water way. However, it is also prone to flooding. The Red River floods thousands of acres of farmland as it overflows its banks. The river crested April 6, 1997, but the continued inflow from its tributaries is preventing the water level from dropping at a regular rate.

SOME KEY THEMES IN THE STUDY OF HUMAN GEOGRAPHY

Human geography studies the ways in which people and societies are regionally different in their distinguishing characteristics. It seeks to understand the flow of people, goods, and ideas from one region to another. Additionally, it examines the ways that different societies perceive, use, and alters the landscapes they occupy. This wide range of interests would seem to imply an unmanageable range and variety of topics. This implication is misleading, however, for the diversified subject matter of human geography can be accommodated within the themes of geography identified in the first chapter. In part 1 of the book, we devote specific attention to three of these themes—the world in spatial terms, human systems, and regions and places.

Two general views emerge from many of the problems facing our world today. The first is cultural and reflects how different social groups are characterized and comprise the individual pieces of the human mosaic. Underlying this perspective are matters related to learned behaviours, attitudes, and group beliefs that are fundamental and identifying features of specific social groups and larger societies. The second view concerns itself with the systems of production, livelihood, spatial organization, and administration—and the institutions appropriate to those systems—that a society erects in response to opportunity, technology, resources, conflict, or the need to adapt and change. This second view recognizes what the French geographers in the early twentieth century called *genre de vie*—the way of life—of a population that might be adopted or pursued no matter what the other intangible cultural traits of that society might be. Interwoven with and unifying these primary

features are the continuing background concern for geographers: society and environment interactions (Chapter 12).

We shall pursue each of these views in separate sections of this book and address the unifying interest of human impact on the earth surface both as an integral part of each chapter and as the topic of our concluding chapter. Throughout, we shall keep returning to a small number of basic observations that underlie all of human geographic study: (1) People and the societies they form are differentiated by a limited set of cultural characteristics and organizational structures; (2) without regard to those cultural and organizational differences, human spatial behaviour has common and recurring motivations and patterns; and (3) cultural variations and spatial actions are rooted in the distribution, number, and movements of people.

These observations are the concerns of the following two chapters, which focus further attention on the four themes of geography. In Chapter 2, a general approach to research is provided. The second part of this chapter pursues the "World in Spatial Terms" theme, and notes how maps can be used as a data source as well as a tool to interpret information. Maps have been an ongoing pursuit of geographers that has transcended cultures.

Chapter 3 examines three important themes in human geography—human systems, regions, and places in the context of globalization. The general physical and behavioural factors that influence spatial interaction are described. This understanding is an important first step in providing a geographical perspective on world, regional, and local processes and problems.

2 THE WORLD IN SPATIAL TERMS—GEOGRAPHIC RESEARCH AND MAPS

Aims

- To understand the research process
- To understand the basic properties of maps and how they show data
- To appreciate the power of geographic information systems

Some Specific Considerations for Review:

1. The sources of information, primary and secondary, which geographers use, pp. 31–37.

2. How the Census of Canada is spatially organized and some problems of using census data, pp. 34–35.

3. Why geographers use maps, and how maps show location and spatial information, pp. 37–51.

4. Other means of visualizing and analyzing spatial data: mental maps, remote sensing, GIS, and models, p. 51–55.

*T*his chapter has two purposes. First, a general approach to conducting research is described, and focuses attention on two general approaches to reasoning, and the nature of data. Second, we examine the properties of maps and how they can (mis)represent information. Understanding the nature of research, such as how questions are posed, research is designed, data are collected and analyzed, and how maps are used to display results, are important to the development of critical thinking skills.

A Research Question: What is the Influence of Place on Human Health?

Human health reflects a complex interplay of two general characteristics: (i) individuals (e.g., age structure, genetic composition, lifestyles, culture), and (ii) the circumstances in which they live both environmental (e.g., exposure to pollution) and social (e.g. access to social services). There is a considerable body of research that has focused attention on the relationship among individual factors, such as smoking, alcohol consumption, obesity, and income levels, on health. There has also been concerted and longstanding research to establish causal relationships between exposure to different environmental conditions and health. However, there is also growing concern about the nature and the extent of relationships among urban form, people, the environment and health. The North American population is becoming increasingly obese. There are also increasing rates of asthma and depression. At the same time, North American lifestyles are becoming increasingly sedentary, and this may be linked, in part, to the structure and form of our communities. However, while there is suspicion about linkages between urban form (or place) and health, there has been little conclusive research.

This point is illustrated in the 2002 Annual Report on the Health of Montrealers by the Régie Régionale de la Santé et des Service Sociaux de Montréal-Centre. It revealed "big gaps" in health indicators based on a person's socio-economic status and place of residence (Figure 2.1). It found that life expectancy increased with income levels—poorer men lived 6.6 years and women 3.6 years less than their higher income counterparts. However, determining the nature and extent of the link between place and health has been a difficult research question, in part, because (i) it is difficult to obtain data at the level of the individual (i.e., a scale problem); and (ii) the absence of appropriate statistical methods (i.e., a technical or methodological problem) (Macintyre et al., 2002). Rising to this type of research challenge is the essence of the work of university and college professors, and those who are involved in research in the public, private, and non-government sectors.

Ross et al. (2004) became intrigued with the link between place and health and specifically posed the following question: "What were the neighbourhood effects (place effects) on health within Montreal?" Using data collected through the Canadian Community Health Survey and the Census of Canada, and applying computer technology to handle large data sets, they applied statistical techniques to answer this research question. They found that neighbourhoods exerted an effect on health status above and beyond the impact of individual risk factors, including smoking, obesity, high stress, and a low sense of belonging to a community. This study is of specific interest to geographers because it was conducted at two scales—the individual and the neighbourhood. Although the neighbourhood effect was found to be small (about 3%) relative to individual factors (e.g., smoking, obesity), they are significant because we can more easily improve the design of our communities (e.g., providing better spaces for walking and recreating) than change individual behaviours (e.g., adopting and affording healthy lifestyles). Ross et al. also found that poor health status was also associated with high levels of self-perceived stress and a low sense of belonging to community. Better community design can increase a person's sense of belonging to a community. The form and structure of Montreal and many other Canadian cities promotes a high level of car usage, which leads to air pollution and a sedentary lifestyle. Achieving healthy cities should be considered as a key goal for public policy and urban planning, and is an area where geographers can make a meaningful contribution.

We will return to this study later in this chapter. For now, appreciate how research questions can develop from previous

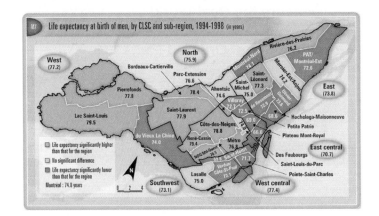

FIGURE 2.1 Life expectancy maps for Montreal.

Source: 2002 Annual Report, "A Profile of Health in Montreal."

research studies, how geography can contribute to public policy, and how there are a mix of challenges, in this case the problems of obtaining health data at the individual level and the initial absence of appropriate statistical tests, which must be overcome in a successful research project.

The Research Process

The research study above asked and answered some of the questions that lie at the core of geography: What is the pattern of life expectancy in Montreal? What factors explain this pattern? What are the opportunities to improve current conditions? To answer these types of questions, geographers develop knowledge by applying their techniques and skills in a systematic and rigorous manner. There are two general approaches to developing knowledge—inductive and deductive reasoning—both of which use a series of logical steps to explain the world around us (see Figure 2.2). However, they are different in that **inductive research** looks at particular facts or events and sees if they can be the basis for formulating a general rule or principle. The steps would generally follow from observations made by the researcher, to patterns observed based on a categorization of the observations, to explanations. An example is the Demographic Transition theory, which will be described in Chapter 4. **Deductive research** more closely follows the "scientific method." It starts with a sense that a general principle exists and research determines if it applies in specific circumstances. Experiments are designed to prove the validity of the generalization. If it is shown to be valid, then a theory or law can be established. The development of the gravity model (Chapter 3) is an example of this type of thinking. The key

in both approaches is to ensure the research question is clear and the appropriate data and analytical techniques are applied that truly test the idea being proposed.

Ethical considerations are a fundamental requirement that researchers must consider. Everyone conducting research must consider the ethical aspects. In Canada, the three major research funding agencies—Social Sciences and Humanities Research Council of Canada (SSHRC), Natural Sciences and Engineering Research Council of Canada (NSERC) and the Canadian Institutes of Health Research (CIHR)—have adopted a set of ethical principles (*The Tri-Council Policy Statement: Ethics in Research with Human Subjects*) to guide research (Table 2.1)

The use of GIS presents some interesting questions related to free and informed consent, and privacy. For instance, should a researcher have access to a car navigation system to track a person's (or number of persons) daily travels without their consent? Whether or not consent is obtained, how can a person's privacy be maintained if their house location is shown on a map?

While each research effort has its own approach (e.g., inductive and deductive thinking), ethical considerations and practical issues (e.g. time and money available, working in remote places), a general research process would likely contain the following elements: (1) clarifying the problem or question, (2) data collection, (3) data analysis, and (4) making conclusions. The following section will consider these four aspects in the context of geographic research.

You are probably aware that problem solving is easier when the problem is clearly defined. Before you think about what data you want to collect, ask why you are collecting it. To this end, think about the many purposes that research projects can pursue. It is often

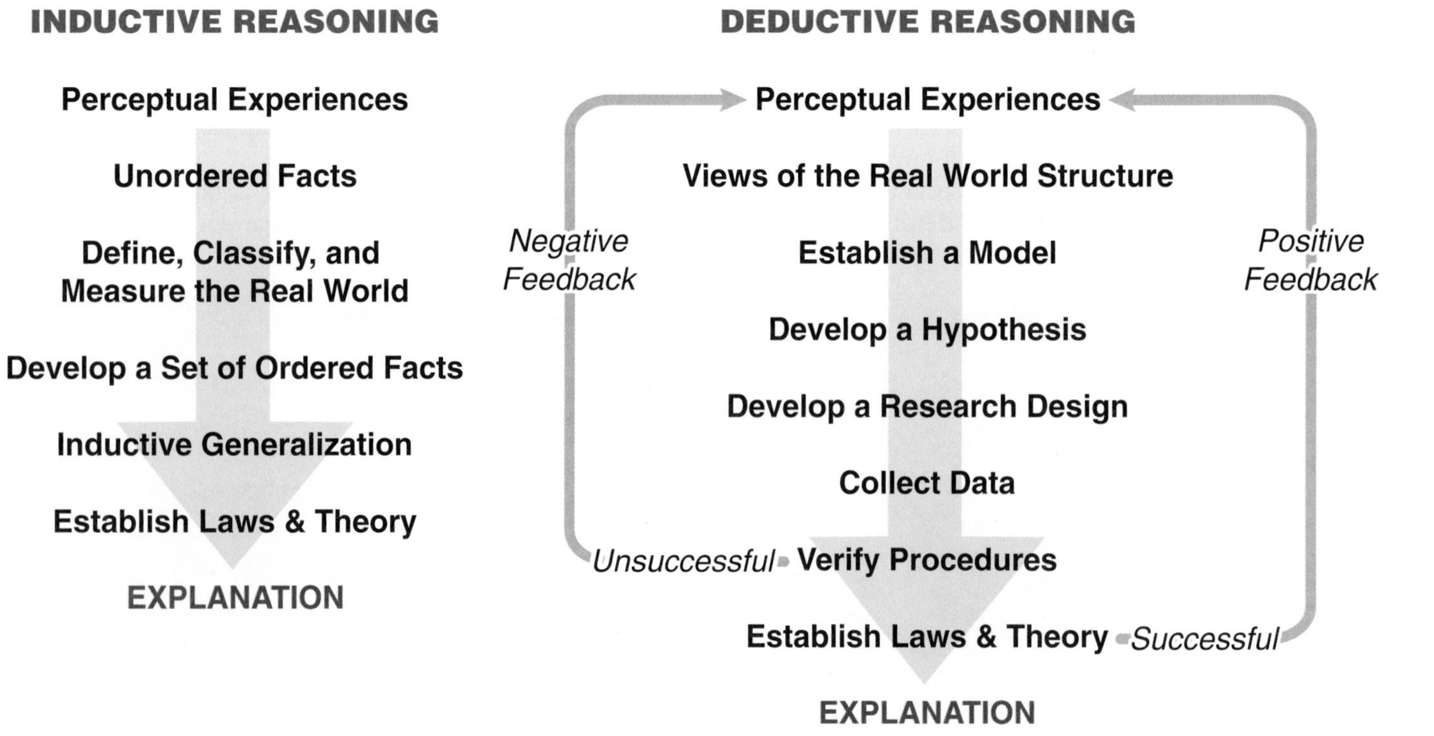

INDUCTIVE REASONING

Perceptual Experiences

Unordered Facts

Define, Classify, and Measure the Real World

Develop a Set of Ordered Facts

Inductive Generalization

Establish Laws & Theory

EXPLANATION

DEDUCTIVE REASONING

Perceptual Experiences

Views of the Real World Structure

Establish a Model

Develop a Hypothesis

Develop a Research Design

Collect Data

Verify Procedures

Establish Laws & Theory ◄ *Successful*

EXPLANATION

Negative Feedback

Positive Feedback

Unsuccessful

FIGURE 2.2 Inductive and deductive reasoning.

TABLE 2.1

Ethical Aspects of Research

The ethical principles that guide research in Canada and most applicable to research in human geography are:

Respect for Human Dignity: Aspires to protect the multiple and interdependent interests of the person—from bodily to psychological to cultural integrity.

Respect for Free and Informed Consent: Requires that people not be forced or pressured into participating in research. This is especially relevant where researchers had previously relied on 'captive audiences' for their subjects—prisons and universities. This also means that prospective research participants must be fully informed about the procedures and risks involved in research and must give their consent to participate.

Respect for Vulnerable Persons: Children, institutionalised persons or others who are vulnerable are entitled to protection and special procedures to protect their interests. At a university, these procedures must be approved by the Ethics Board.

Respect for Privacy and Confidentiality: The researcher promises participants that their identifying information will not be made available to anyone who is not directly involved in the study. This can sometimes take the form of anonymity, which essentially means the participant will not be named or identified throughout the study. Clearly, the anonymity standard is a stronger guarantee of privacy, but it is sometimes difficult to accomplish, especially in situations where participants have to be contacted several times during a study.

Respect for Justice and Inclusiveness: Justice connotes fairness and equity. Procedural justice requires that the ethics review process have fair methods, standards and procedures for reviewing research protocols, and that the process be effectively independent. Justice also concerns the distribution of benefits and burdens of research.

Balancing Harms and Benefits: Harm can be defined as both physical and psychological. The analysis, balance and distribution of harms and benefits are critical to the ethics of human research. Modern research ethics, for instance, require a favourable harms-benefits balance—that is, that the foreseeable harms should not outweigh anticipated benefits. These concerns are particularly evident in biomedical and health research; in research they need to be tempered in areas such as geography, political science, economics, or modern history (including biographies), areas in which research may ethically result in the harming of the reputations of organizations or individuals in public life.

helpful to clarify which specific purpose(s) your research seeks to achieve. Five common purposes found in geographic research are:

- *Description:* A major purpose of geographic inquiry is to describe places or how people perceive places, the flow of people, goods and/or services, events, and how humans interact with the environment. Describing the physical and human characteristics of a region, such as the pattern of mortality in Montreal must be done systematically if it is to be considered research rather than journalism. Descriptive studies would answer questions related to what, where, when, and how. Sometimes, descriptions can involve quantitative measurements in order to establish the strength of relationships.

- *Explanation:* Explanatory studies answer the question "why," such as why do people living in the east end of Montreal have higher mortality rates than those living in the west end? Why do most people immigrating to Canada prefer to live in Toronto, Montreal, and Vancouver?

- *Forecasting and Prediction:* The focus is on the future. What will the health of people be if we do not change current urban planning approaches? How will Canadians change their modes of daily travel if the price of gasoline doubles?

- *Assessment:* Governments and businesses are often interested in knowing if their programs are working effectively, efficiently, and fairly. Defining these terms and determining how to measure them is often a tricky task. For instance, should we measure the efficiency of a government program by how quickly ambulance services serve the public and at what cost? We could also measure efficiency by how quickly people receive required medical procedures. Alternatively, we might ask people who are served by the program about their views of their own health (e.g., stress level) and the efficiency of the health care system. The overall state of a population can be measured directly by relying on quantitative indicators such as mortality rates, life expectancy at birth, activity restrictions, and people's perception of their own health.

- *Prescription:* Identifying changes that will improve the current situation, much like a doctor prescribes drugs to remedy a disease, is a final general research objective. For instance, how should urban form be changed in order to improve health within a neighbourhood?

Having clarified the research question, a researcher is now ready to collect data. There are two types of data sources—primary and secondary. **Primary data** are collected by the researcher or a member of the research team specifically for the research project or program. Within this context, geographers will talk about "collecting data" or "going to the field." Fieldwork in geography may involve anything from a walk around campus to Ph.D. research conducted on faraway places for a year or more. When in the field, you must use your observation skills to their best advantage. Examples of primary data sources include questionnaires and social surveys, interviews, focus groups, observational techniques (e.g., "people watching" and participant observation), and landscape analysis.

Rather than being collected by the researcher or their team, **secondary data** are collected by somebody else or another organization. Note that Ross et al. used secondary data sources, which indicates new analysis on secondary data is considered "research." Geographers often use secondary data collected by government agencies, private organizations (e.g., business reports and statements), or other academic researchers. Census data provided by Statistics Canada are an invaluable source of high quality data (see "The Census of Canada"). Other examples of secondary sources include archives, historical accounts and images, newspapers, censuses, maps, and photographs.

Other federal government agencies (Health Canada, Environment Canada), as well as provincial, territorial, and local government

The first known census to be completed on Canadian soil was initiated by Intendant Jean Talon in 1666. He recorded the age, gender, marital status and occupation of the Colony of New France's 3,215 inhabitants (excluding the Iroquois, who had long lived in the area) in order to aid its planning and development. Some 340 years later, 13.5 million households responded to the census questionnaire issued by Statistics Canada. Eighty percent of the households were asked in 2006 to respond to 8 questions, while the remaining 20% in southern portions of the country responded to an additional 53 questions. Since sampling would not produce accurate results for small populations, all households in northern areas, remote areas, and Indian reserves, completed the longer questionnaire. The census continues to help governments and businesses plan for the future.

Section 8 of *The Constitution Act* of 1867 (formerly *The British North America Act*) required that a census be taken in 1871. Since that time, decennial census data (called a full census) have provided the cornerstone for representative government. Beginning in 1906, the prairie provinces of Manitoba, Alberta, and Saskatchewan began to take a separate census of agriculture every five years to monitor the growth of the West. Since 1956, the Census of Agriculture and the Census of Population have been taken together every five years across the entire country. The following are the major subjects that Statistics Canada can provide information on:

Economy: Business enterprises, Communications, Construction, Manufacturing, National accounts, Prices and price indexes, Science and technology, Service industries, Trade, Transport and warehousing

Land and Resources: Agriculture, Energy, Environment, Primary Industries

People: Arts, culture and recreation, Education, Health, Labour, Personal finance and household finance, Population and demography, Social conditions, Travel and tourism

Nation: Government, Justice

Statistical Methods and Reference: Geography, Reference, Statistical methods

The quality of the data is very good because of the high response rate and the efforts of officials at Statistics Canada who collect and analyze the information. In 2006, just over 18% of all respondents completed their survey online—the first time this option was made available. This development will reduce the time required to process and release census data, which has been somewhat problematic in the past.

Census data are available at various scales, ranging from a city block to the entire country. Key features of its geography are as follows.

The 2006 Census Geography

FIGURE 2.3a A **dissemination block** is an area bounded on all sides by roads and/or boundaries of standard geographic areas. The dissemination block is the smallest geographic area for which population and dwelling counts are disseminated.

Source: Statistics Canada, http://geodepot.statcan .ca/Diss/Reference/COGG/Index_e.cfm.

FIGURE 2.3b The **dissemination area** is a small, relatively stable geographic unit composed of one or more dissemination blocks. It is the smallest standard geographic area for which all census data are disseminated. They usually have populations of 400 to 700 people. The Dissemination Area that comprises the Census Subdivision of Maple Ridge (B.C.) is shown below.

Source: http://geodepot.statcan.ca/Diss/Reference/ COGG/Index_e.cfm.

Dissemination area (400–700 people) within Maple Ridge, British Columbia

agencies also publish substantial amounts of information, as do other national governments, and international organizations (United Nations, Organization for Economic Cooperation and Development (OECD)). Information can range from statistics on transportation, to public attitudes on topics such as immigration, transportation preferences, and perceptions of health and environmental management. Most research projects begin with a search of secondary sources in order to find out what is already known about a topic and what questions remain to be asked/answered.

One must be careful when using secondary data, even those that are of high quality such as Canadian Census data, in order to realize their strengths, weaknesses, and idiosyncrasies. For instance, if you were doing a project on Canadian cities, you would want to make sure you know how urban areas are defined by the census over time. In 2006, an urban area was defined as having a population of at least 1,000 and no fewer than 400 people per square kilometre. In 1931, all incorporated cities, towns, and villages in Canada, regardless of population size or density, were defined as urban. Other problems can also be encountered. A social geography project on Aboriginal populations would have to be sensitive to the changing definition of the term "Aboriginal," and changes to the wording of census questions, and patterns of self-identification. Métis were not included in the census until 1981, and only patrilineal descent (male) was counted until 1981. In areas where there is a small population, Statistics Canada will protect the confidentiality of individual responses by applying random rounding to data (especially socio-economic data). In some instances, this means that some of these census tracts appear to have "zero persons" with certain characteristics. However, you cannot be sure if this is the case or if it is due to random rounding. Go to the Statistics Canada website at www.statcan.ca/start.html to find more about the quality of census data.

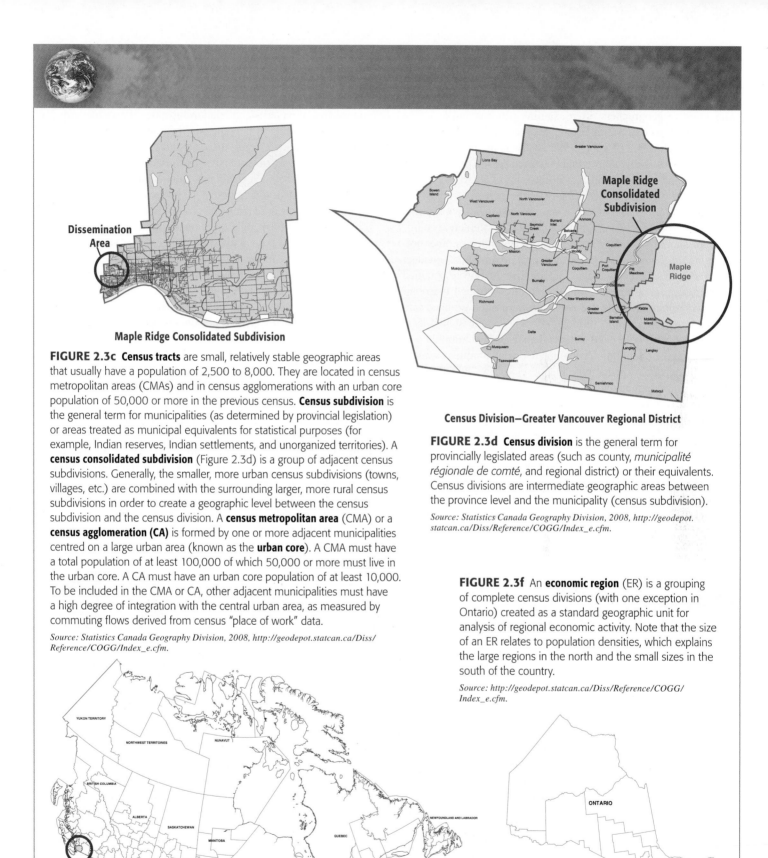

Maple Ridge Consolidated Subdivision

Census Division—Greater Vancouver Regional District

FIGURE 2.3c **Census tracts** are small, relatively stable geographic areas that usually have a population of 2,500 to 8,000. They are located in census metropolitan areas (CMAs) and in census agglomerations with an urban core population of 50,000 or more in the previous census. **Census subdivision** is the general term for municipalities (as determined by provincial legislation) or areas treated as municipal equivalents for statistical purposes (for example, Indian reserves, Indian settlements, and unorganized territories). A **census consolidated subdivision** (Figure 2.3d) is a group of adjacent census subdivisions. Generally, the smaller, more urban census subdivisions (towns, villages, etc.) are combined with the surrounding larger, more rural census subdivisions in order to create a geographic level between the census subdivision and the census division. A **census metropolitan area** (CMA) or a **census agglomeration (CA)** is formed by one or more adjacent municipalities centred on a large urban area (known as the **urban core**). A CMA must have a total population of at least 100,000 of which 50,000 or more must live in the urban core. A CA must have an urban core population of at least 10,000. To be included in the CMA or CA, other adjacent municipalities must have a high degree of integration with the central urban area, as measured by commuting flows derived from census "place of work" data.

Source: Statistics Canada Geography Division, 2008, http://geodepot.statcan.ca/Diss/Reference/COGG/Index_e.cfm.

FIGURE 2.3d **Census division** is the general term for provincially legislated areas (such as county, *municipalité régionale de comté*, and regional district) or their equivalents. Census divisions are intermediate geographic areas between the province level and the municipality (census subdivision).

Source: Statistics Canada Geography Division, 2008, http://geodepot. statcan.ca/Diss/Reference/COGG/Index_e.cfm.

FIGURE 2.3f An **economic region** (ER) is a grouping of complete census divisions (with one exception in Ontario) created as a standard geographic unit for analysis of regional economic activity. Note that the size of an ER relates to population densities, which explains the large regions in the north and the small sizes in the south of the country.

Source: http://geodepot.statcan.ca/Diss/Reference/COGG/Index_e.cfm.

FIGURE 2.3e In 2006, there were 288 census divisions (Figure 2.2e), 5,418 census subdivisions, as well as all 33 census metropolitan areas and 111 census agglomerations.

Another way of classifying data is the distinction made between **quantitative** and **qualitative data**. Quantitative studies often apply a deductive research approach in order to test and verify hypotheses, and develop models (e.g., gravity model). As mentioned in Chapter 1, quantitative geographers often examine patterns and flows on the landscape. In contrast, the behavioural geographers focus attention on the behaviour of people (e.g., individuals, managers, and business people). They believe that how each person perceives and experiences the landscape reflects differences in a person's ability to gather and organize information. It is the perceived landscape that emerges from this process that is of interest to behaviouralists. Rather than asking questions about what kind of interaction and/or landscape should be created on the basis of economic or other normative laws, behaviouralists ask why people do (or do not) conduct certain activities. Perceptual data (quantitative data) were obtained by behavioural geographers from people often through questionnaires and perceptual tests. Respondents were often grouped into categories (e.g., floodplain resident, socio-economic status, level of experience with issue) and statistical analysis is commonly performed. Like the quantitative geographers, behaviouralists wanted to provide general explanations and develop laws and theories. Explaining how humans adjust to hazards, and why certain land use patterns in urban and agricultural existed on landscapes, are two examples of the behaviouralist paradigm in geography. However, note that both types of geographers are obtaining different types of quantitative data.

Data may also be provided through qualitative methods—interviews, observations, journal accounts, and interpretations. From these sources, a researcher can tease out how emotional, aesthetic, and symbolic factors that bind people and place. This set of tools—interviews, observations, and textual interpretations—developed in a variety of disciplines, came to geography in the 1980s. They are often used by feminist geographers (see "Feminist Geography Research Methods"). Unlike quantitative methods, which use statistics and mathematical modelling to generalize, predict, and control spatial patterns and relationships, qualitative methods promote understanding of how the world is viewed, experienced, and constructed. In other words, these methods help geographers investigate the motives, goals, and social relationships of individuals and groups that help to explain how human landscapes, places, and events are created and represented. Interviews are used to elicit information from individuals or groups and may range widely in terms of number of people questioned, duration of the interview, and the length and type of questions posed. Observations may take a variety of forms, ranging from participant observation—whereby the geographer observes through direct engagement with a people or place—to passive observation—whereby the geographer does not actively engage or encounter the site or people, and merely observes non-obtrusively—to personal reflection—the geographer records his or her impressions after experiencing a particular place or social event. The interpretation of texts also provides a means of understanding the human geographical condition. By critically interpreting the content and social construction of images and writings (e.g., advertisements, diaries, films, literature, maps, newspapers, even song lyrics), geographers can gain rich insights into how humans view, experience, and represent their world. Whether to use quantitative methods, qualitative methods, or some combination of the two, depends upon the kind of questions posed, the kind of knowledge sought, and the philosophical and methodological disposition of the geographer.

Data analysis is the third step of the research process. At this stage, the researcher reviews the data that has been obtained,

Feminist Geography Research Methods

In conducting their research, particularly in the areas of urban, social, and development geography, feminist geographers questioned whether there was a better way to apply the established methods—questionnaires, interviews, and case studies. For instance, they found the phrase "administer a questionnaire" somewhat annoying because it implied that a researcher had to be distant from the "research subject" in order to remain "objective." Feminists and others, including post-modernists and post-colonialists, were critical of the traditional research process and power dynamics that distanced "researchers" from "subjects." The most common approach to feminist research has been to apply qualitative methods, and like most researchers, often apply multiple data sources and/or analyses in order to compensate for the weaknesses of one source with the strengths of another. Table 2.2 compares key elements of traditional and feminist research approaches, and illustrates some of the contributions feminists have made to methodology.

Feminists have been recently applying quantitative methods, including GIS. Kwan (2002: 650) suggested that "feminist geographers using GIS methods can experiment and create new visual practices, especially those that can better represent gendered spaces and help construct different spectator positions when compared to conventional GIS methods."

These techniques also carry over to the writing of feminist geographers. While writing in the third person has been the standard rule of "academic writing," feminists advocate the use of the first person singular (e.g., "I, me") to remind both the writer and the reader that an actual person has lived through the events associated with the words and sentences, and that this experience can be very different from another person who lived through those same events. Feminist methods are not that unique in the sense that other approaches will also use qualitative techniques. However, feminist research is distinguished in its "ways of knowing, ways of asking, ways of interpreting, and ways of writing" (Women and Geography Study Group of the IBG, 1997: 109). The methods are used in ways meant to challenge gender differences and unequal gender relations both within the practice of geography, and outside in the larger society, with the intent to help change for the better.

TABLE 2.2

A Comparison of Traditional and Feminist Methods

General Research Stage	Traditional (Patriarchal)	Alternative (Feminist)
Nature of Research Question	Limited, specialized, specific, exclusive. Test hypothesis in order to contribute to theory development.	Broad, inclusive. Develop an understanding of people's experiences.
Data	Reports of attitudes and behaviours obtained through questionnaires, interviews, and archive records. Mode of data collection determined prior to conduct of research.	Feelings, behaviours, thoughts, insights, actions as witnessed or experienced by people obtained through interviews, questionnaires, archive records, journals. Mode of data collection determined by context of research.
Data analysis	Determined prior to research. Deductive approach. Completed when all data are collected. Statistical analysis.	Done during data collection. Relies on development of ideas. Inductive approach.
Analysis/Presentation Format	A research report describing hypothesis, data collection methods, form of analysis, and conclusions. Objective.	A story or a description which includes documentation of the research process—data collection and how patterns were found—and emergent concepts. Subjective, assumes people's interpretations are valid.

Source: Adapted from Reinharz, S. (1983). "Experiential Analysis: A Contribution to Feminist Research." In Theories of Women's Studies, *edited by Gloria Bowles and Renate Duelli Klein, 162–191. Boston: Routledge & Kegan Paul.*

and decides what it contributes to the answering of the research questions. Analysis can take many forms including describing the context or processes of "something" (e.g., a government program), classifying data into categories (e.g., a map of a city's different cultures), drawing graphs, or completing statistical analysis. The last stage of the research process is to make conclusions based on the evidence (data and analysis) that has been collected. This will be influenced by one's philosophy as illustrated by the age-old problem of determining if a glass of water is half full or half empty. While both responses are correct, they provide different interpretations. A universal guide in making conclusions is to ensure that they answer the questions that were initially posed by the research and are adequately supported by the evidence. To better illustrate how four research steps may be used to organize a commentary on the research completed by Ross et al., see "Thinking about Research."

Maps

We now turn our attention to a longstanding and important tool that geographers frequently employ in presenting their results—maps. Geographer H. J. de Blij has suggested that "if a picture is worth a thousand words, a map can be worth a million—but beware" because they can distort reality (as contained in Monmonier, 1996: xi). "All mapmakers use generalization and symbolization to highlight

critical information and to suppress detail of lower priority. All cartography seeks to portray the complex, three-dimensional world on a flat sheet of paper or on a television or video screen. In short . . . all maps must tell white lies" (Monmonier, 1996: xi). A **map** is a two dimensional spatial representation of any part of our world.

Our attention for the remainder of this subsection are on map projections, map features (e.g., scale), types of map, and how data may be portrayed on maps. We shall learn that maps can serve their purpose only if their users have a clear idea of their strengths, limitations, and diversity, and the conventions used in their preparation and interpretation. Knowledge of maps can assist geographers in both gathering and interpreting data, and influencing how others interpret their work.

Map Projections

A map **projection** is simply a system for displaying the curved surface of the earth on a flat sheet of paper. The definition is easy; the process is more difficult. No matter how one tries to "flatten" the earth, it can never be done in such a fashion as to show all earth details in their correct relative sizes, shapes, distances, or directions. Something is always wrong, and the cartographer's—the mapmaker's—task is to select and preserve those earth relationships important for the purpose at hand, and to minimize or accept those distortions that are inevitable but unimportant.

Below is a description, based on the four key steps of research: clarifying the problem, data collection, data analysis, and interpretation. As you become more familiar with the concepts, methods, and findings of a research area, you will be able to extend the comments from descriptive to a constructive commentary.

(1) Clarifying the Problem or Questions

In the study by Ross et al., their purpose was to describe and measure the relationship between neighbourhood effects and health in Montreal. A key geographic question Ross et al. considered carefully pertained to the meaning of the word "neighbourhood" and how should/could it be measured? There are many reasonable responses to the first question and many constraints to its proper measurement. Ross et al. used boundaries suggested by local government and real estate boards, which are published in the book *le Direction de L'habitation*. This source defined 88 neighbourhoods on the Island of Montreal. Since this source did not cover the entire area, Ross et al. used the census subdivisions, which are developed by Statistics Canada, to define the additional 20 neighbourhoods in Montreal. This type of inconsistency is common to many research projects and is difficult to remove.

(2) Data Collection

Ross et al.'s primary data source was secondary and quantitative—the 2000/2001 Canadian Community Health Survey, which is a comprehensive national survey that contains information on health outcomes as well as behavioural and socio-economic information at an individual level. Within Montreal, there was a sample of 1,652 respondents aged 25 to 64 to the survey. Data collected included age, gender, smoking, obesity, stress, sense of community belonging, and household income. Ross et al. measured health outcomes using a health utilities index (HUI), which is based on a respondent's self-reporting of health across eight dimensions: vision, hearing, speech, mobility, dexterity, cognition, emotion, and pain. To measure the influence of neighbourhoods, data were obtained from the 1996 Census of Canada for the following variables: proportion of single-parent families, proportion of recent immigrants, education level, and median household income of the area. Thus, an underlying assumption of the research was that these variables ideally captured all, or at least most of the factors influencing the dimensions of health.

(3) Data Analysis

We will not describe the analysis in detail here—many of you will take (or have to take) statistics courses in upper years. Suffice it to say that a combination of statistical and GIS techniques allowed them to establish the validity of their definition of neighbourhood, and then measure its effect on the HUI.

(4) Making Conclusions

Three major conclusions were made from the information provided above:

- individual risk factors (smoking, obesity, high stress, low household income, low sense of community belonging) have significant negative effects on HUI
- about 3% of variation in health status was attributed to neighbourhoods
- future research is required to pursue the extent and nature of the neighbourhood influence

Source: Ross, N.A., S. Tremblay, and K. Graham. (2004). "Neighbourhood Influences on Health in Montreal, Canada." Social Science and Medicine 59: 1485–1494.

Round Globe to Flat Map

The best way to model the earth's surface accurately, of course, would be to show it on a globe. But globes are not as convenient to use as flat maps and do not allow one to see the entire surface of the earth all at once. Nor can they show very much of the detailed content of areas. Even a very large globe of, say, 1 metre in diameter, compresses the physical or cultural information of some 130,000 square kilometres of earth surface into a space 2.5 centimetres on a side.

Geographers make two different demands on the maps they use to represent reality. One requirement is to show at one glance generalized relationships and spatial content of the entire world; the many world maps used in this and other geography textbooks and in atlases have that purpose. The other need is to show the detailed content of only portions of the earth's surface—cities, regions, countries, hemispheres—without reference to areas outside the zone of interest. Although the needs and problems of both kinds of maps differ, each starts with the same requirement: to transform a curved surface into a flat one.

If we look at the globe directly, only the front—the side facing us—is visible; the back is hidden (Figure 2.4). To make a world map, we must decide on a way to flatten the globe's curved surface on the hemisphere we can see. Then we have to cut the globe map down the middle of its hidden hemisphere and place the two back quarters on their respective sides of the already visible front half. In simple terms, we have to "peel" the map from the globe and flatten it in the same way we might try to peel an orange and flatten the skin. Inevitably, the peeling and flattening process will produce a resulting map that either shows tears or breaks in the surface (Figure 2.5a) or is subject to uneven stretching or shrinking to make it lie flat (Figure 2.5b).

Projections—Geometrical and Mathematical

Of course, mapmakers do not physically engage in cutting, peeling, flattening, or stretching operations. Their task, rather, is to construct or *project* on a flat surface the network of parallels and meridians (the **graticule**) of the globe grid. The idea of projections is perhaps easiest visualized by thinking of a transparent globe with an imagined light source located inside. Lines of latitude and longitude (or of coastlines or any other features) drawn on that globe will cast shadows on any nearby

FIGURE 2.4 An orthographic projection gives us a visually realistic view of the globe; its distortion toward the edges suggests the normal perspective appearance of a sphere viewed from a distance. Only a single hemisphere—one half of the globe—can be seen at a time, and only the central portion of that hemisphere avoids serious distortion of shape.

surface. A tracing of that shadow globe grid would represent a geometrical map projection.

In **geometrical** (or **perspective**) **projections**, the graticule is in theory visually transferred from the globe to a geometrical figure, such as a plane, cylinder, or cone, which, in turn, can be cut and then spread out flat (or *developed*) without any stretching or tearing. The surfaces of cylinders, cones, and planes are said to be **developable surfaces**—cylinders and cones can be cut and laid flat without distortion and planes are flat at the outset (Figure 2.6). In actuality, geometrical projections are constructed not by tracing shadows but by the application of geometry and the use of lines, circles, arcs, and angles drawn on paper. In a planer projection, a portion of the earth's surface is transformed from a perspective point to a flat surface. In polar areas, lines of latitude are represented by a system of *concentric* circles sharing a common point of origin from which radiate the lines of longitude, spaced at true angles. This type of projection shows true direction only between the centre point and other locations on the map.

The location of the theoretical light source in relation to the globe surface can cause significant variation in the projection of the graticule on the developable geometric surface. An **orthographic projection** results from placement of the light source at infinity. A **gnomonic projection** is a type of planer projection, and is produced when the light source is at the centre of the earth. When the light is placed at the *antipode*—the point exactly opposite the point of tangency (point of contact between globe and map)—a **stereographic projection** is produced (Figure 2.7).

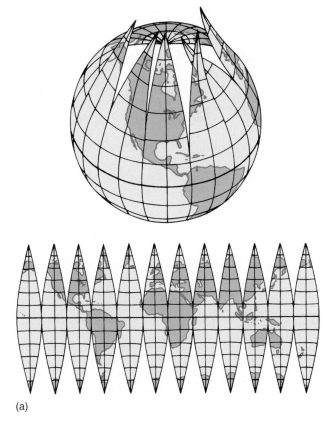

(a)

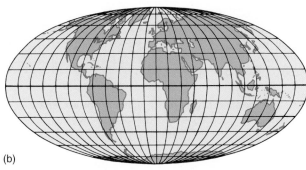

(b)

FIGURE 2.5 (a) A careful "peeling" of the map from the globe yields a set of tapered "gores" which, although individually not showing much stretching or shrinking, do not collectively result in a very useful or understandable world map. (b) It is usually considered desirable to avoid or reduce the number of interruptions by depicting the entire global surface as a single flat circular, oval, or rectangular shape. That continuity of area, however, can be achieved only at the cost of considerable alteration of true shapes, distances, directions, or areas. Although the homolographic (Mollweide) projection shows areas correctly, it distorts shapes.

Source: Redrawn with permission from American Congress Surveying and Mapping, Choosing a World Map. Special Publication No. 2 of the American Cartographic Association, Bethesda, Md. Copyright 1988 American Congress on Surveying and Mapping.

Each projection scheme, however, presents a different arrangement of the globe grid to minimize or eliminate some of the distortions inherent in projecting from a curved to a flat surface. Every projection represents a compromise or deviation from reality to achieve a selected purpose, but in the process of adjustment or compromise, each inevitably contains specific, accepted distortions.

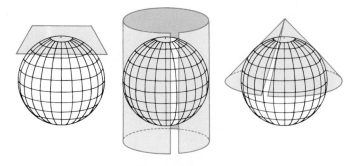

FIGURE 2.6 The theory of geometrical projections. The three common geometric forms used in projections are the plane, the cylinder, and the cone.

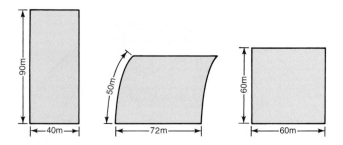

FIGURE 2.8 These three figures are all equal in area despite their different dimensions and shapes.

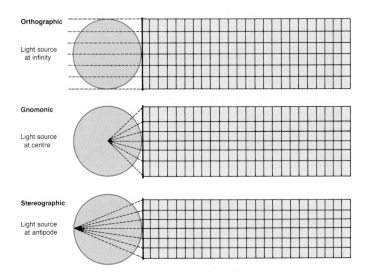

FIGURE 2.7 The effect of light source location on planar surface projections. Note the variations in spacing of the lines of latitude that occur when the light source is moved.

Globe Properties and Map Distortions

Not all of the true properties of the global grid can ever be preserved in any single projection; projections invariably distort some or all of them. The result is that all flat maps, whether geometrically or mathematically derived, also distort in different ways and to different degrees some or all of the four main properties of actual earth surface relationships: area, shape, distance, and direction.

Area

Cartographers use **equal-area**, or **equivalent**, projections when it is important for the map to show the *areas* of regions in correct or constant proportion to earth reality—as it is when the map is intended to show the actual areal extent of a phenomenon on the earth's surface. If we wish to compare the amount of land in agriculture in two different parts of the world, for example, it would be very misleading visually to use a map that represented the same amount of surface area at two different scales. To retain the needed size comparability, our chosen projection must assure that a unit area drawn anywhere on it will always represent the same number of square kilometres (or similar units) on the earth's surface. To achieve *equivalence*, any scale change that the projection imposes in one direction must be offset by compensating changes in the opposite direction. As a result, the shape of the portrayed area is inevitably distorted. A square on the earth, for example, may become a rectangle on the map, but that rectangle has the correct area (Figure 2.8). *A map that shows correct areal relationships always distorts the shapes of regions,* as Figure 2.9a demonstrates.

Shape

Although no projection can reproduce correct shapes for large areas, some do accurately portray the shapes of small areas. These true-shape projections are called **conformal**, and the importance of *conformality* is that regions and features "look right" and have the correct directional relationships. They achieve these properties for small areas by assuring that lines of latitude and longitude cross each other at right angles and that the scale is the same in all directions at any given location. Both these conditions exist on the globe but can be retained for only relatively small areas on maps. Because that is so, the shapes of large regions—continents, for example—are always different from their true earth shapes even on conformal maps. Except for maps for very small areas, *a map cannot be both equivalent and conformal*; these two properties are mutually exclusive, as Figure 2.9b suggests.

Distance

Distance relationships are nearly always distorted on a map, but some projections do maintain true distances in one direction or along certain selected lines. True distance relationships simply mean that the length of a straight line between two points on the map correctly represents the *great circle* distance between those points on the earth. (An arc of a great circle is the shortest distance between two points on the earth's curved surface; the equator is a great circle and all meridians of longitude are half great circles.) Projections with this property can be designed, but even on such **equidistant** maps true distance in all directions is

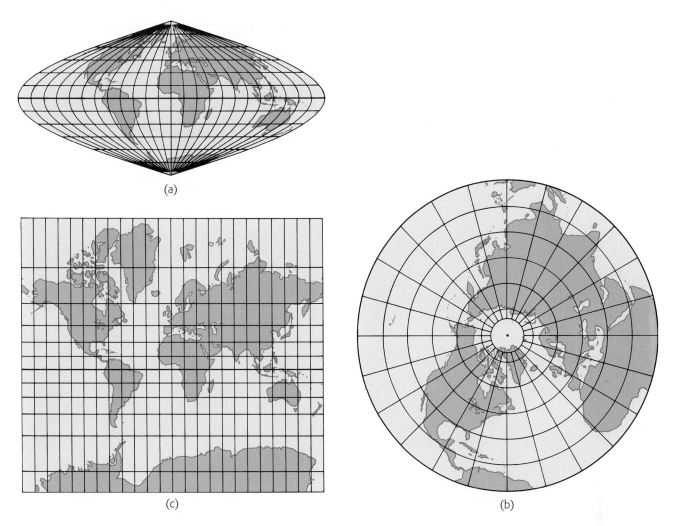

FIGURE 2.9 Sample projections demonstrating specific map properties. (a) The equal-area sinusoidal projection retains everywhere the property of equivalence. (b) The mathematically derived Mercator projection is conformal, displaying true shapes of individual features but greatly exaggerating sizes and distorting shapes away from the equator. (c) A portion of an azimuthal equidistant projection, polar-case. Distances from the centre (North Pole) to any other point are true; extension of the grid to the Southern Hemisphere would show the South Pole infinitely stretched to form the circumference of the map.

shown only from one or two central points. Distances between all other locations are incorrect and, quite likely, greatly distorted as Figure 2.9c clearly shows.

Direction

As is true of distances, directions between all points on a map cannot be shown without distortion. On **azimuthal projections**, however, true directions are shown from one central point to all other points. (An *azimuth* is the angle formed at the beginning point of a straight line, in relation to a meridian.) Directions or azimuths from points other than the central point to other points are not accurate. The azimuthal property of a projection is not exclusive—that is, an azimuthal projection may also be equivalent, conformal, or equidistant. The azimuthal equal-distance ("equidistant") map shown as Figure 2.9c is, as well, a true-direction map from the same North Pole origin.

There has been considerable debate within the cartographic community about which map projection is "best." The Mercator projection, which was frequently placed as wall maps in most

classrooms across Canada during your parents' school days, has had a profound influence how they and others perceive the world (Figure 2.10a). It was developed in 1569 by Gerardus Mercator as a navigation aid because direction is maintained on the map. Draw a line between two points and that provides a compass direction for the trip. However, this benefit comes at a cost—the amount of distortion increases as you move away from the equator. This means that countries such as Canada and the northern hemisphere's continents, appear much larger than they are relative to equatorial countries and the continents of the southern hemisphere, which are located relatively closer to the equator. This map appeared not only in classrooms but was frequently seen in newspapers, books, and atlases. Thus, the Mercator projection became the mental map of the world for Canadians and people living in the northern hemisphere. This was seen as a distinct but inappropriate geographic advantage of the colonial (European) powers over their many colonies located in the southern hemisphere. In response, it was argued that the Mercator Map should only be used for navigation, and that the Gall-Peters Map (Figure 2.10b) should be used for used for other purposes because it preserves

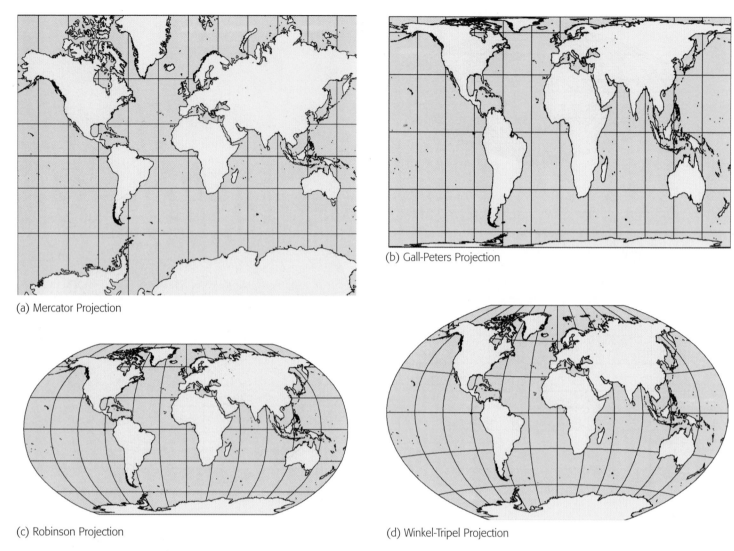

(a) Mercator Projection

(b) Gall-Peters Projection

(c) Robinson Projection

(d) Winkel-Tripel Projection

FIGURE 2.10 The Mercator, Gall-Peters, Robinson, and Winkel-Tripel Map Projections.
© Peter H. Dana/08

area. Originally developed in 1855 by James Gall and popularized Arno Peters in 1973, this projection, like the Mercator, utilizes a rectangular coordinate system but distorts shape, area, scale, and distance. Since it better represents the size of countries, intense lobbying occurred to have the Gall-Peters adopted as "the map of the world." The United Nations Development Programme responded and adopted it in its publications. In truth, neither the Gall-Peters nor the Mercator maps provide an accurate representation of the world—only the globe can do that! A compromise projection is the Robinson projection (Figure 2.10c), developed in 1963 by Arthur H. Robinson. While the projection is neither equal area nor conformal, it produced a more appealing visualization. In 1988, The National Geographic Society adopted the Robinson projection for its publications. It switched 10 years later to the Winkel-Tripel projection (Figure 2.10d), which is a modification of the Robinson projection. It was developed to minimize distortion relative to shapes, distances, and perspective.

The previous discussion suggest that Canada can be mapped a number of ways. The distortion of shape and area in high latitudes that is commonly associated with cylindrical projections has affected Canada by overemphasizing its northern extent and either distorts the shape of high latitude areas or makes them appear very remote (Figure 2.11).

A Cautionary Reminder

Mapmakers must be conscious of the properties of the projections they use, selecting the one that best suits their purposes. It is not ever possible to transform the globe into a flat map without distortion. But cartographers have devised hundreds of possible mathematical and geometrical projections in various modifications and aspects to display to their best advantage the variety of earth features and relationships they wish to emphasize. Some projections are highly specialized and properly restricted to a single limited purpose; others achieve a more general acceptability and utility.

If the map shows only a small area, the choice of a projection is not critical—virtually any can be used. The choice becomes more important when the area to be shown extends over a considerable longitude and latitude; then the selection of a projection clearly

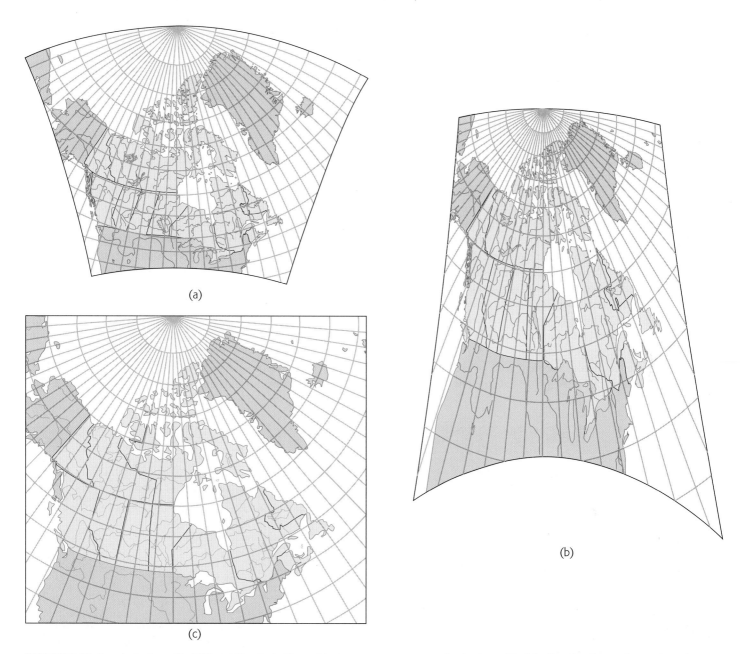

(a)

(b)

(c)

FIGURE 2.11 Canada Portrayed by Different Map Projections. *(a) Transverse Mercator Projection* is a **cylindrical projection** and is conformal. It is often used for mapping continents and oceans, equatorial and mid-latitude, and areas with a reasonably large north-south extent. It is used for the 1:250,000 and 1:50,000 National Topographic System series in Canada (to be discussed very soon), in part because it is relatively easy to match the edges of maps. The USGS also uses this type of projection for its topographic map series. *(b) Gnomonic Azimuthal Projection* is a type of planer map. It maintains (with some limitations) equidistance and true direction. It is well suited for mapping the World (with some limitations), hemispheres, equatorial and mid-latitude areas, continents and oceans, large regions and seas, and polar areas. This type of map is generally used for topographic and navigation purposes, and by the United States Geological Survey, which supplies base and thematic maps covering the United States of America. *(c) Lambert Conformal* **Conic Projection** is conformal and maintains true direction (with some limitations). It is particularly well suited for mapping the continents/ oceans, equatorial and mid-latitude areas, and areas with a reasonably large east-west extent. It is often used to map large countries.

Source: Reproduced with the permission of the Ministry of Public Works and Government Services, 2008. Map Projections, Atlas of Canada, http://atlas.nrcan.gc.ca/site/english/learningresources/carto_corner/map_projections.html.

depends on the purpose of the map. As we have seen, Mercator or gnomonic projections are useful for navigation. If numerical data are being mapped, the relative sizes of the areas involved should be correct, and equivalence is the sought-after map property. Conformality and equal distance may be required in other instances.

While selection of an appropriate projection is the task of the cartographer, understanding the consequences of that selection and recognizing and allowing for the distortions inevitable in all flat maps are the responsibility of the map reader. When skilfully designed maps are read by knowledgeable users, clear and accurate conveyance of spatial information and earth relationships is made convenient and natural.

Map Scale

We have already seen in Chapter 1 that scale (page 18) is a vital element of every map. Because it is a much reduced version of the reality it summarizes, a map generalizes the data it displays. **Scale**—the relationship between size or length of a feature on the map and the same item on the earth's surface—determines the amount of that generalization. The smaller the scale of the map, the larger is the area it covers and the more generalized are the data it portrays. The larger the scale, the smaller is the depicted area and the more accurately can its content be represented (Figure 2.12). An easy way to remember the distinction between small scales and large scales is to compare the numerical value of the representative fraction. The larger the fractional value, the larger the scale (e.g., 1:25,000 is larger than 1:50,000).

Map scale is selected according to the amount of generalization of data that is acceptable and the size of area that must be depicted. The user must consider map scale in evaluating the reliability of the spatial data that are presented. Regional boundary lines drawn on the world maps in this and other books or atlases would cover many kilometres or miles on the earth's surface. They obviously distort the reality they are meant to define, and on small-scale maps major distortion is inevitable. In fact, a general rule of thumb is that the larger the earth area depicted on a map, the greater is the distortion built into the map.

The Globe Grid

Maps have been geographers' longstanding primary tools. With the advent of GIS, they are now used in an even greater variety of ways including as equivalents to notebooks for listing observations, as rough notes, for classifying data, for displaying draft results as patterns, and finally as a means of visualizing spatial conclusions. All spatial analysis starts with locations, and all absolute locations are related to the global grid of latitude and longitude. The key reference points in the *grid system* are the North and South poles and the equator, which are given in nature, and the *prime meridian*, which is agreed on by cartographers. Because a circle contains 360 degrees, the distance between the poles is 180 degrees and between the equator and each pole, 90 degrees (Figure 2.13). *Latitude* measures distance north and south of the equator (0°),

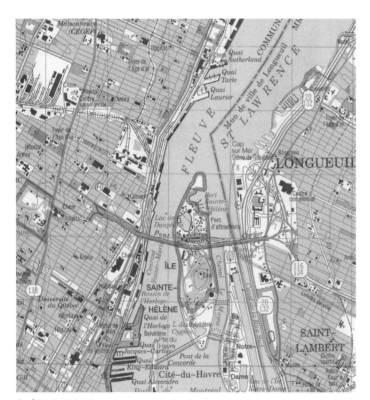

Scale 1:250,000

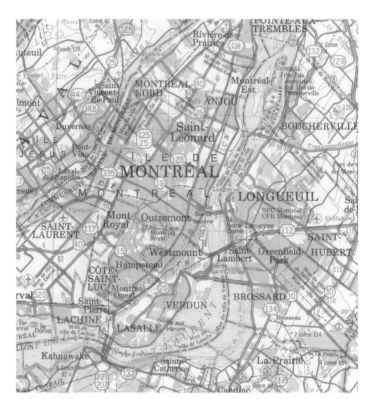

Scale 1:50,000

FIGURE 2.12 The effect of scale on area and detail. These two maps of Squamish, B.C. are from the NTS series and are scales of 1:250,000 and 1:50,000. NTS stands for the National Topographic System which provides topographic map coverage of Canada at scales of 1:500,000, 1:250,000, 1:125,000, 1:50,000, and 1:25,000. The larger the scale, the greater the number and kinds of features that can be included on the map. Scale can be reported in one (or more) of three ways. A verbal scale is given in words ("1 centimetre to 1 kilometre" or "1 inch to 1 mile"). A representative fraction (such as that placed at the left, below each of the maps above) is a statement of how many linear units on the earth's surface are represented by one unit on the map. A graphic scale (such as that placed at the right and below each of the maps above) is a line or bar marked off in map units but labelled in ground units.

Source: © 2006. Produced under licence from Her Majesty the Queen in Right of Canada, with permission of Natural Resources Canada.

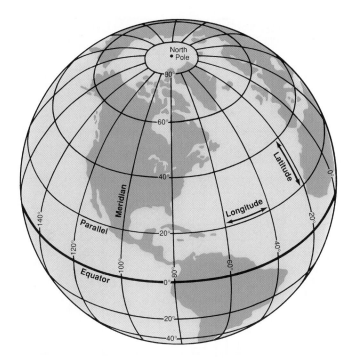

FIGURE 2.13 The grid system of parallels of latitude and meridians of longitude. Since the meridians converge at the poles, parallels become increasingly shorter away from the equator. On the globe, the 60th parallel is only one-half as long as the equator, and a degree of longitude along it measures only about 55 1/2 kilometres (about 34 1/2 miles) compared to about 111 kilometres (about 69 miles) at the equator (0°).

and *parallels* of latitude run due east–west. *Longitude* is the angular distance east or west of the prime meridian and is depicted by north–south lines called *meridians*, which converge at the poles. The properties of the globe grid the mapmaker tries to retain and the map user should look for are as follows:

1. All meridians are of equal length; each is one-half the length of the equator.

2. All meridians converge at the poles and are true north–south lines.

3. All lines of latitude (parallels) are parallel to the equator and to each other.

4. Parallels decrease in length as one nears the poles.

5. Meridians and parallels intersect at right angles.

6. The scale on the surface of the globe is the same in every direction.

Only the globe grid itself retains all of these characteristics. To project it onto a surface that can be laid flat is to distort some or all of these properties and consequently to distort the reality the map attempts to portray.

How Maps Show Location

The properties of the globe grid and of various projections are the concern of the cartographer. Geographers are more interested in the depiction of spatial data and in the analysis of the patterns

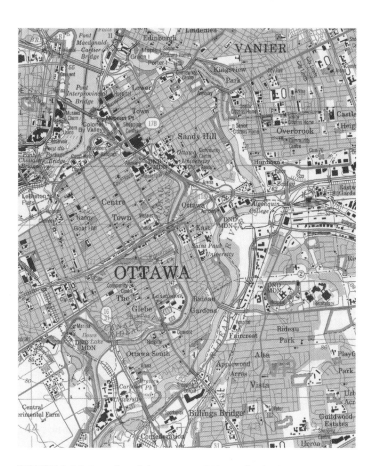

FIGURE 2.14 A portion of the 1:50,000 NTS map for Ottawa (Map 031G05). Topographic maps provide excellent information about ground relief (landforms and terrain), drainage (lakes and rivers), forest cover, administrative areas, populated areas, transportation routes and facilities (including roads and railways), and other artificially-made features. Because so much information is provided about human use of the land, topographic maps are classed as general purpose or reference maps by the International Cartographic Association.

and interrelationships those data present. Out of the myriad of items comprising the content of an area, the geographer must, first, select those that are of concern to the problem at hand and, second, decide on how best to display them for study or demonstration. In that effort, geographers can choose between different types of maps and different systems of symbolization.

General-purpose, reference, or *location maps* make up one major class of maps familiar to everyone. Their purpose is simply to show without analysis or interpretation a variety of natural or human-made features of an area or of the world as a whole. Familiar examples are highway maps, city street maps, topographic maps (Figure 2.14), atlas maps, and the like.

As noted above and in Chapter 1, latitude and longitude form the basis of location. However, since this coordinate system can be difficult to use, others such as the Military Grid, Civilian Grid System, and Universal Transverse Mercator coordinate system have been developed. This subsection devotes attention to the **Universal Transverse Mercator (UTM)** coordinate system because it is often incorporated into GPS systems. The UTM

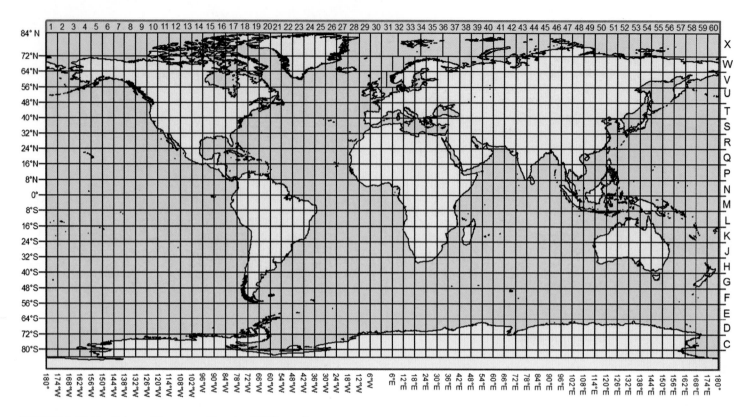

FIGURE 2.15 The Universal Transverse Mercator (UTM) coordinate system

© Peter H. Dana/08

system is based on a grid pattern that divides the earth into 60 zones, each comprising 60 degrees of longitude (Figure 2.15). Each zone is numbered 1 through 60, starting at the international date line (longitude 180°), and proceeding east. West to east, Canada spans zones 7 through 22 (Figure 2.16). Twenty UTM zones extend from 80°S to 84°N. Beginning at 80°S and preceding northward, the bands are lettered 'C' through 'X' (omitting letters 'I' and 'O' in order to avoid confusion with numbers one and zero). Each of these bands is 8° wide with the exception of band X, which is 12° wide. Note that beyond zones C and X, the Universal Polar Stereographic (UPS) grid system is used, and *not* the UTM system. The UTM lettering system covering the latitude zones for Canada are:

— from 72°N lat. to 84°N = "X" (northern 12° zone)
— from 64°N lat. to 72°N = "W"
— from 56°N lat. to 64°N = "V"
— from 48°N lat. to 56°N = "U"
— from 40°N lat. to 48°N = "T"

The Grid Zone Designation is identified by reading the column first and then the row. Winnipeg would be in zone 14U and Toronto 17T (Figure 2.16).

Within each zone, a square grid is superimposed and is aligned in order that vertical grid lines are parallel to the centre of the zone. Location is determined by the UTM grid coordinates, which are expressed as a distance in metres to the east of the central meridian, referred to as the "easting," and a distance in metres to the north of the equator, referred to as the "northing."

The northing values are measured continuously from zero at the Equator, in a northerly direction. To avoid negative numbers for locations south of the Equator, it has been assigned an arbitrary false northing value of 10,000,000 metre. A central meridian through the middle of each 6° zone is assigned an easting value of 500,000 metre. Grid values to the west of this central meridian are less than 500,000; to the east, more than 500,000. Thus, anything west of the central meridian will have an easting less than 500,000 metre. For example, UTM eastings range from 167,000 metre to 833,000 metre at the equator (these ranges narrow towards the poles). In the southern hemisphere, northings decrease as you go southward from the equator, which is given a "false northing" of 10,000,000 metre so that no point within the zone has a negative northing value. In the northern hemisphere, positions are measured northward from the equator, which has an initial "northing" value of 0 metre and a maximum "northing" value of approximately 9,328,000 metre at the 84th parallel—the maximum northern extent of the UTM zones. For instance, the CN Tower, located in zone 17 has a grid coordinates 630084 m east, 4833438 m north. UTM is easier to use than latitude and longitude because it is in a grid (rather than curved) and is in metric units.

The UTM system has been integrated into Canada's National Topographic System, and is represented on the 1:50,000 map sheets in a light blue line (See Figure 2.14). Distances and places can be measured and UTM coordinates determined. For more information go to: http://maps.nrcan.gc.ca/cartospecs/ChapBorder&Grid/ChapBorder&GridEF50/BorGriIntro010704E50.htm.

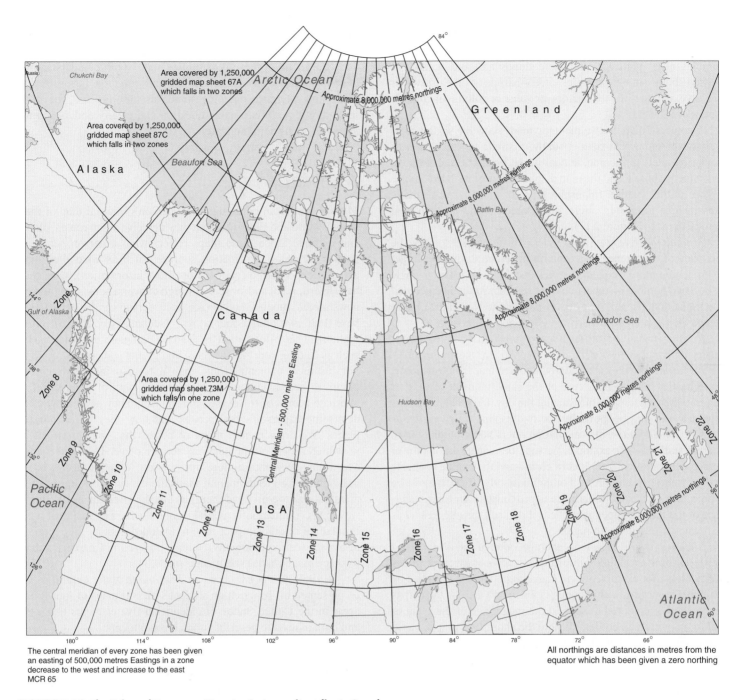

Area covered by 1,250,000 gridded map sheet 67A which falls in two zones

Area covered by 1,250,000 gridded map sheet 87C which falls in two zones

Area covered by 1,250,000 gridded map sheet 73M which falls in one zone

The central meridian of every zone has been given an easting of 500,000 metres Eastings in a zone decrease to the west and increase to the east

MCR 65

All northings are distances in metres from the equator which has been given a zero northing

FIGURE 2.16 The Universal Transverse Mercator System as it applies to Canada

Source: http://www.geod.nrcan.gc.ca/images/utm.jpg.

How Maps Show Other Data—Thematic Maps

Until about the middle of the 18th century, the general-purpose or reference map was the dominant map form, for the primary function of the mapmaker (and the explorer who supplied the new data) was to "fill in" the world's unknown areas with reliable locational information. With the passage of time, scholars saw the possibilities to use the accumulating locational information to display and study the spatial patterns of social and physical data.

The maps they made of climate, vegetation, soil, population, and other distributions introduced the thematic map, the second major class of maps. *Thematic map* is the general term applied to a map of any scale that presents a specific spatial distribution or a single category of data—that is, presents a graphic theme. The way the information is shown on such a map may vary according to the type of information to be conveyed, the level of generalization that is desired, and the symbolization selected. Thematic maps may be either *qualitative* or *quantitative*. The principal purpose of the qualitative map is to show the distribution of a particular class of information. The world location of producing oil fields, the distribution of Canada's national parks, or the pattern of areas of agricultural specialization within a province or country are examples. The interest is in where things are, and nothing is reported about—in the examples cited—barrels of oil extracted or in reserve, number of park visitors, or value or volume of crops or livestock produced.

In contrast, quantitative thematic maps show the spatial characteristic of numerical data. Usually, a single variable such as population, median income, annual wheat production, or average land value is chosen, and the map displays the variation from place to place in that feature. Important types of quantitative thematic maps include graduated circle, dot, isometric and isopleth, and choropleth maps (Figure 2.17).

Graduated circle maps use circles of different size to show the frequency of occurrence of a topic in different places; the larger the circle, the more frequent the incidence. On *dot maps*, a single or specified number of occurrences of the item studied is recorded by a single dot. The dot map serves not only to record data but to suggest their spatial pattern, distribution, and dispersion.

An *isometric map* features lines (*isolines*) that connect points registering equal values of the item mapped (*iso* means "equal"). The *isotherms* shown on the daily weather map connect points recording the same temperature at the same moment of time or the same average temperature during the day. Identical elevations above sea level may be shown by a form of isoline called a *contour line*. On *isopleth maps*, the calculation refers not to a point but to an areal statistic—for example, persons per square kilometre or average percentage of cropland in corn—and the isoline connects average values for unit areas. For emphasis, the area enclosed by isolines may be shaded to indicate approximately uniform occurrence of the thing mapped, and the isoline itself may be treated as the boundary of a uniform region.

A *choropleth map* presents average value of the data studied per pre-existing areal unit—dwelling unit rents or assessed values by city block, for example, or (in Canada) population densities by individual townships within counties. Each unit area on the map is then shaded or coloured to suggest the magnitude of the event or item found within its borders. Where the choropleth map is based on the absolute number of items within the unit area, as it is in Figure 2.17, rather than on areal averaging (total numbers, that is, instead of, for example, numbers per square kilometre), a misleading statement about density may be conveyed.

A *statistical map* records the actual numbers or occurrences of the mapped item per established unit area or location. The actual count of each province's colleges and universities shown on an outline map of Canada or the number of traffic accidents at each street intersection within a city are examples of statistical maps. A *cartogram* uses such statistical data to transform territorial space so that the largest areal unit on the map is the one showing the greatest statistical value (Figure 2.18).

Maps communicate information but, as in all forms of communication, the message conveyed by a map reflects the intent and, perhaps, the biases of its author. Maps are persuasive because of the implied precision of their lines, scales, colour and symbol placement, and information content. But maps, as communication devices, can subtly or blatantly manipulate the message they impart, or contain intentionally false information (Figure 2.19).

Maps, then, can distort and lie as readily as they can convey verifiable spatial data or scientifically valid analyses. The more map users are aware of those possibilities and the more understanding of map projections, symbolization, and common forms of thematic and reference mapping standards they possess, the more likely are they to reasonably question and clearly understand the messages maps communicate.

Mental Maps

Mental maps can be thought of a person's internal map of their known world and illustrate what they perceive about routes, places and regions. Since these maps reflect what a person perceives from a range of information sources, such as what they have actually experienced (primary or direct information), what they have heard, read, and/or seen through conversations, the internet, news media, movies, and books, each person can be expected to have their own unique mental map (secondary or indirect information). This information is used to complete everyday tasks, such as finding your way to class, and giving someone directions. For instance, a mental route map may also include reference points to be encountered on the chosen path of connection or alternate routes of travel (see Figure 1.2). They also allow us to determine a person's preferences and how they define unique places. We draw mental maps of places that are unfamiliar to us, which reflect our perceptions about a place. They can change over time as we obtain more information. Whether drawn by an individual or a group, mental maps are every bit as real as their creators (and we all have them) as are the street maps and highway maps commercially available, and they are a great deal more immediate in their impact on our spatial decisions. The naming of a place (called toponymy), a topic covered in Chapter 6, helps to shape and enhance our mental maps.

In 1960, Kevin Lynch wrote *The Image of the City* in which he presented his research on student's mental maps of four urban areas in the United States. He identified five elements that were and remain used to describe urban environments:

Paths—routes between places, such as walk or bike paths, streets (e.g. route from home to school).

Landmarks—prominent points of interest or particular locations (e.g. home, school).

Nodes—meeting places or centres of activity where pathways cross (e.g. financial district, shopping district).

Districts—regions which are perceived to be homogeneous (e.g. downtown, university, industrial area).

Edges—form the boundaries between districts.

Noting the inclusion and exclusion of these elements, and their prominence on a mental map are useful to interpreting how people perceive their environment. Since Lynch's time, additional techniques have been developed to collect and analyze data from mental maps. These include measuring uni-dimensional aspects (e.g. distance and direction) and two-dimensional aspects as well (e.g. how people draw maps if they are provided with instructions or given a small pre-drawn portion of a map). The latter focuses

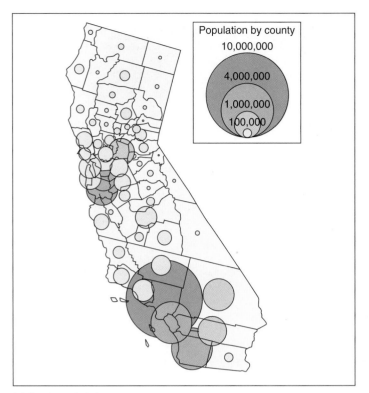

(a) Graduated circle map

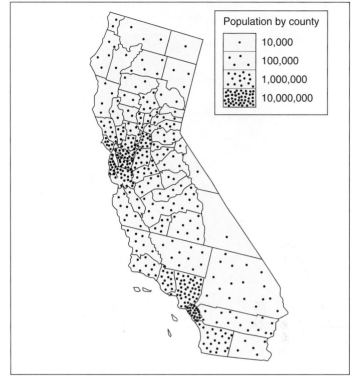

(b) Dot-distribution map

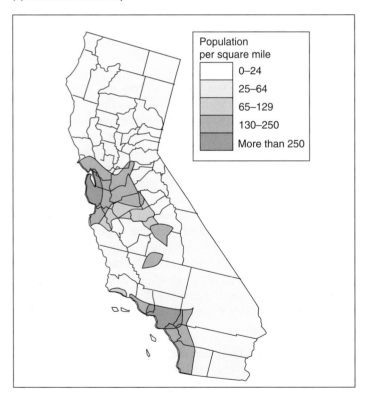

(c) Isopleth map

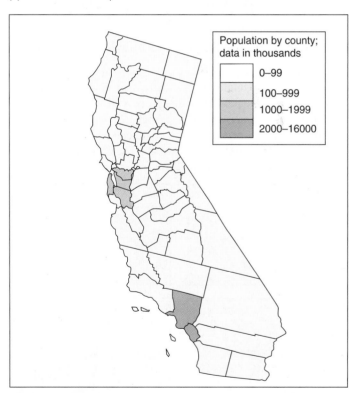

(d) Choropleth map

FIGURE 2.17 Types of thematic maps. Although population is the theme of each, these different California maps present their information in strikingly different ways. (*a*) In the graduated circle map, the area of the circle is approximately proportional to the absolute number of people within each county. (*b*) In a dot-distribution map where large numbers of items are involved, the value of each dot is identical and stated in the map legend. The placement of dots on this map does not indicate precise locations of people within the county, but simply their total number. (*c*) Population density is recorded by the isopleth map, while the choropleth map (*d*) may show absolute values as here or, more usually, ratio values such as population per square kilometre.

Source: From Fred M. Shelley and Audrey E. Clarke, Human and Cultural Geography, © 1994. *Reproduced by permission of The McGraw-Hill Companies.*

FIGURE 2.18 McDonald's Cartogram. This is a cartogram in which each country is sized according to the number of MacDonald's restaurants contained within it. Note how large the United States is to every other country. The continent of Africa is very hard to distinguish. Due to very small number of McDonald's restaurants, some countries have been merged illustrating how maps can simplify reality (lie!).

Source: © Copyright 2006 SASI Group (University of Sheffield) and Mark Newman (University of Michigan).

attention on how mental images and maps are developed while the former indicates the product of that process (Kitchin, 2000).

There are many findings associated with mental map research, which, in part, reinforce comments made in Chapter 1 (see "Physical and Cultural Attributes," "The Changing Attributes of Space"). First, what you know and how you draw it reflects where you have lived (Figure 2.20) and travelled, especially if it is a popular vacation destination. Second, our everyday conversations and media coverage about a place influence our perceptions. For instance, we may choose routes or avoid neighbourhoods not on objective grounds but on how the area is reported in the media (e.g. high crime). In those choices, gender can play an important role. The mental maps of women may well contain danger zones where fear of, for example, sexual assault, harassment, or encounter with persons or conditions felt to be threatening are determinants in routes chosen or times of journey. Third, individuals who are of lower socio-economic groups draw maps that cover smaller geographic areas relative to those of higher socio-economic groups (Figure 2.21). Generally, our areas of awareness generally increase with the increasing mobility that comes with

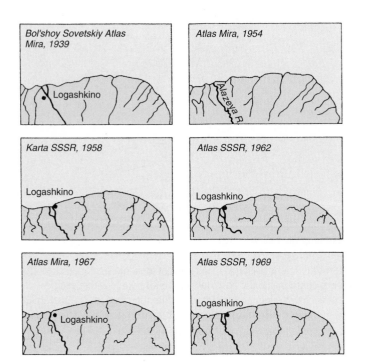

FIGURE 2.19 The wandering town of Logashkino, as traced in various Soviet atlases by Mark Monmonier. Deliberate, extensive cartographic "disinformation" and locational falsification, he reports, became a Cold War tactic of the Soviet Union. We usually use—and trust—maps to tell us exactly where things are located. On the maps shown, however, Logashkino migrates from west of the river away from the coast to east of the river on the coast, while the river itself gains and loses a distributary and, in 1954, the town itself disappears. The changing misinformation, Monmonier suggests, was intended to obscure from potential enemies the precise location of possible military targets.

Source: Mark Monmonier, How to Lie with Maps, *2nd ed. © 1996. Reproduced by permission of the University of Chicago Press.*

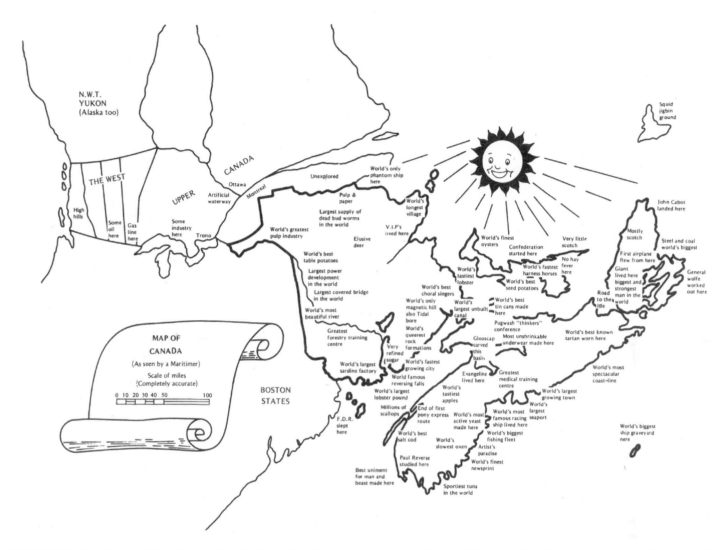

FIGURE 2.20 Mental map of Canada drawn by a Maritimer. Mental maps reflect a person's view of the world. Note the importance and pride reflected in local and regional place values.

Source: R.M. Downs and D. Stea (1977). Maps in Minds: Reflections on Cognitive Mapping. *New York: Harper & Row, Publishers. ISBN: 0-06-041733-1. Figure 1.3, p. 9.*

age, affluence, familiarity, and education, and may be enlarged or restricted for different social groups within the city or country.

Mental maps are becoming more accessible through the web. On Platial.com, over 5,000 custom maps have been drawn, including maps called autobiogeographies, indicating where they have been. Drawing mental maps forms an important element in **neogeography**—people using and creating their own maps, on their own terms, and by combining elements of an existing toolset. A neogeographer geotags pictures and images (i.e. adds information about where an image is located often by using a global positioning system (to be discussed shortly) and locates it on a web-based map, such as Google Maps (maps.google.com), Microsoft Maps (local.live.com), or Yahoo Maps (maps.yahoo .com/beta). People often geotag their photos to make a map of their summer vacation. The popular term for drawing mental maps is **social mapping**—maps that tell people something about a place.

Sometimes government agencies or consultants will use a group facilitator to have members of a community work together to learn more about them, their community, and their resources. Over the past 20 years, there has been an increasing worldwide

interest in, and respect for, traditional knowledge in guiding resource development decisions, such as timber harvesting, oil and gas development, and park planning, as well as land claims agreements between aboriginals and federal/state/provincial governments (Folke et al., 2007). Broadly defined, traditional knowledge is the "cumulative and collective body of knowledge, experience, and values held by societies with a history of subsistence" (Ellis, 2005: 66). Mental maps have been developed by combining the individual discourses and/or mental maps obtained from local people can indicate a community's local knowledge or how it defines its region. In a resource management context, information generated from this type of exercise can enhance sustainability (Figure 2.22). Although it has been employed successfully, the utility and accuracy of this type of exercise remains controversial. Some questions the merits of incorporating qualitative data (i.e., the stories, sketches) onto very accurate locational (i.e., quantitative) maps. On the other hand, as illustrated by some pharmaceutical companies, indigenous knowledge has sometimes been exploited by private interests when the location of their valued resources has been revealed.

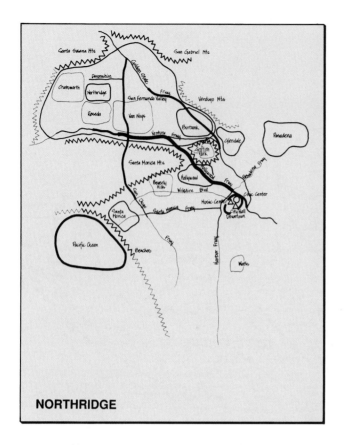

NORTHRIDGE

BOYLE HEIGHTS

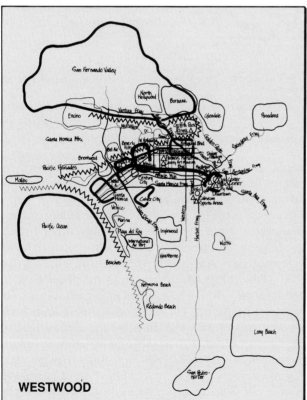

WESTWOOD

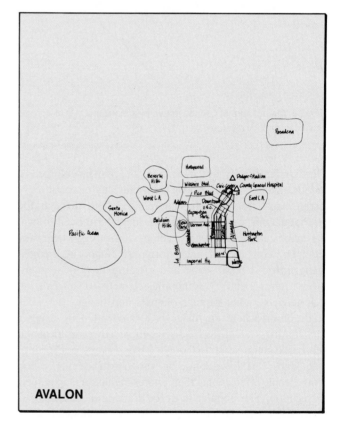

AVALON

FIGURE 2.21 Four mental maps of Los Angeles. The upper and middle-income residents of Northridge and Westwood have expansive views of the metropolis reflecting their mobility and area of travel. Residents of Boyle Heights and Avalon, both minority districts, have a much more restricted and incomplete mental image of the city. Their limited mental maps reflect and reinforce their spatial isolation within the metropolitan area.

Source: From Department of City Planning, City of Los Angeles, The Visual Environment of Los Angeles, 1971. *Reprinted by permission.*

Some Key Themes in the Study of Human Geography

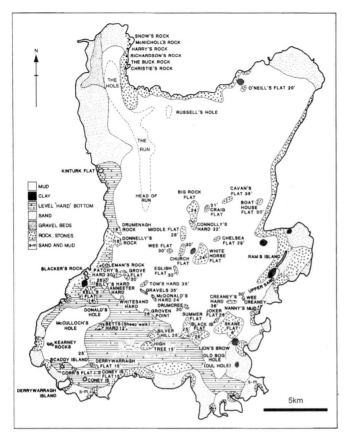

FIGURE 2.22 Mental map of the substrate of Lough Neagh as perceived by local fishermen. A study completed by McKenna et al. (2008) developed a mental map of the substrate of Lough Neagh, Northern Ireland from interviews with local fishers. In this instance, fishers were provided with the outline of Lough Neagh and asked to indicate the substrate on it. The fishers' local knowledge compared very favourably to the information generated from scientific studies.

Source: Copyright © 2008 by John McKenna, Rory, J. Quinn and Daniel J. Donnelly, adapted from maps by Admiralty Chart No. 2163 (1983) and Side-scan Sonar Survey of Lough Neagh. Published here under license by The Resilience Alliance. McKenna, J., R. J. Quinn, D. J. Donnelly and J. A. G. Cooper. 2008. Accurate mental maps as an aspect of local ecological knowledge (LEK): a case study from Lough Neagh, Northern Ireland. Ecology and Society 13(1): 13. [online] URL: http://www.ecologyandsociety.org/vol13/iss1/art13/.

Remote Sensing

Remote sensing detects the nature of an object and the content of an area from a distance. In the early 20th century, fixed-wing aircraft provided a platform for the camera and photographer, and by the 1930s aerial photography from planned positions and routes permitted reliable data gathering for large and small area mapping purposes. Even today, high and low altitude aerial photography with returned film remains a widely used remote sensing technique. Standard photographic film detects reflected energy within the visible portion of the electromagnetic spectrum. It can be supplemented by special sensitized infrared film that has proved particularly useful for the recording of vegetation and hydrographic features, and by non-photographic imaging techniques including thermal scanning (widely used for studying various aspects of water features such as ocean currents and water pollution and, because it can be employed during nighttime hours, for

military surveillance and energy budget observations) and radar mapping (also operative night and day and useful for penetrating clouds and haze).

For more than 30 years, both manned and unmanned spacecraft have supplemented the airplane as the vehicle for imaging earth features. Among the advantages of satellites are the speed of coverage and the fact that views of large regions can be obtained. In addition, they are equipped to record and report back to Earth digitized information from multiple parts of the electromagnetic spectrum including some that are outside the range of human eyesight. Satellites enable us to map the invisible, including atmospheric and weather conditions, in addition to providing images with applications in agriculture and forest inventory, land use classification, identification of geologic structures and mineral deposits, and more. The different sensors of the Landsat satellites are capable of resolving objects between 15 and 60 metres (50 and 200 ft) in size. Even sharper images are yielded by the French SPOT satellite (launched in 1986); its sensors can show objects that are larger than 10 metres (33 ft). Satellite imagery is relayed by electronic signals to receiving stations, where computers convert them into photo-like images for use in long-term scientific research and in current-condition mapping programs. In December 2007, Canada RADARSAT-2 was launched. This commercial radar satellite will be used for marine surveillance, ice monitoring, disaster management, environmental monitoring, resource management, and mapping in Canada and around the world. Its ability to monitor human rights abuses is also being explored (Figure 2.23). The Canada Centre for Remote Sensing provides these and other geographic databases to public and private decision makers, and others too (www.ccrs.nrcan.gc.ca).

Geographic Information Systems (GIS)

Geographic information systems (GIS) extend the use of digitized data and computer manipulation to investigate and display spatial information. A GIS can be envisioned as a set of discrete informational overlays linked by reference to a basic locational grid of latitude and longitude (Figure 2.24). The system then permits the separate display of the spatial information contained in the database. It allows the user to overlay maps of different themes, analyze the relations revealed, and compute spatial relationships. It shows aspects of spatial associations otherwise difficult to display on conventional maps, such as flows, interactions, and three-dimensional characteristics. In short, a GIS database, as a structured set of spatial information, has become a powerful tool for automating geographical analysis and synthesis. A GIS data set may contain the great amount of place-specific information collected and published by Statistics Canada, including population distribution, race, ethnicity, income, housing, employment, industry, farming, and so on. It may also hold environmental information downloaded from satellite imagery or taken from NTS (national topographic system) maps (Figure 2.14) and other governmental and private sources.

GIS makes it possible for a map user not only to see where something is located but to combine other pieces of information in order to increase the level of analysis and information generated.

FIGURE 2.23 Porta Farm, Zimbabwe in 2002 and 2006. In May 2005, the Government of Zimbabwe began Operation Murambatsvina, which in English translates to Operation Restore Order or Drive Out Trash. According to the Government, the intent was to crackdown against illegal housing (e.g. squatter settlements) and black market activities, and reduce the risk of the spread of infectious disease in these areas. However, since this initiative coincided with the results of the March election which saw many of the urban poor voting for the Opposition Party, it has argued that the government's main reason for commencing Operation Murambatsvina was to punish the urban poor for voting for the opposition party. The U.N. estimates the homes of around 700,000 people were destroyed. Over 2.4 million people across Zimbabwe have been affected by the program. Some of this devastation is shown above. In 2002, Porta Farm was home to between 6,000 and 10,000 people who lived in more than 850 homes and other buildings. By 2006, the area had been levelled. Satellite images like these are now being used more frequently to document destruction in many dangerous parts of the world. Amnesty International initiated a project that monitors 12 vulnerable villages in Darfur region of Sudan that uses images produced from commercial satellites that have rented satellites. Find out more at www.eyesondarfur.org.

Terrain Models

Network
- Street centre lines
- Drainage network

Utilities
- Sanitary sewer lines
- Water lines
- Telephone
- Gas/electric

Lots/Ownership
- Lot lines
- Property lines

Zones/Districts
- Comprehensive plan
- Municipal zoning
- Voting precincts
- School districts
- Census tracts/blocks

Base Mapping
- Road pavement
- Buildings/structures
- Fences/parking lots
- Drainage
- Wooded areas
- Spot elevation
- Contour lines
- Recreational facilities

FIGURE 2.24 A model of a geographic information system. A GIS incorporates three primary components: data storage capability, computer graphics programs, and statistical packages. In this example, the different layers of information are to be used in different combinations for city planning purposes. Different data sets, all selected for applicability to the questions asked, may be developed and used in human geography, economic geography, transportation planning, industrial location work, and similar applications.

Reprinted by permission of Shaoli Huang.

The key to the GIS is **geocoding**—the process of assigning absolute location coordinates, such as latitude and longitude, to human and physical features of the earth. For instance, a marketing geographer might combine information on where people buy certain items (think about the last time you were asked for your postal code after buying something at a store) with census information about income and demographics in order to target new products or store locations. An urban geographer might use similar information to determine where affordable housing and social service offices might be best located. GIS allows geographers to determine the relationship between factors, and is becoming increasingly accessible to the public. Google Maps and Google Earth are the simplest and most easily available form of a GIS increasingly used by the general public.

A Canadian geographer, Roger Tomlinson (Figure 2.25), has been identified as the "father" of Geographic Information Systems (GIS). According to him, the strength of the term GIS comes from its

FIGURE 2.25 Roger Tomlinson, the "inventor" of GIS. He was awarded an Order of Canada for his work, which he pioneered the use of worldwide to collect, manage, and manipulate geographical data, changing the face of geography as a discipline. His work with GIS focused on the development of major international GIS programs, ranging widely in geographic scope and content, but with a special emphasis on environmental protection, natural resources management, national parks, and forests.

fundamentals: "the word 'geography' is not going to go away. It has been in use for hundreds (some would say thousands) of years . . . It is clear to me that the overall process is that of earth description; in short, it is geography. It has been demonstrated beyond any refutation that geography matters in human decision making."

GIS is now being combined with satellite-enabled **global positioning systems (GPS)** in cars, cell phones, iPhones, and Black-Berries. This software allows people to find out not only where they are located, but also provides them with directions about how to get to where they want to be. GPS is a satellite-based navigation system, called NAVSTAR, originally developed for military purposes starting in 1978, and is maintained and controlled by the United States Department of Defence. Made fully operational in 1995, it utilizes a set of at least 24 satellites which transmit precise microwave signals to the GPS receiver and allows it to determine its location (within a few metres), speed, direction, and time. The NAVSTAR system is often referred to as *the* GPS, (at least in Canada and the United States) because it was generally available first. The Russians have developed their own system (GLONASS). The Europeans are working on a system—the Galileo positioning system. India and China are considering the development of their own systems.

GIS and GPS are inspiring people to explore their world and re-invigorating people to read and make maps. TV stations use GIS to provide viewers with up-to-date weather forecasts and maps. **Geocaching** is an outdoor "treasure-hunting" activity in which the participants use a GPS receiver to hide and find containers (called "geocaches" or "caches") in local or far-away places. A typical cache is a small waterproof container containing a logbook and "treasure," usually small toys or trinkets. The first time geocaching is reported to have occurred was on May 3, 2000. On that date, to celebrate improved access by the public to more accurate location information, a bucket of trinkets in the woods outside Portland, Oregon and its location was announced on the web (USENET newsgroup sci.geo.satellite-nav). The rule is to take something, leave something, and sign the logbook. According to geocaching.com, there are 513,240 active caches worldwide covering all seven continents.

Systems, Maps, and Models

The content of area is interrelated and constitutes a **spatial system** that, in common with all systems, functions as a unit because its component parts are interdependent. Only rarely do individual elements of area operate in isolation, and to treat them as if they do is to lose touch with spatial reality. The systems of geographic concern are those in which the functionally important variables are spatial: location, distance, direction, density, and the other basic concepts we have reviewed. The systems that they define are not the same as regions, though spatial systems may be the basis for regional identification.

Systems have components, and the analysis of the role of components helps reveal the operation of the system as a whole. To conduct that analysis, individual system elements must be isolated for separate identification and, perhaps, manipulated to see their function within the structure of the system or subsystem. Maps and models are the devices geographers use to achieve that isolation and separate study.

Maps, as we have seen, are effective to the degree that they can segregate at an appropriate level of generalization those system elements selected for examination. By compressing, simplifying, and abstracting reality, maps record in manageable dimension the real-world conditions of interest. A **model** is a simplified abstraction of reality, structured to clarify causal relationships. Maps are a kind of model. They represent reality in an idealized form so that certain aspects of its properties may be seen more clearly. They are a special form of model, of course. Their abstractions are rendered visually and at a reduced scale so they may be displayed, for example, on the pages of this book.

The complexities of spatial systems analysis—and the opportunities for quantitative analysis of systems made possible by computers and sophisticated statistical techniques—have led geographers to use other kinds of models in their work. Model building is the technique social scientists use to simplify complex situations, to eliminate (as does the map) unimportant details, and to isolate for special study and analysis the role of one or more interacting elements in a total system. With this introduction to geography from the perspective of the "World in Spatial Terms," we are able to continue our exploration of geography from three other important themes in the next chapter.

Want to Learn More?

Inductive and Deductive Reasoning:
http://www.socialresearchmethods.net/
kb/dedind.php

2006 Census of Canada:
www2.statcan.ca/ccr_r000_e.htm

Maps

Map Projections: http://atlas.nrcan.gc.ca/
site/english/learningresources/carto_corner/
map_projections.html

U.N. Maps: www.un.org/Depts/
Cartographic/english/htmain.htm

Atlas of Canada, Natural Resources Canada:
http://atlas.nrcan.gc.ca/site/english/
index.html

UTM

Natural Resources Canada: http://maps.
nrcan.gc.ca/cartospecs/ChapBorder&Grid/
ChapBorder&GridEF50/
BorGriIntro010704E50.htm

Geocaching: www.geocaching.org

Parks Canada: http://www.pc.gc.ca/docs/pc/
guide/geocache/index_e.asp

Remote Sensing, Canada Centre for Remote
Sensing: www.ccrs.nrcan.gc.ca

GIS

Environment Canada: http://www.eman-
rese.ca/eman/ecotools/gisarea/intro.html

The Guide to GIS: http://www.gis.com/

Global Positioning Systems, Canadian Space
Agency: http://www.space.gc.ca/asc/eng/
resources/publications/success16.asp

Summary

The research process is generally characterized by four main steps and five common purposes. In order to be rigorous, researchers use a mix of data sources (primary and/or secondary; quantitative and/or qualitative) and/or forms of analysis. The census of Canada is a very reliable secondary source of data and is valuable because data can be tracked over space and time through a range of geographic scales. Maps are an important source of geographic data and a way to present results. All maps are an imperfect rendering of the three-dimensional earth and its parts, on a two-dimensional surface. In that rendering, some or all of the characteristics of the global grid are distorted, but convenience and data manageability are gained. Spatial information may be depicted in a number of ways, each designed to simplify and clarify the infinite complexity of the real-world. GIS allows for the creation, storage, analysis, and visualization of data in both two and three dimensions, and is emerging as a technique all geographers should have some familiarity with. GIS is becoming increasingly more accessible to the general public. Geographers use verbal and mathematical models for the same purpose, to abstract and to analyze.

KEY WORDS

azimuthal projection 41
conformal projection 40
conic projection 43
cylindrical projection 43
deductive research 32
developable surface 39
equal-area (equivalent) projection 40
equidistant projection 40

geocaching 55
geocoding 54
geographic information systems (GIS) 53
geometrical (perspective) projection 39
gnomonic projection 39
global positioning system (GPS) 55
graticule 38

inductive research 32
map 37
mental map 48
mathematical projection 38
model 55
neogeography 51
orthographic projection 39
primary data 33
projection 37

qualitative data 36
quantitative data 36
remote sensing 53
scale 44
secondary data 33
spatial system 55
stereographic projection 39
social mapping 51
Universal Transverse Mercator (UTM) 45

FOR REVIEW

1. What are the major subjects of the Census of Canada?

2. List at least four properties of the globe grid. Why are globe grid properties apt to be distorted on maps?

3. What does prime meridian mean? What happens to the length of a degree of longitude as it approaches the poles?

4. What different ways of displaying statistical data on maps can you name and describe?

5. Look at the maps of Canada in Figure 2.11. Which do you think is the "best" map? What criteria should be applied in determining which is "best"?

6. Using Google Maps. Go to http://www.youtube.com/watch?v=Cd5eu-4kCoA to find a short clip on how to use the Google Map interface. To see some of the power of Google maps, go to http://maps.google.com/. Zoom in on your university/college town. When can begin to see a reasonable level of detail in the street pattern, go to the box "Find Businesses." Type in a general or specific business (e.g., coffee, pizza, insurance; Starbucks, Tim Horton's, Pizza, Pizza, Dominos). How would you describe the pattern of this business relative to accessibility to customers? Press the "Satellite" icon and zoom in on your residence or home. What time of day was this image taken? How can you tell? Google Maps provides high-resolution satellite images for most urban areas in Canada. Compare the level of detail provided within your university town to a nearby rural area.

FOCUS FOLLOW-UP

1. **What are the sources of information, primary and secondary, which geographers use?** pp. 31–37.

   Geographers use a wide range of sources to obtain information. Common primary data sources include surveys, interviews, field observations, and participant observation. Popular secondary data sources include the census, and reliable surveys completed by government agencies, non-government organizations, and the private sector.

2. **How is the Census of Canada spatially organized and what are some problems in using this data source?** pp. 34–35.

   The census geography ranges from city block, dissemination area, census consolidated subdivision, census division, and economic region. Some problems with using census data include the delay in obtaining data once it is collected, although this should become shorter as more data are collected online. Averaging of data, particularly when populations are small, detracts from the precision of data while protecting the confidentiality of respondents.

3. **Why do geographers use maps, and how do maps show spatial information?** pp. 37–51.

   Maps are tools geographers use to identify and delimit regions and to analyze their content. They permit the study of areas and areal features too extensive to be completely viewed or understood on the earth's surface itself. Thematic (single category) maps may be with qualitative or quantitative. Their data may be shown in graduated circle, dot distribution, isometric, chloropleth, statistical, or cartogram form.

4. **In what ways in addition to maps may spatial data be visualized or analyzed?** p. 51–55.

   Informally, we all create "mental maps" reflecting highly personalized impressions and information about the spatial arrangement of things (for example buildings, streets, landscape features). More formally, geographers recognize the content of area as forming a spatial system to which techniques of spatial systems analysis and model building are applicable.

ONLINE LEARNING CENTRE

The World Wide Web has a tremendous number and variety of sites pertaining to geography. To access Web sites, Internet exercises, self-quizzes, videos, and additional study tools relevant to this chapter's content, visit the *Human Geography* Online Learning Centre at **www.mcgrawhill.ca/olc/fellmann.**

3 GEOGRAPHIC PERSPECTIVES ON SPACE

Aims

- To identify the role of a model, the world-systems analysis, in guiding our understanding of globalization
- To better understand the geographer's view of human systems, in the contexts of spatial interaction and human spatial interaction
- To know the essence of "space" from a geographic perspective
- To better understand the concepts of places and regions
- To better appreciate the relevance of geography in our globalized world

Some Specific Considerations for Review:

1. The three perspectives are incorporated into world-systems analysis, pp. 59–64.
2. The three bases for all spatial interaction, pp. 64–66.
3. How the probability of aggregate spatial interaction is measured, pp. 66–70.
4. The special forms and nature of human spatial behaviour, pp. 70–73.
5. The roles of information and perception in human spatial actions, pp. 73–80.

'Space' is often regarded as the fundamental stuff of geography. Indeed, so fundamental that the well-known anthropologist, Edward Hall, once compared it to sex: "It is there but we don't talk about it. And if we do, we certainly don't want to get technical and serious about it" (cited in Barcan and Buchanan, 1999: 7). Indeed, it would be fairly easy to argue that most of the time most geographers do tend to get rather embarrassed when challenged to come out with ideas about what the supposed core of their subject is, and yet they continue to assert its importance. Rather like sex, they argue, without space we would not be here. So is all this just mass disciplinary hypocrisy? Not really. It is just about the extreme difficulty of describing certain aspects of the medium, which is the discipline's message (Thrift, 2003: 95)

Introduction

When he wrote about the 'global village' in 1962, Marshal McLuhan was referring to how the electronic mass media would reduce barriers to communication that time and distance always posed, and allow people to interact on a global basis. Your grandparents and parents, perhaps even McLuhan himself, could not have predicted how quickly and fundamentally our global village has developed and impacted people's lives. The term **'globalization'** is now used to refer to everyone's way of being and living in the global village. While there is no single accepted definition of globalization, it commonly refers the increasing level of "global spatial flows, interconnections and the interdependence of people, and places at a world scale, and which are creating changes in the structures and organizations of society and places" (Davies, 2004: 189). Some of the changes McLuhan foresaw—the faster flows of goods, information and people around the world—supported by improved transportation systems and technology, computers, and the internet have become a reality. Many people now possess cell phones which allow makes them to be accessible 24/7 to people around the world and at relatively low cost. Less likely predicted were suggestions that we would live in a world where many places are similar—the homogenization of the world's economic, financial, cultural, social, and political systems (Figure 3.1). The fact that places appear to be becoming similar is an important spatial manifestation of great interest to geographers.

This chapter provides further insight into 'the geographic perspective'—some of the concepts and methods geographers use in studying regions, human systems, and people and places. Since it is not possible to capture all examples of the perspective in one chapter, the content is selective. The chapter begins with a description of a model based on regions of the world that assists us in understanding the economic dimensions of globalization. This provides a sense of how and why geography is very relevant in solving current problems. It also provides some context for some of the subsequent chapters, which focus some attention on specific aspects of globalization. The next two sections deal with Human Systems and Spatial Interaction, and Human Systems as Human Spatial Behaviour. The former examines the movement of goods and services through space. The latter attends to

FIGURE 3.1 The Streetscape of "Globalization." Globalization suggests that we are becoming the same—that goods like Coke and Nike are available everywhere; that we wear the same clothing and listen to the same music. What elements in the picture suggest that we are living in a global village? Could you guess that this picture is from India? (Also see Figure 1.4.)

the movement of people. Some focus is paid to how some of the concepts mentioned in the text are measured, and in doing so connects to comments made in Chapter 2—conducting research often involves some form of measurement. The final section pays major attention to places.

Globalization: The World-Systems Analysis

Immanuel Wallerstein developed a framework to help understand the development of our modern globalized world. While some people tend to view the world as made up of separate entities, as illustrated in their use of terms such as "First and Third Worlds" or "North and South," Wallerstein maintained that there was only one world system and it was connected through economic relationships. For Wallerstein, the modern world system has always been a capitalist world economy. A world economy refers to "a large geographic zone within which there is a division of labor and hence significant internal exchange of basic or essential goods as well as flows of capital and labor" (Wallerstein, 2006: 23). A capitalist economy is one in which the "*endless*" accumulation of wealth is the main priority. World-system analysis incorporates three important perspectives—historical, dependency theory, and Marxist. Essentially, the world-system is an interdependent economic system of countries, linked through trade and the flow of funds. As we will see, world-systems analysis has both spatial (i.e., regional) and a socio-economic dimensions. A brief review of the framework is provided below.

Between the 9th and 14th centuries, a social and economic system known as **feudalism** dominated most of Western Europe (an exception being Spain and southern France). In brief, it saw kings grant large land holdings to tenants-in-chief (called barons in Britain) in exchange for their military support. This grant of land was known as a "feud" or "fief." The tenant-in-chief usually leased parts of these lands to the knights, who leased land to yeomen. This provided a rigid and static social structure, which was based on an oath of homage by vassals (lower classes) to their lords in return for protection and justice. Under feudalism, power and wealth were concentrated within a very small circle of people (royalty). Marx believed feudalism was an economic system that was based on the control of arable land by the ruling class (the aristocracy). This control led to the development of a class society based on the exploitation of peasants who worked these lands, often under serfdom. Economic activity largely occurred within the context of a nation. As growth within the feudal system became very small, money rents began to replace the feudal obligations. This forced many peasants off the land. However, with the advent of the Industrial Revolution, they found employment in the emerging manufacturing sector. The accumulation of wealth through the trade of goods, particularly manufactured goods, became a hallmark of the new capitalist system and provided for rapid economic growth. The countries that enjoyed this growth also explored new areas and developed colonies.

Wallerstein's incorporation of **dependency theory** into world-systems analysis provided a means to understand the nature and evolution of the relationship between the newly created empire countries and their expanding colonies. Prior to their discovery by Europeans, many places and regions were not part of the world-system, which is defined by economic rather than political, cultural, or social relationships. They remained outside their sphere of trade. As these **external areas** were discovered, many became incorporated into this Western European-oriented world-system. Dependency theory is based on the premise that resources flow from the periphery of poor and underdeveloped states (i.e., often called developing nations) to the core—a set of rich states (i.e., developed countries). From a Marxist perspective, trade benefits the core to the detriment of the periphery as demonstrated by inequalities of wealth between the two (see Chapter 11). Wallerstein maintained that the world-system has and continues to promote the flow of resources from poor, underdeveloped states in the **periphery region** to wealthy states in the **core region.** After 'discovering a colony,' countries of the core region maintained specific political boundaries (see Chapter 7) and enforced their sovereignty through military power. The military also ensured the secure flow of goods from the periphery to the core.

In 1522, Magellan started a voyage that circumnavigated the globe, arriving back in Guadalquivir estuary in Spain 2 years and 351 days after his departure. This started an age of expanded world awareness. As Western European countries discovered new lands, they also became aware of commercial opportunities. In the late 16th and early 17th centuries, newly formed commercial companies such as the Dutch East India Company, the British East India Company (1600), the Dutch East India Company (1602), the Dutch West India Company (1621), the French East India Company (1664), and the Swedish East India Company (1731) extracted goods from recently discovered parts of the world and delivered them to the colonial powers. With varying levels and types of support from their national governments, these companies reflected newly-formed partnerships, which in the cases above, travelled to the East Indies following the discovery of the Cape of Good Hope in 1497. An important aspect of these companies was the power given to them by their respective governments to acquire territory and to essentially exercise the powers of government— the negotiation of treaties and adminisration of justice. Trade monopolies were sometimes established, as illustrated by the Dutch East India Company, which was granted a 21-year monopoly by the Dutch government. In these circumstances, companies could dictate the terms of trade.

Relevant to Canada was the Hudson's Bay Company, which was formed in 1670 by decree of the King of England, who realized that the fur trade could bring wealth to his country. The decree provided a monopoly to the company in all the lands draining into Hudson's Bay. The Hudson's Bay Company established trading posts where many aboriginals delivered furs in exchange for supplies (e.g., blankets, pots, guns, and alcohol). While Hudson Bay officials saw this as a strictly business transaction, aboriginals saw it as, in part, a celebration where smoke and food were shared, singing and dancing occurred, and alcohol was consumed after its introduction by Europeans. After the ceremony, business would be completed. This monopoly was broken with the formation of The North West Company in 1783. The monopoly was restored in 1821 when the companies merged. The economic strength of the Hudson's Bay Company is reflected in its vast network of trading posts covering what is now Canada and parts of the United States (Figure 3.2 and Chapter 7).

During this colonial period, the military presence and intervention by Britain and other colonial powers ensured the flow of trade from the colonies (i.e., periphery) to the core. Some countries, such as Canada, were able to become part of the core, as evidenced by its current membership in the G8 (see Chapter 7). As we will see in Chapter 7, the colonial system was well entrenched into the 20th century (Figure 3.3) and did not undergo radical change until the end of World War II. After 1945, colonies such as India, Pakistan, and Niger were given their political independence. However, some commentators would suggest that the economic dependence of the newly created states in the periphery on their former colonial masters remained. The economy of the periphery is often relegated to **primary industries** rather than **tertiary industries** (see Chapter 9), and the **terms of trade** continued to favour core nations.

More recently, at least five factors have played a major role in shaping our current reality and perception of globalization:

1. **The loosening of controls of the movements of international capital:** International banking can now transfer billions of dollars around the world in response to financial, economic, political, or military crises and opportunities. It is also seen in the foreign investments held by companies and citizens of many countries. For example, Canadians own foreign stocks and bonds directly or through mutual funds and pension plans. Through globalization, London, New York, and Tokyo have emerged as "world cities" (see Chapter 8), which serve as control points for international production, marketing and finance.

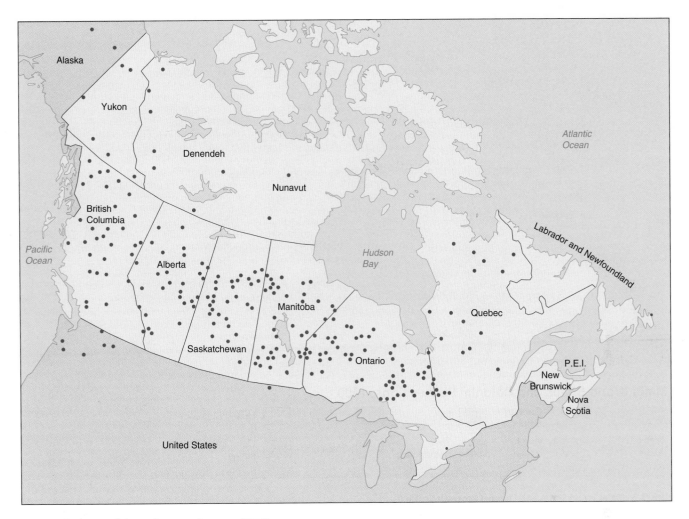

FIGURE 3.2 Trading Posts of the Hudson Bay Company (1850)

Source: Reproduced with permission of Yahoo! Inc., 2008. *http://www.geocities.com/SoHo/Atrium/4832/metis/forts.gif.*

2. **Reduction of trade barriers and tariffs on goods and services between nations:** Since World War II, barriers to international trade have been considerably lowered through international agreements—General Agreement of Trade and Tariffs (GATT), and the World Trade Organization (WTO). Regional economic alliances, such as NAFTA and the European Union (e.g., establishment of the *euro*) (see Chapter 7), have also increased economic integration. The general trend over the past 25 years has favoured "free trade"—the reduction or elimination of tariffs, subsidies, and capital controls. North American, Japanese, and European markets are now being interconnected to Asian, and South and Latin American markets

3. **The Rise of Transnational Corporations:** Transnational corporations (TNCs), discussed more fully in Chapter 10, are a new product of globalization. TNCs will have a head office in one country and subsidiary companies with expertise in specific business products or functions—manufacturing, warehousing, assembly—in many others. There are about 65,000 transnational corporations that control several hundred thousand affiliates worldwide.

4. **Improvements in technology and transportation:** Low-cost high-speed computers, communication satellites, fibre-optic networks, and the Internet are the main technologies of the revolution, with robotics, microelectronics, electronic mail, cellular phones, and more making their contributions. The fact that a consumer in Italy can order a book from Amazon. com or clothes from Land's End, obtain news from CNN, or make an investment through the London Stock Exchange while talking on a cellular phone to a colleague in Tokyo, is revolutionary, and proof that globalization brings about greater world integration and spatial interaction.

5. **The Internationalization of Popular Culture:** The internationalization of popular culture is more apparent to most of the world's people than is the less visible globalization of commerce and industry. In widely different culture realms, teenagers wear Yankee baseball caps, Gap shirts, Levis, and Reeboks; eat at McDonald's; and listen to pop music on their iPod on the way home to play a video game on the family computer. The culture they embrace is largely Western in origin and chiefly American. U.S. movies, television shows, software, music, food, and fashion are marketed worldwide. They influence the beliefs, tastes, and aspirations of people in virtually every country, though their effect is most pronounced on young people. Like the globalization of finance, industry, and commerce, this internationalization of popular culture is

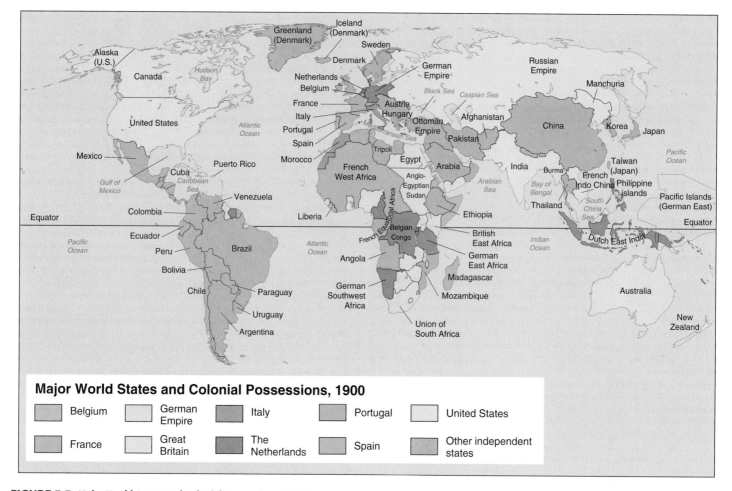

FIGURE 3.3 Major World States and Colonial Possessions, 1900

Source: With thanks to Donald Quataert, History Department, SUNY Binghamton.

further evidence of the transformative nature and impact of modern spatial behaviour and interaction. The adoption of uniform store design and architecture, which are often associated with globalization, affects the sense of place.

The core, periphery, and semi-periphery regions of the world are shown in Figure 3.4. The United States is the dominant economic power. After rebuilding itself after World War II, Japan emerged as a major player in world trade. With the creation and incremental expansion of the European Union, the number of countries considered to be core in that region has grown. With the signing of NAFTA in 1994, Mexico can be included in the core although this is debatable given the predominant role of the United Stated and Canada's more developed and diversified economies. Australia and New Zealand may also be considered part of the current core (Figure 3.4). The core region continues to dominate international trade, and control access to cutting-edge technologies, have well-developed bureaucracies, and highly developed, diverse economies. In particular, the United States has, since World War II, been able to dominate world institutions, such as the International Monetary Fund (IMF) and the World Bank, world trade organizations, such as GATT and the World Trade Organization (WTO), and regional trade agreements, such as NAFTA. The peripheral region continues to include countries that

are often characterized by a reliance on a small number of primary economic activities, less developed bureaucracies, and low economic productivity. One outcome of globalization has been the emergence of a **semi-periphery region**—one that is less reliant on the core region than the periphery region and has attracted considerable investment from the core. Although they can be dominated by the core region, they are also able to exploit some of the countries in the periphery region. China, Russia, and Brazil belong to the emerging semi-periphery region (Figure 3.4). At a global scale, some of the current tensions reflect long-standing needs of the core. For example, the need to ensure a secure flow of goods to the core can be seen in aspects of the current war in Iraq, which some commentators suggest is really a war about access to oil for the United States rather than eliminating terrorism and promoting human rights. The rise of the Chinese economy as a world power is a more recent challenge to the established primacy of the United States and other core nations.

There are also different interpretations about the benefits associated with the current world-system. At a global level, Wallerstein and people who accept dependency theory have concluded that since the 16th century the world economic system has consistently favoured countries in the core region, particularly the United States and Western Europe. For example, the top 500 companies of the world, most of which are from the core region,

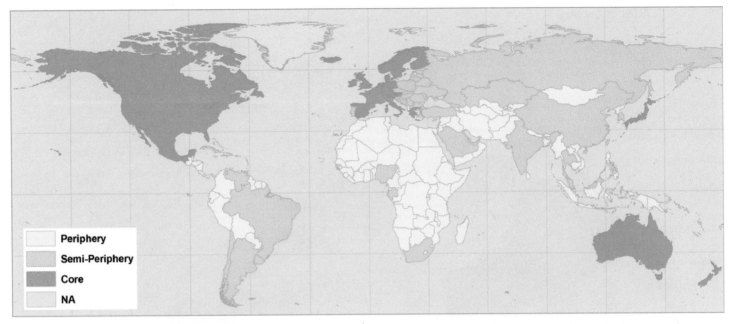

FIGURE 3.4 The Economic Regions of the World—Core, Periphery, and Semi-periphery in the late 20th century. Countries belonging to the core are characterized by high levels of development, a capacity at innovation, a convergence of trade flows, and a reasonable level of military power (although sometimes achieved through alliances, such as NATO). The emergence of a semi-periphery after the 1970s reflects the impact of globalization. A high level of economic development has occurred in countries such as China, Brazil, Malaysia, Korea, and Russia. As the forces of globalization continue to impact the entire world, perhaps the semi-periphery may become the core, in the not too distant future.

Source: (c) Rodrigue, J-P (2008). The Geography of Transport Systems, http://people.hofstra.edu/geotrans/eng/ch7en/conc7/centerperiphery.html.

control about 70% of the world trade, 30% of foreign investments and 30% of the world's GNP. From this perspective, the gains achieved by the corporations have come at the cost of local businesses that are forced to close, local cultures that move to popular culture, and the middle and poor socio-economic class. Resistance to globalization has sometimes been violent. On the other hand, other commentators would suggest that the recent emergence of the semi-periphery is evidence that **neo-liberal** economic policies (e.g., eliminating subsidies, investment in education, health care, infrastructure, trade liberalization, deregulation, privatization of state enterprises) that are associated with globalization have been successful in promoting growth and development among more nations. This difference of views reflects the importance of clarifying one's philosophical stance (Chapter 1) and the nature of the evidence to support one's conclusions (Chapter 2). We will discuss more specific aspects of globalization in many of the subsequent chapters. For now, appreciate the usefulness of an important geographic concept - the region - to assist our understanding of globalization.

Canada and the World-System

The previous section discussed the world at a global scale. It is important to realize that within each region—core, periphery, and semi-periphery—there is great diversity. While Canada, the United States, Britain, Australia, and other countries belong to the core, there are many cultural, social, and political differences. There are also differences within countries. Harold Innis's staples theory (see Chapter 1) and the sense of Canada as a heartland and

hinterland share many similarities with Wallerstein's core, periphery, and semi-periphery regions. According to Bone (2005: 23), the major advantages in applying the core-periphery model to Canada's regional geography are:

- Canada's regional disparities lend themselves to such a spatial framework;
- Relations between Canada's regions, whether economic or political, reflect the core/periphery model; and
- The model is related to Harold Innis's staple thesis, which served to reinterpret Canada's early economic history.

Evidence of the core and periphery in Canada is illustrated in per capita income (Figure 3.5). Highest incomes are in Ontario, especially southern Ontario, Alberta, especially Edmonton, Calgary, and Fort McMurray, and large cities. This pattern reflects the accumulation of wealth in central Canada and the country's urban centres, and high paying jobs associated with some resource development. Within each region and city, cores and peripheries will exist. There are many people who are homeless living in Canada's national and provincial capitals.

Our understanding of Canada can be framed in the context of core and periphery regions. The core has traditionally been viewed as comprising the Windsor–Quebec axis. This view is changing, in part reflecting globalization. Emerging cores are Vancouver and the Edmonton–Calgary Corridor. Vancouver is increasingly becoming an important international centre for international trade. NAFTA has promoted investment in Alberta's

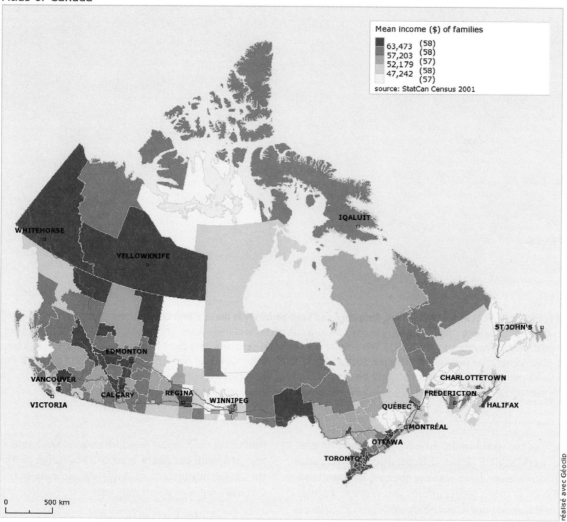

Mean income ($) of families

■	63,473	(58)
	57,203	(58)
	52,179	(57)
	47,242	(58)
		(57)

source: StatCan Census 2001

réalisé avec Géoclip

FIGURE 3.5 Per Capita Income in Canada (2006 by Municipal CSD)

Source: © GEO-STAT, http://www.geostat.ca/realisation/sqlcanada/carto.php?gestion51&lang5en&typind5C&nivgeos5 prov&curIdDom50&curCodeDom5DS&curCodeTheme5pop& curCodeInd5pop65c.

oil and natural gas fields, and contributed to recent exponential economic growth in that province. Oil revenues are enhancing the status of Saskatchewan and Newfoundland. The periphery of Canada consists of the rest of the country in the north, Atlantic, western, and rural areas. Within the periphery, regional centres exist, such as Halifax, Saskatoon, and Winnipeg. Within many urban centres, there is a sense of "core" and "periphery."

For geographers, the significance of world-systems analysis is three-fold. First, it highlights the importance of regions, one of our geographical standards (Chapter 1) at a range of scale—global, regional, national, and local levels. Second, the model is based on the flow of goods and services from one region to another. This is of particular relevance to the study of the world in spatial terms. Third, the recent rise of globalization has made many places throughout the world lose their distinctiveness and look "the same" (Figure 3.1). The reminder of this chapter will provide greater insight in to human systems and spatial interaction, and places and regions.

Human Systems and Spatial Interaction

An important element of globalization is illustrated in the changing nature of transportation—from ships to rail to road to aircraft and later spacecraft. People are able to move themselves, as well as goods and ideas, at much greater speeds and volumes. A focus on **spatial interactions**—the movement of peoples, ideas, and commodities (goods bought and sold) within and between areas—has been of long-standing interest to geographers. Perhaps you have engaged in spatial interaction in moving from different homes with your family or moving to attend college/university. International trade, the movement of tractor-trailers on highways, radio broadcasts, and business or personal telephone calls are more familiar examples. Such movements and exchanges are designed to achieve effective integration between different points of human activity. In a globalized world, movement of whatever

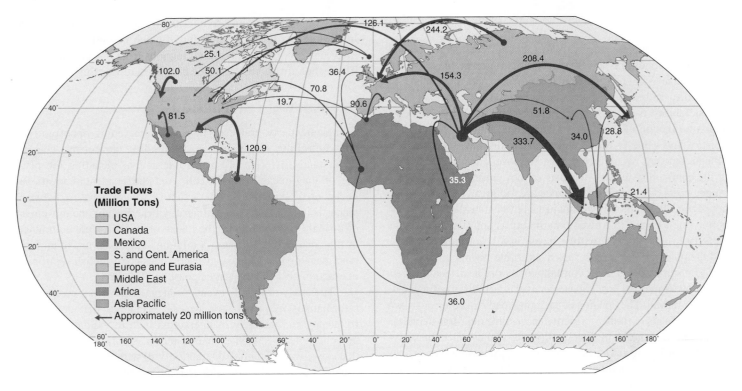

FIGURE 3.6 International crude oil flow by sea, 2003. Complementarity is so basic in initiating interaction that even relatively low-value bulk commodities such as coal, fertilizer, and grain move in trade over long distances. For many years, despite fluctuating prices, petroleum has been the most important commodity in international trade, moving long distances in response to effective supply and demand considerations.

Source: The BP Amoco Statistical Review of World Energy, 2004.

nature satisfies some need or desire. It represents the attempt to smooth out spatially differing availability of required resources, commodities, information, or opportunities. Whatever the particular purpose of a movement, there is inevitably some manner of trade-off balancing the benefit of the interaction with the costs that are incurred in overcoming spatial separation. Because commodity movements represent simple demonstrations of the principles underlying all spatial interactions, let us turn to them first.

Neither the world's resources nor the products of people's efforts are uniformly distributed. Commodity flows are responses to these differences; they are links between points of supply and locales of demand. Such response may not be immediate or even direct. Matters of awareness of supplies or markets, the presence or absence of transportation connections, costs of movement, ability to pay for things wanted and needed—all and more are factors in the structure of trade. Underlying even these, however, is a set of controlling principles governing spatial interaction.

A Summarizing Model

The conviction that spatial interaction reflects areal differences led the geographer Edward Ullman (1912–1976) to speculate on the essential conditions affecting such interactions and to propose an explanatory model. He observed that spatial interaction is effectively controlled by three flow-determining factors that he called *complementarity, transferability,* and *intervening opportunity.* Although Ullman's model deals with commodity flows, it has—as we shall see—applicability to informational

transfers and patterns of human movements in a globalized world. Principles associated with this model and spatial interaction form the basis of location theories that will be discussed in Chapters 8 and 10.

Complementarity

Complementarity refers to the supply and demand relationship between places. For two places to interact, one place must have what another place wants and can secure. That is, one place must have a supply of an item for which there is an effective demand in the other, as evidenced by desire for the item, purchasing power to acquire it, and means to transport it. *Effective* supply and demand are important considerations; mere differences from place to place in commodity surplus or deficit are not enough to initiate exchange. Greenland and the Amazon basin are notably unlike in their natural resources and economies, but their amount of interaction is minimal. Supply and market must come together, as they do in the flow of seasonal fruits and vegetables from California's Imperial Valley to the urban markets of Canada or in the movement of manganese from Ukraine to the steel mills of Western Europe. The massive movement of crude and refined petroleum between spatially separated effective supplies and markets clearly demonstrates complementarity in international trade (Figure 3.6). More generalized patterns of complementarity underlie the exchanges of the raw materials and agricultural goods of less developed countries for the money or industrial commodities of the developed states.

Transferability

Even when complementarity exists, spatial interaction occurs only when conditions of **transferability**—acceptable costs of an exchange—are met. Spatial movement responds not just to availability and demand but to considerations of time and cost. Transferability is an expression of the mobility of a commodity and is a function of three interrelated conditions: (1) the characteristics and value of the product; (2) the distance, measured in time and money, over which it must be moved; and (3) the ability of the commodity to bear the costs of movement. If the time and money costs of traversing a distance are too great, exchange does not occur. That is, mobility is not just a physical matter but an economic one as well. If a given commodity is not affordable upon delivery to an otherwise willing buyer, it will not move in trade, and the potential buyer must seek a substitute or go without.

Transferability is not a constant condition. It differs between places, over time, and in relation to what is being transferred and how it is to be moved. The opening of a logging road will connect a sawmill with stands of timber formerly inaccessible (non-transferable). An increasing scarcity of high-quality ores will enhance the transferability of lower-quality mine outputs by increasing their value. Low-cost bulk commodities not economically moved by air may be fully transferable by rail or water. In short, transferability expresses the changing relationships between the costs of transportation and the value of the product to be shipped.

Intervening Opportunity

The spatial interaction between places is supported by complementarity and transferability. **Intervening opportunities** tend to impede the flow of people, goods, and services between places. For example, the opportunity for people in Manitoba to vacation in Cuba rather than Florida could mean that the spatial interaction between Manitoba and Florida could be replaced by one between Manitoba and Cuba. Other southern destinations also exist—California, Mexico, and the Caribbean. Depending on connections, all might be reached quicker and possibly at less cost. Part of the decision about vacation destinations will reflect a person's expectations— are all the amenities (e.g., tours, beaches, activities) you desire located at your destination and in sufficient quality and quantity? In another example to illustrate intervening opportunity, a shopper is less likely to buy goods at a more distant shop when those same goods are available at the same price at a nearby location.

Similarly, markets and destinations are sought, if possible, close at hand. Growing metropolitan demand in California for fruits grown in the Imperial Valley reduces the importance of Canadian markets for these fruits. The intervening opportunities offered by Ottawa, Kitchener–Waterloo, London, and Hamilton reduce the numbers of job seekers from outside Ontario looking for employment in Toronto. People from Toronto are more likely to ski in the Collingwood–Blue Mountain area, which is relatively near and accessible, than in the Ottawa Valley or Whistler, B.C., which are not. That is, opportunities that are discerned closer at hand reduce the pull of opportunities offered by a distant destination. Patterns of spatial interaction are dynamic, reflecting the changeable structure of apparent opportunity. In the globalized world, we are often quick to uncritically state that products made in distant and developing nations (which essentially reflect an intervening opportunity) are taking jobs from developed nations. This is not always the case (see box "Where was this made?").

Measuring Interaction

Complementarity, transferability, and intervening opportunity— the controlling conditions of commodity movement—help us understand all forms of spatial interaction, including the placing of long-distance phone calls and the residential locational decisions of commuters. Interaction of whatever nature between places is not, of course, meaningfully described by the movement of a single commodity, by the habits of an individual commuter, or the once-only decision of a migrant. The discovery of an Inuit ivory carving in a Calgary gift shop does not establish significant interaction between the Arctic coast and Calgary.

The study of unique events is suggestive but not particularly informative. We often seek general principles that govern the frequency and intensity of interaction both to validate the three preconditions of spatial exchange and to establish the probability that any given potential interaction will actually occur. We are usually concerned here with the probability of aggregate, not individual, behaviour.

Distance Decay

Geographers have traditionally advocated that the distance between locations influences the level of interaction and interaction that occurs between them. This is captured in the phrase the **friction of distance**. That phrase reminds us that distance has a retarding effect on human interaction because there are increasing penalties in time and cost associated with longer-distance, and more expensive interchanges. We visit nearby friends more often than distant relatives; we go more frequently to the neighbourhood convenience store cluster than to the farther regional shopping centre. Telephone calls or mail deliveries between nearby towns are greater in volume than those to more distant locations. An informal study showed that university students living in dormitories are more likely to order out for food if they are close to the delivery drop-off point; students farther away do not order out as often.

Our common experience, clearly supported by maps and statistics tracing all kinds of flows, is that most interactions occur over short distances. That is, interchange decreases as distance increases, a reflection of the fact that transferability costs increase with distance. More generally stated, **distance decay** describes the decline of an activity or function with increasing distance from its point of origin (see Figure 3.7).

Study of all manner of spatial interconnections has led to the very general conclusion that interaction between places is inversely related to the square of the distance separating them. That is, volume of flow between two points 80 kilometres (50 miles) apart would probably be only one-quarter of that between centres at 40 kilometres (25 miles) separation. Such a rigid *inverse-square* relationship is well documented in the physical sciences. For social, cultural, and economic relations, however, it is at best a useful approximation. In human interaction, linear distance is

Where was this Made?

When you buy a $300 iPod that says "Made in China" it suggests that everything occurred in China. In a globalized world, nothing could be further from the truth—many manufactured goods have more than one 'nation of origin' and the single place label hides corporate decisions that reflect the concepts of complementarity, transferability, and intervening opportunity. Corporations usually seek locations where the supply of the materials, labour, and infrastructure is most conducive to producing a reasonable quality good at lowest cost. Apple Inc. provides an example to illustrate these factors at work in the global world. Established in California in 1976, Apple Inc. designs and manufactures

consumer electronics and related software. By 2007, it had about 200 plants located in five countries. Worldwide, over 20,000 people are employed by Apple and sales in 2007 were $24 billion (US)—a figure that is comparable to the gross domestic product of many developing nations (Appendix 1). Many of its products, such as the iPod, require raw materials (e.g., silicon, plastics). Transferability is achieved through an efficient and inexpensive international transport network. In examining the intervening opportunities to locate plants, Apple has shifted its labour intensive testing and assembly operations to China, where low wages are a clear advantage.

In the news media, we often see headlines about trade with China (and other developing countries with cheap labour) taking jobs away from Canada and other developed nations. However, we often fail to appreciate that many of the component parts found in many products labelled "Made in China" are not really "made" there, but rather just assembled there. In the case of Apple's iPod, a Conference Board of Canada Report (2007) finds that of the $300.00 selling price, only $3.00 (1%) goes to China. Other parts—a display from Japan, two critical microchips from the United States—are far more valuable. In this case, geography matters a great deal.

The Apple iPod: where is value actually created?
(approximate iPod value: share, percent)

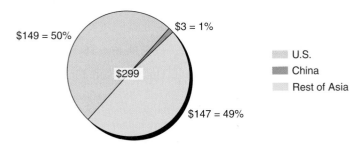

Where is Value Created in an iPod?		
Japan	Hard drive	$73.39
Japan	Display Module	$20.39
United States	Video Processor	$8.36
United States	Portal Player CPU	$4.94
China	Test, Assembly	$3.70
Unknown	Battery pack	$2.89
Japan	Display Driver	$2.88
South Korea	Mobile SDRAM	$2.37
Unknown	Back Enclosure	$2.30
Unknown	Mainboard PCB	$1.90

Sources: Adapted from "Canada's Missing Trade with Asia" by Danielle Goldfarb and Louis Theriault, from The Conference Board of Canada; Linden et al., 2007.

only one aspect of transferability; cost and time are often more meaningful measures of separation.

When the friction of distance is reduced by lowered costs or increased ease of flow, the slope of the distance decay curve is flattened and more total area is effectively united than when those costs are high. When telephone calls are charged by uniform area rates rather than strictly by distance, more calls are placed to the outer margins of the rate area than expected. Highways extend commuting travel ranges to central cities and expand the total area conveniently accessible for weekend recreation and shopping in larger communities.

The assumptions associated with distance decay are being challenged. As transportation and communication technologies have improved, the friction of distance has been reduced and our view of space has shrunk. In 1968, a geographer, Don Janelle, provided an informative and early treatment of these phenomena, which he referred to as **time–space convergence**—that the world

is 'shrinking' as the time required to travel between locations decreases. Early transport innovations that promoted trade were improvements to the construction of ships and railways (use of steel) and the advent of the steam engine. In the 1950s, the development of our global village was promoted through the development of an accessible and affordable jet aircraft (Figure 3.8). Containerization of goods has been the key innovation that has increased the efficient transfer of goods across the world. The standard 20 foot container promotes very efficient transhipment—the transfer from ship to ship, ship to transport-trailer, or ship to train. Reduced transportation costs, especially through the development of containerization for ocean shipping, has allowed some goods produced in developing countries to be sold in distant developed countries, like Canada, at a lower cost than similar goods made within that country. Between 1952 and 1989, the number of dockers and checkers working at Port of New York's was reduced from over 44,000 to 8,000 (Herod, 2007).

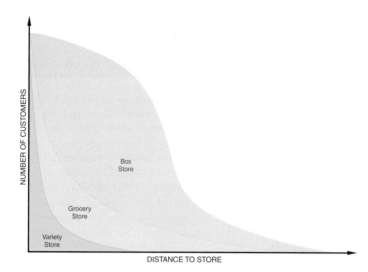

FIGURE 3.7 Distance decay concept. Box stores, such as Canadian Tire, Sam's Club, and Wal-Mart, have a larger number of customers and a greater market distance than that of grocery stores, which are greater than variety stores. Box stores also have a lower distance decay function because they offer a wider range of goods, often at lower prices (due to economies of scale). Therefore, people are more likely to travel a greater distance to shop at a box store, which has implications for stores located in smaller communities and retail outlets located in the urban core of larger centres.

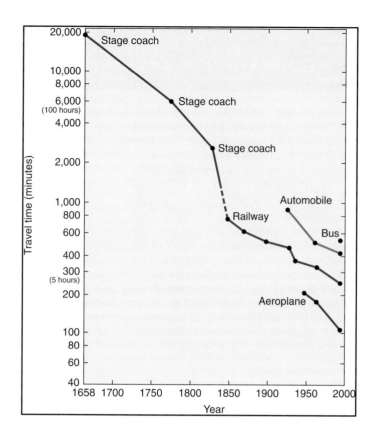

FIGURE 3.8 Time–space convergence as illustrated by travel times from Edinburgh to London since the 17th century. The graph above shows the travel time to travel the 520 km between Edinburgh, Scotland and London, England. Between the 17th and 19th centuries, improvements in road construction and stagecoach engineering, travel times decreased dramatically. After the mid-19th century, further reductions were difficult to achieve. Further declines in travel time were seen with the advent of the railways. Cars, buses, and airplanes significantly lowered travel times. Over the entire time span, initial travel time has been reduced from some 14 days to 100 minutes. Further reductions in travel time are unlikely to be achieved in the near term.

Source: Davies, W.K.D. "Globalization: A Spatial Perspective." Unifying Geography: Common Heritage, *Shared Future.* J.A. Mathews and D.T. Herbert (eds). New York: Routledge. 189–214. 2004.

The Gravity Concept

Interaction decisions are not based on distance or distance/cost considerations alone. The large regional shopping centre attracts customers from a wide radius because of the variety of shops and goods its very size promises. We go to distant big cities "to seek our fortune" rather than to the nearer small town. Migration from one country to another is often associated with the larger size of the country we move to. We are, that is, attracted by the expectation of opportunity that we associate with larger rather than smaller places. That expectation is summarized by another model of spatial interaction, the **gravity model**, which is drawn from the physical sciences.

In the 1850s, Henry C. Carey (1793–1879), in his *Principles of Social Science,* observed that the physical laws of gravity and motion developed by Sir Isaac Newton (1642–1727) were applicable to the aggregate actions of humans. Newton's *law of universal gravitation* states that the attractive pull between any two objects is proportional to the product of their masses and inversely proportional to the square of the distance between them. More simply put, Newton's law tells us that big things attract each other more (have greater gravitational pull) than do small objects, and that things close to each other have stronger mutual attraction than do objects at greater distance—and that the attraction decreases very rapidly with even small increases in separation.

Carey's interests were in the interaction between urban centres and in the observation that a large city is more likely to attract an individual than is a small hamlet. His first interest could be quickly satisfied by simple analogy. He assumed that the expected interaction between two places can be calculated by converting physical mass in the gravity model to population size while retaining the distance component of the Newtonian calculation (for the applicable Newton and Carey equations, see *gravity model* in the Glossary).

In social—rather than physical—science applications of the gravity model, distance may be calculated by travel time or travel cost modifications rather than by straight line separation. Whatever the unit of measure, however, the model assures us that although spatial interaction always tends to decrease with increasing distance between places, at a given distance it tends to expand with increases in the size of the places.

Carey's second observation—that large cities have greater drawing power for individuals than do small ones—was subsequently addressed by the **law of retail gravitation**, proposed by William J. Reilly (1899–1970) in 1931. Using the population and distance inputs of the gravity model, Reilly determined the relative amount of retail trade that two cities would attract from an intermediate place in the vicinity of the *breaking point (BP)*.[1] **Reilly's law** (see the Glossary for the algebraic expression) states that two cities will attract trade from intermediate locales in direct proportion to the populations of the two cities and in inverse proportion to the square of the distance of these two cities to the intermediate place.

The gravity model is often used to assess the spatial interaction of people, goods, and services. Accordingly, the attraction between two objects is *proportional to their mass and inversely proportional to their respective distance*. Consequently, the general formulation of spatial interactions can be adapted to reflect this basic assumption to form the *elementary formulation* of the gravity model:

$$I_{ij} = K \frac{P_i P_j}{D_{ij}^x}$$

where:

- I is the interaction between two places i and j.
- P_i and P_j is the population (or relative importance, mass (e.g., phones) depending on the good or service being studied).
- D_{ij}^x is the intervening distance between i and j. Note that D is raised to the power of X, which indicates that unlike gravity which is always constant, spatial interactions will vary from one type of interaction to another, i.e., they are context specific. For example, since business travel by airplane is less likely to be impacted by distance decay than business travel by car, X would be higher for auto travel than air travel. Empirical studies would have to be completed to determine the X value (otherwise you're "guesstimating").
- K is the proportional constant related to the rate of interaction. For instance, the number of phone calls between two centres might be much larger relative to the number of people who vacation in the two centres (e.g., Canmore and Calgary) but that difference would not be apparent unless a value like K was introduced to scale the expected volume of interaction. K would be low for a number with a good or service with a low transferability, and high for a good or service with a high transferability.

Figure 3.9 provides an example of the gravity concept and how it might be applied in a retail trade context. There are four population centres, A, B, C, and D. In this example, let's assume that $K = 1$, and $X = 2$. The potential interaction of cities A and B is: $(100,000 \times 50,000) / (60 \times 60) = 1,388,888$. Since population and distance are the same, this would also be the potential interaction for A and C. The measure of interaction between B and C is: $(50,000 \times 50,000) / (80 \times 80) = 390,625$.

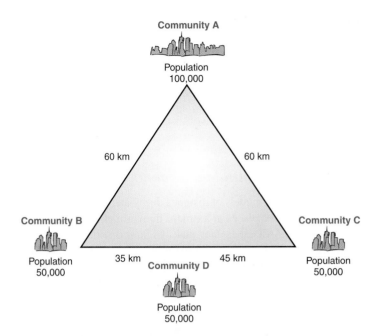

FIGURE 3.9 Gravity concept of spatial interaction. The gravity model has been used to study many problems—population migration, commodity flows, journeys to work or shop, telephone call volumes, and the like. The essence of the model reflects that spatial interaction is a function of the size of centres and the distance between them. Even though the numbers associated with potential interaction that are generated from this example are quite large, it is the relative size of the numbers that are of importance in these types of studies. In this example, we are suggesting that the interaction between A and B (and A and C) is expected to be about 3.6 times the volume of the spatial interaction between cities B and C.

There are some important implicit assumptions that support the gravity model that must also be understood if we are to critically appraise its application for research and to solve real-world problems. Note that the model (in Figure 3.9) does not say anything about the "people" living in communities A, B, and C—it assumes that all people will behave in the same manner. We know that this is not the case and that some people are more willing and able to travel distances to shop than others (e.g., the young, elderly, handicapped, poor, socially disadvantaged). The nature of the local market for each community is assumed to be identical and ignores intervening opportunities. The example provided in Figure 3.9 also fails to account for the influence of community D on the volume of spatial interactions between A and B. The volume is expected to be the same as that between A and C even though there is no intervening city situated along that route. Generally, the model also assumes the transferability is measured by distance between places.

Later studies in location theory, city systems, trade area analysis, and other social topics all suggest that the gravity model can be used to account for a wide variety of flow patterns in

---

[1] The breaking point between two towns is defined as the point up to which one town exerts the controlling retail trade influence and beyond which the other town dominates.

human geography, including population migration, commodity flows, journeys to work or to shop, telephone call volumes, and the like. Each such flow pattern suggests that size as well as distance influences spatial interaction. Carey's observation made some 150 years ago initiated a type of analysis that in modified form is used today for a variety of practical studies that help us better understand the "friction of distance," most often at regional and local scales.

Interaction Potential and Connectivity

Spatial interaction models of distance decay and gravitational pull deal with only two places at a time. The world of reality is rather more complex. All cities, not just city pairs, within a regional system of cities have the possibility of interacting with each other. Indeed, the more specialized the goods produced in each separate centre—that is, the greater their collective complementarity—the more likely it is that such multiple interactions will occur.

A **potential model**, also based on Newtonian physics, provides an estimate of the interaction opportunities available to a centre in such a multicentred network. It tells us the relative position of each point in relation to all other places within a region. It does so by summing the size and distance relationships between all points of potential interaction within an area. The concept of potential is applicable whenever the measurement of the intensity of spatial interaction is of concern—as it is in studies of marketing, land values, broadcasting, commuting patterns, and the like. The recent innovations in transportation and communication have increased the interaction potential and the actual connectivity of people, goods, and services. Look at how many of the students at your university are from other countries, regularly make international phone calls, or have international Internet connections, and one gets a sense of the 'global village.'

The increase in the size, number, and extent of transnational corporations (TNCs), discussed more fully in Chapter 10, is one factor that has contributed to increased connectivity. TNCs will have a head office in one country and subsidiary companies with expertise in specific business products or functions—manufacturing, warehousing, assembly—in many others. There are about 65,000 transnational corporations that control several hundred thousand affiliates worldwide. TNCs are able to take advantage of differential wage rates found in many developing nations. In this way, they can reduce production costs, and decentralize manufacturing facilities and other business functions throughout the world. In doing this, modern manufacturing infrastructure and technology can be diffused to developing nations, which now become more integrated into the global economy. At the same time, the industrial base of developed nations has focused on knowledge-based industries (e.g., high tech), which attract high-wagers.

Movement Biases

Distance decay and the gravity and potential models help us understand the bases for interaction in an idealized area without natural or socio-economic barriers to movement or restrictions on routes followed, and in which only "rational" interaction decisions are made. Even under those model conditions, the pattern of spatial interaction that develops for whatever reason inevitably affects the conditions under which future interactions will occur. An initial structure of centres and connecting flows will tend to freeze into the landscape a mutually reinforcing continuation of that same pattern. The predictable flows of shoppers to existing shopping centres make those centres attractive to other merchants. New store openings increase customer flow; increased flow strengthens the developed pattern of spatial interaction. And increased road traffic calls for the highway improvement that encourages additional traffic volume.

Such an aggregate regularity of flow is called a **movement bias**. We have already noted a *distance bias* favouring short movements over long ones. There is also *direction bias,* in which of all possible directions of movement, actual flows are restricted to only one or a few. Direction bias is simply a statement that from a given origin, flows are not random; rather, certain places have a greater attraction than do others. The movement patterns from an isolated farmstead are likely oriented to a favoured shopping town. On a larger scale, in North America or Siberia, long-distance freight movements are directionally biased in favour of east–west flows. Direction bias reflects not just the orientation but also the intensity of flow. Movements from a single point—from Novosibirsk in Siberia, for example, or from Winnipeg, Canada, or Kansas City in the United States—may occur in all directions; they are in reality more intense along the east–west axis.

These directional biases are in part a reflection of *network bias*, a shorthand way of saying that the presence or absence of links between places strongly affects the likelihood that spatial interaction will occur. A set of routes and the set of places they connect (called nodes by transport geographers) are collectively called a **network**. A **node** within this network is any place that is capable of generating traffic, such as a mall if a traffic study was conducted at a city scale, or any community above a threshold population if the study was at the provincial or national scale. Nodes are connected by links or routes.

A recognition of movement biases and connectivity helps to refine the coarser generalizations of spatial interaction based solely on complementarity, transferability, and intervening opportunity. Other modifying statements have been developed, but each further refinement moves us away from aggregate behaviour toward less predictable individual movements and responses. The spatial interaction questions we ask and the degree of refinement of the answers we require determine the modifications we must introduce into the models we employ.

Human Systems as Human Spatial Behaviour

Humans are not commodities and individually do not necessarily respond predictably to the impersonal dictates of spatial interaction constraints. Yet, to survive, people must be mobile and collectively do react to distance, time, and cost considerations of movement in space and to the implications of complementarity, transferability, and intervening opportunity. Indeed, an exciting line of geographic inquiry involves how individuals make spatial

(a)

(b)

FIGURE 3.10 Our demanded personal space is not necessarily uniform in shape or constant in size. We tolerate strangers closer to our sides than directly in front of us; we accept more crowding in an elevator than in a store. We accept the press of the crowd on a popular beach—as do these students on spring break in the Florida Keys (*a*), but tend to distance ourselves from others in a library (*b*).

behavioural decisions and how those separate decisions may be summarized by models and generalizations to explain collective actions.

Mobility is the general term applied to all types of human territorial movement. Two aspects of that mobility behaviour concern us. The first is the daily or temporary use of space—the journeys to stores, to work, or to school, or for longer periods on vacation, or university students' relocation between home and school dormitory. These types of mobility are often designated as *circulation* and have no suggestion of relocation of residence. The second type of mobility is the longer-term commitment related to decisions to permanently move to a new location. This second form of spatial behaviour is termed **migration**.

Both aspects imply a time dimension. Humans' spatial actions are not instantaneous. They operate over time, frequently imparting a rhythm to individual and group activity patterns and imposing choices among time-consuming behaviours. Elements of both aspects of human spatial behaviour are also embodied in how individuals perceive space and act within it, and how they respond to information affecting their space–behavioural decisions. The nature of those perceptions and responses affect us all in our daily movements. The more permanent movement embodied in migration involves additional and less common decisions and behaviours, as we shall see later in Chapter 4.

Individual Activity Space

One of the realities of life is that groups and countries draw boundaries around themselves and divide space into territories that are, if necessary, defended. Some see the concept of **territoriality**— the emotional attachment to and the defence of home ground—as a root explanation of much of human action and response. It is true that some individual and collective activity appears to be governed by territorial defence responses: the conflict between street groups in claiming and protecting their "turf" (and their

fear for their lives when venturing beyond it), and the sometimes violent rejection by ethnic urban neighbourhoods of any different advancing population group it considers threatening. On a more individualized basis, each of us claims as **personal space** the zone of privacy and separation from others our culture or our physical circumstances require or permit. Anglo-Americans demand greater face-to-face separation in conversations than do Latin Americans. Personal space on a crowded beach or in a department store is acceptably more limited than it is in our homes or when we are studying in a library (Figure 3.10).

For most of us, our personal sense of territoriality is a tempered one. We regard our homes and property as defensible private domains but open them to innocent visitors, known and unknown, or to those on private or official business. Nor do we confine our activities so exclusively within controlled home territories as street-gang members do within theirs. Rather, we have a more or less extended home range, an **activity space** or area within which we move freely on our rounds of regular activity, sharing that space with others who are also about their daily affairs. Figure 3.11 suggests probable activity spaces for a suburban family of five for a day. Note that the activity space is different, and for the mapped day rather limited for each individual, even though two members of the family use automobiles. If one week's activity were shown, more paths would be added to the map, and in a year's time, one or more long trips would probably have to be noted.

The types of trips that individuals make, and thus the extent of their activity space, depend on at least three interrelated variables: their stage in life course (age), the means of mobility at their command, and the demands or opportunities implicit in their daily activities. The first variable, *stage in life*, refers to membership in specific age groups. Children usually travel short distances to elementary schools and longer distances to high schools. After-school activities tend to be limited to walking or bicycle trips to nearby locations. Greater mobility is characteristic of high-school students. Adults responsible for household duties make shopping

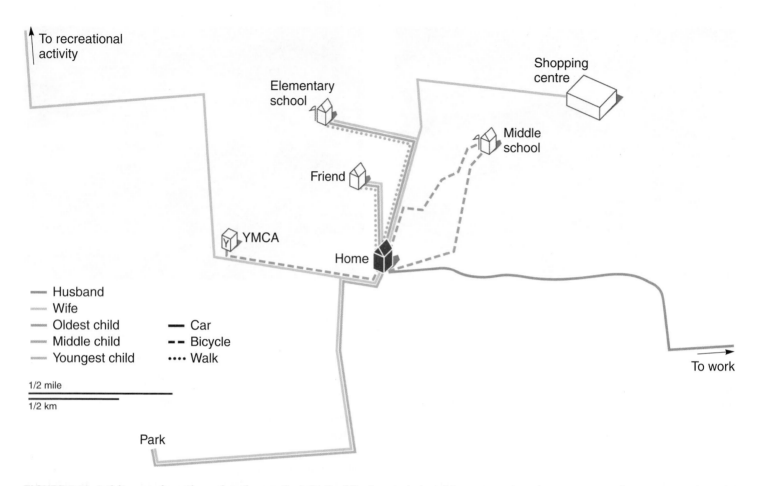

FIGURE 3.11 Activity space for each member of one author's family of five for a typical weekday. Routes of regular movement and areas recurrently visited help to foster a sense of territoriality and to affect one's perceptions of space.

trips and trips related to child care as well as journeys away from home for social, cultural, or recreational purposes. Wage-earning adults usually travel farther from home than other family members. Elderly people may, through infirmity or interests, have less extensive activity spaces.

The second variable that affects the extent of activity space is *mobility*, or the ability to travel. An informal consideration of the cost and effort required to overcome the friction of distance is implicit. Where incomes are high, automobiles are available, and the cost of fuel is reckoned minor in the family budget, mobility may be great and individual activity space large. In societies or neighbourhoods where cars are not a standard means of conveyance, the daily non-emergency activity space may be limited to walking, bicycling, or taking infrequent trips on public transportation. Wealthy suburbanites are far more mobile than are residents of inner-city slums, a circumstance that affects ability to learn about, seek, or retain for work, and to have access to medical care, educational facilities, and social services.

A third factor limiting activity space is the individual assessment of the existence of possible activities or *opportunities*. In subsistence economies where the needs of daily life are satisfied at home, the impetus for journeys away from home is minimal. If there are no stores, schools, factories, or even roads, expectations and opportunities are limited. Not only are activities spatially restricted, but **awareness space**—knowledge of opportunity

locations beyond normal activity space—is minimal, distorted, or absent. In low-income neighbourhoods of modern cities in any country, poverty and isolation limit the inducements, opportunities, destinations, and necessity of travel. Opportunities plus mobility conditioned by life stage bear heavily on the amount of spatial interaction in which individuals engage.

The Tyranny of Time

The daily activities of humans—eating, sleeping, travelling between home and destination, working, or attending classes—all consume time as well as involve space. An individual's spatial reach is restricted because one cannot be in two different places at the same moment or engage simultaneously in activities that are spatially separate. Further, since there is a finite amount of time within a day, and each of us is biologically bound to a daily rhythm of day and night, sleeping and eating, time tyrannically limits the spatial choices we can make and the activity space we can command.

Our daily space-time constraints—our *time–geography*—may be represented by a **space–time prism**, the volume of space and length of time within which our activities must be confined. Its size and shape are determined by our mobility; its boundaries define what we can or cannot accomplish spatially or temporally (Figure 3.12). If our circumstances demand that we walk to work

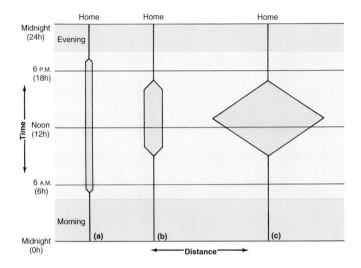

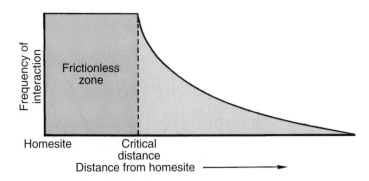

FIGURE 3.12 Space–time prism. An individual's daily prism has both geographical limits and totally surrounding space–time walls. The time (vertical axis) involved in movement affects the space that is accessible, along with the time and space available for other than travel purposes. (*a*) When collecting firewood for household use may take an entire day, as it does in some deforested developing countries, no time or space is left for other activities, and the gatherer's space–time prism may be represented by a straight line. (*b*) Walking to and from work or school and spending the required number of hours there leave little time to broaden one's area of activity. (*c*) The automobile permits an extension of the geographical boundaries of the driver's space–time prism; the range of activity possibilities and locations is expanded for the highly mobile.

FIGURE 3.13 Critical distance. This general diagram indicates how most people observe distance. For each activity, there is a distance beyond which the intensity of contact declines. This is called the critical distance if distance alone is being considered, or the critical isochrone (from Greek isos, "equal," and chronos, "time") if time is the measuring rod. The distance up to the critical distance is identified as a frictionless zone, in which time or distance considerations do not effectively figure in the trip decision.

or school (Figure 3.12b), the sides of our prism are steep and the space available for our activities is narrow. We cannot use time spent in transit for other activities, and the area reasonably accessible to the pedestrian is limited. The space–time prism for the driver (Figure 3.12c) has angled sides and the individual's spatial range is wide. The dimensions of the prism determine what spatially defined activities are possible, for no activity can exceed the bounds of the prism. Since most activities have their own time constraints, the choices of things you can do and the places you can do them are strictly limited. Defined class hours, travel time from residence to campus, and dining hall location and opening and closing hours, for example, may be the constraints on your *space–time path*. If you also need part-time work, your choice of jobs is restricted by their respective locations and work hours, for the job, too, must fit within your daily space–time prism.

Distance and Human Interaction

Most people make many more short-distance trips than long ones, a statement in human behavioural terms of the concept of *distance decay*. If we drew a boundary line around our activity space, it would be evident that trips to the boundary are taken much less often than short-distance trips around the home. The tendency is for the frequency of trips to fall off very rapidly beyond an individual's **critical distance**—the distance beyond which cost, effort, and means strongly influence our willingness to travel. Figure 3.13 illustrates the point with regard to journeys from the home site.

Regular movements defining our individual activity space are undertaken for different purposes and are differently influenced by time and distance considerations. The kinds of activities individuals engage in can be classified according to type of trip: journeys to work, to school, to shop, for recreation, and so on. People in nearly all parts of the world make these same types of journeys, though the spatially variable requirements of culture, economy, and personal circumstance dictate their frequency, duration, and significance to an individual (Figure 3.14). A small child, for example, will make many trips up and down the block but is inhibited by parental admonitions from crossing the street. Different but equally effective distance constraints control adult behaviour.

The journey to work plays a decisive role in defining the activity space of most adults. Formerly restricted by walking distance or by the routes and schedules of public transit systems, the critical distances of work trips have steadily increased in European and North American cities as the private automobile figures more importantly in the movement of workers (Figure 3.15). Daily or weekly shopping may be within the critical distance of an individual, and little thought may be given to the cost or the effort involved. That same individual, however, may relegate shopping for special goods to infrequent trips and carefully consider their cost and effort. The majority of our social contacts tend to be at short distance within our own neighbourhoods or with friends who live relatively close at hand; longer social trips to visit relatives are less frequent. In all such trips, however, the distance decay function is clearly at work (Figure 3.16).

Spatial Interaction and the Accumulation of Information

Critical distances, even for the same activity, are different for each person. The variables of life stage, mobility, and opportunity, together with an individual's interests and demands, help define how often and how far a person will travel. On the basis of these variables, we can make inferences about the amount of

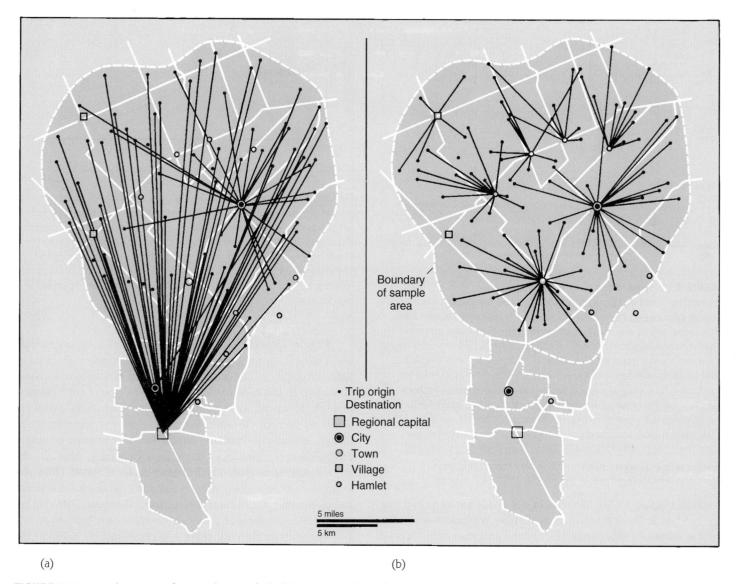

(a)   (b)

FIGURE 3.14 Travel patterns for purchases of clothing and yard goods of (*a*) rural cash-economy Canadians and (*b*) Canadians of the Old Order Mennonite sect. These strikingly different travel behaviours mapped many years ago in midwestern Canada demonstrate the great differences that may exist in the action spaces of different culture groups occupying the same territory. At that time, "modern" rural Canadians, owning cars and wishing to take advantage of the variety of goods offered in the more distant regional capital, were willing and able to travel longer distances than were neighbouring people of a traditionalist culture who had different mobility and whose different demands in clothing and other consumer goods were, by preference or necessity, satisfied in nearby small settlements. Unpublished studies suggest similar contrasts in mobility and purchase travel patterns currently exist between buggy-using Old Order Amish and their car-driving neighbours.

Source: Robert A. Murdie, "Cultural Differences in Consumer Travel," Economic Geography *41, no. 3 (Worcester, Mass.: Clark University, 1965). Redrawn by permission.*

information a person is likely to acquire about his or her activity space and the area beyond. The accumulation of information about the opportunities and rewards of spatial interaction helps increase and justify movement decisions.

For information flows, however, space has a different meaning than it does for the movement of commodities. Communication, for example, does not necessarily imply the time-consuming physical relocations of freight transportation (though in the case of letters and print media it usually does). Indeed, in modern telecommunications, the process of information flow may be instantaneous regardless of distance. The result is space–time convergence to the point of the obliteration of space. A Bell System report tells

us that in 1920, putting through a transcontinental telephone call took 14 minutes and eight operators and cost more than $15.00 for a 3-minute call. By 1940, the call completion time was reduced to less than 1 1/2 minutes, and the cost fell to $4.00. In the 1960s, direct distance dialling allowed a transcontinental connection in less than 30 seconds, and electronic switching has now reduced the completion time to that involved in dialling a number and answering a phone. The price of long-distance conversation essentially disappeared with the advent of voice communication over the Internet in the late 1990s.

The Internet and communication satellites have made worldwide personal and mass communication immediate and data

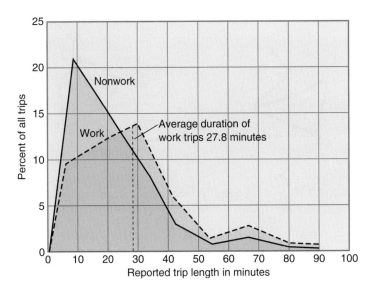

FIGURE 3.15 The frequency distribution of work and non-work trip lengths in minutes in Toronto. More recent studies in different metropolitan areas support the conclusions documented by this graph: work trips are usually longer than other recurring journeys. In the United States in the early 1990s, the average work trip covered 17.1 kilometres (10.6 mi) and half of all trips to work took under 22 minutes; for suburbanites commuting to the central business district, the journey to work involved between 30 and 45 minutes. By 2003, increasing sprawl had lengthened average commuting distances and, because of growing traffic congestion, had increased the average work trip commuting time to about 25 minutes; 15% of workers had commutes of more than 45 minutes, and 2% logged 90-minute one-way commuting times. The situation is similar elsewhere; in the middle 1990s, the average British commuting distance was 12.5 kilometres. Most non-work trips in all countries are relatively short.

Source: Maurice Yeates, Metropolitan Toronto and Region Transportation Study, figure 42, The Queen's Printer, Toronto: 1966.

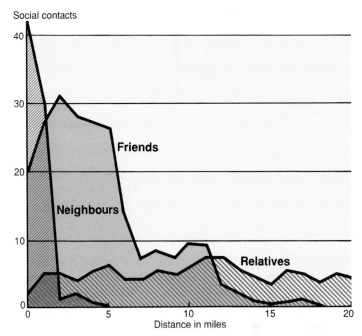

FIGURE 3.16 Social interaction as a function of distance. Visits with neighbours on the same street are frequent; they are less common with neighbours around the corner and diminish quickly to the vanishing point after a residential relocation. Friends exert a greater spatial pull, though the distance decay factor is clearly evident. Visits with relatives offer the greatest incentive for longer distance (though relatively infrequent) journeys.

Source: Frederick P. Stutz, "Distance and Network Effects on Urban Social Travel Fields," Economic Geography 49, no. 2 (Worcester, Mass.: Clark University, 1973), p. 139. Redrawn by permission.

transfers instantaneous. The same technologies that have led to communication space–time convergence have tended toward a space–cost convergence. Domestic mail, which once charged a distance-based postage, is now carried nationwide or across town for the same price. In the modern world, transferability is no longer a consideration in information flows.

A speculative view of the future suggests that as distance ceases to be a determinant of the cost or speed of communication, the spatial structure of economic and social decision making may be fundamentally altered. Determinations about where people live and work, the role of cities and other existing command centres, flows of domestic and international trade, constraints on human mobility, and even the concepts and impacts of national boundaries may fundamentally change with new and unanticipated consequences for patterns of spatial interaction.

Information Flows

Spatially significant information flows are of two types: individual (person-to-person) exchanges and mass (source-to-area) communication. A further subdivision into formal and informal interchange recognizes, in the former, the need for an interposed channel (radio, press, postal service, or telephone, for example) to convey messages. Informal communication requires no such institutionalized message carrier.

Short-range informal *individual communication* is as old as humankind itself. Contacts and exchanges between individuals and within small groups tend to increase as the complexity of social organization increases, as the size and importance of the population centre grow, and as the range of interests and associations of the communicating person expands. Each individual develops a **personal communication field**, the informational counterpart of that person's activity space. Its size and shape are defined by the individual's contacts in work, recreation, shopping, school, or other regular activities. Those activities, as we have seen, are functions of the age, gender, education, employment, income, and so on of each person. An idealized personal communication field is suggested in Figure 3.17.

Each interpersonal exchange constitutes a link in the individual's personal communication field. Each person, in turn, is a node in the communication field of those with whom he or she makes or maintains contact. The total number of such separate informal networks equals the total count of people alive. Despite the number of those networks, all people, in theory, are interconnected by multiple shared nodes (Figure 3.18).

Mass communication is the formal, structured transmission of information in essentially a one-way flow between single points

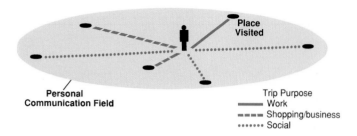

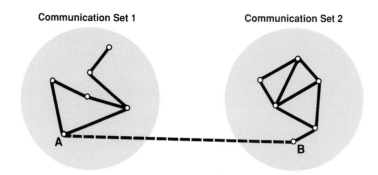

FIGURE 3.17 A personal communication field is determined by individual spatial patterns of communication related to work, shopping, business trips, social visits, and so on.

FIGURE 3.18 Separate population sets are interconnected by the links between individuals. If link A–B exists, everyone in the two sets is linked.

of origin and broad areas of reception. There are few transmitters and many receivers. The mass media are by nature "space filling." From single origin points, they address their messages by print, radio, or television to potential receivers within a defined area. The number and location of disseminating points, therefore, are related to their spatial coverage characteristics, to the minimum size of area and population necessary for their support, and to the capability of the potential audiences to receive their message. The coverage area is determined both by the nature of the medium and by the corporate intent of the agency.

There are no inherent spatial restrictions on the dissemination of printed materials, though of course limitations and restrictions may be imposed by obscenity laws, religious prohibitions (throughout the Islamic world and parts of the Catholic world), restrictions in some countries on certain forms of political speech, and the like. And not everyone has access to bookstores or libraries, or funds to buy printed material, and not everyone can read. Unlike the distance limitations on the transmission of AM or FM radio waves, however, these restrictions are independent of the area over which printed material could be physically distributed and made available.

In the United States, much book and national magazine publishing has localized in metropolitan New York City, as have the services supplying news and print media, both in New York and elsewhere in that country. Paris, Buenos Aires, Moscow, London—indeed, the major metropolises and/or capital cities of other countries—show the same spatial concentration. Regional journals emanate from regional capitals, and major metropolitan newspapers, though serving primarily their home markets, are distributed over (or produce special editions for distribution within) tributary areas whose size and shape depend on the intensity of competition from other metropolises. A spatial information hierarchy has thus emerged.

Hierarchies are also reflected in the market-size requirements for different levels of media offerings. National and international organizations are required to expedite information flows (and, perhaps, to control their content), but market demand is heavily weighted in favour of regional and local coverage. In the electronic media, the result has been national networks with local affiliates acting as the gatekeepers of network offerings and adding to them locally originating programs and news content. A

similar market subdivision is represented by the regional editions of national newspapers and magazines.

The technological ability to fill space with messages from different mass media is unavailing if receiving audiences do not exist. In illiterate societies, publications cannot inform or influence. Unless the appropriate receivers are widely available, television and radio broadcasts are a waste of resources. Perhaps no invention in history has done more to weld isolated individuals and purely person-to-person communicators into national societies exposed to centralized information flows than has the low-cost transistor radio. Its battery-powered transportability converts the remotest village and the most isolated individual into a receiving node of entertainment, information, and political messages. The direct satellite broadcast of television programs to community antennae or communal sets brings that mass medium to remote areas of Arctic Canada, India, Indonesia, and other world areas able to invest in the technology but as yet not served by ground stations.

Innovations in communications technology—the Internet, satellite and fibre-optic networks, electronic mass media—have served to allow for the efficient flow of information between places. In a globalized world, they have contributed to **offshoring**—the establishment of call centres in low-cost locations. When you call someone about your bank account, credit card, or computer, you might be talking with someone in India, the United States, or a distant city in Canada.

Places and Regions

In his book *Geography* (Section 1.2.12), the Greek geographer Strabo maintained that a knowledge of places was conducive to virtue. Given that geographers observe landscapes carefully, they can assess places—to determine a good place from a bad one, based on its physical site, its situation relative to other places, and its human characteristics. This perspective, which emphasizes place as location, is a very traditional one and was a very important aspect of geographical study until the 1950s. This definition of 'place' has now been broadened. At the present time, when a geographer conducts research on 'place,' they may continue to focus on location (absolute or relative). In addition, they may consider the cultural, social, and architectural surroundings (the milieu) which is the context for people's daily actions and interactions; or the feelings associated with a place (sense of place), which play a role in individual and group identity.

We all have a sense of what a region is and all of us refer to regions in our daily lives. We go to "the old neighbourhood," "downtown," or vacation on the "Canadian Shield" or in the Peace River District. These places and regions are based on place characteristics and spatial generalizations that seem useful to us and are understood by people listening to us. We have, in short, engaged in an informal place classification to pass along quite complex spatial, organizational, or content ideas. We have applied the regional concept to bring order to the immense diversity of the earth's surface. Places and regions are central terms in human geography, dating back to Strabo.

Regions play an important role in defining political areas at all scales. In the context of human–environment interactions, the relevance of the region has emerged through the concept of bioregionalism. This idea focuses attention on the delineation of bioregions or ecoregions that are based on natural characteristics, such as watersheds, vegetation, or soil type. It also emphasizes that the region is also a cultural one and that local people's knowledge and participation are essential to solving environmental problems. We will focus more attention on this idea in Chapter 12.

Place as Location

The continent of Africa (Figure 3.19) is home to some 900,000,000 people (14% of the world's population) living in 53 countries, many of which continue to have the same borders that were drawn during a time of European colonisation. Some of the world's poorest countries are located in Africa, including Niger, a former French colony. The concepts of location can assist us in understanding why some countries, such as Niger, are poor and do not receive significant international attention. Due to its absolute location, Niger experiences a subtropical climate, which is very hot and dry, with a large desert. These characteristics mean that it is difficult to grow crops in many parts of the country. During the 1970s, its economy flourished as a result of high levels of uranium production. However, the economy declined in the 1980s when uranium prices dropped. With respect to relative location, Niger is land-locked. Since its relative location is perceived to have little strategic economic or political value, Niger comes to the attention of the developed world only when a significant famine occurs. Clearly, it is a member of Wallerstein's peripheral nations.

Place as Milieu

Milieu refers to the physical or social setting in which something occurs or develops—the background setting. The internationalization of popular culture has often led to the same milieu being copied throughout the world. This is also referred to as the homogenization of place. McDonalds (Figure 1.4) is such a frequently cited example of the globalized milieu that the term "McDonaldization" has been used to describe the process by which

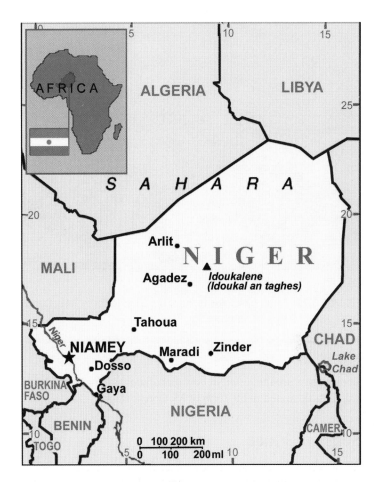

FIGURE 3.19 Map of Africa and Niger

Source: Courtesy of www.thodora.com/maps. Used with permission. http://www.allcountries.org/maps/niger_maps.html.

a society takes on the characteristics of a fast-food restaurant. More specifically, McDonaldization is the way in which "the principles of the fast-food restaurant are coming to dominate more and more sectors of American society as well as of the rest of the world." These principles are:

Efficiency: McDonalds tries to serve people in a minimum amount of time. This can be through the emphasis on self-service and drive-ins in order that staff can focus attention on food preparation and service.

Calculability: allows people to quantify how much they're getting versus how much they're paying. At McDonalds, this is seen in the terms "Big Mac" and "Quarter Pounder." Can you think of similar examples from other food and non-food stores? Workers are often timed to determine if they are providing the service fast enough.

Control: employees have the same uniform and the food is served in the same looking containers.

Predictability: means that no matter where a person goes, they will receive the same service and product. This characteristic is particularly important in shaping places that look the same in order that the customer is not surprised. The reliance on pre-packaging to make Big Macs and other foods also supports predictability.

(a)

(b)

FIGURE 3.20 Paris—France and Ontario. The Eiffel Tower in Paris, France and downtown Paris, Ontario. While both are situated on the banks of a river, they conjure up very different senses of place.

Geographers are interested in how globalization impacts the landscape as illustrated in the form of McDonaldization.

Sense of Place

While globalization has promoted the homogenization of some landscapes, a sense of place is a powerful force that connects people to the rest of the world. Close your eyes and allow your mind to visualize the following places: "dinner table," "home," "downtown," "Paris," and "the Arctic." Some of the places are very familiar and distinctive to you while others may not be. The dinner table you imagine may have the seating arranged in a very specific way, perhaps with your parents at the ends of the table. This arrangement may reflect power and gender structures (e.g., father at the "head of the table," youngest child closest to mother). Chapter 5 examines these aspects in greater detail. Which Paris did you think of—Paris, Ontario or Paris, France (Figure 3.20), and have you ever been to either? If not, were you able to picture either of these places in your mind? Some places evoke strong feelings and images for those who live there as well as those who have never been there. It is widely believed that a strong sense of place enhances people's lives. When our sense of place is violated, perhaps through an urban redevelopment that changes your downtown or home neighbourhood, or a resource development proposal that is perceived to change the landscape of your view of the Arctic, some people tend to become very upset and protest against these proposals. A current tension exists between having uniform places (e.g., McDonald's, Tim Hortons) and having unique places maintained or constructed. Place has cultural, social, and political significance. Sense of place is such a potent force that destroying places during war has been a long-standing military strategy. (Think about the British who burned the White House during the War of 1812, the German attempts to destroy Stalingrad during World War II, and the symbolism of the 9/11 attacks that destroyed the World Trade Towers.)

Sense of place may be generated in several ways. It can reflect distinctive topographic features, such as Niagara Falls. It can reflect memories of significant events, such as the Plains of Abraham, or special places, such as Parliament Hill. Place plays an important role in shaping the identity of people, communities, and nations. This has implications for the development of new places and the maintenance of current places.

Perception of Place

Information and perception influence the way we define and value places and regions. Human spatial interaction, as we have seen, is conditioned by a number of factors. Complementarity, transferability, and intervening opportunities help pattern the movement of commodities and peoples. Flows between points and over area are influenced by distance decay and partially explained by gravity and potential models. Individuals in their daily affairs operate in activity spaces that are partly determined by stage in life, mobility, and a variety of socio-economic characteristics. In every instance of spatial interaction, however, decisions are based on information about opportunity or feasibility of movement, exchange, or want satisfaction.

More precisely, actions and decisions are based on **place perception**—the awareness we have, as individuals, of home and distant places and the beliefs we hold about them. Place perception involves our feelings and understandings, reasoned or irrational, about the natural and cultural characteristics of an area and about its opportunity structure. Whether our view accords with that of others or truly reflects the "real" world seen in abstract descriptive terms is not the major concern. Our perceptions are the important thing, for the decisions people make about the use of their lives or

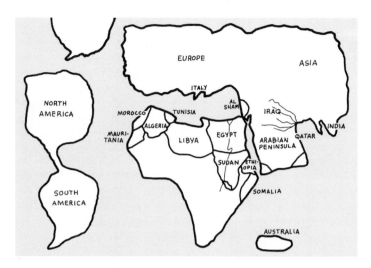

FIGURE 3.21 A Palestinian student's view of the world. The map was drawn by a Palestinian high-school student from Gaza. The map reflects the instruction and classroom impressions the student has received. The Gaza curriculum conforms to the Egyptian national standards and thus is influenced by the importance of the Nile River and pan-Arabism. Al Sham is the old, but still used, name for the area including Syria, Lebanon, and Palestine. The map might be quite different in emphasis if the Gaza school curriculum were designed by Palestinians or if it had been drawn by an Israeli student.

about their actions in space are based not necessarily on reality but on their assumptions and impressions of reality.

The images we form firsthand of our home territory have been in part reviewed in the discussion of mental maps in Chapter 2. The perceptions we have of more distant places are less directly derived (Figure 3.21). In technologically advanced societies, television and radio, magazines and newspapers, books and lectures, travel brochures, and hearsay all combine to help us develop a mental picture of unfamiliar places and of the interaction opportunities they may contain. Again, however, the most effectively transmitted information seems to come from word-of-mouth reports. These may be in the form of letters or visits from relatives, friends, and associates who supply information that helps us develop lines of attachment to relatively unknown areas.

There are, of course, barriers to the flow of information, including that of distance decay. Our knowledge of close places is greater than our knowledge of distant points; our contacts with nearby persons theoretically yield more information than we receive from afar. Yet in crowded areas with maximum interaction potential, people commonly set psychological barriers around themselves so that only a limited number of those possible interactions and information exchanges actually occur. We raise barriers against information overload and to preserve a sense of privacy that permits the filtering out of information that does not directly affect us. There are obvious barriers to long-distance information flows as well, such as time and money costs, mountains, oceans, rivers, and differing religions, languages, ideologies, and political systems.

Barriers to information flow give rise to what we earlier (p. 70) called *direction bias*. In the present usage, this implies a tendency to have greater knowledge of places in some directions than in others. Not having friends or relatives in one part of a country may represent a barrier to individuals, so interest in and knowledge of the area beyond the "unknown" region are low. In the United States, both northerners and southerners tend to be less well informed about each other's areas than about the western part of the country. Traditional communication lines in the United States follow an east–west rather than a north–south direction, the result of early migration patterns, business connections, and the pattern of the development of major cities. In Russia, directional bias favours a north–south information flow within the European part of the country and less familiarity with areas far to the east. Within Siberia, however, east–west flows dominate.

When information about a place is sketchy, blurred pictures develop. These influence the impression—the perception—we have of places and cannot be discounted. Many important decisions are made on the basis of incomplete information or biased reports, such as decisions to visit or not, to migrate or not, to hate or not, even to make war or not. Awareness of places is usually accompanied by opinions about them, but there is no necessary relationship between the depth of knowledge and the perceptions held. In general, the more familiar we are with a locale, the sounder the factual basis of our mental image of it will be. But individuals form firm impressions of places totally unknown to them personally, and these may colour interaction decisions.

One way to determine how individuals envisage home or distant places is to ask them what they think of different locales. For instance, they may be asked to rate places according to desirability—perhaps residential desirability—or to make a list of the 10 best and the 10 worst cities in their country of residence. Certain regularities appear in such inquiries. Figure 3.22 presents some residential desirability data elicited from university students in three provinces of Canada. These and comparable mental maps derived from studies conducted by researchers in many countries suggest that near places are preferred to far places unless much information is available about the far places. Places of similar culture are favoured, as are places with high standards of living. Individuals tend to be indifferent to unfamiliar places and areas, and to dislike those that have competing interests (such as distasteful political and military activities or conflicting economic concerns), or a physical environment perceived to be unpleasant.

On the other hand, places perceived to have superior climates or landscape amenities are rated highly in mental map studies, and are favoured in tourism and migration decisions. The southern and south-western coast of England is attractive to citizens of generally wet and cloudy Britain, and holiday tours to Spain, the south of France, and the Mediterranean islands are heavily booked by the English. A U.S. Census Bureau study indicates that "climate" is, after work and family proximity, the most often reported reason for interstate moves by adults of all ages. International studies reveal a similar migration motivation based not only on climate but also on concepts of natural beauty and amenities.

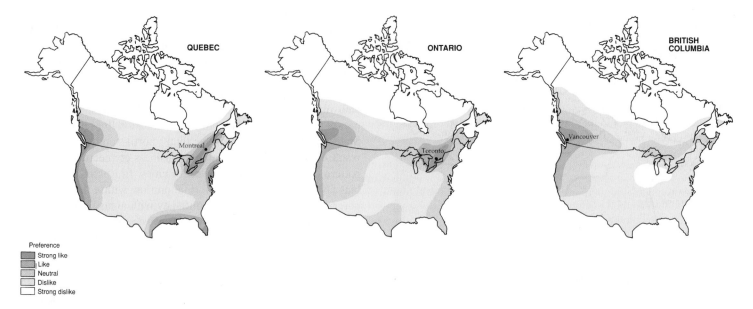

FIGURE 3.22 Residential preferences of Canadians. Each of these maps shows the residential preference of a sampled group of Canadians from the provinces of British Columbia, Ontario, and Quebec, respectively. Note that each group of respondents prefers its own area, but all like the Canadian and U.S. west coasts.

Source: Herbert A. Whitney, "Preferred Locations in North America: Canadians, Clues, and Conjectures," Journal of Geography 83, no. 5, p. 222 (Indiana, Pa.: National Council for Geographic Education, 1984). Redrawn by permission.

 Want to Learn More?

Measuring Interaction

Distance Decay and Tourism: http://jtr.sagepub.com/cgi/content/abstract/42/2/159

Gravity Concept and Retail Trade: http://www.directionsmag.com/features.php?feature_id=5/

Human Spatial Behaviour

The Geography of Information: http://repositories.cdlib.org/iber/cider/C00-111/

Places and Regions

The Geography of Place and River Management: http://www.ingentaconnect.com/content/routledg/cage/2006/00000037/00000002/art00002

Information and Perception and GIS: http://www.directionsmag.com/editorials.php?article_id=2024&trv=1

Summary

In this chapter, attention has been focused on two of geography's well-defined perspectives: (i) human systems as illustrated in the spatial interaction and human spatial behaviour, and (ii) places and regions. The world-systems analysis illustrates how models (or concepts or frameworks) assist researchers—they can act as a guide in helping us understand and solve complex systems and problems, such as globalization. Wallerstein's model consists of three elements—historical, dependency theory, and Marxist perspectives. It suggests that globalization has been occurring for centuries and has benefited a small group of countries in the core region. The model is, in part, spatial because it focuses attention on the economic relationships among core, periphery, semi-periphery, and external regions. Core and periphery regions can been seen at a number of scales—global, national, state/provincial, and local. The flows of goods and services among regions at all scales highlights the relevance and importance of geography, with its longstanding interest in human systems and spatial interaction.

Spatial interaction refers to the movement of goods, information, people, ideas—indeed, of every facet of economy and society—between one place and another. It includes the daily spatial activities of individuals and the collective patterns of their short- and long-distance behaviour in space. The principles and constraints that unite, define, and control spatial behaviour in this sense constitute an essential organizing focus for the study of human geographic patterns of the earth.

We have seen that whatever the type of spatial behaviour or flow, a limited number of recurring mechanisms of guidance and control are encountered. Three underlying bases for spatial interaction are *complementarity*, which encourages flows between areas by balancing supply with demand or satisfying need with opportunity; *transferability*, which affects movement decisions by introducing cost, effort, and time considerations; and *intervening opportunities*, which suggests that costs of overcoming distance may be reduced by finding closer alternate points where needs can be satisfied. The flows of commodities, ideas, or people governed by these interaction factors are interdependent and additive. Flows of commodities establish and reinforce traffic patterns, for example, and also channelize the movement of information and people.

Those flows and interactions may further be understood by the application of uniform models to all forms of spatial interaction from interregional commodity exchanges to an individual's daily pattern of movement. Distance decay tells us of the inevitable decline of interaction with increasing distance. The gravity model suggests that major centres of activity can exert interaction pulls that partly compensate for distance decay. Recognition of movement biases explains why spatial interaction in the objective world may deviate from that proposed by abstract models.

Humans in their individual and collective short- and long-distance movements are responsive to these impersonal spatial controls. Their spatial behaviours are also influenced by their separate circumstances. Each has an activity and awareness space reflective of individual socio-economic and life-cycle conditions. Each differs in mobility. Each has unique wants and needs and perceptions of their satisfaction. Human response to distance decay is expressed in a controlling critical distance beyond which the frequency of interaction quickly declines. That decline is partly conditioned by unfamiliarity with distant points outside normal activity space. Perceptions of home and distant territory therefore colour interaction flows and space evaluations. In turn, those perceptions, well or poorly based, underlie travel and migration decisions, part of the continuing spatial diffusion and interaction of people. It is to people and their patterns of distribution and regional growth and change that we turn our attention in the following chapter.

 KEY WORDS

activity space 71
awareness space 72
complementarity 65
core region 60
critical distance 73
dependency theory 60
distance decay 66
external areas 60
feudalism 59
friction of distance 66

globalization 59
gravity model 68
intervening opportunity 66
law of retail gravitation 69
migration 71
mobility 71
movement bias 70
neo-liberal 63
network 70
node 70

offshoring 76
periphery region 60
personal communication
    field 75
personal space 71
place perception 78
potential model 70
primary industries 60
Reilly's law 69
semi-periphery region 62

space–time prism 72
spatial interaction 64
terms of trade 60
territoriality 71
tertiary industries 60
time–space
    convergence 67
transferability 66

 FOR REVIEW

1. How important an influence has history played in defining core and peripheral regions? How do core regions maintain control over the periphery?

2. Draw a mental map of the core and periphery regions in your university town?

3. What parts of your province would you consider core and periphery? Are there parts of the province which are semi-periphery?

4. What parts, if any, of your university town are "unique?" Explain. Are there elements of a globalization there? What parts, if any, of your university town would you consider to be "placeless." Explain.

5. What is meant by *spatial interaction*? What are the three fundamental conditions governing all forms of spatial interaction? What is the distinctive impact or importance of each of the conditions?

6. What variations in *distance decay* curves might you expect if you were to plot shipments of ready-mixed concrete, potato chips, and computer parts? What do these respective curves tell us about transferability?

7. What is *activity space*? What factors affect the areal extent of an individual's activity space?

8. On a piece of paper, plot your *space–time path* for your movements on a typical class day. What alterations in your established movement habits might be necessary (or become possible) if: (a) instead of walking, you rode a bike? (b) instead of biking, you drove a car? (c) instead of driving, you had to use the bus or go by bike or on foot?

9. What does the thought that transportation and communication are *space-adjusting* imply? In what ways has technology affected the "space adjustment" in commodity flows? In information flows?

10. Recall the places you have visited in the past week. In your movements, were the rules of *distance decay* and *critical distance* operative? What variables affect *your* critical distances?

11. Notice that the Yukon and Northwest Territories are high income areas (Figure 3.5). Do you think this map is "lying"? Why?

FOCUS FOLLOW-UP

1. **What are the three perspectives that are incorporated into world-systems analysis?** pp. 59–64.

   Historical, dependency theory and Marxist. The transition from a feudal society to a capitalist one was closely followed by the discovery of new lands and the establishment of colonies by some western European powers. After World War II, the United States became the predominant world economic power and has dominated world economic, trade and regional trade organizations. Trade between core and periphery nations often does not benefit the latter. The core appropriates the wealth generated from the periphery for its own purposes.

2. **What are the three bases for all spatial interaction?** pp. 64–66.

   Spatial interaction reflects areal differences and is controlled by three "flow-determining" factors. *Complementarity* implies a local supply of an item for which effective demand exists elsewhere. *Transferability* expresses the costs of movement from source of supply to locale of demand. An *intervening opportunity* serves to reduce flows of goods between two points by presenting nearer or cheaper sources.

3. **How is the likelihood of spatial interaction probability measured?** pp. 66–70.

   The probability of aggregate spatial movements and interactions may be assessed by the application of established models. *Distance decay* reports the decline of interaction with increase in separation; the *gravity model* tells us that distance decay can in part be overcome by the enhanced attraction of larger centres of activity; and *movement bias* helps explain interaction flows contrary to model predictions.

4. **What are the forms, attributes, and controls of human spatial behaviour?** pp. 70–73.

   While humans react to distance, time, and cost considerations of spatial movement, their spatial behaviour is also affected by separate conditions of activity and awareness space, of individual economic and life-cycle circumstances, by degree of mobility, and by unique perceptions of wants and needs.

5. **What roles do information and perception play in human spatial actions?** pp. 73–80.

   Humans base decisions about the opportunity or feasibility of spatial movements, exchanges, or want satisfactions on *place perceptions*. These condition the feelings we have about physical and cultural characteristics of areas, the opportunities they possess, and their degree of attractiveness. Those perceptions may not be based on reality or supported by balanced information. Distant places are less well known than nearby ones, for example, and real natural hazards of areas may be mentally minimized through familiarity or rationalization.

ONLINE LEARNING CENTRE

The World Wide Web has a tremendous number and variety of sites pertaining to geography. To access Web sites, Internet exercises, self-quizzes, videos, and additional study tools relevant to this chapter's content, visit the *Human Geography* Online Learning Centre at **www.mcgrawhill.ca/olc/fellmann**.

Performing the Blessing Dance in Long Beach, California, during the Cambodian New Year celebration.

LANDSCAPES OF IDENTITY, PLURALITY, AND ORGANIZATION

*I*n Part One, we reviewed the research process and the role maps play in supporting geographic research and displaying geographic findings. We also described the nature of spatial interaction, the form and nature of human spatial behaviour, the importance of places and regions and the role of information and perception in influencing people's behaviour.

We now turn our attention to the identifying cultural characteristics and organizational structures of people and the societies and landscapes they form. Our first concern is with the principle cultural characteristics or identities of people and the spatial mosaic those identities create. These serve to create a multitude or plurality of cultural groups and cultural landscapes within and between different societies. We ask: What is "culture" and how is it created?

In what pronounced ways are populations distinctive? What notable world and regional spatial patterns of cultural differentiation can we recognize? How do cultural traits and composites change over time and through contact with other, differently constituted groups? And, finally, what are the major concepts and dominant themes pursued by human geographers studying culture?

Although human populations are distinguished from one another in innumerable detailed ways, major points of contrast are relatively few in number and commonly recognized as characteristic cultural traits or identities of distinctive social groups, and herein lays our second concern. Languages spoken, religions practised or espoused, or the composite distinguishing features of ethnicity are among those major elements of contrast. We ask: What constitutes an ethnicity, a language, a religion? Why are these identities considered significant? How might they be classified and "mapped"? And lastly, how are they manifested in cultural landscapes?

Our third concern focuses on how societies formally organize, administer, and control spaces and territories of various peoples through boundaries, laws, and political systems. We ask: Who or what exercises spatial control at the international, national, and local scales? How is power exercised over space? What are the geographic characteristics of

a political state? And how are political boundaries determined? These three concerns will claim our attention in the next three chapters.

To open this section, Chapter 4 focuses on *population*: people in their numbers, movement, distributions, and growth trends. Part of our understanding of those matters in both their global and regional expressions is based on the examination of diffusions and the principles of spatial interaction (Chapter 3), and cultural origins (Chapter 5).

Chapter 5 explains the meaning, characteristics, and components of *culture*, and of the processes of cultural change, diffusion, and divergence. The four themes of *traditional* cultural geography—*ecology, area, history,* and *landscape*—are reviewed and illustrated, followed by an introduction to cultural politics and the work of contemporary geographers on such social identities as class, gender, and "race." The identities of ethnicity, language, and religion are prominent threads in the tapestry of culture, serving both to identify and classify individuals within complex societies, and to distinguish populations and regions of different traditions, tongues, and faiths. *Ethnic identity* represents a form of cultural differentiation of worldwide importance. *Language* is the means of transmission of culture and the medium through which its beliefs and standards are expressed. *Religion* has had a pervasive impact on different culture groups, colouring their perceptions of themselves and their environments, and of other groups of different faiths with whom they come in contact. Fundamental components and spatial expressions of culture, ethnicity, language, and religion command our attention in Chapter 6.

In Chapter 7, we pursue the political ordering of space. We examine the variety of forms and levels—from local to international—of the political organization and control of space. Political boundaries, units, systems, and practices are fundamental features of spatial organization, spatial pattern, and cultural landscapes.

Our concerns in Chapters 4–7, then, are the learned behaviours, attitudes, beliefs, and identities that have significant spatial expression, pattern and organization, and serve in the intricate mosaic of culture.

4 POPULATION: WORLD PATTERNS, REGIONAL TRENDS

Aims

- To know how population is distributed
- To know where and how population increases
- To understand the concept of population density and overpopulation
- To become familiar with Demographic transition theory
- To understand the types and extent of migration
- To become more familiar with population data and projections

Some Specific Considerations for Review:

1. World population distributions, densities, and urban components, pp. 85–91.

2. Data and measures used by population geographers: the meaning and purpose of population cohorts, rates, and other measurements, pp. 92–103.

3. What we are told by the demographic transition model and the demographic equation, pp. 103–107.

4. What kinds of migration movements can be recognized and what influences their occurrence? pp. 107–116.

5. Population projections, controls, and prospects: estimating the future, pp. 116–121.

"Zero, possibly even negative [population] growth" was the 1972 slogan proposed by the prime minister of Singapore, an island country in Southeast Asia. His nation's population, which stood at 1 million at the end of World War II (1945), had doubled by the mid-1960s. To avoid the overpopulation he foresaw, the government decreed "Boy or girl, two is enough" and refused maternity leaves and access to health insurance for third or subsequent births. Abortion and sterilization were legalized, and children born fourth or later in a family were to be discriminated against in school admissions policy. In response, birth rates by the mid-1980s fell to below the level necessary to replace the population, and abortions were terminating more than one-third of all pregnancies.

"At least two. Better three. Four if you can afford it" was the national slogan proposed by that same prime minister in 1986, reflecting fears that the stringencies of the earlier campaign had gone too far. From concern that overpopulation would doom the country to perpetual Third-World poverty, Prime Minister Lee Kuan Yew was moved to worry that population limitation would deprive it of the growth potential and national strength implicit in a youthful, educated workforce adequate to replace and support the present aging population. His 1990 national budget provided for sizable long-term tax rebates for second children born to mothers under 28. Not certain that financial inducements alone would suffice to increase population, the Singapore government annually renewed its offer to take 100,000 Hong Kong Chinese who might choose to leave when China took over that territory in 1997.

The policy reversal in Singapore reflects an inflexible population reality: the structure of the present controls the content of the future. The size, characteristics, growth trends, and migrations of today's populations help shape the well-being of peoples yet unborn but whose numbers and distributions are now being determined. The numbers, age, and sex distribution of people; patterns and trends in their fertility and mortality; their density of settlement and rate of growth all affect and are affected by the social, political, and economic organization of a society. Through population data, we begin to understand how the people in a given area live, how they may interact with one another, how they use the land, what pressure on resources exists, and what the future may bring.

Population geography provides the background tools and understandings of those interests. It focuses on the number, composition, and distribution of human beings in relation to variations in the conditions of earth space. It differs from **demography**, the statistical study of human population, in its concern with *spatial* analysis—the relationship of numbers to area. Regional circumstances of resource base, type of economic development, level of living, food supply, and conditions of health and well-being are basic to geography's population concerns. They are, as well, fundamental expressions of the human–environmental relationships that are the substance of all human geographic inquiry.

This chapter will describe world and Canadian population growth, distribution, and density. These aspects support the view of geography as presenting the "World in Spatial Terms."

Important measures of population related to births, deaths, and population pyramids are explained. The strengths and limitations of population forecasting are provided. Society–environment interactions are explicitly considered in the context of discussing population controls.

Population Growth

In 1950, the world's population was about 2.5 billion people. In mid-1995, the count was 5.6 billion. According to the UN, on March 15, 2008 there were just over 6.6 billion people living on earth. One way of viewing this population growth is to look at the 13-year period between 1995 and 2008, which saw the world grow by about 1 billion people or by 80 million people annually, or some 220,000 per day. Although the rate of global population growth has declined relative to the 1970s, the United Nations still projects that the world will likely contain some 9 billion inhabitants in 2050 (Figure 4.1). Although there is disagreement on specific details, many demographers assume that world population will stabilize at about 10 billion around the year 2100. Others, however, foresee an earlier and lower population peak followed by numerical decline, not stability. All do agree, however, that essentially all of any future growth will occur in countries now considered "less-developed regions" (Figure 4.1). Europe is expected to have a reduction in its population of about 94 million people between 2003 and 2050. North America will grow by some 120 million people. Africa will experience the highest rate of increase, more than doubling its 2003 population. Asia will have the largest absolute increase, growing by about 1.4 billion people by 2050. We will return to these projections and to the difficulties and disagreements inherent in making them later in this chapter. For now, appreciate that world population levels are expected to increase over your lifetime although its distribution will be uneven.

The implications of the present numbers and the potential increases in population are of vital current social, political, and ecological concern. Population numbers were much smaller some 12,000 years ago when continental glaciers began their retreat, people spread to formerly unoccupied portions of the globe, and human experimentation with food sources initiated the Agricultural Revolution. The 5 or 10 million people who then constituted all of humanity obviously had considerable potential to expand their numbers. In retrospect, we see that the natural resource base of the earth had a population-supporting capacity far in excess of the pressures exerted on it by early hunting and gathering groups.

Some observers maintain that despite present numbers or even those we can reasonably anticipate for the future, the adaptive and exploitive ingenuity of humans is in no danger of being taxed. Others, however, compare the earth to a self-contained spaceship and declare with chilling conviction that a finite vessel cannot bear an ever-increasing number of passengers. They point to recurring problems of malnutrition and starvation (though these are realistically more a matter of failures of distribution than of inability to produce enough foodstuffs worldwide). They

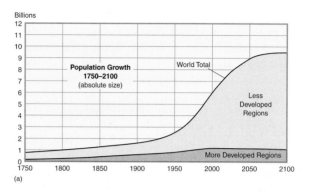

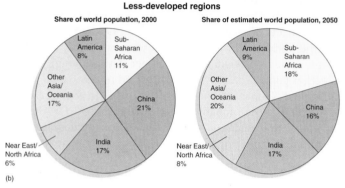

FIGURE 4.1 World population numbers and projections. (*a*) After two centuries of slow growth, world population began explosive expansion after World War II. United Nations demographers project a global population of about 9 billion in 2050. Declining growth rates in much of the developing world have lowered earlier year 2100 estimates of global population from 10 billion to no more than 9.5 billion; some demographers argue for further reducing the number to between 8 and 9 billion. Numbers in more developed regions at mid-century will be the same or lower than at its start thanks to anticipated population loss in Europe. In contrast, the populations of the less-developed regions may increase by almost 60 % between 2000 and 2050. (*b*) While only 80% of world population was found in regions considered "less developed" in 2000 (left diagram), nearly 9 out of 10 of a larger total will be located there in 2050 (right diagram).

Sources: (a) Estimates from Population Reference Bureau and United Nations Population Fund; (b) Based on United Nations and U.S. Bureau of the Census data and projections.

cite dangerous conditions of air and water pollution, the loss of forest and farmland, the apparent nearing exhaustion of many minerals and fossil fuels, and other evidences of strains on world resources as foretelling the discernible outer limits of population growth.

On a worldwide basis, populations grow only one way: the number of births in a given period exceeds the number of deaths. Ignoring for the moment regional population changes resulting from migration, we can conclude that observed and projected increases in population must result from the failure of natural controls to limit the number of births or to increase the number of deaths, or from the success of human ingenuity in circumventing such controls when they exist. In contrast, current estimates of slowing population growth and eventual stability or decline in world totals clearly indicate that humans by their individual

and collective decisions may effectively limit growth and control global population numbers.

World Population Distribution

The millions and billions of people of our discussion are not uniformly distributed over the earth. The most striking feature of the world population distribution map (Figure 4.2) is the very unevenness of the pattern. Some land areas are nearly uninhabited, others are sparsely settled, and still others contain dense agglomerations of people. Until about 2007, most of humanity lived in rural areas. After 2007, however, urbanites will remain dominant with a constantly growing proportion of them residents of very large cities of 1 million or more.

Earth regions of apparently very similar physical makeup show quite different population numbers and densities, perhaps the result of differently timed settlement or of settlement by different cultural groups. Northern and Western Europe, for example, inhabited thousands of years before North America, contain ten times as many people as Canada on about 75% less land; the present heterogeneous population of the Western Hemisphere is vastly denser than was that of earlier Aboriginal peoples.

We can draw certain generalizing conclusions from the uneven, but far from irrational, distribution of population shown in Figure 4.2. First, almost 90% of all people live north of the equator and two-thirds of the total dwell in the mid-latitudes between 20° and 60° North (Figure 4.3). Second, a large majority of the world's inhabitants occupy only a small part of its land surface. More than half the people live on about 5% of the land, two-thirds on 10%, and almost nine-tenths on less than 20%. Third, people congregate in lowland areas; their numbers decrease sharply with increases in elevation. Temperature, length of growing season, slope, and erosion problems, even oxygen reductions at very high altitudes, all appear to limit the habitability of higher elevations. One estimate is that between 50% and 60% of all people live below 200 metres (650 ft), a zone containing less than 30% of total land area. Nearly 80% reside below 500 metres (1650 ft).

Fourth, although low-lying areas are preferred settlement locations, not all such areas are equally favoured. Continental margins have attracted the densest settlement. By United Nations estimates, some 3.8 billion people—about 60% of the world's population—live within roughly 100 kilometres (60 miles) of the ocean, most of them on alluvial lowlands and river valleys. On average, density in coastal areas is about 80 persons per square kilometre (over 200 per square mile), twice the world's average population density. Latitude, aridity, and elevation, however, limit the attractiveness of many seafront locations. Low temperatures and infertile soils of the extensive Arctic coastal lowlands of the Northern Hemisphere have restricted settlement there. Mountainous or desert coasts are sparsely occupied at any latitude, and some tropical lowlands and river valleys that are marshy, forested, and disease-infested are also unevenly settled.

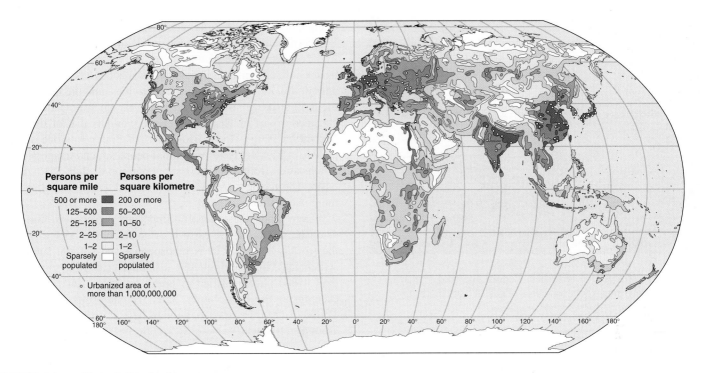

FIGURE 4.2 World population density.

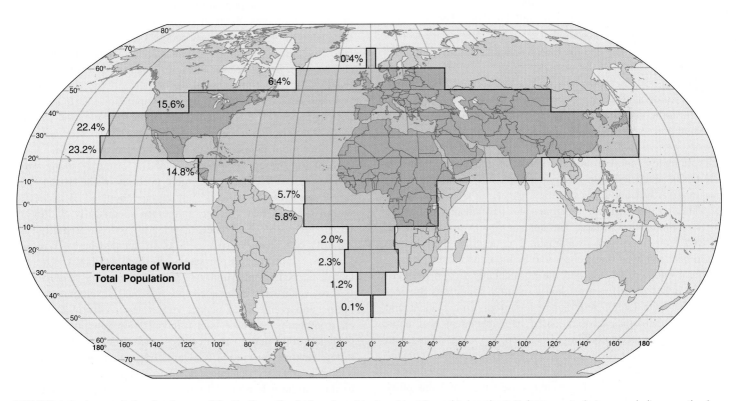

FIGURE 4.3 The population dominance of the Northern Hemisphere is strikingly evident from this bar chart. Only one out of nine people lives south of the equator—not because the Southern Hemisphere is underpopulated, but because it is mainly water.

Within the sections of the world generally conducive to settlement, four areas contain great clusters of population: East Asia, South Asia, Europe, and northeastern United States/southeastern Canada. The *East Asia* zone, which includes Japan, China, Taiwan, and South Korea, is the largest cluster in both area and numbers. The four countries forming it contain nearly 25% of all people on earth; China alone accounts for almost one in five of the world's inhabitants. The *South Asia* cluster

FIGURE 4.4 Terracing of hillsides is one device to extend a naturally limited productive area. The technique is effectively used here in Wakayama Prefecture, southern Honshu, Japan.

of equatorial zones, mid-latitude deserts of both the Northern and Southern Hemispheres, and high mountain areas.

Even parts of these unoccupied or sparsely occupied districts have localized dense settlement nodes or zones based on irrigation agriculture, mining and industrial activities, and the like. Perhaps the most striking case of settlement in an environment elsewhere considered part of the non-ecumene world is that of the dense population in the Andes Mountains of South America and the plateau of Mexico. Here Aboriginal peoples found temperate conditions away from the dry coast regions and the hot, wet Amazon basin. The fertile high basins have served a large population for more than a thousand years.

Even with these locally important exceptions, the non-ecumene portion of the earth is extensive. Some 35% to 40% of the world's land surface is inhospitable and without significant settlement. This is, admittedly, a smaller proportion of the earth than would have qualified as uninhabitable in ancient times or even during the 19th century. Since the end of the Ice Age some 11,000 to 12,000 years ago, humans have steadily expanded their areas of settlement.

Population Distribution in Canada

The distribution of population in Canada reflects many of the previous comments about global trends. Since much of Canada is located in far northern latitudes, the available agricultural land base has played an important role in influencing settlement (Figure 4.5). In 2006, over 86% of Canada's 31.6 million people lived within 300 kilometres of the border with the United States. Another way of describing Canada's population distribution is to note that about 70% of us live south of the 49th parallel, which is the southern border of the Prairie Provinces.

Aboriginal peoples established the general pattern of settlement for subsequent occupants of the country—along water courses in the southern and arable portions of the nation. Currently, most of the nation's population (about 62%) is located within Ontario and Quebec and more specifically within the Great Lakes–St. Lawrence Lowland. Not surprisingly, the majority of Canada's urban centres are located here—Windsor, London, Hamilton, Mississauga, Toronto, Oshawa, Ottawa–Gatineau, Kingston, Montreal, and Quebec City (Figure 4.5). Indeed, waterways influenced the historical development of the nation and continue to play a vital role in current economic, environmental, resource, and transportation functions. Most of Canada's other major urban centres, such as Thunder Bay, Winnipeg, Regina, Saskatoon, Calgary, Edmonton, Vancouver, and Victoria, are also located adjacent to water and most are close to the southern border. Although most of Canada's population is located in Ontario and Quebec, British Columbia and Alberta have recently had the highest rates of growth, primarily from people moving there seeking jobs. Ontario has also had relatively strong growth rates. However, this growth has come at the expense of Atlantic Canada, Quebec, Saskatchewan, and the northern territories, which have been losing their relative share of the nation's population.

is composed primarily of countries associated with the Indian subcontinent—Bangladesh, India, Pakistan, and the island state of Sri Lanka—though some might add to it the Southeast Asian countries of Cambodia, Myanmar, and Thailand. The four core countries alone account for another one-fifth, 21%, of the world's inhabitants. The South and the East Asian concentrations are thus home to nearly one-half the world's people.

Europe—southern, western, and eastern through Ukraine and much of European Russia—is the third extensive world population concentration, with another 12% of its inhabitants. Much smaller in extent and total numbers is the cluster in *northeastern United States/southeastern Canada*. Other smaller but pronounced concentrations are found around the globe: on the island of Java in Indonesia, along the Nile River in Egypt, and in discontinuous pockets in Africa and Latin America.

The term **ecumene** is applied to permanently inhabited areas of the earth's surface. The ancient Greeks used the word, derived from their verb "to inhabit," to describe their known world between what they believed to be the unpopulated, searing southern equatorial lands and the permanently frozen northern polar reaches of the earth. Clearly, natural conditions are less restrictive than Greek geographers believed. Both ancient and modern technologies have rendered habitable areas that natural conditions make forbidding. Irrigation, terracing, diking, and draining are among the methods devised to extend the ecumene locally (Figure 4.4).

At the world scale, the ancient observation of habitability appears remarkably astute. The **non-ecumene**, or *anecumene,* the uninhabited or very sparsely occupied zone, does include the permanent ice caps of the Far North and Antarctica and large segments of the tundra and coniferous forest of northern Asia and North America. But the non-ecumene is not continuous, as the ancients supposed. It is discontinuously encountered in all portions of the globe and includes parts of the tropical rain forests

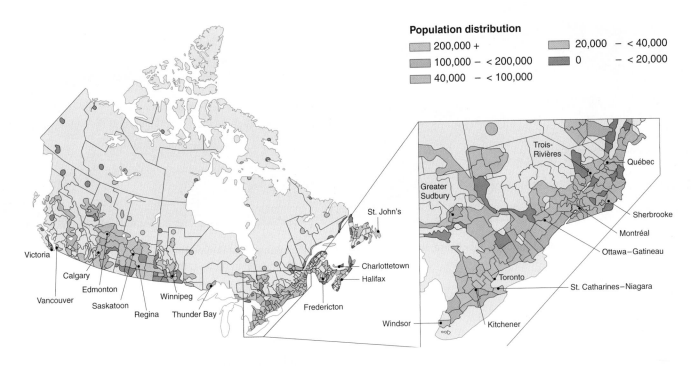

Population distribution

- 200,000 +
- 100,000 − < 200,000
- 40,000 − < 100,000
- 20,000 − < 40,000
- 0 − < 20,000

FIGURE 4.5 **Population distribution in Canada (2006).**

Source: Statistics Canada, http://www.statcan.ca/english/freepub/91-214-XIE/2007000/part4.htm.

Between 1996 and 2006, Canada's Aboriginal population grew by 45% and now exceeds 1 million people. As a share of the entire population, Aboriginals have increased from 2.8% in 1996 to 3.8% in 2006, and live in large and small urban areas, rural areas, and on reserve (Table 4.1). It is clear that the Aboriginal population is becoming increasingly urban (both large and small). In comparison, 81% of non-Aboriginal people were urban dwellers in 2006. According to Statistics Canada, the difference between the two proportions is due mainly to the large share of First Nations people who live on reserves.

The greatest number of Aboriginal people live within the Winnipeg CMA—68,380, which accounts for 10% of its total population. Edmonton, with 52,100 (5% of its population), Vancouver with 40,310 (2%), Toronto with 26,575 (0.5%), Calgary with 26,575 (2%), and Regina with 17,105 (9%), were other major CMA with large aboriginal populations. In terms of a share of the general population, Thompson, Manitoba, Prince Rupert, BC, and Prince Albert, Saskatchewan had 36%, 35%, and 34% Aboriginal population respectively.

Population Density

Margins of habitation could only be extended, of course, as humans learned to support themselves with the resources of new settlement areas. The numbers that could be sustained in old or new habitation zones were and are related to the resource potential of those areas, and the cultural levels and technologies possessed by the occupying populations. The term **population density** expresses the relationship between number of inhabitants and the area they occupy.

Density figures are useful, if sometimes misleading, representations of regional variations of human distribution. The **crude density** or **arithmetic density** of population is the most common and least satisfying expression of that variation. It is the number of people per unit area of land, usually within the boundaries of a political entity (e.g., nation, community). It is easily calculated since all that is required is information on total population and total area. This indicator can, however, be misleading and may

TABLE 4.1

Where Aboriginals Live in Canada (%)

	2001	2006
Urban core	29	31
Other urban	22	22
Rural	20	21
Reserve	29	26

Source: Statistics Canada, 2006, url: http://www12.statcan.ca/english/census06/data/topics/RetrieveProductTable.cfm?TPL=RETR&ALEVEL=3&APATH=3&CATNO=&DETAIL=0&DIM=&DS=99&FL=0&FREE=0&GAL=0&GC=99&GK=NA&GRP=1&IPS=&METH=0&ORDER=1&PID=89121&PTYPE=88971&RL=0&S=1&ShowAll=No&StartRow=1&SUB=734&Temporal=2006&Theme=73&VID=0&VNAMEE=&VNAMEF.

FIGURE 4.6 Tundra vegetation and landscape, Ruby Range, Northwest Territories, Canada. Extensive areas of northern North America and Eurasia are part of the one-third or more of the world's land area considered as non-ecumene, sparsely populated portions of total national territory that affect calculations of arithmetic density.

obscure more of reality than it reveals. The calculation is an average, and a country may contain extensive regions that are only sparsely populated or largely undevelopable, such as Canada's north, along with intensively settled and developed districts (Figure 4.6). A national average density figure, such as Canada's 3.6 people per square kilometre, reveals nothing about either class of territory. In general, the larger the political unit for which crude or arithmetic population density is calculated, the less useful is the figure.

Various modifications may be made to refine density as a meaningful abstraction of distribution. Its descriptive precision is improved if the area in question can be subdivided into comparable regions or units. Thus it is more revealing to know that in 2006, Ontario had a density of 13.4, Western Canada 3.1, Atlantic Canada 4.6, and the territorial north 0.03 persons per square kilometre (Figure 4.7). The calculation may also be modified to provide density distinctions between classes of population—rural versus urban, for example. Rural densities in the United States rarely exceed 115 per square kilometre (300 per square mi), while portions of major cities can have thousands of people in equivalent space.

Another revealing refinement of crude density relates population not simply to total national territory but to that area of a country that is or may be cultivated, that is, to *arable* land. When total population is divided by arable land area alone, the resulting figure is the **physiological density**, which is, in a sense, an expression of population pressure exerted on agricultural land. Table 4.2 makes evident that countries differ in physiological density and that the contrasts between crude and physiological densities of countries point up actual settlement pressures that are not revealed by arithmetic densities alone. The calculation of physiological density, however, depends on uncertain definitions of arable and cultivated land, assumes that all arable land is equally productive and comparably used, and includes only one part of a country's resource base.

Agricultural density is still another useful variant. It simply excludes city populations from the physiological density calculation and reports the number of rural residents per unit of agriculturally productive land. It is, therefore, an estimate of the pressure of people on the rural areas of a country. Other measures of density include:

- **Residential density:** the number of people living in an urban area / the area of residential land;
- **Urban density:** the number of people inhabiting an urban area / the total area of urban land; and
- **Ecological optimum:** the density of population which can be supported by the area's natural resources.

Overpopulation

It is an easy and common step from concepts of population density to assumptions about overpopulation or overcrowding. It is wise to remember that **overpopulation** is a value judgment reflecting an observation or conviction that an environment or territory is unable adequately to support its present population. (A related but opposite concept of *underpopulation* refers to the circumstance of too few people to sufficiently develop the resources of a country or region to improve the level of living of its inhabitants.)

Overpopulation is not the necessary and inevitable consequence of high density of population. Mongolia, a sizable state of 1,565,000 square kilometres (604,000 sq mi) between China and Siberian Russia, has 8 persons per square kilometre (20.5 per sq mi); Iran, only slightly larger, has 43 per square kilometre (110 per sq mi). Macao, a former island possession of Portugal off the coast of China, has some 20,346 persons per square kilometre (52,286 per sq mi). No conclusions about conditions of life, levels of income, adequacy of food, or prospects for prosperity can be drawn from these density comparisons.

Overcrowding is a reflection not of numbers per unit area but of the **carrying capacity** of land—the number of people an area can support on a sustained basis given the prevailing technology. A region devoted to energy-intensive commercial agriculture that makes heavy use of irrigation, fertilizers, and biocides can support more people at a higher level of living than one engaged in the slash-and-burn agriculture described in Chapter 9. An industrial society that takes advantage of resources such as coal and iron ore and has access to imported food will not feel population

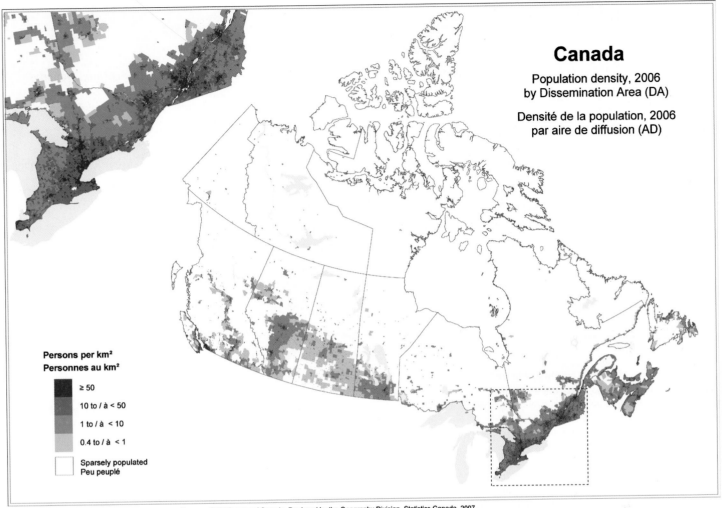

Canada

Population density, 2006
by Dissemination Area (DA)

Densité de la population, 2006
par aire de diffusion (AD)

Persons per km²
Personnes au km²

≥ 50
10 to / à < 50
1 to / à < 10
0.4 to / à < 1
Sparsely populated
Peu peuplé

Sources: 2006 Census of Canada. Produced by the Geography Division, Statistics Canada, 2007.
Recensement du Canada de 2006. Préparé par la Division de la géographie, Statistique Canada, 2007.

FIGURE 4.7 Canada's Population Density by Dissemination Area (2006). Note how Canada's population is distributed along its southern border. Population densities are a relative concept. Although it has one of the lowest population densities in the world (3.3 people/km²), we talk of densely populated areas (> 150), moderately populated areas (between 20 and 150), and sparsely populated areas (< 20). The lowest national population density is Australia's at 3 people per square kilometre. Canada has the second lowest. The United States has 31 people per square kilometre. Monaco has the highest density at 33,104 people per square kilometre. (See Figure 1.11, 4.2, and Appendix A.)

Source: Statistics Canada, 2007, Canadian Demographics at a Glance, *Catalogue number 91-003-XWE*, Portrait of the Canadian Population in 2006: Findings, 2006 *Census Analysis series.*

pressure at the same density levels as a country with rudimentary technology.

Since carrying capacity is related to the level of economic development, maps such as Figure 4.2, displaying present patterns of population distribution and density, do not suggest a correlation with conditions of life. Many industrialized, urbanized countries have lower densities and higher levels of living than do less developed ones.

Overpopulation can be equated with levels of living or conditions of life that reflect a continuing imbalance between numbers of people and carrying capacity of the land. One measure of that imbalance might be the unavailability of food supplies sufficient in caloric content to meet individual daily energy requirements or so balanced as to satisfy normal nutritional needs. Unfortunately, dietary insufficiencies—with long-term adverse implications for life expectancy, physical vigour, and mental development—are most likely to be encountered in the developing countries, where much of the population is in the younger age cohorts.

In the contemporary world, insufficiency of domestic agricultural production to meet national caloric requirements cannot be considered a measure of overcrowding or poverty. Only a few countries are agriculturally self-sufficient. Japan, a leader among the advanced states, is the world's biggest food importer and supplies from its own production only 40% of the calories its population consumes. Its physiological density is high, as Table 4.2 indicates, but it obviously does not rely on an arable land resource for its present development. Largely lacking in either agricultural or industrial resources, it nonetheless ranks well on all indicators of national well-being and prosperity. For countries such as Japan, South Korea, Malaysia, and Taiwan—all of which currently import more than 70% of the grain they consume—a sudden cessation of the international trade that permits the exchange of industrial

TABLE 4.2
Comparative Densities for Selected Countries

Country	Crude Density		Physiological Density[a]		Agricultural Density[b]	
	sq mi	km²	sq mi	km²	sq mi	km²
Argentina	36	14	384	149	44	17
Australia	7	3	100	38	10	4
Bangladesh	2594	1002	4083	1577	3129	1208
Canada	8	3	176	68	36	14
China	353	136	2654	1025	1829	706
Egypt	191	74	6350	2452	3362	1298
India	869	336	1605	620	1176	454
Iran	110	42	1213	468	414	160
Japan	876	338	7321	2827	1562	603
Nigeria	369	142	1131	437	653	252
United Kingdom	635	245	2634	1017	272	105
United States	80	31	404	156	93	36

[a] Total population divided by area of arable land.
[b] Rural population divided by area of arable land.
Rounding may produce apparent conversion discrepancies.

Sources: *World Bank,* World Development Indicators v2003, *and Population Reference Bureau,* World Population Data Sheet.

products for imported food and raw materials would be disastrous. Domestic food production could not maintain the dietary levels now enjoyed by their populations and they, more starkly than many underdeveloped countries, would be "overpopulated."

Some Population Definitions

Demographers employ a wide range of measures of population composition and trends, though all their calculations start with a count of events: of individuals in the population, of births, deaths, marriages, and so on. This "count" was mentioned in Chapter 2—a nation's census. Demographers and population geographers will refine these data in order to make them more meaningful and useful in population analysis. Among these refinements are *rates* and *cohort* measures.

Rates simply record the frequency of occurrence of an event during a given time frame for a designated population—for example, the marriage rate as the number of marriages performed per 1000 population in Canada last year. **Cohort** measures refer data to a population group unified by a specified common characteristic—the age cohort of 1–5 years, perhaps, or the university class of 2009. Basic numbers and rates useful in the analysis of world population and population trends have been reprinted with the permission of the Population Reference Bureau in Appendix A. Examination of them will document the discussion that follows.

Birth Rates

The **crude birth rate (CBR)**, often referred to simply as the *birth rate*, is the annual number of live births per 1000 population. It is "crude" because it relates births to total population without regard to the age or sex composition of that population. The general formula is

$$CBR = \frac{\text{total number of live births in one year}}{\text{total population}} \times 1000$$

The birth rate of a country is, of course, strongly influenced by the age and sex structure of its population, by the customs and family size expectations of its inhabitants, and by its adopted population policies. Since these conditions vary widely, recorded national birth rates vary—in the early 21st century, from a high of 45 to 50 or more in some West African states to lows of 9 or 10 per 1000 in 20 or more European countries. Although birth rates of 30 or above per 1000 are considered *high,* almost one-fifth of the world's people (down from one-half in 1990) live in countries with rates that are that high or higher (Figure 4.8). In these countries—found chiefly in Africa, western and southern Asia, and Latin America—the population is predominantly agricultural and rural, and a high proportion of the female population is young. In many of them, birth rates may be significantly higher than official records indicate. Available data suggest that

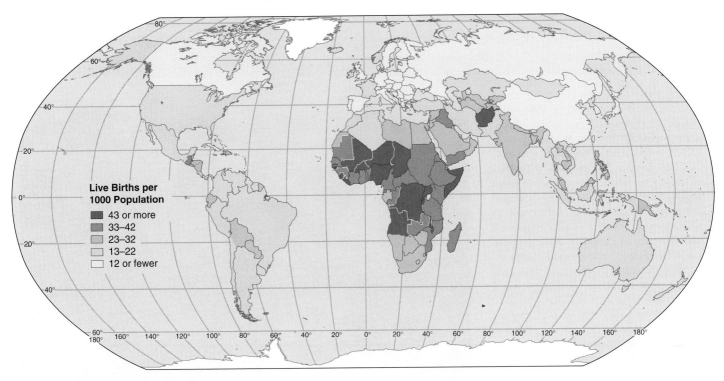

FIGURE 4.8 Crude birth rates. The map suggests a degree of precision that is misleading in the absence of reliable, universal registration of births. The pattern shown serves, however, as a generally useful summary of comparative reproduction patterns if class divisions are not taken too literally. Reported or estimated population data vary annually, so this and other population maps may not agree in all details with data recorded in Appendix A.

Source: Data from Population Reference Bureau, 2007 World Population Data Sheet. Revised with 2007 data (provided by author).

every year around 50 million births go unregistered and therefore uncounted.

Birth rates of less than 18 per 1000 are considered to be *low* and are characteristic of industrialized, urbanized countries. All European countries including Russia, as well as Anglo-America, Japan, Australia, and New Zealand, have low rates as, importantly, do an increasing number of developing states. Some of these, such as China (see "China's Way—and Others"), have adopted effective family planning programs. In others, changed cultural norms have reduced desired family size. *Transitional* birth rates (between 18 and 30 per 1000) characterize some, mainly smaller, developing and newly industrialized countries, though giant India entered that group in 1994.

Religious and political beliefs can also affect birth rates. The convictions of many Roman Catholics and Muslims that their religion forbids the use of artificial birth control techniques often lead to high birth rates among believers. However, dominantly Catholic Italy has nearly the world's lowest birth rate, and Islam itself does not prohibit contraception. Similarly, some European governments—concerned about birth rates too low to sustain present population levels—subsidize births in an attempt to raise those rates.

Fertility Rates

Crude birth rates may display such regional variability because of differences in age and sex composition or disparities in births among the reproductive-age, rather than total, population. The rate is "crude" because its denominator contains persons who have no chance at all of giving birth—males, young girls, and old

women. The **total fertility rate (TFR)** is a more refined and thus more satisfactory statement than the crude birth rate for showing the rate and probability of reproduction among fertile females, the only segment of population who is bearing children.

As a formula, this measure looks like the following:

$$TFR = \frac{\text{number of births}}{\substack{\text{total number of women between} \\ \text{the ages of 15 and 49}}} \times 100$$

The TFR (Figure 4.9) tells us the average number of children that would be born to each woman if, during her childbearing years, she bore children at the current year's rate for women that age. Thus, a TFR of 3 means that the average woman in a population would be expected to have 3 births in her lifetime. The fertility rate minimizes the effects of fluctuation in the population structure and summarizes the demonstrated and expected reproductive behaviour of women. It is thus a more useful and more reliable figure for regional comparative and predictive purposes than the crude birth rate.

Although a TFR of 2.0 would seem sufficient exactly to replace present population (one baby to replace each parent), in reality replacement levels are reached only with TFRs of 2.1 to 2.3 or more because we must consider the affect of mortality, particularly infant and childhood mortalities, childless women, and unexpected deaths in the general population. On a worldwide basis, the TFR in 2007 was 2.33; 20 years earlier it was 3.8. In developed countries, the TFR is about 2.1, while in developing countries, it ranges from about 2.5 to 3.3 (excluding migration).

China's Way—and Others

An ever larger population is "a good thing," Chairman Mao announced in 1965 when China's birth rate was 37 per 1000 and population totalled 540 million. At Mao's death in 1976, numbers reached 852 million, though the birth rate then had dropped to 25. During the 1970s, when it became evident that population growth was consuming more than half of the annual increase in the country's gross domestic product, China introduced a well-publicized campaign advocating the "two-child family" and providing services, including abortions, supporting that program. In response, China's birth rate dropped to 19.5 per 1000 by the late 1970s.

"One couple, one child" became the slogan of a new and more vigorous population control drive launched in 1979, backed by both incentives and penalties to assure its success in China's tightly controlled society. Late marriages were encouraged; free contraceptives, cash awards, abortions, and sterilizations were provided to families limited to a single child. Penalties, including steep fines, were levied for second births. At the campaign's height in 1983, the government ordered the sterilization of either husband or wife for couples with more than one child. Infanticide—particularly the exposure or murder of female babies—was a reported means both of conforming to a one-child limit and of increasing the chances that the one child would be male.

By 1986, China's officially reported crude birth rate had fallen to 18 per 1000, far below the 37 per 1000 then registered among the rest of the world's less developed countries. The one-child policy was effectively dropped in 1984 to permit two-child limits in rural areas where 70% of Chinese population still resides, but in 2002 it was reinstated as nationwide law following documentation of extensive underreporting of rural births. In contrast, newly prosperous urbanites have voluntarily reduced their fertility to well below replacement levels, with childless couples increasingly common.

Nationally, past and current population controls have been so successful that by 2000, China's population was 300 million less than it otherwise would have been. By 2001, indeed, serious concerns were being expressed by demographers and government officials that population decrease, not increase, is the problem next to be confronted. Projections suggest that by 2042, because of lowered fertility rates, China's population numbers will actually start falling. The country is already beginning to face a pressing social problem: a declining proportion of working-age persons and an absence of an adequate welfare network to care for a rapidly growing number of senior citizens.

Concerned with their own increasing numbers, many developing countries have introduced their own less extreme programs of family planning, stressing access to contraception and sterilization. International agencies have encouraged these programs, buoyed by such presumed success as the 21% fall in fertility rates in Bangladesh from 1970 to 1990 as the proportion of married women of reproductive age using contraceptives rose from 3% to 40% under intensive family planning encouragement and frequent adviser visits. The costs per birth averted, however, were reckoned at more than the country's $160 per capita gross domestic product.

Research suggests that fertility falls because women decide they want smaller families, not because they have unmet needs for contraceptive advice and devices. Nineteenth-century northern Europeans without the aid of science had lower fertility rates than their counterparts today in middle-income countries. With some convincing evidence, improved women's education has been proposed as a surer way to reduce births than either encouraged contraception or China's coercive efforts. Studies from individual countries indicate that one year of female schooling can reduce the fertility rate by between 5% and 10%. Yet the fertility rate of uneducated Thai women is only two-thirds that of Ugandan women with secondary education. Obviously, the demand for children is not absolutely related to educational levels.

Instead, that demand seems closely tied to the use value placed on children by poor families in some parts of the developing world. Where those families share in such communal resources as firewood, animal fodder, grazing land, and fish, the more of those collective resources that can be converted to private family property and use, the better off is the family. Indeed, the more communal resources that are available for "capture," the greater are the incentives for a household to have more children to appropriate them. Some population economists conclude that only when population numbers increase to the point of total conversion of communal resources to private property—and children have to be supported and educated rather than employed—will poor families in developing countries want fewer children. If so, coercion, contraception, and education may be less effective as checks on births than the economic consequence of population increase itself.

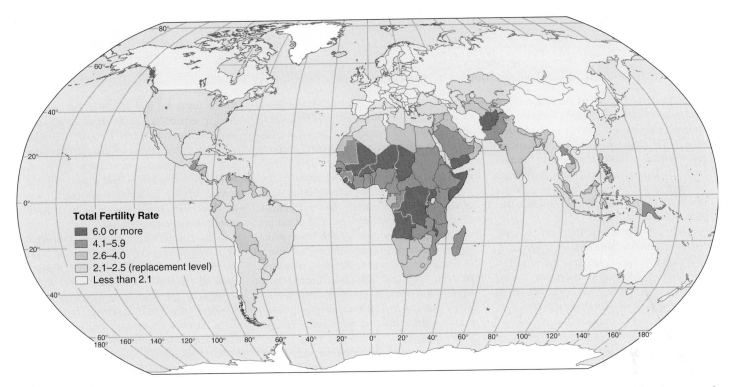

FIGURE 4.9 **Total fertility rate (TFR)** indicates the average number of children that would be born to each woman if, during her childbearing years, she bore children at the same rate as women of those ages actually did in a given year. Since the TFR is age-adjusted, two countries with identical birth rates may have quite different fertility rates and therefore different prospects for growth. Depending on mortality conditions, a TFR of 2.1 to 2.5 children per woman is considered the "replacement level," at which a population will eventually stop growing.

Source: Data from Population Reference Bureau, 2007 World Population Data Sheet. Revised with 2007 data (provided by author).

The concept of *replacement level fertility* is useful here. It marks the level of fertility at which each successive generation of women produces exactly enough children to ensure that the same number of women survive to have offspring themselves. In general, then, the higher the level of mortality in a population, the higher the replacement level of fertility will be. For Mozambique early in the 21st century, for example, the replacement level fertility was 3.4 children per woman.

The recent fertility declines in developing states, however, have been more rapid and widespread than anyone expected. Indeed, the TFRs for so many less developed countries have dropped so dramatically since the early 1960s (Figure 4.10), that earlier widely believed world population projections anticipating 10 billion or more at the end of this century are now generally discounted and rejected. Indeed, worldwide in 2005, 88 countries and territories containing nearly 50% of global population had fertility rates less than 2.1, with more poised to join their ranks. China's decrease from a TFR of 5.9 births per woman in the period 1960–1965 to (officially) about 1.8 in 2000 and comparable drops in TFRs of Bangladesh, Brazil, Mozambique, and other states, demonstrate that fertility reflects cultural values, not biological imperatives. If those values now favour fewer children than formerly, population projections based on earlier, higher TFR rates must be adjusted.

In fact, demographers have long assumed that recently observed developing country—and therefore global—fertility rate declines to the replacement level would continue and in the long run lead to stable population numbers. However, nothing in

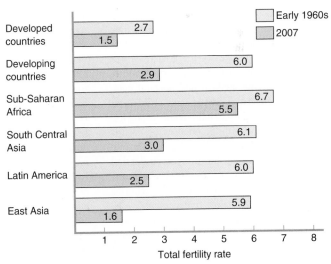

Fertility Declines, 1960s to 2007

FIGURE 4.10 Differential fertility declines. Worldwide fertility has declined dramatically. It is most dramatic in Asia and Latin America, and much more slowly in sub-Saharan Africa. Developed countries as a group have a below-replacement-level of fertility. Europe was far below with a 2007 TFR of 1.5. Canada had a 2007 TFR of 1.5, while the United States has a TFR of 2.1, which is the replacement level.

Source: Population Reference Bureau and United Nations Population Fund.

logic or history requires population stability at any level. Indeed, rather than assume, as in the past, a fertility decline to a constant

For much of the last half of the 20th century, demographers and economists focused on a "population explosion" and its implied threat of a world with too many people and too few resources of food and minerals to sustain them. By the end of the century, those fears for some observers were being replaced by a new prediction of a world with too few rather than too many people.

That possibility was suggested by two related trends. The first became apparent by 1970 when it was noted that the total fertility rates (TFRs) of 19 countries, almost all of them in Europe, had fallen below the **replacement level**—the level of fertility at which populations replace themselves—of 2.1. Simultaneously, Europe's population pyramid began to become noticeably distorted, with a smaller proportion of young and a growing share of middle-aged and retirement-age inhabitants. The decrease in native working-age cohorts had already, by 1970, encouraged the influx of non-European "guest workers" whose labour was needed to maintain economic growth and to sustain the generous security provisions guaranteed to what was becoming the oldest population of any continent.

Many countries of Western and Eastern Europe sought to reverse their birth rate declines by adopting pronatalist policies. The communist states of the East rewarded pregnancies and births with generous family allowances, free medical and hospital care, extended maternity leaves, and child care. France, Italy, the Scandinavian countries, and others gave similar bonuses or awards for first, second, and later births. Despite those inducements, however, reproduction rates continued to fall. By 2004, every one of the 43 European countries and territories had fertility rates below replacement levels, in widespread response to a host of cultural influences and personal lifestyle decisions. Those decisions were influenced by increased educational levels of women with longer years of schooling and deferred marriage ages, opportunities for women to experience challenging professional or employment careers, the increasing cost of rearing multiple children, and the attractiveness of enjoying the increasing number of recreational opportunities that growing prosperity afforded without restrictive family obligations. The effect on national growth prospects has been striking. For example, the populations of Spain and Italy are projected to shrink by a quarter between 2000 and 2050, and Europe as a whole is forecast to shrink by 90 million people by mid-century. "In demographic terms," France's prime minister remarked, "Europe is vanishing."

Europe's experience soon was echoed in other societies of advanced economic development on all continents. By 1995, Canada, Australia, New Zealand, Japan, Taiwan, South Korea, Singapore, and other older and newly industrializing countries (NICs) registered fertility rates below the replacement level. As they have for Europe, simple projections foretold their aging and declining population. Japan's numbers, for example, began to decline in 2006 when its population was older than Europe's; Taiwan forecasts negative growth by 2035.

The second trend indicating to many that world population numbers should stabilize and even decline during the lifetimes of today's university/college cohort is a simple extension of the first: TFRs are being reduced to or below the replacement levels in countries at all stages of economic development in all parts of the world. While only 18% of total world population in 1975 lived in countries with a fertility rate below replacement level, nearly 45% did so by the end of the century. By 2015, demographers estimate, half the world's countries and about two-thirds of its population will show TFRs below 2.1 children per woman. Exceptions to the trend are still will be found in Africa, especially sub-Saharan Africa, and in some areas of South, Central, and West Asia; but even in those regions, fertility rates have been decreasing in recent years. "Powerful globalizing forces [are] at work pushing toward fertility reduction everywhere," was an observation of the French National Institute of Demographic Studies.

That conclusion is plausibly supported by assumptions of the United Nations' 2004 forecast of a decline of long-term fertility rates of most less developed states to an average of 1.9. The same UN assessment envisions that those countries will reach those below-replacement fertilities before 2050. Should these assumptions prove valid, global depopulation could commence by or before mid-century. Between 2040 and 2050, one projection indicates, world population would fall by about 85 million (roughly the amount of its annual growth during much of the 1990s) and shrink further by about 25% with each successive generation.

If the UN scenario is realized in whole or in part, a much different worldwide demographic and economic future is promised than that prophesied so recently by "population explosion" forecasts. Declining rather than increasing pressure on world food and mineral resources would be in our future along with shrinking rather than expanding world, regional, and national economies. Even the achievement of **zero population growth (ZPG)**, a condition for individual countries when births plus immigration equal deaths plus emigration, has social and economic consequences not always perceived by its advocates. These inevitably include an increasing proportion of older citizens, fewer young people, a rise in the median age of the population, and a growing old-age dependency ratio with ever-increasing pension and social services costs borne by a shrinking labour force.

continuing rate of 2.1, the 2004 revision of the United Nations' world population projections predicts a long-term world fertility rate of 2.05—*below* the replacement rate. Should the UN's new assessment of global fertility prove correct, world population would not just stop growing as past UN projections envisioned; it would inevitably decline (see "A Population Implosion?"). Of course, should cultural values change to again favour children, growth would resume. Different TFR estimates imply conflicting population projections and vastly different regional and world population concerns.

Individual country projections based on current fertility rates, it should be noted, may not accurately anticipate population levels even in the near future. As we will see shortly, massive international population movements are occurring in response to political instabilities and, particularly, to differentials in perceived economic opportunities. Resulting migration flows may

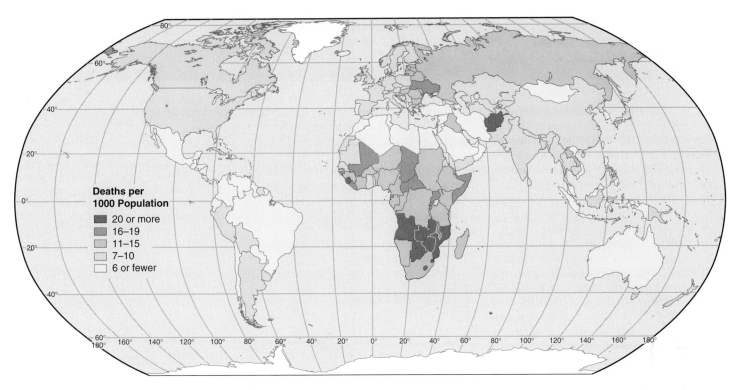

FIGURE 4.11 **Crude death rates** show less worldwide variability than do the birth rates displayed in Figure 4.8. The widespread availability of at least minimal health protection measures and a generally youthful population in the developing countries yield death rates frequently lower than those recorded in "old age" Europe.

Source: Data from Population Reference Bureau, 2007 World Population Data Sheet.

cause otherwise declining national populations to grow. World regional and national fertility rates reported in Appendix A and other sources are summaries that conceal significant variations between population groups. The Caribbean region, for example, showed a total fertility rate of 2.5 in 2007, but the TFRs of individual states ranged from a low of 1.5 in Cuba to a high of 4.0 in Haiti. Among other things, the Canadian average fertility rate of 1.5 did not reveal that the TFR for immigrants was about 3.1, about 1.4 for second generation immigrants, and 1.79 for residents in Saskatchewan.

Death Rates

The **crude death rate (CDR)**, also called the **mortality rate**, is calculated in the same way as the crude birth rate:

$$CDR = \frac{\text{number of deaths in one year}}{\text{total population}} \times 1000$$

In the past, a valid generalization was that the death rate, like the birth rate, varied with national levels of development. Characteristically, highest rates (over 20 per 1000) were found in the less developed countries of Africa, Asia, and Latin America; lowest rates (less than 10) were associated with developed states of Europe and Anglo-America. That correlation became decreasingly valid as dramatic reductions in death rates occurred in developing countries in the years following World War II. Infant mortality rates and life expectancies improved as antibiotics, vaccinations,

and pesticides to treat diseases were made available, and modest improvements were made to providing clean water and sanitation to some communities.

Distinctions between more developed and less developed countries in mortality (Figure 4.11), indeed, have been so reduced that by 1994 death rates for less developed countries as a group actually dropped below those for the more developed states and have remained lower since. Notably, that reduction did not extend to maternal mortality rates (see "The Risks of Motherhood"). Like crude birth rates, death rates are meaningful for comparative purposes only when we study identically structured populations. Countries with a high proportion of elderly people, such as Denmark and Sweden, would be expected to have higher death rates than those with a high proportion of young people, such as Iceland, assuming equality in other national conditions affecting health and longevity. The pronounced youthfulness of populations in developing countries, as much as improvements in sanitary and health conditions, is an important factor in the recently reduced mortality rates of those areas.

To overcome that lack of comparability, death rates can be calculated for specific age groups. The *infant mortality rate (IMR)* is calculated as follows:

$$IMR = \frac{\text{deaths age 1 year or less}}{1000 \text{ live births}} \times 1000$$

Infant mortality rates are significant because it is at these ages that the greatest declines in mortality have occurred, largely as a result

The worldwide levelling of crude death rates does not apply to pregnancy-related deaths. In fact, the maternal mortality ratio—maternal deaths per 100,000 live births—is the single greatest health disparity between developed and developing countries. According to the World Health Organization, approximately 530,000 women die each year from causes related to pregnancy and childbirth; 99% of them live in less developed states where, as a group, the maternal mortality ratio is some 26 times greater than in the more developed countries. Pregnancy complications, childbirth, and abortions in unsafe conditions are the leading causes of death among women of reproductive age throughout the developing world, though the incidence of maternal mortality is by no means uniform, as the chart indicates. According to 2000 data, in Africa the risk is 1 death in 20 pregnancies compared with 1 in 160 in Latin America and the Caribbean, and 1 in 2400 in Europe. Country-level differences are even more striking: in Angola, for example, the lifetime risk is 1 death out of every 7 pregnancies compared to 1 in almost 30,000 in Sweden.

The developing countries as a group in 2000 had a maternal mortality ratio of 440, and 10% of all deaths were due to perinatal and maternal causes; least developed states registered a ratio of 890. In 2000, Asia and Africa recorded almost the same number of maternal deaths (48% and 47% of the world total, respectively), but sub-Saharan African women, burdened with 45% of world maternal mortality, were at greatest statistical risk. There, maternal death ratios in 2000 reached above 1600 in Angola, Malawi, and Niger and to more than 2000 in Sierra Leone; 1 in 16 women in sub-Saharan Africa dies of maternal causes. In contrast, the maternal mortality

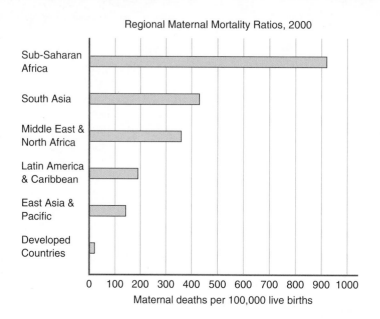

Regional Maternal Mortality Ratios, 2000

Maternal deaths per 100,000 live births

ratio in developed countries as a group (including Russia and eastern Europe) is 20, and in some—Ireland, Austria, and Sweden, for example—it is as low as 2 to 5 (it was 6 in Canada and 17 in the United States in 2000).

The vast majority of maternal deaths in the developing world are preventable. Most result from causes rooted in the social, cultural, and economic barriers confronting females in their home environment throughout their lifetimes: malnutrition, anaemia, lack of access to timely basic maternal health care, physical immaturity due to stunted growth, and unavailability of adequate prenatal care or trained medical assistance at birth. Part of the problem is that women are considered expendable in societies in which their status is low, although the correlation between women's status and maternal mortality is

not exact. In those cultures, little attention is given to women's health or their nutrition, and pregnancy, although a major cause of death, is simply considered a normal condition warranting no special consideration or management. To alter that perception and increase awareness of the affordable measures available to reduce maternal mortality worldwide, 1998 was designated "The Year of Safe Motherhood" by a United Nations interagency group. Legal barriers to abortions are a major contributor to high mortality rates among childbearing-age females because they can look for and obtain illegal abortions, which are usually conducted in unsafe conditions.

Sources: Graph data from WHO, UNICEF, and UNFPA. *Maternal Mortality* (2000).

of the increased availability of health services (Figure 4.12). The drop in infant mortality accounts for a large part of the decline in the general death rate in the last few decades, for mortality during the first year of life is usually greater than in any other year.

Modern medicine and sanitation have increased life expectancy and altered age-old relationships between birth and death rates. In the early 1950s, only five countries, all in northern Europe, had life expectancies at birth of over 70 years. In the first years of the 21st century, some 60 countries outside of Europe and North America—though none in sub-Saharan Africa—were on that list.

The availability and employment of modern methods of health and sanitation have varied regionally, and the least developed countries have least benefited from them. In such underdeveloped and impoverished areas as much of sub-Saharan Africa, the chief causes of death other than HIV/AIDS are those no longer of immediate concern in more developed lands: diseases such as malaria, intestinal infections, typhoid, cholera, and especially among infants and children, malnutrition and dehydration from diarrhea.

HIV/AIDS is the tragic and, among developing regions particularly, widespread exception to observed global improvements

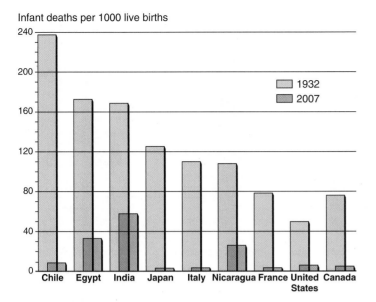

Infant deaths per 1000 live births

FIGURE 4.12 Infant mortality rates for selected countries. Dramatic declines in the rate have occurred in all countries, a result of international programs of health care delivery aimed at infants and children in developing states. Nevertheless, the decreases have been proportionately greatest in the urbanized, industrialized countries, where sanitation, safe water, and quality health care are widely available.

Sources: Data from U.S. Bureau of the Census and Population Reference Bureau.

in life expectancies and reductions in adult death rates and infant and childhood mortalities. AIDS has become the fourth most common cause of death worldwide and is forecast to surpass the Black Death of the 14th century—which caused an estimated 25 million deaths in Europe and 13 million in China—as history's worst-ever epidemic. According to a report by UNAIDS, AIDS is expected to kill 68 million people between 2000 and 2020 in the 45 most affected countries; about 55 million of those deaths will occur in sub-Saharan Africa. The World Health Organization estimated 42 million people to be HIV positive early in the 21st century. Some 95% of those infected live in developing countries, and 70% reside in sub-Saharan Africa, where women account for 60% of all cases. In that hardest-hit region, as much as one-fourth of the adult population in some countries is HIV positive, and average life expectancy has been cut drastically. In South Africa, the life expectancy of a baby born in the early 21st century should be over 66 years; AIDS has cut that down to 50. In Botswana, it is 50 years instead of 70; in Zimbabwe the decline has been to 37 years from 69. Along with the deep cuts in sub-Saharan life expectancies, total population by 2015 is now projected to be 60 million less than it would have been in the absence of the disease. Economically, AIDS will cut an estimated 8% off national incomes in the worst-hit sub-Saharan countries by 2010. Southern Africa's economies are based on farming, and women do much of the farming as well as run households. Because AIDS kills more women than men, sub-Saharan food insecurity is rising and food shortages result because many young adults are too feeble to farm. Malnutrition, starvation, and susceptibility to other diseases are thus AIDS costs added to impersonal national income reductions. HIV/AIDS will be discussed further in Chapter 11.

Population Pyramids

Another means of comparing populations is through the **population pyramid**, a graphic device that represents a population's age and gender composition. The term *pyramid* describes the diagram's shape for many countries in the 1800s, when the display was created: a broad base of younger age groups and a progressive narrowing toward the apex as older populations were thinned by death. Now many different shapes are formed, each reflecting a different population history (Figure 4.13), and some suggest "population profile" is a more appropriate label. By grouping several generations of people, the pyramids or profiles highlight the impact of "baby booms," population-reducing wars, birth rate reductions, and external migrations.

A rapidly growing country such as Uganda has most people in the lowest age cohorts; the percentage in older age groups declines successively, yielding a pyramid with markedly sloping sides. Typically, female life expectancy is reduced in older cohorts of less developed countries, so that for Uganda, the proportion of females in older age groups is lower than in, for example, Sweden. Female life expectancy and mortality rates may also be affected by cultural rather than economic developmental causes (see "100 Million Women Are Missing"). In Sweden, a wealthy country with a very slow rate of growth, the population is nearly equally divided among the age groups, giving a "pyramid" with almost vertical sides. Among older cohorts, as Austria shows, there may be an imbalance between men and women because of the greater life expectancy of the latter. The impacts of war, as Russia's 1992 pyramid vividly demonstrated, were evident in that country's depleted age cohorts and male–female disparities. The sharp contrasts between the composite pyramids of sub-Saharan Africa and Western Europe summarize the differing population concerns of the developing and developed regions of the world; the projection for Botswana suggests the degree to which accepted pyramid shapes can quickly change (Figure 4.14).

The population profile provides a quickly visualized demographic picture of immediate practical and predictive value. For example, the percentage of a country's population in each age group strongly influences demand for goods and services within that national economy. A country with a high proportion of young has a high demand for educational facilities and certain types of health delivery services. In addition, of course, a large portion of the population is too young to be employed (Figures 4.14 and 4.15). On the other hand, a population with a high percentage of elderly people also requires medical goods and services specific to that age group, and these people must be supported by a smaller proportion of workers. As the profile of a national population changes, differing demands are placed on a country's social and economic systems (Figure 4.16). The **dependency ratio** is a simple measure of the number of economic dependents, old or young, that each 100 people in the productive years (usually 15–64) must support. Population pyramids give quick visual evidence of that ratio. Results from the 2006 census indicates that there are now over 4 million Canadians aged 65 and over—an increase of 446,700 since 2001 (+11.5%). In contrast, the number of people aged under-15 declined by almost 146,000 (−2.5%) to 5.6 million during the same period. This is the second consecutive intercensal

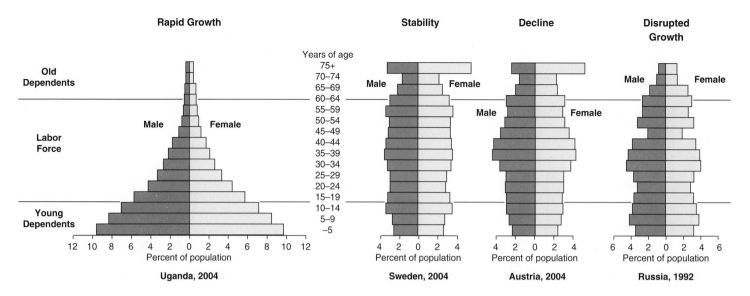

FIGURE 4.13 Four patterns of population structure. These diagrams show that population "pyramids" assume many shapes. The age distribution of national populations reflects the past, records the present, and foretells the future. In countries like Uganda, social costs related to the young are important, and economic expansion is vital to provide employment for new entrants in the labour force. Austria's negative growth means a future with fewer workers to support a growing demand for social services for the elderly. The 1992 pyramid for Russia reported the sharp decline in births during World War II as a "pinching" of the 45–49 cohort, and showed in the large deficits of men above age 65 the heavy male mortality of both world wars and late-Soviet period sharp reductions in Russian male longevity.

Sources: The 2004 pyramids for Uganda, Sweden, and Austria: U.S. Bureau of the Census, International Data Base; and for Russia: Carl Haub, "Population Change in the Former Soviet Republics," Population Bulletin *49, no. 4 (1994).*

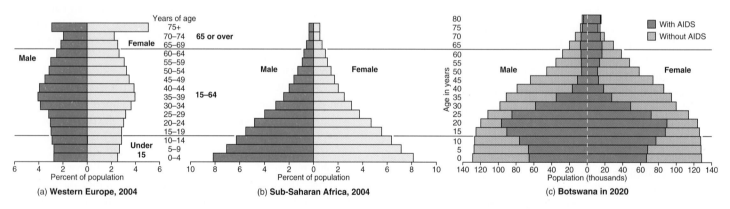

FIGURE 4.14 Summary population pyramids. The 2004 pyramids for (a) Western Europe and (b) sub-Saharan Africa show the sharp contrasts in the age structure of older developed regions with their characteristic lowered birth and total fertility rates and that of the much more youthful developing sub-Saharan states. Even in 2004, about 44% of the sub-Saharan population was below age 15. That percentage, however, was smaller than it had been just five years earlier and hinted at more dramatic declines possible in years to come. Part of the projected decline will come as a result of economic development and changing family size decisions, but for some countries (c) and perhaps for the region as a whole, tremendous pyramid distortions will result from the demographic impact of AIDS. By 2020, the otherwise expected "normal" pyramid of Botswana may well be distorted into a "population chimney" in which there would be more adults in their 60s and 70s than adults in their 40s and 50s.

Sources: (a) and (b) U.S. Bureau of the Census, International Data Base; (c) U.S. Bureau of the Census, World Population Profile *2000.*

period in which the under-15 population has declined, as the last increase was in the 1991 to 1996 period. In 2006, the dependency ratio for Canada was 0.46.

They also foretell future problems resulting from present population policies or practices. The strict family-size rules and widespread preferences for sons in China, for example, skews the pyramid in favour of males and has an impact on the **sex ratio**, which is the ration of males to females in a population. In humans,

the sex ratio at the time of birth (termed secondary sex ratio) is 105 boys to 100 girls. In China, the sex ratio is 113 boys to 100 girls. On the current evidence, about 1 million excess males a year will enter an imbalanced marriage market in China beginning about 2010. Even now, the Chinese population pyramid shows never-married men ages 20–44 outnumber their female counterparts by nearly 2 to 1. The 40 million bachelors China is likely to have in 2020, unconnected to society by wives and children, may pose threats to

100 Million Women are Missing

Worldwide, some 100 million females are missing, victims of nothing more than their gender. In China, India, Pakistan, New Guinea, and many other developing countries, a traditional preference for boys has meant neglect and death for girls, millions of whom are killed at birth, deprived of adequate food, or denied the medical attention provided to sons, favoured as old-age and wealth-gathering insurance for parents. In both China and India, ultrasound and amniocentesis tests are employed, often against government directives, to determine the sex of a fetus so that it can be aborted if it is a female.

The evidence for the missing women starts with one fact: About 105 males are conceived and born for every 100 females. Normally, girls are hardier and more resistant to disease than boys, and in populations where the sexes are treated equally in matters of nutrition and health care, there are about 105 to 106 females for every 100 males. However, the 2001 Census of India found just 93.2 females for every 100 males, while in China, according to the latest census, nearly 10% of all girls of the 1990s birth cohorts are

"missing," and there were 120 boys under age 5 for every 100 girls. China's 2000 Census recorded a national average disparity in births of 117 boys for every 100 girls—a deepening imbalance from the 1990 Census ratio of 111 newborn boys to 100 newborn girls. Even higher 2000 differentials were registered in Hainan and Guangdong provinces in southeastern China with newborn ratios of between 130 and 140 males to 100 females.

Ratio deviations are most striking for second and subsequent births. In China, South Korea, Taiwan, and Hong Kong, for example, the most recent figures for first-child sex ratios are near normal, but rise to 121 boys per 100 girls for a second Chinese child and to 185 per 100 for a third Korean child. On that evidence, the problem of missing females is getting worse. Conservative calculations suggest there are more than 60 million females missing in China alone, almost 5% of the national population and more than are unaccounted for in any other country.

The problem is seen elsewhere. The UN Population Fund reports that countries such as Bahrain, Oman, Qatar, Saudi Arabia, and

United Arab Emirates have male-to-female ratios ranging between 116:100 and 186:100. In much of South and West Asia and North Africa, there are only some 94 females for every 100 males, a shortfall of about 12% of normal (Western) expectations. A 2000 United Nations report on South Asia suggests the "100 million" world total of missing females is a gross understatement. It declares that abortions of female fetuses along with infanticide and the food favouritism shown boys have meant that 79 million lost females are attributable to discrimination in South Asia, including some 40 million in India alone.

But not all poor countries show the same disparities. In sub-Saharan Africa, where poverty and disease are perhaps more prevalent than on any other continent, there are 102 females for every 100 males, and in Latin America and the Caribbean, there are equal numbers of males and females. Cultural norms and practices, not poverty or underdevelopment, seem to determine the fate and swell the numbers of the world's 100 million missing women.

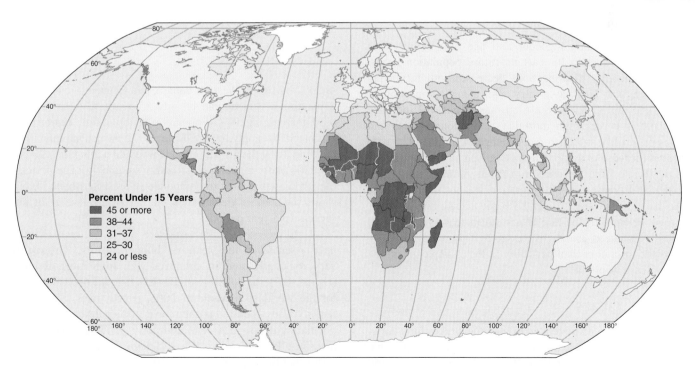

FIGURE 4.15 Percentage of population under 15 years of age. A high proportion of a country's population under 15 increases the dependency ratio of that state and promises future population growth as the youthful cohorts enter childbearing years.

Source: Data from Population Reference Bureau, 2007 World Population Data Sheet.

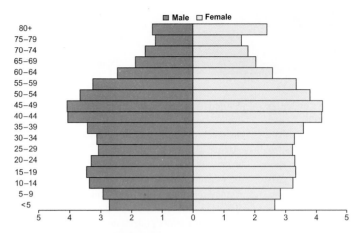

FIGURE 4.16 The progression of the "boomers." The baby boom cohort between 1946 and 1964, shown through this series of population pyramids, has been associated with changing Canadian lifestyles and expenditure patterns. In 1970, Canadian priorities focused on childhood and young adult interests (as evidenced by the growth in post-secondary institutions) and the needs, education, and support of younger age groups. At the turn of the 21st century, boomers formed the largest share of the work-age adult population, and their wants and spending patterns shaped national culture and economy. By 2030, the pyramid suggests their desires and support needs—now for retirement facilities and old-age care—will again be central.

Source: http://www12.statscan.ca/english/census06/analysis/agesex/charts /chart21.htm.

social order and, perhaps, national stability not foreseen or planned when family control programs were put in place, but clearly suggested when made evident by population pyramid distortions.

Natural Increase

Knowledge of a country's gender and age distributions also enables demographers to forecast its future population levels, though the reliability of projections decreases with increasing length of forecast. Thus, a country with a high proportion of young people will experience a high rate of **natural increase** unless there is a very high mortality rate among infants and juveniles or fertility and birth rates change materially. The **rate of natural increase** of a population is derived by subtracting the crude death rate from the crude birth rate. *Natural* means that increases or decreases due to migration are not included. If a country had a birth rate of 22 per 1000 and a death rate of 12 per 1000 for a given year, the rate of natural increase would be 10 per 1000. This rate is usually expressed as a percentage, that is, as a rate per 100 rather than per 1000. In the example given, the annual increase would be 1%.

Doubling Times

The rate of increase can be related to the time it takes for a population to double if the present growth rate remains constant—that is, the **doubling**, or **J-curve**, **time**. Table 4.3 shows that it would take 70 years for a population with a rate of increase of 1% (approximately the rate of growth of Thailand or Argentina at the turn of the century) to double. A 2% rate of increase—recorded

TABLE 4.3
Doubling Time in Years at Different Rates of Increase

Annual percentage increase	Doubling time (years)
0.5	140
1.0	70
2.0	35
3.0	24
4.0	18
5.0	14
10.0	7

TABLE 4.4
Population Growth Yielded by a 2% Rate of Increase

Year	Population
0	1000
5	1104
10	1219
15	1345
20	1485
25	1640
30	1810
35	2000

in 2007 by Libya, Western Sahara, and Ecuador—means that the population would double in only 35 years. Canada recorded a 0.3% increase in 2007. (Population doubling time can be roughly estimated by applying the Rule of 72, which simply involves dividing 72 by the growth rate.) How could adding only 20 people per 1000 cause a population to grow so quickly? The principle is the same as that used to compound interest in a bank. Table 4.4 shows the number yielded by a 2% rate of increase at the end of successive 5-year periods.

Until recently, for the world as a whole, the rates of increase have risen over the span of human history. Growth rates vary regionally, and in countries with high rates of increase (Figure 4.17), the doubling time is less than the 60 years projected for the world as a whole at 2006 growth rates. Should world fertility rates decline (as they have in recent years), theoretical population doubling time would correspondingly increase, as it has since 1990 (Figure 4.18). Although the United Nations estimates that the population of the 50 least developed countries will possibly almost triple between 2000 and 2050, we have learned that doubling time assumptions are inherently misleading and population increases are limited.

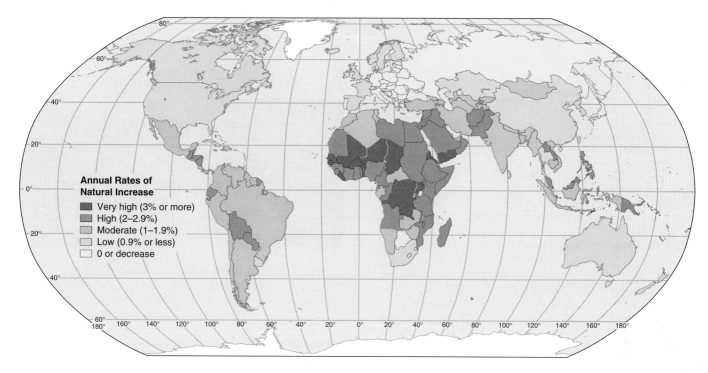

FIGURE 4.17 Annual rates of natural increase. The world's 2007 rate of natural increase (1.2%) would mean a doubling of population in 60 years. Since demographers now anticipate world population—currently well above 6 billion—will stabilize at less than 10 billion (in about a.c.e. 2100), the "doubling" implication and time frame of current rates of increase reflect mathematical, not realistic, projections. Many individual continents and countries, of course, deviate widely from the global average rate of growth and have vastly different doubling times. Africa as a whole has the highest rates of increase, followed by Central America and Western Asia. Anglo-America is prominent among the low-growth areas, and Europe as a whole (including Russia) had a negative natural rate of growth in the early 21st century. Some individual countries show natural rates of increase so small that their doubling times must be measured in millennia. For regions and countries, rates of increase and doubling time projections have more valid implications than do those for the world as a whole.

Source: Data from Population Reference Bureau, 2007.

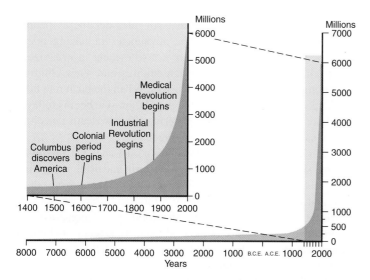

FIGURE 4.18 World population growth 8000 B.C.E. to A.C.E. 2000.
Notice that the bend in the J-curve begins in about the mid-1700s when industrialization started to provide new means to support the population growth made possible by revolutionary changes in agriculture and food supply. Improvements in medical science and nutrition served to reduce death rates near the opening of the 20th century in the industrializing countries.

The Demographic Transition

The theoretical consequence of exponential population growth cannot be realized. Some form of braking mechanism must necessarily operate to control totally unregulated population growth. If voluntary population limitation is not undertaken, involuntary controls of an unpleasant nature may be set in motion.

One attempt to summarize an observed voluntary relationship between population growth and economic development is the **demographic transition** model. It traces the changing levels of human fertility and mortality presumably associated with industrialization and urbanization. Over time, the model assumes, high birth and death rates will gradually be replaced by low rates (Figure 4.19). The *first stage* of that replacement process—and of the demographic transition model—is characterized by high birth and high but fluctuating death rates.

As long as births only slightly exceed deaths, even when the rates of both are high, the population will grow only slowly. This was the case for most of human history until about 1750 A.C.E. Demographers think that it took from approximately 1 A.C.E. to 1650 A.C.E. for the population to increase from 250 million to 500 million, a doubling time of more than a millennium and a half.

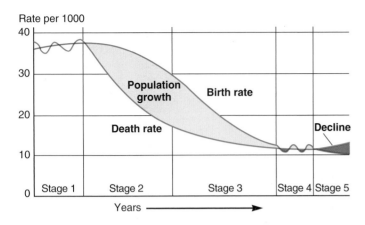

Rate per 1000

FIGURE 4.19 **Stages in the demographic transition.** During the first stage, birth and death rates are both high, and population grows slowly. When the death rate drops and the birth rate remains high, there is a rapid increase in numbers. During the third stage, birth rates decline, and population growth is less rapid. The fourth stage is marked by low birth and death rates and, consequently, by a low rate of natural increase, or even by decrease if death rates should exceed those of births. The negative growth rates of many European countries and the falling birth rates in other regions suggest that a fifth stage, one of population decline, is regionally—and ultimately worldwide—a logical extension of the transition model.

Growth was not steady, of course. There were periods of regional expansion that were usually offset by sometimes catastrophic decline. Wars, famine, and other disasters took heavy tolls. For example, the bubonic plague (the Black Death), which swept across Europe in the 14th century, is estimated to have killed between one-third and one-half of the population of that continent, and epidemic diseases brought by Europeans to the Western Hemisphere are believed to have reduced New World native populations by 95% within a century or two of first contact. The first stage of the demographic transition model is no longer found in any country. By the end of the 20th century, few countries—even in poorer regions of sub-Saharan Africa—had death rates as high as 20 per 1000. However, in several African states birth rates approached or were above 50 per 1000.

The Western Experience

The demographic transition model was developed to explain the population history of Western Europe. That area entered a *second stage* with the industrialization that began about 1750. Its effects—declining death rates accompanied by continuing high birth rates—have been dispersed worldwide even without universal conversion to an industrial economy. Rapidly rising population during the second demographic stage results from dramatic increases in life expectancy. That, in turn, reflects falling death rates due to advances in medical and sanitation practices, improved foodstuff storage and distribution, a rising per capita income, and the urbanization that provides the environment in which sanitary, medical, and food distributional improvements are concentrated (Figure 4.20). Birth rates do not fall as soon as death rates; ingrained cultural patterns change more slowly than technologies. In many agrarian societies, large families are

FIGURE 4.20 **Paris, France, at the start of the 20th century.** A modernizing Europe experienced improved living conditions and declining death rates during that century of progress.

considered advantageous. Children contribute to the family by starting to work at an early age and by supporting their parents in old age.

Many countries in southern Asia and Latin America display the characteristics of this second stage in the population model. Pakistan, with a birth rate of 33 and a death rate of 9, and Guatemala, with respective rates of 34 and 6 (2006 estimates), are typical. The annual rates of increase of such countries are near or above 30 per 1000, and their populations will double in about 20 to 25 years. Such rates, of course, do not mean that the full impact of the Industrial Revolution has been worldwide; they do mean that the underdeveloped societies have been beneficiaries of the life preservation techniques associated with it.

The *third stage* follows when birth rates decline as people begin to control family size. The advantages of having many children in an agrarian society are not so evident in urbanized, industrialized cultures. In fact, such cultures may view children as economic liabilities rather than assets. When the birth rate falls and the death rate remains low, the population size begins to level off. Many countries are now registering the low death rates and transitional birth rates of the third stage.

The classic demographic transition model ends with a *fourth* and final stage characterized by very low birth and death rates. This stage yields at best only very slight percentage increases in population and doubling times stretch to a thousand years or more. A significant and irreversible aging of the world's population is a direct and profound consequence of the worldwide transition from high to low levels of fertility and mortality associated with this fourth stage of the model. In a few countries, death rates have begun to equal or exceed birth rates and populations are actually declining.

This extension of the fourth stage into a *fifth* of population decrease has so far been largely confined to the rich, industrialized world—notably Europe and Japan—but increasingly promises to affect much of the rest of the world as well. Even now, the dramatic decline in fertility recorded in almost all countries since the 1980s suggests that by 2010 at the latest, a majority of the world's population will reside in areas where the only significant population growth will result from demographic momentum (see p. 86), not from second-stage expansion.

The original transition model was devised to describe the experience of northwest European countries as they went from rural-agrarian societies to urban-industrial ones. It may not fully reflect the prospects of all developing countries. In Europe, church and municipal records, some dating from the 16th century, show that people tended to marry late or not at all. In England before the Industrial Revolution, as many as half of all women in the 15–50 age cohort were unmarried. Infant mortality was high, life expectancy low. With the coming of industrialization in the 18th and 19th centuries, immediate factory wages instead of long apprenticeship programs permitted earlier marriage and more children. Since improvements in sanitation and health came only slowly, death rates remained high. Around 1800, 25% of Swedish infants died before their first birthday. Population growth rates remained below 1% per year in France throughout the 19th century.

Beginning about 1860, first death rates and then birth rates began their significant, though gradual, decline. This "mortality revolution" came first, as an *epidemiologic transition* echoed the demographic transition with which it is associated. Many formerly fatal epidemic diseases became endemic, that is, essentially continual within a population, and mortality patterns showed a shift from communicable to noncommunicable diseases. As people developed partial immunities, mortalities associated with them declined. Improvements in animal husbandry, crop rotation, and other agricultural practices, and new foodstuffs (the potato was an early example) from overseas colonies raised the level of health of the European population in general.

At the same time, sewage systems and sanitary water supplies became common in larger cities, and general levels of hygiene improved everywhere (Figure 4.21). Deaths due to infectious, parasitic, and respiratory diseases, and to malnutrition declined, while those related to chronic illnesses associated with a maturing and aging population increased. Western Europe passed from a first stage "Age of Pestilence and Famine" to a presumed ultimate "Age of Degenerative and Human-Origin Diseases." However, recent increases in drug- and antibiotic-resistant diseases, pesticide resistance of disease-carrying insects, and such new scourges of both the less developed and more developed countries as AIDS (acquired immune deficiency syndrome) cast doubt on the finality of that "ultimate" stage (see "Our Delicate State of Health"). Nevertheless, even the resurgence of old and emergence of new scourges such as malaria, tuberculosis, and AIDS (which together cause an estimated 6 million deaths annually) are unlikely to have decisive demographic consequences on the global scale.

In Europe, the striking reduction in death rates was echoed by similar declines in birth rates as societies began to alter their traditional concepts of ideal family size. In cities, child labour laws and mandatory schooling meant that children no longer were important contributors to family economies. As "poor-relief" legislation and other forms of public welfare substituted for family support structures, the insurance value of children declined. Family consumption patterns altered as the Industrial Revolution made more widely available goods that served consumption desires, not just basic living needs. Children hindered rather than aided the achievement of the age's promise of social mobility and lifestyle

FIGURE 4.21 Pure piped water replacing individual or neighbourhood wells, and sewers and waste treatment plants instead of privies, became increasingly common in urban Europe and North America during the 19th century. Their modern successors, such as the Las Vegas, Nevada treatment plant shown here, helped complete the *epidemiologic transition* in developed countries.

improvement. Perhaps most important, and by some measures preceding and independent of the implications of the Industrial Revolution, were changes in the status of women and in their spreading conviction that control over childbearing was within their power and to their benefit.

A Divided World Converging

The demographic transition model described the presumed inevitable course of population events from the high birth and death rates of premodern (underdeveloped) societies to the low and stable rates of advanced (developed) countries. The model failed to anticipate, however, that the population history of Europe was apparently not relevant to all developing countries of the middle and late 20th century. Many developing societies remained in the second stage of the model, unable to realize the economic gains and social changes necessary to progress to the third stage of falling birth rates.

The introduction of Western technologies of medicine and public health, including antibiotics, insecticides, sanitation, immunization, infant and child health care, and eradication of smallpox, quickly and dramatically increased life expectancies in developing countries. Such imported technologies and treatments accomplished in a few years what it took Europe 50 to 100 years to experience. Sri Lanka, for example, sprayed extensively with DDT to combat malaria; life expectancy jumped from 44 years in 1946 to 60 only 8 years later. With similar public health programs, India also experienced a steady reduction in its death rate after 1947. Simultaneously, with international sponsorship, food aid cut the death toll of developing states during drought and other disasters. The dramatic decline in mortality that had emerged only gradually throughout the European world occurred with startling speed in developing countries after 1950.

Death rates have plummeted, and the benefits of modern medicines, antibiotics, and sanitary practices have enhanced both the quality and expectancy of life in the developed and much of the developing world. Far from being won, however, the struggle against infectious and parasitic diseases is growing in intensity and is, perhaps, unwinnable. More than a half century after the discovery of antibiotics, the diseases they were to eradicate are on the rise, and both old and new disease-causing microorganisms are emerging and spreading all over the world. Infectious and parasitic diseases kill between 17 and 20 million people each year; they officially account for one-quarter to one-third of global mortality and, because of poor diagnosis, certainly are responsible for far more. And their global incidence is rising.

The five leading infectious killers are acute respiratory infections such as pneumonia, diarrheal diseases, tuberculosis, malaria, and measles. In addition, AIDS was killing 3 million or more persons yearly early in this century, far more than measles or malaria. The incidence of infection, of course, is much greater than the occurrence of deaths. Nearly 30% of the world's people, for example, are infected with the bacterium that causes tuberculosis, but only 2 to 3 million are killed by the disease each year. More than 500 million people are infected with such tropical diseases as malaria, sleeping sickness, schistosomiasis, and river blindness, with perhaps 3 million annual deaths. Newer pathogens are constantly appearing, such as those causing Lassa fever, Rift Valley fever, Ebola fever, Hantavirus pulmonary syndrome, West Nile encephalitis, hepatitis C, and severe acute respiratory syndrome (SARS), incapacitating and endangering far more than they kill. In fact, at least 30 previously unknown infectious diseases have appeared since the mid-1970s.

The spread and virulence of infectious diseases are linked to the dramatic changes so rapidly occurring in the earth's physical and social environments. Climate warming permits temperature-restricted pathogens to invade new areas and claim new victims. Deforestation, water contamination, wetland drainage, and other human-induced alterations to the physical environment disturb ecosystems and simultaneously disrupt the natural system of controls that keep infectious diseases in check. Rapid population growth and explosive urbanization, increasing global tourism, population-dislocating wars and migrations, and expanding world trade all increase interpersonal disease-transmitting contacts and the mobility and range of disease-causing microbes, including those brought from previously isolated areas by newly opened road systems and air routes. Add in poorly planned or executed public health programs, inadequate investment in sanitary infrastructures, and inefficient distribution of medical personnel and facilities, and the causative role of humans in many of the current disease epidemics is clearly visible.

In response, a worldwide Program for Monitoring Emerging Diseases (ProMED) was established in 1993 and developed a global online infectious disease network linking health workers and scientists in more than 100 countries to battle what has been called a growing "epidemic of epidemics." The most effective weapons in that battle are already known. They include improved health education; disease prevention and surveillance; research on disease vectors and incidence areas (including GIS and other mapping of habitats conducive to specific diseases); careful monitoring of drug therapy; mosquito control programs; provision of clean water supplies; and distribution of such simple and cheap remedies and preventatives as childhood immunizations, oral rehydration therapy, and vitamin A supplementation. All, however, require expanded investment and attention to those spreading infectious diseases—many with newly developed antibiotic-resistant strains—so recently thought to be no longer of concern.

Corresponding reductions in birth rates did not immediately follow, and world population totals soared: from 2.5 billion in 1950 to 3 billion by 1960 and 5 billion by the middle 1980s. Alarms about the "population explosion" and its predicted devastating impact on global food and mineral resources were frequent and strident. In demographic terms, the world was viewed by many as permanently divided between developed regions that had made the demographic transition to stable population numbers and the underdeveloped, endlessly expanding ones that had not.

Birth rate levels, of course, unlike life expectancy improvements, depend less on supplied technology and assistance than they do on social acceptance of the idea of fewer children and smaller families (Figure 4.22). That acceptance began to grow broadly but unevenly worldwide even as regional and world population growth seemed uncontrollable. In 1984, only 18% of world population lived in countries with fertility rates at or below replacement levels (that is, countries that had achieved the demographic transition). By 2000, however, 44% lived in such countries, and early in the 21st century it is increasingly difficult to distinguish between developed and developing societies on the basis of their fertility rates. Those rates in many separate Indian states (Kerala and Tamil Nadu, for example) and in such countries as Sri Lanka, Thailand, South Korea, and China are below those of Canada, the United States, and some European countries. Significant decreases to near the replacement level have also occurred in the space of a single generation in many other Asian and Latin American states with high recent rates of economic growth. Increasingly, it appears that low fertility is becoming a feature of both developed and developing states.

Despite this general substantial convergence in fertility, there still remains a significant minority share of the developing world with birth rates averaging 1.5 to 2 times or more above the replacement level. Indeed, early in the 21st century, almost 1.4 billion persons live in countries or regions where total fertility is still 3.5 or greater (a level not considered high, of course, in the early 1950s when only a quarter of the world's population had a TFR below that mark). For the most part, these current high fertility countries and areas are in sub-Saharan Africa and the northern parts of the Indian subcontinent (see Figure 4.9). Although accounting for less than a quarter of world population, high TFR regions collectively, United Nations demographers predict, will provide the majority of world population growth to at least 2050.

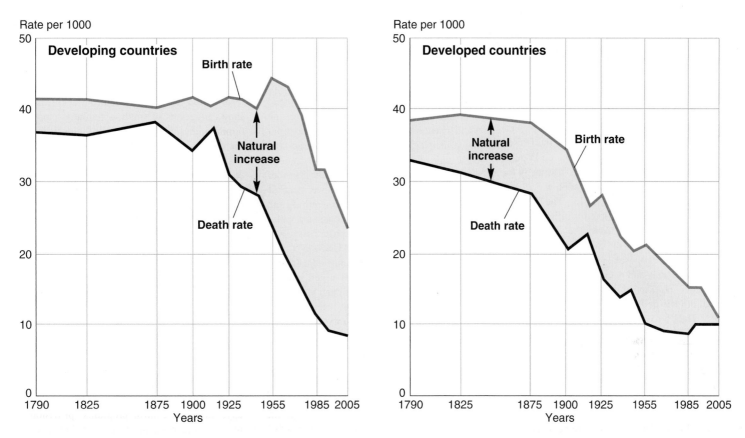

FIGURE 4.22 World birth and death rates to 2005. The "population explosion" after World War II (1939–1945) reflected the effects of drastically reduced death rates in developing countries without simultaneous and compensating reductions in births. By the end of the 20th century, however, three interrelated trends had appeared in many developing world countries: (1) fertility had overall dropped further and faster than had been earlier predicted; (2) contraceptive acceptance and use had increased markedly; and (3) age at marriage was rising. In consequence, the demographic transition had been compressed from a century to a generation in some developing states. In others, fertility decline began to slacken in the mid-1970s, but continued to reflect the average number of children—four or more—still desired in many societies.

Source: Revised and redrawn from Elaine M. Murphy, World Population: Toward the Next Century, *revised ed. (Washington, D.C.: Population Reference Bureau, 1989).*

The established patterns of both high and low fertility regions tend to be self-reinforcing. Low growth permits the expansion of personal income and the accumulation of capital that enhances the quality and security of life and makes large families less attractive or essential. In contrast, in high birth rate regions, population growth consumes in social services and assistance the investment capital that might promote economic expansion. Increasing populations place ever greater demands on limited soil, forest, water, grassland, and cropland resources. As the environmental base deteriorates, productivity declines and population-supporting capacities are so diminished as to make difficult or impossible the economic progress on which the demographic transition depends, an apparent equation of increasing international concern (see "The Cairo Plan").

The Demographic Equation

Births and deaths among a region's population—natural increases or decreases—tell only part of the story of population change. Migration involves the long-distance movement of people from one residential location to another. When that relocation occurs across political boundaries, it affects the population structure of both the origin and destination jurisdictions. The **demographic equation** summarizes the contribution made to regional population change over time by the combination of *natural change* (difference between births and deaths) and *net migration* (the difference between in-migration and out-migration).[1] On a global scale, of course, all population change is accounted for by natural change. The impact of migration on the demographic equation increases as the population size of the areal unit studied decreases.

Migration

Migration—the permanent or planned long-term relocation of residential place and activity space—has been one of the enduring themes of human history and an important device for relieving the pressures of rapid population growth in at least some European countries (Figure 4.23). It has contributed to the evolution of separate cultures, to the diffusion of those cultures and their components by interchange and communication, and to the frequently complex mix of peoples and cultures found in different areas of

---

[1] See the Glossary definition for the calculation of the equation.

Geography and Public Policy

The Cairo Plan

After a sometimes rancorous nine-day meeting in Cairo in September, 1994, the United Nations International Conference on Population and Development endorsed a strategy for stabilizing the world's population at 7.27 billion by no later than 2015. The 20-year program of action accepted by 179 signatory countries sought to avoid the environmental consequences of excessive population growth. Its proposals were therefore linked to discussions and decisions of the UN Conference on Environment and Development held in Rio de Janeiro in June 1992.

The Cairo plan abandoned several decades of top-down governmental programs that promoted "population control" (a phrase avoided by the conference) based on targets and quotas and, instead, embraced for the first time policies giving women greater control over their lives, greater economic equality and opportunity, and a greater voice in reproduction decisions. It recognized that limiting population growth depends on programs that lead women to want fewer children and make them partners in economic development. In that recognition, the Conference accepted the documented link between increased educational access and economic opportunity for women and falling birth rates and smaller families. Earlier population conferences—1974 in Bucharest and 1984 in Mexico City—did not fully address these issues of equality, opportunity, education, and political rights; their adopted goals failed to achieve hoped-for changes in births in large part because women in many traditional societies had no power to enforce contraception and feared their other alternative, sterilization.

The earlier conferences carefully avoided or specifically excluded abortion as an acceptable family planning method. It was the more open discussion of abortion in Cairo that elicited much of the spirited debate that registered religious objections by the Vatican and many Muslim and Latin American states to the inclusion of legal abortion as part of health care, and to language suggesting approval of sexual relations outside of marriage. Although the final text of the conference declaration did not promote any universal right to abortion and excluded it as a means of family planning, some delegations still registered reservations to its wording on both sex and abortion. At conference close, however, the Vatican endorsed the declaration's underlying principles, including the family as "the basic unit of society," the need to stimulate economic growth, and to promote "gender equality, equity, and the empowerment of women." Clearly, the debate concerning the use of abortion as a means to control population will be an ongoing and spirited one.

A special United Nations "Cairo + 5" session in 1999 recommended some adjustments in the earlier agreements. It urged emphasis on measures ensuring safe and accessible abortion in countries where it is legal, called for school children at all levels to be instructed in sexual and reproductive health issues, and told governments to provide special family planning and health services for sexually active adolescents, with particular stress on reducing their vulnerability to AIDS.

In 2004, the UN reported on conclusions reached after a series of regional conferences that assessed progress toward reaching Cairo and Cairo + 5 goals. The consensus was that much remained to be done to broaden programs for the poorest population groups, to invest in rural development and urban planning, to strengthen laws ending discrimination against women, and to encourage donor countries to fully meet their agreed-on contributions to the program (in 2002, those contributions were only half the promised total). Nevertheless, positive Cairo plan results were also seen in declining fertility rates in many of the world's most populous developing countries. Some demographers and many women's health organizations pointedly claim that those declines have little to do with government planning policies. Rather, they assert, current lower and falling fertility rates are the expected result of women assuming greater control over their economic and reproductive lives. The director of the UN population division noted: "A woman in a village making a decision to have one or two or at most three children is a small decision in itself. But . . . compounded by millions and millions . . . of women in India and Brazil and Egypt, it has global consequences."

That women are making those decisions, population specialists have observed, reflects important cultural factors emerging since Cairo. Satellite television brings contraceptive information to even remote villages and shows programs of small, apparently happy families that viewers think of emulating. Increasing urbanization reduces some traditional family controls on women and makes contraceptives easier to find, and declining infant mortality makes mothers more confident their babies will survive. Perhaps most important, population experts assert, is the dramatic increase in most developing states in female school attendance and corresponding reductions in the illiteracy rates of girls and young women who will themselves soon be making fertility decisions. In order to reduce future population growth, a key element of any approach is to ensure women are empowered to make choices about their education, type of employment, and have access to property and finances.

Questions to Consider

1. Do you think it is appropriate or useful for international bodies to promote policies affecting such purely personal or national concerns as reproduction and family planning? Why or why not?

2. Do you think that current international concerns over population growth, development, and the environment are sufficiently valid and pressing to risk the loss of long-enduring cultural norms and religious practices in many of the world's traditional societies? Why or why not?

3. The Cairo plan called for sizeable monetary pledges from developed countries to support enhanced population planning in the developing world. For the most part, those pledges have not been honoured. Do you think the financial obligations assigned to donor countries are justified in light of the many other international needs and domestic concerns faced by their governments? Why or why not?

4. Many environmentalists see the world as a finite system unable to support ever-increasing populations; to exceed its limits would cause frightful environmental damage and global misery. Many economists counter that free markets will keep supplies of needed commodities in line with growing demand and that science will, as necessary, supply technological fixes in the

Geography and Public Policy continued

form of substitutes or expansion of production. In light of such diametrically opposed views of population growth consequences, is it appropriate or wise to base international programs solely on one of them? Why or why not?

5. Rather than suggest that population is the main source of environmental problems, others would suggest it is the high consumption of resources, particularly by the developed world, is the major culprit. At present, about 20% of the world's population consumes 80% of its resources. Developed countries clearly have a large ecological footprint (Chapter 12). Which do you think is the more important problem to solve?

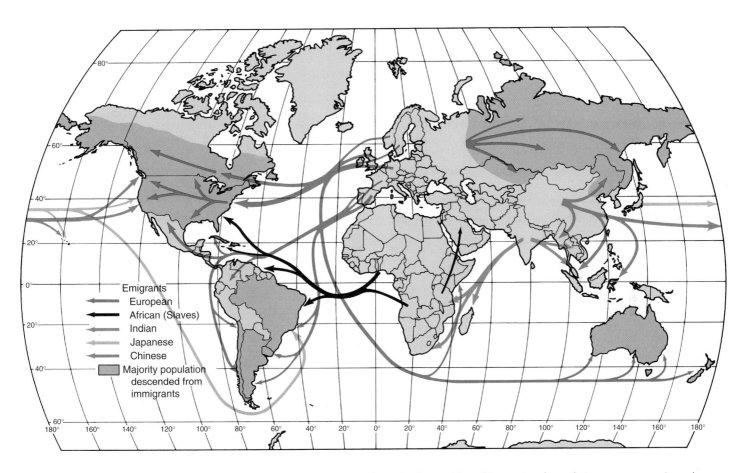

FIGURE 4.23 Principal migrations of recent centuries. The arrows suggest the major free and forced international population movements since about 1700. The shaded areas on the map are regions whose present population is more than 50% descended from the immigrants of recent centuries.

Source: Shaded zones after Daniel Noin, Géographie de la Population *(Paris: Masson, 1979), p. 85.*

the world. Where cross-border movements are massive enough, migration may have a pronounced impact on the demographic equation and result in significant changes in the population structures of both the origin and destination regions. Past European and African migrations, for example, not only altered but substantially created the population structures of new, sparsely inhabited lands of colonization in the Western Hemisphere and Australasia. Despite recent massive movements of economic and political refugees across Asian, African, and Latin American boundaries, emigration today provides no comparable relief for developing countries. Total population numbers are too great to be much affected by migrations of even millions of people. Only a few countries—Afghanistan, Cuba, El Salvador, and Haiti, for example—have as many as 10% of the population emigrated in recent decades.

Massive movements of people within countries, across national borders, and between continents have emerged as a pressing concern of recent decades. They affect national economic structures, determine population density and distribution patterns, alter traditional ethnic, linguistic, and religious mixtures,

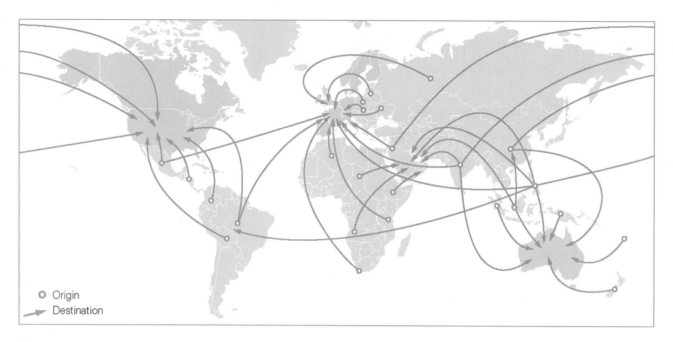

○ Origin
→ Destination

FIGURE 4.24 The Major Pattern of Worker Migration. According to Manpower Inc., the major patterns of worker movement involve the migration to the developed world nations. However, other established and emerging economies, including the Arabian, Gulf States and greater China, are also attracting growing numbers of both skilled and unskilled workers in search of employment.

Source: The Borderless Workforce White Paper, Manpower Inc., Copyright 2008. *The Major Pattern of Worker Migration. Located in* The Borderless Workforce: 2008, *page 5, Figure 2. Published by Manpower Inc.*

and inflame national debates and international tensions. Because migration patterns and conflicts touch so many aspects of social and economic relations, and have become so important a part of current human geographic realities, their specific impact is a significant aspect of several of our topical concerns

Principal Migration Patterns

Migration flows can be discussed at different scales, from massive intercontinental torrents to individual decisions to move to a new house or apartment within the same metropolitan area. At each level, although the underlying controls on spatial behaviour remain constant, the immediate motivating factors influencing the spatial interaction are different, with differing impacts on population patterns and cultural landscapes.

At the broadest scale, *intercontinental* movements range from the earliest peopling of the habitable world to the most recent flight of Asian or African refugees to countries of Europe or the Western Hemisphere. The population structure of the United States, Canada, Australia and New Zealand, Argentina, Brazil, and other South American countries is a reflection and result of massive intercontinental flows of immigrants that began as a trickle during the 16th and 17th centuries and reached a flood during the 19th and early 20th (Figure 4.23). Later in the 20th century, World War II (1939–1945) and its immediate aftermath involved more than 25 million permanent population relocations, all of them international but not all intercontinental.

Migration is one of the defining global issues of the early 21st century for at least three reasons. First and most fundamentally, people are the key to human development—food, raw materials, manufactured goods, and services are the result of their ideas and

labour. Second, as previously mentioned, countries with declining and aging populations are forced to accept migrants or face severe worker shortages. Third, with many countries facing economic and political instability, many people are enticed to migrate (a push factor discussed below). In a globalized world, countries compete for the best workers (Figure 4.24). A 2008 study completed by Manpower Inc. maintained that globally 1 in 35 people, or about 190 million people, was a migrant, and this number is growing by 3% per year. The global workforce is truly multinational. The competition for workers, particularly highly skilled white and blue-collared workers, is intense. Canada competes with India and Bangladesh for call centres. Our auto industry competes with Korea, China, Mexico, and the United States for orders. Brazil, the United States, and the European Union are Canada's main competitors in the air industry. With information more readily available through the Internet, workers can monitor worldwide job prospects and get information about how to obtain work permits at their convenience. If people migrate, they can maintain contact with family and friends through the internet and mobile phones. This is referred to as transnational migration space.

Migration in Canada

Immigration remains an important demographic variable in Canada, and is expected to be the primary contributor to Canada's population growth by mid-century. Historically, Canadian immigration policy was designed to create and maintain a European-oriented society (Figure 4.25). This was first achieved through promoting agriculture in western Canada. After World War II, the focus of policy shifted to attract immigrants to support employment in the manufacturing and construction sectors.

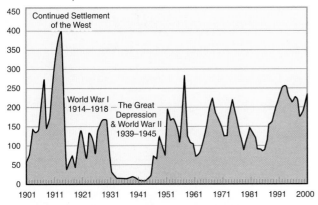

FIGURE 4.25 **Major events and immigration levels in Canada.**

Source: Adapted from Statistics Canada, "Ethnocultural Portrait of Canada: Highlight Tables, 2001 Census," *Catalogue 97F0024XIE2001006, Released January 2003.*

Preference was given to immigrants from Europe, selected Commonwealth countries, and the United States. As a result, before 1961, some 894,000 people immigrated to Canada, most of whom came from the United Kingdom (24.3%), Italy (16.5%), Germany (10.8%), and the Netherlands (8.9%). This favoured-nation policy orientation changed dramatically in the 1960s when legislation was introduced that encouraged immigration from all countries through two innovations. The first allowed Canadians to sponsor family members who wished to come to Canada. The second, which replaced the favoured-nation approach, applied a point system to assess an applicant's suitability for entry into Canada. In this way, immigrants who addressed Canada's skills shortage could be allowed into the country. Of the 1,831,000 people who immigrated to Canada between 1991 and 2001, 10.8% came from the People's Republic of China, 8.5% from India, 6.7% from the Philippines, and 6.5% from Hong Kong. Clearly, the level of immigration has increased. Canada as a multicultural society is discussed in Chapter 5. Between 2001 and 2006, 1.1 million immigrants came to Canada. During that same period, the nation's population grew by 1.6 million. We are already very dependent on immigration to increase the nation's population.

The rate of population of growth in Alberta is the fastest in the country, reflecting in large part, interprovincial migration. Alberta's population grew at a rate of 29.5 per 1,000 (3 times the national average) in 2005–2006. Drawn by its booming economy, 57,100 people left other provinces or territories for Alberta, This represented over 58% of the province's total growth. Only British Columbia (+3,800) and Nunavut (+100) also showed net gains for this period—the other 10 jurisdictions showed net out migration.

Types of Migration

Migrations may be forced or voluntary or, in many instances, reluctant relocations imposed on the migrants by circumstances.

In *forced migrations,* the relocation decision is made solely by people other than the migrants themselves. Some 10 to 12 million Africans were forcibly transferred as slaves to the Western Hemisphere from the late 16th to early 19th centuries. Half or more were destined for the Caribbean, and most of the remainder for Central and South America, though nearly a million arrived in the United States. Australia owed its earliest European settlement to convicts transported after the 1780s to the British penal colony established in southeastern Australia (New South Wales). More recent involuntary migrants include millions of Soviet citizens forcibly relocated from countryside to cities, and from the western areas to labour camps in Siberia and the Russian Far East beginning in the late 1920s. During the 1980s and 1990s, many refugee destination countries in Africa, Europe, and Asia expelled immigrants or encouraged or forced the repatriation of foreign nationals within their borders.

Less than fully voluntary migration—*reluctant relocation*—of some 8 million Indonesians has taken place under an aggressive governmental campaign begun in 1969 to move people from densely settled Java (roughly 775 per square kilometre or 2000 people per square mile) to other islands and territories of the country in what has been called the "biggest colonization program in history." Starting in 1948, the Innu Nation of Labrador was forced to abandon its traditional roamed eastern Quebec and Labrador and settle in permanent communities. The horrendous impacts of this decision—suicide, substance abuse, children at risk—continue to make headlines.

International refugees from war and political turmoil or repression numbered nearly 12 million in 2004, according to the World Refugee Survey. Recently, the flight of people is primarily from developing countries to other developing regions, and many countries with the largest refugee populations are among the world's poorest. Worldwide, the UN estimated, 25 million persons were "internally displaced," effectively internal refugees within their own countries. In a search for security or sustenance, they have left their home areas but not crossed an international boundary.

The great majority of migratory movements, however, are *voluntary* (volitional), representing individual response to the factors influencing all spatial interaction decisions. At root, migrations take place because the migrants believe that their opportunities and life circumstances will be better at their destination than they are at their present location.

Factors influencing Voluntary Migration

Poverty is the great motivator. Some 30% of the world's population—nearly 2 billion persons—have less than $1.00 per day income. Many additionally are victims of drought, floods, and other natural catastrophes or of wars and terrorism. Poverty in developing countries is greatest in the countryside; rural areas are home to around 750 million of the world's poorest people. Of these, some 20 to 30 million move each year to towns and cities, many as "environmental refugees" abandoning land so eroded or exhausted it can no longer support them. In the cities, they join the 40% or more of the labour force that is unemployed or underemployed in their home country and seek legal or illegal entry into more promising economies of the developed world. Among the aging, affluent populations of highly developed countries, retirement amenities figure importantly in perceptions of residential attractiveness of areas. Educational opportunities, changes in life cycle, and environmental attractions or repulsions are but a few other possible migration motivations.

Migration theorists attribute international economic migrations to a series of often overlapping mechanisms. Differentials in wages and job opportunities between home and destination countries are major driving forces in such individual migration decisions. Those differentials are in part rooted in a built-in demand for workers at the bottom of the labour hierarchy in more prosperous developed countries whose own workers disdain low-income, menial jobs. Migrants are available to fill those jobs, some argue, because advanced economies make industrial investment in developing or colonial economies to take advantage of lower labour costs there. New factories inevitably disturb existing peasant economies, employ primarily short-term female workers, and leave a residue of unemployed males available and prone to migrate in search of opportunity. If successful, international economic migrants, male or female, help diversify sources of family income through their remittances from abroad, a form of household security that in itself helps motivate some international economic migration.

Negative home conditions that impel the decision to migrate are called **push factors**. They might include loss of job, lack of professional opportunity, overcrowding or slum clearance, or a variety of other influences including poverty, war, and famine. The presumed positive attractions of the migration destination are known as **pull factors**. They include all the attractive attributes perceived to exist at the new location—safety and food, perhaps, or job opportunities, better climate, lower taxes, more room, and so forth. Very often migration is a result of both perceived push and pull factors. It is *perception* of the areal pattern of opportunities and want satisfaction that is important here, whether or not perceptions are supported by objective reality. In China, for example, a "floating" population of more than 100 million surplus workers has flooded into cities from the countryside, seeking urban employment that exists primarily in their anticipation.

The concept of *place utility* helps us to understand the decision-making process that potential voluntary migrants undergo. **Place utility** is the measure of an individual's satisfaction with a given residential location. The decision to migrate is a reflection of the appraisal—the perception—by the prospective migrant of the current homesite as opposed to other sites of which something is known or hoped for. In the evaluation of comparative place utility, the decision maker considers not only perceived value of the present location, but also expected place utility of potential destinations.

One goal of the potential migrant is to avoid physically dangerous or economically unprofitable outcomes in the final migration decision. Place utility evaluation, therefore, requires assessments not only of hoped-for pull factors of new sites but also of the potentially negative economic and social reception the migrant might experience at those sites. An example of that observation can be seen in the case of the large numbers of young Mexicans and Central Americans who have migrated both legally and illegally to the United States. Faced with poverty and overpopulation at home, they regard the place utility in Mexico as minimal. With a willingness to work, they learn from friends and relatives of job opportunities north of the border and, hoping for success or even wealth, quickly place high utility on relocation to the United States. Many know that dangerous risks are involved in

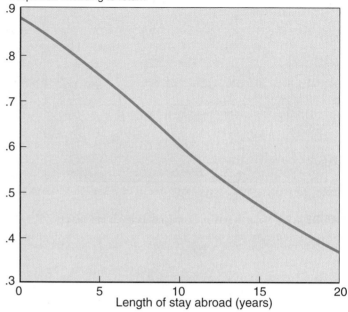

FIGURE 4.26 Intended return migration of Yugoslavs from Germany. As the length of stay in Germany increased, the proportion of Yugoslavs intending to return decreased, but even after 10 years abroad, more than half intended to leave.

Source: Brigitte Waldorf, "Determinants of International Return Migration Intentions," The Professional Geographer 47, no. 2, Fig. 2, p. 132. Association of American Geographers, 1995.

entering the country illegally, but even legal immigrants face legal restrictions or rejections that are advocated or designed to reduce the pull attractions of the United States.

Another migrant goal is to reduce risk and uncertainty. These objectives may be achieved either through a series of transitional relocation stages or when the migrant follows the example of known predecessors. **Step migration** involves the place transition from, for example, rural to central city residence through a series of less extreme locational changes—from farm to small town to suburb and, finally, to the major central city itself. **Chain migration** assures that the mover is part of an established migrant flow from a common origin to a prepared destination. An advance group of migrants, having established itself in a new home area, is followed by second and subsequent migrations originating in the same home district and frequently united by kinship or friendship ties. Public and private services for legal migrants and informal service networks for undocumented or illegal migrants become established and contribute to the continuation or expansion of the chain migration flow. Ethnic and foreign-born enclaves in major cities and rural areas in a number of countries are the immediate result, as we shall see more fully in Chapter 6.

Sometimes the chain migration is specific to occupational groups. For example, nearly all newspaper vendors in New Delhi, in the north of India, come from one small district in Tamil Nadu, in the south of India. Most construction workers in New Delhi come either from Orissa, in the east of India, or Rajasthan, in the northwest. The diamond trade of Mumbai, India, is dominated by a network of about 250 related families who come from a small town several hundred miles to the north.

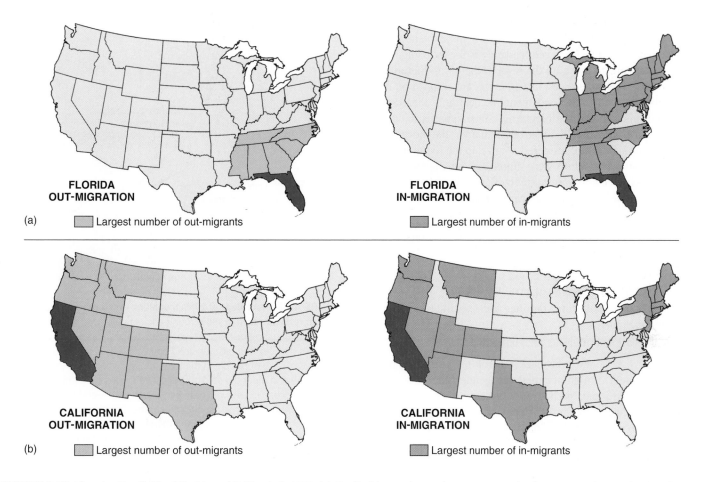

FIGURE 4.27 The migration fields of Florida and California in 1980. (*a*) For Florida, nearby southern states received most out-migrants, but in-migrants, especially retirees, originated from much of the eastern United States. (*b*) For California, the out-migration areas were the western states; the in-migration origins included both western and heavily populated northeastern states.

Source: Kavita Pandit, "Differentiating Between Subsystems and Typologies in the Analysis of Migration Regions: A U.S. Example," The Professional Geographer 46, no. 3, Figs 5 and 6, pp. 342–343. Association of American Geographers, 1994.

Certainly, not all immigrants stay permanently at their first destination. Estimates for Canada indicate that perhaps 40 of each 100 immigrants eventually leave, and about 25% of newcomers to Australia also depart permanently. A corollary of all out-migration flows is, therefore, **counter** (or **return**) **migration**, the likelihood that as many as 25% of all migrants will return to their place of origin (Figure 4.26).

Once established, origin and destination pairs of places tend to persist. Areas that dominate a locale's in- and out-migration patterns make up the *migration fields* of the place in question. As we would expect, areas near the point of origin comprise the largest part of the migration field (Figure 4.27), though larger cities more distantly located may also be prominent as the ultimate destination of hierarchical step migration. Some migration fields reveal a distinctly *channelized* pattern of flow. The channels link areas that are in some way tied to one another by past migrations, by economic trade considerations, or some other affinity. The flow along them is greater than otherwise would be the case but does not necessarily involve individuals with personal or family ties. The former streams of African Americans and whites to northern U.S. cities, of Scandinavians to Minnesota and Wisconsin, and

of U.S. retirees to Florida and Arizona or their European counterparts to Spain, Portugal, or the Mediterranean coast are all examples of **channelized migration**.

Voluntary migration is responsive to other controls that influence all forms of spatial interaction discussed in Chapter 3. Push–pull factors may be equated with *complementarity*; costs (emotional and financial) of residence relocation are expressions of *transferability*. Other things being equal, large cities exert a stronger migrant pull than do small towns, a reflection of the impact of the *gravity model*. The *distance decay* effect has often been noted in migration studies. Movers seek to minimize the *friction of distance*. In selecting between two potential destinations of equal merit, a migrant tends to choose the nearer as involving less effort and expense. And since information about distant areas is less complete and satisfying than awareness of nearer localities, short moves are favoured over long ones. Research indicates that determined migrants with specific destinations in mind are unlikely to be deterred by distance considerations. However, groups for whom push factors are more determining than specific destination pulls are likely to limit their migration distance in response to encountered apparent opportunities.

For them, *intervening opportunity* affects locational decisions. The concept of *hierarchical migration* also helps explain some movement decisions. The observed tendency is for individuals in domestic relocations to move up the level in the urban hierarchy, from small places to larger ones. Often, levels are skipped on the way up; only in periods of general economic decline is there considerable movement down the hierarchy. Since suburbs of large cities are considered part of the metropolitan area, the movement from a town to a suburb is considered a move up the hierarchy.

Observations such as these were summarized in the 1870s and 1880s as a series of "laws of migration" by E. G. Ravenstein (1834–1913). Among those that remain relevant are the following:

1. Most migrants go only a short distance.
2. Longer-distance migration favours big city destinations.
3. Most migration proceeds step-by-step.
4. Most migration is rural to urban.
5. Each migration flow produces a counterflow.
6. Most migrants are adults; families are less likely to make international moves.
7. Most international migrants are young males.

The latter two "laws" introduce the role of personal attributes (and attitudes) of migrants: their age, gender, education, and economic status. Migrants do not represent a cross section of the populace from which they come. Selectivity of movers is evident, and the selection shows some regional differences. In most societies, young adults are the most mobile (Figure 4.28). In Canada and the United States, mobility peaks among those in their 20s, especially the later 20s, and tends to decline thereafter. Among West African cross-border migrants, a World Bank study reveals, the age group 15–39 predominated.

Ravenstein's conclusion that young adult males are dominant in economically pushed international movement is less valid today than when first proposed. In reality, women and girls now comprise 40% to 60% of all international migrants worldwide (see "Gender and Migration"). It is true that legal and illegal migrants to the United States from Mexico and Central America are primarily young men, as were first generation "guest workers" in European cities. But population projections for West European countries suggest that women will shortly make up the largest part of their foreign-born population, and in one-third of the countries of sub-Saharan Africa, including Burkina Faso, Swaziland, and Togo, the female share of foreign-born populations was as large as the male. Further, among rural to urban migrants in Latin America since the 1960s, women have been in the majority.

Female migrants are motivated primarily by economic pushes and pulls. Surveys of women migrants in Southeast Asia and Latin America indicate that 50% to 70% moved in search of employment and commonly first moved while in their teens. The proportion of young, single women is particularly high in rural-to-urban migration flows, reflecting their limited opportunities in increasingly overcrowded agricultural areas. To the push and pull factors normally associated with migration decisions are some-times added family pressures that encourage young women with few employment opportunities to migrate as part of a household's survival strategy. In Latin America, the Philippines,

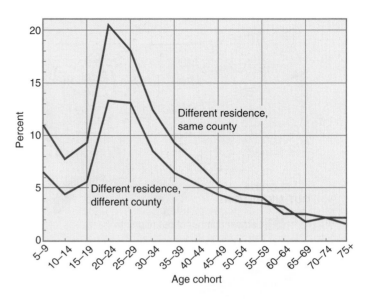

FIGURE 4.28 Percentage of 2000 population over 5 years of age with a different residence than in 1999. Young adults figure most prominently in both short- and long-distance moves in the United States, an age-related pattern of mobility that has remained constant over time. For the sample year shown, 33% of people in their 20s moved whereas fewer than 5% of those 65 and older did so. Short-distance moves predominate; 56% of the 43 million U.S. movers between March, 1999, and March, 2000, relocated within the same county and another 20% moved to another county in the same state. Some two-thirds of intracounty (mobility) moves were made for housing-related reasons; long-distance moves (migration) are likely to be made for work-related reasons.
Source: U.S. Bureau of the Census.

and parts of Asia, emigration of young girls from large, landless families is more common than from smaller families or those with land rights. Their remittances of foreign earnings help maintain their parents and siblings at home.

An eighth internationally relevant observation may be added to those cited in Ravenstein's list: on average, emigrants tend to be relatively well-educated. A British government study reveals three-quarters of Africa's emigrants have higher (beyond high-school) education, as do about half of Asia's and South America's. Of the more than 1 million Asian Indians living in the United States, more than three-quarters of those of working age have at least a bachelor's degree. The loss to home countries can be draining; about 30% of all highly educated West African Ghanaians and Sierra Leoneans live abroad. Outward migration of the educated affects developed countries as well as poorer developing states. Between 1997 and 2002, it is claimed that between 15% and 40% of each year's graduating class from Canadian universities emigrated to the United States, while in Europe, for one example, half the mid-1990s' graduating physics classes of Bucharest University left the country.

For North Americans, the decisions to migrate are more ordinary but individually just as compelling. They appear to involve: (1) changes in life course (e.g., getting married, having children, getting a divorce); (2) changes in the career course (getting a first job or a promotion, receiving a career transfer, seeking work in a new location, retiring); (3) changes of residence associated with individual personality (Figure 4.29). Work-related relocations are

Gender is involved in migration at every level. In a household or family, women and men are likely to play different roles regarding decisions or responsibilities for activities such as child care. These differences, and the inequalities that underlie them, help determine who decides whether the household moves, which household members migrate, and the destination for the move. Outside the household, societal norms about women's mobility and independence often restrict their ability to migrate.

The economies of sending and receiving areas play a role as well. If jobs are available for women in the receiving area, women have an incentive to migrate, and families are more likely to encourage the migration of women as necessary and beneficial. Thousands of women from East and Southeast Asia have migrated to the oil-rich countries of the Middle East, for example, to take service jobs.

The impact of migration is also likely to be different for women and men. Moving to a new economic or social setting can affect the regular relationships and processes that occur within a household or family. In some cases, women might remain subordinate to the men in their families. A study of Greek-Cypriot immigrant women in London and of Turkish immigrant women in the Netherlands found that although these women were working for wages in their new societies, these new economic roles did not affect their subordinate standing in the family in any fundamental way.

In other situations, however, migration can give women more power in the family. In former Zaire [now the Democratic Republic of the Congo], women in rural areas moved to towns to take advantage of job opportunities there, and gain independence from men in the process.

One of the keys to understanding the role of gender in migration is to disentangle household decision-making processes. Many researchers see migration as a family decision or strategy, but some members will benefit more than others from those decisions.

For many years, men predominated in the migration streams flowing from Mexico to the United States. Women played an important role in this migration stream, even when they remained in Mexico. Mexican women influenced the migration decisions of other family members; they married migrants to gain the benefits from and opportunity for migration; and they resisted or accepted the new roles in their families that migration created.

In the 1980s, Mexican women began to migrate to the United States in increasing numbers. Economic crises in Mexico and an increase in the number of jobs available for women in the United States, especially in factories, domestic service, and service industries, have changed the backdrop of individual migration decisions. Now, women often initiate family moves or resettlement efforts.

Mexican women have begun to build their own migration networks, which are key to successful migration and resettlement in the United States. Networks provide migrants with information about jobs and places to live and have enabled many Mexican women to make independent decisions about migrating.

In immigrant communities in the United States, women are often the vital links to social institution services and to other immigrants. Thus, women have been instrumental in the way that Mexican immigrants have settled and become integrated into new communities.

From "Gender, Power, and Population Change" by Nancy E. Riley in *Population Bulletin*, Vol. 52, No. 1, May 1997, pp. 32–33. Reprinted by permission of Population Reference Bureau.

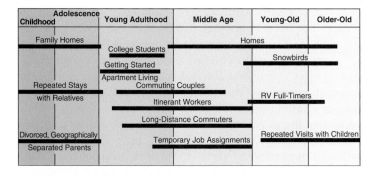

FIGURE 4.29 Examples of multiple residences by stage in life. Each horizontal line represents a period of time in a possible new residence.

Source: K. McHugh, T. Hogan, and S. Happel, "Multiple Residence and Cyclical Migration." The Professional Geographer 47, no. 3. Figure 1, p. 253. Association of American Geographers, 1995.

very important in long-distance (intercounty) migrations, and in both intra- and interprovincial/interstate relocations, more migrants move down the urban hierarchy—that is, from larger to smaller centres—than vice versa. Some observers suggest that pattern of deconcentration reflects modern transportation and communication technologies, more and younger retirees, and the attractions of amenity-rich smaller places. Some people, of course, simply seem to move often for no discernible reason, whereas others, *stayers*, settle into a community permanently. For other developed countries, a different set of summary migration factors may be present. Chapter 4 will provide further information on immigration in Canada.

Urbanization

Pressures on the land resource of countries are increased not just by their growing populations but by the reduction of arable land caused by such growth. More and more of world population increase must be accommodated not in rural areas, but in cities that hold the promise of jobs and access to health, welfare, and other public services. As a result, the *urbanization* (transformation from rural to urban status according to individual state's definition of "urban") of population in developing countries is increasing dramatically. Since the 1950s, cities have grown faster than rural areas in nearly all developing states. Indeed, because of the now rapid flow of migrants from the countryside to cities, population growth in the rural areas of the developing world has essentially stopped. In 2005, the UN reported for the first time in human history, more people lived in urban areas than not. Statistics Canada uses the term "census metropolitan areas" (CMA) to denote areas of Canada that have a core population of at least 100,000 people combined with adjacent urban and rural areas that have a high degree of economic and social integration with that urban area. In this way, urban centres, rather than just the city cores, can be considered in a systematic manner. In 2006, nearly 50% of Canadians—13.9 million people—were living in the country's three largest urban areas: the Montréal CMA, the Vancouver CMA, or the Greater Golden Horseshoe in southern Ontario. There are six CMAs that have populations over 1 million—Toronto (5.1 million), Montreal (3.6 million), Vancouver (2.1 million), Ottawa–Hull (1.1 million), Calgary (1.1 million) and Edmonton (1 million). Collectively, these six CMAs contain about 33% of Canada's total population. Another three CMAs have populations between 500,000 and 1 million—Quebec City, Winnipeg, and Hamilton.

On UN projections, essentially all world population increase between 2000 and 2030 will be in urban areas and almost entirely within the developing regions and countries, continuing a pattern established by 1950 (Figure 4.30). In those areas collectively, cities are growing by more than 3% a year, and the poorest regions are experiencing the fastest growth. By 2020, the UN anticipates, a majority of the population of less developed countries will live in urban areas. In East, West, and Central Africa, for example, cities are expanding by 5% a year, a pace that can double their population every 14 years. Global urban population, just 750 million in 1950, grew to nearly 3 billion by early in the 21st century and is projected to rise to 5.1 billion by 2030. The uneven results of past urbanization are summarized in Figure 4.31.

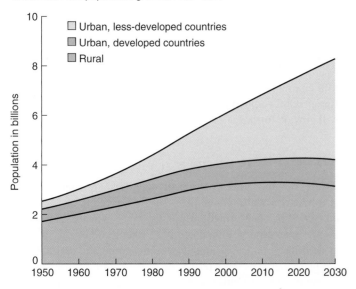

Urban and rural population growth, 1950–2030

FIGURE 4.30 Past and projected urban and rural population growth.
According to UN projections, 60% of the world's total population may be urbanized by 2030.

Data source: United Nations, World Urbanization Prospects: The 2003 Revision; *redrawn from* Population Bulletin *53, no. 1 (1998).*

The sheer growth of those cities in people and territory has increased pressures on arable land and adjusted upward both arithmetic and physiological densities. Urbanization consumes millions of hectares of cropland each year. In Egypt, for example, urban expansion and new development between 1965 and 1985 took out of production as much fertile soil as the massive Aswan dam on the Nile River made newly available through irrigation with the water it impounds.

Population Data and Projections

Population geographers, demographers, planners, governmental officials, and a host of others rely on detailed population data to make their assessments of present national and world population patterns and to estimate future conditions. Birth rates and death rates, rates of fertility and of natural increase, age and sex composition of the population, and other items are all necessary ingredients for their work.

Population Data

Canada is fortunate to have a reliable population database. Unfortunately, census data as reported by some countries may on occasion be more misleading than informative. For much of the developing world, a national census is a massive undertaking. Isolation and poor transportation, insufficiency of funds and trained census personnel, high rates of illiteracy limiting the type of questions that can be asked, and populations suspicious of government data collectors serve to restrict the frequency, coverage, and accuracy of population reports.

However derived, detailed data are published by the major reporting agencies for all national units even when those figures are poorly based on fact or are essentially fictitious. For years, data on the total population, birth and death rates, and other vital statistics for Somalia were regularly reported and annually revised. The fact was, however, that Somalia had never had a census and had no system whatsoever for recording births.

Fortunately, census coverage on a world basis is improving. Almost every country has now had at least one census of its population, and most have been subjected to periodic sample surveys (Figure 4.32). However, only about 10% of the developing world's population live in countries with anything approaching complete systems for registering births and deaths. Estimates are that 40% or less of live births in Indonesia, Pakistan, India, or the Philippines are officially recorded; sub-Saharan Africa has the highest percentage of unregistered births (71%), according to UNICEF. Apparently, deaths are even less completely reported than births throughout Asia. And whatever the deficiencies of Asian states, African statistics are still less complete and reliable. It is, of course, on just these basic birth and death data that projections about population growth and composition are founded.

Population Projections

For all their inadequacies and imprecision, current data reported for country units form the basis of **population projections,**

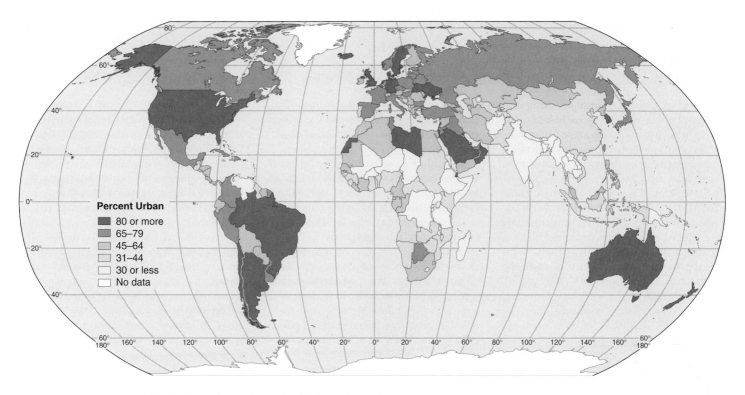

FIGURE 4.31 Percentage of national population that is classified as urban. Urbanization has been particularly rapid in the developing continents. In 1950, only 17% of Asians and 15% of Africans were urban. By 2004, 35% of Africans and nearly 40% of Asians were city dwellers, and collectively, the less-developed areas contained 70% of the world's city population.

Source: Data from Population Reference Bureau.

FIGURE 4.32 By the early 21st century, most countries of the developed and developing worlds had conducted a relatively recent census, although some were of doubtful completeness or accuracy. The photo shows an enumerator interviewing a Quito resident during the Ecuador census of 2001.

estimates of future population size, age, and sex composition based on current data. Projections are not forecasts, and demographers are not the social science equivalent of meteorologists. Weather forecasters work with a myriad of accurate observations applied against a known, tested model of the atmosphere. The demographer, in contrast, works with sparse, imprecise, out-of-date, and missing data applied to human actions that will be unpredictably responsive to stimuli not yet evident.

Population projections, therefore, are based on assumptions for the future applied to current data that are, themselves, frequently suspect. Since projections are not predictions, they can never be wrong. They are simply the inevitable result of calculations about fertility, mortality, and migration rates applied to each age cohort of a population now living, and the making of birth rate, survival, and migration assumptions about cohorts yet unborn. Of course, the perfectly valid *projections* of future population size and structure resulting from those calculations may be dead wrong as *predictions*.

Population Controls

This section focuses attention on society–environment interactions—how human populations impact the earth to support life. All population projections include an assumption that at some point in time population growth will cease and plateau at the replacement level. Without that assumption, future numbers become unthinkably large. For the world at unchecked present growth rates, there would be 1 trillion people three centuries from now, 4 trillion four centuries in the future, and so on. Although there is reasonable debate about whether the world is now overpopulated and about what either its optimum or maximum sustainable population should be, totals in the trillions are beyond any reasonable expectation.

Population projections can be useful and instructive but of necessity are based on current evaluations of future events. In making them, demographers are guided by controlling assumptions about the future levels of birth and death rates and, in some cases, amount of migration. These assumptions are based on answers to such questions as: What are the present levels of fertility, of literacy, and of education? Does the government have a policy to influence population growth? What is the status of women? What might be the impact of, for example, HIV/AIDS on life expectancies?

Along with these questions must be weighed the likelihood of socio-economic change, for it is generally assumed that as a country "develops," a preference for smaller families will cause fertility to fall to the replacement level of about two children per woman. But when can one expect this to happen in less developed countries? And for the majority of more developed countries with fertility currently below replacement level, can one assume that fertility will rise to avert eventual disappearance of the population and, if so, when?

Predicting the pace of fertility decline is most important, as illustrated by one earlier set of United Nations long-range projections for Africa. As with many projections, these were issued in a "series" to show the effects of different assumptions. The "low" projection for Africa assumed that replacement-level fertility would be reached in 2030, which would put the continent's population at 1.4 billion in 2100. If attainment of replacement-level fertility were delayed to 2065, the population would reach 4.4 billion in 2100. That difference of 3 billion serves as a cautionary note on both the acceptability of distant projections and the need to consider not only the possibilities but also the probabilities of future events.

Unfortunately, demographers usually cast their projections in an environmental vacuum, ignoring the realities of soils, vegetation, water supplies, and climate that ultimately determine feasible or possible levels of population support. Inevitably, different analysts present different assessments of the absolute carrying capacity of the earth. At an unrealistically low level, the World Hunger Project in the 1990s calculated that the world's ecosystem could, with then-current agricultural technologies and with equal distribution of food supplies, support on a sustained basis no more than 5.5 billion people, a number already far exceeded. Many agricultural economists, in contrast—citing present trends and prospective increases in crop yields, fertilizer efficiencies, and intensification of production methods—are confident that the earth can readily feed 10 billion or more on a sustained basis. Nearly all observers, however, agree that physical environmental realities make unrealistic purely demographically based projections of a world population two or three times its present size.

Thomas Robert **Malthus** (1766–1834), an English economist and demographer, put the problem succinctly in a treatise published in 1798: All biological populations have a potential for increase that exceeds the actual rate of increase, and the resources for the support of increase are limited. In later publications, Malthus amplified his thesis by noting the following:

1. Population is inevitably limited by the means of subsistence.
2. Populations invariably increase with increase in the means of subsistence unless prevented by powerful checks.
3. The checks that inhibit the reproductive capacity of populations and keep it in balance with means of subsistence are either "private" (moral restraint, celibacy, and chastity) or "destructive" (war, poverty, pestilence, and famine).

The deadly consequences of Malthus's dictum that unchecked population increases geometrically while food production can increase only arithmetically[2] have been reported throughout human history, as they are today. Starvation, the ultimate expression of resource depletion, is no stranger to the past or present. By conservative estimate, some 100 people worldwide will starve to death during the 2 minutes it takes you to read this page; half will be children under 5. They will, of course, be more than replaced numerically by new births during the same 2 minutes.

Losses are nearly always recouped. All battlefield deaths, perhaps 70 million, in all of humankind's wars over the past 300 years equal less than a one-year replacement period at present rates of natural increase.

Yet, inevitably—following the logic of Malthus, the apparent evidence of history, and our observations of animal populations—equilibrium must be achieved between numbers and support resources. When overpopulation of any species occurs, a population dieback is inevitable. The madly ascending leg of the J-curve is bent to the horizontal, and the J-curve is converted to an S-curve. It has happened before in human history, as Figure 4.33 summarizes. The top of the **S-curve** represents a population size consistent with and supportable by the exploitable resource base. When the population is equivalent to the carrying capacity of the occupied area, it is said to have reached a **homeostatic plateau**.

In animals, overcrowding and environmental stress apparently release an automatic physiological suppressant of fertility. Although famine and chronic malnutrition may reduce fertility in humans, population limitation usually must be either forced or self-imposed. The demographic transition to low birth rates matching reduced death rates is cited as evidence that Malthus's first assumption was wrong: human populations do not inevitably grow geometrically. Fertility behaviour, it was observed, is conditioned by social determinants, not solely by biological or resource imperatives.

Although Malthus's ideas were discarded as deficient by the end of the 19th century in light of the European population

---

[2] "Within a hundred years or so, the population can increase from five-fold to twenty-fold, while the means of subsistence . . . can increase only from three to five times," was the observation of Hung Liangchi of China, a spatially distant early 19th century contemporary of Malthus.

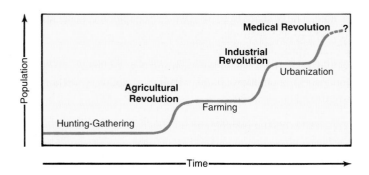

FIGURE 4.33 The steadily higher *homeostatic plateaus* (states of equilibrium) achieved by humans are evidence of their ability to increase the carrying capacity of the land through technological advance. Each new plateau represents the conversion of the J-curve into an S-curve.

experience, the concerns he expressed were revived during the 1950s. Observations of population growth in underdeveloped countries and the strain that growth placed on their resources inspired the viewpoint that improvements in living standards could be achieved only by raising investment per worker. Rapid population growth was seen as a serious diversion of scarce resources away from capital investment and into unending social welfare programs. In order to lift living standards, the existing national efforts to lower mortality rates had to be balanced by governmental programs to reduce birth rates. **Neo-Malthusianism**, as this viewpoint became known, has been the underpinning of national and international programs of population limitation primarily through birth control and family planning.

Neo-Malthusianism has had a mixed reception. Asian countries, led by China and India, have in general—though with differing successes—adopted family planning programs and policies. In some instances, success has been declared complete. Singapore established its Population and Family Panning Board in 1965, when its fertility rate was 4.9 lifetime births per woman. By 1986, that rate had declined to 1.7, well below the 2.1 replacement level for developed countries, and the board was abolished as no longer necessary. Caribbean and South American countries, even the poorest and most agrarian, have also experienced declining fertility rates, though often these reductions have been achieved despite pronatalist views of governments influenced by the Roman Catholic Church.

Africa and the Middle East have generally been less responsive to the neo-Malthusian arguments because of ingrained cultural convictions among people, if not in all governmental circles, that large families with six or seven children are desirable. Although total fertility rates have begun to decline in most sub-Saharan African states, they still remain nearly everywhere far above replacement levels. Islamic fundamentalism opposed to birth restrictions is also a cultural factor in the Near East and North Africa. However, the Muslim theocracy of Iran has endorsed a range of contraceptive procedures and developed one of the world's more aggressive family planning programs.

Other barriers to fertility control exist. When first proposed by Western states, neo-Malthusian arguments that family planning was necessary for development were rejected by many less developed countries. Reflecting both nationalistic and Marxist concepts, they maintained that remnant colonial-era social, economic, and class structures rather than population increase hindered development. Some government leaders think there is a correlation between population size and power, and pursue pronatalist policies, as did Mao's China during the 1950s and early 1960s. And a number of American economists called *cornucopians* expressed the view, beginning in the 1980s, that population growth is a stimulus, not a deterrent, to development and that human minds and skills are the world's ultimate resource base. Since the time of Malthus, they observe, world population has grown from 900 million to over 6 billion without the predicted dire consequences—proof that Malthus failed to recognize the importance of technology in raising the carrying capacity of the earth. Still higher population numbers, they suggest, are sustainable, perhaps even with improved standards of living for all.

A third view, modifying cornucopian optimism, admits that products of human ingenuity, such as the Green Revolution's increases in food production, have managed to keep pace with rapid population growth since 1970. But its advocates argue that scientific and technical ingenuity to enhance food production do not automatically appear; both complacency and inadequate research support have hindered continuing progress in recent years. And even if further advances are made, they observe, not all countries or regions have the social and political will or capacity to take advantage of them. Those that do not, third-view advocates warn, will fail to keep pace with the needs of their populace and will sink into varying degrees of poverty and environmental decay, creating national and regional—though not necessarily global—crises.

Population Prospects

Regardless of population philosophies, theories, or cultural norms, the fact remains that many or most developing countries are showing significantly declining population growth rates. Global fertility and birth rates are falling to an extent not anticipated by pessimistic Malthusians and at a pace that suggests a peaking of world population numbers sooner—and at lower totals—than previously projected (see "A Population Implosion?" p. 96). In all world regions, steady and continuous fertility declines have been recorded over the past years, reducing fertility from global 5-children-per-woman levels in the early 1950s to less than 3-per-woman levels early in the present century.

Momentum

Reducing fertility levels even to the replacement level of about 2.1 births per woman does not mean an immediate end to population growth. Because of the age composition of many societies, numbers of births will continue to grow even as fertility rates per woman decline. The reason is to be found in **population** (or **demographic**) **momentum**, and the key to that is the age structure of a country's population.

When a high proportion of the population is young, the product of past high fertility rates, larger and larger numbers enter the childbearing age each year; that is the case for major parts of the world early in the 21st century. The populations of developing countries are far younger than those of the established industrially developed regions (see Figure 4.15), with nearly one-third (in Asia and Latin America) to over 40% (in Africa) below the age of 15. The consequences of the fertility of these young people are yet to be realized. A population with a greater number of young people tends to grow rapidly regardless of the level of childbearing. The results will continue to be felt until the now-youthful groups mature and work their way through the population pyramid.

Inevitably, while this is happening, even the most stringent national policies limiting growth cannot stop it entirely. A country with a large present population base will experience large numerical increases despite declining birth rates. Indeed, the higher fertility was to begin with and the sharper its drop to low levels, the greater will be the role of momentum even after rates drop below replacement. A simple comparison of South Korea and the United Kingdom may serve to demonstrate the point. The two countries had (in 2002) the same level of fertility, with women averaging about 1.6 children each. Between that year and 2025, the larger population of the U.K. (without considering immigration or the births associated with newcomers) was projected to decline by 2 million persons while the smaller, more youthful South Korea was expected to continue growing, adding 2 million people.

The realities of population momentum (Figure 4.34) have, for some demographers, cast serious doubt on the UN's projection of a world population stabilizing at abut 9.5 billion by 2100. Instead, they note, a large share of current world population is concentrated in the 15–40 age span where birth rates are high. Even if everyone everywhere adopted a policy of only two children per couple, it would take (because of momentum) approximately 70 years before world population would stabilize at about 12 billion, far above the UN projection.

Aging

Eventually, of course, young populations grow older, and even the youthful developing countries are beginning to face the consequences of that reality. The problems of a rapidly aging population that already confront the industrialized economies are now being realized in the developing world as well. Globally, there will be more than 1 billion persons 60 years of age and older by 2025, and 1.5 billion by 2050, when the world will contain more people aged 60 and above than children under the age of 15. That momentous reversal in relative proportions of young and old already occurred in 1998 in the more developed regions. The progression toward older populations is considered irreversible, the result of the now-global demographic transition from high to low levels of fertility and mortality. The youthful majorities of the past are unlikely to occur again, for globally, the population of older persons early in the century was growing by 2% per year—much faster than the population as a whole—and between 2025 to 2030, the 60 + growth rate will reach 2.8% per year. By 2050, the UN projects, one out of five persons worldwide will be 60 years old or older.

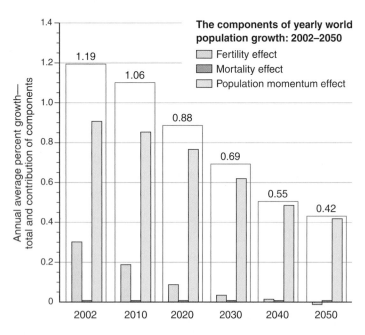

FIGURE 4.34 Effects of population momentum, 2002–2050. Worldwide declines in total fertility rates will not soon be reflected by equivalent declines in the growth of population. Because of past fertility levels, the numbers of women in their childbearing years are increasing both absolutely and relative to the rest of the population. As a result, fertility's contribution to global growth will steadily decline, and population momentum will account for a growing share of projected world population increase.

Source: U.S. Bureau of the Census, 2004.

FIGURE 4.35 These senior residents of a Moroccan nursing home are part of the rapidly aging population of many developing countries. Worldwide, the over-60 cohort will number some 22% of total population by 2050 and be larger than the number of children less than 15 years of age. But by 2020, a third of Singapore citizens will be 55 or older, and China will have as large a share of its population over 60—about one in four—as will Europe. Already, the numbers of old people in the world's poorer countries are beginning to dwarf those in the rich world. At the start of the 21st century, there were nearly twice as many persons over 60 in developing countries as in the advanced ones, but most are without the old-age assistance and welfare programs developed countries have put in place.

About 80% of the mid-century elderly folk will live in the less developed world, for the growth rate of older people is three times as high in developing countries as in the developed ones. In the developing world, older persons are projected to make up 20% of the population by 2050, in contrast to the 8% over age 60 in the developing world in 2000. Since the pace of aging is much faster in the developing countries, they will have less time than the developed world did to adjust to the consequences of that aging. And those consequences will be experienced at lower levels of personal and national income and economic strength.

In both rich and poor states, the working-age populations will face increasing burdens and obligations. The potential support ratio, or PSR (the number of persons aged 15–64 years per one citizen aged 65 or older), has steadily fallen. Between 1950 and 2000, it dropped from 12 to 9 workers for each older person; by mid-century, the PSR is projected to drop to 4. The implications for social security schemes and social support obligations are obvious and made more serious because the older population itself is aging. By the middle of the century, one-fifth of older persons will be 80 years or older and on average require more support expenditures for health and long-term care than do younger seniors. The consequences of population aging appear most intractable for the world's poorest developing states that generally lack health, income, housing, and social service support systems adequate to the needs of their older citizens. To the social and economic implications of their present population momentum, therefore, developing countries must add the aging consequences of past patterns and rates of growth (Figure 4.35).

Want to Learn More?

Population Growth

Population Reference Bureau: http://www.prb.org

Demographic Transition Theory: http://en.wikipedia.org/wiki/Demographic_transition

Population Projections

World: http://www.un.org/popin/wdtrends.htm

Canada: http://dsp-psd.communication.gc.ca/Collection-R/Statcan/91-520-XIB/91-520-XIB-e.html

Summary

Birth, death, fertility, and growth rates are important in understanding the numbers, composition, distribution, and spatial trends of population. Recent "explosive" increases in human numbers and the prospects of continuing population expansion may be traced to sharp reductions in death rates, increases in longevity, and the impact of demographic momentum on a youthful population largely concentrated in the developing world. Control of population numbers historically was accomplished through a demographic transition first experienced in European societies that adjusted their fertility rates downward as death rates fell and life expectancies increased. The introduction of advanced technologies of preventive and curative medicine, pesticides, and famine relief have reduced mortality rates in developing countries without, until recently, always a compensating reduction in birth rates. Recent fertility declines in many developing regions suggest the demographic transition is no longer limited to the advanced industrial countries, and promise world population stability earlier and at lower numbers than envisioned just a few years ago.

The demographic future for the next 50 years is as follows. The population will be 2 to 4 billion people bigger by 2050, and nearly all of that growth will be in less developed countries. In some developed nations, such as Canada, population increases will largely reflect immigration. Future population growth, in absolute and relative terms, will be less than the recent past. Populations will be more urban than at any time in the past. Finally, the population will be much older, on average, than it is now. Collectively, population pressures will force governments at all levels to serve their citizens' changing needs and aspirations. Thus, population has implications for urban geography, resource management, development, the international economic system, and health and well-being geography. We will investigate some of these issues in subsequent chapters.

People are unevenly distributed over the earth. The ecumene, or permanently inhabited portion of the globe, is discontinuous and marked by pronounced differences in population concentrations and numbers. East Asia, South Asia, Europe, and northeastern United States/southeastern Canada represent the world's greatest population clusters, though smaller areas of great density are found in other regions and continents. Since growth rates are highest and population doubling times generally shorter in world regions outside these four present main concentrations, new patterns of population localization and dominance are taking form.

A respected geographer once commented that "population is the point of reference from which all other elements [of geography] are observed." Certainly, population geography is the essential starting point of the human component of the human–environment concerns of geography. But human populations are not merely collections of numerical units; nor are they to be understood solely through statistical analysis. Societies are distinguished not just by the abstract data of their numbers, rates, and trends, but by experiences, beliefs, understandings, and aspirations that collectively constitute that human spatial and behavioural variable called *culture*. It is to that fundamental human diversity that we next turn our attention.

KEY WORDS

agricultural density   90
arithmetic density   89
carrying capacity   90
chain migration   112
channelized migration   113
cohort   92
counter migration   113
crude birth rate (CBR)   92
crude death rate (CDR)   97
crude density   89
demographic equation   107
demographic transition   103

demography   85
dependency ratio   99
doubling time   102
ecological optimum   90
ecumene   88
homeostatic plateau   118
J-curve time   102
Malthus   118
migration   107
mortality rate   97
natural increase   102
neo-Malthusianism   119

non-ecumene   88
overpopulation   90
physiological density   90
place utility   112
population (demographic)
    momentum   119
population density   89
population geography   85
population projection   116
population pyramid   99
pull factor   112
push factor   112

rate of natural increase   102
rates   92
replacement level   96
residential density   90
return migration   113
S-curve   118
sex ratio   100
step migration   112
total fertility rate (TFR)   93
urban density   90
zero population growth
    (ZPG)   96

FOR REVIEW

1. How do the *crude birth rate* and the *fertility rate* differ? Which measure is the more accurate statement of the amount of reproduction occurring in a population?

2. How is the *crude death rate* calculated? What factors account for the worldwide decline in death rates since 1945?

3. How is a *population pyramid* constructed? What shape of "pyramid" reflects the structure of a rapidly growing country? Of a population with a slow rate of growth? What can we tell about future population numbers from those shapes?

4. What variations do we discern in the spatial pattern of the *rate of natural increase* and, consequently, of population growth? What rate of natural increase would double population in 35 years?

5. How are population numbers projected from present conditions? Are projections the same as predictions? If not, in what ways do they differ?

6. Describe the stages in the *demographic transition*. Where has the final stage of the transition been achieved? Why do some analysts doubt the applicability of the demographic transition to all parts of the world?

7. Contrast *crude population density*, *physiological density*, and *agricultural density*. For what differing purposes might each be useful? How is *carrying capacity* related to the concept of density?

8. What considerations appear to influence the decision to migrate? How do perceptions of *place utility* induce or inhibit migration?

9. What is a *migration field*? Some migration fields show a *channelized* flow of people. Select a particular channelized migration flow (such as the movement of Scandinavians to Michigan, Wisconsin, and Minnesota, or people from the Great Plains to California, or African Americans to the North U.S.) and speculate why a channelized flow developed.

10. What was Malthus's underlying assumption concerning the relationship between population growth and food supply? In what ways do the arguments of *neo-Malthusians* differ from the original doctrine? What governmental policies are implicit in *neo-Malthusianism?*

11. Why is *population momentum* a matter of interest in population projections? In which world areas are the implications of demographic momentum most serious in calculating population growth, stability, or decline?

FOR REVIEW

12. Refer to Figure 4.5—"Population distribution in Canada (2006)." How do you think this pattern will change during your lifetime? On other words, what are the changes in the ecumene and the non-ecumene? Explain why you think these changes will occur?

13. Refer to Appendix A—"2007 World Population Data." Examine the "population growth rate" column. What countries have the highest and lowest growth rates? What stage of the demographic transition model are they currently experiencing? For those with the highest rates, what changes do you think are required for them to enter the next stage of the model?

14. Refer to Go to Appendix B— "Population pyramids for Canadian provinces and territories." (a) Which ones have the oldest population? The youngest? What reasons would you propose to explain this? (b) Which province/territory has the fewest individuals between the ages of 20 and 50? Which one had the most individuals between the ages of 20 and 50? What reasons would you propose to explain this? (c) Which province/territory has the highest dependency ratio? Which one has the lowest? What are the implications of this pattern for each province/territory?

15. Why or why not is density the best indicator or measure of overpopulation. If not, which indicator would you suggest best measures overpopulation? Why?

16. What is the best spatial scale to measure population density—community, province/state, country, world, or other (e.g., watershed)? Explain why.

FOCUS FOLLOW-UP

1. **What descriptive generalizations can be made about world population distributions and densities?** pp. 85–91.

   World population is primarily concentrated north of the equator, in lower (below 200 metres) elevations, along continental margins. Major world population clusters include *East Asia* with 25% of the total, *South Asia* with over 20%, *Europe* and *northeastern United States/ southeastern Canada* with significant but lesser shares of world population. Other smaller but pronounced concentrations are found discontinuously on all continents. Within the permanently inhabited areas—the "ecumene"—population densities vary greatly. Highest densities are found in cities; almost one-half of the world's people are urban residents now and the vast majority of world population growth over the first quarter of the 21st century will occur in cities of the developing world.

2. **What are some basic terms and measures used by population geographers?** pp. 92–103.

   A *cohort* is a population group, usually an age group, treated as a unit. *Rates* record the frequency of occurrence of an event over a given unit of time. Rates are used to trace a wide range of population features and trends: births, deaths, fertility, infant or maternal mortality, natural increase, and others. Those rates tell us both the present circumstances and likely prospects for national, country group, or world population structures. Population pyramids give visual evidence of the current age and sex cohort structure of countries or country groupings.

3. **What are meant and measured by the demographic transition model and the demographic equation?** pp. 103–107.

   The *demographic transition* model traces the presumed relationship between population growth and economic development. In Western countries, the transition model historically displayed four stages: (a) high birth and death rates; (b) high birth and declining death rates; (c) declining births and reduced growth rates; and (d) low birth and death rates. A fifth stage of population decline is observed for some aging societies. The transition model has been observed to be not fully applicable to all developing states. The *demographic equation* attempts to incorporate cross-border population migration into projections of national population trends.

4. **What kinds of migration movements can be recognized and what influences their occurrence?** pp. 107–116.

   Migration means the permanent relocation of residence and activity space. It is subject to all the principles of spatial interaction and behaviour and represents both a survival strategy for threatened people and a reasoned response to perceptions of opportunity. Migration has been enduring throughout human history and occurs at separate scales from intercontinental to regional, and includes flights of refugees and relocations of retirees. Negative home conditions (push factors) coupled with perceived positive destination attractions (pull factors) are important, as are age and sex of migrants and the spatial search they conduct. Step and chain migration and return migratory flows all affect patterns and volume of flows.

5. **What are population projections, and how are they affected by various controls on population growth?** pp. 116–121.

   Population projections are merely calculations of the future size, age, and sex composition of regional, national, or world populations; they are based on current data and manipulated by

FOCUS FOLLOW-UP continued

varying assumptions about the future. As simple calculations, projections cannot be wrong. They may, however, totally misrepresent what actually will occur because of faulty current data or erroneous assumptions used in their calculation. They may also be invalid because of unanticipated self-imposed or external brakes on population growth, such as changing family size desires or limits on areal carrying capacity that slow or halt current growth trends. Even with such growth limitations, however, population prospects are always influenced greatly by *demographic momentum*, the inevitable growth in numbers promised by the high proportion of younger cohorts yet to enter childbearing years in the developing world, and by the consequences of global population aging.

ONLINE LEARNING CENTRE

The World Wide Web has a tremendous number and variety of sites pertaining to geography. To access Web sites, Internet exercises, self-quizzes, videos, and additional study tools relevant to this chapter's content, visit the *Human Geography* Online Learning Centre at **www.mcgrawhill.ca/olc/fellmann**.

CULTURES, LANDSCAPES, AND IDENTITIES

Aims

- To appreciate the concepts of culture and landscape
- To understand the processes of cultural change
- To introduce the dominant themes of cultural geography
- To explain how cultural identities are political and spatial

Some Specific Considerations for Review:

They buried them nearly 1,000 years ago at a sacred site now called the "Moose Bay Burial Mound" situated in what is now part of the Crooked Lake Provincial Park, near the Qu'Appelle River Valley in Saskatchewan. The actual burials themselves were the final step in a complex, year-long mourning ritual of this Plains Indian society. Several days following their initial deaths, the bodies were tightly wrapped in buffalo hides and placed atop a scaffold with gifts of food and assorted implements: birch bark containers, stone scrappers, pottery, and stone pipes. This was followed by a period of religious ceremonies, including mourning and feasts. About a year later, the remains of the deceased were unwrapped, rubbed with ochre, and placed in a buried mound. This circular site was first stripped of its sod and a wooden post was erected in its centre. The remains, along with artifacts required in the next life, were placed around the post, and a tipi-like structure erected to cover it all. Tons of earth was then hauled to cover the entire site, and a mound was inscribed in the landscape for centuries to come.

Not until 1968, when modern day archaeologists excavated the site and found skeletal remains of three adults males and nine other adolescents or children, did this swell in an otherwise hilly natural environment reveal itself as the sacred burial site of an ancient Aboriginal cultural group. Indeed, thousands of mounds representing numerous aboriginal groups were built throughout North America between 1000 B.C.E. and 1600 A.C.E. They speak to both the ancient occupation of these lands by humans and the timeless and universal cultural practice of paying homage to our dead through ritual and remembrance (Canada's Digital History, 2006).

As shown by their tools and equipment, their behaviours and beliefs, these ancient Aboriginals displayed highly developed and distinctive characteristics, primitive only from the vantage point of our own different technologies and customs. They represented the culmination of a long history of development of skills, of invention of tools, and of creation of lifestyles that set them apart from peoples elsewhere in Europe, Asia, and Africa, who possessed still different cultural heritages.

To the layperson, "culture" means the arts (literature, painting, music, and the like). Artistic products are indeed cultural creations, but so too are the seemingly infinite totality of all other human creations: systems of shared belief (e.g., religion or democracy); the knowledge, customs, rituals, and habits acquired and practiced by members of a society (e.g., burials, mathematical skills, table manners, shaving); communication in all its forms (e.g., language, television, body gestures, spatial arrangements); and the shared experiences of our everyday lives (e.g., graduations, breakfast foods, traffic jams). Because culture is virtually the sum total of a shared, learned 'way of life,' it encompasses the human experience in its entirety. To say culture is everything humans practise, make, or learn is correct, but such a sweeping definition holds little analytical direction for the social scientist: where and how does one begin to study 'everything'? For the purposes of this book, let us accept that **culture** is the specialized behavioural patterns, understandings, adaptations, and social systems that summarize a group of people's learned way of life. 'Behavioural patterns' are recurring human actions at any number of scales, from the everyday and seemingly insignificant—dinner,

weekly laundry, bus routes—to national elections or international warfare of historic importance: all are repeated again and again over time and space. What we know, comprehend, and believe constitute 'understandings,' and the tools and methods we invent and use—clothing, housing, fishing, farming—are the means by which we 'adapt' to the environments we inhabit. The relationships among individuals, groups, institutions, and organizations, be they with family, co-workers, fellow citizens at large, or institutions and organizations, such as universities or corporations, comprise 'social systems.' Collectively these constitute a people's 'learned way of life': culture is thus nurtured from birth, not innate at birth.

In this sense of the term, culture is an ever-present part of the regional differences that are the essence of human geography. In fact, "cultural geography" was synonymous with "human geography" for the first half of the 20th century. As the discipline grew, "human" geography developed into numerous specialized subfields, as the chapters in this textbook attest. For a human geographer, the visible and material manifestations of culture—buildings, cities, clothing, farms, factories, roads, tools—as well as the invisible or immaterial manifestations of culture—customs, knowledge, language, political beliefs, religion, values—are all parts of the spatial diversity and similarities studied within the discipline. Cultural differences over time and space may present contrasts as great as those between the Stone Age ivory hunters and modern urban North Americans, or be as subtle as the differing "feel" of urban Paris, Moscow, or New York, or as obvious as the sharp contrasts of rural Zimbabwe and the U.S. Midwest (Figure 5.1).

On the other hand, cultural uniformity may occur between entire continents, as is the case with the global prevalence of capitalism, the English language, and Christianity, or among individual households in the same residential neighbourhood composed of identical townhouses, filled with the same appliances, and occupied by people of comparable economic standing and lifestyle. Such differences and similarities of people around the world or across the street speak to the complexities of "culture." For the geographer, the task is to identify culture in its many forms as it is manifest in the landscape, and to understand and explain the spatial processes that produce and reproduce that cultural landscape.

Describing what is observed is a crucial first step, hence the geographical concept of **landscape** and its inclusion in the title of this textbook. Taken at face value, *land* refers to the environment—that which sustains and surrounds us—and *scape* means view: a landscape is literally a view of the arrangement in physical space of human activities and artifacts. But of course the concept has much more depth than this literal explanation suggests. As Relph notes (1989):

> Landscapes are many sided phenomena. In their most obvious sense they are visible environments which not only have aesthetic and symbolic properties but also serve many purposes, some of which are immediately apparent, like car parks and tree houses, while others are more subtle, such as property speculation. Considerable expenditures of time, effort and money are required to make and modify built environments, so it is unlikely that their appearances are mere accidents.

(a)

(b)

FIGURE 5.1 Cultural contrasts are clearly evident between (*a*) a subsistence maize plot in Zimbabwe and (*b*) the extensive fields and mechanized farming of the U.S. Midwest.

Observations of those appearances lead to questions, and this is the genesis of geographical inquiry. Why, since humankind constitutes a single species, are cultures so varied over space and time? What and where were the origins of the different culture regions we now observe? How, from whatever limited areas individual culture traits developed, were they diffused over a wider portion of the globe? How did people who had roughly similar origins come to display significant areal differences in technology, social structure, ideology, and the innumerable other expressions of human geographic diversity?

What are the variety of resource use strategies evident between various cultural groups and their natural environments? What do the changes to the natural environment by a particular people tell us about their way of life? And what are the social, economic, and political processes giving rise to such a plurality of human activities, landscapes, and identities?

To answer such questions, a number of themes and numerous concepts have emerged in cultural geography that help us to conceptually organize our approach to, and our understanding of, something as seemingly all encompassing as culture. What follows is an overview of the four traditional themes of cultural geography—cultural *history*, cultural *area*, cultural *ecology*, and cultural *landscape*—followed by a fifth theme—cultural *politics*—which is the principal focus of most contemporary cultural geographers. But before we look at how geographers have sought to understand landscapes of human activities, we need to consider what constitutes "culture" and the processes that create and change it.

Characteristics and Components of Culture

Culture is a human creation: it is invented, practised, changed, and maintained by human beings. People make cultures and transmit them within a society to succeeding generations by imitation, instruction, and example. In short, it is learned, not biological.

It has nothing to do with instinct or with genes. As members of a social group, individuals acquire integrated sets of behavioural patterns, environmental and social perceptions, and knowledge of existing technologies. Of necessity, each of us learns the culture in which we are born and reared. But we need not—indeed, cannot—learn their totality. Age, gender, status, or occupation may dictate the aspects of the cultural whole in which an individual becomes integrated.

Characteristics of Culture

Culture is *plural*. The diversity of human cultures is perhaps most evident at an international global scale, when we compare say, the dietary practices of the Maasai in Kenya (Figure 5.2) with those of the typical North American. But even at a national, regional, or city scale, diversity abounds: the majority of Quebecers speak French whereas English speakers dominate the rest of Canada; the livelihood of rural Northern Ontarians is tied much more directly to resource extraction than the more service and commerce based employment of urbanites in Southwestern Ontario; and the influx of large numbers of Asian immigrants to Greater Vancouver in recent years has changed the face of the city's neighbourhoods. Plurality is no less evident at the scale of the individual human being. You yourself have a pluralistic cultural identity—ancestral heritage, language, nationality, gender, religion, and economic class, to name but a few of your many cultural characteristics—which makes you and everyone else part of several subculture groups simultaneously. Consequently, societies are "multicultural": composed of many cultures and cultural groups whose way of life expresses their identities.

Multiculturalism takes four forms in Canada. First, it is a *fact*. As noted above, Canada is comprised of people from virtually all over the world. Toronto, Ontario, for example, is arguably the most diverse city in the world, with one in two residents having been born outside of the country, and over 100 dialects and languages spoken. Second, it is an *ideology*: a set of beliefs celebrating cultural diversity. These beliefs are commensurate

Culture is thus a *medium of expression*. Human beings are unique in that we use virtually everything and anything to communicate meanings directly and indirectly to ourselves and to other people. Cities, clothing, education, entertainment, food, housing, shopping malls, transportation, tools, occupations—virtually everything humans know, use, or invent—reveals something about culture, if only indirectly. This is because the material objects we build, the social systems and relationships we practise, and the ideas, beliefs, and values we mentally construe are themselves cultural. These do not simply reflect culture; they *are* culture (Figure 5.3). As discussed later in Chapter 6, language is arguably the most important means of transmitting culture because it is both direct and comprehensive: it permits precise communication

FIGURE 5.2 The formerly migratory Maasai of Kenya are now largely sedentary, partially urbanized, and frequently owners of fenced farms. Cattle formed the traditional basis of Maasai culture and were the evidence of wealth and social status. They provided, as well, the milk and blood important in the Maasai diet. Here, a herdsman catches blood released from a small neck incision he has just made.

FIGURE 5.3 Both the traditional rice farmer of rural Japan and the harried commuter of Tokyo are part of a common Japanese culture. They occupy, however, vastly different positions in its social structure.

with the principles of freedom, tolerance, and respect for individual differences. Among the underlying assumptions of this ideology are the ideals that all cultural groups are equal, accommodation and mutual understanding will promote social harmony, and that diversity must be actively managed, not simply tolerated. Third, it is a *government policy*. Initiated by Prime Minister Trudeau in 1971, it became legally entrenched in 1988 under the *Multicultural Act*. Under this law, everyone is entitled to equal treatment, protection from "racial" discrimination, equality of opportunity, and the right to remain culturally different. Fourth, it is an *ongoing process*. Cultural conflicts between members of our diverse society occur regularly, but these can be minimized through promoting and practising the values inherent in the ideology of multiculturalism, and as a last resort, resolved peacefully in a court of law (see "Geography and Public Policy: Multiculturalism: Balancing our Cultural Differences").

Geography and Public Policy

Multiculturalism: Balancing our Cultural Differences

As an ongoing process whereby Canadians attempt to resolve cultural conflicts among a diversity of cultural groups, the ideals inherent in the policies of "multiculturalism" are useful guidelines. Putting policy into practice, however, is difficult. Tolerating, encouraging, and celebrating diversity does promote inclusion and fairness for all, but does this mean that each and every way of doing and thinking must be acceptable? Below are a series of cultural conflicts that have emerged in Canada's multicultural society in recent years. Each one is an instance where differences in ways of doing and thinking have generated a controversy in need of resolution. Think about each issue and where you stand.

Religious Expression

A Muslim girl in a large city was sent home from her secondary school for wearing a hijab, a head covering she must wear due to her religious beliefs. She was dismissed because the school dress code does not permit distinctive clothing that would indicate a student's religion. Should secondary schools be permitted to ban religious dress given that "freedom of religion and expression" is entrenched in the Charter of Rights and Freedoms?

Free Speech

A university professor gained notoriety for controversial views on "race" expressed in the scholar's published academic articles and through class lectures. There were calls by some students and faculty to levels as high as the provincial premier's office to fire the professor because of his "racist" views. Should the freedom of speech extend to those who voice what others regard as racist ideas?

Public Affection

Two 12-year-old girls were dismissed from their elementary school for the day, much to the anger of their respective parents, because they were observed kissing each other in the cafeteria by teachers. No such expulsion had occurred previously when boy–girl partners exchanged similar forms of public affection. Should all such public displays of affection be tolerated or prohibited at elementary schools? And should distinctions be made according to sexual orientation?

Recreational Activity

"New" Canadians in a small town located in a largely rural area organized a bullfighting event, much as they had done in their previous homeland. Under current Canadian laws, bullfighting is considered a form of animal cruelty and is not permitted by anyone. The organizers of the event cited that this practice was part of their cultural heritage and they should be allowed to proceed. Should existing laws stand, or should culture serve as a defence in such instances, thus permitting the event to proceed? Why?

National Symbol

The red serge coat, breeches, boots, and Stetson hat of the Royal Canadian Mounted Police comprise a uniform recognized as a symbol of Canada to Canadians and others around the world. Since 1990, the Stetson hat may be substituted by a turban for those officers of the Sikh faith who must wear one in accordance with their religion. Should such an accommodation have been made? Why or why not?

Questions to Consider

1. Select one of the above issues and switch your initial position. Devise an alternative argument opposing your original position, and then re-evaluate both sides. What might this tell you about the complexities of balancing cultural differences?

2. Virtually all successful social relationships involve accommodation, a mutual give and take. This holds true for both relationships of two people or entire societies. How much accommodation do you expect from new immigrants to adopt mainstream ways of doing and thinking? And how far are you willing to modify your own ways of doing and thinking to accommodate newcomers? This is the very balancing act that multicultural societies must address. Consider not only such issues as the wearing of religious symbols, but dress, language, food, and attitudes towards the gender roles of men and women.

3. Opponents to Canada's "multiculturalism" argue that "unity through diversity" is false. If the only commonality we share is our differences then there is nothing substantive to bind us together as a society. Do you think diversity in Canadian society is for the better or for the worse? Why?

---

between people about virtually any aspect of a culture. Language is the primary means through which a way of life is learned. Consequently, language is one of the most sophisticated cultural creations, and is itself a key marker of cultural identity.

Culture is also inherently *spatial*, and this is of primary importance to the geographer. In other words, how space is used, organized, arranged and ascribed meaning by people, are forms of culture. Where and why humans locate and arrange their activities, objects, and themselves in physical space; the modifications they make to the "physical" or natural environment; the kinds of "human" or built environments they construct in which to live, work, and socialize; the meanings, values, sentiments, and identities they attribute and attach to places; even how the human body—itself a space—is dressed, groomed, and behaves in various settings: all are expressions of culture. One of the goals of the cultural geographer is to learn how to interpret space in order to understand what it reveals about culture, and thus what it says about human beings and the geographies they construct.

Culture is *politics* by another name. Power is intrinsic to the very production and expression of culture. **Power** exists whenever there is an uneven relationship and the stronger or dominant party—an individual person, a cultural group, citizens of a city, an entire society, country, or group of countries—has the ability to influence, if not determine, the actions of the weaker or subordinate. The roots of power are numerous, but the basic foundation is access to resources others possess to the same degree: wealth, knowledge, physical strength, technology, land, labour, raw materials, and so forth. Those cultural groups with the most power are able to protect and promote their own interests and ways of life more effectively than less powerful groups. Culture is therefore a "site of struggle" (Jackson, 1989): various cultural groups conflict, contest, and negotiate with one another to have their own way of life if not privileged, then certainly accepted by others. As will be shown below, these struggles necessarily involve space.

Components of Culture

For analytical purposes, the traits and complexes of culture—its building blocks and expressions—may be grouped and examined as three subsets of the whole (Leslie White, 1900–1975).

The **ideological subsystem** consists of ideas, beliefs, and knowledge of a culture, and of the ways in which these things are expressed in speech or other forms of communication. Mythologies and theologies, legend, literature, philosophy, and folk wisdom make up this category. Passed on from generation to generation, these abstract belief systems, or **mentifacts**, tell us what we ought to believe, what we should value, and how we ought to act. Beliefs form the basis of the socialization process. Often we know—or think we know—what the beliefs of a group are from their oral or written statements. Sometimes, however, we must depend on the actions or objectives of a group to tell us what its true ideas and values are. "Actions speak louder than words" or "Do as I say, not as I do" are commonplace recognitions of the fact that actions, values, and words do not always coincide. Two basic strands of the ideological subsystem—language and religion—are the subject of Chapter 6.

The **technological subsystem** is composed of the material objects, together with the techniques of their use, by means of which people are able to live. The objects are the tools and other instruments that enable us to feed, clothe, house, defend, transport, and amuse ourselves. We must have food, we must be protected from the elements, and we must be able to defend ourselves. Huxley termed the material objects we use to fill these basic needs **artifacts** (Figure 5.4). In Chapter 11 we will examine the relationship between technological subsystems and regional patterns of economic development.

The **sociological subsystem** of a culture is the sum of those expected and accepted patterns of interpersonal relations that find their outlet in economic, political, military, religious, kinship, and other associations. These **sociofacts** define the social organization of a culture. They regulate how the individual functions relative to the group—whether it be family, church, or state. There are no "givens" as far as the patterns of interaction in any of these associations are concerned, except that most cultures possess a variety of formal and informal ways of structuring behaviour. Differing patterns of behaviour are learned and are transmitted from one generation to the next (Figure 5.5).

Classifications are necessarily arbitrary, and these classifications of the subsystems and components of culture are no exception. The three-part categorization of culture, while helping us to appreciate its structure and complexity, can simultaneously obscure the many-sided nature of individual elements of culture. A dwelling, for example, is an artifact providing shelter for its occupants. It is, simultaneously, a sociofact reflecting the nature of the family or kinship group it is designed to house, and a mentifact summarizing a culture group's convictions about appropriate

(a)

(b)

FIGURE 5.4 (*a*) This Balinese farmer working with draft animals uses tools typical of the lower technological levels of subsistence economies. (*b*) Cultures with advanced technological subsystems use complex machinery to harness inanimate energy for productive use.

design, orientation, and building materials of dwelling units. In the same vein, clothing serves as an artifact of bodily protection appropriate to climatic conditions, available materials and techniques, or the activity in which the wearer is engaged. But garments also may be sociofacts, identifying an individual's role in the social structure of the community or culture, and mentifacts, evoking larger community value systems (Figure 5.6).

And finally, the characteristics and components of culture are *dynamic*. Culture is in a perpetual process of change, of becoming different, because people themselves change: different ways of doing and thinking are invented, which alter the material objects, systems of organization, and thoughts and beliefs of the cultures people create. Similarly, differing ways of doing and thinking will come to prominence or fade as the dominant and subordinate

FIGURE 5.5 All societies prepare their children for membership in the culture group. In each of these settings, certain values, beliefs, skills, and proper ways of acting are being transmitted to the youngsters.

(a)   (b)   (c)

FIGURE 5.6 (*a*) When clothing serves primarily to cover, protect, or assist in activities, it is an *artifact*; (*b*) Some garments are *sociofacts,* identifying a role or position within the social structure: the distinctive "uniforms" of the soldier, the cleric, or the beribboned ambassador immediately proclaim their respective roles in a culture's social organizations; (*c*) The sometimes mandatory burkas or chadors worn by Muslim women are *mentifacts,* indicative not specifically of the role of the wearer but of the values of the culture the wearer represents.

cultural groups of a society change. And of course, culture not only varies over time but over space. One need only travel from one's own hometown to another to notice subtle cultural variations over space; travel to a foreign country can make these differences striking. Cultural changes, be they slow or rapid, small and local, or large and global, manifest themselves in the human landscape at varying scales. The geographer not only tries to document cultures in and over time and space, but more importantly, attempts to understand and explain the many social, economic, and political processes that create the identities of cultural landscapes. To study culture as a geographer is to study the processes of change in the landscapes of human activities (see "Geography and Public Policy: Multiculturalism: Balancing our Cultural Differences").

Processes of Cultural Change

Because creating culture is an active process, and modification is intrinsic to its very construction, change is a fundamental focus of cultural geography. Admittedly, most cultures are essentially slow to change. Indeed, most societies have an innate resistance to change because new or different ways may be perceived by some as an unwelcome threat to the established order. Similarly, at the level of the individual, change requires effort—learning new skills, rethinking one's beliefs, altering behaviours—that need not be expended if the *status quo*—the existing state of affairs—remains unaltered. Nevertheless, entire societies, the individuals who comprise them, and the cultures they make are always in a state of flux.

Some changes are major and pervasive. The transition from hunter-gatherer to sedentary farmer, for example, affected markedly every facet of the cultures experiencing that change. Profound, too, has been the impact of the Industrial Revolution and its associated urbanization on all societies it has touched.

Not all change is so extensive as that following the introduction of agriculture or the Industrial Revolution. Many changes are so slight individually as to go almost unnoticed at their inception, though cumulatively they may substantially alter the affected culture. Think of how the culture of Canada differs today from what you know it to have been in 1970—not in essentials, perhaps, but in the innumerable electronic telecommunication devices that have been introduced, and in the social, behavioural, and recreational changes they and other technological changes have wrought. Among these latter have been shifts in employment patterns to include greater participation by women in the waged workforce, and associated adjustments in attitudes toward the role of women in the society at large. Such cumulative changes occur because the cultural traits of any group are not independent; they are clustered in a coherent and integrated pattern. Change on a small scale will have wide repercussions as associated traits arrive at accommodation with the adopted adjustment. Change, both major and minor, and within or between cultures, is induced by *innovation, diffusion, acculturation,* and *assimilation.*

Innovation

Innovation implies changes to a culture that result from ideas created within the social group itself and adopted by the culture. The novelty may be an invented improvement in material technology, like the bow and arrow or the computer chip, or it may involve the development of non-material forms of social structure and interaction: feudalism, for example, or democracy. Regardless of its form, innovation is a driving force for cultural change, but what induces innovation? If a society is at equilibrium with its environment and has no unmet needs, innovation has no adaptive value and no reason to occur. Necessity is the parent of innovation.

All cultures are amalgams of innumerable innovations spread spatially from their points of origin and integrated into the structure of the receiving societies. It has been estimated that no more than 10% of the cultural items of any society are traceable to innovations created by its members, and that the other 90% come to the society through diffusion (see "A 'Homemade' Global Culture"). Since the pace of innovation is affected strongly by the mixing of ideas among alert, responsive people, and is increased by exposure to a variety of cultures, the most active and innovative historical origins of culture were those at crossroads and those deeply involved in distant trade and colonization. Ancient Mesopotamia and classical Greece and Rome had such crossroads and involvements, as did West Africa after the 5th century and, much later, England during the Industrial Revolution and the spread of its empire. The same can be said of the United States for much of the 20th century and the emergent 21st century.

Innovation—invention—frequently under stress, has marked the history of humankind. As we have seen, growing populations at the end of the Ice Age necessitated an expanded food base. In response, domestication of plants and animals appears to have occurred independently in more than one world area. Indeed, a most striking fact about early agriculture is the universality of its development or adoption within a relatively short span of human history. In 10,000 B.C.E., the world population of no more than 10 million was exclusively hunter-gatherers. By 1500 A.C.E., only 1% of the world's 350 million people still followed that way of life. The revolution in food production affected every facet of the threefold subsystems of culture in every society accepting it. All innovation has a radiating impact on the web of culture; the more basic the innovation, the more pervasive its consequences.

In most contemporary societies, innovative change has become common, expected, and inevitable. The rate of invention, at least as measured by the number of patents granted, has steadily increased, and the period between idea conception and product availability has been decreasing. A general axiom is that the more ideas available and the more minds able to exploit and combine them, the greater the rate of innovation. The spatial implication is that larger urban centres of advanced technologies tend to be centres of innovation. This is not just because of their size but because of the number of ideas interchanged. Indeed, ideas not only stimulate new thoughts and viewpoints but also create circumstances in which the society must develop new solutions to maintain its forward momentum (Figure 5.7).

Diffusion

Diffusion is the process by which an idea or innovation is transmitted from one individual or group to another across space. Diffusion may assume a variety of forms, each different in its

A Canadian has been described as a person wearing English tweeds, a Hong Kong shirt and Spanish shoes, who sips Brazilian coffee sweetened with Philippine sugar from a Bavarian cup while eating American apple pie topped with Swiss cheese, sitting at a Danish desk over a Persian rug, after driving home in a German car from an Italian movie with an African friend . . . who then writes, in both English and French, to their Member of Parliament—a system of government modelled after the British—using a Japanese computer, requesting that something be done about the high cost of gasoline imported from the Middle East.

This tongue in cheek portrait is amusing in so far as it accentuates the diversity of Canadian society: we are a country premised on cultures from around the world: we are a 'global' culture. With the major exception of First Nations people—the original peoples who "first" occupied what is now Canada—all of us can trace our family heritage back to someplace else. Almost 20% of us were born outside Canada, coming from over 168 different countries in the world, with over 1 in 10 of us being a "visible minority" (person of colour). In addition to the "official" languages of English and French, we speak more than 100 languages. Over three-quarters of us are Christian, almost 7% are Muslim, Jewish, Buddhist, Hindu, Sikh or other, and 16% of us have no religious affiliation at all. In terms of ethnicity, language, and religion, we are "multicultural." But what is "culture"? How is it "multiple"? And how does geography help us to understand cultures both within Canada and around the world?

Source: Adapted from Statistics Canada, 2001.

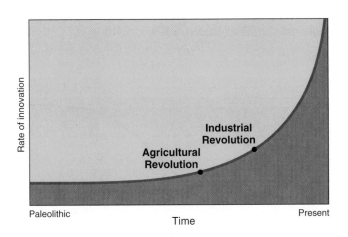

FIGURE 5.7 The trend of innovation through human history. Hunter-gatherers, living in equilibrium with their environment and their resource base, had little need for innovation and no necessity for cultural change. The Agricultural Revolution accelerated the diffusion of the ideas and techniques of domestication, urbanization, and trade. With the Industrial Revolution, dramatic increases in all aspects of socio-economic innovation began to alter cultures throughout the world.

impact on social groups. Basically, however, two processes are involved: (1) People move, for any of a number of reasons, to a new area and take their culture with them. For example, 18th century British, French, and Spanish immigrants to North American colonies brought along crops and farming techniques, building styles, or concepts of government alien to their new home. (2) Information about an innovation (e.g., hybrid corn or compact discs) may spread throughout a society, perhaps aided by local or mass media advertising; or new adopters of an ideology or way of life—for example, a new religious creed—may be inspired or recruited by immigrant or native converts. The former is known as *relocation diffusion*, the latter as *expansion diffusion* (Figure 5.8).

Expansion diffusion involves the spread of an item or idea from one place to others. In the process, the thing diffused also remains—and is frequently intensified—in the origin area. Islam, for example, expanded from its Arabian Peninsula origin locale across much of Asia and North Africa. At the same time, it strengthened its hold over its Near Eastern birthplace by displacing pagan, Christian, and Jewish populations. When expansion diffusion affects nearly uniformly all individuals and areas outward from the source region, it is termed *contagious diffusion*. The term implies the importance of direct contact between those who developed or have adopted the innovation and those who newly encounter it, and is reminiscent of the course of infectious diseases (Figure 5.9).

If an idea has merit in the eyes of potential adopters, and they themselves become adopters, the number of contacts of adopters with potential adopters will compound. Consequently, the innovation will spread slowly at first and then more and more rapidly until saturation occurs or a barrier is reached. The incidence of adoption under contagious diffusion is represented by the S-shaped curve in Figure 5.10. The rate of diffusion of a trait or idea may be influenced by *time–distance decay* (see Chapter 3), which simply tells us that the spread or acceptance of an idea is usually delayed as distance from the source of the innovation increases.

In some instances, however, geographic distance is less important in the transfer of ideas than is communication between major centres or important people. News of new clothing styles, for example, quickly spreads internationally between major cities and only later filters down irregularly to smaller towns and rural areas. The process of transferring ideas first between larger places or prominent people and only later to smaller or less important points or people is known as *hierarchical diffusion*. The Christian faith in Europe, for example, spread from Rome as the principal centre to provincial capitals and thence to smaller Roman settlements in largely pagan occupied territories.

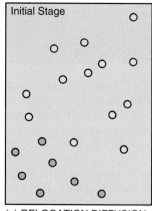

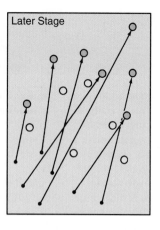

(a) RELOCATION DIFFUSION

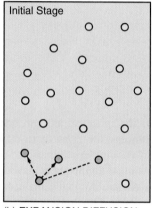

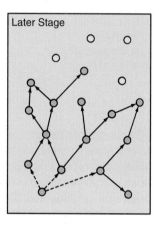

(b) EXPANSION DIFFUSION

FIGURE 5.8 Patterns of diffusion. (*a*) In *relocation diffusion*, innovations or ideas are transported to new areas by carriers who permanently leave the home locale. The "Pennsylvania Dutch" barn (Figure 5.27) was brought to Pennsylvania by German immigrants and spread to other groups and areas southward through Appalachia and westward into Ohio, Indiana, Illinois, and Missouri, Not all farmers or farm districts in the path of advancement adopted the new barn design. (*b*) In *expansion diffusion*, a phenomenon spreads from one place to neighbouring locations, but in the process remains and is often intensified in the place of origin.

Source: Redrawn by permission from Spatial Diffusion, *by Peter R. Gould, Resource Paper no. 4, page 4, Association of American Geographers, 1969.*

While the diffusion of ideas may be slowed by time–distance decay, their speed of spread may be increased to the point of becoming instantaneous through the *space–time compression* (Chapter 3) made possible by modern communication. Given access to radios; telephones; worldwide transmission of television news, sports, and entertainment programs; and—perhaps most importantly—to computers and the Internet, people and areas distantly separated can immediately share in a common fund of thought and innovation.

Stimulus diffusion is a third form of expansion diffusion. The term summarizes situations in which a fundamental idea, though not the specific trait itself, stimulates imitative behaviour within a receptive population. Canada's nation-wide 'blue box' recycling programs is a case in point. Begun in Kitchener, Ontario, in 1981, as a means to divert from landfill materials that could be recycled

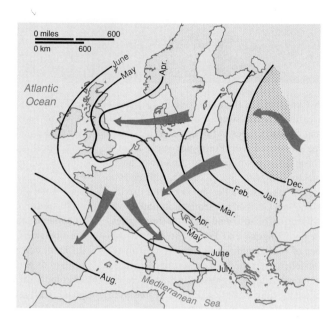

FIGURE 5.9 The process of *contagious diffusion* is sensitive to both time and distance, as suggested by the diffusion pathways of the European influenza pandemic of 1781. The pattern there was a wavelike radiation from a Russian nodal origin area.

Source: Based on Gerald F. Pyle and K. David Patterson, Ecology of Disease 2, *no. 3 (1984): 179.*

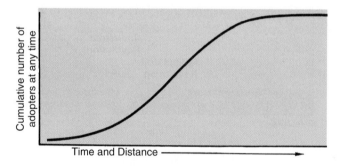

FIGURE 5.10 The diffusion of innovations over time and distance. The number of adopters of an innovation rises at an increasing rate over an increasing distance until the point at which about one-half of the total who ultimately decide to adopt the innovation have made the decision. At that point, the number of adopters increases at a decreasing rate.

into new products—paper, plastics, metal, and glass—the idea spread. Reducing household wastes through curbside collection, thus reducing landfill space, saving energy and lowering greenhouse gases, swept Ontario over the next ten years. In 1989, the province was awarded the first ever United Nations Environment Award for this innovative contribution to lessen pollution. Delegations from across the country and around the globe converged in Ontario to see how this recycling system worked, and how they might initiate similar recycling projects of their own. The specific traits of the collection techniques, the variety of materials collected, even the colour of the collection box may vary over space, but the *idea* of curbside recycling was diffused by stimulating imitative behaviour.

In **relocation diffusion**, the innovation or idea is physically carried to new areas by migrating individuals or populations that possess it (Figure 5.8a). Mentifacts or artifacts are therefore introduced into new locales by new settlers who become part of populations not themselves associated or in contact with the origin area of the innovation. The spread of religions by settlers or conquerors is a clear example of relocation diffusion, as was the diffusion of agriculture to Europe from the Middle East (Figure 5.26). Christian Europeans brought their faiths to areas of colonization or economic penetration throughout the world. At the world scale, massive relocation diffusion resulted from the European colonization and economic penetration that began in the 16th century. More localized relocation diffusion continues today as Asian refugees or foreign "guest workers" bring their cultural traits to their new areas of settlement in Europe or North America.

Innovations in the technological or ideological subsystems may be relatively readily diffused to, and accepted by, cultures that have basic similarities and compatibilities. Continental Europe and North America, for example, could easily and quickly adopt the innovations of the Industrial Revolution diffused from England with which they shared a common political, social, economic, and technological background. Industrialization was not quickly developed in Asian and African societies of totally different cultural conditioning. Diffusion also depends on the nature of power relations exercised between various societies. Industrialization was not introduced into these peripheral regions because they contributed the resource extraction component of a world colonial economy dictated by Europe and North America. This unequal role in the world economy shaped many social characteristics of Asian and African regions that might have made industrialization difficult: low levels of urbanization, low wages, and the export of surplus wealth.

On the ideological level, too, successful diffusion depends on acceptability of the innovations. The United Kingdom of Great Britain, for example, remains wedded to its own currency, the British pound, despite its membership in the European Union. This union of 25 independent European states, founded in 1993 to enhance political, economic, and social cooperation, now uses the "euro" as its currency. The British have so far resisted this change for largely sentimental and symbolic reasons. When a social group is inappropriately unresponsive—mentally, psychologically, or economically—to changing circumstances and to innovation, it is said to exhibit **cultural lag**.

It is not always possible, of course, to determine the precise point of origin or the routes of diffusion of innovations now widely adopted (see "Documenting Diffusion"). Nor is it always certain whether the existence of a cultural trait in two different areas is the result of diffusion or of **independent** (or *parallel*) **invention**. Cultural similarities do not necessarily prove that diffusion has occurred. The pyramids of Egypt and of the Central American Maya civilization most likely were separately conceived and are not necessarily evidence, as some have proposed, of pre-Columbian voyages from the Mediterranean to the Americas. A Neolithic monument-building culture, after all, has only a limited number of shapes from which to choose.

Historical examples of independent, parallel invention are numerous: logarithms by Napier (1614) and Burgi (1620), the calculus by Newton (1672) and Leibnitz (1675), and the telephone by Elisha Gray and Alexander Graham Bell (1876), are commonly cited. Who invented what at specific times and locations is often more a function of politics than science. Nevertheless, it appears beyond doubt that agriculture was independently developed not only in both the New World and the Old but also in more than one society in each of the hemispheres.

Acculturation and Transfer

A culture group or individual member may undergo major modifications in their own identifying traits by willingly adopting some or all of the characteristics of another, dominant culture group. This process of modification is called **acculturation**. The classic example of this is the cultural transfer experienced by immigrants as they learn, appropriate, and practise the values, attitudes, behaviours, customs, technologies, speech, and spaces of their receiving society. During this process—one that is quite slow for many individuals and groups—the immigrant group loses its separate cultural identity as it accepts over time the culture of the larger host community. Although acculturation most usually involves a minority group adopting the patterns of the dominant population, the process can be reciprocal. That is, the dominant group may also adopt at least some patterns and practices typical of the minority group. The entire process has numerous variables that may interact in different ways, altering the speed and degree of cultural transfer.

Immigrant groups arrive at their destinations with already existing sets of production techniques and skills. They bring established ideas of "appropriate" dress, foods, and building styles, and they have religious practices, marriage customs, and other cultural expressions in place and ingrained. That is, immigrants carry to their new homes a full complement of artifacts, sociofacts, and mentifacts. They may modify, abandon, or even pass these on to the host culture, depending on a number of interacting influences: (1) the background of the arriving group; (2) its social and spatial distance from the charter group; (3) the disparity between new home and origin-area environmental conditions; (4) the importance given by the migrants to the economic, political, or religious motivations that caused them to relocate; and (5) the kinds of encountered constraints that force personal, social, or technical adjustments on the new arrivals. Generally speaking, acculturation tends to be most rapid when the immigrant group shares many of the basic traits similar to the host society, is relatively well educated and wealthy, and finds political or social advantage to transferring cultural identities.

Immigrant groups rarely transferred intact all of their culture traits to North America. Invariably, there have been modifications as a result of the necessary adjustment to new circumstances or physical conditions. In general, if a transplanted ethnic trait was usable in the new locale, it was retained. Simple inertia suggested there was little reason to abandon the familiar and comfortable when no advantage accrued. If a trait or a set of traits was essential to group identity and purpose—the religious convictions of the rural Mennonites of Waterloo County, Ontario, for example, or of urban Hasidic Jews—its retention was certain. But ill-suited habits or techniques would be abandoned if superior practices were encountered, and totally inappropriate practices would be discarded. German settlers in Texas, for example, found that the

The places of origin of many ideas, items, and technologies important in contemporary cultures are only dimly known or supposed, and their routes of diffusion are speculative at best. Gunpowder, printing, and spaghetti are presumed to be the products of Chinese inventiveness; the lateen sail has been traced to the Near Eastern culture world; the mold-board plow is ascribed to 6th-century Slavs of northeastern Europe. The sequence and routes of the diffusion of these innovations has not been documented.

In other cases, such documentation exists, and the process of diffusion is open to analysis. Clearly marked is the diffusion path of the custom of smoking tobacco, a practice that originated among Amerindians. Sir Walter Raleigh's Virginia colonists, returning home in 1586, introduced smoking in English court circles, and the habit very quickly spread among the general populace. England became the source region of the new custom for northern Europe; smoking was introduced to Holland by English medical students in 1590. Dutch and English together spread the habit by sea to the Baltic and Scandinavian areas and overland through Germany to Russia. The innovation continued its eastward diffusion, and within a hundred years tobacco had spread across Siberia and was, in the 1740s, reintroduced to the American continent at Alaska by Russian fur traders. A second route of diffusion for tobacco smoking can be traced from Spain, where the custom was introduced in 1558, and from which it spread more slowly through the Mediterranean area into Africa, the Near East, and Southeast Asia.

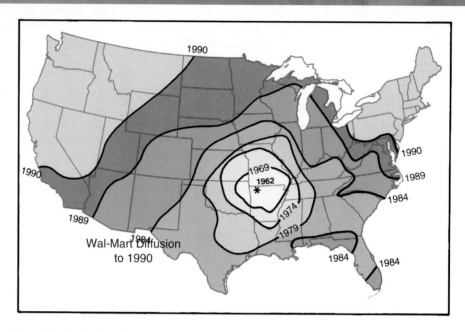

Wal-Mart Diffusion to 1990

Source: Map based on data from Thomas O. Graff and Dub Ashton, "Spatial Diffusion of Wal-Mart: Contagious and Reverse Hierarchical Elements." Professional Geographer 46, no. 1 (1994): 19–29.

In more recent times, hybrid corn was first adopted by imaginative farmers of northern Illinois and eastern Iowa in the mid-1930s. By the late 1930s and early 1940s, the new seeds were being planted as far east as Ohio and north to Minnesota, Wisconsin, and northern Michigan. By the late 1940s, all commercial corn-growing districts of the United States and southern Canada were cultivating hybrid corn varieties.

A similar pattern of diffusion marked the expansion of the Wal-Mart stores chain. From its origin in northwest Arkansas in 1962, the discount chain had dispersed throughout the United States by the 1990s to become the country's largest retailer in sales volume. In its expansion, Wal-Mart displayed "reverse hierarchical" diffusion, initially spreading by way of small towns before opening its first stores in larger cities and metropolitan areas (see map). For a dynamic map showing the diffusion and density of Wal-Mart in the U.S. from 1962 through 2005, see "The Diffusion of Wal-Mart and Economies of Density" at http://www.youtube.com/watch?v=EGzHBtoVvpc.

vine and other familiar mid-latitude fruits did not thrive there. Old-country agricultural traditions were, they discovered, not fully transferable and had to be altered.

In many instances, close contact between two different groups may involve adjustments of the original cultural patterns of both rather than disappearance of either. For example, changes in Japanese political organization and philosophy were imposed by occupying Americans after World War II, and the Japanese voluntarily adopted some more frivolous aspects of American life. In turn, American society was enriched by the selective importation of Japanese cuisine, architecture, and philosophy, demonstrating the two-way nature of cultural diffusion. Where that two-way flow reflects a more equal exchange of cultural outlooks and ways of life, a process of *transculturation* has occurred. That process is observable within the United States as massive South

and Central American immigration begins to intertwine formerly contrasting cultures, altering both.

Assimilation

When integration has been achieved, **assimilation** has occurred. Full assimilation may be seen as a three-part process. **Behavioural assimilation** is integration into a common behavioural pattern through shared experience, language, intermarriage, and sense of history. **Structural assimilation** refers to the fusion of immigrant groups with the social systems and occupations of the host society and the adoption of common attitudes and values. Structural assimilation is a two-way street. Not only does it require immigrant groups to absorb majority cultural values and practices, but it also demands that the majority society give full and unrestricted acceptance to members of the minority group and allow them to rise to positions of authority and power. The extent of behavioural and structural assimilation is frequently measured by the degree of **spatial assimilation**: the overlap, intersection, and sharing of physical space between two previously separate cultural groups (e.g., immigrants and hosts). The greater the degree of spatial integration between the groups—sharing the same workplace, shops, recreational sites, and residential neighbourhoods—the greater the degree of cultural assimilation will be.

Precisely what threshold of cultural transfer must be attained to constitute assimilation is debatable today. Immigrant minorities in North America no longer suffer the isolation from their homelands that of necessity hastened their acculturation into assimilation in the past. As mentioned in Chapter 4, the new ease of personal long-distance communication via telephone and email, of cheap and easy international travel that maintains and renews home territory ties, the globalization of print and broadcast news and ready availability of home country newspapers and magazines on the Internet, and a host of other means of retaining close association and continuing identity with original national and cultural origins, give immigrant groups and individuals enhanced capabilities to survive without full integration into the majority society of their new homes. In a multicultural society such as Canada's, where cultural diversity is not only tolerated but actively managed, assimilation has become more of a continuum, rather than an absolute. Newcomers are more likely to become assimilated into a cultural mosaic, where much of their original culture can be maintained, rather than into one uniform, homogenous culture of the dominant host.

Assimilation no longer necessarily means that cultural identities or awareness of cultural differences is lost. *Competition theory*, in fact, suggests that as cultural minorities begin to achieve success and enter into mainstream social and economic life, awareness of cultural differences may be heightened. Frequently, ethnic identity, for example, may be most clearly experienced and expressed by those who can most successfully assimilate but who choose to promote group awareness and ethnic mobilization movements. That promotion, the theory holds, is a reflection of pressures of urban life and the realities of increased competition. Those pressures transform formerly isolated groups into recognized, self-assertive ethnic minorities pursuing goals and interests dependent on their position within the larger society.

Similarly, the concept of **hybridity** suggests that cultural identities are not lost entirely when two or more cultural groups intermingle and exchange various aspects of their respective cultures. Adopting cultures do not usually accept intact items originating outside the receiving society. Diffused ideas and artifacts commonly undergo some alteration of meaning or form that makes them acceptable to a borrowing group. The process of cross-breeding or fusing cultures is called hybridity and is a major feature of culture change. It can be seen in alterations to religious ritual and dogma made by convert societies seeking acceptable conformity between old and new beliefs; the mixture of Catholic rites and theological and magical elements taken from West African religions that produced voodooism in Haiti is an example. On a more familiar level, hybridity is reflected in subtle or blatant alterations of imported cuisines to make

them conform to the demands of North America's palate and its fast-food franchises (Figure 5.11).

Resistance to Change

Of course not all cultural change is readily accepted, willingly chosen, or free from resistance and barriers. Every relocated immigrant group may be subject to forces of rejection both toward and from the dominant host society.

Rejection factors internal to the immigrant group that aid in the retention of cultural identification include isolation and rebound. The group or individual members may seek cultural isolation through physical separation in remote areas or raise barriers of a social nature to assure its separation from corrupting influences. Social isolation can be effective even in congested urban environments if it is buttressed by distinctive costume, beliefs, or practices (Figure 5.12). Group segregation may even result in the retention of customs, clothing, or dialects discarded in the original home area. Rejection factors may also involve **culture rebound**, a belated adoption of group consciousness and re-establishment of identifying traits. These may reflect an attempt to reassert old values and to achieve at least a modicum of social separation. The wearing of dashikis, the popularity of Ghanian-origin kente cloth, or the celebration of Kwanzaa by North American blacks seeking identification with African roots, are examples of culture rebound. Ethnic identity is fostered by the nuclear family and ties of kinship, particularly when reinforced by residential proximity. It is preserved by such group activities as distinctive feasts or celebrations and by marriage customs; by ethnically identified clubs, such as the Turnverein societies of German communities or the Sokol movement of athletic and cultural centres among the former Czechs and by ethnic churches (Figure 5.13).

Conversely, a host society may reject an immigrant group and its culture, or a dominant cultural group may reject a minority one, due to a misplaced fear of the "other" or on the false premise of cultural or biological superiority. **Xenophobia** is the fear of or aversion to strangers or foreigners, often manifesting itself in the form of "ethnophobia": fear of a particular ethnic group. Newcomers with "strange" ways or different ethnicities are thus rejected on no other grounds than their difference.

Ethnocentrism is the term describing a tendency to evaluate other cultures against the standards of one's own. It implies the feeling that one's own ethnic or cultural group is superior. Ethnocentrism can divide multicultural societies by establishing rivalries and provoking social and spatial discord and isolation. Ethnocentricism should not be confused with holding one's own culture in high esteem. Pride in one's own cultural identities can be a sustaining and comforting emotion, giving familiar values and support to an individual in the face of life's complexities. **Racism**—the unfounded belief that social behaviour and cognitive ability is attributable to an arbitrary biological attribute (e.g., skin tone, size of nose, hair colour)—is perhaps more divisive. As will be discussed below, having pride in one's own distinct "race" is a misnomer.

Of course, cultural change can be forced upon others against their will. History is rich with instances of various cultural groups conquering or colonizing others and then imposing their own

FIGURE 5.11 Foreign foods, modified for Canadian tastes and Canadian palates growing accustomed to dishes from all cultures, together represent *hybridity* in action.

FIGURE 5.12 Ultra-orthodox Hasidim, segregating themselves by dress and custom, seek social isolation and shun corrupting outside influences even in the midst of New York City's congestion.

FIGURE 5.13 These young girls, dressed in traditional garb for a Los Angeles Greek Orthodox Church festival, show the close association of ethnicity and religion in the American mosaic.

ways. The subordinate or subject population is either forced to adopt the culture of the new ruling group, introduced through relocation diffusion, or does so voluntarily, overwhelmed by the superiority in numbers or the technical level of the conqueror. Tribal Europeans in areas of Roman conquest, native populations in the wake of Slavic occupation of Siberia, and Native Americans stripped of their lands following European settlement of North America, experienced this kind of cultural modification or adoption. Repressive laws, violent resistance, and cultural annihilation have resulted. Ramifications are numerous and often enduring.

For example, in Canada, only recently has the federal government formally acknowledged and apologized to Chinese Canadians for the discriminatory "head tax" it once enforced. As of 1885, all Chinese who immigrated to the country—and only the Chinese—had to pay what was in effect a racist entrance fee. This separated families who could not afford the price of admission, which created a "bachelor society" of Chinese males in Canada, and impacted families in both countries for generations to come. This tax ended in 1923, when Chinese were barred from immigrating altogether: the trans-Canada railway had been completed, and their cheap labour was no longer needed. The apology some eight decades later was welcomed by the few surviving "tax" payers and their immediate descendents.

Similarly, Basques and Catalans of Spain, and Corsicans, Bretons, and Normans of France have only recently seen their respective central governments relax strict prohibitions on teaching or using the languages that identified those ethnic groups. On the other hand, in Bulgaria, ethnic Turks, who unofficially comprise 10% of the total population, at least temporarily officially ceased to exist in 1984 when the government obliged Turkish speakers and Muslims to replace their Turkish and Islamic names with Bulgarian and Christian ones. The government also banned their language and strictly limited practice of their religion. The intent was to impose an assimilation not sought by the minority.

The Sinhalese comprise 75% of Sri Lanka's population, but the minority Tamils have waged years of guerrilla warfare to defend what they see as majority threats to their culture, rights, and property. In India, Kashmiri nationalists fight to separate their largely Muslim valley from the Hindu majority society. Expanding ethnic minorities made up nearly 8.5% of China's 2000 population total. Some, including Tibetans, Mongols, and Uighurs, face assimilation largely because of massive migrations of ethnic Chinese into their traditional homelands. And in many multi-ethnic African countries, single-party governments seek to impose a sense of national unity on populations whose primary and nearly unshakable loyalties are rooted in their tribes and regions and not the state that is composed of many tribes.

Across the world, conflicts between ethnic groups within states have proliferated in recent years. Armenia, Azerbaijan, Burma, Burundi, Ethiopia, Indonesia, Iraq, Russia, Rwanda, and the former Yugoslavia, are others in a long list of countries where ethnic tensions have erupted into civil conflict.

In extreme cases, of course, small and, particularly, primitive indigenous groups brought into contact with conquering or absorbing societies may simply cease to exist as separate cultural entities. Although presumably such cultural loss has been part of all of human history, its occurrence has been noted and its pace quickened over the past 500 years. By one informed estimate, at least one-third of the world's inventory of human cultures has totally disappeared since 1500 A.C.E., along with their languages, traditions, ways of life and, indeed, their very identity or remembrance. This loss is particularly disturbing if one considers cultural diversity as important to humanity as biodiversity is to the planet's ecosystems.

And finally, there are various kinds of **diffusion barriers** that minimize or negate cultural change. Diffusion barriers are any conditions that hinder either the flow of information or the movement of people and thus retard or prevent the acceptance of an innovation. Because of the *friction of distance*, generally the farther two areas are from each other, the less likely is interaction to occur, an observation earlier summarized by the term *time–distance decay*. Distance as a factor in spatial interaction was explored in Chapter 3. It is sufficient to note here that distance may be an *absorbing barrier*, halting the spread of an innovation.

Interregional contact can also be hindered by the physical environment and by a lack of receptivity by a contacted culture. Oceans and rugged terrain can and have acted as physical *interrupting barriers*, delaying or deflecting the path of diffusion. Cultural obstacles that are equally impenetrable may also exist. Should reluctant adopters or non-adopters of innovations intervene between hearths and receptive cultures, the spread of an innovation can be slowed. It can also be delayed when cultural contact is overtly impeded by governments that interfere with radio reception, control the flow of foreign literature, and discourage contact between their citizens and foreign nationals.

More commonly, barriers are at least partially *permeable*; they permit passage (acceptance) of at least some innovations encountering them. The more similar two cultural areas are to each other, the greater is the likelihood of the adoption of an innovation, for diffusion is a selective process. The receiver culture may adopt some goods or ideas from the donor society and reject others. The decision to adopt is governed by the receiving group's own culture.

Political restrictions, religious taboos, and other social customs are cultural barriers to diffusion. The French Canadians, although close geographically to many Anglo-Canadian centres of diffusion such as Ottawa and Toronto, strive to be only minimally influenced by them. Both their language and culture complex govern their selective acceptance of Anglo influences, such as Quebec's Bill 101, designed to preserve and enforce the integrity of their distinctive French culture. This is a language policy that clarifies, among other things, the rules of use of French and English in public signage, education, and health care. In a more extreme fashion, Afghan Taliban and other Mideast militant fundamentalist groups adamantly or violently reject Western

(a)

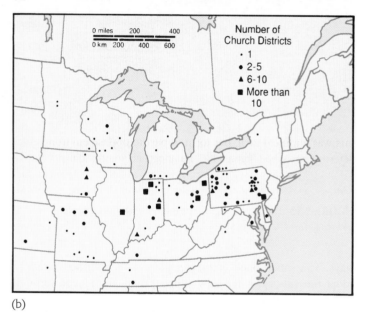

(b)

FIGURE 5.14 (*a*) Motivated by religious conviction that the "good life" must be reduced to its simplest forms, Old Order Amish communities shun all modern luxuries of the majority secular society around them. Children use horse and buggy, not school bus or automobile, on their daily trip to this rural school in east central Illinois. (*b*) **Distribution of Old Order Amish communities** in the United States.

Source: (b) Redrawn by permission from Annals of the Association of American Geographers, *William K. Crowley, vol. 68, p. 262, Association of American Geographers, 1978.*

socio-cultural values, seeking to preserve their religious and cultural purity through isolation from secular, non-Islamic influences. Traditional groups, perhaps controlled by firm religious conviction, may very largely reject culture traits and technologies of the larger society in whose midst they live (see Figure 5.14).

The processes of cultural change, therefore, include numerous variables and take many forms, much more than this cursory overview suggests. What is the geographer to make of these processes? It is no easy task studying the cultural geographies people create if that creation is in a perpetual state of flux. Cultural geographers have risen to this challenge by developing several themes and key concepts that assist in organizing how to approach and question "culture" from geographical perspectives.

Themes of Traditional Cultural Geography

The cultural *ecology* of a particular group is distributed over a cultural *area*, has a particular cultural *history* or development, and is manifest in a cultural *landscape*.

This phrase above captures the essence of traditional cultural geography as conceived by Carl Sauer (1889–1975). His influence on cultural geography, indeed human geography in general, was immense. As a professor of Geography at the University of Berkeley for over 50 years (1923–1975), he not only founded American cultural geography, he was arguably the most influential human geographer in the United States and Canada during the last century. His lectures and research left an indelible mark not only in human geography but in other social, historical, and biological sciences as well (Sauer, 1952).

Sauer established and led what has been subsequently called the "Berkeley School" of cultural geography. This perspective conceived of cultural geography as "the application of the idea of culture to geographic problems" (Wagner and Mikesell, 1962). Such a perspective is taken for granted today, but in the 1920s this was a radical idea, put forth in part to oppose environmental determinism (see Chapter 1). The approach sought to unify physical and human geography—specifically how human activities changed the natural environment—by examining the diffusion of culture over areas through time. In other words, cultural geography sought to observe and assess the spread and impact of human activities, technologies, and beliefs on and over land through time. It was a largely historical approach seeking to understand how humans had altered their environments. It endorsed a humane and responsible use of the environment as exemplified by ancient and modern rural cultures.

This *Sauerian* or *Berkeley* approach to cultural geography literally defined the field and dominated it well into the 1980s. Since then, this approach has come to be known as *traditional* cultural geography, consisting of four overlapping themes: cultural *ecology*, cultural *area*, cultural *history*, and cultural *landscape* (Wagner and Mikesell, 1962).

Cultural Ecology

Cultural ecology is that part of traditional cultural geography which draws upon anthropology to study the relationship between a cultural group and its natural environment, and the resource use strategy that results. A **natural resource** is a physically occurring item that a population perceives to be necessary and useful to its maintenance and wellbeing. Crude oil, for example was not considered highly valuable or especially useful until the 1850s when a refining process was invented permitting a clean burn: the global economy is now premised on this fossil fuel. Saudi Arabia, site of the world's largest known oil reserves, where oil has always been located throughout human history but not always valued, is now a

FIGURE 5.15 The park-like landscape of grasses and trees characteristic of the tropical savanna is seen in this view from Kenya, Africa.

site of international economic and political importance. Resources are, therefore, culturally, spatially, and temporally specific: they are whatever materials a cultural group extracts and uses from the physical environment at a particular time to satisfy needs or wants. **Environment** in this context means the totality of things that in any way affect an organism. Humans exist within a natural environment—the sum of the physical world—that they have modified by their individual and collective actions.

The impacts of human actions, both deliberate and inadvertent, modifying or even destroying the natural environment, are perhaps as old as humankind itself. People have used, altered, and replaced the vegetation in wide areas of the tropics and midlatitudes. They have hunted to extinction vast herds and whole species of animals. They have, through overuse and abuse of the earth and its resources, rendered sterile and unpopulated formerly productive and attractive regions.

Fire has been called the first great tool of humans, and the impact of its early and continuing use is found on nearly every continent. Poleward of the great rain forests of equatorial South America, Africa, and South Asia lies the *tropical savanna* of extensive grassy vegetation separating scattered trees and forest groves (Figure 5.15). The trees appear to be the remnants of naturally occurring tropical dry forests, thorn forests, and scrub now largely obliterated by the use, over many millennia, of fire to remove the unwanted and unproductive trees, and to clear off old grasses for more nutritious new growth. The grasses supported the immense herds of grazing animals that were the basis of hunting societies. After independence, the government of Kenya in East Africa sought to protect its national game preserves by prohibiting the periodic use of fire. It quickly found that the immense herds of gazelles, zebras, antelope, and other grazers (and the lions and other predators that fed on them) that tourists came to see were being replaced by less-appealing browsing species—rhinos, hippos, and elephants. With fire prohibited, the forests began to reclaim their natural habitat and the grassland fauna was replaced.

Other examples of adverse human impact abound. The *Pleistocene overkill*—the Stone Age loss of whole species of large animals on all inhabited continents—is often ascribed to the unrestricted hunting to extinction carried on by societies familiar with fire to drive animals and hafted (with handles) weapons to slaughter them. With the use of these, according to one estimate, about 40% of African large-animal genera passed to extinction. The majority of large animal, reptile, and flightless bird species had disappeared from Australia around 46,000 years ago; in North America, some two-thirds of original large mammals had succumbed by 11,000 years ago under pressure from the hunters migrating to and spreading across the continent. Similar destruction of key marine species—Caribbean sea turtles, sea cows off the coast of Australia, sea otters near Alaska, and others elsewhere—as early as 10,000 years ago resulted in environmental damage whose effects continue to the present.

Not only destruction of animals but of the life-supporting environment itself has been a frequent consequence of human misuse of area. North Africa, the "granary of Rome" during the days of the Roman Empire, became wasted and sterile in part because of mismanagement. Easter Island in the South Pacific was covered lushly with palms and other trees when Polynesians settled there about 400 A.C.E. By the beginning of the 18th century, Easter Island had become the barren wasteland it remains today. Deforestation increased soil erosion, removed the supply of timbers needed for the vital dugout fishing canoes, and made it impossible to move the massive stone statues that were significant in the islanders' religion (Figure 5.16). With the loss of livelihood resources and the collapse of religion, warfare broke out and the population was decimated. A similar tragic sequence is occurring on Madagascar in the Indian Ocean today. Despite current romantic notions, not all early societies lived in harmony with their environment.

Contemporary societies have altered the natural environment in ways and at scales unprecedented in human history. We have altered our climates and polluted our air, land, and water at a global level. We have cleared forests, ploughed grasslands, dammed rivers, opened vast open-pit mines, and constructed expansive cities, streets, and highways. More often than not, the changes we have set in motion create unplanned landscapes and unwanted environmental and social conditions. Canada's own 'James Bay Hydroelectric Project' is such an instance. Commenced in 1975 after an agreement was reached between the Cree and Inuit—Aboriginals who occupied, hunted, and fished the land—and the Government of Quebec—that wished to generate and sell electricity—vast tracks of forested land were flooded adjacent to La Grande River. Subsequent biodegradation of trees and other organic materials resulted in the formation of dangerously high levels of mercury in the surrounding ecosystem, eventually contaminating the Cree who consumed the toxic fish. The ill effects of mercury poisoning on the human nervous systems of local inhabitants and the ongoing legal issues over land rights and financial restitution between First Nations people and government was an unforeseen impact of the ecological dominance of humans.

FIGURE 5.16 Now treeless, Easter Island once was lushly forested. The statues (some weighing up to 85 tonnes) dotting the island were rolled to their locations and lifted into place with logs.

The interrelations of people to their natural environment, their perceptions and use of it, and their impact on it, are the interwoven themes of cultural ecology. Like the anthropologist who seeks to understand *how* people live, these assist the geographer to understand how and where people live. Perhaps most importantly, cultural ecology assists in broadening our resource use strategies by identifying those human activities and processes that degrade the natural, and consequently human, landscape. The perpetual human dilemma lies in the reality that what people need and want in support and supply from the environment generally exceeds in form and degree what they are able to yield in an unaltered state. To satisfy their perceived needs, humans have learned to manipulate their environment. The greater those needs, the larger the population, and the more technologically advanced and complex the society, the greater is the human impact on the natural landscape. In sprawling urban industrial societies, the cultural landscape has come to outweigh the natural physical environment in its impact on people's daily lives. It interposes itself between "nature" and humans, and residents of the cities of such societies—living and working in climate-controlled buildings, driving to enclosed shopping malls—can go through life with very little contact with or concern about the physical environment (Figure 5.17).

Geography and other social and environmental sciences compel us to be concerned with a fundamental question for humanity: how can we extract our requirements from the natural environment without destroying the very basis of our life support? This question spans all scales, from one's own household up to and including the entire planet. 'Going green,' both locally and globally, means finding answers about our cultural ecologies toward living a more balanced human–environment relationship.

Cultural Area

Whereas the theme of cultural ecology seeks answers to questions involving the human–environment interaction, the theme of cultural area seeks to locate culture in space. More precisely, **cultural area** is a unit in space inhabited at a given period by people characterized by a shared culture. The task here is to isolate

FIGURE 5.17 The physical and cultural landscapes in juxtaposition. Advanced societies are capable of so altering the circumstances of nature that the cultural landscapes they create become the controlling environment. The city of Cape Town, South Africa, is first and foremost a "built environment" atop and within its physical surroundings.

for special study those more fundamental cultural variables that give structure and spatial order to societies. But what units of space are used? And what aspects of a culture are isolated?

We begin with *culture traits*, the smallest distinctive items of culture. **Culture traits** are units of learned behaviour ranging from the language spoken to the tools used or the games played. A trait may be an object (a fishhook, for example), a technique (weaving and knotting of a fishnet), a belief (in the spirits resident in water bodies), or an attitude (a conviction that fish is superior to other animal protein). Of course, the same trait—the Christian religion, perhaps, or the Spanish language—may be part of more than one culture. Traits are the most elementary expression of culture, the building blocks of the complex behavioural patterns of distinctive groups of peoples.

Individual cultural traits that are functionally interrelated comprise a **culture complex**. The existence of such complexes is universal. Keeping cattle was a *culture trait* of the Maasai of Kenya and Tanzania. Related traits included the measurement of personal wealth by the number of cattle owned, a diet containing milk and the blood of cattle, and disdain for labour unrelated to herding. The assemblage of these and other related traits yielded a culture complex descriptive of one aspect of Maasai society

(Figure 5.2). In exactly the same way, religious complexes, business behaviour complexes, sports complexes, and others can easily be recognized in any society.

In North America, for example, a culture complex exists around the automobile. Americans often buy car brands and models to reflect their income, employment, or status in society. Cinema, television, and sports often have autos at their heart; movies such as *American Graffiti* and the mass popularity of NASCAR races are familiar examples. Even rites of passage may focus on the automobile: driver education in high school, passing the driving exam and, perhaps, getting a car of one's own as a teenager, or the common practice of decorating automobiles at the end of a wedding ceremony.

When cultural traits and complexes are plotted on maps, the areal character of the components of culture is revealed. Although human geographers are interested in the spatial distribution of these individual elements of culture over small areas, their usual concern is with the **culture region**, a large portion of the earth's surface occupied by populations sharing recognizable and distinctive cultural characteristics. Examples include the political organizations societies devise, the religions they espouse, the form of economy they pursue, and even the type of clothing they wear,

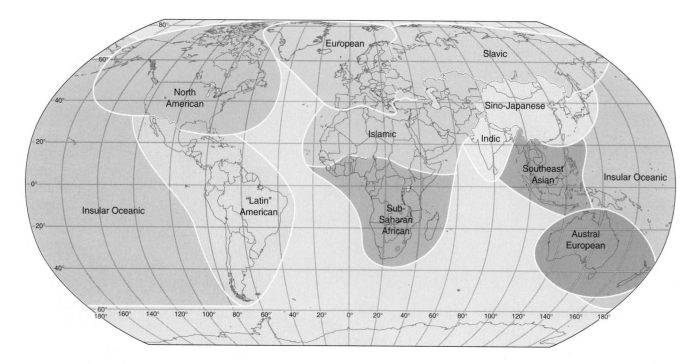

FIGURE 5.18 Culture realms of the modern world. This is just one of many possible subdivisions of the world into multifactor cultural regions.

eating utensils they use, or kind of housing they occupy. There are as many such conceptual culture regions as there are culture traits and complexes recognized for population groups. We must, therefore, keep in mind that within any one recognized culture region, groups united by the specific mapped characteristics may be competing and distinctive in other important cultural traits.

A set of culture regions showing related culture complexes and landscapes may be grouped to form a **culture realm**. The term recognizes a large segment of the earth's surface area having an assumed fundamental uniformity in its cultural characteristics and showing a significant difference in them from adjacent realms. Culture realms are, in a sense, cultural areas at the broadest scale of recognition. In fact, the scale is so broad and the diversity within the recognized realms so great that the very concept of realm may mislead more than it informs.

Indeed, the current validity of distinctive culture realms has been questioned in light of an assumed globalization of all aspects of human society and economy. The result of that globalization, it has been suggested, is a homogenization of cultures as economies are integrated and uniform consumer demands are satisfied by standardized commodities produced by international corporations. Despite that growing globalism in all facets of life and economy, however, the world is far from homogenized. Although an increased sameness of commodities and experiences is encountered in distant places, even common and standardized items of everyday life—branded soft drinks, for example, or American fast-food franchises—take on unique regional meanings and roles, conditioned by the total cultural mix they enter. Those multiple regional cultural mixes are often defiantly distinctive and separatist as recurring incidents of ethnic conflict, civil war, and strident regionalism attest. Rather than levelling and removing regional contrasts, as frequently predicted, globalization continues to be countered by powerful forces of regionalism, place identity, and ethnicity.

If a global culture can be discerned, it may best be seen as a combination of multiple territorial cultures, rather than a standardized uniformity. It is those territorially different cultural mixtures that are recognized by the culture realms suggested on Figure 5.18, which itself is only one of many such possible divisions. The spatial pattern and characteristics of these generalized realms will help us place the discussions and examples of human geography of later chapters in their regional context.

Culture Hearths

The term **culture hearth** is used to describe such centres of innovation and invention from which key culture traits and elements moved to exert an influence on surrounding regions. The hearth may be viewed as the point of origin or "cradle" of any culture group whose developed systems of livelihood and life created distinctive cultural ecologies, cultural areas, and as discussed below, cultural histories, and cultural landscapes. Most of the thousands of hearths that evolved across the world in all regions and natural settings remained at low levels of social and technical development. Only a few developed the trappings of *civilizations*. The definition of that term is not precise, but indicators of its achievement are commonly assumed to be writing, metallurgy, long-distance trade connections, astronomy and mathematics, social stratification and labour specialization, formalized governmental systems, and a structured urban culture.

Several major culture hearths emerged in the Neolithic period. Prominent centers of early creativity were found in Egypt, Crete, Mesopotamia, the Indus Valley of the Indian subcontinent, northern China, southeastern Asia, several locations in sub-Saharan

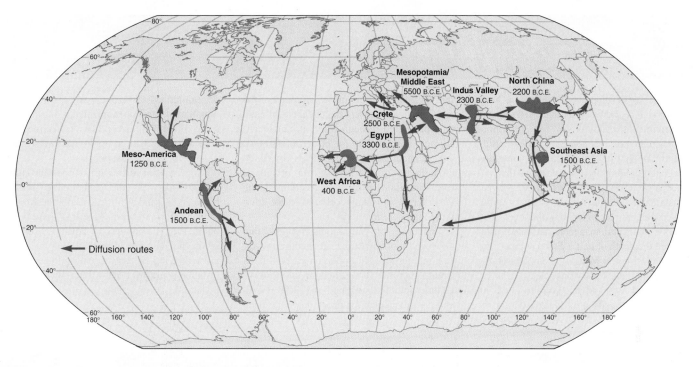

FIGURE 5.19 Early culture hearths of the Old World and the Americas. The B.C.E. (Before the Common Era) dates approximate times when the hearths developed complex social, intellectual, and technological bases and served as cultural diffusion centres.

Africa, in the Americas, and elsewhere (Figure 5.19). They arose in widely separated areas of the world, at different times, and under differing ecological circumstances. Each displayed its own unique mix of culture traits and amalgams.

All were urban centred, the indisputable mark of civilization first encountered in the Near East 5500–6000 years ago, but the urbanization of each was differently arrived at and expressed (Figure 5.20). In some hearth areas, such as Mesopotamia and Egypt, the transition from settled agricultural village to urban form was gradual and prolonged. In Minoan Crete, urban life was less explicitly developed than in the Indus Valley, where early trade contacts with the Near East suggest the importance of exchange in fostering urban growth (see "Cities Brought Low"). Trade seems particularly important in the development of West African culture hearths, such as Ghana and Kanem. Coming later (from the 8th to the 10th centuries) than the Nile or Mesopotamian centres, their numerous stone-built towns seem to have been supported both by an extensive agriculture whose origins were probably as early as those of the Middle East and, particularly, by long-distance trade across the Sahara. The Shang kingdom on the middle course of the Huang He (Yellow River) on the North China Plain had walled cities containing wattle-and-daub buildings but no monumental architecture.

Each culture hearth showed a rigorous organization of agriculture resulting in local productivity sufficient to enable a significant number of people to engage in non-farm activities. Therefore, each hearth region saw the creation of a stratified society that included artisans, warriors, merchants, scholars, priests, and administrators. Each also developed or adopted astronomy, mathematics, and the all-essential calendar. Each, while advancing in cultural diversity and complexity, exported technologies, skills, and learned behaviours far beyond its own boundaries.

As discussed above, the spread of culture may occur along lines or "avenues" of various forms of diffusion outwards from the cultural hearth or origin, but similar cultural traits may emerge between two or more distinct and spatially segregated cultural groups without any contact whatsoever. For example, whether the idea of writing originated in Mesopotamia at least 5,000 years ago and then spread outward to Egypt, the Indus Valley, Crete, and perhaps even China, *or* both Mesopotamia and Egypt developed writing—albeit in different forms—independently in separate hearths remains unresolved to this day. Adherents of the former position accept diffusionism—the belief that cultural similarities occur primarily, perhaps even solely, by spatial spread (diffusion) from one or at most a very few common origin sites—while the latter accept the idea of parallel creation called **multilinear evolution**: peoples in similar ecological circumstances but separate locations will develop *similar* but not *identical* cultural traits and complexes to explain the common characteristics of widely separated cultures developed under similar ecological circumstances.

In any event, the common characteristics deriving from multilinear evolution and the spread of specific culture traits and complexes contained the roots of **cultural convergence**, a concept particularly important today. That term describes the sharing of technologies, organizational structures, and even cultural traits and artifacts that is so evident among widely separated societies in a modern world united by instantaneous communication and efficient transportation. Convergence in those worldwide terms is, for many observers, proof of the pervasive globalization of culture.

Sustainable development requires a long-term balance between human actions and environmental conditions. When either poor management of resources by an exploiting culture or natural environmental alteration unrelated to human actions destroys that balance, a society's use of a region is no longer "sustainable" in the form previously established. Recent research shows that over 4000 years ago an unmanageable natural disaster spelled the death of half a dozen ancient civilizations from the Mediterranean Sea on the west to the Indus Valley on the east.

That disaster took the form of an intense 300-year drought that destroyed the rain-based agriculture on which many of the early civilizations were dependent. Although they prospered through trade, urban societies were sustained by the efforts of farmers. When, about 2200 B.C.E., fields dried and crops failed through lack of rain, urban and rural inhabitants alike were forced to flee the dust storms and famine of intolerable environmental deterioration.

Evidence of the killer drought that destroyed so many Bronze Age cultures—for example, those of Mesopotamia, early Minoan Crete, and the Old Kingdom in Egypt—includes cities abandoned in 2200 B.C.E. and not reoccupied for over 300 years; deep accumulations (20–25 cm, or 8–10 in.) of windblown sand over farmlands during the same three centuries; abrupt declines in lake water levels; and thick lake and seabed deposits of windblown debris.

Similar, but differently timed drought periods—such as the catastrophic aridity between 800 and 1000 A.C.E. that destroyed Mayan culture in Meso-America—have been blamed for the collapse of advanced societies in the New World as well. Not even the most thriving of early urban cultures were immune to restrictions arbitrarily imposed by nature.

FIGURE 5.20 Urbanization was invariably a characteristic of culture hearths of both the Old and the New Worlds. Pictured is the Pyramid of the Moon and Avenue of the Dead at Teotihuacán, a city that at its height between 300 and 700 A.C.E. spread over nearly 18 square kilometres (7 square miles). Located some 50 kilometres (30 miles) northeast of Mexico City in the Valley of Mexico, the planned city of Teotihuacán featured broad, straight avenues and an enormous pyramid complex. The Avenue of the Dead, bordered with low stone-faced buildings, was some 3 kilometres (nearly 2 miles) in length.

Cultural area is a particularly important theme of cultural geography because of its emphasis on the spatial distribution of cultural traits and complexes, both in the past and in contemporary societies. The "area" itself is one of "relative uniformity" rather than absolute: there are degrees of similarity and difference among cultural groups at varying spatial scales. The task of the geographer in this instance is to identify cultural traits and complexes, organize them into primarily three geographical or spatial categories—area, point, lines—and attempt to explain the patterns that emerge. In other words, what cultural traits and complexes exist over an area? Where is their point of origin or "cultural hearth"? And how has this culture spread through lines or avenues of diffusion?

Cultural History

In order to identify and describe the processes that have helped to create a cultural ecology, cultural area, or cultural landscape, the geographer must necessarily adopt an historical perspective. Because change occurs over both space and time, one cannot examine one dimension without the other. **Cultural history** is primarily concerned with reconstructing the local and regional sequence or successions of cultures, with a particular emphasis on cultural origins *(hearths)* and cultural dispersals *(avenues)* (Figure 5.19). By examining such cultural traits and complexes as architecture, documents, language, oral histories, place names, religions, and technologies, geographers try to "map" the sequences in the occupation of an area by different cultural groups and link these people with cultural groups in other areas exhibiting similar characteristics. This kind of research helps to establish the origin or cultural hearth of a given cultural feature in a specific time and place, the avenues, times and manner of its dispersion, the distribution and extent of cultural areas, and the character of the former cultural landscape. The problems of cultural history necessarily extend back to the very origins of humanity itself. By tracing our development over land and time, many insights into human history become evident.

Early Humanity as Hunter-Gatherers

Earlier humans found the physical environment more immediate and controlling than we do today. Some 11,000 years ago—during the *Paleolithic* or Old Stone Age—the massive glaciers—moving ice sheets of great depth—that had covered much of the land and water of the Northern Hemisphere (Figure 5.21) began to retreat. Animal, plant, and human populations that had been spatially confined by both the ice margin and the harsh climates of middle-latitude regions began to spread, colonizing newly opened territories. All were **hunter-gatherers**, pre-agricultural people dependent on the year-round availability of plant and animal foodstuffs they could secure with the limited variety of rudimentary stone tools and weapons at their disposal. Tundra vegetation, the mosses, lichens, and low shrubs of Europe were food staples. Southeastern Europe and southern Russia had forest, tundra, and grasslands, and the Mediterranean areas had forest cover (Figure 5.22). Gigantic herds of herbivores—reindeer, bison, mammoth, and horses—browsed, bred, and migrated throughout the tundra and the grasslands. An abundant animal life filled the forests.

Human migration northward into present-day Sweden, Finland, and Russia demanded a much more elaborate set of tools and provision for shelter and clothing than had previously been required. It necessitated the crossing of a number of ecological barriers and the occupation of previously avoided difficult environments. By the end of the Paleolithic period, humans had spread to all the continents but Antarctica, carrying with them their adaptive hunting-gathering

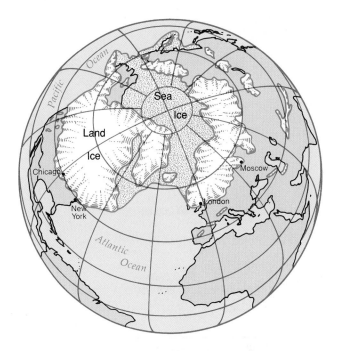

FIGURE 5.21 Maximum extent of glaciation. In their fullest development, glaciers of the most recent Ice Age covered large parts of Eurasia and North America. Even areas not covered by ice were affected as ocean levels dropped and rose, and climate and vegetation regions changed with glacial advance and retreat.

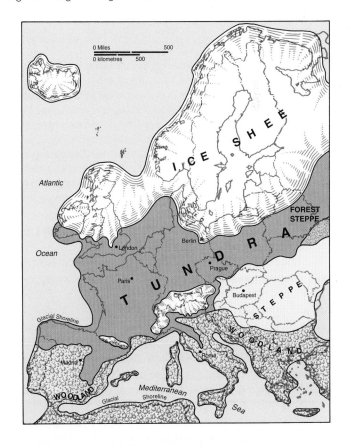

FIGURE 5.22 Late Paleolithic environments of Europe. During the late Paleolithic period, new food-gathering, shelter, and clothing strategies were developed to cope with harsh and changing environments, so different from those in Europe today.

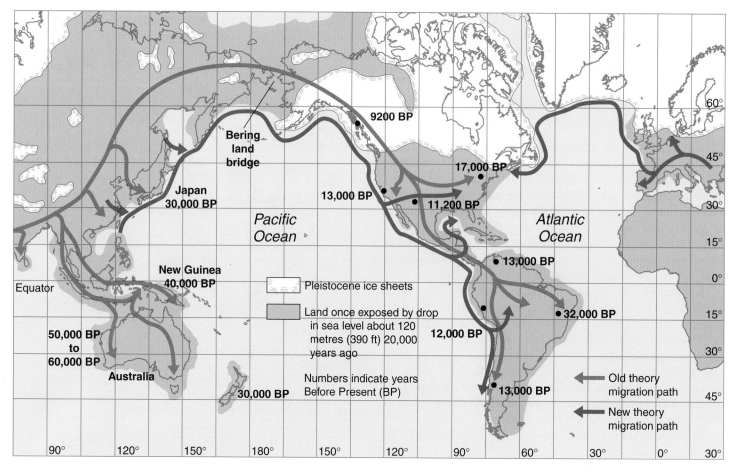

FIGURE 5.23 Settlement of the Americas and the Pacific basin. Genetic studies suggest humans spread around the globe from their Old World origins beginning some 100,000 years ago. Their time of arrival in the Western Hemisphere, however, is uncertain. The older view claimed that earliest migrants to the Americas, the ancestors of modern Amerindian groups, crossed the Bering land bridge in three different waves beginning 11,500 years ago. Recent evidence suggests that those North Asian land migrants encountered (and conquered or absorbed) earlier occupants who had arrived from Europe, Polynesia, and coastal East Asia by boat travelling along frozen or open shorelines. Although genetic and linguistic research yields mixed conclusions, physical evidence considered solid by some investigators indicates that the first Asian arrivals came at least 22,000 years ago, and more likely 30,000 or more years ago. Eastern United States artifacts that have been assigned dates of 17,000 to 30,000 years ago hint at European arrivals as early as those of coastal Asians; a South Carolina site found in 2004 has been dated at 50,000 years ago. Many researchers, however, caution that any New World population dates earlier than 18,000 years ago are questionable and that first migrants from that period probably were most closely related to prehistoric Jomon and later Ainu groups of Japan who crossed over the Bering land bridge.

cultures and social organizations. The settlement of the lands bordering the Pacific Ocean is suggested in Figure 5.23.

While spreading, the total population also increased. But hunting and foraging bands require considerable territory to support a relatively small number of individuals. There were contacts between groups and, apparently, even planned gatherings for trade, socializing, and selecting mates from outside the home group. Nevertheless, the bands tended to live in isolation. Estimates place the Paleolithic population of the entire island of Great Britain, which was on the northern margin of habitation, at only some 400–500 persons living in widely separated families of 20–40 people. Total world population at about 9000 B.C.E. probably ranged from 5 to 10 million. Variations in the types of tools characteristic of different population groups steadily increased as people migrated and encountered new environmental problems. By the end of the Ice Age (about 11,000 to 12,000 years ago), language, religion, long-distance trade, permanent settlements, and social stratification within groups appear to have been well developed in many European culture areas.

What was learned and created was transmitted within the cultural group. The increasing variety of adaptive strategies and technologies, and the diversity of non-economic creations in art, religion, language, and custom meant an inevitable cultural variation of humankind. That diversification began to replace the rough social uniformity among hunting and gathering people that had been based on their similar livelihood challenges, informal leadership structures, small-band kinship groups, and the like (Figure 5.24).

Agricultural Origins and Technological Innovations

The *Mesolithic* (Middle Stone Age) period, from about 11,000 to 5000 B.C.E. in Europe, marked the transition from the collection of food to its production. As rapid climatic fluctuation adversely affected their established plant and animal food sources of hunter-gatherers, people independently in more than one world area experimented with the *domestication* of plants and animals.

FIGURE 5.24 Hunter-gatherers practised the most enduring lifestyle in human history, trading it for the more arduous life of farmers under the necessity to provide larger quantities of less diversified foodstuffs for a growing population. For hunter-gatherers (unlike their settled farmer rivals and successors), age and gender differences, not caste or economic status, were and are the primary basis for the division of labour and of interpersonal relations. Here a San (Bushman) hunter of Botswana, Africa, stalks his prey. Men also help collect the gathered food that constitutes 80% of the San diet.

There is no agreement on whether the domestication of animals preceded or followed that of plants. The sequence may well have been different in different areas. The domestication of plants, like that of animals, appears to have occurred independently in more than one world region over a time span of between 10,000 and perhaps as long as 20,000 years ago. A strong case can be made that most widespread Eurasian food crops were first cultivated in the Near East beginning some 10,000 years ago and dispersed rapidly from there across the mid-latitudes of the Old World. However, clear evidence also exists that African peoples were raising crops of wheat, barley, dates, lentils, and chickpeas on the floodplains of the Nile River as early as 18,500 years ago, while farming in the Americas appeared in Mexico no more than 5000 years ago.

Full-scale domestication of food plants, like that of animals, can be traced to a limited number of origin areas from which its techniques spread (Figure 5.25). Although there were several source regions, certain uniformities united them. In each, domestication focused on plant species selected apparently for their capability of providing large quantities of storable calories or protein, and there was a population already well fed and able to devote time to the selection, propagation, and improvement of plants available from a diversified vegetation. Outside of those regions, wild plants reproducing from seeds were more common along with the objects of domestication. Although there was some duplication, each of the origin areas developed crop complexes characteristic of itself alone, as Figure 5.25 summarizes. From each, there was dispersion of crop plants to other areas, slowly at first under primitive systems of population movement and communication (Figure 5.26), more rapidly and extensively with the onset of European exploration and colonization after 1500 A.C.E. The regional contrasts between hunter-gatherer and sedentary

agricultural societies increased. Where the two groups came in contact, farmers were the victors and hunter-gatherers the losers in competition for territorial control.

As time progressed and humanity moved into what is now referred to as the *Neolithic* (New Stone Age) period, from 8000 to 3500 B.C.E., this cultural transition was refined and brought complex and revolutionary changes in human life. Culture began to alter at an accelerating pace, and change itself became a way of life. In an interconnected adaptive web, technological and social innovations came with a speed and genius surpassing all previous periods. Humans learned the arts of spinning and weaving plant and animal fibres. They learned to use the potter's wheel and to fire clay and make utensils. They developed techniques of brick making, mortaring, and construction, and they discovered the skills of mining, smelting, and casting metals. On the foundation of such technical advancements, a more complex exploitative culture appeared and a more formal economy emerged. A stratified society based on labour and role specialization replaced the rough equality of adults in hunting and gathering economies. Special local advantages in resources or products promoted the development of long-distance trading connections, which the invention of the sailboat helped to maintain.

By the end of the Neolithic period, certain spatially restricted groups, having created a food-producing rather than a foraging society, undertook the purposeful restructuring of their environment. They began to modify plant and animal species; to manage soil, terrain, water, and mineral resources; and to utilize animal energy to supplement that of humans. They used metal to make refined tools and superior weapons—first pure copper and later the alloy of tin and copper that produced the harder, more durable bronze. Humans had moved from adopting and shaping to the art of creating.

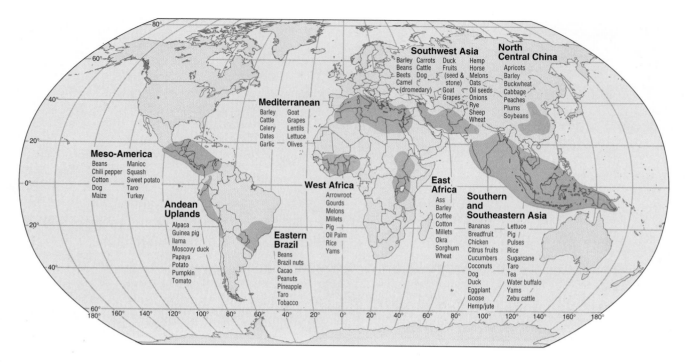

FIGURE 5.25 Chief centres of plant and animal domestication. The Southern and Southeastern Asia centre was characterized by the domestication of plants such as taro, which are propagated by the division and replanting of existing plants (vegetative reproduction). Reproduction by the planting of seeds (e.g., maize and wheat) was more characteristic of Meso-America and Southwest Asia. The African and Andean areas developed crops reproduced by both methods. The lists of crops and livestock associated with the separate origin areas are selective, not exhaustive.

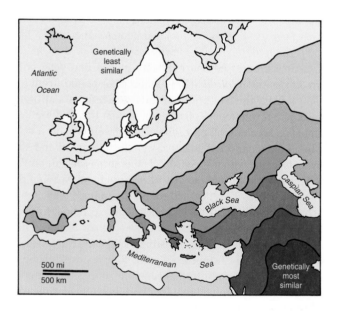

FIGURE 5.26 The migration of first farmers out of the Middle East into Europe starting about 10,000 years ago is presumably traced by blood and gene markers. If the gene evidence interpretation is valid, the migrants spread at a rate of about 1 kilometre (five-eighths of a mile) per year, gradually interbreeding with and replacing the indigenous European hunter-gatherers throughout that continent.

Source: L. Luca Cavalli-Sforza, Paolo Menozzi, and Alberto Piazza. The History and Geography of Human Genes. *Copyright © 1994 Princeton University Press, Princeton, N.J.*

As people gathered together in larger communities, new and more formalized rules of conduct and control emerged, especially important where the use of land was involved. We see the beginnings of governments to enforce laws and specify punishments for wrongdoers. The protection of private property, so much greater in amount and variety than that carried by the nomad, demanded more complex legal codes, as did the enforcement of the rules of societies increasingly stratified by social privileges and economic status.

Religions became more formalized and rituals developed appropriate to seasons of planting, irrigation, harvesting, and thanksgiving. In daily life, occupations became increasingly specialized. Metalworkers, potters, sailors, priests, merchants, scribes, and in some areas, warriors complemented the work of farmers and hunters. Such increasingly complex social stratification, technological innovations, and emergent urbanization were premised on agricultural surplus: readily available and abundant food supplies liberated societies to pursue and develop other non-agrarian ways of living.

Modernity and the Industrial Revolution

Modernity, or the Modern Era, is the term given to the last two to three hundred years of Western culture. The distinguishing feature of this period was the rise of the Industrial Revolution. This revolution was certainly not limited to industry nor was its development as sudden as the term suggests. This was a period of immense cultural transformation in the way goods were produced, how people obtained food, shelter, and clothing, and the very organization of the economy, politics, society, and space. At its core were a series of technological inventions and new ideas that originated in Great Britain in the late 1700s, gradually diffusing east through Europe and west to North America (1800s), and then to Eastern Europe, Southeast Asia, and Japan (mid 1900s), and

Landscapes of Identity, Plurality, and Organization

more recently China and other parts of the globe. This created an unprecedented expansion in human productivity that resulted in a substantially higher standard of material living, as well as new modes of spatial, social, and economic organization, with political and environmental ramifications.

Prior to the Industrial Revolution, industry in Britain and elsewhere was geographically dispersed into what is termed "cottage industries": small-scale operations with low, time-consuming outputs of a unique product, run by craftspeople out of their own home. This changed with the introduction of centralized energy sources and mechanized methods of mass production. One of the first and most important technological inventions leading to the development of "factories" was James Watt's steam engine (circa 1765). His steam engine could pump water—an energy source—more efficiently than watermills, let alone humans or animals.

This innovation initiated a series of technological developments. The iron industry was among the first industries to increase production through extensive use of the steam engine and other technological advances. The steam engines enabled the ovens used to smelt iron ore to be heated more economically at higher temperatures than was previously possible. This advance in the iron industry in turn generated innovations in coal mining, engineering, and transportation. Wood had become scarce so iron factories began to locate near coal mines for ready supplies of coal to feed the steam engines and blast furnaces. Hundreds of new kinds of machines made out of steel and iron, and powered by coal and steam, required new technical expertise to repair, maintain, and develop these engineered tools (circa 1795). The construction of canals and a new transportation marvel, the railway (circa 1825), further enhanced the concentration and diffusion of factories, by allowing easier access to bring raw materials in and take finished products out to markets. The manufacturing of woven fabric also underwent a major change. New technologies hastened the conversion of rough cotton to usable thread followed by weaving. Developments in the textile industry, in turn, generated innovations in what became the chemical industry. Traditional methods of bleaching fabric in the sun or boiling it in a solution of ash and sour milk gave way to the use of sulphuric acid—obtained from burning coal—and then subsequently modified to a chlorine gas and lime solution (circa 1800). The chemical industry gave rise to yet another spin-off industry, food processing. With the increasing number of factory workers concentrated in cities, where one could not easily grow or obtain fresh produce, food preservation became a problem. Drying, fermenting, and pickling, known for centuries, had limited utility. The tin can was invented (circa 1840) and the process of canning later refined with the use of chemicals such that the production of canning increased tenfold in 1861.

These and numerous other cultural innovations changed the cultures of societies themselves from largely rural and agrarian to industrialized and urban economies, affecting the organization and division of land and labour. This ushered in the rise of capitalism (free market economies), its antithesis, Communism (centrally planned economies), and unprecedented levels of **economic imperialism**: the economic exploitation of one state by another through political and often military means. The transformations in the physical and human landscapes induced by the mass production, mass consumption, and environmental degradation of the industrial revolution have been global in scale and will impact humanity and the Earth for centuries to come.

By understanding past human geographies, such as those of early hunters-gatherers, agrarian societies, and modernity, one can better appreciate and more fully understand contemporary geographies. It is to our own advantage to know what humanity has done to the world and to itself: knowledge of the past will have practical implications for both our present and the future.

Cultural Landscapes

The fourth and final theme of traditional cultural geography is an overarching one that anchors the other three. Remember that none of the themes is mutually exclusive—they overlap—and this is particularly evident when one considers the breadth of a **cultural landscape**: the tangible physical record of modification to the earth's surface by a cultural group. By this traditional definition, a landscape is necessarily an historical record of a particular group's human–environment relationship over an area. Meinig (1979) has noted that the "environment sustains us as creatures; landscape displays us as culture." This is a loaded phrase worth pondering.

If the natural "environment" provides for our biological needs as living organisms, viewing or "scaping" that which lays before us, as well as the arrangements in space of human activities and artifacts that are actually expressed in the "land" itself, reveals or displays our many and varied cultures. In other words, both the "scape" and the "land" are human built creations that both reveal humanity's "culture" and are themselves, cultural creations, and therein lies the utility of this concept. Chapter 1 of this text introduced many of the major philosophies and approaches geographers employ: these are the sorts of perspectives or views through which we can approach or scape our world. For example, a humanistic perspective might view an urban landscape, say a residential neighbourhood, for the meanings people attach to the houses—affection, security, family, and the like—whereas a more pragmatic and economic perspective may consider the material wealth or market value of the housing itself. That same residential neighbourhood could be viewed as a landscape of nature—the flora and fauna present—a landscape of problems—the polluted air, contaminated soil, crime—or any number of ways. Indeed, the variety and variations in *ways* to view a landscape is a perpetual source of new questions, and questions are the very engine of research and geographical inquiry. What is actually viewed or seen to be manifest in the "land" also reveals a cultural group's traits and complexes, be they sociofacts, mentifacts, or artifacts. The residential neighbourhood mentioned above, for example, could display a cultural group's household social organization of "family," the environmental values practised within the home through recycling waste and composting, and the house itself and its material contents—say electrical appliances and telecommunication devices—would indicate the priorities and levels of technology present.

Interpreting or "reading" a landscape provides us with evidence, clues, and insights into culture, but it can be a difficult task. Landscapes are not viewed in a laboratory under controlled conditions: we view landscapes in the messy, confusing, contradictory, and changing conditions that are the world around us. They have multiple layers of history and authorship, are subject to various interpretations and personal biases, and pose as many questions as we can possibly imagine. What is recent and what, if anything, is ancient? What is exceptional and what is ordinary? What is intentional and planned, and what is accidental and by chance? What has been made by human beings and what has been given by nature?

There are several guidelines or axioms that do assist us in making sense of the "display" before us (Meinig, 1979). Among them is the idea discussed above and worth restating here, that *landscapes reveal culture to us, because they are themselves cultural creations*. Landscapes do not simply mirror or reflect our ways of doing and thinking, they are themselves a way of doing and thinking. For instance, a sophisticated network of national highways does not simply "reflect" a society's priority, technology, and culture—although it certainly does so—it *is* a priority, a technology, a form of culture. Furthermore, virtually anything in a human landscape conveys meaning: it tells us something about people and their culture. This is the axiom of landscape equality —*all items reveal and are culture*—but what one observes must be guided by the question posed, lest everything be observed, so nothing is observed. To contextualize and thus appreciate the meanings revealed, *knowledge of historical development is vital*. Because culture is dynamic, landscapes change; and as noted above, they change over time and space. Why a particular building is located in a certain location and takes the form it does can only be understood by delving into the history of its creation. Similarly, *a landscape must be situated in its geographical context*, the so-called "geographic axiom." Meanings are made, in part, due to their context, their relationship with other things. A small residential home located on a quiet street with similar structures will have a very different economic meaning—price—if located on a four lane road surrounded by large commercial and office buildings. And finally, *the cultural landscape cannot be viewed independently of the natural or physical landscape*. Humans "create" their cultures within a physical environment, and these creations are in part a function of that natural context. A city where heavily insulated brick houses are built upon cement foundations, topped with slanted, shingled-roofs, replete with central heating and air conditioning, takes this cultural form in part as a response to the climatic conditions of the natural environment: strong winds, heavy precipitation, and extreme fluctuations in temperatures.

The Ethnic Landscape

Landscape evidence of ethnicity may be as subtle as the greater number and size of barns in the German-settled areas of the Ozarks, or the designs of churches, or the names of villages. The evidence may be as striking as the buggies of the Amish communities, the massive Dutch (really, German-origin) barns of southeastern Pennsylvania (Figure 5.27), the adobe houses of Mexican-American settlements in the Southwest, or the abundance of Asian-themed shopping malls in suburban Toronto. The ethnic landscape, however defined, may be a relic, reflecting old ways no longer pursued, indicating the influx of a new cultural group into

FIGURE 5.27 The Pennsylvania Dutch barn, with its origins in southern Germany, has two levels. Livestock occupy the ground level; on the upper level, reached by a gentle ramp, are the threshing floor, haylofts, and grain and equipment storage. A distinctive projecting forebay provides shelter for ground-level stock doors and unmistakably identifies the Pennsylvania Dutch barn. The style, particularly in its primitive log form, was exported from its eastern origins, underwent modification, and became a basic form in the Upland (i.e., off the Coastal Plain) South, Ohio, Indiana, Illinois, and Missouri. An example of a distinctive ethnic imprint on the landscape, the Pennsylvania Dutch barn also became an example of cultural transfer from an immigrant group to the charter group.

an area it previously did not occupy. It may contain evidence of artifacts or designs imported, found useful, and retained, or it may illustrate how newcomers alter an existing cultural landscape. In some instances, the physical or customary trappings of ethnicity may remain unique to one or a very few communities. In others, the diffusion of ideas or techniques may have spread introductions to areas beyond their initial impact.

Take, for example, the traditional French system for claiming and allotting farmland in the "New World" of North America. This cultural signature on the landscape has been particularly enduring. The *long lot* was a surveyed elongated holding typically about 10 times longer than wide, stretching far back from a narrow river frontage (Figure 5.28). The back of the lot was indicated by a roadway roughly parallel to the line of the river, marking the front of a second series (or *range*) of long lots. The system had the advantage of providing each settler with a fair access to fertile land along the floodplain, lower-quality river terrace land, and remote poorer-quality back areas on the valley slopes serving as woodlots. Dwellings were built at the front of the holding, in a loose settlement alignment called a *côte*, where access was easy and the neighbours were close. These cultural traits are still very much evident today.

A more contemporary and urban example illustrates how new immigrants may change the ethnic identity of a cultural landscape (Buzzelli, 2000). Prior to World War II, the St. Clair retail strip in Toronto was called "Little Britain," due to the overwhelming predominance of residents originally from Britain, and the many shops and services operated by, and catering to, this cultural group. In the post-war period, this neighbourhood—one in need

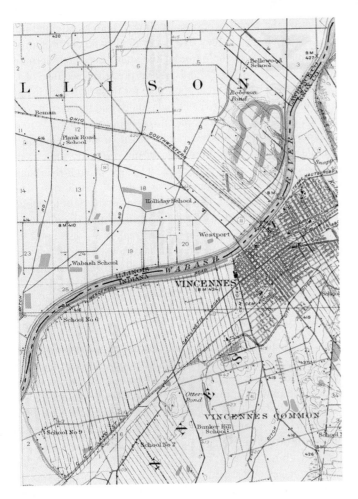

FIGURE 5.28 A portion of the Vincennes, Indiana–Illinois, topographic quadrangle (1944) showing evidence of original French long-lot survey. Note the importance of the Wabash River in both long-lot and Vincennes street-system orientations. This U.S. Geological Survey map was originally published at the fractional scale of 1:62,500.

Source: U.S. Geological Survey map.

and examination of the "landscapes of human activities" that our human geographies are revealed.

Cultural Politics: Space, Identities, and Environment

A fifth theme of cultural geography began to emerge in the 1980s and has come to dominate the field today: cultural politics. With the rise of the *Quantitative Revolution* in the 1960s and 1970s (see Chapter 1), traditional cultural geography became overshadowed by those fields within human geography that could more readily employ this new approach, such as economic and urban geography, and as a result, the prevalence of the Berkley School waned. By the late 1970s and during the 1980s, however, cultural geography began to take on a different tone, one rooted primarily in Great Britain and subsequently spreading to the United States, Canada, and other Anglo countries. This so-called *new* cultural geography initially drew upon the interdisciplinary work of *cultural studies* and the works of scholars such as Stuart Hall (1980) and Raymond Williams (1981). As noted by Sadar and Loon (1997: 6–8), cultural studies is difficult to define because it straddles traditional academic disciplines—anthropology, political science, psychology, geography and others—as well as contemporary political movements, intellectual modes and methods of inquiry, such as feminism, Marxism, as post-modernism. Unifying it all is the perspective that the subject matter at hand is viewed in terms of cultural practices and their relations to power: the "goal is to expose power relationships and examine how these relationships influence and shape cultural practices" (Sadar and Loon, 1997: 9). Culture is viewed as a politically-charged social creation.

Among the prominent scholars promoting this perspective within geography is Britain's Peter Jackson, Canada's Audrey Kobayashi, and America's Don Mitchell. Jackson was among the first geographers to promote this perspective when he pleaded in 1980 for cultural geography to "better understand the geography of culture and society as they work together to shape the experience of everyday life." By the end of the decade, Jackson (1989) published *Maps of Meaning*, a textbook linking cultural geography with the larger interdisciplinary body of "cultural studies." In it, he encouraged geographers to recognize that "culture is a site of contested meanings": geographers responded. The 1990s saw an explosion of works on "contested sites" in cultural geography. Issues of class, ethnicity, "race," gender and sexuality came to the fore. Kobayashi's work on multiculturalism (1993), racism (1999), gender (1994), human rights (1998), and immigration (2002), particularly her work on the Japanese-Canadian migrant experience (1994), exemplified this new concern with political culture. By the new millennium, Don Mitchell (2000) published *Cultural Geography: A Critical Introduction*, in which he reviewed in detail the development and application of this political approach to cultural geography. He takes Jackson's notion of culture as a contested site further still. Culture, Mitchell argues, is *war*: "a struggle over identities and the power to shape, determine and . . . emplace those identities" (2000: 11). Culture is thus viewed as a politically-charged, social and *spatial* construct.

of maintenance and re-investment—became a major reception area for new immigrants, primarily Italian immigrants, drawn there by relatively inexpensive rents. They brought with them their "Italian" culture, and as the numbers grew, their presence transformed "Little Britain" into "Little Italy": many of the Georgian architectural features and red clay brick of buildings were overlain by white stucco, mosaic tile, marble, archway facades, and grey paint; sidewalk patios and large plate glass windows were added to restaurants and cafes; and the names of shops, shop owners, and specialty foods and services became Italian. And this cycle of landscape change continues today. By the early 21st century, a new wave of immigrants is entering this neighbourhood, and it appears this cultural landscape is once again poised to undergo a change in ethnic identity.

A cultural landscape, then, holds the potential to tell us a great deal about a people's way of life, and the natural environment in which that life is lived. In fact, the very concept of cultural landscape is central to human geography, as the title of this text book emphasizes. It is through the systematic description

This so-called *new* cultural geography provides a more critical approach to the concepts and practices of culture and landscape relative to the more traditional descriptive accounts of geographers such as Sauer. Culture is not regarded as simply something material to be described and located in space, but also something immaterial in need of explanation. To understand cultures and landscapes, therefore, one must examine the political struggles among various cultural groups for their place in society. The focus is on cultural struggle and the battle for identity formation—the meanings, values, and ideas people make for themselves and others—which necessarily involve questioning power—domination, resistance, and negotiation—among and between various people within and across societies. This means that landscapes are not conceptualized as something static to be observed, but something active, and engaging: a process that works to produce and reproduce the social and political systems that create the attributes and characteristics of cultural identity. The goal, according to Mitchell (2000: xvii), is to identify, analyze and "intervene in social and political struggle." The intent is to strive toward cultural justice: to ensure individual human rights, obligations, and freedoms are met.

Rather than usurping traditional cultural geography as some have argued, this new approach may be viewed as an additional *fifth* theme of cultural geography—*cultural politics*—a theme that enhances and augments, rather than rivals and replaces, the four traditional themes noted above. They remain fundamental to human geography, and consequently they resonate throughout this textbook. But just how does cultural politics enhance cultural geography? Why the need to explain culture? What is the role of space in the production of culture? Why the emphasis on power and identities, and politics and the environment? And what is the intention of doing so?

Culturalism and "Super-Organic" Culture

Arguably the most important contribution cultural studies and its emphasis on cultural politics has brought to cultural geography is the need to *explain* culture, rather than simply *describe* culture. Of course description is vital—one must first identify, classify, and map the geographies before us—but mere description, as detailed, insightful, and intriguing as it may be, not only fails to ask some fundamental questions about the actual production of culture, it can inadvertently lead to **culturalism**: the use of culture to explain culture. To say that people behave, think, and use certain technologies *because of their culture* explains nothing about culture. Indeed, such thinking gives external independence and causative power to culture, rendering the very idea of culture **super-organic**: *super*—meaning above or beyond—and *organic*—referring to human beings.

From this culturalist perspective, culture is beyond human control—it is a naturally occurring, external entity that has the power to govern people—so humanity at large and individuals in particular are simply subject to its forces. Culture can then be used—and has been used—to explain, excuse, and justify any number of inequalities: the homeless living on the street may be *explained* by their preference for this way of life, rather than

questioning the larger economic, political, and social conditions of the society in which they live; individuals who commit atrocities against others in the name of the state, say Nazi Germany, may be *excused* on the grounds of the prevailing culture of the era, rather than being held accountable for their own actions; and the current income disparity between males and females in North America can be *justified* on the sexist belief that male workers are superior, without consideration given to the likelihood of male bias in hiring and promotion in the primarily male dominated workplace. Culture may be used inappropriately as a causal explanation for social, economic, or political conditions, when in fact social, economic, and political processes help to explain the production of culture. There is truth in the statement that we make our culture and then culture makes us—we make our economy for example, and then that economy impacts us—but appreciate that this relationship is driven solely by humans: culture is a human-made creation.

Space and Power

Space, too, is an integral part of the process of producing and thus explaining culture. Various individuals, groups, and institutions in any society create and occupy differing spaces of social, economic, and political power. In this context, space takes on three kinds of meanings: physical location, social status, and lived experience. *Physical location* refers to the actual space occupied: a certain floor of an office building, a particular neighbourhood of a city, a region within a country, an entire continent, may be physically more advantaged or disadvantaged relative to other locations. *Social status* refers to the place or rank occupied in social space: the position of a middle-aged medical doctor in society is, for instance, generally ascribed higher stature than an unemployed student. The *lived experience* refers to the places experienced in the course of everyday life, and these will vary depending upon an individual's lifestyle, tastes, education, income, religion, gender, and so forth. Because there are variations in the resources accompanying these spaces—differences in wealth, knowledge, privilege, status, and technology but to name a few—and due to the variety and variations in these spaces that individual people and groups produce and occupy, cultures are not only plural, but created within a context of uneven power. Some people and the spaces in which they live, work, play, and create their cultural identities have more or less power than others. Consequently, there is a continuum of cultural power within and across societies, ranging from the most dominant cultural groups whose meanings, values, and ways are privileged and imposed upon other less powerful groups—the subordinate cultural groups—whose ways and identities are marginalized. As noted above, those cultural groups with the most power are able to protect and promote their own interests and ways of life—their cultural subsystems of ideologies, technologies, and social relationships—more effectively than less powerful cultural groups.

Exercising power, either to dominate or resist others, may range from the passive, indirect, gentle, and persuasive to the active, direct, violent, and threatening. For example, people could resist global poverty by passively wearing symbolic ribbons or wrist bands proclaiming support for more government aid to developing countries, or they could take to the streets in a

FIGURE 5.29 Spatial exclusion can be exercised in highly visible ways, as this racist sign erected in a residential neighbourhood illustrates vividly.

violent rampage outside government offices and demand change. Similarly, a religious group could seek peaceful co-existence with non-members by practising mutual respect and tolerance, or proclaim zero tolerance for the religious beliefs of others and seek to both eradicate other religions and their followers. Not only are there numerous ways power can be practised, it can take many forms. Remember that culture is a medium of expression and a site of struggle, so resistance and domination can be expressed through virtually any cultural creation, including space (see Figure 5.29).

Space—be it physical, social, or lived—plays a key role in the exercise of power through exclusion, expulsion, containment, and inclusion. If one cultural group wishes to protect and promote its own interests and way of life, it may do so by **exclusion**: denying access to *others* from their physical space—residential neighbourhoods—their social space—business, friendship, and kinship relationships—and their lived experiences—the sites and interactions of their daily activities. Such has been the case between the dominant Catholics and subordinate Protestants in Northern Ireland, the dominant *Whites* and subordinate *Blacks* in parts of the United States, and between the dominant wealthy and the subordinate poor in most every society (Figure 5.30). **Expulsion**—forced departure—may also be used by a cultural group: the dominant cultural group may completely remove those subordinate groups deemed undesirable. At worse are the horrific instances of the removal and murder of Jews and others in Nazi Germany, and more recently the *ethnic cleansing* in the former Yugoslavia by both Serbians and Croatians against one another. Less extreme and more common are the instances where subordinate groups are informed that their presence is unwanted and their departure encouraged by the dominant group through various means: rude comments, inflammatory graffiti, repeated employment denial, defamation of property, or personal injury.

Containment is yet another spatial strategy: place the *other* in locations elsewhere, out of sight, and keep them there. *Bantustans* for Blacks in White South Africa and some *reservations* for Aboriginals in Canada exemplify this technique. It is not often that containment is so blatantly orchestrated or visible. Red light districts, gay villages, and immigrant neighbourhoods, for instance, may also be forms of containment, produced through prejudice and the marketplace. Certain groups and activities may be deemed undesirable by the dominant group in society, but are tolerated if kept to spaces they themselves do not want to occupy. The most undesirable areas will have the lowest rents, making them the most viable locations to live and work for those with the least financial resources—the least powerful —often those of a subordinate culture. **Inclusion** means an individual or group is granted access to the space or spaces of an *other* cultural group and the resources therein. This could be a temporary inclusion—a Chinese festival in Vancouver where members of the general public are invited to come and join in the celebrations and a local community centre—or so permanent that the differences between two or more groups literally vanishes, and all are considered equal. The right for women to vote (1925) and the right for gays and lesbians to marry (2005) in Canada are two examples of previously excluded groups—women and gays/lesbians—who are now included with men and heterosexuals who previously had exclusive rights to vote in elections and marry in civil ceremonies. Of course various cultural groups aspire to different positions in society. Some subordinate groups seek to become dominant, others equal, and still others may wish to remain largely excluded. Similarly, some dominant groups may wish to remain dominant while others may wish to divest themselves of exclusive power and share their resources. The variations are innumerable and make for a highly diverse set of landscapes where differences are negotiated, maintained, or resisted through space on a perpetual process of making and remaking cultures.

Spatial resistance can be practised in many ways, as exemplified by the Mennonites. They are an ethnic religious group with a long history of religious persecution (Bowen, 2001). Emerging in 16th century Europe, they have repeatedly used migration in their quest for religious freedom. In the late 17th century, large-scale migrations of Mennonites to North America began when they landed in Pennsylvania, and continued well into the 20th century when 20,000 arrived in Canada, fleeing the communist takeover of Russia. The past century has seen Mennonites from both Europe and North America move to Paraguay and Mexico. Although the vast majority of these moves have been motivated in part by economic circumstances, one group of the most conservative of all Mennonites, the 6500 members of the *Old Colony*, located currently in La Crete, Alberta, move whenever a threat to their way of life is perceived. Their cultural identity is maintained and perpetuated through a standard mode of dress, the use of a German dialect, rural living on a family farm, and conformity to a strict set of values and behaviours consistent with their own ideals of Christianity. The ultimate goal of the *Old Colony* is separation from the outside world, a world they believe will detract them from their promise to remain true to their God. Their quest for religious freedom from the dominance of other cultural groups employs three self-imposed and selected spatial strategies of resistance:

FIGURE 5.30 A house is the single largest purchase most people make. The size, location, and quality of one's home are, arguably, highly visible indices of the occupant's economic class. Some homeowners live beyond their means, and others under, but generally speaking housing and economic class are closely linked.

(1) migration—they relocate elsewhere; (2) exclusion—they deny access to others; and (3) containment—they are a self-contained community in spaces of their own, on their own.

Identities

If culture is a site of struggle between various cultural groups to practise their own way of life, *culture wars* are ultimately battles for recognition and legitimacy of identity. It is through a way of life that one's identity is expressed, and culture, as noted above, is the medium through which that identity is expressed, be it through material objects—art, clothing, food, housing, and so forth—activities—celebrations, dance, weddings, work—or immaterial creations, such as attitudes, beliefs, and values. Everyone has a pluralistic cultural identity—ancestral heritage, language, nationality, and religion, to name but a few of the many cultural characteristics used to identify one's culture to one's self and to others—but precisely which cultural **identities** matter will vary over time and space. In an ideal world, for example, one's religion should not be grounds for exclusion, expulsion, or containment—but in certain times and spaces, as history clearly shows, such an identity may get one killed. Just when and where different identities matter is the very point in examining the cultural politics of space. The task of this fifth theme of cultural geography, therefore, is to examine cultural identities through the lens of power to see how those identities are socially and spatially constructed, negotiated, resisted, or maintained. But which identities does geography study?

Among the identities considered major markers of cultural differences—and thus sites of struggle—include *class*, *gender*, and '*race*.' These can be divisive identities in many societies as various individuals and groups with varying degrees of power compete to have their own cultures, their own identities, if not dominate, then accepted or at least tolerated, by others. **Class**, in the narrowest sense of the term, is determined by economic position. A person's place in the economy has a major impact on the spaces where they will live, work, and play, their social status, and lifestyle choices and constraints (Figure 5.30). Precisely how people are categorized into various economic classes can be both broad and varied, as will become evident in the subsequent chapters on livelihood and economy. Class could be based upon any number or combination of variables: income—*upper, middle, or lower*; property—*owners, users, renters*; occupation—*skilled, semi-skilled, unskilled*; economic sector—*intellectual, administrative, managerial, labour*; educational attainment—*university, college, secondary, or primary school*, among others. The particulars of the classification aside, the point is that class conflict arises because people in various positions in the economy occupy different spaces with opposing interests, values, and ways of living. For example, a factory owner may wish to move operations to a distant country where labour costs are cheaper; the current workers would be vehement in their opposition to such a move: class conflict. Given the complexities of economies, the diversity of roles people play in their operation, and the plurality of experiences people have as a result, one can see how class is an identity rife with cultural conflicts, and therefore of major interest to geographers.

Gender is often used as a synonym for *sex* by the layperson, but within geography the two terms have different meanings. People are born of a sex—male or female—and this distinction is a biologically-created physical characteristic. Minimal physical

Women and the "Traditional" Home

From a patriarchal perspective, the "place of a woman is in the home." Although such an extreme position is not held by most North Americans, the notion that the home is primarily a place of childrearing, nurturing, and domesticity, remains prevalent. These qualities tend to be engendered as feminine cultural traits in our society. Home is regarded as a private place, where females remain largely responsible for performing the many chores of maintaining the household—cooking, cleaning, and childrearing—without pay. Whereas men tend to occupy places of paid employment, status, and power outside the home in "public" spaces, most women for much of the last century have been "housewives," responsible for sustaining the private space of the household and the "family."

And yet popular notions of what constitutes a "family" do not hold true for the majority of North Americans. Held up by many as the "traditional" family, those Canadian households composed of mom, dad, and the children form a minority at 44%, including both married and common-law couples. Although the "traditional" family remains the most common structure, the majority of Canadians have alternative compositions: no children, no children at home, divorced, separated, single, partner lives elsewhere, or separated. Family takes on multiple forms and meanings for different people (Statistics Canada, 2001).

Feminist geographers have challenged the unspoken assumptions, "normalcy," and practices inherent in such notions of the home. The rigid gender roles, the ideals of the "dream" home, the constitution of the family, and the dualism of home/work and private space/public place are questioned and critiqued. What kind of place is the home from the woman's standpoint? What are her experiences and meanings attributable to the home, be they positive or negative?

and biological variations aside, differences between males and females are invented. **Gender** is a socially-created and learned set of cultural characteristics: one is not born a *man* or a *woman* but rather socialized—taught—how to behave, dress, and live as a *masculine* or *feminine* person (see "Women and the 'Traditional' Home"). Virtually any cultural creation can be inscribed or *engendered* with varying degrees of masculine or feminine identity: clothes (suit/dress), food (steak/tofu), occupations (mechanic/hairdresser), human behaviour (assertive/passive), and of course spaces (executive office/daycare centre) (Figure 5.31). Gender identities, like all cultural creations, are dynamic and flexible: they vary over time and space, and changes can and do induce conflict. Generally speaking the dominant gender-based culture is masculine and male, and as the subordinate feminine and female culture struggles toward equality in North American and the rest of the world, the so-called *battle of the sexes* unfolds. This is a much more complex process than suggested here, but suffice to say that geographers are very interested in the impact gender identities have on the creation of cultural landscapes because

they are such a prevalent yet often overlooked aspect of landscape production.

A 'race' has traditionally been defined as a group of individuals sharing common genetic attributes that determine that group's physical appearance, social behaviours, and cognitive abilities. Physical attributes, such as skin colour, hair, eyes, and nose width, are the prevalent markers of race: Caucasoid *(White)*, Negroid *(Black)*, and Mongoloid *(Yellow)*. Contemporary thinking rejects entirely this concept of race! Examination of the human genome indicates that race has little or no biological meaning: there are no DNA hallmarks of race; the human species is too young to divide into separate biological groups; and superficial surface characteristics, such as skin colour, are a function of only 0.01% of human genes (Figure 5.32). There is one biological race—*the human race*—and the belief that human beings can be segregated into a series of distinct races are now widely regarded as false. Instead, **race** is regarded as a socially-constructed cultural identity, the product of racism rather than biology. *Racism* is an ideology whereby people are classified into racial categories and

FIGURE 5.31 Throughout most of the Western world, conventional gender roles dictate that males wear suits and females wear dresses. There is nothing inherently biological or absolute about these gender codes: they are socially constructed and therefore flexible. Until the early part of the 20th century, women did not wear pants, and contemporary society now regards this piece of clothing as gender neutral.

subsequently ranked according to the superiority or inferiority of supposed racial differences. This is manifest through actions, attitudes, and policies that attribute social, cultural, and cognitive characteristics to people based solely on arbitrary physical criteria (e.g., skin tone). Race as a biological category does not exist, but people are *racialized* through social and spatial practices: they are assigned racist identities by others.

For instance, several years ago during a business trip to Red Lake, Ontario, a small community about 500 kilometres north-west of Thunder Bay, a man checked himself into a small hotel. He quickly placed his luggage in his assigned room and immediately departed to attend his afternoon business meeting. Upon his return he noticed that his room was filthy: it smelled heavily of cigarette smoke and alcohol; there were cigarette burns on the rug, the bedspread and curtains; the bathroom was unclean; and there was no safety chain on the door. The man complained to the staff and was assigned a slightly better, but still substandard, room.

After checking out the next morning, the man was informed by others in Red Lake that the hotel had a policy of assigning a specific set of rooms—'Indian Rooms'—to those whom the staff identified as Aboriginal. The provincial police investigated the matter, subsequently reported it to the Ontario Human Rights Commission, which in turn ruled that the man's human rights had indeed been violated. The former executive director of the Independent First Nations Alliance was paid a modest amount in damages for his racist treatment. Spatial allocation based on *race* perception is discriminatory and illegal in Canada. Nevertheless,

FIGURE 5.32 Because of its visibility, skin tone was used as one of the key markers in socially-constructed categorization of "race." And yet, immediate family members who share the same close biology can be of varying complexions.

cultural conflicts due to racism persist and continue to create landscapes of inequality in dire need of explanation and resolution. Geographers assist through anti-racist research, which reveals, explains, and challenges the creation and consequences of racism.

Environmental Politics

In addition to viewing cultural identities in a society through a lens of power, a society's relationship with their environment can also be examined and critiqued as a 'site of struggle' among differing resource use strategies. The traditional theme of cultural ecology, explained above, has been reinvigorated through an emphasis on the power relations between differing cultural groups, their natural environment, and the resource use strategies employed. **Political ecology** is the term used to refer to this approach that links politics and the economy to issues of environmental control and change (Watts, 2000). The social system that produces, distributes and consumes goods and services—*the economy*—is inherently *political* because social systems necessarily involve the exercise of authority and power. In this way the extraction of natural resources and the management of the environment are inextricably linked to the economic livelihoods of people and the exercise of power by individuals, groups, and institutions.

A classic study in political ecology on soil erosion by Blaikie (1985) that was briefly mentioned in Chapter 1, will serve to illustrate these linkages. Conventional assessments of soil erosion in developing countries had traditionally used a colonial model, whereby land degradation through farming was framed around such problems as government mismanagement, overpopulation, and flawed markets. Instead, Blaikie viewed the problem at the level of households—the immediate resource manager—and found that living costs compelled farming households to extract as much as possible from the environment, which exacerbated soil erosion. The novelty of this approach made explicit the failure of existing soil conservation schemes: the problem of soil erosion was intrinsic to the low economic class of farmers, their lack of power relative to the state, and the variations by class in perceptions and proposed solutions to soil erosion. Land degradation was shown to be grounded in economic class, and was ultimately a political issue.

From a cultural political perspective, identities and human-environment relations are created through social and spatial processes amidst an uneven playing field of power. Cultural groups have different interests at stake, occupy different kinds of spaces, and have different identities and relations to the natural environment. Regardless of one's opinion about a particular cultural group, identity, or issue, the theme of cultural politics encourages tough questions about the production of culture and the role of space in its production. Who or what cultural group is dominant or subordinate? Why? How? *Where*? Which cultural group benefits from certain cultural practices? Certain environmental practices? Who or what group does not? Which cultural identities are acceptable or unacceptable? When? *Where*? Who decides, and on what basis? Is there a more just, fair, and inclusive landscape a society might build? How might space in that landscape be more equitably and peacefully shared? Answers to such questions help geographers to *explain* cultures, and understanding how cultures work through space is necessary in order to intervene in those processes that perpetuate social intolerance, inequality, and human-environment imbalance (see "Want to Learn More?").

Want to Learn More?

Aboriginal Canadians

"The Aboriginal Canada Portal" provides access to other online resources, contacts, information, and government programs and services: http://www.aboriginalcanada.gc.ca/

"First Nations Statistics" provides statistics and measurements of First Nations people: http://www.firststats.ca/

Cultural Landscapes

"Cultural Landscapes" exhibits numerous large-scale maps, such as individual land surveys, county land ownership maps and atlases, large-scale topographic maps, and thematic maps showing economic activity: memory.loc.gov/ammem/gmdhtml/setlhome.html

"Parks Canada—An Approach to Aboriginal Cultural Landscapes" provides access to a large collection of landscape materials addressing Aboriginal Canadians: http://www.pc.gc.ca/docs/r/pca-acl/sec4/index_e.asp

Cultural Politics

"Seven Oaks" is an online Canadian magazine that reports on contemporary issues of social justice and issues of class, gender, and "race": http://www.sevenoaksmag.com/index.html

"Rabble News" offers alternative political views to mainstream news events: http://www.rabble.ca/

"Anti-Racism Canada" provides a description of numerous anti-racism websites in Canada and elsewhere: http://www.angelfire.com/linux/nickshomepage/antiracecan.html

Early Humanity and Innovations

"Story of Farming" illustrates and discusses various aspects of early farming around the world: http://www.historylink101.com/lessons/farm-city/story-of-farming.htm

"Industrial Revolution—Timeline of Textile Machinery" outlines the major inventions and timeline of textile machinery: inventors.about.com/library/inventors/blindustrialrevolutiontextiles.htm

"The Diffusion of Technology" describes how technologies are adopted by individuals and organizations: http://www.umsl.edu/~rkeel/280/soctechchange/soctech5.htm

Summary

Culture lies at the root of human geography. To study the diversity of ways people interact with the natural environments they occupy, and the plurality of built environments they create, is an immense and interesting challenge, particularly in light of increased globalization. As the subsequent chapters show, geographers have developed specialized subfields to address the many strands in the web of culture. In this chapter, the concept of *culture* itself has been discussed, with particular emphasis on the spatial and social processes through which culture is expressed, displayed, and changed over time in the landscape. Change is induced by innovations that spread outward from their origin points, carried by migrants through relocation diffusion, or adopted by others through a variety of expansion diffusion and acculturation processes. Although diffusion barriers exist, most successful or advantageous innovations find adopters, and both cultural modification and cultural convergence of different societies result. *Traditional cultural geography* seeks to observe and describe the spread and impact of human activities, technologies, and beliefs of cultural groups over

time—*cultural history*—to the natural environment—*cultural ecology*—as distributed over a particular space—*cultural area*—as manifest in a *cultural landscape*. It takes an historical approach to changes in a particular group's human–environment relationship. Contemporary or *new* cultural geography takes a political approach to explain the creation of culture and the social mechanisms of cultural and environmental change. The focus is upon culture as a *site of struggle* for identity—the meanings, values, and ideas people make for themselves and others—which requires examining who has the *power* to dominate other cultural groups, and which cultural groups are subordinate to others and why, be it a local or global scale. Physical, social, and lived *spaces* play a fundamental role in the exercise of power, through *exclusion, expulsion, containment*, and *inclusion. Class, "race," and gender* are among the primary markers of cultural identity and conflict. By understanding how social intolerance and inequality work in the production of cultural landscapes, cultural geography may assist in the intervention of such processes.

 ## KEY WORDS

acculturation 135
artifact 130
assimilation 136
behavioural
    assimilation 136
class 156
containment 155
culturalism 154
cultural area 142
cultural convergence 145
cultural ecology 141
cultural history 147
cultural lag 135
cultural landscape 151
culture 126

culture complex 143
culture hearth 144
culture realm 144
culture rebound 137
culture region 143
culture trait 143
diffusion 132
diffusion barrier 140
economic imperialism 151
environment 141
ethnocentrism 137
exclusion 155
expansion diffusion 133
expulsion 155
gender 157

hunter-gatherer 147
hybridity 137
identities 156
ideological subsystem 130
inclusion 155
independent invention 135
innovation 132
landscape 126
mentifact 130
modernity 150
multilinear evolution 145
natural resource 141
power 129
political ecology 159
race 157

racism 137
relocation diffusion 135
sociofact 130
sociological subsystem 130
space 154
spatial assimilation 137
structural assimilation 136
super-organic 154
technological
    subsystem 130
xenophobia/
    ethnophobia 137

 ## FOR REVIEW

1. What is included in the concept of *culture*? How is culture transmitted? What personal characteristics affect the aspects of culture that any single individual acquires or fully masters?

2. What do we mean by *domestication*? When and where did the domestication of plants and animals occur? What impact on culture and population numbers did plant domestication have?

3. What is a *culture hearth*? What new traits of culture characterized the early

hearths? Identify and locate some of the major culture hearths that emerged at the close of the Neolithic period.

4. What do we mean by *innovation*? By *diffusion*? What different patterns of diffusion can you describe? Discuss the role played by innovation and diffusion in altering the cultural structure in which you are a participant from that experienced by your great-grandparents.

5. What are *class*, *"race,"* and *gender*? How might each of these cultural

identities display themselves on the cultural landscape?

6. What are the components or subsystems of the three-part system of culture? What characteristics are included in each of the subsystems?

7. What are the main cultural regions in Canada? Consider both the importance of geographical scale in your categorization and the dense concentration of population close to the U.S. border.

FOCUS FOLLOW-UP

1. **What are the characteristics and components of culture?** pp. 127–132.

   Culture is a complex human creation. It is plural, a medium of expression and identity, and inherently spatial and political. Culture not only displays and reveals the landscapes, areas, histories, and ecologies of humanity, the creation of culture is itself a social and spatial process, a *site of struggle*, where different individuals and groups negotiate with others for their own ways of doing and thinking.

2. **How did cultures develop and diverge, and where did cultural advances originate?** pp. 132–141.

   From Paleolithic hunting and gathering to Neolithic farming and then to city civilizations, different groups made differently timed cultural transitions. All early cultural advances had their origins in a few areally distinct "hearths."

3. **What are the components of culture and forms of culture change?** pp. 141–153.

   All cultures contain ideological, technological, and sociological components that work together to create cultural integration. Cultures change through innovations they themselves invent or that diffuse from other areas and are accepted or adapted.

4. **What is cultural politics and how does it relate to identities and space?** pp. 153–159.

   Cultural politics views culture as a politically charged site of struggle between dominant and subordinate cultural groups over social identities—the markers of cultural differences, such as class, gender, ethnicity, religion, and language—and the spaces where they are created and contested.

ONLINE LEARNING CENTRE

The World Wide Web has a tremendous number and variety of sites pertaining to geography. To access Web sites, Internet exercises, self-quizzes, videos, and additional study tools relevant to this chapter's content, visit the *Human Geography* Online Learning Centre at **www.mcgrawhill.ca/olc/fellmann.**

6

GEOGRAPHIES OF ETHNICITY, LANGUAGE, AND RELIGION: THREADS OF DIVERSITY AND UNITY

Aims

- To understand the concept of ethnicity and its constitution in space
- To appreciate the areal extent and diversity of languages
- To explain the roles and distributions of major religions
- To illustrate how these three cultural identities both unify and diversify people

Some Specific Considerations for Review:

Ethnicity

Language

Religion

Geographies of Ethnicity

"An enthnocultural profile of Canada at the outset of the 21st century shows a nation that has become increasingly multiethnic and multicultural. This portrait is diverse and varies from province to territory, city to city, and community to community. Immigration to Canada over the past 100 years has shaped Canada, with each new wave of immigrants adding to the nation's ethnic and cultural composition. Half a century ago, most immigrants came from Europe. Now most newcomers are from Asia. As a result, the number of visible minorities in Canada is growing. In answering the 2006 Census question on ethnic ancestry, Canadians listed more than 200 ethnic groups, reflecting a varied, rich cultural mosaic as the nation started the new millennium.[1]"

Canada is a cultural composite, as increasingly are most of the countries of the world. The majority of the world's societies, even those outwardly seemingly most homogeneous, house distinctive **ethnic groups**, populations who feel themselves bound together by a common origin and set off from other groups by ties of culture, language, religion, or nationality. Ethnic diversity is a near-universal part of human geographic patterns; the current some 200 or so independent countries are home to at least 5000 ethnic groups. In the 2006 Census, Canadians reported more than 200 different ethnic origins. European states house increasing numbers of African and Asian immigrants and guest workers from outside their borders, and have effectively become multiethnic societies. Refugees and job seekers are found in alien lands throughout both hemispheres. Cross-border movements and resettlements in Southeast Asia and Africa are well-reported current events. European colonialism created pluralistic societies in tropical lands through introduction of both ruling elites and, frequently, non-indigenous labouring groups. Polyethnic Russia, Afghanistan, China, India, and most African countries have native—rather than immigrant—populations more characterized by ethnic, linguistic, and religious diversity than by uniformity.

Globally speaking, there are between 3000–8000 languages, depending upon how one defines language, and whether or not "dead" languages—those no longer spoken, such as Latin—are included in the count. Some linguists predict that the number of "living" world languages will number around 600 by the turn of the next century. Most of the loss will be in indigenous languages due to declines in the number of speakers who use the language on any regular basis. Religions are plural and numerous, too. Depending upon how it is defined, there are as many as 270 large religious groups, and many smaller ones: there are over 34,000 separate Christian groups alone. Ethnicity, like language and religion, can be difficult to define, but however conceptualized, it is clear that they are basic components of cultures, the learned ways of life of different human communities. They help identify who and what we are and clearly place us within larger communities of persons with similar identities and characteristics, while simultaneously marking us and making us distinct from others. These cultural identities are important threads in the cultural–geographic web of our complex world. The multiple movements, diffusions, migrations, and mixings of peoples of different ethnicities, languages, and religions are among the processes and identities that concern human geographers. We are concerned with the spatial distributions and interactions of ethnic, linguistic, and religious groups, and of the cultural characteristics and influences underlying them.

In this chapter, examination of ethnicity and spatial patterns will concentrate on Anglo-America (the United States and Canada). Originally, this region was occupied by a multitude of distinctive Aboriginal peoples, each with their own territory, culture, and language. Over time, these populations were overwhelmed and displaced by a wide spectrum of Old World ethnic groups. Although Anglo-America lacks the numerous homelands that gave territorial identity and unity to immigrant ethnics in their countries of origin, it has provided a case study of how distinctive culture groups partition space, and place their claims and imprints on it. Their languages and religions have also left their mark upon our cultural landscapes.

Languages evolve in place, responding to the dynamics of human thought, experience, and expression, and to the exchanges and borrowings ever more common in a closely integrated world. They disperse in space, carried by streams of migrants, colonizers, and conquerors. They may be rigorously defended and preserved as essential elements of cultural identity, or abandoned in the search for acceptance into a new society. To trace their diffusions, adoptions, and disappearances is to understand part of the evolving course of historical cultural geography. Religions, too, are dynamic, sweeping across national, linguistic, and cultural boundaries by conversion, conviction, and conquest. Their broad spatial patterns—distinctive culture regions in their own right—are also fundamental in defining the culture realms outlined in Figure 5.18, while at a different scale religious differences may contribute to the cultural diversity and richness within the countries of the world.

Ethnic Identities in Space

Each summer for over two decades some 40,000 people gather on the waterfront of Halifax to celebrate and experience a diversity of dance, art, and food: Chinese dragon races, handcrafted Latin American ornaments, and dishes from Ghana, Greece, and Jamaica. Each merchant, artist, and performer is part of the larger collective

---

[1] From Statistics Canada, 2005. Geographies of Ethnicity.

cultural group called Canadians, yet each has preserved a distinctive small-group identity within the larger collective group. Similar cultural festivals are held throughout Canada and the United States each year (Figure 6.1), and are expressions of ethnicity.

Ethnicity is a surprisingly difficult concept (Hiebert, 2000). The word itself is derived from the Greek word "ethos" meaning distinct "people." Precisely which characteristics researchers use to distinguish an "ethnicity" and which cultural expressions are used by social groups to define their own distinct ethnicity varies considerably. Among these variations are two commonly held misconceptions. First is the notion that ethnicity refers only to minority groups. In fact, everyone—including majority groups—may claim an ethnicity. Second is the interchangeable use of the term ethnicity with "race." As discussed in the previous chapter, race is a fallacious classification system whereby social behaviour and cognitive ability are attributed to people based solely on arbitrary physical characteristics. Merely substituting the term ethnicity for race, yet clinging to the idea that a group's behaviour and ability is a function of biology does not negate racist thinking. For example, Black Americans, like Asian Americans and Hispanics, have had thrust on them an assumed common ethnicity that does not, in fact, exist. Because of common physical or linguistic characteristics, quite dissimilar ethnic groups have often been categorized by the white, English-speaking majority in ways totally at odds with the realities of their separate national origins or cultural inheritances.

Ethnicity is a cultural marker used by people to define their personal identity as both individuals and members of a larger group. No single trait denotes ethnicity. It may be based on any one, or an entire set of unique customs, distinct traditions, ancestral heritage, national origin, language, or religion. Whichever cultural characteristics establish the ethnic identity, and regardless of the degree of attachment and importance individuals feel toward their ethnicity or the frequency of ethnic group social interactions and relations, ethnicity is always based on a real or perceived understanding by its members that they are in some fundamental ways different from others who do not share their distinguishing characteristics or cultural heritage. In this sense, ethnicity is simultaneously inclusive—bringing "same" individuals together—and exclusive—distinguishing groups as different from "others."

Ethnicity is also an inherently spatial concept because the identity of "same" or "different" is necessarily a function of spatial context. An individual's ethnic identity could be virtually irrelevant and seemingly invisible if they shared the same ethnicity as everyone else in their society: all the spaces of that society—including those of the aforementioned individual—would express the same kinds of ethnic identity. Conversely, an individual's ethnicity could become highly relevant and visible if most everyone else in society shared a different ethnicity or set of ethnicities: most other spaces would express other ethnicities, making that individual and the spaces in which they express their own ethnicity different and thus highly visible. Geographers are interested in areas or regions where there are sufficient numbers of an ethnic group or groups with ample social interaction and cohesion to render the spatial expressions of ethnic identities

FIGURE 6.1 The annual Ninth Avenue International Fair in New York City became one of the largest of its kind. Similar festivals celebrating North America's ethnic diversity are found in cities and small towns across the continent.

visible. Consequently, ethnic groups are associated with clearly recognized territories—either larger homeland districts or smaller rural or urban enclaves—in which they are primary or exclusive occupants and upon which they have placed distinctive cultural marks. Since territory and ethnicity are inseparable concepts, ethnicity becomes an important concern in the cultural patterning of space and clearly an item of human geographic interest. Furthermore, since ethnicity is often identified with language and religious practices that distinguish a minority ethnic group from the surrounding majority cultures, it follows that we discuss language and religion in this chapter.

The cultural contexts in which ethnic identities emerge and become relevant to members of these social groups occur whenever there is a territorial conflict over the exercise of a group's ethnic identity. Generally speaking this takes two forms: an ethnic group may resist their cultural inclusion and domination by another group by spatially excluding themselves from that other group; or an ethnic group may resist their lack of cultural inclusion and acceptance by another group by spatially excluding themselves in order to create a welcoming and familiar social and economic place of their own. Whereas conquered ethnic groups usually struggle for independence, immigrant ethnic groups usually struggle for equality in their new societies (Hiebert, 2000: 236).

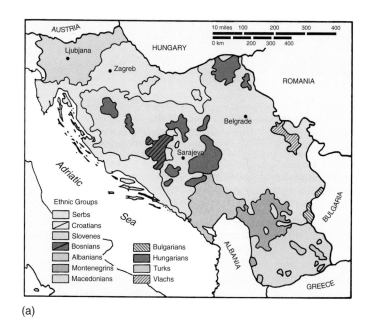

(a)

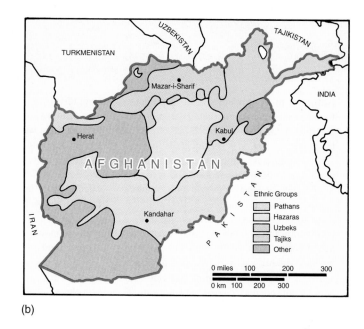

(b)

FIGURE 6.2 (*a*) **Ethnicity in former Yugoslavia.** Yugoslavia was formed after World War I (1914–1918) from a patchwork of Balkan states and territories, including the former kingdoms of Serbia and Montenegro, Bosnia-Herzegovina, Croatia-Slavonia, and Dalmatia. The authoritarian central government created in 1945 began to disintegrate in 1991 as non-Serb minorities voted for regional independence. In response, Serb guerillas backed by the Serb-dominated Yugoslav military engaged in a policy of territorial seizure and "ethnic cleansing" to secure areas claimed as traditional Serb "homelands." Religious differences between Eastern Orthodox, Roman Catholic, and Muslim adherents compound the conflicts rooted in nationality. (*b*) **Afghanistan** houses Pathan, Tajik, Uzbek, and Hazara ethnic groups speaking Pashto, Dari Persian, Uzbek, and several minor languages, and split between majority Sunni and minority Shia Moslem believers. Ethnic and local warlord rivalries and regional guerilla resistance to the NATO-supported central government contribute to national instability.

Ethnic Homelands

In the first instance, there is a real or perceived threat of domination or conquest by another external and powerful group. Consequently, members of an ethnic group may resist by laying claim to their own territory in order to ensure the survival of their cultural practices. In extreme instances, this takes the form of territorial isolation, which is a strong and supporting trait of ethnic separatism that assists individual groups in retaining their identification.

In Europe, Asia, and Africa, ethnicity and territorial identity are inseparable. Ethnic minorities are first and foremost associated with *homelands*. This is true of the Welsh, Bretons, and Basques of Western Europe (Figure 7.20); the Slovenes, Croatians, or Bosnians of Eastern Europe (Figure 6.2a); the non-Slavic "nationalities" of Russia; and the immense number of ethnic communities of South and Southeast Asia. These minorities have specific spatial identity even though they may not have political independence.

Where ethnic groups are intermixed and territorial boundaries imprecise—former Yugoslavia (Figure 6.2a) is an example—or where a single state contains disparate, rival populations—the case of many African and Asian (Figure 6.2b) countries—conflict among groups can be serious if peaceful relations or central governmental control break down. The outcome is not only an alteration of the ethnic composition of regions and states, but of the ethnic mix in, usually, adjacent areas and countries to which assaulted and displaced populations have fled as refugees.

Isolationism and political disruptions notwithstanding, the close association of territoriality and ethnicity is well recognized and accepted throughout much of the world. Indigenous ethnic groups have developed over time in specific locations and, through ties of kinship, language, culture, religion, and shared history, have established themselves in their own and others' eyes as distinctive peoples with their own culture in defined homeland areas. The boundaries of most countries of the world encompass a number of ethnic minorities, whose demands for special territorial recognition have increased rather than diminished with advances in economic development, education, and self-awareness (Figure 6.2).

The dissolution of the Soviet Union in 1991, for example, not only set free the 14 ethnically based union republics that formerly had been dominated by Russia and Russians, but also opened the way for many smaller ethnic groups—the Chechens of the northern Caucasus, for example—to seek recognition and greater local control from the majority populations, including Russians, within whose territory their homelands lay. In Asia, the Indian subcontinent was subdivided to create separate countries with primarily religious-territorial affiliations, and the country of India itself has adjusted the boundaries of its constituent states to accommodate linguistic-ethnic realities. Other continents and countries show a similar acceptance of the importance of ethnic territoriality in their administrative structure (see "The Rising Tide of Nationalism").

Nationalism is an ideology—a mentifact—founded on the notion that a people with common characteristics such as ethnicity, language, or religion constitute a distinct and separate political community. This notion is premised on both imagination and territory. Simply because people share one or more cultural identities, language for instance, does not mean that they necessarily share a common political interest or will ever interact directly or indirectly with one another. National identity is a shared but imagined sense of unity and belonging. The sense of attachment is tied necessarily to land: nations require a space or territory of their own to exercise and protect their national interests.

The rise of nationalist movements commenced with the birth of nation-states in Europe after the Napoleonic period (1799–1815). Countries like England, France, and Italy promoted the idea that their respective state territories were occupied by a homogeneous ethnic group or nation: "Englishman," "Frenchman," and so forth. The reasons for the growth and diffusion of nationalism in the 19th century are many and complex. Suffice to say that governments responded effectively to the new demands of an increasingly urbanized and industrial society, and there were advantages for governments to promote national unity and cohesion: nationalism served political interests.

Nationalism in the late 20th and early 21st centuries is associated with decolonization, the economic advancement of developing countries, and the struggle for regional equality or independence within existing states (e.g., Quebec independence). Indeed, calls for ethnic self-assertion and demands for national independence and cultural purification of homeland territories are spreading. To some, these demands and the conflicts they frequently engender are the expected consequences of the decline of strong central governments and imperial controls. It has happened before. The disintegration of British, French, and Dutch colonial control after World War II resulted in new state formation in Africa, South and East Asia, and Oceania. Similarly, the former Soviet Union and its Eastern European satellites fragmented in the late 1980s and early 1990s (see Figure 6.2a).

Democracies, too, at least before legal protections for minorities are firmly in place, risk disintegration or division along ethnic, tribal, or religious lines. African states with their multiple ethnic loyalties (see Figure 7.6) have frequently used those divisions to justify restricting political freedoms and continuing one-party rule. Such ethnically inspired civil wars and regional revolts show the fragility of some political structures.

In Anglo-America, there are at least two cases, both primarily Canadian, where territorial claim and ethnic distinctiveness come together as "homelands." The first is the clearly delineated province of Quebec, which is overwhelmingly French, and the second are the widely dispersed and varied lands of First Nations.

French Concentration and Dispersal

The stamp of the French charter group on Canada is overwhelming. Quebec—with ethnic concentrations extending into Ontario, New Brunswick, Nova Scotia and northern-most Maine—is one of two extensive regions in North America where regional delimitation on purely ethnic lines is possible or appropriate. In language, religion, legal principles, system of land tenure, the arts, cuisine, philosophies of life, and landscapes of rural and urban occupance, Quebec stands apart from the rest of Canada (Figure 6.3). Its distinctiveness and self-assertion have won it special consideration and treatment within the political structure of the country.

Quebec is a province of some 1.5 million square kilometres (600,000 sq mi) with 7.4 million people, more than 82% of whom have French as their native tongue (see Figure 6.28) and adhere to the Roman Catholic faith. Quebec City is the cultural hearth of French Canada, though the bilingual Montreal metropolitan area, with a population of 3.5 million, is the largest centre of Quebec, and the largest French speaking city outside of France. The sense of cultural identity prevalent throughout French Canada imparted a spirit of nationalism not similarly expressed in other ethnic provinces of North America. Laws and guarantees recognizing and strengthening the position of French language and culture within the province assure the preservation of this distinctive North American cultural region, even if the movement for full political separation from the rest of Canada is not successful. The political implications of this are discussed in Chapter 7.

But Quebec is certainly not the only province with French speakers. As Figure 6.28 illustrates, Francophones are dispersed across Canada. Outside Quebec, they account for 4.4% of the population: Ontario's Francophones number over half a million; New Brunswick has just under a quarter of a million; Alberta and British Columbia have some 60,000 each; and Manitoba has just over 45,000 (Statistics Canada, 2008). Quebec is certainly the hearth of Francophones, but they are very much a part of the rest of Canada.

First Nations Diversity

The second instance of territorial and ethnic distinctiveness involves Aboriginals and their reserves. The term "Aboriginal" refers to all of the original inhabitants of North America and their descendents: those people who can trance their ancestry back to those present prior to European settlement. Just over 1.3 million Canadians report some Aboriginal ancestry or ethnicity, but not all identify themselves as an "Aboriginal person": a North American Indian, Métis, or Inuit (Statistics Canada, 2001). These three groups constitute the First Nations, and comprise almost 1 million people, or 3.3% of Canada's population. Roughly 65% of First Nations people live off **reserves** and more than two-thirds of those live in urban areas. The remaining 375,000 Indians, Métis, and Inuit live on reserves: land areas, both rural and urban, "reserved" for the exclusive use of First Nations peoples (Figure 6.4). The term *reserve* is defined by the *Indian Act*—federal legislation first introduced in 1876 to govern First Nations and federal government relations—as a "tract

(a)

(b)

FIGURE 6.3 (*a*) The hotel Château Frontenac stands high above the lower older portion of Quebec City, where many streets show the architecture of French cities of the 18th century carried over to the urban heart of modern French Canada. (*b*) Rural Richelieu Valley in the Eastern Townships of Quebec Province.

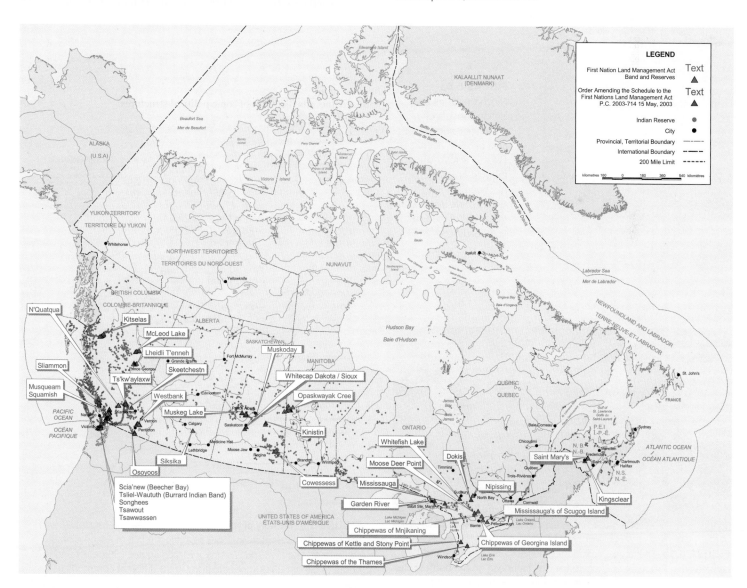

FIGURE 6.4 First Nations reserves in Canada. There are more than 600 First Nations reserves spread throughout Canada, most of which are quite small. They are self-governed in accordance with the Indian Act, and as such both land and the personal property of band and residents are exempt from provincial and federal taxation.

Source: http://www.lsd.nrcan.gc.ca/english/fnlmi_e.asp.

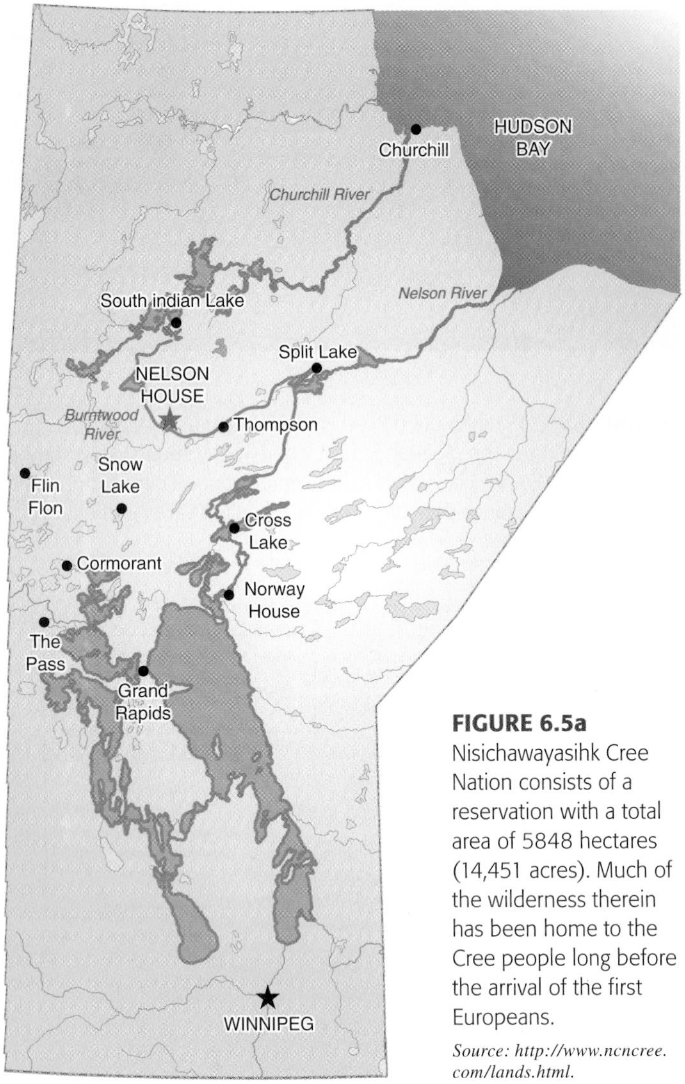

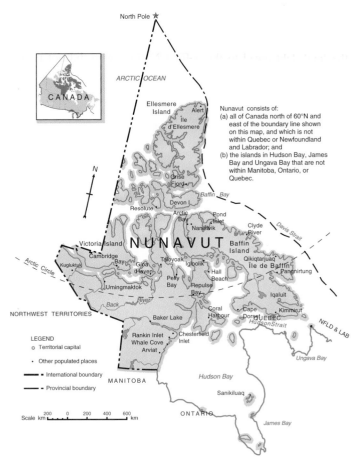

FIGURE 6.5a
Nisichawayasihk Cree Nation consists of a reservation with a total area of 5848 hectares (14,451 acres). Much of the wilderness therein has been home to the Cree people long before the arrival of the first Europeans.

Source: http://www.ncncree. com/lands.html.

of land, the legal title to which is vested in Her Majesty, that has been set apart by Her Majesty for the use and benefit of a band." The Act also declares that land reserved for the benefit and use of a band which is not vested in the Crown is also subject to the same provisions governing reserves.

Although reserves are clearly defined spaces of ethnic identity, one must recognize the cultural diversity within First Nations, the origins of these homelands and the ongoing negotiations over land claims. American Indians, Métis, and Inuit have their own histories and cultural differences, with a broad spectrum of lifestyles, values, and customs. The reserves themselves comprise an area less than 1% of Canada's land base, yet are homeland to 610 bands or communities, who make up 52 Nations (e.g., Cree, Iroquois, Mohawk), and speak more than 52 languages. Some reserves are small, remote, and support only a dozen people, while others, such as the Peter Ballantyne Reserve in Saskatchewan or the Six Nations Reserve in Ontario, are populated by over 8000 residents (Figure 6.5). Some are

FIGURE 6.5b The largest community, business, and government centre within this reserve is located at Nelson House on the north shore of Footprint Lake at the convergence of the Burntwood, Footprint, and Rat Rivers. The Cree name Nisichawayasihk means, "Where three rivers meet." This community is approximately 80 kilometres (50 miles) west of Thompson in Northern Manitoba.

FIGURE 6.6 Territory of Nunavut. Nunavut, meaning "our land," was established as a territory in 1999 as a direct result of a land claims settlement. The area spans some 2 million square kilometres and is home to almost 29,000 people living in 26 different communities. None of the communities are accessible by rail or road: everything and everyone enters or leaves by plane or boat.

Source: http://atlas.gc.ca/site/english/maps/reference/provincesterritories/nunavut/ referencemap_image_view.

wealthy, others are not. The latter do have problems with unemployment, inadequate housing, and a variety of health and social problems that warrant Canada's collective concern. There are differences in the formation of the reserves themselves as well. Those which were imposed upon First Nations by missionaries and colonial administrators before Confederation were, in fact, ghettos: i.e., people were forced to move onto them, and in many cases this involved relocation far from their traditional lands. Others were areas that bands had historically occupied and were established through land grants from the government or negotiated through treaties (Figure 6.6).

Negotiations over treaties and Aboriginal rights continue to this day. Treaties emerged some 300 years ago between the British Crown and many First Nations living in what became Canada (Figure 6.7). These agreements are intended to outline the obligations both parties have to ensure a peaceful and prosperous partnership: they are fundamental building blocks in the creation and continuation of the country. Many Aboriginals regard the historical treaties as sacred, and the Government of Canada views treaties, both historic and modern, as key components in federal–First Nations relations. Conflicts, however, do persist, most notably in the form of "treaty land entitlements" or TLEs. These land claims are intended to settle peacefully the land debt owed to those First Nations who did not receive all the land they were entitled to under historical treaties signed by the Crown and First Nations. As of 2002, there were 117 specific claims under negotiation and another 491 under assessment (Indian and Northern Affairs, 2004). Regardless of the legal status of these varied homelands, and the cultural diversity within Aboriginal communities, these territories remain vital to First Nations people for their sense of ethnic identities and the continuation of their cultures.

Ethnic Enclaves and Ghettos

Unlike those ethnic groups above who struggle to exert their identity and independence from an external or conquering cultural group, immigrant ethnic groups usually aspire for acceptance and equality with their host society. Here, ethnic groups may resist their lack of cultural inclusion and acceptance by the majority group through spatially excluding themselves to their own smaller rural or urban enclaves. The minority ethnic group is subject to a real or perceived sense of social exclusion by other cultural groups and seeks strength, safety, and reassurance among their own members through occupying spaces inscribed with their own identity. In North American cities, these take the form of the "Chinatowns" and "Little Italys," which provide both the spatial refuge and the

FIGURE 6.7 Historical Indian treaties in Canada. Historical agreements, or treaties, between the British Crown or Government of Canada and First Nations affect 369 First Nations composed of 499,000 people and impact nine provinces and three territories.

Source: Reproduced with permission of Natural Resources Canada 2008, courtesy of the Atlas of Canada. http://atlas.nrcan.gc.ca/site/english/maps/historical/indiantreaties/historicaltreaties.

support systems essential to new arrivals in an alien culture realm. Asian and West Indian immigrants in London and other English cities, and foreign guest workers—originally migrant and temporary labourers, usually male—that reside in Continental European communities assume similar spatial separation (Figure 6.8). While serving a support function, this **segregation** is as much the consequence of the housing market and of public and private restriction as it is simply of self-selection. In Southeast Asia, Chinese communities remain aloof from the majority culture not as a transitional phase to incorporation with it but as a permanent chosen isolation. When an ethnic cluster does persist because its occupants choose to preserve it, their behaviour reflects the internal cohesiveness of the group and its desire to maintain an enduring **ethnic enclave** or neighbourhood.

By retaining what is familiar of the old in a new land, ethnic enclaves have reduced cultural shock and have paved the way for the gradual process of adaptation that prepares both individuals and groups to operate effectively in the new, larger **host society** —the established, dominant group.

Internal Controls

The clustering of specific groups into discrete, ethnically homogeneous urban neighbourhoods is best understood as the result of internal controls of group defensiveness and conservatism. The self-elected segregation of ethnic groups can be seen to serve four principal functions—defence, support, preservation, and "attack."

First, it provides *defence*, reducing individual immigrant isolation and exposure by physical association within a limited area. The walled and gated Jewish quarters of medieval European cities have their present-day counterparts in the clearly marked and defined "turfs" of street gang members and the understood exclusive domains of ethnic neighbourhoods. In British cities, it has been observed that West Indians and Asians fill identical slots in the British economy and reside in the same sorts of areas, but they tend to avoid living in the *same* areas. West Indians avoid Asians; Sikhs isolate themselves

FIGURE 6.8 "Guest workers"—frequently called by their German name, *Gastarbeiter*—have substantially altered the ethnic mix in formerly unicultural cities of Western Europe. The restaurant shown here is in an Algerian neighbourhood of Paris, France. On average, foreigners comprise nearly 10% of Western Europe's labour force. They form the majority of the workforce in many Middle Eastern countries; between 60% and 90% of the workers of the Persian Gulf countries of Bahrain, Kuwait, Oman, Qatar, Saudi Arabia, and the United Arab Emirates are foreigners.

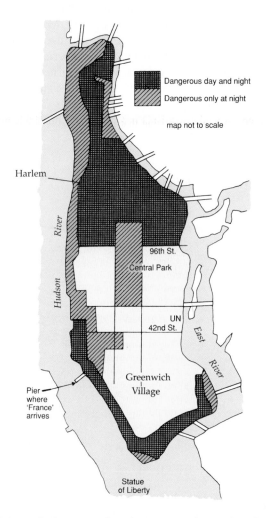

Dangerous day and night
Dangerous only at night

map not to scale

Harlem

Hudson River

East River

96th St.
Central Park

UN
42nd St.

Greenwich Village

Pier where 'France' arrives

Statue of Liberty

FIGURE 6.9 A "safety map" of Manhattan. According to the editors of the French newspaper *l'Aurore,* all of western and southern Manhattan fringe areas and any place north of 96th street—then (late 1970s) all largely ethnic and racial minority districts—were best avoided, particularly at night.

Source: From l'Aurore as reproduced in Peter Jackson, Ethnic Groups and Boundaries, *School of Geography, Oxford University, 1980.*

Geography and Public Policy

An Asian-Themed Mall in Suburban Toronto—An Enclave with Land-Use Conflicts

Retaining familiar cultural practices and identities is easier in self-selected enclaves, but this does not mean all practices are permitted by the dominant "host" society. As geographers Preston and Lo (2000) explain in their study of land-use conflicts over Asian-themed malls in suburban Richmond Hill near Toronto, ethnic groups who are free to choose where and how to live may still encounter intense opposition to their cultural practices, indicating choice has its limitations and acculturation presents challenges.

With almost 20% of the population of Richmond Hill of Chinese ethnicity by the mid-1990s, it is not surprising that plans for a major commercial establishment, specifically an "Asian-themed" mall, emerged at that time in response to the growing demand for access to Chinese goods and services in a familiar Chinese setting. Asian-themed malls are designed and operated in ways that differ from the typical suburban mall. Instead of using major retailers or "anchors" to attract customers indirectly to the smaller shops and services, a large number of very small retail outlets are concentrated in one location. Much more space is given to food outlets—up to 50%—than is normally the case, and can themselves act as the mall's anchor. An Asian-themed mall also tends to be entirely enclosed—windowless—a feature that is the norm for large regional malls, but not for neighbourhood shopping centres, which usually take the form of a strip plaza: individual shops under one roof, each with their own storefront window and direct access from the parking lot. Finally, unlike the norm where a single mall property owner leases space to retail tenants, in the Asian-themed mall each retail unit are owned separately.

The Richmond Hill town council, and ultimately the Ontario Municipal Board, would not accommodate the developer's proposed deviations from the norm. The 132 retail units would have to be reduced to only 30, the amount of floor space devoted to food outlets substantially decreased, and more parking spaces would be required. The mall was never built.

This land use conflict demonstrates the challenges Canadian society has in coming to terms with how to incorporate ethnic diversity into the built environment. On one hand, Canada is committed to promoting diversity, ensuring fair and equitable treatment for all, and enhancing the ability of all to participate fully in society, and yet incorporating these values into the built environment—in this instance an Asian-themed mall with an ethnic identity deviating from the dominant norm—is problematic.

---

from Muslims; Bengalis avoid Punjabis. In London, patterns of residential isolation even extends to West Indians of separate island homelands.

Their own defined ethnic territory provides members of the group with security from the hostility of antagonistic social groups, a factor also underlying the white flight in the United States, whereby "whites" flee from "black" inner cities to "garrison" suburbs. That outsiders view at least some closely defined ethnic communities as homogeneous, impenetrable, and hostile is suggested by Figure 6.9, a "safety map" of Manhattan published in the newspaper *l'Aurore* for the guidance of French tourists.

Second, the ethnic neighbourhood provides *support* for its residents in a variety of ways. The area serves as a halfway station between the home country and the alien society, to which admittance will eventually be sought. It acts as a place of initiation and indoctrination, providing supportive lay and religious ethnic institutions, familiar businesses, job opportunities where language barriers are minimal, and friendship and kinship ties to ease the transition to a new society (see "Geography and Public Policy: An Asian-Themed Mall in Suburban Toronto").

Third, the ethnic neighbourhood may provide a *preservation* function, reflecting the ethnic group's positive intent to preserve and promote such essential elements of its cultural heritage as language and religion. The preservation function represents a disinclination to be totally absorbed into the charter society, and a desire to maintain those customs and associations seen to be essential to the conservation of the group. For example, Jewish dietary laws are more easily observed by, or exposure to potential marriage partners within the faith is more certain in, close-knit communities than when individuals are scattered.

Finally, ethnic spatial concentration can serve what has been termed the *assertion* or *attack* function, a peaceful and legitimate search for, particularly, political representation by a concentration of electoral power. Voter registration drives among African and Hispanic Americans represent concerted efforts to achieve the promotion of group interests at all governmental levels.

External Controls

When the ethnic cluster is perpetuated by external constraints and discriminatory actions, it has come to be termed a **ghetto**. When the majority culture or rival minorities perceive an ethnic group as threatening, the group tends to be spatially isolated by external "blocking" tactics designed to confine the rejected minority and to resist its "invasion" of already occupied urban neighbourhoods. The more tightly knit the threatened group, the more adamant and overt are its resistance tactics. When confrontation measures (including, perhaps, threats and vandalism) fail, the invasion of dominant-group territory by the rejected minority proceeds until a critical

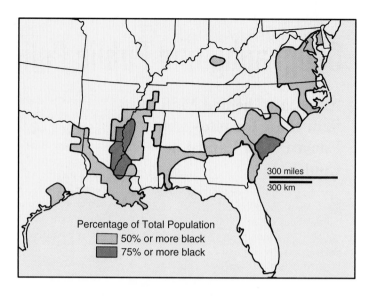

FIGURE 6.11 African American concentrations, 1850.

FIGURE 6.10 The outward expansion of ethnic and nationality groups in Chicago. "Often," Samuel Kincheloe observed in the 1930s, "[minority] groups first settle in a deteriorated area of a city somewhere near its centre, then push outward along the main streets." More recently, many—particularly young, innovative, and entrepreneurial—immigrants have avoided traditional first locations in central cities and from their arrival have settled in metropolitan area suburbs and outlying cities where economic opportunity and quality of life is perceived as superior to conditions in the primary inner city.

Source: The American City and Its Church, by Samuel Kincheloe. Copyright 1938 by Friendship Press, New York.

percentage of newcomer housing occupancy is reached. That level, the **tipping point**, may precipitate a rapid exodus by the former majority population. Invasion, followed by succession, then results in a new spatial pattern of ethnic dominance. Where forced segregation limits residential choices, ethnic minorities may be confined to the older, low-cost housing areas, typically close to the city centre. Growing ethnic groups that maintain voluntary spatial association frequently expand the area of their dominance by growth outward from the core of the city in a radial pattern. That process has long been recognized in Chicago (Figure 6.10) and has, in that and other American cities, typically been extended beyond the central city boundaries into at least the inner fringe of the suburbs.

African Americans, involuntary immigrants to the United States, have, traditionally, found strong resistance to their territorial expansion from the largely Anglo groups. "White–black" urban relations and patterns of black ghetto formation and expansion have differed in different sections of the country. Prior to the Civil War (Figure 6.11), blacks were largely confined to rural areas of the South and Southeast. Even today, when almost half of African Americans reside outside of the South, a southern regionalization of blacks is still evident (Figure 6.12).

A revealing typology of African American ghettos helps to explain this spatial distribution (Figure 6.13). In the South, the white majority, with total control of the housing market, was able to assign residential space to blacks in accordance with white, not black, self-interest. In the early southern ghetto of such pre-Civil War cities as Charleston and New Orleans, African Americans were assigned small dwellings in alleys and back streets within and bounding the white communities where they worked as house and garden slaves. The classic southern ghetto for newly free blacks was composed of specially built, low-quality housing on undesirable land—swampy, perhaps, or near industry or railroads—and was sufficiently far from better-quality white housing to maintain full spatial and social segregation. In the North, on the other hand, African Americans were open competitors with other claimants for space in a generalized housing market. The early northern ghetto represented a "toehold" location in high-density, aged, substandard housing on the margin of the central business district. The classic northern ghetto is a more recent expansion of that initial enclave to surround the central business district (CBD) and to penetrate, through invasion and succession, contiguous zones as far as the numbers and the rent-paying ability of the growing African American community will carry. Finally, in new Western and Southwestern cities not tightly hemmed in by resistant ethnic neighbourhoods or ethnic suburbs, the black community may display a linear expansion from the CBD to the suburban fringe. Nevertheless, by 2000, the African American population (12% of all Americans) had become more urbanized than the general population: 86% were residents of metropolitan areas compared to 75% for all Americans combined.

"Racial" or ethnic discrimination in urban areas generally expresses itself in the relegation of the most recent, most alien, most rejected minority to the poorest available housing. That confinement has historically been abetted by the concentration of the newest, least assimilated ethnic minorities at the low end of the occupational structure. Distasteful, menial, low-paying service

Landscapes of Identity, Plurality, and Organization

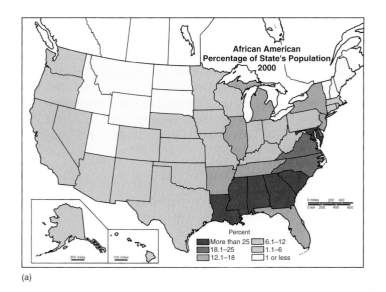
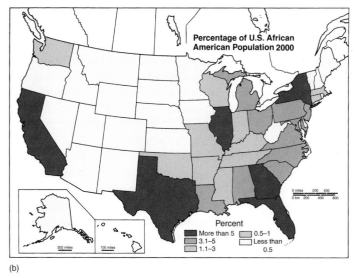

(a)   (b)

FIGURE 6.12 Evidences of African American concentration, 2000. (*a*) The left-hand map indicates the importance of African Americans in the total population of the individual states. They are particularly significant in the largely rural, relatively low-population states of the Southeast in a pattern reminiscent of their distribution in 1850 (Figure 6.11). (*b*) The right-hand map makes clear the African American response to employment opportunities now more widely available than 150 years ago in the urbanized, industrialized states of the Northeast, Midwest, and California. However, the South was still the home of almost 55% of African Americans in 2000, reflecting both tradition and a pronounced return migration in the later 20th century.

Source: Data from U.S. Bureau of the Census.

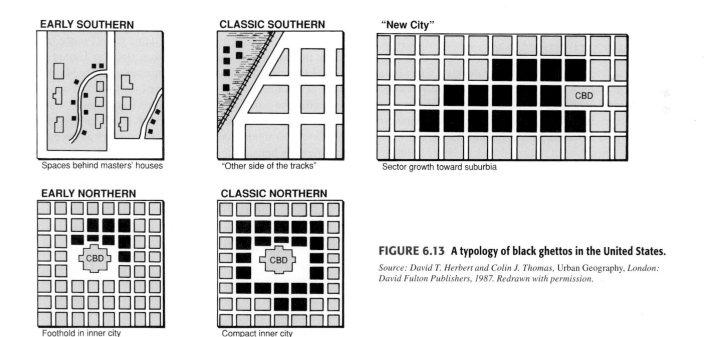

FIGURE 6.13 A typology of black ghettos in the United States.

Source: David T. Herbert and Colin J. Thomas, Urban Geography, *London: David Fulton Publishers, 1987. Redrawn with permission.*

and factory employment, unattractive to the dominant group, is available to those new arrivals even when other occupational avenues may be closed. The dockworkers, street cleaners, slaughterhouse employees, and sweatshop garment workers of earlier America had and have their counterparts in other regions. In England, successive waves of West Indians and Commonwealth Asians took the posts of low-pay hotel and restaurant service workers, transit workers, refuse collectors, manual labourers, and

the like; Turks in German cities and North Africans in France play similar low-status employment roles.

In the United States, there has been a spatial association between the location of such employment opportunities—the inner-city central business district (CBD) and its margins—and the location of the oldest, most dilapidated, and least desirable housing. Proximity to job opportunity and the availability of cheap housing near the CBD, therefore, combined to concentrate the U.S.

immigrant slum near the heart of the 19th-century central city. In the second half of the 20th century, the suburbanization of jobs, the rising skill levels required in the automated offices of the CBD, and the effective isolation of inner-city residents by the absence of public transportation or their inability to pay for private transport, maintained the association of the least competitive minorities and the least desirable housing area. But now those locations lack the promise of entry-level jobs formerly close at hand.

That U.S. spatial association does not necessarily extend to other cultures and urban environments. In Latin American cities, newest arrivals at the bottom of the economic and employment ladder are most apt to find housing in squatter or slum areas on the outskirts of the urban unit, while prestigious housing claims room near the city centre. European and Canadian cities, too, have retained a larger proportion of upper income groups at the urban centre than have their American counterparts, with a corresponding impact on the distribution of lower-status, lower-income housing.

As we have seen, both voluntarism and discrimination have historically influenced the changing pattern of ethnic clustering within metropolitan areas. Generally, the spatial pattern of ethnicity that has developed in Canada and the United States is more intricate and shifting than in many other pluralistic societies; it is not based on the dominance of one single ethnic group, but on interplay between numerous ethnic groups with varying degrees of power. The resulting ethnic landscapes are highly fluid and change over time, driven always by the constant stream of newcomers to the continent.

Immigration Streams

The ethnic diversity found on the Anglo-American scene today is the product of continuous flows of immigrants through space—some 70 million of them by the start of the 21st century—representing, at different periods, movements to this continent of members of nearly all of the cultures and ethnicities of the world. These flows have always been designed and carefully managed. The European powers that first colonized the continent, and later both the American and Canadian governments, have opened and closed borders to immigrants based primarily upon economic and demographic needs (see Chapter 4). Newcomers bring needed skills, expertise, and labour, as well as expand the size of the population. Both help to stimulate and sustain economic growth by filling jobs and creating demand for more goods and services. Accordingly, as economic and demographic needs change over time, the government increases or decreases the flow of immigrants. Even unwanted flows—streams of illegal immigrants or "aliens"—are managed in the sense that attempts are made to close them through border patrols, physical barriers, check points, and various forms of surveillance. Consequently, immigrant streams come in "waves," with peaks and troughs of both legal and illegal immigrants. For the United States, these streams have taken the form of three distinct immigrant waves, all of which, of course, followed much earlier Amerindian arrivals.

The first wave, lasting from pioneer settlement to about 1870, was made up of two different groups. One comprised arrivals from western and northern Europe, with Britain and Germany best represented. Together with the Scots and Scotch-Irish, they established a majority society controlled by Protestant Anglo-Saxons and allied groups. The Europeans dominated numerically the second group of first-wave immigrants. Africans forced to the New World made up nearly 20% of U.S. population in 1790. The mass immigration that occurred beginning after the middle of the 19th century began to reduce both the northwest European dominance of American society and the percentage of blacks within the growing total population.

That second immigrant wave, from 1870 to 1921, was heavily weighted in favour of eastern and southern Europeans, who comprised more than 50% of new arrivals by the end of the 19th century. The second period ended with congressional adoption of a quota system regulating both the numbers of individuals who would be accepted and the countries from which they could come. That system, plus a world depression and World War II (1939–1945), greatly slowed immigration until a third-wave migration was launched during the 1960s. At that time, the old national quota system of immigrant regulation was replaced by one more liberal in its admission of Latin Americans. Nevertheless, by 1970, only 4.8% of the population was foreign born. By 2000 nearly 11% of the population, or some 30 million people, had been born abroad, and over 30% of total population growth of the United States between 1990 and 2000 was accounted for by legal and illegal immigration. Along with more recent Asian arrivals, Latin Americans became the largest segment of new arrivals.

Canada experienced three quite different immigration streams. Until 1760, most settlers came from France. After that date, the pattern abruptly altered as a flood of United Kingdom (English, Irish, and Scottish) immigrants arrived. Many came by way of the United States, fleeing, as Loyalists, to Canada during and after the American Revolutionary War. Others came directly from overseas. Another pronounced shift in arrival pattern occurred during the early and mid-20th century as the bulk of new immigrants began originating in Continental Europe after World Wars I and II (Figure 6.14). During the last 40 years, changes in Canada's immigration policies have altered the flow of migrants yet again. Whereas prior to 1961, 90% of immigrants were European, the largest source of newcomers is now Asia. Of the 1.8 million immigrants who came to Canada between 1991 and 2001, 58% were from Asia. The People's Republic of China, followed by India, the Philippines, Hong Kong, Sri Lanka, Pakistan, and Taiwan now account for over 40% of all immigrants to Canada. By 2001, 18.4% of all Canadians had been born outside of the country, surpassed only by the 22.2% of foreign-born peoples in 1931; immigration accounted for more than one-half of Canada's population growth between 1996 and 2001. The 10 leading ethnicities in 2001 (of more than 200 different ethnic origins reported) are listed in Table 6.1 (see "Nations of Immigrants").

In both the United States and Canada, these immigrant streams have channelled themselves into specific **migration fields**: areas that draw the majority of immigrants. Pre-existing contacts with friends and relatives who arrived earlier (**chain migration**), the perception of the best economic opportunities in certain places, and direct flights to major "gateway" cities from

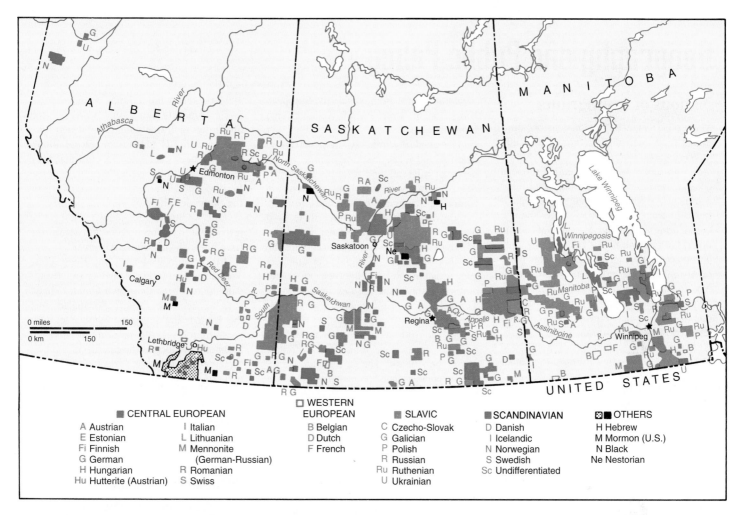

FIGURE 6.14 Ethnic diversity in the Prairie Provinces of Canada. In 1991, 69% of all Canadians claimed some French or British ancestry. For the Prairie Provinces, with their much greater ethnic mixture, only 15% declared any British or French descent. Immigrants comprise a larger share of Canadian population than they do of the U.S. population. Early in the 20th century, most newcomers located in rural western Canada and by 1921 about half the population of the Prairie Provinces was foreign born. Later immigrants concentrated in the major metropolitan centres. In 2001, some 40% of Toronto's population was foreign born and 35% of Vancouver's. In the period 1981 to 1991, 48% of Canada's immigrants were from Asia and only 25% from Europe, the traditionally dominant source region. From 1991 to 2001, the disparity increased: to 58% and 20%.

Source: D.G.G. Kerr, A Historical Atlas of Canada, *2nd edition, 1966. Thomas Nelson & Sons Ltd., 1966.*

TABLE 6.1			
Canadian Population ranked by Claimed Ethnic Origin, 2006			
Rank	**Ethnic Group**	**Rank**	**Ethnic Group**
1	Canadian	6	German
2	English	7	Italian
3	French	8	Chinese
4	Scottish	9	North American Indian
5	Irish	10	Ukrainian

Source: Statistics Canada, 2008.

Geography and Public Policy

Nations of Immigrants

Many other countries are "nations of immigrants" and their numbers are dramatically increasing. In Canada, the United States, Australia, and New Zealand, early European colonists and, later, immigrants from other continents, overwhelmed indigenous populations. In each, immigration has continued, contributing not only to national ethnic mixes but maintaining or enlarging the proportion of the population that is foreign born. In Australia, as one example, that proportion now equals 25%; for Canada it is some 18%.

In Latin America, foreign population domination of native peoples was and is less complete and uniform than in Anglo-America. While in nearly all South and Central American states, European and other non-native ethnic groups dominate the social and economic hierarchy, in many they constitute only a minority of the total population. In Paraguay, for example, the vast majority of inhabitants are native Paraguayans who pride themselves on their Native American descent, and Amerindians comprise nearly half the population of Peru, Bolivia, and Ecuador. But European ethnics make up over 90% of the population of Argentina, Uruguay, Costa Rica, and southern Chile, and about 50% of the inhabitants of Brazil.

The original homelands of those immigrant groups are themselves increasingly becoming multiethnic. Several European countries are now home to many more foreign-born people. Some 20% of Switzerland's population, 13% of France's, 10% of Sweden's, and over 9% of Germany's are of foreign birth. Many came as immigrants and refugees fleeing unrest or poverty in postcommunist Eastern Europe. Many are "guest workers" and their families who were earlier recruited in Turkey and North Africa; or they are immigrants from former colonial or overseas territories in Asia, Africa, and the Caribbean. More than 7% of Germany's

inhabitants come from outside the European Union, as do over 3% of Holland's and Belgium's.

The trend of ethnic mixing is certain to continue and accelerate. Cross-border movements of migrants and refugees in Africa, Asia, the Americas, as well as in Europe are continuing common occurrences, reflecting growing incidences of ethnic strife, civil wars, famines, and economic hardships. But of even greater long-term influence are the growing disparities in population numbers and economic wealth between the older developed states and the developing world. The population of the world's poorer countries is growing twice as fast as Europe's of the late 19th century, when that continent fed the massive immigration streams across the Atlantic. The current rich world, whose population is projected to stabilize well below 1.5 billion, will increasingly be a magnet for those from poorer countries, where numbers will rise from some 4 billion to more than 6.5 billion by 2025 A.C.E. and to nearly 8 billion in a half-century. The economic and population pressures building in the developing world ensure greater international and intercontinental migration, and a rapid expansion in the numbers of "nations of immigrants."

Many of those developed host countries are beginning to resist that flow. Although the Universal Declaration of Human Rights declares individuals are to be free to move within or to leave their own countries, no right of admittance to any other country is conceded. Political asylum is often—but not necessarily—granted; refugees or migrants seeking economic opportunity or fleeing civil strife or starvation have no claims for acceptance. Increasingly, they are being turned away. The Interior Minister of France advocates "zero immigration"; Germany's government closed its doors in 1993 by increasing border controls and changing its constitutional right to asylum; Britain in

1994 tightened immigration rules even for foreign students and casual workers. And all European Union countries—which have no common EU policies on illegal immigration—have measures for turning back refugees who come via another EU country. In 1995, the EU's members materially narrowed the definition of who may qualify for asylum. Additional individual and collective restrictions have been enforced during the later 1990s and into the 21st century.

Nor is Europe alone. Hong Kong ejects Vietnamese refugees; Congo orders Rwandans to return to their own country; India tries to stem the influx of Bangladeshis; the United States rejects "economic refugees" from Haiti. Algerians are increasingly resented in France as their numbers and cultural presence increase. Turks feel the enmity of a small but violent group of Germans, and East Indians and Africans find growing resistance among the Dutch. In many countries, policies of exclusion or restriction appear motivated by unacceptable influxes of specific ethnic or national groups.

Questions to Consider

1. Do you think all people everywhere should have a universal right of admittance to a country of choice equivalent to their declared right to depart their homelands? Why or why not?

2. Do you think it appropriate that destination states make a distinction between political and economic refugees? Why or why not?

3. Do you think it legitimate for countries to establish immigration quotas based on national origin or to classify certain potential immigrants as unacceptable or undesirable on the grounds that their national, ethnic, or religious origins are incompatible with the culture of the prospective host country? Why or why not?

---

abroad, make some areas more amenable to the needs and aspirations of newcomers than others (see Chapter 4, "Migration").

Individual cities and counties in the U.S. showed very high concentrations of the foreign born at the end of the 20th century. New York City, for example, received one million immigrants in the 1990s, and by 2000, 40% of its population had been born abroad. Similar proportionate immigration flows and foreign-born ratios were recorded for Dade County

Landscapes of Identity, Plurality, and Organization

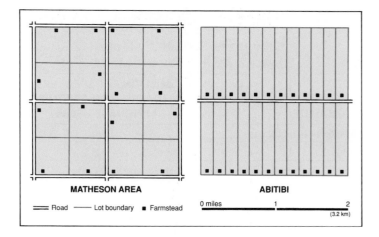

FIGURE 6.15 Land survey in Canada. Adjacent areas of Canada demonstrate the effects of different survey systems and cultural heritages on rural settlement patterns. The regular plots of Ontario in English Canada (left map) display the isolated farmsteads characteristic of much of rural Anglo-America. The long-lot survey of Quebec in French Canada (right map) shows the lot-front alignments of rural dwellings.

Source: Redrawn by permission from Annals of the Association of American Geographers, *George I. McDermott, vol. 51, p. 263, Association of American Geographers, 1961.*

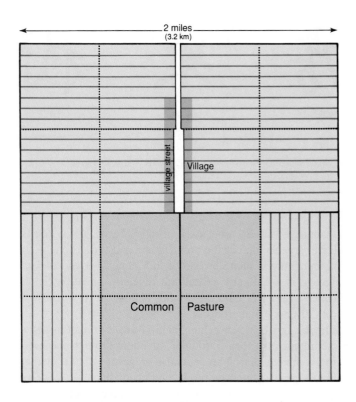

FIGURE 6.16 A transplanted ethnic landscape. The German-speaking Mennonites settled in Manitoba in the 1870s and recreated the agricultural village of their European homeland. Individual farmers were granted strip holdings in the separate fields to be farmed in common with the other villagers. The farmsteads themselves, with elongated rear lots, were aligned along both sides of a single village street in an Old World pattern.

Source: Redrawn from Carl A. Dawson, Group Settlement: Ethnic Communities in Western Canada. *vol. 7, Canada Frontiers of Settlement (Toronto: Macmillan Company of Canada, 1936), p. 111.*

(Miami) Florida, the Silicon Valley, California, counties of San Mateo and Santa Clara, and others. Monterey Park, California, has a population that is 60% Asian, the vast majority recent Chinese immigrants.

In Canada, almost three-quarters (73%) of the immigrants who arrived during the 1990s live in greater Toronto, Vancouver, and Montreal. Given over just one-third of the total Canadian population lives in these three areas, immigrants constitute an increasingly large proportion of these urban populations. The census metropolitan area of Toronto in particular has been the single largest migration field in Canada, attracting 40% and 43% of all immigrants during the 1980s and 1990s, respectively. Only 6% of new immigrants in the 1990s settled outside of urban centres with populations of less than 100,000

inhabitants. This accounts for the growing ethnic, linguistic, and religious diversity of Canada's cities.

See Figures 6.15 and 6.16 for examples of settlement patterns in Ontario, Quebec, and Manitoba.

Language and Diversity

Language is the most important medium of transmitting, sustaining, and modifying cultures, including the identities of ethnicity and religion. As noted in the previous chapter, language is both direct and comprehensive: it permits precise communication between people about virtually every aspect of a culture. Forever changing and evolving, language in spoken or written form makes possible the cooperative efforts, the group understandings, and shared behaviour patterns that distinguish culture groups. It is what enables parents to teach their children what the world they live in is like and what they must do to become functioning members of society. Some argue that the language of a society structures the perceptions of its speakers. By the words that it contains and the concepts that it can formulate, language is said to determine the attitudes, the understandings, and the responses of the society to which it belongs.

The more than 6 billion people on earth speak many thousands of different languages. Knowing that more than 1500 languages

HOUSE

RICE

TREE

FIGURE 6.17 All literate Chinese, no matter which of the many languages of China they speak, recognize the same ideographs for house, rice, and tree.

and language variants are spoken in sub-Saharan Africa gives us a clearer appreciation of the political and social divisions in that continent. Europe alone has some 225 languages and dialects. Language is a hallmark of cultural diversity, an often fiercely defended symbol of cultural identity helping to distinguish the world's diverse social groups.

In the broadest sense, language is any systematic method of communicating ideas, attitudes, or intent through the use of mutually understood signs, sounds, or gestures. It is perhaps the most sophisticated cultural creation of humanity. For our geographic purposes, we may define **language** as an organized system of spoken words by which people communicate with each other with mutual comprehension. But such a definition fails to recognize the gradations among and between languages, or to grasp the varying degrees of mutual comprehension between two or more of them. The language commonly called "Chinese," for example, is more properly seen as a group of distinct but related languages—Mandarin, Cantonese, Hakka, and others—that are as different from each other as are such comparably related European languages as Spanish, Italian, French, and Romanian. "Chinese" has uniformity only in the fact that all of the varied Chinese languages are written alike. No matter how it is pronounced, the same symbol for "house" or for "rice," for example, is recognized by all literate speakers of any Chinese language variant (Figure 6.17). Again, the language known as "Arabic" represents a number of related but distinct tongues, so Arabic spoken in Morocco differs from Palestinian Arabic roughly as Portuguese differs from Italian.

Languages differ greatly in their relative importance, if "importance" can be taken to mean the number of people using them. More than half of the world's inhabitants are native speakers of just eight of its thousands of tongues, and at least half regularly use or have competence in just four of them. That restricted language dominance reflects the reality that the world's linguistic diversity is rapidly shrinking. Of the at most 7000 tongues still remaining, between 20% and 50% are no longer being learned by children and are effectively dead. One estimate anticipates that no more than 600 of the world's current living languages will still be in existence in 2100 A.C.E. Table 6.2 lists those languages currently spoken as a native or second tongue by 40 million or more people, a list that includes nearly 90% of the world's population. At the other end of the scale are a number of rapidly declining languages whose speakers number in the hundreds or, at most, the few thousands.

TABLE 6.2	
Languages Spoken by More Than 40 Million People, 2004	
LANGUAGE	**MILLIONS OF SPEAKERS (NATIVE PLUS SECOND LANGUAGE USERS)**
Mandarin (China)	1076
English	551
Hindi/Urdu [a] (India, Pakistan)	498
Spanish	427
Russian	267
Bengali (Bangladesh, India)	215
Portuguese	195
Malay-Indonesian	176
Japanese	132
French	131
German	128
Javanese	78
Korean (Korea, China, Japan)	78
Wu (China)	78
Telugu (India)	77
Tamil (India, Sri Lanka)	76
Marathi (India)	73
Panjabi (India, Pakistan)	72
Yue/Cantonese (China)	72
Vietnamese	69
Italian	67
Turkish	63
Swahili (East Africa)	50
Egyptian Arabic [b]	48
Min (China)	48
Jinyu (China)	47
Ukrainian	47
Gujarati (India, Pakistan)	46
Polish	44

[a]Hindi and Urdu are basically the same language: Hindustani. Written in the devangari script, it is called *Hindi,* the official language of India; in the Arabic script it is called *Urdu,* the official language of Pakistan.

[b]Collectively the many, often mutually unintelligible versions of colloquial Arabic are used by at least 260 million native speakers. Classical or literary Arabic, the language of the Koran, is uniform and standardized but is restricted to formal usage as a spoken tongue.

Source: Based on data from *Ethnologue* and others.

The diversity of languages is simplified when we recognize among them related *families.* A **language family** is a group of languages descended from a single, earlier tongue. By varying estimates, from at least 30 to perhaps 100 such families of languages are found worldwide. The families, in turn, may be subdivided into subfamilies, branches, or groups of more closely related tongues. Some 2000 years ago, Latin was the common language spoken throughout the Roman Empire. The fall of the empire in the

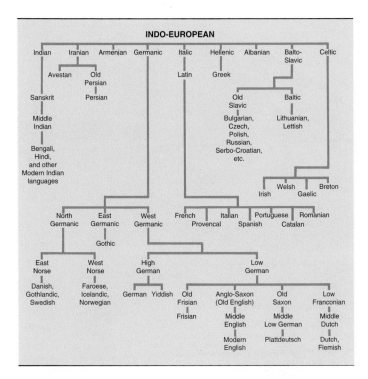

FIGURE 6.18 The Indo-European linguistic family tree. Euskara (Basque), Estonian, Finnish, and Hungarian are the only European languages not in the Indo-European family (see also Figure 6.22).

5th century A.C.E. broke the unity of Europe, and regional variants of Latin began to develop in isolation. In the course of the next several centuries, these Latin derivatives, changing and developing as all languages do, emerged as the individual *Romance* languages—Italian, Spanish, French, Portuguese, and Romanian—of modern Europe and of the world colonized by their speakers. Catalan, Sardinian, Provençal, and a few other spatially restricted tongues are also part of the Romance language group.

Family relationship between languages can be recognized through similarities in their vocabulary and grammar. By tracing regularities of sound changes in different languages back through time, linguists are able to reconstruct earlier forms of words and, eventually, determine a word's original form before it underwent alteration and divergence. Such a reconstructed earlier form is said to belong to a **protolanguage**. In the case of the Romance languages, of course, the well-known ancestral tongue was Latin, which needs no such reconstruction. Its root relationship to the Romance languages is suggested by modern variants of *panis*, the Latin word for "bread": *pane* (Italian), *pain* (French), *pan* (Spanish), *pão* (Portuguese), *pîine* (Romanian). In other language families, similar word relationships are less confidently traced to their protolanguage roots. For example, the *Germanic* languages, including English, German, Dutch, and the Scandinavian tongues, are related descendants of a less well-known proto-Germanic language spoken by peoples who lived in southern Scandinavia and along the North Sea and Baltic coasts from the Netherlands to western Poland. The classification of languages by origin and historical relationship is called a *genetic classification*.

Of the principal recognized language clusters of the world, the Indo-European family is the largest, embracing most of the languages of Europe and a large part of Asia, and the introduced—not the native—languages of the Americas (Figure 6.18). All told, languages in the Indo-European family are spoken by about half the world's peoples.

World Pattern of Languages

The present world distribution of major language families (Figure 6.19) records not only the migrations and conquests of our linguistic ancestors, but also the continuing dynamic pattern of human movements, settlements, and colonizations of more recent centuries. Indo-European languages have been carried far beyond their Eurasian homelands from the 16th century onwards by western European colonizers in the Americas, Africa, Asia, and Australasia. In the process of linguistic imposition and adoption, innumerable indigenous languages and language groups in areas of colonization have been modified or totally lost. Most of the estimated 1000 to 2000 *Amerindian* tongues of the Western Hemisphere disappeared in the face of European conquest and settlement (Figure 6.20).

The Slavic expansion eastward across Siberia beginning in the 16th century obliterated most of the *Paleo-Asiatic* languages there. Similar loss occurred in Eskimo and Aleut language areas. Large linguistically distinctive areas comprise the northern reaches of both Asia and America (see Figure 6.19). Their sparse populations are losing the mapped languages as the indigenous people adopt the tongues of the majority cultures of which they have been forcibly made a part. In the Southern Hemisphere, the several hundred original *Australian* languages also loom large spatially on the map but have at most 50,000 speakers, exclusively Australian aborigines. Numerically and effectively, English dominates that continent.

Examples of linguistic conquest by non-Europeans also abound. In Southeast Asia, formerly extensive areas identified with different members of the *Austro-Asiatic* language family have been reduced through conquest and absorption by *Sino-Tibetan* (Chinese, Thai, Burmese, and Lao, principally) expansion. Arabic—originally a minor *Afro-Asiatic* language of the Arabian Peninsula—was dispersed by the explosive spread of Islam through much of North Africa and southwestern Asia, where it largely replaced a host of other locally variant tongues and became the official or the dominant language of more than 20 countries and over 250 million people. The more than 300 Bantu languages found south of the "Bantu line" in sub-Saharan Africa are variants of a proto-Bantu carried by an expanding, culturally advanced population that displaced more primitive predecessors (Figure 6.21).

Language Diffusion

Languages are dynamic: they live, die, change, and diffuse over the world because their speakers cease to exist, modify their system of communication, or occupy new territories. *Language diffusion*

FIGURE 6.19 World language families.

Language families are groups of individual tongues that had a common but remote ancestor. By suggesting that the area assigned to a language or language family uses that tongue exclusively, the map pattern conceals important linguistic detail. Many countries and regions have local languages spoken in territories too small to be recorded at this scale. The map also fails to report that the population in many regions is fluent in more than one language or that a second language serves as the necessary vehicle of commerce, education, or government. Nor is important information given about the number of speakers of different languages; the fact that there are more speakers of English in India or Africa than in Australia is not even hinted at by a map at this scale.

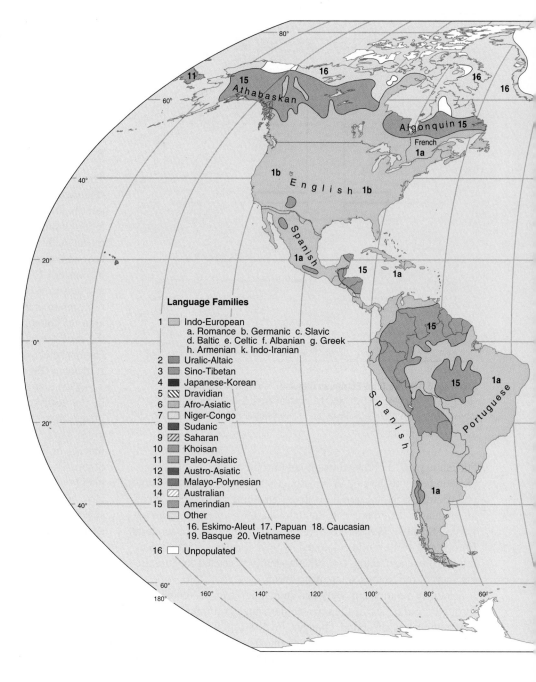

Language Families

1 ☐ Indo-European
   a. Romance b. Germanic c. Slavic
   d. Baltic e. Celtic f. Albanian g. Greek
   h. Armenian k. Indo-Iranian
2 ☐ Uralic-Altaic
3 ☐ Sino-Tibetan
4 ■ Japanese-Korean
5 ☒ Dravidian
6 ☐ Afro-Asiatic
7 ☐ Niger-Congo
8 ■ Sudanic
9 ☒ Saharan
10 ☐ Khoisan
11 ☐ Paleo-Asiatic
12 ■ Austro-Asiatic
13 ■ Malayo-Polynesian
14 ☒ Australian
15 ☐ Amerindian
   ☐ Other
      16. Eskimo-Aleut 17. Papuan 18. Caucasian
      19. Basque 20. Vietnamese
16 ☐ Unpopulated

or "spread" as a geographical event represents the increase or relocation through time in the area over which a language is spoken. The Bantu of Africa or the English-speaking settlers of North America displaced preexisting populations and replaced as well the languages previously spoken in the areas of penetration. Therefore, we find one explanation of the spread of language families to new areas of occurrence in massive population relocations such as those accompanying the colonization of the Americas or of Australia. That is, languages may spread because their speakers occupy new territories.

Latin, however, replaced earlier Celtic languages in western Europe not by force of numbers—Roman legionnaires, administrators, and settlers never represented a majority population—but by the gradual abandonment of their former languages by native

populations brought under the influence and domination of the Roman Empire and, later, of the Western Christian church. Adoption rather than eviction of language was the rule followed in perhaps the majority of historical and contemporary instances of language spread. Knowledge and use of the language of a dominating culture may be seen as a necessity when that language is the medium of commerce, law, civilization, and personal prestige. It was on that basis, not through numerical superiority, that Indo-European tongues were dispersed throughout Europe and to distant India, Iran, and Armenia. Likewise, Arabic became widespread in western Asia and North Africa not through massive population relocations but through conquest, religious conversion, and dominating culture. That is, languages may spread because they acquire new speakers.

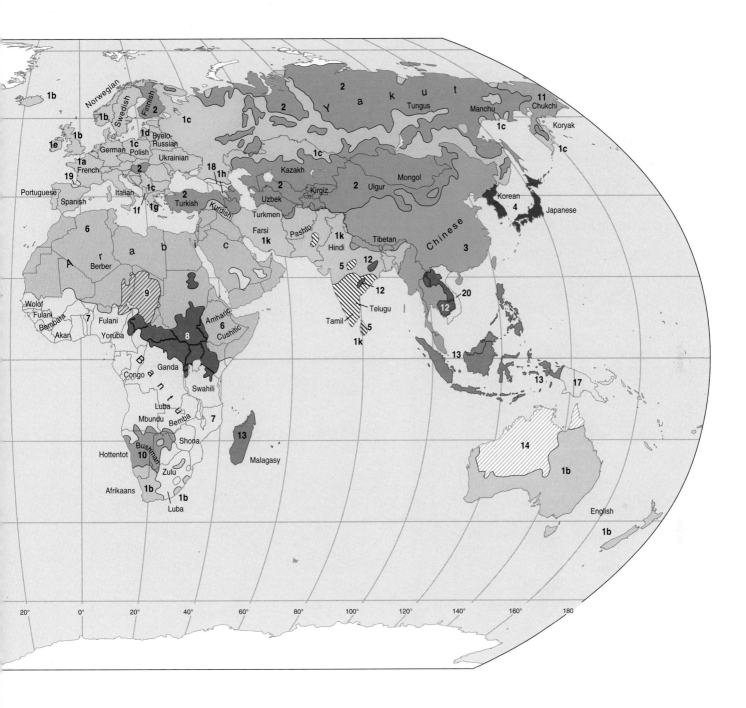

Either form of language spread—dispersion of speakers or acquisition of speakers—represents one of the *spatial diffusion* processes introduced in Chapter 5. Massive population relocation in which culture is transported to and made dominant in a new territory is a specialized example of *relocation diffusion*. When the advantages of a new language are discerned and it is adopted by native speakers of another tongue, a form of *expansion diffusion* has occurred along with partial or total *acculturation* of the adopting population. Usually, those who are in or aspire to positions of importance are the first to adopt the new language of control and prestige. Later, through schooling, daily contact, and business or social necessity, other, lower social strata of society may gradually be absorbed into the expanding pool of language adopters.

Such *hierarchical diffusion* of an official or prestigious language has occurred in many societies. In India during the 19th century, the English established an administrative and judicial system that put a very high premium on their language as the sole medium of education, administration, trade, and commerce. Proficiency in it was the hallmark of the cultured and educated person (as knowledge of Sanskrit and Persian had been in earlier periods under other conquerors of India). English, French, Dutch, Portuguese, and other languages introduced during the acquisition of empire retain a position of prestige and even status as the official language in multilingual societies, even after independence has been achieved by former colonial territories. In Uganda and other former British possessions in Africa, a stranger may be addressed in English by one who wishes to display his or her education and

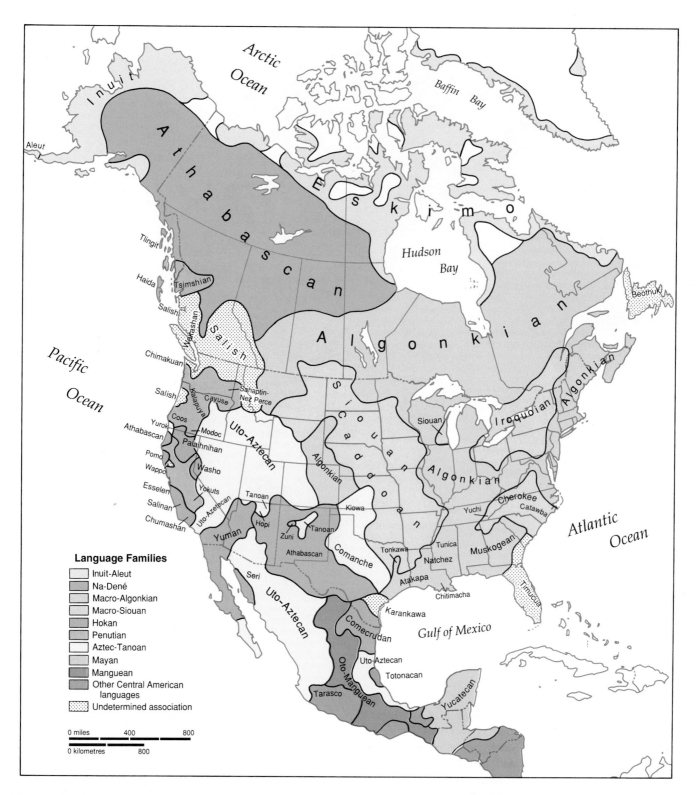

FIGURE 6.20 Amerindian language families of North America. As many as 300 different North American and more than 70 Meso-American tongues were spoken at the time of first European contact. The map summarizes the traditional view that these were grouped into nine or 10 language families in North America, as many as five in Meso-America, and another 10 or so in South America. More recent research, however, suggests close genetic relationships between Native American tongues, clustering them into just three families: Inuit in the extreme north and Greenland; Na-Dené in Canada and the U.S. Southwest, and Amerind elsewhere in the hemisphere. Because each family has closer affinities with Asian language groups than with one another, it is suggested that each corresponds to a separate wave of Asian migration to the Americas: the first giving rise to the Amerind family, the second to the Na-Dené, and the last to the Inuit. Many Amerindian tongues have become extinct; others are still known only to very small groups of mostly elderly speakers.

Source: Data from various sources, including C. F. and F. M. Voegelin, Map of North American Indian Languages *(Seattle: University of Washington Press, 1986).*

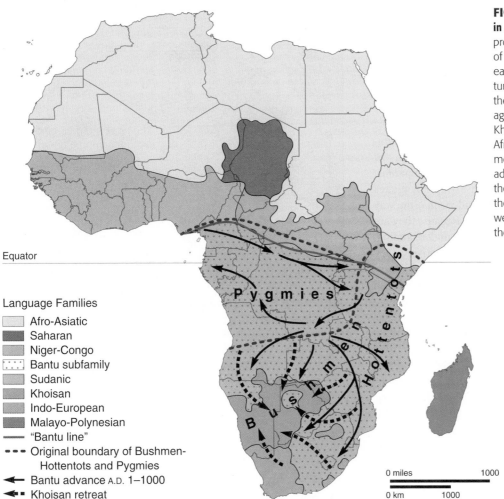

FIGURE 6.21 Bantu advance, Khoisan retreat in Africa. Linguistic evidence suggests that proto-Bantu speakers originated in the region of the Cameroon-Nigeria border, spread eastward across the southern Sudan, then turned southward to Central Africa. From there they dispersed slowly eastward, westward, and against slight resistance, southward. The earlier Khoisan-speaking occupants of sub-Saharan Africa were no match against the advancing metal-using Bantu agriculturalists. Pygmies, adopting a Bantu tongue, retreated deep into the forests; Bushmen and Hottentots retained their distinctive Khoisan "click" language but were forced out of forests and grasslands into the dry steppes and deserts of the southwest.

Equator

Language Families

- ▢ Afro-Asiatic
- ▨ Saharan
- ▨ Niger-Congo
- ⦂ Bantu subfamily
- ▨ Sudanic
- ▨ Khoisan
- ▨ Indo-European
- ▨ Malayo-Polynesian
- — "Bantu line"
- ‑ ‑ ‑ Original boundary of Bushmen-Hottentots and Pygmies
- ← Bantu advance A.D. 1–1000
- ◄‑‑ Khoisan retreat

0 miles 1000
0 km 1000

social status, though standard Swahili, a second language for many different culture groups, may be chosen if certainty of communication is more important than pride.

As a diffusion process, language spread may be impeded by barriers or promoted by their absence. Cultural barriers may retard or prevent language adoption. Speakers of Greek resisted centuries of Turkish rule of their homeland, and the language remained a focus of cultural identity under foreign domination. Breton, Catalan, Gaelic, and other localized languages of Europe remain symbols of ethnic separateness from surrounding dominant national cultures and controls.

Physical barriers to language spread have also left their mark (see Figure 6.19). Migrants or invaders follow paths of least topographic resistance and disperse most widely where access is easiest. Once past the barrier of the Pamirs and the Hindu Kush mountains, Indo-European tongues spread rapidly through the Indus and Ganges river lowlands of the Indian subcontinent but made no headway in the mountainous northern and eastern border zones. The Pyrenees Mountains serve as a linguistic barrier separating France and Spain. They also house the Basques who speak the only language—*Euskara* in their tongue—in southwestern Europe that survives from pre-Indo-European times (Figure 6.22). Similarly, the Caucasus Mountains between the Black and Caspian seas

FIGURE 6.22 In their mountainous homeland, the Basques have maintained a linguistic uniqueness despite more than 2000 years of encirclement by dominant lowland speakers of Latin or Romance languages. This sign of friendly farewell gives its message in both Spanish and the Basque language, Euskara.

Geographies of Ethnicity, Language, and Religion   183

separate the Slavic speakers to the north and the areas of *Ural-Altaic* languages to the south. At the same time, in their rugged topography they contain an extraordinary mixture of languages, many unique to single valleys or villages, lumped together spatially if not by origin into a separate *Caucasian* language family.

Language Change

Migration, segregation, and isolation give rise to separate, mutually unintelligible languages because the society speaking the parent protolanguage no longer remains unitary. Comparable changes occur normally and naturally within a single language in word meaning, pronunciation, vocabulary, and *syntax* (the way words are put together in phrases and sentences). Because they are gradual, minor, and made part of group use and understanding, such changes tend to go largely unnoticed. Yet, cumulatively, they can result in language change so great that in the course of centuries an essentially new language has been created. The English of 17th-century Shakespearean writings or the King James Bible (1611) sounds stilted to our ears. Few of us can easily read Chaucer's 14th-century *Canterbury Tales*, and 8th-century *Beowulf* is practically unintelligible.

Change may be gradual and cumulative, with each generation deviating in small degree from the speech patterns and vocabulary of its parents, or it may be massive and abrupt. English gained about 10,000 new words from the Norman conquerors of the 11th century. In some 70 years (1558–1625) of literary and linguistic creativity during the reigns of Elizabeth I and James I, an estimated 12,000 words—based on borrowings from Latin, Greek, and other languages—were introduced.

Discovery and colonization of new lands and continents in the 16th and 17th centuries greatly and necessarily expanded English as new foods, vegetation, animals, and artifacts were encountered and adopted along with their existing aboriginal American, Australian, or African names. The Indian languages of the Americas alone brought more than 200 relatively common daily words to English, 80 or more from the North American native tongues and the rest from Caribbean, Central, and South American. More than two thousand more specialized or localized words were also added. *Moose, raccoon, skunk, maize, squash, succotash, igloo, toboggan, hurricane, blizzard, hickory, pecan*, and a host of other names were taken directly into English; others were adopted second hand from Spanish variants of South American native words: *cigar, potato, chocolate, tomato, tobacco, hammock*. More recently, and within a short span of years, new scientific and technological developments have enriched and expanded the vocabularies not only of English but of all languages spoken by modern societies by adding many words of Greek and Latin derivation.

The Story of English

English itself is a product of change, an offspring of proto-Germanic (see Figure 6.18) descending through the dialects brought to England in the 5th and 6th centuries by conquering Danish and North German Frisians, Jutes, Angles, and Saxons. Earlier Celtic-speaking inhabitants found refuge in the north and west of Britain and in the rugged uplands of what are now Scotland and Wales. Each of the transplanted tongues established

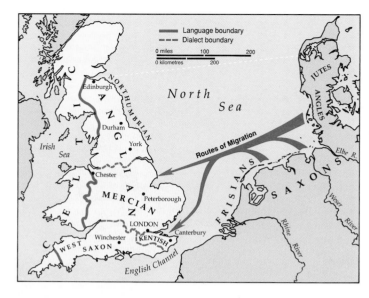

FIGURE 6.23 Old English dialect regions. In structure and vocabulary, Old English brought by the Frisians, Angles, Saxons, and Jutes was purely Germanic, with many similarities to modern German. It owed practically nothing to the Celtic it displaced, though it had borrowings from Latin. Much of Old English vocabulary was lost after the Norman conquest. English today has twice as many words derived from Latin and French as from the Germanic.

its own area of dominance, but the West Saxon dialect of southern England emerged in the 9th and 10th centuries as Standard Old English (Figure 6.23) on the strength of its literary richness.

It lost its supremacy after the Norman Conquest of 1066, as the centre of learning and culture shifted northeastward from Winchester to London, and French rather than English became the language of the nobility and the government. When the tie between France and England was severed after the loss of Normandy (1204), French fell into disfavour and English again became the dominant tongue, although now as the French-enriched Middle English used by Geoffrey Chaucer and mandated as the official language of the law courts by the Statute of Pleading (1362). During the 15th and 16th centuries, English as spoken in London emerged as the basic form of Early Modern English.

During the 18th century, attempts to standardize and codify the rules of English were unsuccessful. But the *Dictionary of Samuel Johnson* (published 1755)—based on cultured language of contemporary London and the examples of major authors—helped establish norms of proper form and usage. A worldwide diffusion of the language resulted as English colonists carried it as settlers to the Western Hemisphere and Australasia; through merchants, conquest, or territorial claim, it established footholds in Africa and Asia. In that spatial diffusion, English was further enriched by its contacts with other languages. By becoming the accepted language of commerce and science, it contributed, in turn, to the common vocabularies of other tongues.

Within some 400 years, English has developed from a localized language of 7 million islanders off the European coast to a truly international language with some 375 million native speakers, perhaps the same number who use it as a second language, and another 750 million who have reasonable competence in English as a foreign language. With over one half billion speakers worldwide,

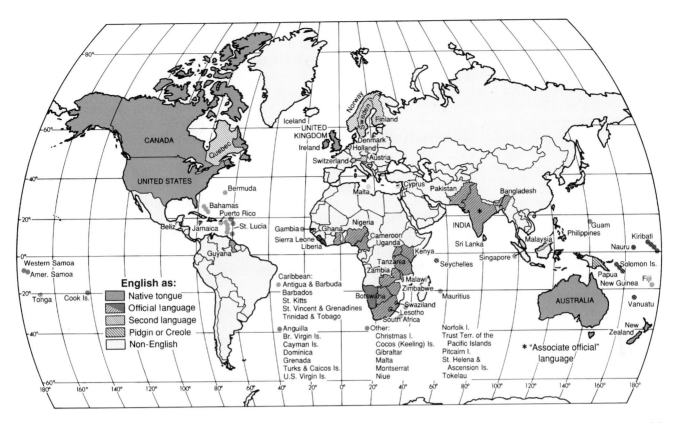

FIGURE 6.24 International English. In worldwide diffusion and acceptance, English has no past or present rivals. Along with French, it is one of the two working languages of the United Nations and the effective common language of the workers and committees of European Union institutions; some two-thirds of all scientific papers are published in it, making it the first language of scientific discourse, and it is the accepted language of international air traffic control. English is the sole or joint official language of more nations and territories, some too small to be shown here, than any other tongue. It also serves as the effective unofficial language of administration in other multilingual countries with different formal official languages. "English as a second language" is indicated for countries with near-universal or mandatory English instruction in public schools. Not evident on this map is the full extent of English penetration of Continental Europe, where more than 80% of secondary school students (and 92% of those of European Union states) study it as a second language.

English also serves as an official language of some 60 countries (Figure 6.24), far exceeding in that role French (32), Arabic (25), or Spanish (21), the other leading current international languages. At the end of the 20th century, over 78% of Internet Web pages used English (Japanese was second with 2.5%). No other language in history has assumed so important a role on the world scene.

Standard and Variant Languages

People who speak a common language such as English are members of a **speech community**, but membership does not necessarily imply linguistic uniformity. A speech community usually possesses both a **standard language**—comprising the accepted community norms of syntax, vocabulary, and pronunciation—and a number of more or less distinctive *dialects* reflecting the ordinary speech of areal, social, professional, or other subdivisions of the general population.

Standard Language

A dialect may become the standard language through identity with the speech of the most dominant and most powerful members of the larger speech community. A rich literary tradition may help establish its primacy, and its adoption as the accepted written and spoken norm in administration, economic life, and education will solidify its position, minimizing linguistic variation and working toward the elimination of deviant, non-standard forms. The dialect that emerges as the basis of a country's standard language is often the one identified with its capital or centre of power at the time of national development. Standard French is based on the dialect of the Paris region, a variant that assumed dominance in the latter half of the 12th century and was made the only official language in 1539. Castilian Spanish became the standard after 1492 with the Castile-led reconquest of Spain from the Moors and the export of the dialect to the Americas during the 16th century. Its present form, however, is a modified version associated not with Castile but with Madrid, the modern capital of Spain. Standard Russian is identified with the speech patterns of the former capital, St. Petersburg, and Moscow, the current capital. Modern Standard Chinese is based on the Mandarin dialect of Beijing. In England, *Received Pronunciation*—"Oxford English," the speech of educated people of London and southeastern England and used by the British Broadcasting System—was until recently the accepted standard though it is now being modified or replaced by a generalized southern accent called "Estuary English."

Other forces than the political may affect language standardization. In its spoken form, Standard German is based on norms established and accepted in the theatre, the universities, public speeches, and radio and television. The Classical or Literary Arabic of the Koran became the established norm from the Indian to the Atlantic Ocean. Standard Italian was derived from the Florentine dialect of the 13th and 14th centuries, which became widespread as the language of literature and economy.

In many societies, the official or unofficial standard language is not the dialect of home or daily life, and populations in effect have two languages. One is their regional dialect they employ with friends, at home, and in local community contacts; the other is the standard language used in more formal situations. In some cases, the contrast is great; regional variants of Arabic may be mutually unintelligible. Most Italians encounter Standard Italian for the first time in primary school. In India, the several totally distinct official regional languages are used in writing and taught in school but have no direct relationship to local speech; citizens must be bilingual to communicate with government officials who know only the regional language but not the local dialect.

Dialects

Just as no two individuals talk exactly the same, all but the smallest and most closely knit speech communities display recognizable speech variants called **dialects**. Vocabulary, pronunciation, rhythm, and the speed at which the language is spoken may set groups of speakers apart from one another and, to a trained observer, clearly mark the origin of the speaker. In George Bernard Shaw's play *Pygmalion,* on which the musical *My Fair Lady* was based, Henry Higgins—a professor of phonetics—is able to identify the London neighbourhood of origin of a flower girl by listening to her vocabulary and accent. In many instances, such variants are totally acceptable modifications of the standard language; in others, they mark the speaker as a social, cultural, or regional "outsider" or "inferior." Professor Higgins makes a lady out of the uneducated flower girl simply by teaching her upperclass pronunciation.

Shaw's play tells us dialects may coexist in space. Cockney and cultured English share the streets of London; Black English and Standard American are heard in the same school yards throughout the United States. In many societies, **social dialects** denote social class and educational level. Speakers of higher socio-economic status or educational achievement are most likely to follow the norms of their standard language; less-educated or lower-status persons or groups consciously distinguishing themselves from the mainstream culture are more likely to use the **vernacular**—non-standard language or dialect native to the locale or adopted by the social group. In some instances, however, as in Germany and German-Switzerland, local dialects are preserved and prized as badges of regional identity.

Different dialects may be part of the speech patterns of the same person. Professionals discussing, for example, medical, legal, financial, or scientific matters with their peers employ vocabularies and formal modes of address and sentence structure that are quickly changed to informal colloquial speech when the conversation shifts to sports, vacations, or personal anecdotes. Even gender may be the basis for linguistic differences added to other determinants of social dialects. More commonly, we think of dialects in

spatial terms. Speech is a geographic variable; each locale is apt to have its own, perhaps slight, language differences from neighbouring places. Such differences in pronunciation, vocabulary, word meanings, and other language characteristics tend to accumulate with distance from a given starting point. When they are mapped, they help define the **linguistic geography**—the study of the character and spatial pattern of dialects and languages—of a generalized speech community.

Every dialect feature has a territorial extent. The outer limit of its occurrence is a boundary line called an **isogloss** (the term *isophone* is used if the areal variant is marked by difference in sound rather than word choice), as shown in Figure 6.25. Each isogloss is a

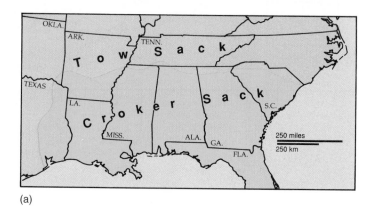

(a)

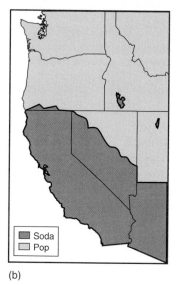

(b)

FIGURE 6.25 (*a*) **Dialect boundaries.** Descriptive words or terms for common items are frequently employed indicators of dialect difference. The limit of their areas of use is marked by an isogloss, such as that shown here for now-obsolete terms describing a coarse sack. Usually such boundary lines appear in clusters, or bundles; together, they help define the frontier of the dialect under study. (*b*) **The isogloss separating "pop" from "soda" in common usage in Western United States.** Maps such as this visually record variations over space in word usage or accent or pronunciation. Despite the presumed influence of national radio and television programs in promoting a "general" or "standard" American word usage, regional variations persist.

Source: (a) Adapted from Gordon R. Wood, Vocabulary Change: A Study of Variation in Regional Words in Eight of the Southern States *(Carbondale: Southern Illinois University Press, 1971), Map 81, p. 357. Used by permission of the publisher; (b) Adapted and generalized from a portion of "Generic Names for Soft Drinks—by County."*

Non-native speakers of English far outnumber those for whom English is the first language. Most of the more than 1 billion people who speak and understand at least some English as a second language live in Asia; they are appropriating the language and remaking it in regionally distinctive fashions to suit their own cultures, linguistic backgrounds, and needs.

It is inevitable that widely spoken languages separated by distance, isolation, and cultural differences will fragment into dialects that, in turn, evolve into new languages. Latin splintered into French, Spanish, Italian, and other Romance languages; the many national variants of spoken Arabic are effectively different tongues. English is similarly experiencing that sort of regional differentiation, shaped by the variant needs and inputs of its far-flung community of speakers, and following the same path to mutual unintelligibility. Although Standard English may be one of or the sole official language of their countries of birth, millions of people around the world claiming proficiency in English, or English as their national language, cannot understand each other. Even teachers of English from India, Malaya, Nigeria, or the Philippines, for example, may not be able to communicate in their supposedly common tongue—and find cockney English of London utterly alien.

The splintering of spoken English is a fact of linguistic life and its offspring—called "World Englishes" by linguists—defy frequent attempts by different governments to remove localisms and encourage adherence to international standards. Singlish (Singapore English) and Taglish (a mixture of English and Tagalog, the dominant language of the Philippines) are commonly cited examples of the multiplying World Englishes, but equally distinctive regional variants have emerged in India, Malaysia, Hong Kong, Nigeria, the Caribbean, and elsewhere. One linguist suggests that beyond an "inner circle" of states where English is the first and native language—for example, Canada, Australia, United States—lies an "outer circle" where English is a second language (Bangladesh, Ghana, India, Kenya, Pakistan, Zambia, and many others) and where the regionally distinctive World Englishes are most obviously developing. Even farther out is an "expanding circle" of such states as China, Egypt, Korea, Nepal, Saudi Arabia, and others where English is a foreign language and distinctive local variants in common usage have not yet developed.

Each of the emerging varieties of English is, of course, "correct," for each represents a coherent and consistent vehicle for communication with mutual comprehension between its speakers. Each also represents a growing national cultural confidence and pride in the particular characteristics of the local varieties of English, and each regional variant is strengthened by local teachers who do not themselves have a good command of the standard language. Conceivably, these factors may mean that English will fragment into scores or hundreds of mutually unintelligible tongues. But equally conceivably, the worldwide influence of globalized business contacts, the Internet, worldwide North American radio and television broadcasts, near-mandatory use of English in scientific publication, and the like, will mean a future English more homogeneous and, perhaps, more influenced and standardized by North American usage.

Most likely, observers of World Englishes suggest, both divergence and convergence will take place. While use of English as the major language of communication worldwide is a fact in international politics, business, education, and the media, increasingly, speakers of English learn two "dialects"—one of their own community and culture and one in the international context. While the constant modern world electronic and literary interaction between the variant regional Englishes make it likely that the common language will remain universally intelligible, it also seems probable that mutually incomprehensible forms of English will become entrenched as the language is taught, learned, and used in world areas far removed from contact with first-language speakers and with vibrant local economies and cultures independent of the Standard English community. "Our only revenge," said a French official, deploring the declining role of French within the European Union, "is that the English language is being killed by all these foreigners speaking it so badly."

distinct entity, but taken together isoglosses give clear map evidence of dialect regions that in their turn may reflect topographic barriers and corridors, long-established political borders, or past migration flows and diffusions of word choice and pronunciation.

Geographic or **regional dialects** may be recognized at different scales. On the world scene, for example, British, American, Indian, and Australian English are all acknowledged distinctive dialects of the same evolving language (see "World Englishes"). Regionally, in Britain alone, one can recognize Southern British English, Northern British English, and Scottish English, each containing several more localized variants. Italy contains the Gallo-Italian and Venetian dialect groups of the north, the Tuscan dialects of the center, and a collection of southern Italian dialects; within the 20 regions of Italy, 10 to 18 main dialects are still spoken today. Japanese has three recognized dialect groups.

Indeed, all long-established speech communities show their own structure of geographic dialects whose number and diversity tend to increase in areas longest settled and most fragmented and isolated. For example, the local speech of Newfoundland—isolated off the Atlantic coast of mainland Canada—retains much of the 17th-century flavour of the four West Counties of England from which the overwhelming majority of its settlers came. Yet the isolation and lack of cultural mixing of the islanders have not led to a general Newfoundland "dialect"; settlement was coastal and in the form of isolated villages in each of the many bays and indentations. There developed from that isolation and the passage of time nearly as many dialects as there are bay settlements, with each dialect separately differing from Standard English in accent, vocabulary, sounds, and syntax. Isolation has led to comparable linguistic variation among the 47,000 inhabitants of the 18 Faeroe

Islands between Iceland and Scotland; their Faeroese tongue has 10 dialects.

Pidgins and Creoles

Language is rarely a total barrier in communication between peoples, even those whose native tongues are mutually incomprehensible. Bilingualism or multilingualism may permit skilled linguists to communicate in a jointly understood third language, but long-term contact between less able populations may require the creation of new language—a pidgin—learned by both parties. In the past 400 years, more than 100 new languages have been created out of the mixings of peoples and cultures throughout the world.

A **pidgin** is an amalgam of languages, usually a simplified form of one, such as English or French, with borrowings from another, perhaps non-European local language. In its original form, a pidgin is not the mother tongue of any of its speakers; it is a second language for everyone who uses it, a language generally restricted to such specific functions as commerce, administration, or work supervision. For example, such is the variety of languages spoken among the some 270 ethnic groups of the Democratic Republic of the Congo that a special tongue called Lingala, a hybrid of Congolese dialects and French, was created to permit, among other things, issuance of orders to army recruits drawn from all parts of the country.

Pidgins are initially characterized by a highly simplified grammatical structure and a sharply reduced vocabulary, adequate to express basic ideas but not complex concepts. For example, fanagalo, a pidgin created earlier in South Africa's gold mines to allow spoken communication between workers of different tribes and nationalities and between workers and Afrikaner bosses, is being largely abandoned. Since the mid-1990s, workers have increasingly been schooled in basic English as fanagalo—which lacks the vocabulary to describe how to operate new, automated mining machinery and programmable winches with their multiple sensors and warnings in English—became decreasingly useful. If a pidgin becomes the first language of a group of speakers—who may have lost their former native tongue through disuse—a **creole** has evolved. In their development, creoles invariably acquire a more complex grammatical structure and enhanced vocabulary.

Creole languages have proved useful integrative tools in linguistically diverse areas; several have become symbols of nationhood. Swahili, a pidgin formed from a number of Bantu dialects with major vocabulary additions from Arabic, originated in the coastal areas of East Africa and spread inland, first by Arab ivory and slave caravans, and later by trade during the period of English and German colonial rules. When Kenya and Tanzania gained independence, they made Swahili the national language of administration and education. Other examples of creolization are Afrikaans (a pidginized form of 17th-century Dutch used in the Republic of South Africa); Haitian Creole (the language of Haiti, derived from the pidginized French used in the slave trade); and Bazaar Malay (a pidginized form of the Malay language, a version of which is the official national language of Indonesia).

Lingua Franca

A **lingua franca** is an established language used habitually for communication by people whose native tongues are mutually incomprehensible. For them it is a *second language*, one learned in addition to the native tongue. Lingua franca, literally "Frankish tongue," was named from the dialect of France adopted as their common tongue by the Crusaders assaulting the Muslims of the Holy Land. Later, it endured as a language of trade and travel in the eastern Mediterranean, useful as a single tongue shared in a linguistically diverse region.

Between 300 B.C.E. and 500 A.C.E., the Mediterranean world was unified by Common Greek. Later, Latin became a lingua franca, the language of empire and, until replaced by the vernacular European tongues, of the Church, government, scholarship, and the law. Outside the European sphere, Aramaic served the role from the 5th century B.C.E. to the 4th century A.C.E. in the Near East and Egypt; Arabic followed Muslim conquest as the unifying language of that international religion after the 7th century. Mandarin Chinese and Hindi in India, both formerly and today, have a lingua franca role in their linguistically diverse countries. The immense linguistic diversity of Africa has made regional lingua francas there necessary and inevitable (Figure 6.26), and in a polyglot world, English increasingly serves everywhere as the global lingua franca.

Official Languages

Governments may designate a single tongue as a country's **official language**, the required language of instruction in the schools and universities, government business, the courts, and other official and semi-official public and private activities. In societies in which two or more languages are in common use **(multilingualism,)** such an official language may serve as the approved national lingua franca, guaranteeing communication among all citizens of differing native tongues. In many immigrant societies, such as the United States, only one of the many spoken languages may have implicit or official government sanction.

Nearly every country in linguistically complex sub-Saharan Africa has selected a European language—usually that of their former colonial governors—as an official language (Figure 6.27), only rarely designating a native language or creole as an alternate official tongue. Indeed, less than 10% of the population of sub-Saharan Africa live in countries with any indigenous African tongue given official status. Nigeria has some 350 clearly different languages and is dominated by three of them: Hausa, Yoruba, and Ibo. For no Nigerian is English a native tongue, yet throughout the country English is the sole language of instruction and the sole official language. Effectively, all Nigerians must learn a foreign language before they can enter the mainstream of national life. Most Pacific Ocean countries, including the Philippines (with between 80 and 110 Malayo-Polynesian languages) and Papua New Guinea (with over 850 distinct Papuan tongues), have a European language as at least one of their official tongues.

Increasingly, the "purity" of official European languages has been threatened by the popular and widespread inclusion of English words and phrases in everyday speech, press, television,

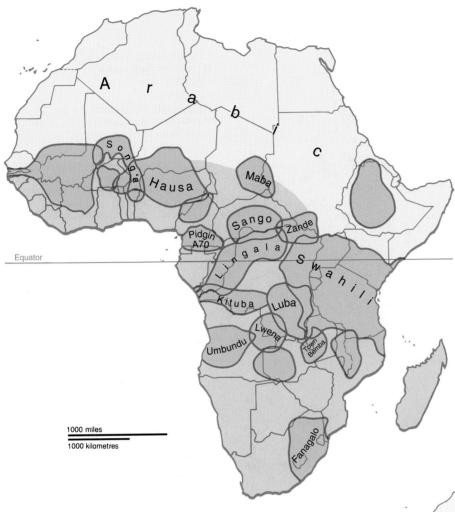

FIGURE 6.26 Lingua francas of Africa. The importance and extent of competing lingua francas in sub-Saharan Africa change over time, reflecting the spread of populations and the relative economic or political stature of speakers of different languages. In many areas, an individual may employ different lingua francas, depending on activity: dealing with officials, trading in the marketplace, conversing with strangers. Among the elite in all areas, the preferred lingua franca is apt to be a European language. When a European tongue is an official language (Figure 6.27) or the language of school instruction, its use as a lingua franca is more widespread. Throughout northern Africa, Arabic is the usual lingua franca for all purposes.

Source: Adapted from Bernd Heine, Status and Use of African Lingua Francas *(Munich, Germany: Weltforum Verlag; and New York: Humanities Press, 1970).*

and the Internet. So common has such adoption become, in fact, that some nearly new language variants are now recognized: *franglais* in France and *Denglish* in Germany are the best-known examples. Both have spurred resistance movements from officially sanctioned language monitors of, respectively, the French Academy and the Institute for the German Language. Poland, Spain, and Latvia are among other European states seeking to preserve the purity of their official languages from contamination by English or other foreign borrowings. Japan's Council on the Japanese Language is doing the same.

In some countries, multilingualism has official recognition through designation of more than a single state language. Canada and Finland, for example, have two official languages (*bilingualism*), reflecting rough equality in numbers or influence of separate linguistic populations comprising a single country. In a few multilingual countries, more than two official languages have been designated. Bolivia and Belgium have three official tongues and Singapore has four. South Africa's constitution designates 11 official languages, and India gives official status to 18 languages at the regional, though not at the national, level.

Multilingualism may reflect significant cultural and spatial divisions within a country. In Canada, the Official Languages Act of 1969 accorded French and English equal status as official languages of the Parliament and of government throughout

FIGURE 6.27 Europe in Africa through official languages. Both the linguistic complexity of sub-Saharan Africa and the colonial histories of its present political units are implicit in the designation of a European language as the sole or joint "official" language of the different countries.

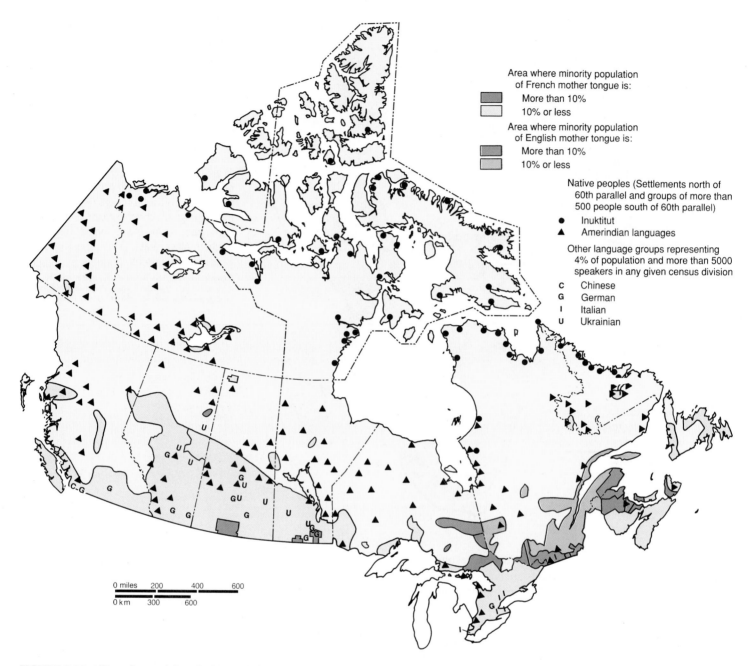

FIGURE 6.28 Bilingualism and diversity in Canada. The map shows areas of Canada that have a minimum of 5000 inhabitants and include a minority population identified with an official language.

Source: Commissioner of Official Languages, Government of Canada.

the nation. French-speakers are concentrated in the Province of Quebec, however, and constitute a culturally distinct population sharply divergent from the English-speaking majority of other parts of Canada (Figure 6.28). Within sections of Canada, even greater linguistic diversity is recognized; the legislature of the Northwest Territories, for example, has eight official languages —six native, plus English and French.

Few countries remain purely *monolingual*, with only a single language of communication for all purposes among all citizens, though most are officially so. Past and recent movements of peoples as colonists, refugees, or migrants have assured that most of the world's countries contain linguistically mixed populations.

Maintenance of native languages among such populations is not assured, of course. Where numbers are small or pressures for integration into an economically and socially dominant culture are strong, immigrant and Aboriginal (native) linguistic minorities tend to adopt the majority or official language for all purposes. On the other hand, isolation and relatively large numbers of speakers may serve to preserve native tongues. In Canada, for example, Aboriginal languages with large populations of speakers—Cree, Ojibwe, and Inuktitut—are well maintained in their areas of concentration (respectively, northern Quebec, the northern prairies, and Nunavut). In contrast, much smaller language groups in southern and coastal British Columbia have a much lower ratio of retention among native speakers.

Landscapes of Identity, Plurality, and Organization

Language, Territoriality, and Landscape

The designation of more than one official language does not always satisfy the ambitions of linguistically distinct groups for recognition and autonomy. Language is an inseparable part of group identity and a defining characteristic of ethnic and cultural distinction. The view that cultural heritage is rooted in language is well-established and found throughout the world, as is the feeling that losing linguistic identity is the worst and final evidence of discrimination and subjugation. Language has often been the focus of separatist movements, especially of spatially distinct linguistic groups outside the economic heartlands of the strongly centralized countries to which they are attached.

Language and Territoriality

In Europe, highly centralized France, Spain, Britain—and Yugoslavia and the Soviet Union before their dismemberment—experienced such language "revolts" and acknowledged, sometimes belatedly, the local concerns they express. Until 1970, when the ban on teaching regional tongues was dropped, the spoken regional languages and dialects of France were ignored and denied recognition by the state. Since the late 1970s, Spain not only has relaxed its earlier total rejection of Basque and Catalan as regional languages and given state support to instruction in them, but also has recognized Catalan as a co-official language in its home region in northeastern Spain. In Britain, parliamentary debates concerning greater regional autonomy in the United Kingdom have resulted in bilingual road and informational signs in Wales, a publicly supported Welsh-language television channel, and compulsory teaching of Welsh in all schools in Wales.

In fact, throughout Europe beginning in the 1980s, non-official native regional languages have increasingly not only been tolerated but encouraged—in Western Europe, particularly, as a buffer against the loss of regional institutions and traditions threatened by a multinational "superstate" under the European Union. The Council of Europe, a 41-nation organization promoting democracy and human rights, has adopted a charter pledging encouragement of the use of indigenous languages in schools, the media, and public life. That pledge recognizes the enduring reality that of some 500 million people in Eastern and Western Europe (not including immigrants and excluding the former USSR), more than 50 million speak a local language that is not the official tongue of their country. The language charter acknowledges that cultural diversity is part of Europe's wealth and heritage and that its retention strengthens, not weakens, the separate states of the continent and the larger European culture realm as a whole.

Many other world regions, less permissive than Europe is becoming, have continuing linguistically based conflict. Language has long been a divisive issue in South Asia, for example, leading to wars in Pakistan and Sri Lanka, and periodic demands for secession from India by southern states such as Tamil Nadu, where the Dravidian Tamil language is defended as an ancient tongue as worthy of respect as the Indo-European official language, Hindi. In Russia and several other successor states of the former USSR (which housed some 200 languages and dialects), linguistic diversity forms part of the justification for local separatist movements, as it did in the division of Czechoslovakia into Czech- and Slovak-speaking successor states, and in the violent dismemberment of former Yugoslavia.

Language on the Landscape: Toponymy

Language is also inscribed in the cultural landscape, revealing histories and displaying the identities of those linguistic cultural groups who claimed the land

Toponyms—place names—are language on the land, the record of past inhabitants whose namings endure, perhaps corrupted and disguised, as reminders of their existence and their passing. **Toponymy** is the study of place names, a special interest of linguistic geography. It is also a revealing tool of historical cultural geography, for place names become a part of the cultural landscape that remains long after the name givers have passed from the scene.

In England, for example, place names ending in *chester* (as in Winchester and Manchester) evolved from the Latin *castra*, meaning "camp." Common Anglo-Saxon suffixes for tribal and family settlements were *ing* (people or family) and *ham* (hamlet or, perhaps, meadow) as in Birmingham or Gillingham. Norse and Danish settlers contributed place names ending in *thwaite* ("meadow") and others denoting such landscape features as *fell* (an uncultivated hill) and *beck* (a small brook). The Celts, present in Europe for more than 1000 years before Roman times, left their tribal names in corrupted form on territories and settlements taken over by their successors. The Arabs, sweeping out from Arabia across North Africa and into Iberia, left their imprint in place names to mark their conquest and control. *Cairo* means "victorious," *Sudan* is "the land of the blacks," and *Sahara* is "wasteland" or "wilderness." In Spain, a corrupted version of the Arabic *wadi*, "watercourse," is found in *Guadalajara* and *Guadalquivir*.

In the New World, not one people but many placed names on landscape features and new settlements. In doing so they remembered their homes and homelands, honoured their monarchs and heroes, borrowed and mispronounced from rivals, followed fads, recalled the Bible, and adopted and distorted Amerindian names. Homelands were recalled in New England, New France, or New Holland; settlers' hometown memories brought Boston, New Bern, New Rochelle, and Cardiff from England, Switzerland, France, and Wales. Monarchs were remembered in Virginia for the Virgin Queen Elizabeth, Carolina for one English king, Georgia for another, and Louisiana for a king of France. Washington, D.C.; Jackson, Mississippi and Michigan; Austin, Texas; and Lincoln, Illinois memorialized heroes and leaders. Names given by the Dutch in New York were often distorted by the English; Breukelyn, Vlissingen, and Haarlem became Brooklyn, Flushing, and Harlem. French names underwent similar twisting or translation, and Spanish names were adopted, altered, or, later, put into such bilingual combinations as Hermosa Beach. Amerindian tribal names—the Yenrish, Maha, Kansa—were modified, first by French and later by English speakers—to Erie, Omaha, and Kansas. A faddish "Classical Revival" after the Revolution gave us Troy, Athens, Rome, Sparta, and other ancient town names and later spread them across the country. Bethlehem, Ephrata, Nazareth, and Salem came from the Bible. Names adopted were transported as settlement moved westward across the United States.

Place names, whatever their language of origin, frequently consist of two parts: *generic* (classifying) and *specific* (modifying or particular). *Big River* in English is found as *Rio Grande* in Spanish, *Mississippi* in Algonquin, and *Ta Ho* in Chinese. The *order* of generic and specific, however, may alter between languages and give a clue to the group originally bestowing the place name. In English, the specific usually comes first: *Hudson River, Bunker Hill, Long Island*. When, in the United States, we find *River Rouge* or *Isle Royale*, we also find evidence of French settlement—the French reverse the naming order. Some generic names can be used to trace the migration paths across the United States of the three Eastern dialect groups. Northern dialect settlers tended to carry with them their habit of naming a community and calling its later neighbours by the same name modified by direction—Lansing and East Lansing, for example. *Brook* is found in the New England settlement area, *run* is from the Midland dialect, *bayou* and *branch* are from the Southern area.

European colonists and their descendants gave place names to a physical landscape already adequately named by indigenous peoples. Those names were sometimes adopted, but often shortened, altered, or—certainly—mispronounced. The vast territory that local Amerindians called "Mesconsing," meaning "the long river," was recorded by Lewis and Clark as "Quisconsing," later to be further distorted into "Wisconsin." *Milwaukee* and *Winnipeg*, *Potomac* and *Niagara*, *Adirondack*, *Chesapeake*, *Shenandoah*, and *Yukon*; the names of 27 of the 50 United States; and the present identity of thousands of North American places and features, large and small, had their origin in Native American languages.

In the Northwest Territories of Canada, Indian and Inuit place names are returning. The town of Frobisher Bay has reverted to its Inuit name *Iqaluit* ("place of the fish"); Resolute Bay becomes *Kaujuitok* ("place where the sun never rises") in Inuktitut, the language of the Inuit; the Jean Marie River returns to *Tthedzehk'edeli* ("river that flows over clay"), its earlier Slavey, pre-colonial name. These and other official name changes reflect the decision of the territory's Executive Council that community preference will be the standard for all place names, no matter how entrenched European versions might be.

It was a decision that recognized the importance of language as a powerful unifying thread in the culture complex of peoples. In India, for example, the changing of various long-accepted municipal place names—*Mumbai* instead of Bombay, *Chennai* but not Madras, or *Thiruvananthapuram* replacing Trivandrum—demonstrates both post-colonial pride and growing Hindu nationalism. Language may serve as a fundamental evidence of ethnicity and be the fiercely defended symbol of the history and individuality of a distinctive social group. Hispanic Americans demand the right of instruction in their own language, and Basques wage civil war to achieve a linguistically based separatism. Indian states were adjusted to coincide with language boundaries, and the Polish National Catholic Church was created in America, not Poland, to preserve Polish language and culture in an alien environment.

Patterns of Religion

Religions, like languages, are cultural inventions, but unlike language, which is an attribute of all people, religion varies in its cultural role—dominating among some societies, unimportant or denied totally in others. While established religious institutions tend to be conservative and resistant to change, religion as a culture trait is dynamic. Religions may be imposed by conquest, adopted by conversion, or be defended and preserved in the face of surrounding hostility or indifference.

All societies have *value systems*—common beliefs, understandings, expectations, and controls—that unite their members and set them off from other, different culture groups. Such a value system is termed a **religion** when it involves systems of formal or informal worship and faith in the sacred and divine. In a more inclusive sense, religion may be viewed as a unified system of beliefs and practices that join all those who adhere to them into a single moral community. Religion may intimately affect all facets of a culture. Religious belief is by definition an element of the ideological subsystem; formalized and organized religion is an institutional expression of the sociological subsystem. And religious beliefs strongly influence attitudes toward the tools and rewards of the technological subsystem.

Non-religious value systems can exist—humanism, capitalism, or Marxism, for example—that are just as binding on the societies that espouse them as are more traditional religious beliefs. Even societies that largely reject religion—that are officially atheistic or secular—are strongly influenced by traditional values and customs set by predecessor religions, in days of work and rest, for example, or in legal principles.

Since religions are formalized views about the relation of the individual to this world and to the hereafter, each carries a distinct conception of the meaning and value of this life, and most contain strictures about what must be done to achieve salvation. These beliefs become interwoven with the traditions of a culture. For Muslims, the observance of the *sharia* (law) is a necessary part of *Islam*, submission to Allah. In classical Judaism, the keeping of the *Torah*, the Law of Moses, involved ritual and moral rules of holy living. For Hindus, the *dharma*, or teaching, includes the complex laws enunciated in the ancient book of Manu. Ethics of conduct and human relations rather than religious rituals are central to the Confucian tradition of China, while the Sikh *khalsa*, or holy community, is defined by various rules of observance, such as prohibiting the cutting of one's hair.

Economic patterns may be intertwined with past or present religious beliefs. Traditional restrictions on food and drink may affect the kinds of animals that are raised or avoided, the crops that are grown, and the importance of those crops in the daily diet. Occupational assignment in the Hindu caste system is in part religiously supported. In many countries, there is a state religion—that is, religious and political structures are intertwined. Buddhism, for example, has been the state religion in Myanmar, Laos, and Thailand. By their official names, the Islamic Republic of Pakistan and the Islamic Republic of Iran proclaim their identity of religion and government. Despite Indonesia's overwhelming Muslim majority, that country sought and formerly found domestic harmony by recognizing five official religions and a state ideology—*pancasila*—whose first tenet is belief in one god.

The landscape imprint of religions may be both obvious and subtle. The structures of religious worship—temples, churches, mosques, stupas, or cathedrals—landscape symbols such as shrines or statues, and such associated land uses as monasteries may give an immediately evident and regionally distinctive cultural character to an area. "Landscapes of death" may also be visible regional variables, for different religions and cultures dispose of their dead in different manners. Cemeteries are significant and reserved land uses among Christians, Jews, and Muslims who typically bury their deceased with headstones or other markers and monuments to mark graves. Egyptian pyramids or elaborate mausoleums like the Taj Mahal are more grandiose structures of entombment and remembrance. On the other hand, Hindus and Buddhists have traditionally cremated their dead and scattered their ashes, leaving no landscape evidence or imprint.

Some religions may make a subtle cultural stamp on the landscape through recognition of sacred places and spaces not otherwise built or marked. Grottos, lakes, single trees or groves, such rivers as the Ganges or Jordan, or special mountains or hills, such as Mount Ararat or Mount Fuji, are examples that are unique to specific religions and express the reciprocal influences of religion and environment.

Global Patterns and Flows

The nature of the different classes of religions is reflected in their distributions over the world (Figure 6.29) and in their number of adherents. **Universalizing religions** tend to be expansionary, carrying their message to new peoples and areas. Christianity, Islam, and Buddhism are the major world universalizing religions, faiths that claim applicability to all humans and that seek to transmit their beliefs through missionary work and conversion. Membership in universalizing religions is open to anyone who chooses to make some sort of symbolic commitment, such as baptism in Christianity. No one is excluded because of nationality, ethnicity, or previous religious belief.

Ethnic religions, unless their adherents are dispersed, tend to be regionally confined or to expand only slowly and over long periods. Ethnic religions have strong territorial and cultural group identification. One usually becomes a member of an ethnic religion by birth or by adoption of a complex lifestyle and cultural identity, not by simple declaration of faith. These religions do not usually proselytize, and their members form distinctive closed communities identified with a particular ethnic group or political unit. An ethnic religion—for example, Judaism, Indian Hinduism, or Japanese Shinto—is an integral element of a specific culture; to be part of the religion is to be immersed in the totality of the culture.

Tribal or **traditional religions** tend to contract spatially as their adherents are incorporated increasingly into modern society and converted by proselytizing faiths. Tribal, or traditional religions are special forms of ethnic religions distinguished by their small size, their

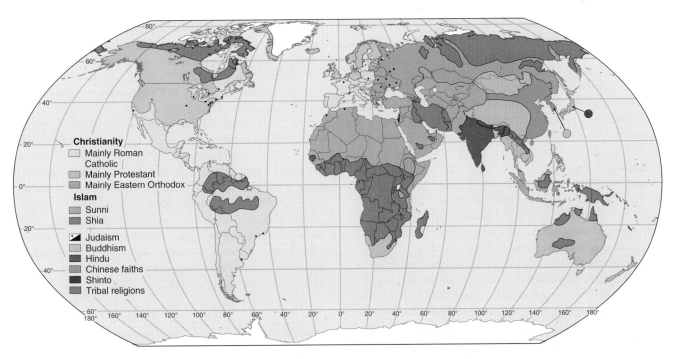

FIGURE 6.29 Principal world religions. The assignment of individual countries to a single religion category conceals a growing intermixture of faiths in European and other western countries that have experienced recent major immigration flows. In some instances, those influxes are altering the effective, if not the numerical, religious balance. In nominally Christian, Catholic France, for example, low church-going rates suggest that now more Muslims than practising Catholics reside there and, considering birth rate differentials, that someday Islam may be the country's predominant religion as measured by the number of practising adherents. Secularism—rejection of religious belief—is common in many countries but is not locationally indicated on this map.

unique identity with localized culture groups not yet fully absorbed into modern society, and their close ties to nature. **Animism** is the name given to their belief that life exists in all objects, from rocks and trees to lakes and mountains, or that such inanimate objects are the abode of the dead, of spirits, and of gods. **Shamanism** is a form of tribal religion that involves community acceptance of a *shaman*, a religious leader, healer, and worker of magic who, through special powers, can intercede with and interpret the spirit world.

As we expect in human geography, the map in Figure 6.29 records only the latest stage of a constantly changing cultural reality. The map (at this scale) cannot present a full picture of current religious affiliation or regionalization. Few societies are homogeneous, and most modern ones contain a variety of different faiths or, at least, variants of the dominant professed religion. Frequently, members of a particular religion show areal concentration within a country. Thus, in urban Northern Ireland, Protestants and Catholics reside in separate areas whose boundaries are clearly understood. The "Green Line" in Beirut, Lebanon, marked a guarded border between the Christian East and the Muslim West sides of the city, while within the country as a whole regional concentrations of adherents of different faiths and sects are clearly recognized (Figure 6.30). Religious diversity within countries may reflect the degree of toleration a majority culture affords minority religions. In dominantly (90%) Muslim Indonesia, Christian Bataks, Hindu Balinese, and Muslim Javanese for many years lived in peaceful coexistence. By contrast, the fundamentalist Islamic regime in Iran has persecuted and executed those of the Baha'i faith.

More than half of the world's population probably adheres to one of the major universalizing religions: Christianity, Islam, or Buddhism. Of these three, Figure 6.29 indicates, Christianity and Islam are most widespread; Buddhism is largely an Asian religion. Hinduism, the largest ethnic faith, is essentially confined to the Indian subcontinent, showing the spatial restriction characteristic of most ethnic and traditional religions even when found outside of their homeland area. Small Hindu emigrant communities in Africa, Southeast Asia, England, or the United States, for example, tend to remain isolated even in densely crowded urban areas. Although it is not localized, Judaism is also included among the ethnic religions because of its identification with a particular people and cultural tradition.

Extensive areas of the world are peopled by those who practise tribal or traditional religions, often in concert with the universalizing religions to which they have been outwardly converted. Tribal religions are found principally among peoples who have not yet been fully absorbed into modern cultures and economies or who are on the margins of more populous and advanced societies. Although the areas assigned to tribal religions in Figure 6.29 are large, the number of adherents is small and declining.

One cannot assume that all people within a mapped religious region are adherents of the designated faith or that membership in a religious community means active participation in its belief system. **Secularism**, an indifference to or rejection of religion and religious belief, is an increasing part of many modern societies, particularly of the industrialized nations and those now or formerly under communist regimes. In England, for example, the state Church of England claims 20% of the British population as communicants, but only 2% of the adult population attends its Sunday services. Two-thirds of the French describe themselves as Catholic, and less than 5% regularly go to church. Even in devoutly Roman Catholic South American

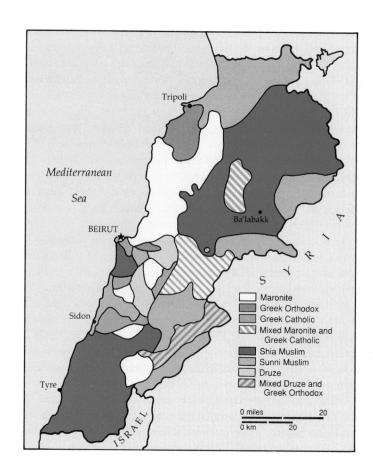

FIGURE 6.30 Religious regions of Lebanon. Religious territoriality and rivalry contributed to a prolonged period of conflict and animosity in this troubled country.

states, low church attendance attests to the rise of at least informal secularism. In Colombia, only 18% of people attend Sunday services; in Chile, the figure is 12%, in Mexico 11%, and Bolivia 5%.

Similarly in Canada, 83% of the population identifies with a religion, yet only one-third of Canadians aged 15 and over attends a religious service at least once a month. Unlike the United States, where there is no large section of the country overwhelmingly dominated by a specific denomination, Quebec's 88% Roman Catholic presence in Canada is unique in North America. As Figure 6.31 illustrates, there is an absence of any "second rank" religious affiliation. The "leading" position of the United Church of Canada in the Canadian West or of the Anglican Church in the Atlantic region of Newfoundland is much less commanding. Much of interior Canada shows a degree of cultural mixing and religious diversity only hinted at by Figure 6.31, where only the largest church memberships are noted. Nevertheless, Catholicism has a much stronger presence in Canada as a whole than in the United States.

The Principal Religions

Each of the major religions has its own unique mix of cultural values and expressions, each has had its own pattern of innovation and spatial diffusion (Figure 6.32), and each has had its own impact on the cultural landscape. Together they contribute importantly to the worldwide pattern of human diversity.

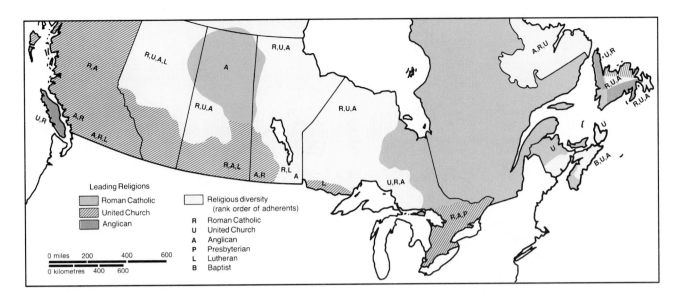

FIGURE 6.31 Religious affiliation in Canada. The richness of Canadian religious diversity is obscured by the numerical dominance of a small number of leading Christian denominations.

Sources: Based on Statistics Canada, Population *(Ottawa, 1984); and* The National Atlas of Canada.

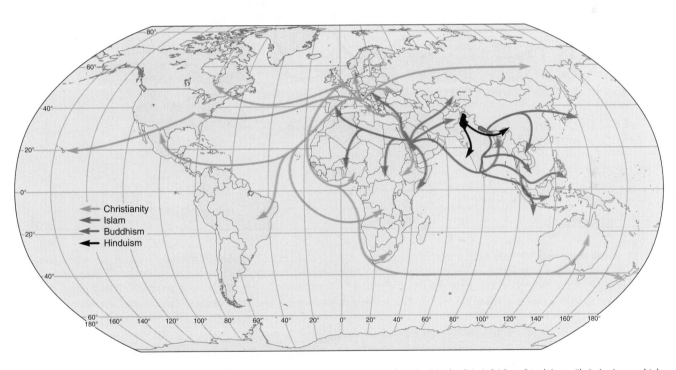

FIGURE 6.32 Innovation areas and diffusion routes of major world religions. The monotheistic (single deity) faiths of Judaism, Christianity, and Islam arose in southwestern Asia, the first two in Palestine in the eastern Mediterranean region and the last in western Arabia near the Red Sea. Hinduism and Buddhism originated within a confined hearth region in the northern part of the Indian subcontinent. Their rates, extent, and directions of diffusions are suggested here and detailed on later maps.

Judaism

We begin our brief overview of world faiths with **Judaism**, whose belief in a single God laid the foundation for both Christianity and Islam. Unlike its universalizing offspring, Judaism is closely identified with a single ethnic group and with a complex set of beliefs and laws. It emerged some 3000 to 4000 years ago in the Near East, one of the ancient culture hearth regions (see Figure 5.19). This became a distinctively *ethnic* religion, the determining factors of which are descent from Israel (the patriarch Jacob), the Torah (law and scripture), and the traditions of the culture and the faith. Early military success gave the Jews a sense of territorial and political identity to supplement their religious self-awareness. Later conquest by non-believers led to their dispersion (*diaspora*) to much of the Mediterranean world and farther east into Asia by 500 A.C.E. (Figure 6.33).

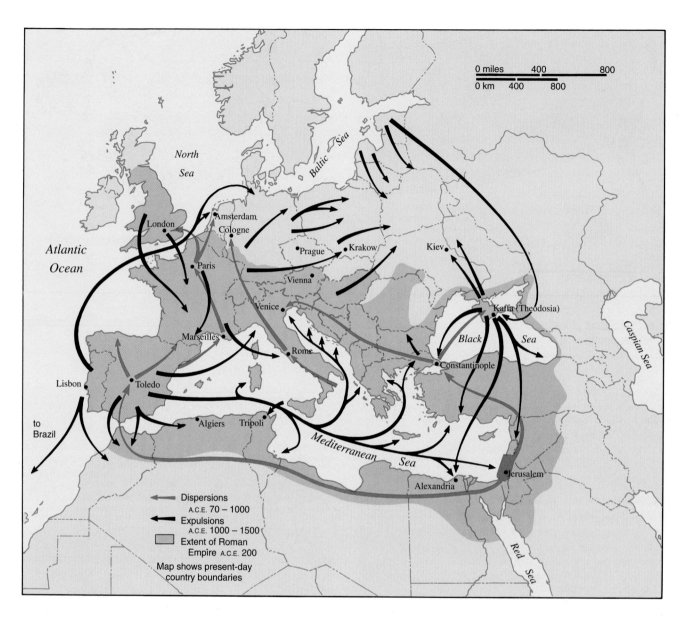

FIGURE 6.33 Jewish dispersions, 70–1500 A.C.E. A revolt against Roman rule in 66 A.C.E. was followed by the destruction of the Jewish Temple four years later and an imperial decision to Romanize the city of Jerusalem. Judaism spread from the hearth region by *relocation diffusion*, carried by its adherents dispersing from their homeland to Europe, Africa, and eventually in great numbers to the Western Hemisphere. Although Jews established themselves and their religion in new lands, they did not lose their sense of cultural identity and did not seek to attract converts to their faith.

Alternately tolerated and persecuted in Christian Europe, they were occasionally expelled from countries, and usually, as outsiders of different faith and custom, isolated in special residential quarters (ghettos). The mass destruction of Jews in Europe before and during World War II—the Holocaust—drastically reduced their representation among that continent's total population. The establishment of the state of Israel in 1948 represented a reversal of the preceding 2000-year history of dispersal and relocation diffusion. Israel became largely a country of immigrants, an ancient homeland again identified with a distinctive people and an ethnic religion.

Judaism's imprint on the cultural landscape includes space for the practice of communal burial; the spread of cultivated citron in Mediterranean areas due to Jewish ritual needs; and the cultivation of the vine for the religious use of grape wine. The

synagogue as place of worship has tended to be less elaborate than its Christian counterpart and appears in the landscape wherever Jews gather to worship.

Christianity

Christianity had its origin in the life and teachings of Jesus, a Jewish preacher of the 1st century of the modern era, whom his followers believed was the messiah promised by God.

Christianity's mission was conversion and missionary work was critical to its diffusion. As a universal religion of salvation and hope, it spread quickly among the underclasses of both the eastern and western parts of the Roman Empire, carried to major cities and ports along the excellent system of Roman roads and

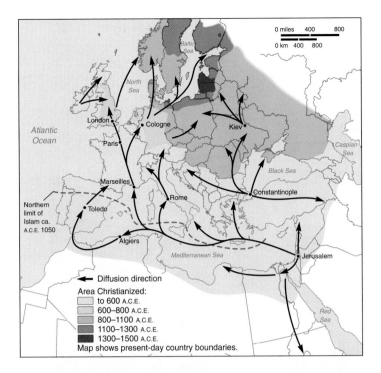

FIGURE 6.34 Diffusion paths of Christianity, 100–1500 A.C.E. Routes and dates are for Christianity as a composite faith. No distinction is made between the Western church and the various subdivisions of the Eastern Orthodox denominations.

sea lanes (Figure 6.34). *Expansion diffusion* followed the establishment of missions and colonies of converts in locations distant from the hearth region. Important among them were the urban areas that became administrative seats of the new religion. For the Western Church, Rome was the principal centre for dispersal, through *hierarchical diffusion*, to provincial capitals and smaller Roman settlements of Europe. From those nodes and from monasteries established in pagan rural areas, *contagious diffusion* disseminated Christianity throughout the continent. The acceptance of Christianity as the state religion of the empire by the Emperor Constantine in 313 A.C.E. was also an expression of hierarchical diffusion of great importance in establishing the faith throughout the full extent of the Roman world. Finally, and much later, *relocation diffusion*, missionary efforts, and in Spanish colonial areas, forced conversion of Aboriginals brought the faith to the New World with European settlers (see Figure 6.29).

In Anglo-America today, the beliefs and practices of various immigrant groups and the innovations of domestic congregations have created a particularly varied spatial patterning, though intermingling rather than rigid territorial division is characteristic of the North American, particularly United States, scene. While 85% of Canadian Christians belong to one of three denominations (Roman Catholic, Anglican, or United Church of Canada), it takes at least 20 denominations to account for 85% of religious adherents in America.

The mark of Christianity on the cultural landscape has been prominent and enduring (Figure 6.35). In common with Muslims and Jews, Christians practise burial in areas reserved for the dead. The cemetery—whether connected to the church, separate from it, or unrelated to a specific denomination—has traditionally been a significant land use within urban areas. Frequently, the separate cemetery, originally on the outskirts of the community, becomes with urban expansion a more central land use and often one that distorts or blocks the growth of the city.

Islam

Islam—the word means "submission" (to the will of God)—springs from the same Judaic roots as Christianity and embodies many of the same beliefs: There is only one God, who may be revealed to humans through prophets; Adam was the first human; Abraham was one of his descendants. Mohammed is revered as the prophet of *Allah* (God), succeeding and completing the work of earlier prophets of Judaism and Christianity, including Moses, David, and Jesus.

Islam served to unify an Arab world sorely divided by tribes, social ranks, and multiple local deities. Mohammed was a resident of Mecca but fled in 622 A.C.E. to Medina, where the Prophet proclaimed a constitution and announced the universal mission of the Islamic community. By the time of Mohammed's death in 632 A.C.E., all of Arabia had joined Islam. The new religion swept quickly by *expansion diffusion* outward from that source region over most of Central Asia and, at the expense of Hinduism, into northern India (Figure 6.36). The advance westward was particularly rapid and inclusive in North Africa and western Europe. Later, by *relocation diffusion*, Islam was dispersed into Indonesia, southern Africa, and the Western Hemisphere. Muslims now form the majority population in 39 countries, with Asia having the largest absolute number, and Africa having the highest proportion of Muslims among its population—more than 42%.

The mosque—place of worship, community club house, meeting hall, and school—is the focal point of Islamic communal life and the primary imprint of the religion on the cultural landscape. Its principal purpose is to accommodate the Friday communal service mandatory for all male Muslims. It is the congregation rather than the structure that is important. Small or poor communities are as well served by a bare whitewashed room as are larger cities by architecturally splendid mosques with domes and minarets. With its perfectly proportioned, frequently gilded or tiled domes, its graceful, soaring towers and minarets (from which the faithful are called to prayer), and its delicately wrought parapets and cupolas, the carefully tended mosque is frequently the most elaborate and imposing structure of the town (Figure 6.37) (see "Gender and Religion").

Hinduism

Hinduism is the world's oldest major religion. Though it has no datable founding event or initial prophet, some evidence traces its origin back 4000 or more years. Hinduism is not just a religion but an intricate web of religious, philosophical, social, economic, and artistic elements comprising a distinctive Indian civilization. Its estimated 850 million to 1 billion adherents are largely confined to India, where it claims 80% of the population.

Hinduism derives its name from its cradle area in the valley of the Indus River. From that district of present-day Pakistan, it spread by *contagious diffusion* eastward down the Ganges River and southward throughout the subcontinent and adjacent regions

FIGURE 6.35 The building of Notre Dame Cathedral of Paris, France, begun in 1163, took more than 100 years to complete. Perhaps the best known of the French Gothic churches, it was part of the great period of cathedral construction in Western Europe during the late 12th and the 13th centuries. Between 1170 and 1270, some 80 cathedrals were constructed in France alone. The cathedrals were located in the centre of major cities; their plazas were the sites of markets, public meetings, morality plays, and religious ceremonies. They were the focus of public and private life and the symbol not only of the faith but of the pride and prosperity of the towns and regions that erected them.

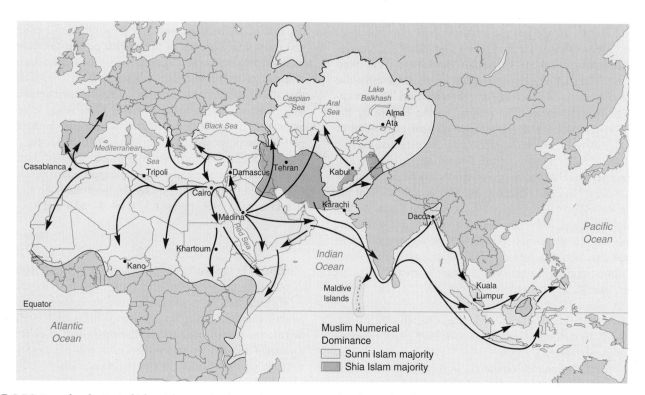

FIGURE 6.36 Spread and extent of Islam. Islam predominates in over 35 countries along a band across northern Africa to Central Asia, northwestern China, and the northern part of the Indian subcontinent. Still farther east, Indonesia has the largest Muslim population of any country. Islam's greatest development is in Asia, where it is second only to Hinduism, and in Africa, where some observers suggest it may be the leading faith. Current Islamic expansion is particularly rapid in the Southern Hemisphere.

Landscapes of Identity, Plurality, and Organization

A person's sense and practice of religion has a strong gender component: men and women differ in their levels of involvement, commitment to, and practice of religion. Women tend to be more religious than men; they are more likely to be interested in religion; they exhibit a stronger religious commitment: they pray more frequently; and they attend religious services more regularly. Studies have also shown that these attributes and practices not only hold true across the life course—from youth into old age—but are consistent regardless of the type of religion or religious institution (e.g., Christian to mystic or church to cult).

Social scientists have two general explanations for these findings. The first is sociological and suggests that females are taught to be more religious than men. Feminine gender roles encourage females to be more passive, submissive, obedient, and nurturing than males who are engendered as masculine and thus socialized to be more assertive and independent. In fact, both females and males who exhibit the aforementioned "feminine" traits tend to be more religious. Religions tend to require adherence to codes of conduct and ways of thinking that necessitate compliance on the part of their devotees. It follows that people with dispositions agreeable to such demands—dispositions that are particularly encouraged in females—are more likely to be religious.

The second explanation is geographical. Females are argued to be more religious than males because of their "place" in society: the location and social station they occupy in male-dominated societies. The lower participation rates in waged labour outside the home leave more time and flexibility for religious activities, as well as a greater need to seek an extension of their own social identity outside the home. Religion is also considered part of the household activities: the greater responsibility women take for childrearing in particular and the overall well-being of the family in general includes the family's spirituality.

Although females tend to be the primary followers of religion, males—both deities and mortals—tend to be the spiritual leaders of most major religions. God is conceived as a "father," and most institutions are male dominated. The Catholic Church forbids women to be either pope or priest, and only since the 1970s have females been permitted as rabbis in virtually all branches of Judaism, with the exception of the Orthodox. Muslims, too, have traditionally ordained only male imans, but several female imans do exist, most notably in China.

Religion, like other cultural complexes, is infused with prescribed gender roles, social practices, and institutions.

Source: Miller and Hoffman (1995).

FIGURE 6.37 The common architectural features of the mosque make it an unmistakable landscape evidence of the presence of Islam in any local culture. The Blue Mosque in Istanbul, Turkey, would not be out of place architecturally in Muslim Malaysia or Indonesia.

by amalgamating, absorbing, and eventually supplanting earlier native religions and customs (see Figure 6.32). Its practice eventually spread throughout southeastern Asia, into Indonesia, Malaysia, Cambodia, Thailand, Laos, and Vietnam, as well as into neighbouring Myanmar (Burma) and Sri Lanka. The largest Hindu temple complex is in Cambodia, not India, and Bali remains a Hindu pocket in dominantly Islamic Indonesia. Hinduism's more recent growing presence in western Europe and North America reflects a *relocation diffusion* of its adherents.

A Hindu is one born into a caste, a member of a complex social and economic—as well as religious—community. Hinduism accepts and incorporates all forms of belief; adherents may believe in one god or many or none. It emphasizes the divinity of the soul and is based on the concepts of reincarnation and passage from one state of existence to another in an unending cycle of birth and death in which all living things are caught. The **caste** (meaning "birth") structure of society is an expression of the eternal transmigration of souls. For the Hindu, the primary aim of this life is to conform to prescribed social and ritual duties and to the rules of conduct for the assigned caste and profession. The castes are subdivided into thousands of *jati* groups defined by geography and occupation. Caste rules define who you can mingle with, where you can live, what you may wear, eat, and drink, and how you can earn your livelihood.

The practice of Hinduism is rich with rites and ceremonies, festivals and feasts, processions and ritual gatherings of literally millions of celebrants. Pilgrimages to holy rivers and sacred places, for example, are thought to secure deliverance from sin or pollution and to preserve religious worth (Figure 6.38). Temples and shrines are everywhere; their construction brings merit to their owners—the villages or individuals who paid for them. Within them, innumerable icons of gods in various forms are enshrined, the objects of veneration, gifts, and daily care. All temples have a circular spire as a reminder that the sky is the real dwelling place of the god who temporarily resides within the temple (Figure 6.39). The temples, shrines, daily rituals and worship, numerous specially garbed or marked holy men and ascetics, and the ever-present sacred animals mark the cultural landscape of Hindu societies.

FIGURE 6.38 Pilgrims at dawn worship in the Ganges River at Varanasi (Banares), India, one of the seven most sacred Hindu cities and the reputed earthly capital of Siva, Hindu god of destruction and regeneration. Hindus believe that to die in Varanasi means release from the cycle of rebirth and permits entrance into heaven.

FIGURE 6.39 The Hindu temple complex at Khajraho in central India. The creation of temples and the images they house has been a principal outlet of Indian artistry for more than 3000 years. At the village level, the structure may be simple, containing only the windowless central cell housing the divine image, a surmounting spire, and the temple porch or stoop to protect the doorway of the cell. The great temples, of immense size, are ornate extensions of the same basic design.

Buddhism

Numerous reform movements have derived from Hinduism over the centuries, some of which have endured to the present day as major religions on a regional or world scale. The largest and most influential of these dissident movements has been **Buddhism**, a universalizing faith founded in the 6th century B.C.E. in northern India by Siddhartha Gautama, the Buddha (*Enlightened One*). The Buddha's teachings were more a moral philosophy that offered an explanation for evil and human suffering, rather than a formal religion. He viewed the road to enlightenment and salvation to lie in understanding the "four noble truths": existence involves suffering; suffering is the result of desire; pain ceases when desire is destroyed; the destruction of desire comes through knowledge of correct behaviour and correct thoughts. In Buddhism, which retains the Hindu concept of *karma* (deeds and conduct in previous lives), the ultimate objectives of existence are the achievement of *nirvana*, a condition of perfect enlightenment, and cessation of successive rebirths. All can aspire to ultimate enlightenment, a promise of salvation that raised the Buddha in popular imagination from teacher to inspiration and Buddhism from philosophy to universalizing religion.

Contact or *contagious diffusion* spread the belief system throughout India, where it was made the state religion in the 3rd century B.C.E. It was carried elsewhere into Asia by missionaries, monks, and merchants. Present-day spatial patterns of Buddhist adherence reflect the schools of thought, or *vehicles*, that were dominant during different periods of dispersion of the basic belief system (Figure 6.40). Earliest, most conservative, and closest to the origins of Buddhism was *Theravada* (Vehicle of the Elders) Buddhism, which was implanted in Sri Lanka and Southeast Asia

beginning in the 3rd century B.C.E. *Mahayana* (Greater Vehicle) was the dominant tradition when Buddhism was accepted into East Asia—China, Korea, and Japan—in the 4th century A.C.E. and later. *Vajrayana* (the Diamond Vehicle) was dominant when the conversion of Tibet and neighbouring northern areas began, first in the 7th century and again during the 10th and 11th centuries. Tibetan Buddhism was further dispersed, beginning in the 14th century, to Mongolia, northern China, and parts of southern Russia. Today, the number of adherents of Buddhism is estimated to lie between 225 million and 500 million.

In all of its many variants, Buddhism imprints its presence vividly on the cultural landscape. Equally widespread are the three main types of buildings and monuments: the *stupa*, a commemorative shrine; the temple or pagoda enshrining an image or relic of the Buddha; and the monastery, some of them the size of small cities (Figure 6.41). Common, too, is the *bodhi* (or *bo*) tree, a fig tree of great size and longevity. Buddha is said to have received enlightenment seated under one of them at Bodh Gaya, India, and specimens have been planted and tended as an act of reverence and symbol of the faith throughout Buddhist Asia.

East Asian Ethnic Religions

When Buddhism reached China from the south some 1500 to 2000 years ago and was carried to Japan from Korea in the 7th century, it encountered and later amalgamated with already well established ethical belief systems. The Far Eastern ethnic religions are hybrids. In China, the union was with Confucianism and Taoism; in Japan, it was with Shinto.

There are no churches or clergy in **Confucianism**, though its founder believed in a Heaven seen in naturalistic terms, and the Chinese custom of ancestor worship as a mark of gratitude and respect was encouraged. After his death, the custom was expanded to include worship of Confucius himself in temples erected for that purpose. With its emphasis on ethics and morality rooted in Chinese traditional wisdom, Confucianism formed the basis of the belief system of China.

It was joined by, or blended with, **Taoism**, an ideology that according to legend was first taught by Lao-tsu in the 6th century B.C.E. Its central theme is *Tao*, the Way, a philosophy teaching that eternal happiness lies in total identification with nature and deploring passion, unnecessary invention, unneeded knowledge, and government interference in the simple life of individuals. It involves deities, spirits, magic, temples, and priests. Along with Confucianism and Taoism, Buddhism became one of the honoured Three Teachings, and to the average person, there was no distinction in meaning or importance between a Confucian temple, Taoist shrine, or Buddhist stupa.

Similarly, **Shinto**—The Way of the Gods—is basically a structure of customs and rituals rather than an ethical or moral system. It observes a complex set of deities, including deified emperors, family spirits, and the divinities residing in rivers, trees, certain animals, mountains, and, particularly, the sun and moon. The centres of worship are the numerous shrines and temples in which the gods are believed to dwell and which are approached through ceremonial *torii*, or gateway arches (Figure 6.42).

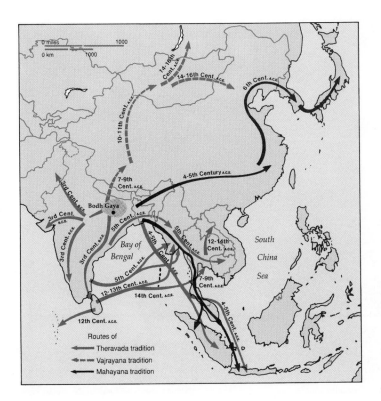

FIGURE 6.40 Diffusion paths, times, and "vehicles" of Buddhism.

FIGURE 6.41 The golden stupas of the Swedagon pagoda, Yangon, Myanmar (Rangoon, Burma).

FIGURE 6.42 Torii gate at Meiji Shrine in Tokyo, Japan.

Landscapes of Identity, Plurality, and Organization

Ethnicity, Religion, and Language: 'At Risk' Practices in a Globalizing World

Among the positive attributes of a globalizing world, are the increased opportunities for some people to learn, share and exchange cultural practices. Learning about the ethnicities, religions and languages of others may encourage mutual understanding, respect and cooperation: it can enrich lives by fostering and spreading cultural diversity. Globalization can also deplete lives by promoting cultural homogeneity—*uniformity*—at the expense of more marginalized cultures and cultural practices. Given the primary engine of globalization is economics, specifically global capitalism, and the international language of business is English, thus privileging Anglophone cultures, what are the implications for the diversity and distributions of the numerous ethnicities, religions, and languages practiced by humanity in an increasingly globalized world?

Such questions are a hot topic of debate and research among scholars across the disciplines, and one central issue they have raised is worth considering here: language rights and cultural loss. The growing widespread use, visibility, and availability of the English language in its various forms have given rise to what is termed *'Global English.'* Because of the growing number of English speakers as a first or additional language, many argue that English is becoming too dominant, lessening the need to learn or speak other languages, while at the same time marginalizing those speakers of other languages. Many see globalization as threatening the perpetuity of minority languages and marginalizing ethnic, religious, and other cultural differences in the process. Remember: language is the key means through which culture is taught, learned, transferred, and practised, and is fundamental marker of identity. The loss of a language is the loss of an entire culture.

Combating this risk of cultural loss is a call to ensure 'language rights' as part of the larger umbrella of 'human rights,' which has wide spread institutional support through, for example, the United Nations. Because language cannot be isolated from other cultural practices, language rights cannot be separated from other forms of cultural discrimination, be it ethnic or religious. Of course the privileged status of English, or the minority status of, say, Cree, arises from the political, social, and economic position status and power of those language users rather than the languages themselves. Minimizing or eradicating discrimination is thus a highly politicized process that entails policy formation, educational reforms, policy enforcement, and the necessary resources to do so.

At the micro-scale an individual's everyday life, simply practising one's native tongue, one's ethnic heritage, and one's religion is an act of resistance against cultural homogeneity and cultural loss.

Source: Mooney and Evans, 2007a, 2007b.

Want to Learn More?

Ethnicities in Canada

Citizenship and Immigration Canada
Explore the many facets of Canada's immigration process, including how others apply to enter Canada, what happens when they arrive, and related topics.
http://www.cic.gc.ca/english/index.asp

Metropolis, Canada
Canadian researchers, including geographers, are part of an international forum for comparative research and public policy development about population migration, cultural diversity, and the challenges of immigrant integration in cities in Canada and around the world.
http://canada.metropolis.net/index_e.html

Statistics Canada: People and Society
Maps, tables, and numerous other data bout Canadian ethnicities and languages are available at this website.
http://atlas.nrcan.gc.ca/site/english/maps/peopleandsociety#immigration

Religious Matters

Families of Religion
Learn more about the history and belief systems of both major and minor religions. Links to other religion specific sites are available here.
http://www.interfaithcalendar.org/Familiesofreligions.htmw

If the world were a village of 1000 people. . .
To place the size of various religions and numerous other cultural identities and economic indicators in perspective, this website scales down humanity to a village of 1000 people.
http://www.gdrc.org/uem/1000-village.html

Places of Peace and Power
Maps and photographs of sacred places from around the world are listed here in alphabetical order by country.
http://www.sacredsites.com/pages/atlas.html

Languages

Aboriginal Languages of Canada
Results about Aboriginal language uses and users are available from "The 2001 Aboriginal Peoples Survey."
http://www.statcan.ca/english/freepub/89-589-XIE/language.htm

Information about Esperanto
Esperanto is a language, but not of any country or ethnic group: it is a neutral, international language.
http://www.esperanto.net/info/index_en.html

Language Varieties
There are varieties of language that differ from the standard variety that is normally used in the media and educational institution. Explore the many pidgins, regional dialects, and minority dialects at this website.
http://www.une.edu.au/langnet/index.html

Summary

Ethnicity, language, and religion are symbols of identity, serving both as threads of unity and diversity in the complex web of human cultures. Depending upon the spatial and cultural contexts, these identities can assume varying degrees of importance, serving to include and unify people, or exclude and divide them.

Ethnic diversity is a reality in most countries of the world and is increasing in many of them. Immigration, refugee streams, guest workers, and job seekers all contribute to the mixing of peoples and cultures in an area. The mixing is not complete, however. In much of the world, spatial separation identifies home territories within which the ethnic group is dominant and with which it is identified. In societies of immigrants—Anglo-America, for example—such homelands are rare, French Quebec and Aboriginal lands being the major exceptions. Ethnic enclaves of self selection or forced ghettos of imposed separation from the larger host society are more common. Ethnicity is one of the threads of diversity in the spatial cultural fabric. Throughout the world, ethnic groups have imprinted their presence on the landscapes in which they have developed or to which they have transported their culture.

Language and religion are fundamental components of culture and often intrinsic to ethnic diversity. They serve to identify and categorize individuals within a single society and to separate peoples and nations of different tongues and faiths. By their pronunciation and choice of words, we quickly recognize districts of origin and educational levels of speakers of our own language, and easily identify those who originally had different native tongues. In some societies, religion may serve as a similar identifier of individuals and groups who observe distinctive modes or rhythms of life dictated by their separate faiths. Both language and religion are mentifacts, parts of the ideological subsystem of culture; both are transmitters of culture as well as its identifiers. Both have distinctive spatial patterns—reflecting past and present processes of spatial interaction and diffusion—that are basic to the recognition of world culture realms.

Languages may be grouped genetically—by origin and historical development—but the world distribution of language families depends as much on the movement of peoples and histories of conquest and colonization as it does on patterns of linguistic evolution. Linguistic geography studies spatial variations in languages, variations that may be minimized by encouragement of standard and official languages or overcome by pidgins, creoles, and lingua francas. Toponymy, the study of place names, helps document that history of movement.

Religion is a less pronounced identifier or conveyer of culture than is language. While language characterizes all peoples, religion varies in its impact and influence on culture groups. Some societies are dominated in all aspects by their controlling religious belief: Hindu India, for example, or Islamic Iran. Where religious beliefs are strongly held, they can unite a society of adherents and divide nations and peoples holding divergent faiths. Although religions do not lend themselves to easy classification, their patterns of distribution are as distinct and revealing as are those of languages. They, too, reflect past and present patterns of migration, conquest, and diffusion, part of the larger picture of dynamic cultural geography.

Ethnicity, language, and religion are important and evident components of spatial cultural variation. They are, however, only part of the total complex of cultural identities that distinguish individuals and groups from one another, within, and between societies. The spatial politics of organizing this human mosaic is the focus of the next chapter.

KEY WORDS

animism   194
Buddhism   201
caste   199
chain migration   174
Christianity   196
Confucianism   201
creole   188
dialect   186
ethnic enclave   170
ethnic group   163
ethnic religion   193
ethnicity   164

geographic (regional)
   dialect   187
ghetto   171
Hinduism   197
host society   170
Islam   197
isogloss   186
Judaism   195
language   178
language family   178
lingua franca   188
linguistic geography   186

migration fields   174
multilingualism   188
nationalism   166
official language   188
pidgin   188
protolanguage   179
religion   192
reserve   166
secularism   194
segregation   170
shamanism   194
Shinto   201

social dialect   186
speech community   185
standard language   185
Taoism   201
tipping point   172
toponym   191
toponymy   191
tribal (traditional)
   religion   193
universalizing religion   193
vernacular   186

FOR REVIEW

1. How does *ethnocentrism* contribute to preservation of group identity? In what ways might an ethnic group sustain and support new immigrants?

2. How are the concepts of *ethnicity* and *culture* related?

3. How may *segregation* be measured? Does ethnic segregation exist in the cities of world areas outside of North America? If so, does it take different form than in North American cities?

4. What forces external to ethnic groups help to create and perpetuate immigrant neighbourhoods? What functions beneficial to immigrant groups do ethnic communities provide?

5. Why might one consider language the dominant differentiating element of culture separating societies?

6. Cite examples that indicate the significance of religion as a cultural dominant in the internal and foreign relations of nations.

7. How does the classification of religions as *universalizing*, *ethnic*, or *tribal* help us to understand their patterns of distribution and spatial diffusion?

8. The issue of 'language' rights and practices, specifically English and French, has been with Canadians since confederation, but more recently we have seen issues of religion and ethnicity come to the fore: why might this be the case? Think of a contemporary religious or ethnic issue you may have seen in the news to illustrate an example.

FOCUS FOLLOW-UP

1. **What are the implications and bases of "ethnicity," and how have historic immigration streams shaped North American multiethnicity?** pp. 163–174.

   Ethnicity implies a "people" or "nation," a large group classified according to common religious, linguistic, or other aspects of cultural origin or background. In common with nearly all countries, the United States and Canada are multiethnic. Past and current immigration streams—earlier primarily European, more recently Asian and Latin American—have intricately mixed their populations.

2. **What patterns of ethnic diversity and segregation exist in the world's urban areas, and how are they created or maintained?** pp. 174–177.

   Ethnic communities, clusters, and neighbourhoods are found in cities worldwide. They are a measure of the social distance that separates minority from majority or other minority groups. Segregation measures the degree to which culture groups are not uniformly distributed within the total population. Although different world regions show differing patterns, all urban segregation is based on external restrictions of isolation and discrimination or ethnic group internal separatism controls of defence, mutual support, and cultural preservation.

3. **How are the world's languages classified and distributed?** pp. 177–185.

   The some 6000 languages spoken today may be grouped within a limited number of language families that trace their origins to common protolanguages. The present distribution of tongues reflects the current stage of continuing past and recent dispersion of their speakers and their adoption by new users. Languages change through isolation, migration, and the passage of time.

4. **What are standard languages and what kinds of variants from them can be observed?** pp. 185–190.

   All speakers of a given language are members of its speech community, but not all use the language uniformly. The standard language is that form of speech that has received official sanction or acceptance as the "proper" form of grammar and pronunciation. Dialects, regional and social, represent non-standard or vernacular variants of the common tongue. A pidgin is a created, composite, simple language designed to promote exchange between speakers of different tongues. When evolved into a complex native language of a people, the pidgin has become a creole. Governments may designate one or more official state languages (including, perhaps, a creole such as Swahili).

5. **What is the cultural role of religion?** pp. 192–193.

   Like language, religion is a basic identifying component of culture, a mentifact that serves as a cultural rallying point. Frequently, religious beliefs and adherence divide and alienate different groups within and among societies. Past and present belief systems of a culture may influence its legal norms, dietary customs, economic patterns, and landscape imprints.

6. **What are the principal world religions and how are they distinguished in patterns of innovation, diffusion, and landscape imprint?** pp. 195–203.

   The text briefly traces those differing origins, spreads, and cultural landscape impacts of Judaism, Christianity, Islam, Hinduism, Buddhism, and certain East Asian ethnic religions.

ONLINE LEARNING CENTRE

The World Wide Web has a tremendous number and variety of sites pertaining to geography. To access Web sites, Internet exercises, self-quizzes, videos, and additional study tools relevant to this chapter's content, visit the *Human Geography* Online Learning Centre at **www.mcgrawhill.ca/olc/fellmann**.

7 THE POLITICAL ORDERING OF SPACE

Aims:

- To know what a state and a nation are
- To understand how the modern state has evolved
- To know what are geographic characteristics of states
- To understand different types of boundaries and boundary disputes
- To identify the forces that bring states together and apart
- To understand why and how states project power and cooperate with each other
- To become familiar with the role of local governments

Some Specific Considerations for Review:

In 1998, The Government of Canada asked the Supreme Court of Canada to consider the legal question of Quebec separating from Canada. One of the responses provided by the Court is provided below.

Question 1: *Under the Constitution of Canada, can the National Assembly, legislature or government of Quebec effect the secession of Quebec from Canada unilaterally?*

The Constitution is more than a written text. It embraces the entire global system of rules and principles which govern the exercise of constitutional authority. A superficial reading of selected provisions of the written constitutional enactment, without more, may be misleading. It is necessary to make a more profound investigation of the underlying principles animating the whole of the Constitution, including the principles of federalism, democracy, constitutionalism and the rule of law, and respect for minorities. Those principles must inform our overall appreciation of the constitutional rights and obligations that would come into play in the event that a clear majority of Quebecers votes on a clear question in favour of secession.

The Court in this Reference is required to consider whether Quebec has a right to unilateral secession. Arguments in support of the existence of such a right were primarily based on the principle of democracy. Democracy, however, means more than simple majority rule. Constitutional jurisprudence shows that democracy exists in the larger context of other constitutional values. Since Confederation, the people of the provinces and territories have created close ties of interdependence (economic, social, political and cultural) based on shared values that include federalism, democracy, constitutionalism and the rule of law, and respect for minorities. A democratic decision of Quebecers in favour of secession would put those relationships at risk. The Constitution vouchsafes order and stability, and accordingly secession of a province "under the Constitution" could not be achieved unilaterally, that is, without principled negotiation with other participants in Confederation within the existing constitutional framework.

Our democratic institutions necessarily accommodate a continuous process of discussion and evolution, which is reflected in the constitutional right of each participant in the federation to initiate constitutional change. This right implies a reciprocal duty on the other participants to engage in discussions to address any legitimate initiative to change the constitutional order. A clear majority vote in Quebec on a clear question in favour of secession would confer democratic legitimacy on the secession initiative which all of the other participants in Confederation would have to recognize.

Quebec could not, despite a clear referendum result, purport to invoke a right of self-determination to dictate the terms of a proposed secession to the other parties to the federation. The democratic vote, by however strong a majority, would have no legal effect on its own and could not push aside the principles of federalism and the rule of law, the rights of individuals and minorities, or the operation of democracy in the other provinces or in Canada as a whole. Democratic rights under the Constitution cannot be divorced from constitutional obligations. Nor, however, can the reverse proposition be accepted: the continued existence and operation of the Canadian constitutional order could not be indifferent to a clear expression of a clear majority of Quebecers that they no longer wish to remain in Canada. The other provinces and the federal government would have no basis to deny the right of the government of Quebec to pursue secession should a clear majority of the people of Quebec choose that goal, so long as in doing so, Quebec respects the rights of others. The negotiations that followed such a vote would address the potential act of secession as well as its possible terms should in fact secession proceed. There would be no conclusions predetermined by law on any issue. Negotiations would need to address the interests of the other provinces, the federal government and Quebec and indeed the rights of all Canadians both within and outside Quebec, and specifically the rights of minorities.

The negotiation process would require the reconciliation of various rights and obligations by negotiation between two legitimate majorities, namely, the majority of the population of Quebec, and that of Canada as a whole. A political majority at either level that does not act in accordance with the underlying constitutional principles puts at risk the legitimacy of its exercise of its rights, and the ultimate acceptance of the result by the international community.

The task of the Court has been to clarify the legal framework within which political decisions are to be taken "under the Constitution" and not to usurp the prerogatives of the political forces that operate within that framework. The obligations identified by the Court are binding obligations under the Constitution. However, it will be for the political actors to determine what constitutes "a clear majority on a clear question" in the circumstances under which a future referendum vote may be taken. Equally, in the event of demonstrated majority support for Quebec secession, the content and process of the negotiations will be for the political actors to settle. The reconciliation of the various legitimate constitutional interests is necessarily committed to the political rather than the judicial realm precisely because that reconciliation can only be achieved through the give and take of political negotiations. To the extent issues addressed in the course of negotiation are political, the courts, appreciating their proper role in the constitutional scheme, would have no supervisory role.[1]

According to Canada's Supreme Court (Figure 7.1), a Constitution, which is the legal basis upon which countries conduct themselves, is more than a written document, and democracy is more than applying majority rule. In Canada, implementing the Constitution in a democratic manner is, in part, a process of negotiation among different levels of government. The process of building and maintaining a nation is as old as human history. From clans to kingdoms, human groups have laid claim to territory and have organized themselves in a variety of manners (often under a Constitution) and administered their affairs within it. Indeed, political organizations of society are as fundamental an expression of culture and cultural differences as are forms of economy or religious beliefs. Geographers are interested in that structuring because it is both an expression of the human organizations of space that is

---

[1] Available from: http://scc.lexum.umontreal.ca/en/1998/1998rcs2-217/1998rcs2-217.html.

FIGURE 7.1 The Supreme Court of Canada. The SCC is created under Canada's Constitution, is the highest court of Canada, and is the final court of appeal within the Canadian legal system. It hears appeals of decisions made by provincial, territorial, and federal courts (lower courts), and its decisions are binding upon all lower courts of Canada. Its decisions assist in interpreting the laws of Canada and its Constitution.

FIGURE 7.2 These flags, symbols of separate member states, grace the front of the United Nations building in New York City. Although central to political geographic interest, states are only one level of the political organization of space.

closely related to other spatial evidences of culture, such as ethnicity, religion, and language.

Political geography is the study of the organization and distribution of political phenomena, including their impact on other spatial components of society and culture. Nationality is a basic element in cultural variation among people, and political geography traditionally has had a primary interest in country units, or *states* (Figure 7.2). Of particular concern have been spatial patterns that reflect the exercise of central governmental control, such as questions of boundary delimitation and effect. Increasingly, however, attention has shifted both upward and downward on the political scale. On the world scene, international alliances, regional compacts, and producer cartels—some requiring the surrender of at least a portion of national sovereignty—have increased in prominence since World War II, representing new forms of spatial interaction. At the local level, voting patterns, the merging of municipal governments, changing electoral boundaries and political fragmentation have directed public attention to the significance of area in the domestic political process.

In this chapter, we discuss some of the characteristics of political entities, examine the problems involved in defining jurisdictions, seek the elements that lend cohesion to a political entity, explore the implications of partial surrender of sovereignty, and consider the significance of the fragmentation of political power. We begin with states (countries) and end with local political systems.

Emphasis here on political entities should not make us lose sight of the reality that states are rooted in the operations of the economy and society they represent, that social and economic disputes are as significant as border confrontations, and that in some regards, transnational corporations and other nongovernmental agencies may exert more influence in international affairs than do the separate states in which they are housed or operate. Some of those expanded political considerations are alluded to in the discussions that follow.

National Political Systems

One of the most significant elements in cultural geography is the nearly complete division of the earth's land surface into separate country units. Even Antarctica is subject to the rival territorial claims of seven countries, although these claims have not been pressed because of the Antarctic Treaty of 1959 (Figure 7.3). A second element is that this division into country units is relatively recent. Although countries and empires have existed since the days of ancient Egypt and Mesopotamia, only in the last century has the world been almost completely divided into independent governing entities. Now people everywhere accept the idea of the state and its claim to sovereignty within its borders as normal.

States, Nations, and Nation-States

Before we begin our consideration of political systems, we need to clarify some terminology. Geographers use the words *state* and *nation* somewhat differently than the way they are used in everyday speech; sometimes confusion arises because each word has more than one meaning. A state can be defined as either (1) any of the political units forming a federal government (e.g., one of the Canadian provinces), or as (2) an independent political entity holding sovereignty over a territory (e.g., Canada). In this latter sense, *state* is synonymous with *country* or *nation*. That is,

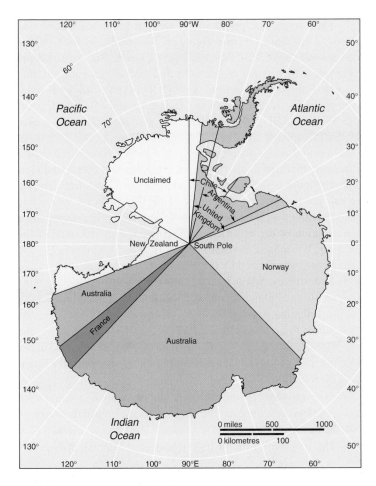

FIGURE 7.3 Territorial claims in Antarctica. Seven countries claim sovereignty over portions of Antarctica, and those of Argentina, Chile, and the United Kingdom overlap. The Antarctic Treaty of 1959 froze those claims for 30 years, banned further land claims, and made scientific research the primary use of the continent. The treaty was extended for 50 years in 1991. Antarctica is neither a sovereign state—it has no permanent inhabitants or local government—nor a part of one.

a nation can also be defined as: (1) an independent political unit holding sovereignty over a territory (e.g., a member of the United Nations); but it can also be used to describe (2) a community of people with a common culture and territory (e.g., the Kurdish nation). The second definition is *not* synonymous with state or country. For instance, the Quebec Assembly sees itself as a nation and wishes other Canadian governments to accept this view. In 2006, all parties in the Canadian parliament voted to recognize the Québécois as a nation within a united Canada. According to Prime Minister Stephen Harper, this motion provides no recognition of Quebec sovereignty and is only symbolic in nature.

To avoid confusion, we shall define a **state** on the international level as an independent political unit occupying a defined, permanently populated territory and having full sovereign control over its internal and foreign affairs. We will use *country* as a synonym for the territorial and political concept of "state." Not all recognized territorial entities are states. Antarctica, for example, has neither established government nor permanent population, and it is, therefore, not a state. Nor are *colonies* or *protectorates* recognized as states. Although they have a defined extent, permanent

inhabitants, and some degree of separate governmental structure, they lack full control over all of their internal and external affairs. More importantly, they lack recognition as states by the international community, a decisive consideration in the proper use of the term "state."

We use nation in its second sense, as a reference to people, not to political structure. A **nation** is a group of people with a common culture occupying a particular territory, bound together by a strong sense of unity arising from shared beliefs and customs. Language and religion may be unifying elements, but even more important are an emotional conviction of cultural distinctiveness and a sense of ethnocentrism. The Cree nation exists because of its cultural uniqueness, not by virtue of territorial sovereignty.

The composite term **nation-state** properly refers to a state whose territorial extent coincides with that occupied by a distinct nation or people or, at least, whose population shares a general sense of cohesion and adherence to a set of common values (Figure 7.4a). That is, a nation-state is an entity whose members feel a natural connection with each other by virtue of sharing language, religion, or some other cultural characteristic strong enough both to bind them together and to give them a sense of distinction from all others outside the community. Although all countries strive for consensus values and loyalty to the state, few can claim to be true nation-states since few are or have ever been wholly uniform ethnically. Iceland, Slovenia, Poland, and the two Koreas are often cited as acceptable examples.

A *binational* or *multinational state* is one that contains more than one nation (Figure 7.4b). Often, no single ethnic group dominates the population. In the constitutional structure of the former Soviet Union (before 1988), one division of the legislative branch of the government was termed the Soviet of Nationalities. It was composed of representatives from civil divisions of the Soviet Union populated by groups of officially recognized "nations": Ukrainians, Kazakhs, Tatars, Estonians, and others. In this instance, the concept of nationality was territorially less than the extent of the state.

Alternatively, a single nation may be dispersed across, and be predominant in, two or more states. This is the case with the *partnation state* (Figure 7.4c). Here, a people's sense of nationality exceeds the areal limits of a single country. An example is the Arab nation, which dominates 17 states.

Finally, there is the special case of the *stateless nation*, a people without a state. The Kurds, for example, are a nation of some 20 million people divided among six states and dominant in none (Figure 7.4d). Kurdish nationalism has survived over the centuries, and many Kurds nurture a vision of an independent Kurdistan. Other stateless nations include Gypsies (Roma), Basques, and Palestinians.

The Evolution of the Modern State

The concept and practice of political organization of space and people arose independently in many parts of the world. Certainly, one of the distinguishing characteristics of very early culture hearths—including those shown in Figure 5.19—was the political organization of their peoples and areas. The larger and

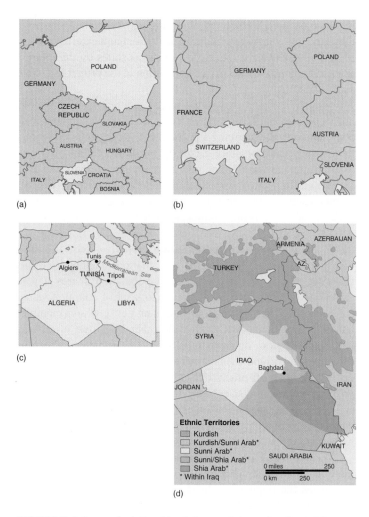

FIGURE 7.4 Types of relationships between states and nations. (*a*) **Nation-states.** Poland and Slovenia are examples of states occupied by a distinct nation or people. (*b*) **A multinational state.** Switzerland shows that a common ethnicity, language, or religion is not necessary for a strong sense of nationalism. (*c*) **A part-nation state.** The Arab nation extends across and dominates many states in northern Africa and the Middle East. (*d*) **A stateless nation.** An ancient group with a distinctive language, the Kurds are concentrated in Turkey, Iran, and Iraq. Smaller numbers live in Syria, Armenia, and Azerbaijan.

more complex the economic structures they developed, the more sophisticated became their mechanisms of political control and territorial administration.

Our Western orientations and biases may incline us to trace ideas of spatial political organization through their Near Eastern, Mediterranean, and Western European expressions. Mesopotamian and classical Greek city states, the Roman Empire, and European colonizing kingdoms and warring principalities were, however, not unique. Southern, southeastern, and eastern Asia had their counterparts, as did sub-Saharan Africa and the Western Hemisphere. Although the Western European models and colonization strongly influenced the forms and structures of modern states in both hemispheres, the cultural roots of statehood run deeper and reach further back in many parts of the world than European example alone suggests.

The current and predominant view of the modern state was strongly influenced by the Treaty of Westphalia in 1648, which saw an end to the Thirty Years War in Europe. The Thirty Years War refers to a series of declared and undeclared conflicts that occurred throughout central Europe between 1618 and 1648. The main participants were the Hapsburg Holy Roman Emperors Ferdinand II and Ferdinand III, and their Spanish cousin Philip IV, against the French, Swedish, Danish, and Dutch. In addition to this international conflict, a civil war occurred within Germany that saw many of the principalities that comprised Germany (Figure 7.5) fight with or against the Hapsburgs. To add to this confusion, over the course of the Thirty Years War, some principalities fought on both sides of the conflict. To provide some appreciation of the historical context and the significance of the Peace of Westphalia, consider the political environment in Europe that were characterized by the following:

- A desire by Spain to maintain control over what is today southern Holland despite the signing of a 12-year agreement in 1609 that stated otherwise;
- Since France was fearful of becoming encircled by the Habsburg Empire (Spain, the Spanish Netherlands, and upper portions of Italy), it actively supported rebels during the Spanish rebellion;
- The intrusion of the Catholic popes, who had significant political influence at the time, into the internal affairs of Spain; and
- The rulers of northern Italy who feared Spanish domination of the region.

On top of these and other political dimensions, it was also, in part, a religious conflict among Catholics, Lutherans, and Calvinists.

What is of significance to our discussion is the Treaty of Westphalia, which brought an end to this conflict. It incorporated the following four basic principles that are fundamental in shaping current international political relations:

- The sovereignty of nation-states and the related right of political self determination;
- The legal equality between nation-states;
- The binding nature of international treaties between states; and
- Non-intervention of one state into the internal affairs of the other states.

It also demonstrated the need for international cooperation if long-lasting peace among nations was to be achieved. In 1648, these principles were new and changed the nature of future conflicts in Europe. By recognizing a country's sovereignty over a specific territory, future wars were about conflicts of the state rather than religion. As a middle class developed as part of the Industrial Revolution, the role of royalty declined and power was transferred to the people. The French Revolution (1789–1795) is one well-known element of this struggle for power.

During the period of European exploration that occurred in the 17th, 18th, and 19th centuries, many parts of Africa, Asia, and the Americas were divided into colonies based on the principles of the state associated with the Peace of Westphalia. Usually the colonial claims were given fixed and prescribed boundaries where none had been formally defined. For indigenous peoples

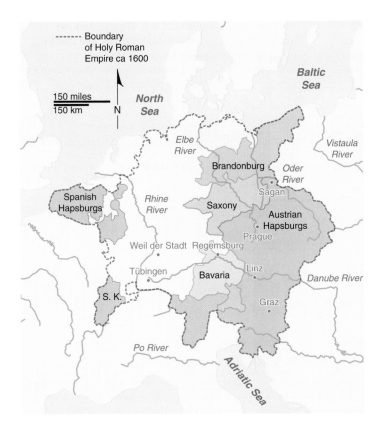

FIGURE 7.5 Present day Germany at the time of the Thirty Years War.

in these countries, the concept of territory was different. In North America, for instance, territorial boundaries shifted in response to the migration of herds (e.g., buffalo, bison, elk), land was owned communally and not by individuals, and in some instances hunting grounds were shared with other tribes. The entire concept of individuals owning property and nations having fixed boundaries—things societies from developed countries take for granted—are completely foreign to Aboriginals in Canada. They see themselves very much as stewards of the land. In other parts of the world, great empires arose, again with recognized outer limits of influence or control: Mongol and Chinese, Benin and Zulu, Ican and Aztec. Upon them where they still existed, and upon the less formally organized spatial patterns of effective tribal control, European colonizers imposed their arbitrary new administrative boundaries to the land. In fact, groups that had previously had very little in common and little contact with one another were now part of the same colony (Figure 7.6). The new divisions were not based on culturally or physically defined lines. Instead, the boundaries simply reflected the spatial limits of the colonizing empire's power and territory. The difference in the pre- and post-Westphalian period view of the state is reflected in the previously mentioned dual meanings of the word "state."

You will recall the Wallerstein's World Systems Analysis (Chapter 3) identified the European colonial period as an important historical element that influenced globalization. **Colonialism** may be defined as the control by one nation (i.e., extension of sovereignty) over another, dependent area. Colonialism is achieved by the establishment of settler colonies that exert direct rule

(e.g., laws, control) on indigenous populations, who are often displaced (i.e., unwanted or forced migration) or exterminated (i.e., genocide). The colonizing nation exploits natural resources of the colony (see Figure 3.2) and its people. It often imposes other cultural, social, political, economic, and financial norms on the indigenous population. This unbalanced relationship gave rise to the development of "core" and "periphery" nations, which has shaped the current the current world system.

As these former colonies have gained political independence, they have retained the idea of the state. They have generally accepted—in the case of Africa, by a conscious decision to avoid pre-colonial territorial or ethnic claims that could lead to war—the borders established by their former European rulers (Figure 7.7). One problem that many of the new countries face is "nation building"—developing feelings of loyalty to the state among their arbitrarily associated citizens. For example, the Democratic Republic of the Congo, the former Belgian Congo, contains some 270 frequently antagonistic ethnic groups. Julius Nyerere, president of Tanzania, noted in 1971, "These new countries are artificial units, geographic expressions carved on the map by European imperialists. These are the units we have tried to turn into nations."

The idea of separate statehood grew slowly at first and, more recently, has accelerated rapidly. In 1776, there were about 35 empires, kingdoms, and countries in the entire world. By 1939, that number had only doubled to about 70. Following the end of World War II in 1945, the colonial era ended and a rapid increase in the number of sovereign states began. From the former British Empire and Commonwealth, there have come the independent countries of India, Pakistan, Bangladesh, Malaysia, Myanmar (Burma), and Singapore in Asia, and Ghana, Nigeria, Kenya, Uganda, Tanzania, Malawi, Botswana, Zimbabwe, and Zambia in Africa. Even this extensive list is not complete. A similar process has occurred in most of the former overseas possessions of the Netherlands, Spain, Portugal and France. By 1990, independent states totalled some 180, and their number increased again following—among other political geographic developments—the disintegration during the 1990s of the USSR, Czechoslovakia, and Yugoslavia, which created more than 20 countries where only three had existed before (Figure 7.8).

The proliferation of states means that about half of the world's independent countries in the early 21st century had small populations. All told, some 90 countries had populations under 5 million, 56 had less than 2.5 million, and 33 had fewer than a half-million population. The great increase in the number of smaller countries is an affirmation of the ideal of nation-state but poses some challenges (see "The Ministates").

Another term often used interchangeably with colonialism is **imperialism**, which refers to the less formal control one nation exerts on another. This can manifest itself in several forms but most often it is through economic influence and/or military control. Since the end of World War II, the United States has been perceived by some people as adopting an imperialist policy with a goal to dominate the world for its own benefit. On the other hand, others would suggest many US actions since that time have promoted and defended democracy and freedom throughout the world. On the other hand, there are many examples of U.S. covert

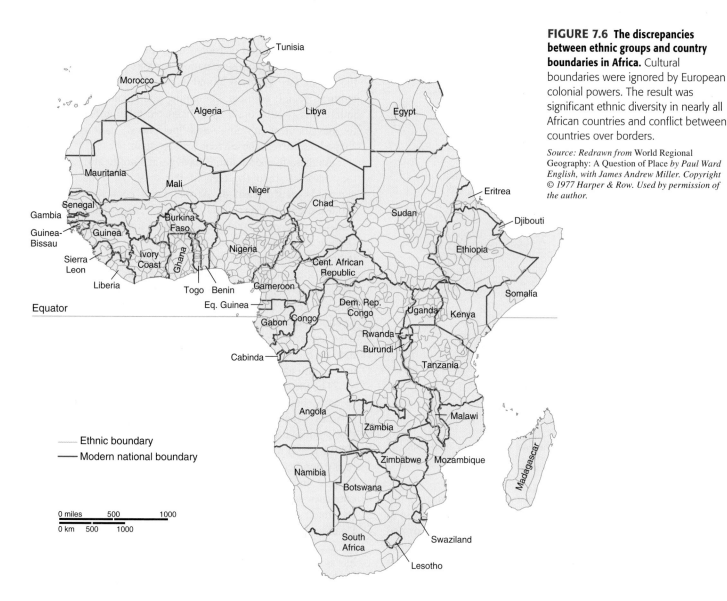

FIGURE 7.6 The discrepancies between ethnic groups and country boundaries in Africa. Cultural boundaries were ignored by European colonial powers. The result was significant ethnic diversity in nearly all African countries and conflict between countries over borders.

Source: Redrawn from World Regional Geography: A Question of Place *by Paul Ward English, with James Andrew Miller. Copyright © 1977 Harper & Row. Used by permission of the author.*

operations, which would appear to be contrary to the principles of Westphalia:

- the Bay of Pigs Invasion (Cuba) (1961);
- spending $3 million to influence election in Chile (1964) and tried to kidnap the head of the Chilean army (1970);
- the Vietnam War (1964–1975);
- the invasion of Grenada (1983) in order to overthrow a Marxist junta;
- the invasion of Panama (1989) in order to overthrow its President, Manuel Noriega;
- the invasion on Afghanistan (2001) in order to overthrow the Taliban in response to the attacks of September 11; and
- the invasion on Iraq (2003) to overthrow Saddam Hussein.

The USSR also established itself as an imperial power after World War II. Using its military power, it controlled Central and Eastern Europe (Bulgaria, Czechoslovakia, East Germany, Poland, and Romania). It established a communist form of government and economy. In 1956, it invaded Hungary, and invaded Czechoslovakia in 1968 in order to re-establish its control. The "Cold War," which will be discussed later in this chapter, was essentially a conflict between the imperial powers of the United States and the USSR.

Globalization and Pressures on State Primacy

The state and nation-state have been the long-established focus of political geography in recognition of their presumed unalterable control over the administrative organization of space. Although for tradition and convenience we shall keep that focus in much of the following discussion, we should also realize that the validity of that state-centric view of the world is increasingly under assaults from multiple new agents of economic and social power. Among them are:

1. The globalization of economies and the emergence of transnational corporations whose economic and production decisions are unrelated to the interests of any single state, including their home office state. Those decisions—outsourcing of

(a) COLONIAL AFRICA, 1939

FIGURE 7.7 Africa—from **colonies to states**. (*a*) Africa in 1939 was a patchwork of foreign claims and alien rule, some dating from the 19th century, others of more recent vintage. For example, Germany lost its claim to South West Africa, Tanganyika, Togoland, and the Cameroons after World War I, and Italy asserted control over Ethiopia during the 1930s. (*b*) **Africa in 2004** was a mosaic of separate states. Their dates of independence are indicated on the map. French West Africa and French Equatorial Africa have been extensively subdivided. Most of the current countries retain the boundaries of their former colonial existence, though the continent's structure of political influence and regional power has changed through civil wars and neighbouring state interventions. These marked the decline of earlier African principles of inviolability of borders and non-interference in the internal affairs of other states.

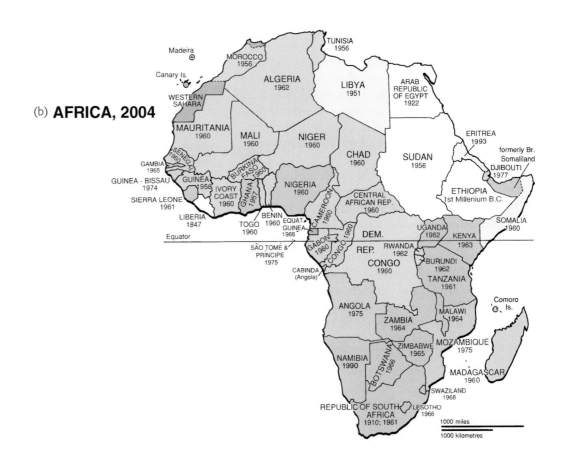

FIGURE 7.8 By mid-1992, 15 newly independent countries had taken the place of the former USSR.

production and services, for example—may be detrimental to the employment structure, tax base, and national security of any single state and limit the applicability of national economic planning and control.

2. The proliferation of international and supranational institutions initially concerned with financial or security matters but all representing the voluntary surrender of some traditional state autonomy. The World Trade Organization, regional trade blocs like the North American Free Trade Association, the European Union, and a host of other international conventions and agreements all limit the independence of action of each of their members and thus diminish absolute state primacy in matters economic and social.

3. The emergence and multiplication of non-governmental organizations (NGOs) whose specific interests and collective actions cut across national boundaries and unite people sharing common concerns about, for example, globalization, the environment, economic and social injustice, AIDS efforts, and the like. The well-publicized protests and pressures exerted by NGOs channel social pressures to influence or limit governmental actions.

4. The massive international migration flows that tend to undermine the state as a cultural community with assured and expected common values and loyalties. The Internet, cheap telephone calls, and easy international travel, permit immigrant retention of primary ties with their home culture and state, discouraging their full assimilation into their new social environment or the transfer of loyalties to their adopted country.

5. The increase in nationalist and separatist movements in culturally composite states, weakening, through demands for independence or regional autonomy, the former unquestioned primacy of the established state.

Some of these agents and developments have been touched on in earlier chapters; others will be reviewed in this, particularly in the section on Centrifugal Forces (p. 225). All represent recent and strengthening forces that, in some assessments of political geographic reality, weaken the validity of a worldview in which national governments and institutionalized politics are all-powerful.

Some Geographic Characteristics of States

Every state has certain geographic characteristics by which it can be described and that set it apart from all other states. A look at the world political map confirms that every state is unique. The size, shape, and location of any one state combine to distinguish it from all others. These characteristics are of more than academic interest because they also affect the power and stability of states.

Location

The absolute and relative locations of a state are factors that can influence its "success." Although both Canada and Russia are extremely large, their *absolute location* in upper middle latitudes reduces their size advantages when agricultural potential is considered. To take another example, Iceland has a reasonably compact shape, but its location in the North Atlantic Ocean, just south of the Arctic Circle, means that most of the country is barren, with settlement confined to the rim of the island.

A state's *relative location*, its position compared to that of other countries, is as important as its absolute location. *Landlocked* states, those lacking ocean frontage and surrounded by other states, are at a commercial and strategic disadvantage (Figure 7.9) (see Chapter 3, "Place as Location"). They lack easy access to both maritime (sea-borne) trade and the resources found in coastal waters and submerged lands. Typically, a landlocked country arranges to use facilities at a foreign port plus to have the right to travel to that port. Bolivia, for example, has secured access to the Chilean port of Arica, the Peruvian port of Ilo, and the Argentinean city of Rosario on the Parana River (Figure 7.10). The number of landlocked states—about 40—increased greatly with the dissolution of the Soviet Union and the creation of new, smaller nation-states out of such former multinational countries as Yugoslavia and Czechoslovakia.

In a few instances, a favourable relative location constitutes the primary resource of a state. Singapore, a state of only 580 square kilometres (224 sq mi), is located at a crossroads of world shipping and commerce. Based on its port and commercial activities and buttressed by its more recent industrial development, Singapore has become a notable Southeast Asian economic success. In general, history has shown that countries benefit from a location on major trade routes, not only from the economic advantages such a location carries, but also because they are exposed to the diffusion of new ideas and technologies.

Cores and Capitals

Many states have come to assume their present shape, and thus the location they occupy, as a result of growth over centuries. They grew outward from a central region, gradually expanding into surrounding territory. The original nucleus, or **core area**, of a state usually contains its most developed economic base, densest population and largest cities, the most highly developed transportation systems, and—at least formerly if no longer—the resources which sustained it. All of these elements become less intense away

Totally or partially autonomous political units that are small in area and population pose some intriguing questions. Should size be a criterion for statehood? What is the potential of ministates to cause friction among the major powers? Under what conditions are they entitled to representation in international assemblies like the United Nations?

Of the world's growing number of small countries, more than 40 have under 1 million, the population size adopted by the United Nations as the upper limit defining "small states," though not too small to be members of that organization. Nauru has about 12,000 inhabitants on its 21 square kilometres (8.2 sq mi). Other areally small states like Singapore (580 sq km; 224 sq mi) have populations (4.2 million) well above the UN criterion. Many are island countries located in the Caribbean, or the Pacific or Indian Ocean (such as Grenada, Tuvalu, and Maldives), but Europe (Vatican City and Andorra), Asia (Bahrain and Brunei), Africa (Djibouti and Equatorial Guinea), and South and Central America (Suriname, Belize) have their share.

Many ministates are vestiges of colonial systems that no longer exist. Some of the small countries of West Africa and the Arabian Peninsula fall into this category. Others, such as Mauritius, served primarily as refuelling stops on transoceanic shipping lanes. However, some occupy strategic locations (such as Bahrain, Malta, and Singapore), and others contain valuable minerals (Kuwait, Nauru, and Trinidad). The possibility of

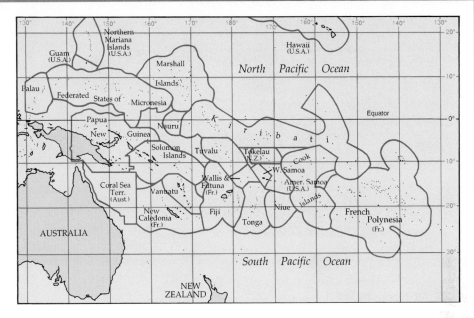

claiming 370-kilometre-wide (200 nautical mile) zones of adjacent seas adds to the attraction of yet others.

Their strategic or economic value can expose small islands and territories to unwanted attention from larger neighbours. The 1982 war between Britain and Argentina over the Falkland Islands (claimed as the Islas Malvinas by Argentina) and the Iraqi invasion of Kuwait in 1990 demonstrate the ability of such areas to bring major powers into conflict and to receive world attention that is out of proportion to their size and population.

The proliferation of tiny countries raises the question of their representation and their voting weight in international assemblies. Should there be a minimum size necessary for participation in such bodies? Should countries receive a vote proportional to their population? New members accepted into the United Nations in 1999 and 2000 included four small Pacific island countries, all with populations under 100,000: Nauru, Tonga, Kiribati, and Tuvalu. Within the United Nations, the Alliance of Small Island States (AOSIS) has emerged as a significant power bloc, controlling more than one-fifth of UN General Assembly votes—far more than the combined voting strength of all the countries of South America.

---

from the national core. Transportation networks thin, urbanization ratios and city sizes decline, and economic development is less concentrated on the periphery than in the core. The outlying resource base may be rich but generally is of more recent exploitation with product and benefit tending to flow to the established heartlands. The developed cores of states, then, can be contrasted to their subordinate peripheries. As noted in Chapter 3, this *core-periphery* idea is also applicable in an international developmental context (Chapter 11).

Easily recognized and unmistakably dominant national cores include the Paris Basin of France, London and southeastern England, Moscow and the major cities of European Russia, northeastern United States and southeastern Canada, and the Buenos Aires megalopolis in Argentina. Not all countries have such clearly defined cores—Chad, or Mongolia, or Saudi Arabia, for example—and some may have two or more rival core areas.

Ecuador, Nigeria, Democratic Republic of the Congo, and Vietnam are examples of multi-core states.

The capital city of a state is usually within its core region and frequently is the very focus of it, dominant not only because it is the seat of central authority but because of the concentration of population and economic functions as well. That is, in many countries the capital city is also the largest or *primate* city, dominating the structure of the entire country. Paris in France, London in the United Kingdom, and Mexico City are examples of that kind of political, cultural, and economic primacy (see Figure 8.17).

This association of capital with core is common in what have been called the *unitary states*, countries with highly centralized governments, relatively few internal cultural contrasts, a strong sense of national identity, and borders that are clearly cultural as well as political boundaries. Most European cores and capitals are of this type. It is also found in many newly independent countries

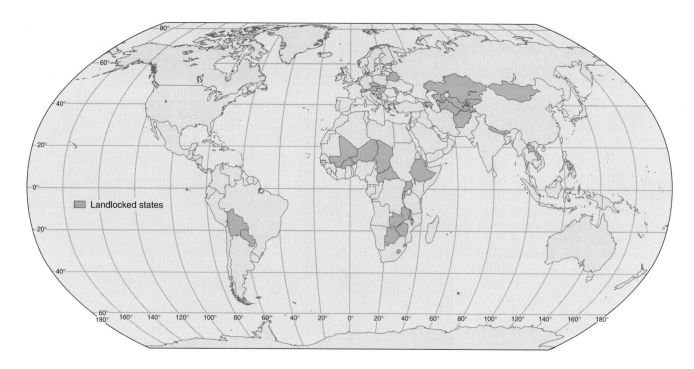

FIGURE 7.9 Landlocked states.

Afghanistan	Botswana	Hungary	Malawi	San Marino	Uganda
Andorra	Burkina Faso	Kazakhstan	Mali	Serbia and	Uzbekistan
Armenia	Burundi	Kyrgyzstan	Moldova	Montenegro	Vatican City
Austria	Central African	Laos	Mongolia	Slovakia	(Holy See)
Azerbaijan	Republic	Lesotho	Nepal	Swaziland	West Bank
Belarus	Chad	Liechtenstein	Niger	Switzerland	Zambia
Bhutan	Czech Republic	Luxembourg	Paraguay	Tajikistan	Zimbabwe
Bolivia	Ethiopia	Macedonia	Rwanda	Turkmenistan	

whose former colonial occupiers established a primary centre of exploitation and administration and developed a functioning core in a region that lacked an urban structure or organized government. With independence, the new states retained the established infrastructure, added new functions to the capital, and, through lavish expenditures on governmental, public, and commercial buildings, sought to create prestigious symbols of nationhood.

In *federal states*, associations of more or less equal provinces or states with strong regional governmental responsibilities, the national capital city may have been newly created or selected to serve as the administrative center. Although part of a generalized core region of the country, the designated capital was not its largest city and acquired few of the additional functions to make it so. Ottawa, Canada; Washington, D.C.; and Canberra, Australia, are examples (Figure 7.11).

A new form of state organization, *regional* government or *asymmetric federalism*, is emerging in Europe as formerly strong unitary states acknowledge the autonomy aspirations of their several subdivisions, and grant to them varying degrees of local administrative control while retaining in central hands authority over matters of nationwide concern, such as monetary policy, defence, foreign relations, and the like. That new form of federalism involves recognition of regional capitals, legislative assemblies, administrative bureaucracies, and the like. The

asymmetric federalism of the United Kingdom, for example, now involves separate status for Scotland, Wales, and Northern Ireland, with their own capitals at Edinburgh, Cardiff, and Belfast, respectively. That of Spain recognizes Catalonia and the Basque country with capitals in Barcelona and Vitoria, respectively. In Canada, the establishment of the self-governing Inuit arctic territory of Nunavut in 1999 has been followed by other recognized Indian claims of home territory land use control: that of the Haida in British Columbia, the Dogrib (Tlicho) in the Northwest Territories, and the Cree in northern Quebec, for example.

All other things being equal, a capital located in the centre of the country provides equal access to the government, facilitates communication to and from the political hub, and enables the government to exert its authority easily. Many capital cities, such as Washington, D.C., were centrally located when they were designated as seats of government but lost their centrality as the state expanded.

Some capital cities have been relocated outside of peripheral national core regions, at least in part to achieve the presumed advantages of centrality. Two examples of such relocation are from Karachi inland to Islamabad in Pakistan, and from Istanbul to Ankara, in the centre of Turkey's territory. A particular type of relocated capital is the *forward-thrust capital* city—one that has been deliberately sited in a state's interior to signal the

Landscapes of Identity, Plurality, and Organization

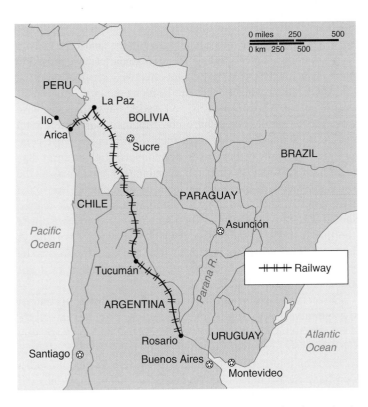

FIGURE 7.10 Like many other landlocked countries, Bolivia has gained access to the sea through arrangements with neighbouring states. Unlike most landlocked countries, however, Bolivia can access ports on two oceans.

government's awareness of regions away from an off-centre core and its interest in encouraging more uniform development. In the late 1950s, Brazil relocated its capital from Rio de Janeiro to the new city of Brasilia to demonstrate its intent to develop the vast interior of the country. The West African country of Nigeria has been building the new capital of Abuja near its geographic centre since the late 1970s, with relocation there of government offices and foreign embassies in the early 1990s.

The British colonial government relocated Canada's capital six times between 1841 and 1865, in part seeking centrality to the mid-19th-century population pattern and in part seeking a location that bridged the colony's cultural divide (Figure 7.12). A Japanese law of 1997 calling for the relocation out of Tokyo of the parliament building, Supreme Court, and main ministries by 2010 is more related to earthquake fears and a search for seismic safety than to enhanced convenience or governmental efficiency.

Boundaries: The Limits of the State

We noted earlier that no portion of the earth's land surface is outside the claimed control of a national unit, and that even uninhabited Antarctica has had territorial claims imposed upon it (see Figure 7.3). Each of the world's states is separated from its neighbours by *international boundaries*, or lines that establish the limit of each state's jurisdiction and authority. Consistent with Westphalian principles, boundaries indicate where the sovereignty of one state ends and that of another begins.

FIGURE 7.11 Canberra, the planned capital of Australia, was deliberately sited about halfway between the country's two largest cities, Sydney and Melbourne. Planned capitals are often architectural showcases, providing a focus for national pride.

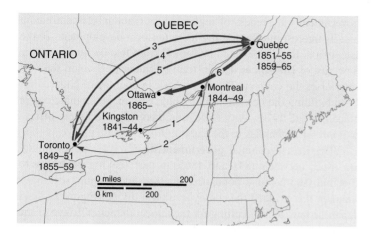

FIGURE 7.12 Canada's migratory capital. Kingston was chosen as the first capital of the united Province of Canada in preference to either Quebec, capital of Lower Canada, or Toronto, that of Upper Canada. In 1844, governmental functions were relocated to Montreal where they remained until 1849, after which they shifted back and forth—as the map indicates—between Toronto and Quebec. An 1865 session of the provincial legislature was held in Ottawa, the city that became the capital of the Confederation of Canada in 1867.

Source: Redrawn with permission from David B. Knight, A Capital for Canada *(Chicago: University of Chicago, Department of Geography, Research Paper No. 182, 1977), Figure 1, p. vii.*

Within its own bounded territory, a state administers laws, collects taxes, provides for defence, and performs other such governmental functions. Thus, the location of the boundary determines the kind of money people in a given area use, the legal code to which they are subject, the army they may be called upon to join, and the language and perhaps the religion children are taught in school. These examples suggest how boundaries serve as powerful reinforcers of cultural variation over the earth's surface.

Territorial claims of sovereignty, it should be noted, are three-dimensional. International boundaries mark not only the outer limits of a state's claim to land (or water) surface, but are also projected downward to the centre of the earth in accordance with international consensus allocating rights to subsurface resources. States also project their sovereignty upward, but with less certainty because of a lack of agreement on the upper limits of territorial airspace. Properly viewed, then, an international boundary is a line without breadth; it is a vertical interface between adjacent state sovereignties.

Before boundaries were delimited, nations or empires were likely to be separated by *frontier zones*, ill-defined and fluctuating areas marking the effective end of a state's authority. Such zones were often uninhabited or only sparsely populated and were liable to change with shifting settlement patterns. Many present-day international boundaries lie in former frontier zones, and in that sense the boundary line has replaced the broader frontier as a marker of a state's authority.

Natural and Geometric Boundaries

Geographers have traditionally distinguished between "natural" and "geometric" boundaries. **Natural** (or **physical**) **boundaries** are those based on recognizable physiographic features, such as

mountains, rivers, and lakes. Although they might seem to be attractive as borders because they actually exist in the landscape and are visible dividing elements, many natural boundaries have proved to be unsatisfactory. That is, they do not effectively separate states.

Many international boundaries lie along mountain ranges, for example in the Alps, Himalayas, and Andes, but while some have proved to be stable, others have not. Mountains are rarely total barriers to interaction. Although they do not invite movement, they are crossed by passes, roads, and tunnels. High pastures may be used for seasonal grazing, and the mountain region may be the source of water for irrigation or hydroelectric power. Nor is the definition of a boundary along a mountain range a simple matter. Should it follow the crests of the mountains or the *water divide* (the line dividing two drainage areas)? The two are not always the same. Border disputes between China and India are in part the result of the failure of mountain crests and headwaters of major streams to coincide (Figure 7.13).

Rivers can be even less satisfactory as boundaries. In contrast to mountains, rivers foster interaction. River valleys are likely to be agriculturally or industrially productive and to be densely populated. For example, for hundreds of miles the Rhine River serves as an international boundary in Western Europe. It is also a primary traffic route lined by chemical plants, factories, and power stations, and dotted by the castles and cathedrals that make it one of Europe's major tourist attractions. It is more a common intensively used resource than a barrier in the lives of the nations it borders. With any river, it is not clear precisely where the boundary line should lie: along the right or left bank, along the centre of the river, or perhaps along the middle of the navigation channel. Even an agreement in accordance with international custom that the boundary be drawn along the main channel may be impermanent if the river changes its course, floods, or dries up.

The alternative to natural boundaries is **geometric (or artificial) boundaries**. Frequently delimited as segments of parallels of latitude or meridians of longitude, they are found chiefly in Africa, Asia, and the Americas. The western portion of the United States–Canada border, which follows the 49th parallel, is an example of a geometric boundary. Many such were established when the areas in question were colonies, the land was only sparsely settled, and detailed geographic knowledge of the frontier region was lacking.

Boundaries Classified by Settlement

Boundaries can also be classified according to whether they were laid out before or after the principal features of the cultural landscape were developed. An **antecedent boundary** is one drawn across an area before it is well populated, that is, before most of the cultural landscape features were put in place. To continue our earlier example, the western portion of the United States–Canada boundary is such an antecedent line, established by a treaty between the United States and Great Britain in 1846.

Boundaries drawn after the development of the cultural landscape are termed **subsequent**. One type of subsequent boundary is **consequent** (also called *ethnographic*), a border drawn to accommodate existing religious, linguistic, ethnic, or economic differences between countries. An example is the boundary

FIGURE 7.13 Several international borders run through the jumble of the Himalayas. The mountain boundary between India and China has long been in dispute.

FIGURE 7.14 Like Hadrian's Wall in the north of England or the Great Wall of China, the Berlin Wall was a demarcated boundary. Unlike them, it cut across a large city and disrupted established cultural patterns. The Berlin Wall, therefore, was a subsequent superimposed boundary. The dismantling of the wall in 1990 marked the reunification of Germany; any of it that remains standing as a historic monument is a relic boundary.

drawn between Northern Ireland and Eire (Ireland). Subsequent **superimposed boundaries** may also be forced on existing cultural landscapes, a country or a people by a conquering or colonizing power that is unconcerned about pre-existing cultural patterns. The colonial powers in 19th-century Africa superimposed boundaries upon established African cultures without regard to the tradition, language, religion, or tribal affiliation of those whom they divided (see Figure 7.6).

When Great Britain prepared to leave the Indian subcontinent after World War II, it was decided that two independent states would be established in the region: India and Pakistan. The boundary between the two countries, defined in the partition settlement of 1947, was thus both a *subsequent* and a *superimposed* line. As millions of Hindus migrated from the northwestern portion of the subcontinent to seek homes in India, millions of Muslims left what would become India for Pakistan. In a sense, they were attempting to ensure that the boundary would be *consequent*, that is, that it would coincide with a division based on religion.

If a former boundary line that no longer functions as such is still marked by some landscape features or differences on the two sides, it is termed a **relic boundary** (Figure 7.14). The abandoned castles dotting the former frontier zone between Wales and England are examples of a relic boundary. They are also evidence of the disputes that sometimes attend the process of boundary making.

Boundary Disputes

Boundaries create many possibilities and provocations for conflict. Since World War II, almost half of the world's sovereign states have been involved in border disputes with neighbouring countries. Just like householders, states are far more likely to have disputes with their neighbours than with more distant parties. It follows that the more neighbours a state has, the greater the likelihood of conflict. Although the causes of boundary disputes and open conflict are many and varied, they can reasonably be placed into four categories.

1. **Positional disputes** occur when states disagree about the interpretation of documents that define a boundary and/or the way the boundary was delimited. Such disputes typically arise when the boundary is antecedent, preceding effective human settlement in the border region. Once the area becomes populated and gains value, the exact location of the boundary becomes important. The boundary between Argentina and Chile, originally defined during Spanish colonial rule and formalized by treaty in 1881, was to follow "the most elevated crests of the Andean Cordillera dividing the waters" between east- and west-flowing rivers. Because the southern Andes had not been adequately explored and mapped, it was not apparent that the crest lines (highest peaks) and the watershed divides do not always coincide. In some places, the water divide is many miles east of the highest peaks, leaving a long, narrow area of some 52,000 square kilometres (20,000 sq mi) in dispute (Figure 7.15). In Latin America as a whole, the 21st century began with at least 10 unresolved border disputes, some dating back to colonial times.

2. **Territorial disputes** over the ownership of a region often, though not always, arise when a boundary that has been superimposed on the landscape divides an ethnically homogeneous population. Each of the two states then has some justification for claiming the territory inhabited by the ethnic group in question. We noted previously that a single nation may be dispersed across several states (see Figure 7.4d). Conflicts can arise if the people of one state want to annex a territory whose population is ethnically related to that of the state but now subject to a "foreign" government. This type of expansionism is called **irredentism**. In the 1930s, Hitler used the existence of German minorities in Czechoslovakia and Poland to justify German invasion and occupation of

those countries. More recently, Somalia has had many border clashes with Ethiopia over the rights of Somalis living in that country, and the area of Kashmir has been a cause of dispute and open conflict between India and Pakistan since the creation of the two countries (Figure 7.16).

3. Closely related to territorial conflicts are **resource disputes**. Neighbouring states are likely to covet the resources—whether they may be valuable mineral deposits, fertile farmland, or rich fishing grounds—lying in border areas and to disagree over their use. The United States has been involved in disputes with both its neighbours—Mexico and Canada—over resources. The waters of the Colorado River and Gulf of Mexico have been sources of disagreement between Mexico and the United States. Longstanding disputes over resources between Canada and the United States have concerned the Georges Bank and Beaufort Sea.

One of the causes of the 1990–1991 war in the Persian Gulf was the huge oil reservoir known as the Rumaila field, lying mainly under Iraq with a small extension into Kuwait (Figure 7.17a).

Because the two countries were unable to agree on percentages of ownership of the rich reserve, or a formula for sharing production costs and revenues, Kuwait pumped oil from Rumaila without any international agreement. Iraq helped justify its invasion of Kuwait by contending that the latter had been stealing Iraqi oil in what amounted to economic warfare.

According to the *Canadian Geographic* (2004), there are six specific maritime boundary disputes between Canada and other countries:

- Northwest Passage: The United States fails to recognize Canada's claim to sovereignty and views it as an international waterway.
- Beaufort Sea: There is a disputed region of about 6250 square nautical miles with the United States. This is significant because Canada has issued oil and gas exploration permits for the region that could be challenged.
- The Continental Shelves with the United States, Russia, and Denmark/Greenland: While Canada has yet to declare its

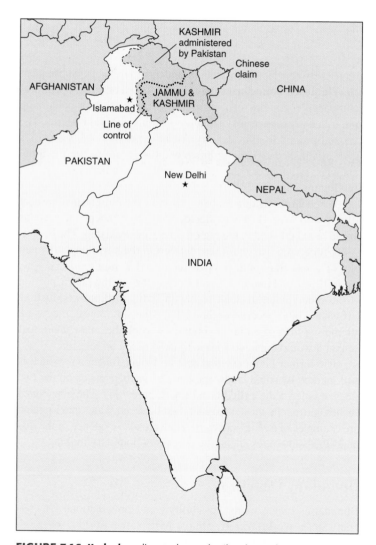

FIGURE 7.15 The disputed boundary between Argentina and Chile in the southern Andes. The treaty establishing the boundary between the two countries preceded adequate exploration and mapping of the area, leaving its precise location in doubt and in contention. After years of friction, the last remaining territorial dispute between Chile and Argentina in the Andes was settled in an accord signed in late 1998.

FIGURE 7.16 Kashmir, a disputed area that has been the cause of two wars between India and Pakistan. The resolution of the problem of possession of Kashmir may be a permanent partition along the cease-fire line, though the continuing Chinese claim to a portion of eastern Kashmir clouds the ownership picture.

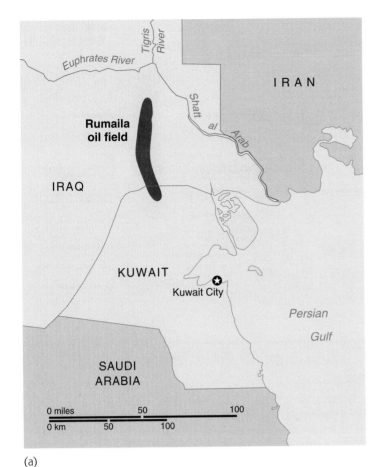

(a)

(b)

FIGURE 7.17 (*a*) **The Rumaila oil field.** One of the world's largest petroleum reservoirs, Rumaila straddles the Iraq–Kuwait border. Iraqi grievances over Kuwaiti drilling were partly responsible for Iraq's invasion of Kuwait in 1990. (*b*) To stem the flow of undocumented migrants entering California from Baja California, the United States in 1993 constructed a fence 3 metres (10 feet) high along the border.

continental shelf in the Arctic Ocean, it is expected that when it does, it will overlap with claims already made by its northern neighbours.

- Dixon Entrance, B.C.: located just south of the Alaska Panhandle, this disputed 2250-square nautical mile area contains access to salmon fishing area.
- Juan de Fuca Strait, B.C.: is a relatively small 15-square nautical mile area that has implications for fishing and navigation.
- Georges Bank and Machias Seal Island, Bay of Fundy: The United States and Canada disagree on the border location. A popular bird-watching area, the island is situated in the middle of the disputed area.

In addition to these maritime disputes, Canada and Denmark both lay claim to Hans Island located off the coast of east Ellesmere Island. In 2007, several countries increased their efforts to assert sovereignty over the Arctic Ocean. Some of the key participants and activities included:

- Canada, which announced a $70 million initiative to map its portion of the Arctic Ocean floor

- Russia, which sent a scientific expedition on an ice breaker for six weeks to study the Lomonosv Ridge, which it believes is geologically linked to the Siberian continental shelf.
- United States, which is also increasing its efforts to survey the ocean floor in the vicinity of Alaska
- Denmark, which is also mapping the ocean floor, and
- Norway, which is suggesting that nations cooperate rather than compete in their scientific research. Norwegian oil companies are also expanding their activities in the Barents Sea.

A map of disputed territory in the Arctic that states might claim in the future is provided in Figure 7.18. Given that there are significant resource development opportunities within the Arctic, including an estimated 20% of the undiscovered and recoverable oil and gas resources, the outcomes of these resource disputes will have significant.

4. **Functional disputes** arise when neighbouring states disagree over policies to be applied along a boundary. Such policies may concern immigration, the movement of traditionally nomadic groups, customs regulations, or land use. U.S. relations with Mexico, for example, have been affected by the increasing number of illegal aliens and the flow of drugs entering the United States from Mexico (Figure 7.17b).

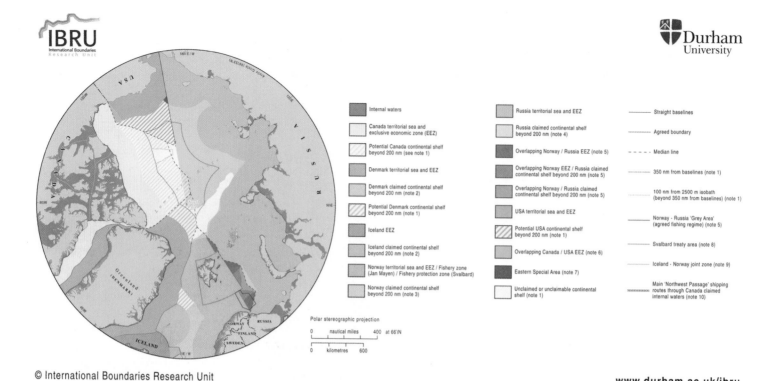

FIGURE 7.18 Maritime Jurisdiction and Boundaries in the Arctic Region. Researchers at Durham University produced the map above based on geological data and international law. Rights over the resources of the seabed beyond 200 nautical miles from coastal baselines are determined by the physical extent of the continental shelf. Among the unresolved claims are those between Canada and the United States, and Norway and Russia.

Source: The International Boundaries Research Unit (IBRU) at Durham University. http://www.dur.ac.uk/ibru/resources/arctic. pdf.

Centripetal Forces: Promoting State Cohesion

At any moment in time, a state is characterized by forces that promote unity and national stability and by others that disrupt them. Political geographers refer to the former as **centripetal forces**. These are factors that bind together the people of a state, enable it to function and give it strength. **Centrifugal forces**, on the other hand, destabilize and weaken a state. If centrifugal forces are stronger than those promoting unity, the very existence of the state will be threatened. In the sections that follow, we examine four centripetal (uniting) forces—nationalism, unifying institutions, effective organization and administration of government, and systems of transportation and communication—to see how they can promote cohesion.

Nationalism

One of the most powerful of the centripetal forces is **nationalism**, an identification with the state and the acceptance of national goals. Nationalism is based on the concept of allegiance to a single country and the ideals and the way of life it represents; it is an emotion that provides a sense of identity and loyalty and of collective distinction from all other peoples and lands (see Chapter 6, "The Rising Tide of Nationalism").

States purposely try to instil feelings of allegiance in their citizens, for such feelings give the political system strength.

People who have such allegiance are likely to accept common rules of action and behaviour and to participate in the decision-making process establishing those rules. In light of the divisive forces present in most societies, not everyone, of course, will feel the same degree of commitment or loyalty. The important consideration is that the majority of a state's population accepts its ideologies, adheres to its laws, and participates in its effective operation. For many countries, such acceptance and adherence has come only recently and partially; in some, it is frail and endangered.

Recall that true nation-states are rare; in only a few countries do the territory occupied by the people of a particular nation and the territorial limits of the state coincide. Most countries have more than one cultural group that considers itself separate in some important way from other citizens. In a multicultural society, nationalism helps integrate different groups into a unified population. This kind of consensus nationalism has emerged in countries such as Canada, the United States, and Switzerland, where different culture groups have joined together to create political entities commanding the loyalties of all their citizens.

States promote nationalism in a number of ways. *Iconography* is the study of the symbols that help unite people. National anthems and other patriotic songs; flags, national sports teams, and officially designated or easily identified flowers and animals; and rituals and holidays are all developed by states to promote nationalism and attract allegiance. By ensuring that all citizens, no matter how diverse the population may be, will have at least these symbols in common, they impart a sense of belonging to a political entity called, for example, Japan or Canada. In some countries, certain documents, such as the Constitution Act in Canada, the Magna Carta in England, or the Declaration of Independence in the United States, serve the same purpose. Royalty may fill the need: in Sweden, Japan, and the United Kingdom, the monarchy functions as the symbolic focus of allegiance. Such symbols are significant, for symbols and beliefs are major components of the ideological subsystem of every culture. When a society is very heterogeneous, composed of people with different customs, religions, and languages, belief in the national unit can help weld them together.

Since Confederation, successive Canadian governments have pursued a range of strategies with varying degrees of success to bring the nation together. Some of these include:

- The system of equalization payments that have been guaranteed through the Constitution since 1867, by which funds are transferred through the federal government from the "have provinces" (usually Ontario, Alberta, sometimes British Columbia and Saskatchewan) to the "have not provinces" in order that a minimum level of service for health care, education, and other social programs can be provided across the nation. The changing structure of the Canadian economy, particularly as it relates to the dramatic decline of the manufacturing sector in Ontario, will challenge current approaches to equalization. In 2008, Ontario was declared a "have not" province, while Newfoundland and Labrador will, for the first time, contribute to the equalization fund.
- John A. Macdonald's promise to construct a railway running across the country from east to west.
- Implementation of tariffs to nurture the development of Canadian industries in the face of competition from the United States and Britain.
- The ownership and/or control of important industries, such as railway and airlines, in order to ensure adequate levels of service to all parts of the country, particularly less populated areas of the periphery.
- The ownership and regulation of television and radio stations ensures minimum levels of Canadian content, which promotes Canadian culture.
- The federal bilingualism programs of the 1960s. These are founded on the premise that Canada has two founding nations—English and French—whose cultures and languages should have primacy. This belief led to the passage of the Official Languages Act in 1969, through which Canada became officially bilingual (see Chapter 6, "Official Languages").

These and other centripetal initiatives have been introduced, in part, to overcome some of Canada's main centrifugal forces: its culture, physical geography, and large size, dispersed settlement patterns, regionalism, and decentralized federal system.

Unifying Institutions

Institutions can also help to develop the sense of commitment and cohesiveness essential to the state. Schools, particularly elementary schools, are among the most important of these.

Children learn the history of their own country and relatively little about other countries. Schools are expected to instil the society's goals, values, and traditions, to teach the common language that conveys them, and to guide youngsters to identify with their country.

Other institutions that advance nationalism are the armed forces and, sometimes, a state church. The armed forces are of necessity taught to identify with the state. They see themselves as protecting the state's welfare from what are perceived to be its enemies. In about one-quarter of the world's countries, the faith of the majority of the people has by law been designated the state religion. In such cases, the religion may become a force for cohesion, helping unify the population. This is true of Buddhism in Thailand, Hinduism in Nepal, Islam in Pakistan, and Judaism in Israel. In countries like these, the religion and the church are so identified with the state that belief in one is transferred to allegiance to the other.

The schools, the armed forces, and the church are just three of the institutions that teach people what it is like to be members of a state. As institutions, they operate primarily on the level of the sociological subsystem of culture, helping to structure the outlooks and behaviours of the society. But by themselves, they are not enough to give cohesion, and thus strength, to a state. Indeed, each of the institutions we have discussed can also be a destabilizing centrifugal force.

Organization and Administration

A further bonding force is public confidence in the effective organization of the state. Can it provide security from external aggression and internal conflict? Are its resources distributed and allocated in such a way as to be perceived to promote the economic welfare of all its citizens? Are all citizens afforded equal opportunity to participate in governmental affairs (see "Legislative Women")? Do institutions that encourage consultation and the peaceful settlement of disputes exist? How firmly established are the rule of law and the power of the courts? Is the system of decision making responsive to the people's needs?

The answers to such questions, and the relative importance of the answers, will vary from country to country, but they and similar ones are implicit in the expectation that the state will promote the welfare and protect the safety of its citizens. If those expectations are not fulfilled, the loyalties promoted by national symbols and unifying institutions may be weakened or lost.

Transportation and Communication

A state's transportation network fosters political integration by promoting interaction between areas and by joining them economically and socially. The role of a transportation network in uniting a country has been recognized since ancient times. The saying that all roads lead to Rome had its origin in the impressive system of roads that linked Rome to the rest of its empire. Centuries later, a similar network was built in France, joining Paris to the various parts of the country. Often the capital city is better connected to other cities than the outlying cities are to one another. In France, for example, it can take less time to travel from one city to another by way of Paris than by direct route.

Women, a majority of the world's population, in general fare poorly in the allocation of such resources as primary and higher education, employment opportunities and income, and health care. That their lot is improving is encouraging. In nearly every developing country, women have been closing the gender gap in literacy, school enrolment, and acceptance in the job market.

But in the political arena—where power ultimately lies—women's share of influence is increasing only slowly and selectively. In 2004, fewer than 15 countries out of a world total of over 200 had women as heads of government: presidents or prime ministers. Nor did they fare much better as members of parliaments. Women in early 2005 held just 16% of all the seats in the world's legislatures. The proportion of women holding cabinet level office was 14.3%.

Only in 26 countries did women in 2005 occupy one-quarter or more of the seats in the lower or single legislative House. Of these 26, 13 were European and 5 were African. Rwanda and Sweden were the most equitable, with 49% and 45%, respectively, of their members' female. In no country were women a legislative majority, and a number of countries had no female representatives at all. Although half the countries with women making up one-quarter of the legislature were in Europe, in much of Europe women held but a small minority of legislative seats. This low representation included both established democracies of Northern and Western Europe and virtually all the countries of Southern and Eastern Europe. In contrast, in 65 countries women make up 10% or less of the legislature.

Although in the Parliament of the European Union women comprised 30% of members in 2005, they held only 14% of the seats in the Greek parliament, 12% of France's National Assembly, and 11% of Italy's Chamber of Deputies. Japan made an even poorer showing with but a 7% female membership. Arab states average only 6%. Nor did the United States show a very significant number of women members. At the start of the 109th Congress (2005–2007), only 14 women served in the Senate (14% female) and 65 in the House of Representatives (15% female). At that time, both numbers were at their highest-ever levels.

In 1921, women in Canada were allowed to vote and run for Parliament for the first time.

Agnes MacPhail, representing the riding of Grey Southeast, Ontario, was the first female elected to the House of Commons. There was some legal difficulty in getting a woman appointed to the Senate because the British North America Act (BNA) (now known as the Constitution Act, 1867) identified that only "qualified persons" could be appointed to the Senate. Since the BNA used the word "persons" when it referred to more than one person, and the word "he" when it referred to an individual, those individuals wanting the status quo argued that only men could legally be "persons." In 1927, Emily Murphy, Henrietta Muir Edwards, Nellie McClung, Louise McKinney, and Irene Parlby, all from Alberta and known collectively as the "Famous Five," asked the Supreme Court of Canada to answer whether or not the word "person" in section 24 of the British North America Act included female persons. After taking five weeks to consider its decision, the Supreme Court determined that women were not considered as a person under the BNA. The "Famous Five" appealed this decision to the Privy Council of England, which was at this time Canada's highest court of appeal. In 1929, it decided that "the exclusion of women from all public offices is a relic of days more barbarous than ours. And to those who would ask why the word "person" should include females, the obvious answer is, "why should it not?" In 1930, Cairine Wilson of Ontario was appointed as Canada's first female Senator.

In the later 1990s, women's legislative representation began to expand materially in many developed and developing democracies, and their "fair share" of political power began to be formally recognized or enforced. In Western countries, particularly, improvement in female parliamentary participation has become a matter of plan and pride for political parties and, occasionally, for governments themselves.

The widely recognized minimum benchmark to ensure a critical mass of women parliamentarians has been set at 30%. As indicated in the data contained in Table 7.1, Canada has not reached this threshold in recent times. In terms of the representation of women in the lower house of parliament, Canada currently ranks 45th internationally. Visible minority women and Aboriginal women are even further under-represented. In fact, just three Aboriginal women have been elected to the Canadian House of Commons since 1921.

Political parties from Mexico to China have tried to correct female under-representation, usually by setting quotas for women candidates, and a few governments—including Belgium and Italy—have tried to require their political parties to improve their balance. France went further than any other country in acknowledging the right of women to equal access to elective office when in 1999 it passed a constitutional amendment requiring *parité*—parity or equality. A year later, the National Assembly enacted legislation requiring the country's political parties to fill 50% of the candidacies in all elections in the country (municipal, regional, and European Parliament) with women, or lose a corresponding share of their state-provided campaign funding. India similarly proposed to reserve a third of the seats in parliament for women.

Quotas are controversial, however, and often are viewed with disfavour even by avowed feminists. Some argue that quotas are demeaning because they imply women cannot match men on merit alone. Others fear that other groups—for example, religious groups or ethnic minorities—would also seek quotas to guarantee their proportionate legislative presence.

A significant presence of women in legislative bodies makes a difference in the kinds of bills that get passed and the kinds of programs that receive governmental emphasis. Regardless of party affiliation, women are more apt than their male counterparts to sponsor bills and vote for measures affecting child care, elderly care, women's health care, medical insurance, and bills affecting women's rights and family law.

TABLE 7.1

Women in the Canadian House of Commons

Year	Total Number Of Seats	Seats Held By Women	% Of Seats Held By Women
1984	282	27	9.6
1988	295	39	13.3
1993	295	53	18.0
1997	301	62	20.6
2000	301	62	20.6
2004	308	65	21.1
2006	308	64	20.8

Roads and railroads have played a historically significant role in promoting political integration. In Canada and the United States, they not only opened up new areas for settlement but increased interaction between rural and urban districts. Because transportation systems play a major role in a state's economic development, it follows that the more economically advanced a country is, the more extensive its transport network is likely to be (see Figure 9.4). At the same time, the higher the level of development, the more resources there are to be invested in building transport routes. The two reinforce one another.

Transportation and communication, while encouraged within a state, are frequently curtailed or at least controlled between them as a conscious device for promoting state cohesion through limitation on external spatial interaction (Figure 7.19). The mechanisms of control include restrictions on trade through tariffs or embargoes, legal barriers to immigration and emigration, and limitations on travel through passports and visa requirements.

Centrifugal Forces: Challenges to State Authority

State cohesion is not easily achieved or, once gained, invariably retained. Destabilizing *centrifugal forces* are ever-present, sowing internal discord and challenges to the state's authority. Transportation and communication may be hindered by a country's shape or great size, leaving some parts of the state not well integrated with the rest. A country that is not well organized or administered stands to lose the loyalty of its citizens. Institutions that in some states promote unity can be a divisive force in others.

Organized religion, for example, can be a potent centrifugal force. It may compete with the state for people's allegiance—one reason the former USSR and other communist governments suppressed religion and promoted atheism. Conflict between majority and minority faiths within a country—as between Catholics and Protestants in Northern Ireland, or Hindus and Muslims in Kashmir and Gujarat State in India—can destabilize social order. Opposing sectarian views within a single, dominant faith can also promote civil conflict. Recent years have seen particularly Muslim militant groups attempt to overturn official or constitutional policies of secularism or replace a government deemed insufficiently ardent in its imposition of religious laws and regulations. Islamic fundamentalism led to the 1979 overthrow of the Shah of Iran; more recently, Islamic militancy has been a destabilizing force in, among other countries, Afghanistan, Algeria, Iraq, Tunisia, Egypt, and Saudi Arabia.

Nationalism, in contrast to its role as a powerful centripetal agency, is also a potentially disruptive centrifugal force. The idea of the nation-state is that states are formed around and coincide with nations. It is a small step from that to the notion that every nation has the right to its own state or territory. Centrifugal forces may be very strong in countries containing multiple nationalities and unassimilated minorities, racial or ethnic conflict, contrasting cultures, and a multiplicity of languages or religions. Such states are susceptible to nationalist challenges from within their borders *if* the minority group has an explicit territorial identification and believes that its right to *self-determination*—the right of a group to govern itself in its own state—has not been satisfied.

A dissident minority that has total or partial secession from the state as its primary goal is said to be guided by **separatism** or **autonomous nationalism**. In recent years, such nationalism has created currents of unrest within many countries, even long-established ones. Canada, for example, houses a powerful secessionist movement in French-speaking Quebec, the country's

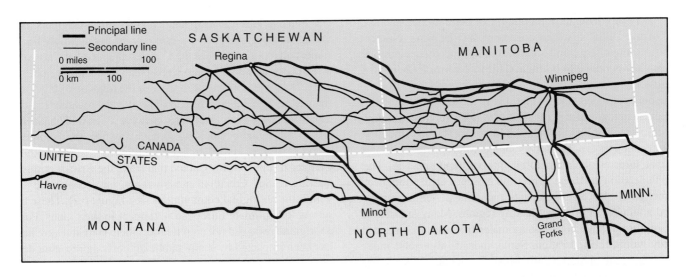

FIGURE 7.19 Canadian–U.S. railroad discontinuity. Canada and the United States developed independent railway systems connecting their respective prairie regions with their separate national cores. Despite extensive rail construction during the 19th and early 20th centuries, the pattern that emerged even before recent track abandonment was one of discontinuity at the border. Note how the political boundary restricted the ease of spatial interaction between adjacent territories. Many branch lines approached the border, but only eight crossed it. In fact, for over 480 kilometres (300 miles), no railway bridged the boundary line. The international border—and the cultural separation it represents—inhibits other expected degrees of interaction. Telephone calls between Canadian and U.S. cities, for example, are far less frequent than would be expected if distance alone were the controlling factor.

largest province. In October, 1995, a referendum to secede from Canada and become a sovereign country failed in Quebec by a razor-thin margin. Quebec's nationalism is fuelled by strong feelings of collective identity and distinctiveness, a desire to protect its language and culture, and by the conviction that the province's ample resources and advanced economy would permit it to manage successfully as a separate country. (See "Thinking about the Boundaries of a Separate Quebec" on page 228.)

In Western Europe, five countries (the United Kingdom, France, Belgium, Italy, and Spain) house separatist political movements whose members reject total control by the existing sovereign state and who claim to be the core of a separate national entity (Figure 7.20). Their basic demand is for *regional autonomy*, usually in the form of self-government or "home rule" rather than complete independence. Accommodation of those demands has resulted in some degrees of **devolution**—the transfer of some central powers to regional or local governments—and in the forms of asymmetric federalism discussed earlier (p. 216) with the United Kingdom and Spain as examples.

Separatist movements affect many states outside of Western Europe and indeed are more characteristic of developing countries, especially those formed since the end of World War II and containing disparate groups more motivated by enmity than affinity. The Basques of Spain and the Bretons of France have their counterparts in the Palestinians in Israel, the Sikhs in India, the Moros in the Philippines, the Tamils in Sri Lanka, and many others. Separatist movements are expressions of **regionalism**, minority group self-awareness and identification with a region rather than with the state.

The countries of Eastern Europe and the republics of the former Soviet Union have seen many instances of regionally rooted nationalist feelings. Now that the forces of ethnicity, religion, language, and culture are no longer suppressed by communism, ancient rivalries are more evident than at any time since World War II. The end of the Cold War aroused hopes of decades of peace. Instead, the collapse of communism and the demise of the USSR spawned dozens of smaller wars. Numerous ethnic groups large and small are asserting their identities and what they perceive to be their right to determine their own political status.

The national independence claimed in the early 1990s by the 15 former Soviet constituent republics did not assure the satisfaction of all separatist movements within them. Many of the new individual countries are themselves subject to strong destabilizing forces that threaten their territorial integrity and survival. The Russian Federation itself, the largest and most powerful remnant of the former USSR, has 89 components, including 21 "ethnic republics" and a number of other nationality regions. Many are rich in natural resources, have non-Russian majorities, and seek greater autonomy within the federation. Some, indeed, want total independence. One, the predominantly Muslim republic of Chechnya, in 1994 claimed the right of self-determination and attempted to secede from the federation, provoking a bloody civil war that escalated again in 1996 and 1999. Under similar separatist pressures, Yugoslavia shattered into five pieces in 1991–1992; more peacefully, Czechs and Slovaks agreed to split former Czechoslovakia into two ethnically based states in 1993.

Recently, several European governments have moved peacefully in the direction of regional recognition and devolution. In France, 22 regional governments were established in 1986; Spain has a program of devolution for its 17 "autonomous communities," a program that Portugal is beginning to emulate. Italy, Germany, and the Nordic countries have, or are developing, similar recognitions of regional communities with granted powers of local administration and relaxation of central controls.

The two preconditions common to all regional autonomist movements are *territory* and *nationality*. First, the group must be concentrated in a core region that it claims as a national homeland, and seek to regain control of land and power that it believes were unjustly taken from it. Second, certain cultural characteristics must provide a basis for the group's perception of separateness, identity, and unity. These might be language, religion, or distinctive group customs and institutions that promote feelings of group identity at the same time that they foster exclusivity. Normally, these cultural differences have persisted over several generations and have survived despite strong pressures toward assimilation.

Other characteristics common to many separatist movements are a *peripheral location* and *social* and *economic inequality*. Troubled regions tend to be peripheral, often isolated in rural pockets, and their location away from the seat of central government engenders feelings of alienation and exclusion. They perhaps sense what has been called the *law of peripheral neglect*, which observes that the concern of the capital for its controlled political space decreases with increasing distance from it. Second, the dominant culture group is often seen as an exploiting class that has suppressed the local language, controlled access to the civil service, and taken more than its share of wealth and power. Poorer regions complain that they have lower incomes and greater unemployment than prevail in the rest of the state and that "outsiders" control key resources and industry. Separatists in relatively rich regions believe that they could exploit their resources for themselves and do better economically without the constraints imposed by the central state.

Settling long-standing land claims from aboriginals and providing for aboriginal self-government are increasingly becoming important political issues in Canada and involve vast amounts of territory in what is considered to be Canada's periphery. Figure 7.21 provides a European view of the division of land between themselves and the aboriginals. The Royal Proclamation of 1763 identified an unspecified area of what is now Canada for the use of aboriginal people, and forbade any unauthorized purchase or possession of those lands by non-native settlers. As noted in Chapter 6 (pp. 165–169), since that time, the British government, and after 1867 Canadian governments, have concluded treaties with some aboriginal communities (see Figure 6.7). These treaties served to legitimate European settlement in their lands. For those aboriginals who did not sign treaties, their land and way have life has been impacted by many public and private resource development activities.

The federal government recognizes two general types of aboriginal land claims in Canada. First, specific claims pertain to problems arising from the administration of Indian treaties, the *Indian Act*, Indian funds, and disposition of Indian land. Second, comprehensive claims are based on the concept of continuing aboriginal rights and title that have not been dealt through a treaty

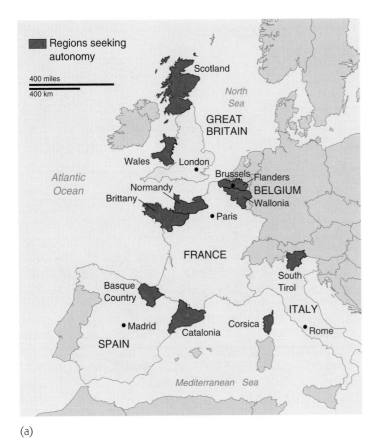

(a)

(b)

FIGURE 7.20 (*a*) **Regions in Western Europe seeking autonomy.** Despite longstanding state attempts to assimilate these historic nations culturally, each contains a political movement that has sought or is seeking a degree of self-rule recognizing its separate identity. Separatists on the island of Corsica, for example, want to secede from France, and separatists in Catalonia demand independence from Spain. The desires of nationalist parties in both Wales and Scotland were partially accommodated by the creation in 1999 of their own parliaments and a degree of regional autonomy, an outcome labelled "separation but not divorce" from the United Kingdom. (*b*) Demonstrators carry a giant Basque flag during a march to call for independence for the Basque region.

or other legal agreement. Comprehensive settlements usually involve a number of components including financial compensation, land, forms of local government, access to wildlife resources, and mechanisms to protect aboriginal culture and language (see Chapter 6—"First Nation Diversity"). Comprehensive claims cover about half of Canada, and include the James Bay and Northern Quebec Agreement (1975), Nunavut Agreement (1993), the Gwich'in of the Upper Mackenzie Delta Final Agreement (1992), the Yukon Territory Umbrella Agreement (1993), and the Sahtu Dene and Métis of the Great Bear Lake Region Final Agreement (1994) (Figure 6.7). While there has been some progress, much more remains to be done. Under Liberal Prime Minister Paul Martin, the Kelowna Accord, which refers to a working paper entitled *Strengthening Relationships and Closing the Gap* and roundtable discussion at the First Ministers' Meeting in Kelowna BC, was announced. The working paper focused on the need to the education and employment levels, and living conditions for Aboriginal peoples. To these ends, $5 billion was to be spent over

a 10-year period. However, with the defeat of the Martin Government in 2006, the Conservative Government led by Stephen Harper was not satisfied with the approach taken in the Kelowna Accord. We wait to see effective action on this item.

The Projection of Power

Territorial and political influence or control by a state need not necessarily halt at its recognized land borders. Throughout history, states have projected power beyond their home territories where such power could credibly be applied or asserted. Imperial powers such as Rome, Czarist Russia, and China extended control outward over adjacent peoples and territories through conquest or *suzerainty*—control over vassal states. The former Soviet Union, for example, not only conquered and incorporated such adjacent states as Estonia, Latvia, and Lithuania but also, claiming to be first among equals, asserted the right to intervene militarily to preserve communist regimes wherever they appeared threatened.

Geography and Public Policy

Thinking about the Boundaries of a Separate Quebec

Several of the questions associated with the possible secession of Quebec from the rest of Canada include: How should the debt be divided? How should federal assets be divided? What are the implications for treaty rights and obligations? Would Quebec be automatically a member of NAFTA? From a political geography perspective, a very interesting question asks, "What would Quebec's boundaries be after secession?" To understand how this question might be answered, we must consider the history and territorial development of Canada as depicted on maps (Figures 17.21–17.30).

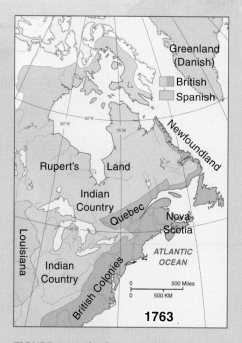

FIGURE 7.21 The first permanent settlement, located in what is now the Province of Quebec, was established in 1608 by Samuel de Champlain at what is now Quebec City. When Canada was initially settled by Europeans, it was a French colony that had significant influence over much of North America. Under the Treaty of Paris (1763), which signalled the defeat of the French by the British, all eastern North America became British. Louisiana was ceded to the Spanish. The French retained the islands of Saint-Pierre and Miquelon. The Hudson's Bay Company administered Rupert's Land. The Province of Quebec was formed as a result of the Royal Proclamation of 1763. Its territory was a thin band to the south and west of "Indian Country." Quebec extended from about the Ottawa River eastward along the St. Lawrence shoreline to about Anticosti Island. This boundary reflected the reality that although the British defeated the French, the French population in Canada outnumbered the British well into the 19th century. The British had a stronger presence within the 13 colonies of what is now the United States. European powers had limited reach into the interior of the continent and relied upon military alliances and trade relations with First Nations to support their territorial sovereignty.

Source: http://atlas.nrcan.gc.ca/site/english/maps/ archives/4thedition/historical/083-84. Reproduced with permission of Natural Resources Canada 2008, courtesy of the Atlas of Canada.

FIGURE 7.22 In order to gain the further support of Canadians against the Americans in the impending war against the colonies, Britain issued the Quebec Act in 1774. It extended the territory of Quebec from the Labrador coast along a line much further north of the St. Lawrence River and extending west beyond Lake Superior. Its southern border ran along the Mississippi/Missouri and Ohio Rivers. The British hoped that by expanding Quebec's territory, economic growth would increase, access to the interior would be provided, and Quebec's support in the upcoming war assured. Note how the size of the "Indian Country" relative to the previous figure and how the colonies' growth is contained. The passage of the Quebec Act displeased many Americans and First Nations. Years after the end of the Revolutionary War, the Treaty of Paris (1783) settled the issue of the border between America and what would become Canada. Based on the European principles of statehood that evolved from the Peace of Westphalia, Britain agreed to recognize the independence of the United States. The border of the Province of Quebec was significantly reduced to be only those lands on the north shore of the Great Lakes—essentially equivalent to current southern Quebec and southern Ontario. First Nations territory essentially disappeared from the map.

Source: http://atlas.nrcan.gc.ca. Reproduced with permission of Natural Resources Canada 2008, courtesy of the Atlas of Canada.

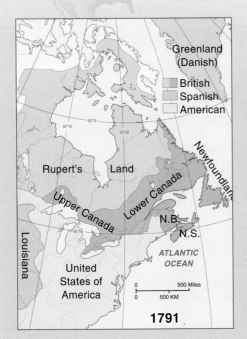

FIGURE 7.23 Until 1791, there had always been a single Province of Quebec within the Great Lakes–St. Lawrence lowland. With the passage of the Canada Act (1791), the British divided the colony of Quebec into Upper and Lower Canada. The dividing line between the two provinces was the Ottawa River. Lower Canada retained French civil law and their laws based on French traditions. In 1809, Anticosti Island and the area of Labrador were transferred from the control of Lower Canada to the administration of Newfoundland. In 1825, Anticosti Island and Labrador (except for the coast of Labrador that was to remain under the control of Newfoundland) were transferred back to Quebec. Outside Canada, Spain ceded Louisiana back to France in 1800. The United States purchased Louisiana from France in 1803.

Source: http://atlas.nrcan.gc.ca. Reproduced with permission of Natural Resources Canada 2008, courtesy of the Atlas of Canada.

FIGURE 7.24 By 1841, Lower Canada remained predominantly French but a powerful urban-based English-speaking population emerged (largely located in Montreal) who controlled the commerce. Upper Canada was predominately English. Following the completion of Lord Durham's report, a Royal Proclamation (1841) merged the former of provinces of Upper and Lower Canada to create a single Province of Canada, which remained divided into two parts, Canada East and Canada West. The institutional structure of the Province of Canada largely reflected the previous patterns on Upper and Lower Canada. Canada East and Canada West each had equal representation in the new colonial parliament, and each had its own set of administrative agencies. For the first time since the British victory over the French, there is not a separate government exclusively representing Quebec. Fundamental principles of the new government structure were equal representation and equal recognition of French and English-speaking populations. Outside Canada, the international boundary from the Rocky Mountains to the Pacific is agreed upon in the Oregon Treaty (1846). The name "New Caledonia" is used to describe the northern portion of the Oregon Territory. In 1849, The Hudson's Bay Co. is granted Vancouver Island to develop as a colony.

Source: http://atlas.nrcan.gc.ca. Reproduced with permission of Natural Resources Canada 2008, courtesy of the Atlas of Canada.

FIGURE 7.25 The British North America (BNA) Act (1867), which served as Canada's constitution until it was repatriated in 1982, created the provinces of Ontario, Quebec, Nova Scotia, and New Brunswick. The BNA Act created provincial governments, which have jurisdiction over local issues, control of resources, and other responsibilities. The Province of Quebec at this time occupies what is now southern Quebec. Outside of Canada, the United States purchased Alaska from Russia in June 1867.

Source: http://atlas.nrcan.gc.ca. Reproduced with permission of Natural Resources Canada 2008, courtesy of the Atlas of Canada.

Continued

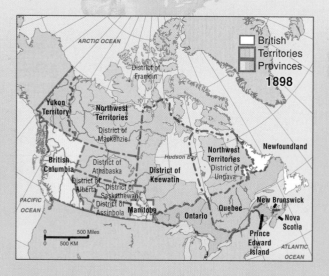

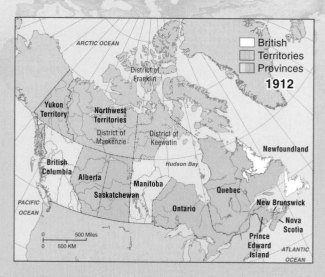

FIGURE 7.26 The provinces of Manitoba (1870), British Columbia (1871), and Prince Edward Island (1873) joined Canada. In 1897, boundaries were changed in the Districts of Mackenzie, Keewatin, Ungava, and Yukon. The District of Yukon becomes a distinct territory from the Northwest Territories. The land formerly held by the Hudson's Bay Company (Rupert's Land) was purchased by Canada. In 1898, the boundaries of Quebec were extended northward to the Eastman River.

Source: http://atlas.nrcan.gc.ca/site/english/maps/historical/ territorialevolution/1898. Reproduced with permission of Natural Resources Canada 2008, courtesy of the Atlas of Canada.

FIGURE 7.27 Saskatchewan and Alberta joined Canada in 1905. The boundaries of Manitoba, Ontario, and Quebec were extended northward to the Ungava Peninsula. Part of this new territory was now part of the James Bay Project, which generates massive amounts of electricity. Significant mining and forestry activities occur within this region.

Source: http://atlas.nrcan.gc.ca/site/english/maps/historical/ territorialevolution/1912. Reproduced with permission of Natural Resources Canada 2008, courtesy of the Atlas of Canada.

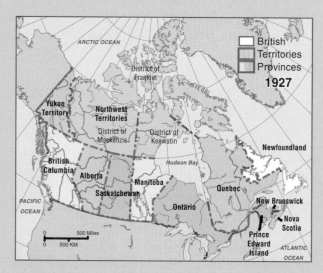

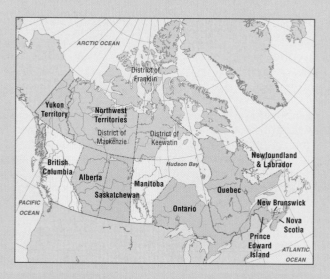

FIGURE 7.28 In 1925, Canada's boundaries were extended northward pursuant to provisions of international law. In 1927, the boundary between Canada and Newfoundland was defined by the Imperial Privy Council in Britain. This decision was unpopular within Quebec and it has never been officially recognized by Governments of Quebec. This stance has contributed to friction between the two provinces.

Source: http://atlas.nrcan.gc.ca/site/english/maps/historical/ territorialevolution/1927. Reproduced with permission of Natural Resources Canada 2008, courtesy of the Atlas of Canada.

FIGURE 7.29 Prior to 1949, Newfoundland and Labrador enjoyed the status of a "country." After a bitterly fought plebiscite campaign between those who wished the country to remain independent and those who wished to join Canada, Newfoundland and Labrador become the 10th province in Canadian Confederation with the boundaries as delimited in 1927. The vote was close—52% to 48%—supporting the move to Canada.

Source: http://atlas.nrcan.gc.ca/site/english/maps/historical/ territorialevolution/1949. Reproduced with permission of Natural Resources Canada 2008, courtesy of the Atlas of Canada.

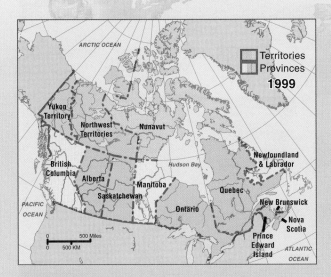

FIGURE 7.30 In 1999, Nanavut became Canada's third territory. The boundaries of this new territory respect the traditional Aboriginal concept of territoriality.

Source: http://atlas.nrcan.gc.ca/site/english/maps/historical/ territorialevolution/1999. Reproduced with permission of Natural Resources Canada 2008, courtesy of the Atlas of Canada.

It is this historical context that contributes to the French-speaking population within Quebec seeing themselves as constantly resisting assimilation and needing to preserve their language and culture. The desire to promote their language and culture is best illustrated by the formation of the Parti Québécois (PQ) in 1968. Initially, it promoted the idea of national sovereignty for Quebec from Canada as well as a social democratic set of programs. After the election of a PQ Government in 1976, a referendum was held in 1980 asking the people of Quebec to support negotiations for independence. The referendum lost by a margin of 59.6% to 40.4%. After proposed reforms to the Canadian Constitution failed (i.e., the Charlottetown Accord and the Meech Lake Accord) and with the question of Quebec's status within Canada still unresolved to its satisfaction, the PQ government held a second referendum in 1995 that called for a Unilateral Declaration of Independence. It lost by a margin of less than 1%—50.4% to 49.6%. If successful it would have authorized Quebec to proclaim itself a sovereign nation and negotiate a new political and economic relationship with the rest of Canada. In 1996, the federal government responded to this threat by asking the Supreme Court to rule on its legality (See Opening of Chapter). In 1999, the federal government passed the Clarity Act that established the framework for the secession of any province. It focused attention on the process for separation (i.e., a clear question that is supported by a clear majority of the population) and did not provide any final determination of boundaries. In response, Quebec's National Assembly passed Bill 99, entitled "An Act respecting the exercise of the fundamental rights and prerogatives of the Québec people and the Québec State," which directly challenged the Clarity Act because it maintained that the people of Québec had the right of self-determination.

There are at least three perspectives on the question of Quebec's borders if it were to secede from Canada. The first is based on the principle of *uti possidetis juris*, which is a concept of international law that defines borders of newly sovereign states on the basis of their previous admin-istrative borders. This view, which would see no changes in Quebec's current boundaries, was supported by five international law experts who were asked in 1992 to prepare an opinion on Quebec's territorial integrity by a provincially appointed Commission on the Future of Quebec. However, the application of this principle is likely inappropriate in the case of Quebec because the legal right to self-determination only exists for colonies (e.g., portions of Africa, Asia, and Latin America) or previously sovereign states that lost their sovereignty (e.g., the Baltic States of Estonia, Latvia, and Lithuania that were forcibly incorporated into the Soviet Union). Self-determination is provided for populations who live under foreign control, have little influence over how they are governed, and are subjected to racial and other forms of discrimination. Clearly, these circumstances are non-existent in Quebec.

As mentioned elsewhere in this chapter, what the PQ is essentially proposing is secession. While there is no international right to secession and it is certainly not encouraged by the international community, it is not prohibited either. This view is implicitly supported by the Supreme Court of Canada opinion, which ruled that Quebec had neither the right under international nor Canadian law to unilaterally declare its independence. It supported a view that in any referendum the question should be clear and it should be supported by a clear majority. However, it did not specify what constituted a clear question or majority. While the Parti Quebecois argues that "fifty percent plus one" is sufficient, the 1999 Clarity Act indicates that it will be the Parliament of Canada that will determine if a referendum question is clear and if a sufficient majority has been obtained. These requirements were not in place when Newfoundland joined Canada.

If there was no negotiated agreement of the boundaries of an independent Quebec, it would have to demonstrate effective political control over its territory and population. Once this was established, perhaps as quickly as a matter of months, the international community would likely recognize Quebec as a state. Thus, people's decisions to continue to pay taxes to Canada Revenue Agency or to a similar Quebec agency, use stamps issued by Canada Post rather than "Quebec Post," and respect the enforcement of law by the RCMP over its "Quebec counterpart" would reflect the success of Quebec secession. In the absence of a negotiated agreement, Canada could also try to assert its control over territory that it views as its own—likely those portions of Quebec that were added after 1867. It would be argued that the former territory of Rupert's Land was obtained by Quebec only because it was part of the Canadian federation and its continued control over these lands requires it to remain within Canada. It is in these northern portions of the province that Quebec has invested billions of dollars in the massive James Bay hydroelectric diversion projects. French-speaking Canadians in northern Quebec currently outnumber Aboriginal people.

A third perspective on the borders of a new Quebec would advocate the partitioning of within the pre- and post-1867 boundaries of Quebec. This view is promoted on the basis that the regions within the province, particularly around Montreal and northern Quebec, expressed a strong desire to remain in Canada in the 1995 referendum and a separate referendum by Aboriginal people living in Quebec. No doubt the struggle to control and declare sovereignty over Quebec in the event of secession will be an intensive one that will involve its boundaries.

Sources: D.B. Knight, "Canada and Its Political Fault Lines: Reconciliation or Disintegration?" in D. Bennett (ed.) *Tension Areas of the World* (2nd edition), Debuque, Iowa: Kendall Hunt, 1998; D.B. Knight, "Bounding Whose Territory? Potential Conflict Between A State and A Province Desiring Statehood," *Geopolitics* 4(2): 2000, 209–238.

Colonial empires such as those of England, France, Spain, and Portugal exerted home state control over non-contiguous territories and frequently retain influence even after their formal colonial dominion has been lost. The Commonwealth (originally, the British Commonwealth of Nations), for example, is a free association of some 50 countries that recognize the British sovereign as head of the Commonwealth and retain use of the English language and legal system. The French Community comprises autonomous states formerly part of the French colonial empire that opted to remain affiliated with the Community, that generally retain the French language and legal system, have various contractual cooperative arrangements with the former ruling state, and have in the instance of African members occasionally called on France to intervene militarily to protect established regimes.

The United States has also projected its early imperialist power through a number of mechanisms. It purchased the Louisiana territory from France, and Alaska from Russia. It fought wars and won territory from Spain. American foreign policy has been driven, according to some people, by a desire to access foreign markets for the benefit of the nation. As noted earlier, it has supported the overthrow (or attempted overthrows) of governments of many nations including Nicaragua, Cuba, Iran, and more recently Iraq. Finally, through the processes of globalization, American culture is seen through the dominance of its movies, music, and industries (Figure 7.31).

Geopolitical Assessments

Geopolitics is a branch of political geography that considers the strategic value of land and sea area in the context of national economic and military power and ambitions. In that light, geopolitical concerns and territorial assessments have always influenced the policies of governments. "Manifest Destiny" rationalized the westward territorial spread of the United States; the Monroe Doctrine declared the Western Hemisphere off-limits to further European colonization; creation of a "Greater East Asia Co-Prosperity Sphere" justified Japan's Asian and Pacific aggression before and during World War II.

Modern geopolitics was rooted in the early 20th-century concern of an eminent English geographer, Halford Mackinder (1861–1947), with the world balance of power at a time of British expansion and overseas empire. Believing that the major powers would be those that controlled the land, not the seas, he developed what came to be known as the **heartland theory**. The greatest land power, he argued, would be sited in Eurasia, the "World-Island" containing the world's largest landmass in both area and population. Its interior or heartland, he warned, would provide a base for world conquest, and Eastern Europe was the core of that heartland. Mackinder warned, "Who rules East Europe commands the Heartland, who rules the Heartland commands the World-Island, who rules the World-Island commands the World."[2]

Developed in a century that saw first Germany and then the Soviet Union dominate East Europe, and the decline of Britain as a superpower, Mackinder's theory impressed many. Even earlier, Alfred Mahan (1840–1914) recognized the core position of Russia

FIGURE 7.31 A form of American economic and cultural imperialism. For some people the "McDonaldization" of landscape and culture is a very visible sign of America's economic imperialism. This picture, taken in downtown San Jose, Costa Rica, contains at least two examples of America's global economic influence.

in the Asian landmass and anticipated conflict between Russian land power and British sea power, though Mahan argued that control of the world's sea lanes to protect commerce and isolate an adversary was the key to national strength. Near the end of World War II, Nicholas Spykman (1894–1943) also agreed that Eurasia was the likely base for potential world domination, but argued that the coastal fringes of the landmass, not its heartland, were the key (Figure 7.32). The continental margins, Spykman reasoned, contained dense populations, abundant resources, and had controlling access both to the seas and to the continental interior. His **rimland theory**, published in 1944, stated "Who controls the Rimland rules Eurasia, who rules Eurasia controls the destinies of the world."[3]

The rimland has tended throughout history to be politically fragmented, and Spykman concluded that it would be to the advantage of both the United States and the USSR if it remained that way.

By the end of World War II, the Heartland was equated in American eyes with the USSR. To prevent Soviet domination of the World-Island, U.S. foreign policy during the Cold War was based on the notion of **containment**, or confining the USSR within its borders by means of a string of regional alliances in the Rimland: The North Atlantic Treaty Organization (NATO) in Western Europe, the Central Treaty Organization (CENTO) in West Asia, and the Southeast Asia Treaty Organization (SEATO).

---

[2] Halford J. Mackinder, *Democratic Ideals and Reality* (London: Constable, 1919), p. 150.

[3] Nicholas J. Spykman, *The Geography of the Peace* (New York: Harcourt Brace, 1944), p. 43.

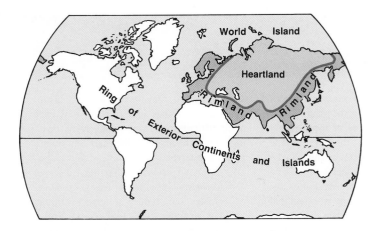

FIGURE 7.32 Geopolitical viewpoints. Both Mackinder and Spykman believed that Eurasia possessed strategic advantages, but they disagreed on whether its heartland or rimland provided the most likely base for world domination. Mahan recognized sea power as the key to national strength, advocating American occupation of the Hawaiian Islands, control of the Caribbean, and construction of an interocean canal through Central America.

Military intervention was deemed necessary where communist expansion, whether Soviet or Chinese, was a threat—in Berlin, the Middle East, and Korea, for example.

A simple spatial model, the **domino theory**, was used as an adjunct to the policy of containment. According to this analogy, adjacent countries are lined up like dominoes; if one topples, the rest will fall. In the early 1960s, the domino theory was invoked to explain and justify U.S. intervention in Vietnam, and in the 1980s, the theory was applied to involvement in Central America. As mentioned earlier, other commentators would view these as examples of U.S. imperialism.

These (and other) models aimed at realistic assessments of national power and foreign policy stand in contrast to "organic state theory" based on the 19th-century idea of German geographer Friedrich Ratzel (1844–1904) that the state acted as if it were an organism conforming to natural laws and forced to grow and expand into new territories (*Lebensraum*) in order to secure the resources needed for survival. Without that growth, the state would wither and die. These ideas, later expanded in the 1920s by the German Karl Haushofer (1869–1946) as *Geopolitik*, were used by the Nazi party as the presumed intellectual basis for the wartime theories of race superiority and need for territorial conquest. Repudiated by events and Germany's defeat, *Geopolitik* for many years gave bad odour to any study of geopolitics, which only recently has again become a serious subfield of political geography.

In a rapidly changing world, many analysts believe the older geopolitical concepts and ideas of geostrategy no longer apply. A number of developments have rendered them obsolete: the dissolution of the USSR and the presumed end of the Cold War; the proliferation of nuclear technology; and the rise of Japan, China, and Western Europe to world power status. Geopolitical reality is now seen less in terms of military advantage and confrontation—the East-West rivalry of the Cold War era—and more as a reflection of other forms of competition.

One of those forms expresses itself in violent assaults carried out by individuals and groups motivated by their total rejection of an established order they despise. Traditional geopolitical theories and assessments have dealt with projections of state power and influence embodied in military and economic strength. The study of modern imperialism is an important element of contemporary geopolitics. As a series of destructive incidents throughout the world before and after the tragic September 11, 2001 assaults on the World Trade Center and the Pentagon—and the aroused response to them from the United States and other governments—made clear, terrorism, including state-sponsored terrorism, must also be recognized as a substantially different form of global geopolitical activity. Terrorism, the use or threat of violence to advance a political cause, was usually thought of as dissident individual or small group assault on civilian populations to weaken state authority; force change in governmental policy; or erode the social, cultural, or political organization of a society. Under Canada's Anti-Terrorism Act, the Government of Canada has, as of June 2008, identified 40 organizations as "terrorist" and been outlawed (see "Terrorism and Political Geography").

The factors that have contributed to the current rise of terrorism are complex. However, religious or faith-based groups are particularly prominent on the late 20th and early 21st centuries' terrorist rosters. In their home countries, one frequent objective of these terrorist organizations is to replace existing secular or westernized governments with regimes committed to strict enforcement of fundamentalist religious law. On the international scene, however, they have primarily targeted the United States, its allies, and its citizens. The car bombing of the World Trade Center in New York in 1993, the bombing of American embassies in Kenya and Tanzania in 1998, the bombs exploded in three Spanish commuter railroad stations on a 2004 March morning, and the London subway and bus bombing in July 2005—collectively with the loss of hundreds of lives and many thousands of injuries—were the work of terrorist individuals and groups. The al-Qaeda network, responsible for the attacks of 9/11, was the creation of Osama bin Laden, who issued a 1998 *fatwa*, or religious judgment, claiming it was the duty of Muslims to conduct holy war against the United States for its support of both the state of Israel and the ruling Saudi Arabian royal family. Governments and citizens of European Union countries have also been subject to al-Qaeda terrorism at home and abroad. For some people, and much to the surprise of other individuals, the United States has been perceived to have frequently committed terrorism as illustrated by when it bombed a pharmaceutical factory in Sudan (1998) and much of the city of Fallujah, Iraq (2004). The one group view these and other similar acts as imperialism, while the other group would maintain they were premised, among other things, on promoting democracy.

Two other types of global competition are also evident on the modern geopolitical scene. One is economic rivalry within the developed world and between economic core countries and emerging peripheral states—the North–South split (see Chapter 11)—and expressed in the development of international blocs aligned by economic interests. The rise of China as a world economic power that competes against the United States will be a story that will be in the news frequently during your lifetime.

"Where were you when the world stopped turning?" Asks Alan Jackson in his song about the September 11, 2001, terrorist attacks on the United States. You probably know the answer to his question, and you probably always will. Of course, the world didn't really stop turning, but that's how it felt to millions of Americans, Canadians, and others with no previous exposure to terrorism.

What is terrorism? How does it relate to political geography? Do all countries experience terrorism? Is terrorism new? Is there a way to prevent it? Attempting to answer these questions, difficult as they are, may help us understand the phenomenon.

Terrorism is the calculated use of violent acts against civilians and symbolic targets to publicize a cause, intimidate or coerce a civilian population, or affect the conduct of a government. *International terrorism*, such as the attacks of September 11, 2001, include acts that transcend national boundaries. International terrorism is intended to intimidate people in other countries. *Domestic terrorism* consists of acts by individuals or groups against the citizens or government of their own country. *State terrorism* is committed by the agents of a government. *Subnational terrorism* is committed by nongovernmental groups. Whatever its agency or level, terrorism is a weapon designed to intimidate populations and, often, to influence government actions or policies.

State terrorism is probably as old as the concept of a state. As early as 146 B.C.E., for example, Roman forces sacked and completely destroyed the city of Carthage, burning it to the ground, slaughtering its population, and sowing salt on the fields so that no crops could grow. Governments have used systematic policies of violence and intimidation to further dominate and control their own populations. Nazi Germany, the Pol Pot regime in Cambodia, and Stalinist Russia are 20th-century examples of state terrorism. Heads of state ordered the murder, imprisonment, or exile of enemies of the state—politicians, intellectuals, dissidents—anyone who dared to criticize the government. In Rwanda, the former Yugoslavia, and Saddam Hussein's Iraq, state terrorism aimed against ethnic and religious minorities provided the government with a method of consolidating power;

in each case, genocide, or mass murder of ethnic minority groups, was the result.

Subnational terrorism is of more recent vintage, coinciding with the rise of the nation-state. Sub national terrorism can be perpetrated by those who feel wronged by their own or another government. For example, ethnic groups in a minority who feel that the central government has taken their territory and absorbed them into a larger political entity, such as the Basques in Spain, have used terrorist activities to promote their cause and resist the government. Ethnic and religious groups that have been split by national boundaries imposed by others sometimes have used terrorism to make governance difficult. Political, ethnic, or religious groups or individuals who feel oppressed by their own government, such as the Oklahoma City bombers in the United States, have committed acts of domestic terrorism.

Nearly every country has experienced some form of terrorism at some point since the mid-19th century. These acts have been as various as the anarchist assassinations of political leaders in Europe during the 1840s and in the United States in the late 19th century, the abduction of Canadian government officials by the Front Libération du Québec (FLQ) in 1970, and the release of sarin gas in the Tokyo subways in 1995 by the group Aum Shinrikyo.

Canada has not been immune from terrorism in recent times. The Air India bombing resulted in the deaths of 329 people in 1985. More recently, in June 2006, 17 people, who security officials believed were preparing for large-scale terrorist attacks in southern Ontario, including detonating truck bombs, invading various buildings such as Parliament Hill (Ottawa) and the CBC offices (Toronto), and beheading Prime Minister Stephen Harper, were charged with a wide range of offences.

The political and religious aims of these attackers, however, can cause confusion on the world stage. In 2001, the Reuters News Agency told its reporters to stop using the word *terrorism*, because "one person's terrorist is another's freedom fighter." The definition of terrorism rests on the ability to define motives and the outlook of the observer.

Although it may be difficult to distinguish among types of terrorism, it is even more difficult to prevent it. Generally speaking, governments and international bodies respond to terrorist acts in one of four ways:

1. Reducing or addressing the causes of terrorism. In some cases, political change can reduce a terrorist threat. For example, the 1998 Good Friday Agreement in Northern Ireland led to a reduction of terrorist acts; the Spanish government's granting of some regional autonomy to the Basques helped lessen the violent actions of the ETA (Basque separatists) and reduced the support of many Basque people for such acts.

2. Increasing international cooperation in the surveillance of sub-national groups. Spurred by terrorist crimes in Bahrain and Saudi Arabia, the Arab Gulf States agreed in 1998 to exchange intelligence regarding terrorist groups, to share information regarding anticipated terrorist acts, and to assist each other in investigating terrorist crimes.

3. Increasing security measures in a country. In the United States, following September 11, 2001, the government organized a Department of Homeland Security, federalized air traffic screening, and increased efforts to reduce financial support for foreign terrorist organizations. In concert, Canada, the European Union, and many other countries froze the assets of any group on its list of terrorist organizations.

4. Using military means, either unilaterally or multilaterally, against terrorists or governments that sponsor terrorists. Following the September 11, 2001, World Trade Center and Pentagon assaults, the United States led a coalition of countries, including Canada, in attacking the government of Afghanistan, which had harboured Osama bin Laden's al-Qaeda terrorist organization.

Each response to terrorism is expensive, politically difficult, and potentially harmful to the life and liberty of citizens. Governments must decide which response or combination of responses is likely to have the most beneficial effect.

The other is competition rooted in more fundamental and perhaps enduring conflicts between different "civilizations." It has been suggested that the world will increasingly be shaped by the interactions and conflicts among seven or eight major civilizations: Western, Confucian, Japanese, Islamic, Hindu, Slavic, Latin American, and possibly African. It is thought that the differences among such civilizations are basic and antagonistic, rooted in enduring differences of history, language, culture, tradition, and religion (see Chapter 5). These differences, the argument runs, are less easily resolved than purely political and economic ones. They underlie such recent clashes as Indian rivalries between Hindus and Muslims, those of Sri Lanka between Hindu Tamils and Buddhist Sinhalese, multicultural conflicts in former Yugoslavia and between Armenians and Azeris in the Caucasus, and among and within other states and areas where "civilizations" come in contact and competition. They also motivate some Muslim faith-based groups' animosity against Western states and the globalization of their economies, societies, and popular cultures.

International Political Systems

As changing geopolitical theories and outlooks suggest, in many ways individual countries are now weaker than ever before. Many are economically frail, others are politically unstable, and some are both. Strategically, no country is safe from military attack, for technology now enables us to shoot weapons halfway around the world. Some people believe that no national security is possible in the atomic age.

The recognition that a country cannot by itself guarantee either its prosperity or its own security has led to increased cooperation among states. In a sense, these cooperative ventures are replacing the empires of yesterday. They are proliferating quickly, and they involve countries everywhere. They are also adding a new dimension to the concept of "political boundaries" since the associations of states have themselves limits that are marked by borders of a higher spatial order than those between individual states. Such boundaries as the former Iron Curtain, the current division between NATO (North Atlantic Treaty Organization) and non-NATO states, or that between the European Union area and other European countries represent a different scale of the political ordering of space.

Supranationalism

Associations among states represent a new dimension in the ordering of national power and national independence. Recent trends in economic globalization and international cooperation suggest to some that the sovereign state's traditional responsibilities and authorities are being diluted by a combination of forces and partly delegated to higher-order political and economic organizations. Even corporations and nongovernmental economic and communication agencies often operate in controlling ways outside of nation-state jurisdiction.

The rise of transnational corporations dominant in global markets, for example, limits the economic influence of individual countries; cyberspace and the Internet are controlled by no one and are largely immune to the state restrictions on the flow of information exerted by many governments. Those information flows help create and maintain the growing number of international *nongovernmental organizations* (*NGOs*), estimated at over 20,000 in number and including such well-known groups as Greenpeace, Amnesty International, and Doctors without Borders. NGOs, through petitions, demonstrations, court actions, and educational efforts, have become effective influences on national and international political and economic actions. And increasingly, individual citizens of any country have their lives and actions shaped by decisions not only of local and national authorities, but by those of regional economic associations (the North American Free Trade Agreement, for example), multinational military alliances (NATO), and global political agencies (the United Nations).

The roots of such multistate cooperative systems are ancient—for example, the leagues of city states in the ancient Greek world or the Hanseatic League of free German cities in Europe's medieval period. The creation of new ones has been particularly active since 1945. They represent a world trend toward a **supranationalism** comprised of associations of three or more states created for mutual benefit and to achieve shared objectives. Although many individuals and organizations decry the loss of national independence that supranationalism entails, the many supranational associations in existence early in the 21st century are evidence of their attraction and pervasiveness. Almost all countries, in fact, are members of at least one—and most of many—supranational groupings. All at least are members of the United Nations.

The United Nations and Its Agencies

The United Nations (UN) is the only organization that tries to be universal, and even it is not all-inclusive. With its membership expanded from 51 countries in 1945 to 191 by 2005, the UN is the most ambitious attempt ever undertaken to bring together the world's nations in international assembly and to promote world peace. Stronger and more representative than its predecessor, the League of Nations, it provides a forum where countries may discuss international problems and regional concerns and a mechanism, admittedly weak but still significant, for forestalling disputes or, when necessary, for ending wars. The United Nations also sponsors 40 programs and agencies aimed at fostering international cooperation with respect to specific goals. Among these are the World Health Organization (WHO), the Food and Agriculture Organization (FAO), and the United Nations Educational, Scientific, and Cultural Organization (UNESCO). Many other UN agencies and much of the UN budget are committed to assisting member states with matters of economic growth and development.

Member states have not surrendered sovereignty to the UN, and the world body is legally and effectively unable to make or enforce a world law. Nor is there a world police force. Although there is recognized international law adjudicated by the International Court of Justice, rulings by this body are sought only by countries agreeing beforehand to abide by its arbitration. In 2002, a UN treaty was signed (without U.S. participation) creating a permanent International Criminal Court able to investigate and prosecute those individuals accused of crimes against humanity, genocide, and crimes of war. The United Nations has no authority over the military forces of individual countries.

A pronounced change both in the relatively passive role of the United Nations and in traditional ideas of international relations has begun to emerge. Long-established rules of total national sovereignty that allowed governments to act internally as they saw fit, free of outside interference, are fading as the United Nations increasingly applies a concept of "interventionism." The Persian Gulf War of 1991 was UN authorized under the old rules prohibiting one state (Iraq) from violating the sovereignty of another (Kuwait) by attacking it. After the war, the new interventionism sanctioned UN operations within Iraq—against the Iraqi government's will—to protect the Kurds against punitive actions by the Iraqi government. Later, the UN intervened with troops and relief agencies in Somalia, Bosnia, and elsewhere, invoking an "international jurisdiction over inalienable human rights" that prevails without regard to state frontiers or sovereignty considerations. However, the U.S.-led attack of Iraq in 2003 was not supported by the United Nations.

Whatever the long-term prospects for interventionism replacing absolute sovereignty, for the short term the United Nations remains the only institution where the vast majority of the world's countries can collectively discuss matters of international political and economic concerns, and attempt peacefully to resolve their differences. It has been particularly influential in formulating a Law of the Sea.

Maritime Boundaries

Boundaries define political jurisdictions and areas of resource control. But claims of national authority are not restricted to land areas alone. Water covers about two-thirds of the earth's surface, and increasingly countries have been projecting their sovereignty seaward to claim adjacent maritime areas and resources. A basic question involves the right of states to control water and the resources that it contains. The inland waters of a country, such as rivers and lakes, have traditionally been considered within the sovereignty of that country. Oceans, however, are not within any country's borders. Are they, then, to be open to all states to use, or may a single country claim sovereignty and limit access and use by other states?

For most of human history, the oceans remained effectively outside individual national control or international jurisdiction. The seas were a common highway for those daring enough to venture on them, an inexhaustible larder for fishermen, and a vast refuse pit for the muck of civilization. By the end of the 19th century, however, most coastal countries claimed sovereignty over a continuous belt 3 or 4 nautical miles wide (a *nautical mile*, or *nm*, equals 1.15 statute miles, or 1.85 km). At the time, the 3-nm limit represented the farthest range of artillery and thus the effective limit of control by the coastal state. Though recognizing the rights of others to innocent passage, such sovereignty permitted the enforcement of quarantine and customs regulations, allowed national protection of coastal fisheries, and made claims of neutrality effective during other people's wars. The primary concern was with security and unrestricted commerce. No separately codified laws of the sea existed, however, and none seemed to be needed until after World War I.

A League of Nations Conference for the Codification of International Law, convened in 1930, inconclusively discussed maritime legal matters and served to identify areas of concern that were to become increasingly pressing after World War II. Important among these was an emerging shift from interest in commerce and national security to a preoccupation with the resources of the seas, an interest fanned by the *Truman Proclamation* of 1945. Motivated by a desire to exploit offshore oil deposits, the U.S. government under this doctrine laid claim to all resources on the continental shelf contiguous to its coasts. Other states, many claiming even broader areas of control, hurried to annex their own adjacent marine resources. Within a few years, a quarter of the earth's surface was appropriated by individual coastal countries.

An International Law of the Sea

Unrestricted extensions of jurisdiction and disputes over conflicting claims to maritime space and resources led to a series of United Nations conferences on the Law of the Sea. Meeting over a period of years, delegates from more than 150 countries attempted to achieve consensus on a treaty that would establish an internationally agreed-upon "convention dealing with all matters relating to the Law of the Sea." The meetings culminated in a draft treaty in 1982, the **United Nations Convention on the Law of the Sea (UNCLOS)**.

The convention delimits territorial boundaries and rights by defining four zones of diminishing control (Figure 7.33):

- A *territorial sea* of up to 12 nm (19 km) in breadth over which coastal states have sovereignty, including exclusive fishing rights. Vessels of all types normally have the right of innocent passage through the territorial sea, though under certain circumstances, non-commercial (primarily military and research) vessels can be challenged.
- A *contiguous zone* to 24 nm (38 km). Although a coastal state does not have complete sovereignty in this zone, it can enforce its customs, immigration, and sanitation laws and has the right of hot pursuit out of its territorial waters.
- An **exclusive economic zone** (**EEZ**) of up to 200 nm (370 km) in which the state has recognized rights to explore, exploit, conserve, and manage the natural resources, both living and nonliving, of the seabed and waters (see Figure 7.34). Countries have exclusive rights to the resources lying within

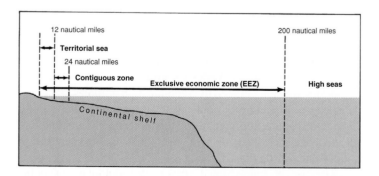

FIGURE 7.33 Territorial claims permitted by the 1982 United Nations Convention on the Law of the Sea (UNCLOS).

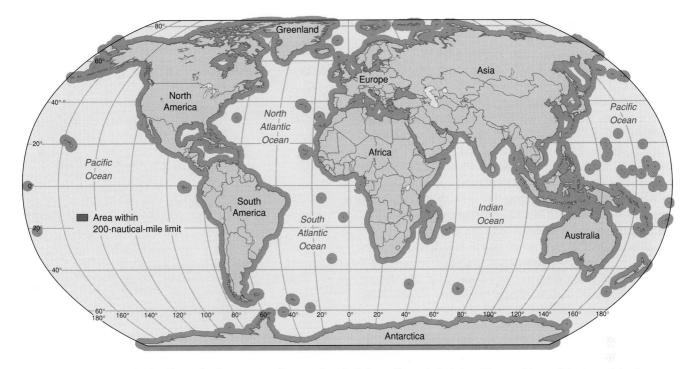

FIGURE 7.34 The 200-nautical mile exclusive economic zone (EEZ) claims of coastal states. The provisions of the Law of the Sea Convention have in effect changed the maritime map of the world. Three important consequences flow from the 200-nm EEZ concept: (1) islands have gained a new significance, (2) countries have a host of new neighbours, and (3) the EEZ lines result in overlapping claims. EEZ lines are drawn around a country's possessions as well as around the country itself. Every island, no matter how small, has its own 200-nm EEZ.

the continental shelf when this extends farther, up to 350 nm (560 km), beyond their coasts. The traditional freedoms of the high seas are to be maintained in this zone.

- The *high seas* beyond the EEZ. Outside any national jurisdiction, they are open to all states, whether coastal or landlocked. Freedom of the high seas includes the right to sail ships, fish, fly over, lay submarine cables and pipelines, and pursue scientific research. Mineral resources in the international deep seabed area beyond national jurisdiction are declared the common heritage of humankind, to be managed for the benefit of all the peoples of the earth.

By the end of the 1980s, most coastal countries, including Canada, had used the UNCLOS provisions to proclaim and reciprocally recognize jurisdiction over 12-nm territorial seas and 200-nm (370 km) economic zones. Despite reservations held by the United States and a few other industrial countries about the deep seabed mining provisions, the convention received the necessary ratification by 60 states and became international law in 1994. However, as noted earlier, there are disagreements between Canada and the U.S. about precise delineation of some maritime boundaries.

UN Affiliates

Other fully or essentially global supranational organizations with influences on the economic, social, and cultural affairs of states and individuals have been created. Most are specialized international agencies, autonomous and with their own differing memberships but with affiliated relationships with the United Nations and operating under its auspices. Among them are the Food and Agriculture

Organization (FAO), the International Bank for Reconstruction and Development (World Bank), the International Labor Organization (ILO), the United Nations Children's Fund (UNICEF), the World Health Organization (WHO), and—of growing economic importance—the World Trade Organization (WTO).

The WTO, which came into existence at the start of 1995, has become one of the most significant of the global expressions of supranational economic control. It is charged with enforcing the global trade accords that grew out of years of international negotiations under the terms of the General Agreement on Tariffs and Trade (GATT). The basic principle behind the WTO is that the 148-plus (2005) member countries should work to cut tariffs, dismantle non-tariff barriers to trade, liberalize trade in services, and treat all other countries uniformly in matters of trade. Any preference granted to one should be available to all.

Increasingly, however, regional rather than global trade agreements are being struck, and free trade areas are proliferating. Only a few WTO members are not already part of some other regional trade association. Such areal associations—some 80 of them by 2004—it can be argued, make world trade less free by scrapping tariffs on trade among member states but retaining them separately or as a group on exchanges with non-members.

Regional Alliances

In addition to their membership in such international agencies, countries have shown themselves willing to relinquish some of their independence to participate in smaller multinational systems. These groupings may be economic, military, or political, and many have been formed since 1945. Cooperation in the economic sphere seems to come more easily to states than does military and political collaboration.

Economic Alliances

Among the oldest, most powerful, and far-reaching of the regional economic alliances are those that have evolved in Europe, particularly the European Union and its several forerunners. Shortly after the end of World War II, the Benelux countries (Belgium, the Netherlands, and Luxembourg) formed an economic union to create a common set of tariffs and to eliminate import licences and quotas. Formed at about the same time were the Organization for European Cooperation (1948), which coordinated the distribution and use of Marshall Plan funds, and the European Coal and Steel Community (1952), which integrated the development of that industry in the member countries. A few years later, in 1957, the *European Economic Community* (*EEC*), or *Common Market*, was created, composed at first of only six states: France, Italy, West Germany, and the Benelux countries.

To counteract these Inner Six, as they were called, other countries in 1960 formed the European Free Trade Association (EFTA). Known as the Outer Seven, they were the United Kingdom, Norway, Denmark, Sweden, Switzerland, Austria, and Portugal (Figure 7.35). Between 1973 and 1986, three members (the United Kingdom, Denmark, and Portugal) left EFTA for membership in the Common Market and were replaced by Iceland and Finland. Other Common Market additions were Greece in 1981, and Spain and Portugal in 1986. Austria, Finland, and Sweden became members of the **European Union** (**EU**), as the organization embracing the Common Market is now called, in 1995. Invitations to preliminary entry negotiations, conditional on continued economic restructuring, were issued to Poland, the Czech Republic, Hungary, Slovenia, and Estonia in mid-1997 (Figure 7.36). At meetings in 2000, the EU pledged they would be ready to receive new members in 2004. That pledge was confirmed in 2002 with the decision to admit—subject to their acceptance by referendum—former Soviet bloc nations from Estonia on the north to Slovenia in the south, and adding as well the island states of Malta and Cyprus. These 10 additions increase the EU's land mass by 23%, raise its total population to more than 450 million people, and expand its economy to rival and perhaps exceed that of the United States. They make the EU the world's largest and richest bloc of nation-states.

Over the years, members of the European Union have taken many steps to integrate their economies and coordinate their policies in such areas as transportation, agriculture, and fisheries. A Council of Ministers, a Commission, a European Parliament, and a Court of Justice give the European Union supranational institutions with effective ability to make and enforce laws. By January 1, 1993, the EU had abolished most remnant barriers to free trade and the free movement of capital and people, creating a single European market. In another step toward economic and monetary union, the EU's single currency, the *euro*, replaced separate national currencies in 1999. And all applicant members in 2002 added 80,000 pages of EU law to their own legal systems.

We have traced this European development history, not because the full history of the EU is important to remember, but simply to

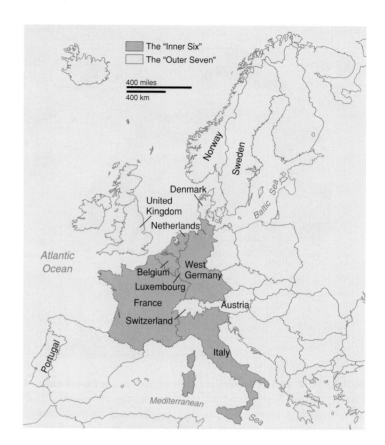

FIGURE 7.35 The original Inner Six and Outer Seven of Europe.

illustrate the fluid process by which regional alliances are made. Countries come together in an association, some drop out, and others join. New treaties are made, and new coalitions emerge. Indeed, a number of such regional economic and trade associations have been added to the world supranational map. None are as encompassing in power and purpose as the EU, but all represent a cession of national independence to achieve broader regional goals.

NAFTA, the North American Free Trade Agreement launched in 1994 and linking Canada, Mexico, and the United States in an economic community aimed at lowering or removing trade and movement restrictions among the countries, is perhaps the best known to North American students. The Americas as a whole, however, have other similar associations with comparable trade enhancement objectives, though frequently they—in common with other world regional alliances—have social, political, and cultural interests also in mind. CARICOM (Caribbean Community and Common Market), for example, was established in 1974 to further cooperation among its members in economic, health, cultural, and foreign policy arenas. MERCOSUR—the Southern Cone Community Market—which unites Brazil, Argentina, Uruguay, and Paraguay in the proposed creation of a customs union to eliminate levies on goods moving among them, is a South American example.

A similar interest in promoting economic, social, and cultural cooperation and development among its members underpins the Association of Southeast Asian Nations (ASEAN), formed in 1967. A similar, but much less wealthy African example is

FIGURE 7.36 The 25 members of the European Union (EU) as of January 2004. Accession talks with Romania, Bulgaria, and Turkey (an applicant since 1987) were underway in 2004. The EU has stipulated that in order to join, a country must have stable institutions guaranteeing democracy, the rule of law, human rights, and protection of minorities; a functioning market economy; and the ability to accept the obligations of membership, including the aims of political, economic, and monetary union.

ECOWAS, the Economic Community of West African States. The Asia Pacific Economic Cooperation (APEC) forum includes China, Japan, Australia, Canada, and the United States among its 18 members and has a grand plan for "free trade in the Pacific" by 2020. More restricted bilateral and regional preferential trade arrangements have also proliferated, numbering some 230 at the end of 2004, up from only 50 in 1990, with another 60 or so under negotiation. They create a maze of rules, tariffs, and commodity agreements that result in trade restrictions and preferences contrary to the free trade intent of the World Trade Organization.

Some supranational alliances, of course, are more cultural and political in orientation than these cited agencies. The League of Arab States, for example, was established in 1945 primarily to promote social, political, military, and foreign policy cooperation among its 22 members. In the Western Hemisphere, the Organization of American States (OAS) founded in 1948 concerns itself largely with social, cultural, human rights, and security matters affecting the hemisphere. A similar concern with peace and security underlay the Organization of African Unity (OAU) formed in 1963 by 32 African countries and, by 2001, expanded to 53 members and renamed the African Union.

Economic interests, therefore, may motivate the establishment of most international alliances, but political, social, and cultural objectives also figure largely or exclusively in many. Although the alliances themselves may change, the idea of single- and multiple-purpose supranational associations has been permanently added to the national political and global realities of the 21st century.

The world map pattern those alliances create must be recognized to understand the current international order.

Three further points about regional international alliances are worth noting. The first is that the formation of a coalition in one area often stimulates the creation of another alliance by countries left out of the first. Thus, the union of the Inner Six gave rise to the treaty among the Outer Seven. Similarly, a counterpart of the Common Market was the Council of Mutual Economic Assistance (CMEA), also known as Comecon, which linked the former communist countries of Eastern Europe and the USSR through trade agreements.

Second, the new supranational unions tend to be composed of contiguous states (Figure 7.37). This was not the case with the recently dissolved empires, which included far-flung territories. Contiguity facilitates the movement of people and goods. Communication and transportation are simpler and more effective among adjoining countries than among those far removed from one another, and common cultural, linguistic, historical, and political traits and interests are more to be expected in spatially proximate countries.

Finally, it does not seem to matter whether countries are alike or distinctly different in their economies, as far as joining economic unions is concerned. There are examples of both. If the countries are dissimilar, they may complement each other. This was one basis for the European Common Market. Dairy products and furniture from Denmark are sold in France, freeing that country to specialize in the production of machinery and clothing. On the other hand, countries that produce the same raw materials hope that by joining together in an economic alliance, they might be able to enhance their control of markets and prices for their products. The Organization of Petroleum Exporting Countries (OPEC), see Chapter 9, is a case in point. Other attempts to form commodity cartels and price agreements between producing and consuming nations include the International Tin Agreement, the International Coffee Agreement, and others.

Military and Political Alliances

Countries form alliances for other than economic reasons. Strategic, political, and cultural considerations may also foster cooperation. *Military alliances* are based on the principle that unity assures strength. Such pacts usually provide for mutual assistance in the case of aggression. Once again, action breeds reaction when such an association is created. The formation of the North Atlantic Treaty Organization (NATO), a defensive alliance of many European countries and the United States, was countered by the establishment of the Warsaw Treaty Organization, which joined the USSR and its satellite countries of Eastern Europe. Both pacts allowed the member states to base armed forces in one another's territories, a relinquishment of a certain degree of sovereignty uncommon in the past.

Military alliances depend on the perceived common interests and political goodwill of the countries involved. As political realities change, so do the strategic alliances. NATO was created to defend Western Europe and North America against the Soviet military threat. When the dissolution of the USSR and the Warsaw Pact removed that threat, the purpose of the NATO

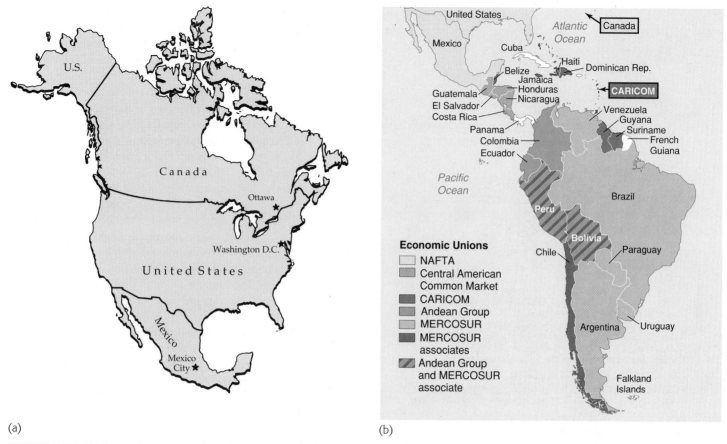

(a)

(b)

FIGURE 7.37 (*a*) **The North American Free Trade Agreement (NAFTA)** is intended to unite Canada, the United States, and Mexico in a regional free trade zone. Under the terms of the treaty, tariffs on all agricultural products and thousands of other goods were to be eliminated by the end of 1999. In addition, all three countries are to ease restrictions on the movement of business executives and professionals. If fully implemented, the treaty will create one of the world's richest and largest trading blocs. (*b*) Western Hemisphere economic unions in 2005. In addition to these subregional alliances, President George H. W. Bush in 1990 proposed a "free trade area of the Americas" to stretch from Alaska to Cape Horn.

alliance became less clear and, during the 1990s, its members put its relationships with Eastern European states and Russia under review. Most of those countries sought ways to foster cooperation with NATO, and three of them—Poland, Hungary, and the Czech Republic—joined the alliance in 1999 (Figure 7.38).

All international alliances recognize communities of interest. In economic and military associations, common objectives are clearly seen and described, and joint actions are agreed on with respect to the achievement of those objectives. More generalized mutual concerns or appeals to historical interest may be the basis for primarily *political alliances.* Such associations tend to be rather loose, not requiring their members to yield much power to the union. Examples are the Commonwealth of Nations (formerly the British Commonwealth), composed of many former British colonies and dominions, and the Organization of American States, both of which offer economic as well as political benefits.

There are many examples of abortive political unions that have foundered precisely because the individual countries could not agree on questions of policy and were unwilling to subordinate individual interests to make the union succeed. The United Arab Republic, the Central African Federation, the Federation of Malaysia and Singapore, and the Federation of the West Indies fall within this category.

Although many such political associations have failed, observers of the world scene speculate about the possibility that "superstates" will emerge from one or more of the economic or political alliances that now exist. Will a "United States of Europe," for example, under a single government be the logical outcome of the successes of the EU? No one knows, but as long as the individual state is regarded as the highest form of political and social organization (as it is now) and as the body in which sovereignty rests, such total unification is unlikely.

Local and Regional Political Organizations

The most profound contrasts in cultures tend to occur among, rather than within states, is one reason political geographers traditionally have been primarily interested in country units. The emphasis on the state, however, should not obscure the fact that for most of us it is at the local level that we find our most intimate and immediate contact with government and its influence on the administration of our affairs. In Canada, for example, an individual is subject to the decisions and regulations made by a

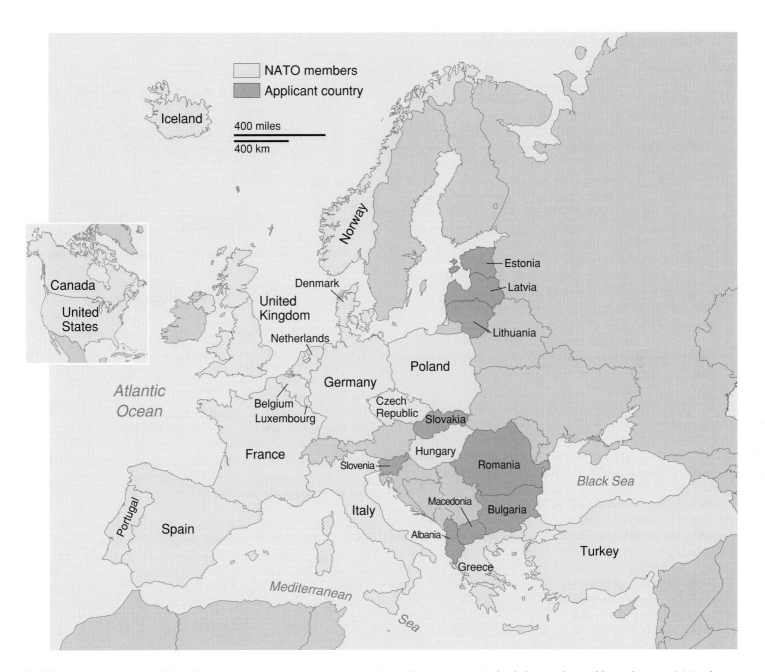

FIGURE 7.38 The NATO military alliance at the end of 2004 had 19 members. Three countries (Poland, the Czech Republic, and Hungary) joined the alliance in 1999, the first enlargement since Spain became a member in 1982. Nine other countries have applied for membership. Proponents of expansion argue that it is necessary in order to create a zone of stability and security throughout Europe. Opponents contend that enlargement is a divisive move that will cast a shadow over the future of relations with Russia, which is opposed to expansion so close to its borders.

school board, the local municipality, the county, the province, and, perhaps, a host of special-purpose agencies—all in addition to the laws and regulations issued by the federal government and its agencies. Among other things, local political entities determine where children go to school, the minimum size lot on which a person can build a house, and where one may legally park a car. Different countries are characterized by sharply differing personal and business tax rates; differing controls on the sale of firearms, alcohol, and tobacco; variant administrative systems for public services; and different levels of expenditures for them.

All of these governmental entities are *spatial systems*. Because they operate within defined geographic areas and because they make behaviour-governing decisions, they are topics of interest to political geographers. In the concluding sections of this chapter, we examine two aspects of political organization at the local and regional level. Our emphasis will be on the Canadian and U.S. scene simply because their local political geography is familiar to most of us. We should remember, however, Anglo-American structures of municipal governments, minor civil divisions, and special-purpose districts have counterparts in other regions of the world.

The Geography of Representation

Beneath the federal, provincial, and territorial governments, there are thousands of local government agencies/bodies in Canada. These include regional governments, municipalities, cities, towns and villages, counties, and townships. In addition, there are school boards, water districts, police boards, airport authorities, and other special-purpose agencies, such as the National Energy Board, the conservation districts in Manitoba, and conservation authorities in Ontario. Although the number of agencies does not change greatly from year-to-year, many boundary lines are redrawn each year.

When the size or shape of a district is based on population numbers or distribution, *redistricting* or *reapportionment* is made necessary by shifts in population, as areas gain or lose people. While many people use these terms interchangeably, they have distinct meanings:

- *Reapportionment* is the process of dividing the number of parliamentary representatives among the province's population in order to assure—as close as possible—electoral districts (or ridings) of equal size.
- *Redistricting* is the drawing of district lines in order to demarcate the riding boundaries.

The following discussion examines these processes applied at the federal level. At the time of Confederation in 1867, The British North America Act, 1867 (after 1982 referred to as the Constitution Act, 1867) established a parliament composed of two houses. The upper house, or Senate, comprised 72 members who were appointed by the Government—24 representing each of the three regions—Quebec, Ontario, and the Maritimes. The lower house, or House of Commons, was composed of 181 members, who were elected by the people. Initially the four founding provinces had the following number of representatives: 82 for Ontario, 65 for Quebec, 19 for Nova Scotia, and 15 for New Brunswick. In order that each province's representation in the House of Commons continued to reflect its population, section 51 of the Constitution Act, 1867 stated that the number of seats allocated to each province would be recalculated after each 10-year (decennial) census, starting with the 1871 Census (see Chapter 2). Since that time, three rules have developed that determine the number of ridings per province and territory. These are:

1. *Provincial Quotient:* The number of MPs within a province is calculated by dividing the total population of all the provinces by 279 (this is the number of seats allotted to the provinces in 1986, when the law was established and is referred to as the "National Quotient," which was 107,220 for 2001). The population of the province is then divided by the quotient so obtained, rounding up totals in excess of 0.5 as one additional seat. The equation is as follows:

   Provincial Quotient = provincial population / [population of all provinces / 279]

   Using 2001 Census data, British Columbia had a population of 3,907,738, while the population of all the provinces combined was 29,914,315.

   Using the formula, the number of MPs for BC = 3,907,738 / [29,914,315 / 279] = 36.45

Therefore, BC is allotted 36 electoral ridings in Canada's parliament.

2. *Minimum Number of MPs Per Province:* If the total number of members that would be assigned to a province using the "Provincial Quotient" approach is less than the total number assigned to that province on the date of section 51 of the Constitution Act coming into force (March 6, 1986), the number of members would be increased. This ensures that the province will have at least the same number of MPs as were held previously.

3. *The "Senatorial Clause":* First adopted in 1915, it states that a province cannot have fewer seats in the House of Commons than it does in the Senate.

Table 7.2 indicates the effect of the provincial quotient and the minimum numbers of MPs for each province following the 2001 Census.

Proposed changes by the Harper Government in 2007 have been questioned, particularly by Ontarians, on the basis of fairness. The Bill addresses the need to increase representation in British Columbia and Alberta, which has seen their populations increase recently without an proportional increase in the seats allocated to them in the House of Commons. Implementation of the Bill in 2011 would see the ratio of population to seats in the House of Commons be raised to 10.3:10 for Alberta and 13.4:13 for British Columbia. Quebec would have a ratio of 23.1:22.7. Ontario perceives it is being short-changed in this process because its ration would be 35.2:39.4. This proposed change, in addition to the seats guaranteed provinces under the Constitution, raises questions about the principle of representation by population in the House of Commons.

The analysis of how boundaries are drawn around voting districts is one aspect of **electoral geography**, which also addresses the spatial patterns yielded by election results and their relationship to the socio-economic characteristics of voters. In a democracy, it might be assumed that election districts should contain roughly equal numbers of voters, that electoral districts should be reasonably compact, and that the proportion of elected representatives should correspond to the share of votes cast for a given political party. Problems arise because the way in which the electoral boundary lines are drawn can maximize, minimize, or effectively nullify the representational power of a group of people.

Gerrymandering is the practice of drawing the boundaries of voting districts so as to unfairly favour one political party over another, to fragment voting blocs, or to achieve other non-democratic objectives (Figure 7.39). A number of strategies have been employed over the years for that purpose. *Stacked* gerrymandering involves drawing circuitous boundaries to enclose pockets of strength or weakness of the group in power; it is what we usually think of as "gerrymandering." The *excess vote* technique concentrates the votes of the opposition in a few districts, which they can win easily, but leaves them few potential seats elsewhere. Conversely, the *wasted vote* strategy dilutes the opposition's strength by dividing its votes among a number of districts.

Assume that *X* and *O* represent two groups with an equal number of voters but different policy preferences. Although there are equal numbers of *X*s and *O*s, the way electoral districts are drawn

TABLE 7.2

Representation Formula for Canadian Parliament Following the 2001 Census

Province/ Territory	Seats in Previous Parliament	Population (2001 Census)	Divide by National Quotient (107,220)	Rounded Result			Total Seats
Newfoundland and Labrador	7	512,930	4.784	5	1	1	7
Prince Edward Island	4	135,294	1.262	1	3	0	4
Nova Scotia	11	908,007	8.469	8	2	1	11
New Brunswick	10	729,498	6.804	7	3	0	10
Quebec	75	7,237,479	67.501	68	0	7	75
Ontario	95	11,410,046	106.417	106	0	0	106
Manitoba	14	1,119,583	10.442	10	0	4	14
Saskatchewan	14	978,933	9.130	9	0	5	14
Alberta	21	2,974,807	27.745	28	0	0	28
British Columbia	28	3,907,738	36.446	36	0	0	36
Nunavut	—	26,745					1
Northwest Territories	2	37,360					1
Yukon Territory	1	28,674					1
National Total	**282**	**30,007,094**					**308**

Source: Government of Canada.

affects voting results. In Figure 7.40a, the Xs are concentrated in one district and will probably elect only one representative of four. The power of the Xs is maximized in Figure 7.40b, where they may control three of the four districts. The voters are evenly divided in Figure 7.40c, where the Xs have the opportunity to elect two of the four representatives. Finally, Figure 7.40d shows how both political parties might agree to delimit the electoral districts to provide "safe seats" for incumbents. Such partitioning offers little chance for change.

Figure 7.40 depicts a hypothetical district, compact in shape with an even population distribution and only two groups competing for representation. In actuality, voting districts are often oddly shaped because of such factors as the city limits, current population distribution, and transportation routes—as well as past gerrymandering. Further, in any large area, many groups vie for power. Each electoral interest group promotes its version of fairness in the way boundaries are delimited. Minority interests, for example, seek representation in proportion to their numbers so that they will be able to elect representatives who are concerned about and responsive to their needs.

Canada has not been immune to gerrymandering at both federal and provincial levels. In order to avoid this problem, there has been a trend starting in Manitoba in the 1950s to use independent boards to determine electoral boundaries. The task of redrawing federal electoral districts has been done by a set of independent electoral boundary commissions since 1964. After the decanal census, a set of commissions has the task of redesigning Canada's electoral boundaries. This is accomplished by forming 10 federal electoral boundaries—one for each province—to consider and report on any changes required to the boundaries of the electoral districts. The territories (Northwest Territories, Yukon Territory, and Nunavut) constitute one electoral district each, so no federal adjustments are required in these jurisdictions. To keep the process at arm's length from the political process, each province's Chief Justice appoints the chair of the commission. Another judge usually chairs the commissions, but any resident of the province is eligible. The Speaker of the House of Commons selects another two members of the commission (both must be residents of the province).

To find out more about the history and development of this process, go to the Elections Canada website at: www.elections.ca/scripts/fedrep/federal_e/RED/representation_e.htm#history.

The Fragmentation of Political Power

Canada has a fragmented political pattern. Each of the provinces contains minor civil divisions—municipalities—under provincial control, and all (cities, towns, villages, and rural municipalities) are governed by elected councils. Ontario and Quebec also have counties that group smaller municipal units for certain purposes. In general, municipalities are responsible for police and fire protection, local jails, roads and hospitals, water supply and sanitation, and schools, duties that are discharged either by elected agencies or appointed commissions.

THE GERRY-MANDER. (Boston, 1811.)

FIGURE 7.39 The original gerrymander. The term gerrymander originated in 1811 from the shape of a U.S. electoral district formed in Massachusetts while Elbridge Gerry was governor. When an artist added certain animal features, the district resembled a salamander and quickly came to be called a gerrymander.

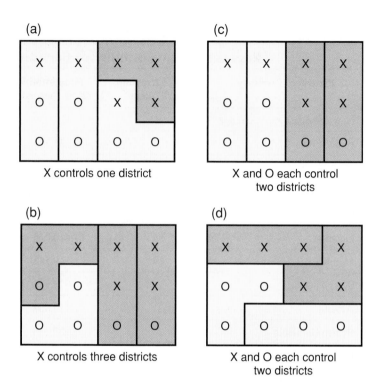

FIGURE 7.40 Alternative districting strategies. Xs and Os might represent Conservatives and Liberals, urban and rural voters, or any other distinctive groups.

Boundary drawing at any electoral level is never easy, particularly when political groups want to maximize their representation and minimize that of opposition groups. Furthermore, the boundaries that we may want for one set of districts may *not* be those that we want for another. For example, water-oriented districts must take natural drainage features into account, whereas police boards may be based on the distribution of the population or the number of kilometres of street to be patrolled, and school attendance zones must consider the numbers of school-aged children and the capacities of individual schools.

Most North Americans live in large and small cities. In Canada these, too, are subdivided, not only into wards or precincts for voting purposes but also into special purpose bodies for such functions as fire and police protection, water and electricity supply, education, recreation and sanitation. These districts almost never coincide with one another, and the larger the urban area, the greater the proliferation of small, special-purpose agencies. Although no Canadian community has quite the multiplication of governmental entities plaguing many U.S. urban areas, major Canadian cities may find themselves with complex and growing systems of similar nature. Even before its major expansion on January 1, 1998, for example, Metropolitan Toronto had more than 100 identified authorities that could be classified as "local governments."

The existence of such a great number of districts in metropolitan areas may cause inefficiency in public services and hinder the orderly use of space. *Zoning by-laws,* for example, controlling

the uses to which land may be put, are determined by each municipality and are a clear example of the effect of political decisions on the division and development of space. Unfortunately, in large urban areas, the efforts of one community may be hindered by the practices of neighbouring communities. Thus, land zoned for an industrial park or shopping mall in one city may abut land zoned for single-family residences in an adjoining municipality. Each community pursues its own interests, which may not coincide with those of its neighbours or the larger region.

Inefficiency and duplication of effort characterize not just zoning but many of the services provided by local governments. The efforts of one community to avert air and water pollution may be, and often are, counteracted by the rules and practices of other towns in the region, although provincial and national environmental protection standards are now reducing such potential conflicts. Social as well as physical problems spread beyond city boundaries. Thus, nearby suburban communities are affected when a central city lacks the resources to maintain high-quality schools or to attack social ills. The provision of health care facilities, electricity and water, transportation, and recreational space affects the whole region and, many professionals think, should be under the control of a single consolidated metropolitan government.

The growth in the number and size of metropolitan areas has increased awareness of their administrative and jurisdictional problems. Too much governmental fragmentation and too little local control are both seen as metropolitan problems demanding attention and solution. The one concern is that multiple jurisdictions prevent the pooling of resources to address metropolitan-wide needs. The other is that local community needs and interests are subordinated to social and economic problems of a core city for which outlying communities feel little affinity or concern.

Want to Learn More?

The Evolution of the Modern State

http://en.wikibooks.org/wiki/
International_Relations:Evolution_of_the_
Modern_State_System

Political Boundary Setting in Africa

Abstract of an Article: www.springerlink
.com/content/qu867q6x87470p37/

How to Resolve Maritime Boundary Disputes

www.chathamhouse.org.uk/pdf/research/il/
ILP140206.doc

The United Nations

www.un.org/english/

Regional Alliances

The Marshall Plan
http://usinfo.state.gov/usa/infousa/facts/
democrac/57.htm

The European Union
http://europa.eu/

NAFTA
www.nafta-sec-alena.org/DefaultSite/index
.html

CARICOM
www.caricom.org/

MERCOSUR
www.mercosurtc.com/

ASEAN
www.aseansec.org/

APEC
www.apec.org/

Military Alliances

NATO www.nato.int/

Summary

The sovereign state is the dominant entity in the political subdivision of the world. It constitutes an expression of cultural separation and identity as pervasive as that inherent in language, religion, or ethnicity. A product of 18th-century political philosophy, the idea of the state was diffused globally by colonizing European powers. In most instances, the colonial boundaries they established have been retained as their international boundaries by newly independent countries.

The greatly varying physical characteristics of states contribute to national strength and stability. Relative location influences countries' economies and international roles, while national cores and capitals are the heartlands of states. Boundaries, the legal definition of a state's size and shape, determine the limits of its sovereignty. They may or may not reflect pre-existing cultural landscapes and in any given case may or may not prove to be viable. Whatever their nature, boundaries are at the root of many international disputes. Maritime boundary claims, particularly as reflected in the UN Convention on the Law of the Sea, add a new dimension to traditional claims of territorial sovereignty.

State cohesiveness is promoted by a number of centripetal forces. Among these are national symbols, a variety of institutions, and confidence in the aims, organization, and administration of government. Also helping to foster political and economic integration are transportation and communication connections. Destabilizing centrifugal forces, particularly ethnically based separatist movements, threaten the cohesion and stability of many states. Assessments of the possession and projection of national power have always coloured international relations. The validity of older geopolitical theories has recently been questioned in light of new developments involving organized terrorism and global competition between conflicting "civilizations."

Although the state remains central to the partitioning of the world, a broadening array of political entities affects people individually and collectively. Recent decades have seen a significant increase in supranationalism, in the form of a number and variety of global and regional alliances to which states have surrendered some sovereign powers. At the other end of the spectrum, expanding Anglo-American urban areas and governmental responsibilities raise questions of fairness in districting procedures and of effectiveness when political power is fragmented.

KEY WORDS

antecedent boundary 218
artificial boundary 218
autonomous nationalism 225
centrifugal force 222
centripetal force 222
colonialism 211
consequent (ethnographic) boundary 218
containment 232
core area 214
devolution 226

domino theory 233
electoral geography 242
European Union (EU) 238
exclusive economic zone (EEZ) 236
functional dispute 221
geometric boundary 218
geopolitics 232
gerrymandering 242
heartland theory 232
imperialism 211

irredentism 219
nation 209
nationalism 222
nation-state 209
natural boundary 218
physical boundary 218
political geography 208
positional dispute 219
regionalism 226
relic boundary 219
resource dispute 220

rimland theory 232
separatism 225
state 209
subsequent boundary 218
superimposed boundary 219
supranationalism 235
territorial dispute 219
terrorism 234
United Nations Convention on the Law of the Sea (UNCLOS) 236

FOR REVIEW

1. What are the differences between a *state*, a *nation*, and a *nation-state*? Why is a colony not a state? How can one account for the rapid increase in the number of states since World War II?

2. What attributes differentiate states from one another? How do a country's size and shape affect its power and stability? How can a piece of land be both an *enclave* and an *exclave*?

3. How can boundaries be classified? How do they create opportunities for conflict? Describe and give examples of three types of border disputes.

4. How does the United Nations Convention on the Law of the Sea define zones of diminishing national control? What are the consequences of the concept of the 200-nm *exclusive economic zone*?

5. Distinguish between *centripetal* and *centrifugal* political forces. What are some of the ways national cohesion and identity are achieved?

6. What characteristics are common to all or most regional autonomist movements? Where are some of these movements active? Why do they tend to be on the periphery rather than at the national core?

7. What types of international organizations and alliances can you name? What were the purposes of their establishment? What generalizations can you make regarding economic alliances?

8. How did MacKinder and Spykman differ in their assessments of Eurasia as a likely base for world conquest? What post-1945 developments suggest that there may be no enduring correlation between location and national power?

9. Why does it matter how boundaries are drawn around electoral districts? Theoretically, is it always possible to delimit boundaries "fairly"? Support your answer.

10. What reasons can you suggest for the great political fragmentation in Canada? What problems stem from such fragmentation?

11. Examine Figure 7.18 which gives Canada sovereignty over the Northwest Passage—currently an area under dispute with the United States. Complete research to determine of it is international waters (the US position) or not (the Canadian).

12. Some commentators have suggested that world organizations, such as the WTO, are extensions of US imperialism. Research this question.

FOCUS FOLLOW-UP

1. **What are the types and geographic characteristics of countries and the nature of their boundaries?** pp. 209–222.

   States are internationally recognized independent political entities. When culturally uniform, they may be termed nation-states. Their varying physical characteristics of size, shape, and location have implications for national power and cohesion. Boundaries define the limits of states' authority and underlie many international disputes.

2. **How do states maintain cohesiveness, instil nationalism, and project power internationally?** pp. 222–235.

   Cohesiveness is fostered through unifying institutions, education, and efficient transport and communication systems. It may be eroded by minority group separatist wishes and tendencies.

Older geopolitical theories of state military power projection have been modified by concepts of economic rivalry and conflicting cultural ideals.

3. **Why are international alliances proliferating, and what objectives do they espouse and serve?** pp. 235–240.

   In an economically and technologically changing world, alliances are presumed to increase the security and prosperity of states. The UN claims to represent and promote worldwide cooperation; its Law of the Sea regulates use and claims of the world's oceans. Regional alliances involving some reduction of national independence promote economic, military, or political objectives of groups of states related spatially or ideologically. They are expressions of the growing trend toward *supranationalism* in international affairs.

4. **What problems are evident in defining local political divisions in North America, and what solutions have been proposed or instituted?** pp. 240–244.

   The great political fragmentation within Canada and the United States reflects the creation of special-purpose agencies to satisfy a local or administrative need. States, counties, townships, cities, and innumerable special-purpose districts all have defined and often overlapping boundaries and functions. Voting rights, reapportionment, and local political boundary adjustments represent areas of continuing political concern and dispute. In the United States, racial gerrymandering is a current legal issue in voting district definition.

ONLINE LEARNING CENTRE

The World Wide Web has a tremendous number and variety of sites pertaining to geography. To access Web sites,

Internet exercises, self-quizzes, videos, and additional study tools relevant to this chapter's content, visit the *Human*

Geography Online Learning Centre at **www. mcgrawhill.ca/olc/fellmann**.

*Internationalization of commerce plays an
increasing role in America's economy.*

DYNAMIC SPACES OF CITIES AND ECONOMIES

The preceding chapters of Part Two focused on prominent characteristics of culture, cultural identities, and the political organization of space. The unifying theme stressed the cultural diversity of humanity, the spatial patterns of primary social markers—ethnicity, language, and religion—and the political systems employed to organize and control space. In Part 3 of our study of human geography, the theme switches from the construction of cultural identities and the political organization of space to the functional and dynamic spaces of cities and economies. Change, as we have seen, is the recurring theme of human societies, and in few other regards is change so pervasive as it is in the urban environment and in the economic orientations and activities of the modern world.

Urbanization has always accompanied economic advancement. Manufacturing, trade, and services imply concentrations, networks, and flows of workers, managers, merchants, and supporting populations and institutions. Chapter 8 looks at the systems of cities that contain an increasing proportion of the population of all culture realms. In them, too, are concentrated a growing share of the world's productive activities.

Cities, we shall see, are functional entities producing and exchanging goods, performing services, and administering the space economy for the larger, increasingly global society of which they are the operational focus. The functions they house and the kind of economy that has shaped them help determine the size and spatial patterns of the urban systems. Within those systems, each city is a separate landscape entity, distinct from surrounding non-urban areas. Internally, each displays a complex of land use arrangements and social geographies, in part unique to it but in part, as well, influenced by the cultural, economic, and ideological setting that it reflects. Both city systems and internal city structures are fundamental features of spatial organization and of cultural differentiation.

Food and raw material production still dominate the landscape of some economies and areas, but increasingly the world's people are engaging in activities—labelled secondary, tertiary, and quarternary—that involve the processing and exchange of produced primary materials and the provision of personal, business, and professional services. Simultaneously, economically advanced societies are becoming "post-industrial" while those less advanced seek the prosperity and benefits that are promised by "development." Cultural convergence, through shared technologies and intertwined economies, has served to reduce the distinguishing features that formerly were preserved in economic isolation. Increasingly, economic development of peoples in all parts of the world has imposed new pressures on the environment to accommodate new patterns of production and exploitation.

Our concern in Chapters 9, 10, and 11 will be with the dynamic changes in economic patterns and orientations of regions and societies that have emerged with the development and integration of the world's space economy. These patterns of livelihood, production, and exchange augment and complement the understandings of regional cultural differentiation we have already explored. They add an awareness of the economic unity, diversity, and change so prominent in modern society and so essential to our fuller appreciation of the spatial mosaic of culture.

CHAPTER

URBAN SYSTEMS AND URBAN STRUCTURES

Aims

- To introduce the nature and spatial organization of urban settlements
- To identify economic and social patterns and processes of urban systems
- To explain the formation of suburbs and central cities
- To convey the global diversity of urban structures

Some specific considerations for review:

*C*airo was a world-class city in the 14th century. Situated at the crossroads of Africa, Asia, and Europe, it dominated trade on the Mediterranean Sea. By the early 1300s, it had a population of half a million or more, with 10- to 14-storey buildings crowding the city centre. A Cairo chronicler of the period recorded the construction of a huge building with shops on the first floors and apartments housing 4000 people above. One Italian visitor estimated that more people lived on a single Cairo street than in all of Florence. Travellers from all over Europe and Asia made their way to Cairo, and the shipping at its port of Bulaq outdistanced that of Venice and Genoa combined. The city contained more than 12,000 shops, some specializing in luxury goods from all over the world—Siberian sable, chain mail, musical instruments, luxurious cloth, and exotic songbirds. Travellers marvelled at the size, density, and variety of Cairo, comparing it favourably with Venice, Paris, and Baghdad.

Today, Cairo is a vast, sprawling metropolis, plagued by many of the problems common to the urbanization of developing countries in which population growth has far outstripped economic development. The 1970 population of Egypt was 35.3 million; it had grown to more than 76 million by 2004, thanks to migrants flocking from the countryside, improved health care in general, a dramatic drop in infant mortality, and lengthening of life expectancy. An estimated 15 million people reside in the Cairo greater metropolitan area; the metro area contains 45% of all Egyptian urban dwellers and 20% of the entire population of the country. Cairo city alone holds 11 million residents at a density of more than 32,000 per square kilometre (83,000 per sq mi). And the city continues to grow, spreading onto valued farmland and decreasing food production for the country's increasing population.

A steady stream of migrants arrives daily in Cairo where, they hope, opportunities will be available for a better and brighter life than in the crowded countryside. The city is the symbol of modern Egypt, a place where young people are willing to undergo deprivation for the chance to "make it." But real opportunities continue to be scarce. The poor, of whom there are millions, crowd into row after row of apartment houses, many of them poorly constructed. Tens of thousands more live in rooftop sheds or small boats on the Nile; a half million find shelter living between the tombs in the Northern and Southern Cemeteries—known as the Cities of the Dead—on Cairo's eastern edge. On occasion, buildings collapse; the earthquake of October 12, 1992, measuring 5.9 on the Richter scale, did enormous damage, levelling thousands of structures.

One's first impression when arriving in central Cairo is of opulence, a stark contrast to what lies outside the city centre. High-rise apartments, regional headquarter buildings of multinational corporations, and modern hotels stand amid clogged streets, symbols of the new Egypt (Figure 8.1). New suburban developments and exclusive residential communities create enclaves for the wealthy whose plush apartments are but a short distance from the slums that house a largely unemployed 20% of Cairo's population. Like cities nearly everywhere in the developing world, Cairo has experienced explosive growth that finds an increasing proportion of the country's population housed in an urban area without the economy or facilities to support them all. Street congestion and idling traffic generate

FIGURE 8.1 **Sprawling Cairo, Egypt.** The population growth in the greater metropolitan area—from some 3 million in 1970 to an estimated 15 million today—has been mirrored in most developing countries. The rapid expansion of urban areas and populations brings housing shortages, inadequate transportation and other infrastructure development, unemployment, poverty, and environmental deterioration.

air pollution now worse than that of Mexico City, long the holder of that world record. Both the Nile River and the city's treated drinking water show dangerous levels of lead and cadmium, the unwanted by-products of the local lead smelter.

An Urbanizing World

Figure 8.2 gives evidence that the growth of major metropolitan areas was astounding in the 20th century. Some 411 metropolitan areas each had in excess of 1 million people in 2000; in 1900, there were only 12. Expectations are for 564 "million cities" in 2015. As many as 25 metropolises had populations of more than 10 million people in 2006, the United Nations calls them *megacities* (Figure 8.3). In 1900, none was of that size. It follows, of course, that since the world's total population has greatly increased over the centuries, so too would its urban component—from 2% in 1800 to half in 2007. The urban share of the total has everywhere increased greatly as urbanization has spread to all parts of the globe. Indeed, in 2007, for the first time in history, more people are living in cities than in rural areas.

The amount of urban growth differs from continent to continent and from region to region (Figure 8.4), but nearly all countries have two things in common: the proportion of their people living in cities is rising, and the cities themselves are large and growing. In consequence, most of the world's people are city dwellers. Over half the world's population now lives in cities and urban majorities exist in essentially all regions of the world (Figure 8.5)—reaching 60% of the world's population by 2030. The vast majority of urban growth will occur in low- to middle-income countries of the developing world, but even the

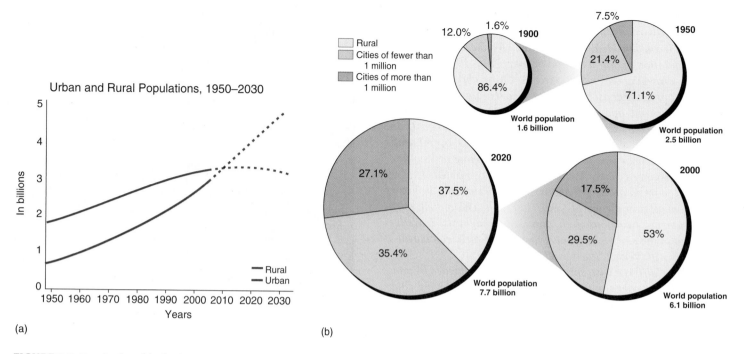

FIGURE 8.2 Trends of world urbanization document the steady decline in rural population proportions throughout the 20th century. (*a*) Since 1950, the growth rate of the rural component has slackened compared to the urban rate. (*b*) The United Nations estimates that virtually all the population growth expected during 2000–2020 will be concentrated in the urban areas of the world and that small and medium-sized cities will increase more rapidly than will megacities.

Sources: (a) United Nations, World Urbanization Prospects: The 2003 Revision; (b) Population Reference Bureau, United Nations, and other sources.

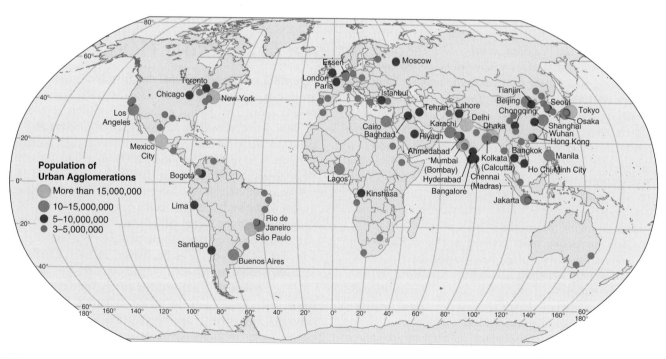

FIGURE 8.3 Metropolitan areas of 3 million or more in 2006. Only metropolitan areas with a population of 5 million or more are named. Massive urbanized districts are no longer characteristic only of the industrialized, developed countries. They are now found on every continent, in all latitudes, as part of most economies and societies. Not all cities in congested areas are shown.

Source: Data from United Nations Population Division.

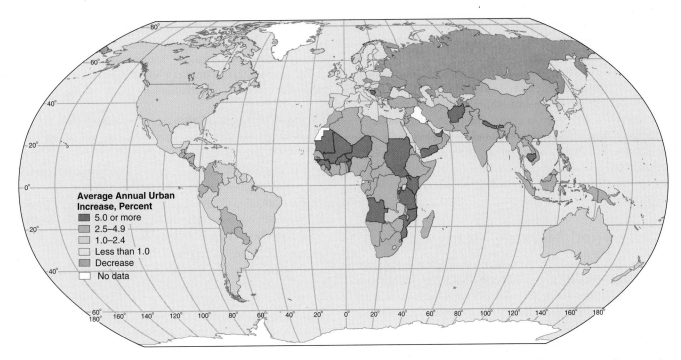

FIGURE 8.4 Average annual urban population growth rates, 1995–2004. In general, developing countries show the highest percentage increases in their urban populations, and the already highly urbanized and industrialized countries have the lowest—less than 1% per year in most of Europe. Demographers anticipate that population increase in cities in developing countries will be the distinguishing demographic trend of the 21st century. In contrast to their patterns of growth, the cities of Russia and most of the states formerly within its empire have experienced population decline since the break-up of the Soviet Union in 1991. An urban growth rate of 5% means that a country's city population will double in just 14 years.

Source: Data from United Nations Population Division.

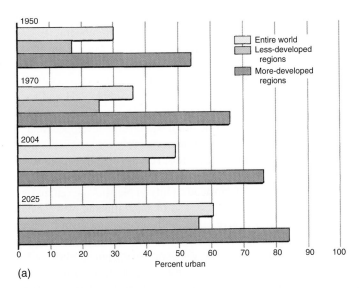

(a)

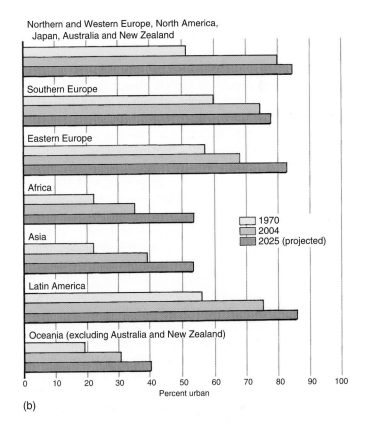

(b)

FIGURE 8.5 (*a*) **Percentage of population that was urban.** The rapid growth of urban percentages in the developing world is clearly shown here. The UN projects that the less-developed regions will have accounted for 93% of global urban population increase that occurs between 1970 and 2020. (*b*) **World regional urbanization levels.** Within the larger continental summaries shown, regional differences in urbanization levels may be pronounced. Within Asia, for example, national levels range (2004) from about 8% in East Timor to over 90% in Israel and Qatar and 100% for Kuwait and Singapore. The World Bank claims too-liberal national definitions of urban overstate the city dweller portion of Latin American population; the Bank calculates the region's 2004 urban component was less than 60%, not the 75% shown here. See also Figure 4.31.

Source: Data from United Nations Population Division.

high-income, highly developed states—with low or negative rates of natural population increase—will experience multicultural expansion from international migrants seeking opportunities in their cities. Worldwide in 2006, there were at least 200 million documented international migrants (and untold millions more not officially traced), almost all of whom—whatever their destination country—seek refuge in cities. The result everywhere is growing urban multiculturalism with attendant problems of social fragmentation and minority segregation, isolation, and poverty affecting primarily the largest cities of the inflow states. The proportion of people living in urban areas in Canada has grown from 37% in 1901, to 76% in 1976, and to 80% in 2006.

Mega-cities and Merging Metropolises

The emergence of mega-cities—a term originally coined by the UN in the 1970s—aroused dire predictions that there would soon be cities of totally unmanageable size—25 million inhabitants or more. At that time it was thought that by the early 1980s, supercities would dominate the world urban structure and distort the economies and city hierarchies of countries everywhere. The UN anticipated that 22 cities of 10 million or more size would be present in 2015. Fears as well were voiced of catastrophic human poverty and unbearable environmental deterioration thought certain to accompany such mega-city growth. Those size predictions now appear to have been overblown in many cases, reflecting simple projections of estimated past percentage and numerical increases. In reality, both personal migration choices and corporate and government investment decisions have resulted in growth rates and city sizes below those once anticipated. Largest cities have proved not to be the fastest growing agglomerations; mega-cities in 1975 held 2% of world population; in 2006 they contained only 4% of world population and are expected to hold less than 5% by 2015. Although data are not totally conclusive, the earlier rapid expansion of many mega-cities has been slowing, and some of the largest may now, in fact, be stabilized or even losing population. While São Paulo and Mexico City may, indeed, have stabilized, mid-size cities such as Curitiba (Brazil) and Monterrey (Mexico) within the same countries are growing, with at least part of their growth representing out-migrants from the mega-cities and government programs encouraging investment and population retention within smaller towns and mid-sized cities. While it is certain that growth rates have slowed for most developing country mega-cities in recent years, even those lower rates represent more new residents each year than during the middle of the 20th century because the rates are applied to an expanding population base.

When separate major metropolitan complexes of whatever size expand along the superior transportation facilities connecting them, they may eventually meet, bind together at their outer margins, and create the extensive metropolitan regions or **conurbations** suggested on Figure 8.3. Where this increasingly common pattern has emerged, the urban landscape can no longer be described in simple terms. No longer is there a single city with a single downtown area set off by open countryside from any other urban unit in its vicinity. Rather, we must now recognize extensive regions of continuous urbanization made up of multiple centres that have come together at their edges.

Megalopolis, encountered later in Chapter 10, is the major conurbation of North America, a nearly continuous urban string that stretches from north of Boston (southern Maine) to south of Washington, D.C. (southern Virginia). Other North American present or emerging conurbations include

- the southern Great Lakes region stretching from north of Milwaukee through Chicago and eastward to Detroit, Cleveland, and Pittsburgh;
- the Coastal California zone of San Francisco—Los Angeles—San Diego—Tijuana, Mexico;
- the Canadian "core region" conurbation from Montreal to Windsor, opposite Detroit, Michigan, where it connects with the southern Great Lakes region;
- the Vancouver—Portland strip ("Cascadia") in the West, and the Gulf Coast and the Coastal Florida zones in the Southeast (Figure 8.6).

Outside North America, examples of conurbations are numerous and growing, still primarily in the most industrialized European and East Asian (Japanese) districts, but forming as well in other world regions where urban clusters and mega-cities emerged in developing countries still primarily rural in residential pattern (see Figure 8.3).

Settlement Roots

The major cities of today had humbler origins, their roots lying in the clustered dwellings which everywhere have been the rule of human settlement. People are gregarious and cooperative. Even Stone Age hunters and gatherers lived and worked in groups, not as single individuals or isolated families. Primitive cultures are communal for protection, cooperative effort, sharing of tasks by age and gender, and for more subtle psychological and social reasons. Communal dwelling became the near-universal rule with the advent of sedentary agriculture wherever it developed, and the village became the norm of human society.

In most of the world still, most rural people live in nucleated settlements, that is, in villages or hamlets, rather than in dispersed dwellings or isolated farmsteads. Only in North America, parts of northern and western Europe, and in Australia and New Zealand do rural folk tend to live apart, with houses and farm buildings located on land that is individually worked. In those regions, farmsteads tend to be spatially separate one from another, and the farm village is a much less common settlement form. Communal settlements were not, of course, unknown in North America. Mormon Utah, Mennonite Manitoba, and other districts of cluster migration (see Figure 5.14) were frequently village-centred, as were such cooperative and utopian communities as Oneida, New York; Amana, Iowa; New Harmony, Indiana; the various Shaker settlements; and others of the 19th century. Elsewhere in the world, villages and hamlets were the settlement norm, though with size and form that varied by region and culture. Intensity of agricultural land use, density of population, complexity and specialization of life and livelihood, and addition of functions other than the purely residential affected the size, distribution, external form, and internal structure of settlements (Figures 8.7 and 8.8).

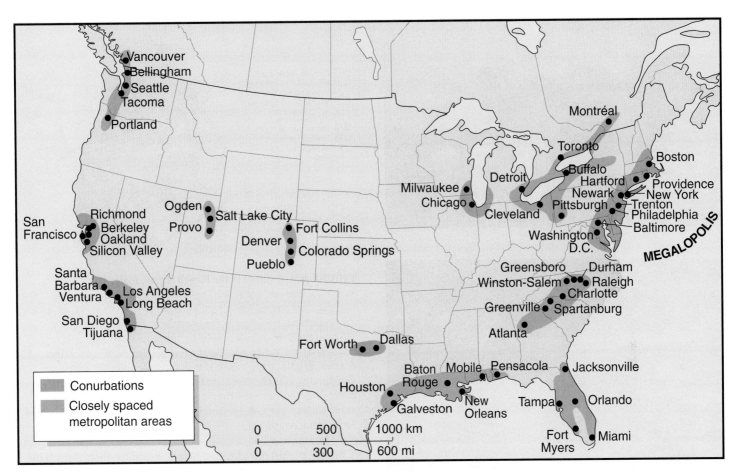

FIGURE 8.6 Megalopolis and other North American conurbations. The northeast U.S. Boston-to-Norfolk urban corridor comprises the original and largest *Megalopolis* and contains the economic, political, and administrative core of the United States. A Canadian counterpart core region anchored by Montreal and Toronto connects with U.S. conurbations through Buffalo, New York, and Detroit, Michigan. For some of their extent, conurbations fulfill their classic definition of continuous built-up urban areas. In other portions, they are more statistical than landscape entities, marked by counties that qualify as "urban" or "metropolitan" even though land uses may appear dominantly rural.

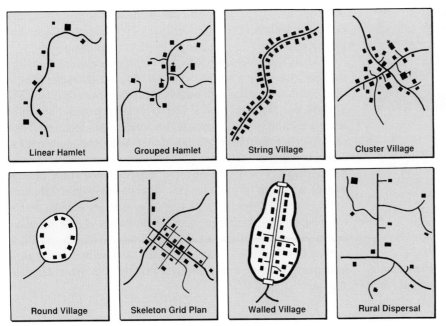

FIGURE 8.7 Basic settlement forms. The smallest organized rural clusters of houses and non-residential structures are commonly called *hamlets*, and may contain only 10–15 buildings. *Villages* are larger agglomerations, although not as sizeable or functionally complex as urban *towns*. The distinction between village and town is usually a statistical definition that varies by country.

Source: Redrawn from Introducing Cultural Geography, *2nd ed., by Joseph E. Spencer and William L. Thomas. © 1978 John Wiley & Sons, Inc. Used by permission of John Wiley & Sons, Inc.*

(a)

(b)

(c)

FIGURE 8.8 Rural settlements in largely subsistence economies vary from the rather small populations characteristic of compact African villages, such as the Zulu village, or kraal, in South Africa shown in (a), to more dispersed and populous settlements such as the Nepalese high pasture summer village of Konar seen in (b), to the very large, densely populated Indian rural communities like that seen in (c).

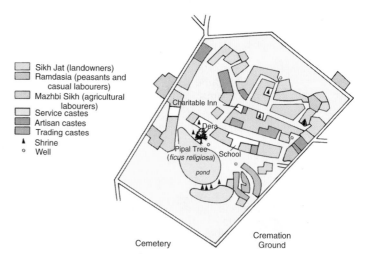

Sikh Jat (landowners)
Ramdasia (peasants and casual labourers)
Mazhbi Sikh (agricultural labourers)
Service castes
Artisan castes
Trading castes
▲ Shrine
○ Well

FIGURE 8.9 A village in the Punjab region, India. In the 1960s, Kunran village had some 1000 inhabitants of several different occupational castes. Most numerous were the Sikh Jat (landowners: 76 households), Ramdasia (peasants and casual labourers: 27 households), and Mazhbi Sikh (agricultural labourers: 12 households). Other castes (and occupations) included Tarkhan (carpenter), Bazigar (acrobat), Jhiwar (water carrier), Sunar (goldsmith), Nai (barber), and Bania (shopkeeper). The trades, crafts, and services they (and others) pursued created a more complex land use pattern than is implied by the generalized village forms depicted on Figure 8.7.

Source: Redrawn with permission from Jan O. M. Broek and John M. Webb, A Geography of Mankind, © 1968 McGraw-Hill, Inc.

Rural settlements in developing countries are often considered as expressions of subsistence economic systems in which farming and fishing cultures produce no more than their individual families can consume. That clearly is not always the case. Even in the poorest farm settlements of India or Bangladesh, for example, there is a good deal of trading, buying, and selling of farm goods and family crafts for other needed commodities, and at least some village land is used for other than residential purposes (Figure 8.9). The farming or fishing settlement itself, however, may be nearly self-contained, with little commercial exchange with neighbouring villages or between villages and distant cities.

When trade does develop between two or more rural settlements, they begin to take on new physical characteristics as their inhabitants engage in additional types of occupations. The villages lose the purely social and residential character of subsistence agricultural settlements and assume urban features. There is a tendency for the houses to cluster along the main road or roads, creating a linear, cross, or star-like pattern. No longer are the settlements nearly completely self-contained; they become part of a system of communities. The beginnings of urbanization are seen in the types of buildings that are erected and in the heightened importance of the main streets and of the roads leading to other settlements. The location of villages relative to one another becomes significant as the once self-sufficient rural settlements become towns and cities engaged in urban activities and interchange.

The Nature of Cities

Cities are among the oldest marks of civilization. Dating from at least 6000 years or more ago, they originated in—or diffused from—the culture hearths that first developed sedentary agriculture. They are as well among the newest experiences of a growing share of the world's population. Whether ancient or modern, all cities show recurring themes and regularities appropriate to their time and place of existence.

First, all of them perform functions—have an economic base—generating the income necessary to support themselves and their contained population. Second, none exists in a vacuum; each is part of a larger society, culture, and economy with which it has essential reciprocal connections. That is, each is a unit in a system of cities and a focus for a surrounding non-urban area. Third, each urban unit has a more or less orderly internal arrangement of land uses, social groups, and economic functions. These arrangements may be partially planned and controlled and partially determined by individual decisions and market forces. Finally, all cities, large or small, ancient or modern, have experienced problems of land use, social conflict, and environmental concern. Yet cities, though flawed, remain the capstone of our cultures, the organizing foci of modern societies, cultures, and economies, and the magnet of people everywhere.

Whatever their size, age, or location, urban settlements exist for the efficient performance of functions required by the society that creates them. They reflect the saving of time, energy, and money that the agglomeration of people and activities implies. The more accessible the producer to the consumer, the worker to the workplace, the citizen to the town hall, the worshiper to the church, or the lawyer or doctor to the client, the more efficient is the performance of their separate activities, and the more effective is the integration of urban functions.

Urban areas may provide all or some of the following types of functions: retailing, wholesaling, manufacturing, professional and personal services, entertainment, business and political administration, military defence, educational and religious functions, and transportation and communication services. Because all urban functions and people cannot be located at a single point, cities themselves must take up space, and land uses and populations must have room within them. Because interconnection is essential, the nature of the transportation system will have an enormous bearing on the total number of services that can be performed, and the efficiency with which they can be carried out. The totality of people and functions of a city constitutes a distinctive cultural landscape whose similarities and differences from place to place are the subjects for urban geographic analysis.

Some Definitions

Urban units are not of a single type, structure, or size. Their common characteristic is that they are nucleated, non-agricultural settlements. At one end of the size scale, urban areas are hamlets or small towns with at most a single, short main street of shops; at the opposite end, they are complex, multifunctional metropolitan areas or supercities (Figure 8.10). The word *urban* is often used to describe such places as a town, city, suburb, and metropolitan area, but it is a general term, not used to specify a particular type or size of settlement. Although the terms designating the different types of urban settlement, like *city*, are employed in common speech, not everyone uses them in the same way. What is recognized as a city by a resident of rural Newfoundland might not at all be afforded that name and status by an inhabitant of South western

(a)

(b)

FIGURE 8.10 The differences in size, density, and land use complexity are immediately apparent between (*a*) New York City and (*b*) a small Ohio town. Clearly, one is a city, one is a town, but both are *urban*.

Ontario. It is necessary in this chapter to agree on the meanings of terms commonly employed but varyingly interpreted.

The words **city** and **town** denote nucleated settlements, multifunctional in character, including an established central business district and both residential and non-residential land uses. Towns are smaller in size and have less functional complexity than cities, but they still have a nuclear business concentration. **Suburb** implies a subsidiary area, a functionally specialized segment of a larger urban complex. It may be dominantly or exclusively residential, industrial, or commercial, but by the specialization of its land uses and functions, a suburb is not self-sufficient. It depends on and is integrated with urban areas outside of its boundaries. Suburbs can, however, be independent political entities. For large cities having many suburbs, it is common to call that part of the urban area contained within the official boundaries of the main city around which the suburbs have been built the **central city**.

Some or all of these urban types may be associated into larger landscape units. The **urbanized area** refers to a continuously built-up landscape defined by building and population densities with no reference to political boundaries. It may be viewed as the *physical city* and may contain a central city and many contiguous cities, towns, suburbs, and other urban tracts. A **metropolitan area**, on the other hand, refers to a large-scale *functional* entity, perhaps containing several urbanized areas, discontinuously built-up but nonetheless operating as an integrated economic whole. Figure 8.11 shows these areas in a hypothetical American county.

The concept of "metropolitan" can vary between countries and may be redefined from time to time to summarize the realities of the changing population, physical size, and functions of urban regions. In Canada, Statistics Canada currently defines a **census metropolitan area (CMA)** as consisting of one or more adjacent municipalities situated around a major urban core with a population of at least 100,000 (see Chapter 2). To form a census agglomeration, the similar but smaller version of the CMA, the urban core must have a population of at least 10,000. In addition to its 33 census metropolitan areas, which are home to 25.1 million Canadians in 2006, urban Canada is also comprised of 111 mid-size urban centres, which are referred to as census agglomerations areas (CAs) by Statistics Canada (Tables 8.1 and 8.2). These areas have an urban core of at least 10,000 but are not CMAs. Some of the highest growth rates in Canada between 2001 and 2006 occurred within CAs, many of which are located in Alberta (Table 8.2). Some 4.1 million Canadians lived in its 111 CAs. In the United States, the Bureau of the Census currently defines metropolitan statistical areas as comprised of a central county or counties with at least one urbanized area of at least 50,000 population, plus adjacent outlying counties with a high degree of social and economic integration with the central county as measured by commuting volumes. A metropolitan statistical area is a similar but smaller version of the metropolitan concept. It is based on a central city county

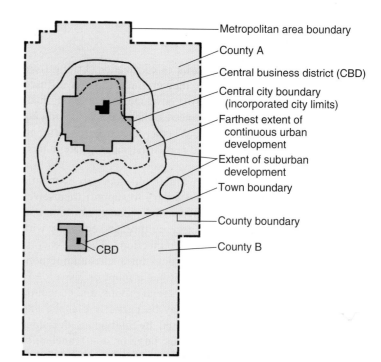

FIGURE 8.11 A hypothetical spatial arrangement of urban units within a metropolitan area. Sometimes official limits of the central city are very extensive and contain areas commonly considered suburban or even rural. On the other hand, older eastern U.S. cities (and some such as San Francisco in the West) more often have restricted limits and contain only part of the high-density land uses and populations of their metropolitan or urbanized areas.

with at least one urban cluster of between 10,000 and 50,000 population plus outlying counties with considerable social and economic integration with it. When comparing metropolitan areas between countries and over time, one must keep such differences in mind (see Tables 8.1, 8.2, 8.3, and 8.4).

The Location of Urban Settlements

Urban centres are functionally connected to other cities and to rural areas. In fact, the reason for the existence of an urban unit is not only to provide services for itself, but for others outside of it. The urban centre is a consumer of food, a processor of materials, and an accumulator and dispenser of goods and services. But it must depend on outside areas for its essential supplies and as a market for its products and activities.

In order to adequately perform the tasks that support it and to add new functions as demanded by the larger economy, the city must be efficiently located. That efficiency may be marked by centrality to the area served. It may derive from the physical characteristics of its site. Or placement may be related to the resources, productive regions, and transportation network of the country so that the effective performance of a wide array of activities is possible.

TABLE 8.1

Population (2006) and Growth Rate (2001–2006) in Canada's CMAs

Rank	CMA	2006 Population	Growth Rate (%)
1	Toronto, ON	5,113,149	9.2
2	Montreal, QUE	3,635,571	5.3
3	Vancouver, BC	2,116,581	6.5
4	Ottawa–Gatineau, ON/QUE	1,130,761	5.9
5	Calgary, AB	1,079,310	13.4
6	Edmonton, AB	1,034,945	10.4
7	Quebec, QUE	715,515	4.2
8	Winnipeg, MB	694,668	2.7
9	Hamilton, ON	692,911	4.6
10	London, ON	457,720	5.1
11	Kitchener, ON	451,235	8.9
12	St Catherines–Niagara, ON	390,317	3.5
13	Halifax, NS	372,858	3.8
14	Oshawa, ON	330,594	11.6
15	Victoria, BC	330,088	5.8
16	Windsor, ON	323,342	5.0
17	Saskatoon, SK	233,923	3.5
18	Regina, SK	194,971	1.1
19	Sherbrook, QUE	186,952	6.3
20	St. John's, NFLD	181,113	4.7
21	Barrie, ON	177,061	19.2
22	Kelowna, BC	162,276	9.8
23	Abbotsford, BC	159,020	7.9
24	Greater Sudbury/Grand Sudbury, ON	158,258	1.7
25	Kingston, ON	152,358	3.8
26	Saguenay, QUE	151,643	−2.1
27	Trois-Rivières, QUE	141,529	2.9
28	Guelph, ON	127,009	8.2
29	Moncton, NB	126,424	6.5
30	Brantford, ON	124,607	5.5
31	Thunder Bay, ON	122,907	0.8
32	Saint John, NB	122,389	−0.2
33	Peterborough, ON	116,570	5.1

Source: Adapted from Statistics Canada, "Portrait of the Canadian Population in 2006," 2006 Census, p. 22, Catalogue no. 97-550-XIE. Found at http://www12.statcan.ca/english/census06/analysis/popdwell/pdf/97-550-XIE2006001.pdf.

TABLE 8.2

Fastest Growing mid-size cities (CAs) in Canada (% increase 2001–2006)

Rank	Census Agglomeration	% Increase
1	Okotoks, AB	46.7
2	Wood Buffalo, AB	23.6
3	Grande Prairie, AB	22.3
4	Red Deer, AB	22.0
5	Yellowknife, NWT	13.1
6	Lloydminster, SK/AB	12.8
7	Canmore, AB	11.6
8	Medicine Hat, AB	11.5
9	Saint-Jean-sure-Richelieu, QUE	9.9
10	Joliette, QUE	9.8

Source: Adapted from Statistics Canada, "Portrait of the Canadian Population in 2006," 2006 Census, p. 24, Catalogue no. 97-550-XIE. Found at http://www12.statcan.ca/english/census06/analysis/popdwell/pdf/97-550-XIE2006001.pdf.

TABLE 8.3

Largest Combined Metropolitan Statistical Areas in United States (Population in 2007)[a]

Rank	CMSA	Population
1	New York–Newark–Bridgeport, NY–NJ–CT–PA	21,961,994
2	Los Angeles–Long Beach–Riverside, CA	17,755,322
3	Chicago–Naperville–Michigan City, IL–IN–WI	9,745,165
4	Washington–Baltimore–Northern Virginia, DC–MD–VA–WV	8,241,912
5	Boston–Worcester–Manchester, MA–RI–NH	7,476,689
6	San Jose–San Francisco–Oakland, CA	7,264,887
7	Dallas–Fort Worth, TX	6,498,410
8	Philadelphia–Camden–Vineland, PA–NJ–DE–MD	6,385,461
9	Houston–Baytown–Huntsville, TX	5,729,027
10	Atlanta–Sandy Springs–Gainesville, GA–AL	5,626,400

Source: http://www.census.gov/popest/metro/tables/2007/CBSA-EST2007-02.xls.

[a] The U.S. Census Bureau defines a Consolidated Metropolitan Statistical area (CMSA) as an area composed of more than one Metropolitan Statistical area and containing more than 1 million people.

TABLE 8.4

Fastest Growing Metropolitan Statistical Areas in the United States[b] (% increase 2000–2007)

Rank	Metropolitan statistical area	% Increase
1	Palm Coast, FL	77.4
2	St. George, UT	48.1
3	Greeley, CO /1	34.8
4	Cape Coral–Fort Myers, FL	33.9
5	Bend, OR	33.5
6	Las Vegas–Paradise, NV	33.5
7	Raleigh–Cary, NC	31.4
8	Provo–Orem, UT	30.9
9	Gainesville, GA	29.3
10	Phoenix–Mesa–Scottsdale, AZ	28.5

[b] The U.S. Census Bureau defines a Metropolitan Statistical area (MSA) as an economically integrated urbanized area in one or more contiguous counties.

Source: http://www.census.gov/popest/metro/tables/2007/CBSA-EST2007-07.xls.

In discussing urban settlement location, geographers usually mention the significance of site and situation, concepts already introduced in Chapter 1 (see Figures 1.8 and 1.9). You will recall that *site* refers to the exact terrain features associated with the city, as well as—less usefully—to its absolute (globe grid) location. Classifications of cities according to site characteristics have been proposed, recognizing special placement circumstances. These include *break-of-bulk* locations such as river crossing points where cargoes and people must interrupt a journey; *head-of-navigation* or *bay head* locations where the limits of water transportation are reached; and *railhead* locations where the railroad ended. In Europe, security and defence—island locations or elevated sites—were considerations in earlier settlement locations. Waterpower sites of earlier stages and coalfield sites of later phases of the Industrial Revolution (Chapters 9 and 10) represent a union of environmental and cultural-economic considerations.

If site suggests absolute location, *situation* indicates relative location that places a settlement in relation to the physical and cultural characteristics of surrounding areas. Very often it is important to know what kinds of possibilities and activities exist in the area near a settlement, such as the distribution of raw materials, market areas, agricultural regions, mountains, and oceans. Although in many ways more important than site in understanding the functions and growth potentials of cities, situation is more nearly unique to each settlement and does not lend itself to easy generalization.

The site or situation that originally gave rise to an urban unit may not remain the essential ingredient for its growth and development for very long. Agglomerations originally successful for whatever reason may by their success attract people and activities totally unrelated to the initial localizing forces. By what has been called a process of "circular and cumulative causation" (see p. 260), a successful urban unit may acquire new populations and functions attracted by the already existing markets, labour force, and urban facilities.

The Functions of Cities

The key concept is *function*—what cities actually do within the larger society and economy that established them. No city stands alone. Each is linked to other towns and cities in an interconnected city system; each provides services and products for its surrounding tributary region—its *hinterland* or trade area. Those linkages reflect complementarity and the processes of spatial interaction that we explored in Chapter 3; they are rooted in the different functions performed by different units within the urban system. However, not all of the activities carried on within a city are intended to connect that city with the outside world. Some are necessary simply to support the city itself. Together, these two levels of activity make up the **economic base** of an urban settlement.

The Economic Base

Part of the employed population of an urban unit is engaged either in the production of goods or the performance of services for areas and people outside the city itself. They are workers engaged in "export" activities, whose efforts result in money flowing into the community. Collectively, they constitute the **basic sector** of the city's total economic structure. Other workers support themselves by producing goods or services for residents of the urban unit itself. Their efforts, necessary to the well-being and the successful operation of the settlement, do not generate new money for it but comprise a **service** or **non-basic sector** of its economy. These people are responsible for the internal functioning of the urban unit. They are crucial to the continued operation of its stores, professional offices, city government, local transit, and school systems.

The total economic structure of an urban area equals the sum of its basic and non-basic activities. In actuality, it is the rare urbanite who can be classified as belonging entirely to one sector or another. Some part of the work of most people involves financial interaction with residents of other areas. Dentists, for example, may have mainly local patients and thus are members of the non-basic sector, but the moment they provide a service to someone from outside the community, they bring new money into the city and become part of the basic sector.

Variations in basic employment structure among urban units characterize the specific functional role played by individual cities. Most centres perform many export functions, and the larger the urban unit, the more multifunctional it becomes. Nonetheless, even in cities with a diversified economic base, one or a very small number of export activities, tends to dominate the structure of the community and to identify its operational purpose within a system of cities.

Such functional specialization permits the classification of cities into categories: manufacturing, retailing, wholesaling, transportation, government, and so on. Such specialization may also evoke images when the city is named: Ottawa, Canada, in government; Detroit, Michigan, or Tokyo, Japan, as manufacturing centres; Tulsa, Oklahoma, for oil production; Nice, France, as a resort, and so on. Certain large regional, national, or world capitals—as befits major multifunctional concentrations—call up a whole series of mental associations, such as New York with banking, the stock exchange, entertainment, the fashion industry, port activities, and others.

Simmons and McCann (2006) examined employment growth rates by sector in Canada for the period 1991–2003 (Table 8.5). They observed that the greatest growth took place in retail and wholesale activities, and in business and other commercial activities. While these favour big cities, they are not always well-paying jobs. They also suggested that the slow growth in the manufacturing sector was related to the Canada–US Free Trade Agreement of 1989. They suggested that it promoted a more specialized and city-based labour force in order to compete with other manufacturing centres from around the world.

Base Ratios

Assuming it were possible to divide with complete accuracy the employed population of a city into totally separate basic and service (non-basic) components, a ratio between the two employment groups could be established. With exception for some high-income communities, this *basic/non-basic ratio* is roughly similar for urban units of similar size irrespective of their functional specializations. Further, as a settlement increases in size, the number of non-basic personnel grows faster than the number of new basic workers. Thus, in cities with a population of 1 million, the ratio is about two non-basic workers for every basic worker. The addition

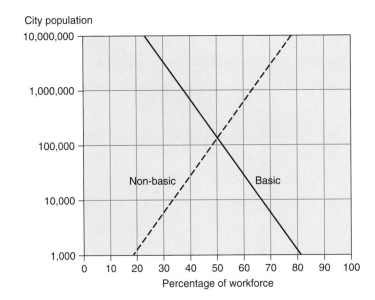

FIGURE 8.12 A generalized representation of the proportion of the work force engaged in basic and non-basic activities. As settlements become larger, a greater proportion of the workforce is employed in non-basic activities. Larger centres are therefore more self-contained.

of 10 new basic employees implies the expansion of the labour force by 30 (10 basic, 20 non-basic) and an increase in total population equal to the added workers plus their dependants. A **multiplier effect** thus exists, associated with economic growth. The term implies the addition of non-basic workers and dependants to a city's total employment and population as a supplement to new basic employment. The size of the multiplier effect is determined by the community's basic/non-basic ratio (Figure 8.12).

TABLE 8.5				
Employment Growth by Economic Sector in Canada, 1991–2003				
	Employment (000s)	**1991–2003 Change (000s)**	**Percentage Change**	**Share of GDP (%)**
Agriculture, fishing, and forestry	440	−161	−26.8	2.3
Mining	150	−2	−1.5	3.6
Manufacturing	2,047	203	14.4	17.3
Construction	643	146	29.5	5.4
Transportation and utilities	725	37	5.4	7.2
Trade	2,349	416	21.5	11.8
Finance and Real Estate	803	51	6.8	20.1
Business Services and Communication	1,680	617	57.6	10.7
Commercial Services	1,689	361	27.4	5.5
Community Services (education and health)	2,314	244	11.8	10.5
Public Administration	766	−4	−0.5	5.7
TOTAL	**13,606**	**2,268**	**20.0**	**100.0**

Source: Simmons and McCann (2006).

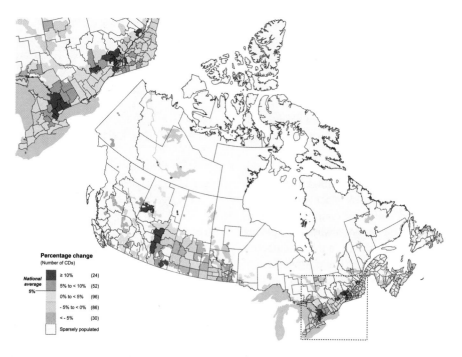

FIGURE 8.13 Population Growth in Canada: 2001–2006 by Census Division.

Source: 2001 to 2006 Censuses of Canada. Produced by the Geography Division, Statistics Canada, 2007. Located in Catalogue no. 97-550-XIE, p. 43. Found on http://www12.statcan.ca/english/census06/analysis/popdwell/pdf/97-550-XIE2006001.pdf.

The changing numerical relationships shown in Figure 8.12 are understandable when we consider how settlements add functions and grow in population. A new industry selling services to other communities requires new workers who thus increase the basic workforce. These new employees, in turn, demand certain goods and services, such as clothing, food, and medical assistance, which are provided locally. Those who perform such services must themselves have services available to them. For example, a grocery clerk must also buy groceries. The more non-basic workers a city has, the more non-basic workers are needed to support them, and the application of the multiplier effect becomes obvious.

The growth of cities may be self-generating—"circular and cumulative"—in a way related not to the development of industries that specialize in the production of material objects for export, like automobiles and paper products, but to the attraction of what would be classified as *service* activity. Banking and legal services, a sizeable market, a diversified labour force, extensive public services, and the like, may generate additions to the labour force not basic by definition, but non-basic. In recent years, service industries have developed to the point where new service activities serve older ones. For example, computer systems firms aid banks in developing more efficient computer-driven banking systems.

In much the same way as settlements grow in size and complexity, so do they decline. When the demand for the goods and services of an urban unit falls, obviously fewer workers are needed, and both the basic and the services components of a settlement system are affected. There is, however, a resistance to decline that impedes the process and delays its impact. That is, settlements can grow rapidly as migrants respond quickly to the need for more workers, but under conditions of decline, those who have developed roots in the community are hesitant to leave or may be financially unable to move to another locale. Tables 8.1 and 8.2, and Figure 8.13 show that between 2001 and 2006, six of the 15 CMAs that had growth rates higher than the national average (5.4%) were in the Greater Golden Horseshoe—Barrie (19.2%), Oshawa (11.6%), Toronto (9.2%), Kitchener (8.9%), Guelph (8.2%) and Brantford (5.5%). Calgary and Edmonton also experienced very high growth rates—13.4% and 10.4% respectively. Eight CAs had growth rates of more than 10%: seven of the eight were located in Alberta. Declines were experienced in some of the regions of Quebec, the prairies and eastern Canada.

Systems of Urban Settlements

The functional structure of a settlement affects its current size and growth prospects. At the same time, its functions are a reflection of that community's location and its relationships with other urban units in the larger city system of which all are a part. A simple but revealing threefold functional classification of urban settlements recognizes them as either transportation centres, special-function cities, or central places. Each class has its own characteristic spatial arrangement; together, the three classes help explain the distributional pattern and the size and functional hierarchies of the entire city system.

The spatial pattern of *transportation centres* is that of alignment—along seacoasts, major and minor rivers, canals,

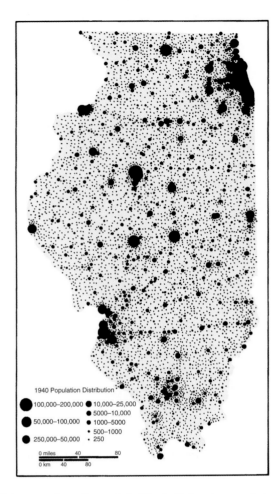

1940 Population Distribution

● 100,000–200,000	● 10,000–25,000
	• 5000–10,000
● 50,000–100,000	• 1000–5000
	· 500–1000
● 250,000–50,000	· 250

```
0 miles    40        80
0 km    40    80
```

FIGURE 8.14 Urban alignments in Illinois. Railroads preceded settlement in much of the Anglo-American continental interior, and urban centres were developed—frequently by the railroad companies themselves—as collecting and distributing points expected to grow as the farm populations increased. Located at constant 8- to 10-kilometre (5- to 6-mile) intervals in Illinois, the rail towns were the focal points of an expanding commercial agriculture. The linearity of the town pattern in 1940, at the peak of railroad influence, unmistakably marks the rail routes. Also evident are such special-function clusterings as the Chicago and St. Louis metropolitan districts and the mining towns of Southern Illinois. In addition to the linear and cluster patterns, the smallest towns show the uniform distribution characteristic of the "central places" discussed on page 268.

or railways. Routes of communication form the orienting axes along which cities developed and on which at least their initial functional success depended (Figure 8.14). *Special-function cities* are those engaged in mining, manufacturing, or other activities, the localization of which is related to raw material occurrence, agglomeration economies, or the circular and cumulative attractions of constantly growing market and labour concentrations. Special-function cities show a pattern of urban clustering—such as the mining and manufacturing cities of the Ruhr district of Germany, the Midlands of England, or the Donets Basin in Ukraine, for example. More familiarly, they appear in the form of the multifunctional metropolitan concentrations recognized by the Census Metropolitan Areas

of Canada, the Metropolitan Statistical Areas of the United States, or in such massive urbanized complexes as metropolitan Tokyo, Moscow, Paris, London, Buenos Aires, and others worldwide.

A common property of all settlements is centrality, no matter what their recognized functional specializations. Every urban unit provides goods and services for a surrounding area tributary to it. For many, including mining or major manufacturing centres, service to tributary areas is only a very minor part of their economic base. Some settlements, however, have that rural service and trade function as their dominant role, and these make up the third simplified category of cities: *central places*.

The Urban Hierarchy

Perhaps the most effective way to recognize how systems of cities are organized is to consider the **urban hierarchy**, a ranking of cities based on their size and functional complexity. One can measure the numbers and kinds of functions each city or metropolitan area provides. The hierarchy is then like a pyramid; a few large and complex cities are at the top and many smaller, simpler ones are at the bottom. There are always more smaller cities than larger ones.

When a spatial dimension is added to the hierarchy as in Figure 8.15, it becomes clear that an areal system of metropolitan centres, large cities, small cities, and towns exists. Goods, services, communications, and people flow up and down the hierarchy. The few high-level metropolitan areas provide specialized functions for large regions, while the smaller cities serve smaller districts. The separate centres interact with the areas around them, but since cities of the same level provide roughly the same services, those of the same size tend not to serve each other unless they provide some very specialized activity, such as housing a political capital of a region, or a major hospital or university. Thus, the settlements of a given level in the hierarchy are not independent but interrelated with communities of other levels in that hierarchy. Together, all centers at all levels in the hierarchy constitute an urban system.

World Cities

Standing at the top of national systems of cities are a relatively few agglomerations of cities that may be termed **world cities**. This term designates cities based on their functionality in the economic globalization process, and should not be confused with the term 'mega-cities,' which uses demographic criterion of population size (Beaverstock, Taylor, and Smith, 1999). Calcutta is a mega-city but not a world city; Zurich is a world city but not a mega-city; and New York and Mexico City are both. World class status may be identified using different criteria. One is to identify and rank the locational preferences of multinational corporation (MNC) headquarters: those cities with the highest concentration are world class (e.g., Tokyo, London, New York City). Another is based on the idea of 'control centres.' World class cities have the highest concentrations and control of capital: major financial institutions, MNCs, international institutions, and a rapidly growing business sector, among others

FIGURE 8.15 A functional hierarchy of U.S. metropolitan areas. Only the major metropolitan areas are shown. The hierarchy includes smaller urban districts (not shown) that depend on or serve the larger centres.

Source: Redrawn from P. L. Knox, ed., The United States: A Contemporary Human Geography. *Harlow, England. Longman, 1988, Fig. 5.5, p. 144.*

(e.g., London, Paris, Los Angeles). A third approach uses not the economic base of the cities themselves as a marker, but the highest levels and extent of internationalization of the service and financial sectors. Such cities serve as 'command centres' in the organization of the world economy (e.g., London, Paris, New York City). Still another approach ranks cities by the presence of international financial centres to identify the so-called 'Capitals of Capitals' (e.g., Hong Kong, Frankfurt, London). A fifth approach uses four key services that are argued to constitute the formation of world cities: accounting, advertising, banking, and law (Beaverstock, Taylor, and Smith, 1999). When these four variables are combined cities can be organized, ranked, and then mapped (Figure 8.16). London, New York, Paris, and Tokyo are generally recognized as dominant world cities in each approach. They contain the highest number of transnational service offices and headquarters of multinational corporations and dominate commerce in their respective parts of the world. Each is directly linked to a number of other primary- and secondary-level world cities, all bound together in complex networks that control the organization and management of the global system of finance.

Rank-Size and Primacy

The development of city systems on a global scale invites inquiry about the organization of city systems within regions or countries. The observation that there are many more small than large cities within an urban system ("the larger the fewer") is itself a statement about city hierarchies we normally expect. In some countries, especially those with complex economies and a long urban history, the city size hierarchy is summarized by the **rank-size rule**. It tells us that the nth largest city of a national system of cities will be $1/n$ the size of the largest city. That is, the second largest settlement will be 1/2 the size of the largest, the 10th biggest will be 1/10 the size of the first-ranked city. Although no national city system exactly meets the requirements of the rank-size rule, that of Russia and the United States closely approximates it.

Rank-size ordering is less applicable to countries with developing economies or where the city system is dominated by a **primate city**, one that is far more than twice the size of the second-ranked city. In fact, there may be no obvious "second city" at all, for a characteristic of a primate city hierarchy is one very large city, few, or no intermediate-sized cities, and many subordinate smaller settlements. For example, metropolitan Seoul (estimated at nearly 20 million) contains over 40% of the total population and one-half of the urban population of South Korea, and Luanda has almost two-thirds of Angola's urban folk. The capital cities of many developing countries display that kind of overwhelming primacy. In part, their primate city pattern is a heritage of their colonial past, when economic development, colonial administration, and transportation and

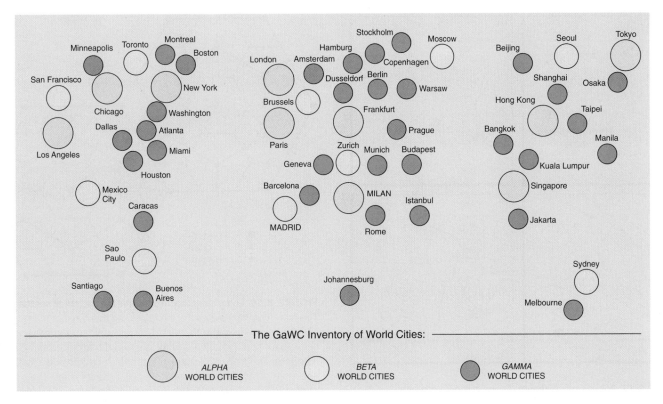

FIGURE 8.16 The 'Globalization and World Cities' (GaWC) inventory not only illustrates the location and concentrations of global service centres it clearly expresses what has been termed "uneven globalization": world cities are clearly not evenly distributed around the globe.

Source: Beaverstock et al., 1999. J.V. Beaverstock, P.J. Taylor and R.G. Smith, A Roster of World Cities. Cities 16, 6 (1999), pp. 445–458.

trade activities were concentrated at a single point (Figure 8.17); Kenya (Nairobi is the primate city) and many other African countries are examples.

In other instances—Egypt (Cairo) or Mexico (Mexico City), for example—development and population growth have tended to concentrate disproportionately in a capital city whose very size attracts further development and growth. Many European countries—Austria, the United Kingdom, and France are familiar examples—also show a primate structure, often ascribed to the former concentration of economic and political power around the royal court in a capital city that was, perhaps, also the administrative and trade centre of a larger colonial empire.

Central Places

An effective way to realize the meaning of influence zones and to grasp how cities and towns are interrelated is to consider urban settlements as **central places**, that is, as centres for the distribution of economic goods and services to surrounding non-urban populations. They are at the same time essential links in a system of interdependent urban settlements. Central places show size and spacing regularities not seen where special function or transportation cities predominate. That is, instead of showing patterns of clustering or alignment, central places display a regularity of distribution, with towns of about the same size and performing about the same number and kind of functions located about the same distance from each other.

In 1933, the German geographer **Walter Christaller** (1893–1969) attempted to explain those observed regularities of size, location, and interdependence of settlements. He recognized that

his **central place theory** could best be visualized in rather idealized, simplified circumstances. Christaller assumed that the following propositions were true:

1. Towns that provide the surrounding countryside with such fundamental goods as groceries and clothing would develop on a uniform plain with no topographic barriers, channelization of traffic, or variations in farm productivity.

2. The farm population would be dispersed in an even pattern across that plain.

3. The characteristics of the people would be uniform; that is, they would possess similar tastes, demands, and incomes.

4. Each kind of product or service available to the dispersed population would have its own *threshold*, or minimum number of consumers needed to support its supply. Because such goods as sports cars or fur coats are either expensive or not in great demand, they would have a high threshold, whereas a fewer number of customers within smaller tributary areas would be needed to support a small grocery store.

5. Consumers would purchase goods and services from the nearest opportunity (store or supplier).

When all of Christaller's assumptions are considered simultaneously, they yield the following results:

1. Since each customer patronizes the nearest centre offering the needed goods, the agricultural plain is automatically divided into non-competing market areas—*complementary regions*—where each individual town (and its merchants) has a sales monopoly.

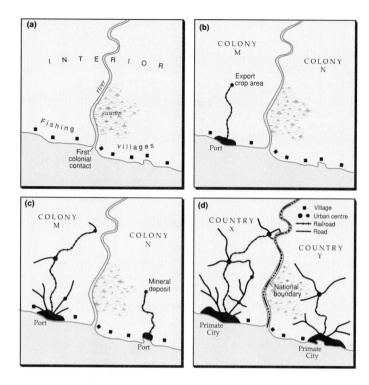

FIGURE 8.17 Primate city evolution. At first colonial contact (*a*), settlements are coastal and unconnected with each other. Joining a newly productive hinterland by European-built railroad to a new colonial port (*b*) begins to create a pattern of core-periphery relations and to focus European administration, trade, and settlement at the port. Mineral discoveries and another rail line in a neighbouring colony across the river (*c*) mark the beginnings of a new set of core-periphery relationships and of a new multifunctional colonial capital nearby but unconnected by land with its neighbour. With the passage of time and further transport and economic development, two newly independent nations (*d*) display *primate city* structures in which further economic and population growth flows to the single dominating centres of countries lacking balanced regional transport networks, resource development, and urban structures. Both populations and new functions continue to seek locations in the primate city where their prospects for success are greatest.

Source: Adapted from E. S. Simpson, The Developing World: An Introduction. *(Harlow, Essex, England: Longman Group UK Limited, 1987).*

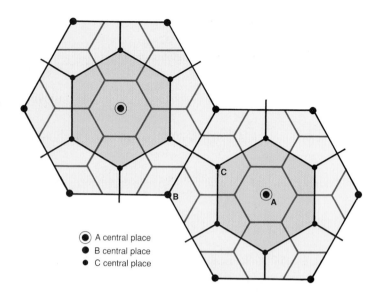

FIGURE 8.18 Complementary regions and the pattern of central places. The two "A" central places are the largest on this diagram of one of Christaller's models. The "B" central places offer fewer goods and services for sale and serve only the areas of the intermediate-sized hexagons. The many "C" central places, which are considerably smaller and more closely spaced, serve still smaller market areas. The goods offered in the "C" places are also offered in the "B" and "A" places, but the latter offer considerably more and more specialized goods. Notice that places of the same size are equally spaced.

Source: Arthur Getis and Judith Getis, "Christaller's Central Place Theory." Journal of Geography, *1966. Used with permission of the National Council for Geographic Education.*

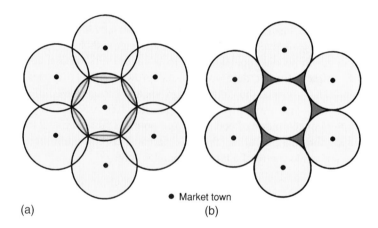

FIGURE 8.19 The derivation of complementary regions. (*a*) If the hypothetical region were totally covered by circular complementary regions, areas of overlap would occur. Since Christaller's assumption was that people will only shop at the nearest centre, areas of overlap must be divided so that those on each side of the boundary are directed to their nearest service point. (*b*) Circular areas too small to cover the region completely result in impermissible unserved populations.

2. Those market areas will take the form of a series of hexagons that cover the entire plain, as shown in Figure 8.18. Since the hypothetical plain must be completely subdivided, no area can be unserved and none can have equal service from two competing centres (Figure 8.19).

3. There will be a central place at the centre of each of the hexagonal market areas.

4. The largest central places (with the largest market areas) will supply all the goods and services the consumers in that area demand and can afford.

5. The size of the market area of a central place will be proportional to the number of goods and services offered from that place.

6. Contained within or at the edge of the largest market areas are central places serving a smaller population and offering fewer

goods and services. As Figure 8.19 indicates, the central place pattern shows a "nesting" of complementary regions in which part or all of multiple lower-order service areas are contained within the market area of a higher-order centre.

In addition, Christaller reached two important conclusions. First, towns of the same size (functional level) in the central place system will be evenly spaced, and larger towns (higher-order places) will be farther apart than smaller ones. This means that many more small than large towns will exist. In Figure 8.18, the ratio of the number of small towns to towns of the next larger size is 3 to 1. This distinct, step-like series of towns in size classes differentiated by both size and function is called a *hierarchy of central places.*

Second, the system of towns is interdependent. If one central place were eliminated, the entire system would have to readjust in its spatial pattern, its offered goods, or both. Consumers need a variety of products, each of which has a different minimum number of customers required to support it. The towns containing many goods and services become regional retailing centres, while the smaller central places serve just the people immediately in their vicinity. Customers are willing to travel great distances to buy expensive luxury items, but not basic foodstuffs like bread or milk. The higher the threshold of a desired product, the farther, on average, the consumer must travel to purchase it.

These conclusions have been shown to be generally valid in widely differing areas of the world. When varying incomes, cultures, landscapes, and transportation systems are taken into account, the results, though altered to some extent, hold up rather well. They are particularly applicable to agricultural areas (Figure 8.14). One has to stretch things a bit to see the model operating in highly industrialized areas where cities are more than just retailing centres. And, of course, the central place pattern originally established by pedestrian and horse-and-wagon movement has proved impermanent in the face of advances in transportation and communication. In the United States, the advent of improved rural roads and the reliable auto and truck in the 1930s began the economic erosion and disappearance of some of lowest-order farm town central places because more mobile customers increasingly bypassed them in favour of the greater variety and cost competition in larger, more distant towns. That erosion has continued farther up the hierarchy as both big-box discount chains (Wal-Mart, Future Shop, etc.) entered the retail structure and as, through Internet access, an increasing volume of retail trade and services are obtained electronically with no physical customer movement required at all.

Therefore, in an increasingly industrializing and modernizing world, pure central place theory has decreasing applicability as the sole explanation of observed urban spatial patterns.

Network Cities

In recent years, a new kind of urban spatial pattern has begun to appear, one seemingly divorced from the more recognized hierarchical orderings of cities we have reviewed. A **network city** evolves when two or more previously independent nearby cities, potentially complementary in functions, strive to cooperate by developing between them high-speed transportation corridors and communications infrastructure. For example, since the reunion of Hong Kong and China proper in 1997, an infrastructure of highway and rail lines, and of communications improvements has been developed to help integrate Hong Kong with Guangzhou, the huge, rapidly growing industrial and economic hub on the mainland. In Japan, three distinctive, nearby cities—Kyoto, Osaka, and Kobe—are joining together to compete with the Tokyo region as a major centre of commerce. Kyoto, with its temples and artistic treasures, is the cultural capital of Japan; Osaka is a primary commercial and industrial centre; and Kobe is a leading port. Their complementary functional strengths are reinforced by high-speed rail transport connecting the cities and by an airport (Kansai) designed to serve the entire region.

In Europe, the major cities of Amsterdam, Rotterdam, and The Hague, together with intermediate cities such as Delft, Utrecht, and Zaanstad, are connected by high-speed rail lines and a major airport that serves them all collectively. Each of these cities has special functions not duplicated in the others, and planners have no intention of developing competition between them. This region—called the Randstad—is second only to London in its popularity for international head offices, putting it in a strong position to compete for dominant world city status.

No similar network city has yet developed in the United States. The New York–Philadelphia, the Chicago–Milwaukee, the San Francisco–Oakland, or the Los Angeles–San Diego city pairings do not yet qualify for network city status since there has been no concerted effort to bring their competing interests together into a single structure of complementary activities.

Inside the City

The structure, patterns, and spatial interactions of systems of cities make up only half of the story of urban settlements. The other half involves the distinctive cultural landscapes that are the cities themselves. An understanding of the nature of cities is incomplete without a knowledge of their internal characteristics. So far, we have explored the location, the size, and the growth and decline tendencies of cities within hierarchical urban systems. Now we look into the city itself to better understand how its land uses are distributed, how social areas are formed, and how institutional controls, such as zoning by-laws, affect its structure. We will begin our discussion primarily on U.S. and Canadian cities. Later in this chapter, we will review urban land use patterns and social geographies in different world settings.

It is a common observation that recurring patterns of land use arrangements and population densities exist within urban areas. There is a certain sameness to the ways cities are internally organized, especially within one particular culture sphere like North America or Western Europe. The major variables shaping those North American regularities were accessibility, a competitive market in land, the transportation technologies available during the periods of urban growth, and the collective consequences of individual residential, commercial, and industrial locational decisions.

The Competitive Bidding for Land

For its effective operation, the city requires close spatial association of its functions and people. As long as those functions were few and the population small, pedestrian movement and pack-animal haulage were sufficient for the effective integration of the urban community. With the advent of large-scale manufacturing and the accelerated urbanization of the economy during the 19th century, however, functions and populations—and therefore city areas—grew beyond the interaction capabilities of pedestrian movement alone. Increasingly, efficient and costly mass transit systems were installed. Even with their introduction, however, only land within walking distance of the mass transit routes or terminals could successfully be incorporated into the expanding urban structure.

Usable—because accessible—land, therefore, was a scarce commodity, and by its scarcity it assumed high-market value and demanded intensive, high-density utilization. Because of its limited supply of usable land, the industrial city of the mass transit era (the late 19th and early 20th centuries) was compact, was characterized by high residential and structural densities (Figure 8.20), and showed a sharp break on its margins between urban and non-urban uses. The older central cities of, particularly, the north-eastern United States and south-eastern Canada were of that vintage and pattern.

Within the mass transit city, parcels of land were allocated among alternate potential users on the basis of the relative ability of those users to outbid their competitors for a chosen site. There was, in gross generalization, a continuous open auction of land in which users would locate, relocate, or be displaced in accordance with "rent-paying ability." The attractiveness of a parcel, and therefore the price that it could command, was a function of its accessibility. Ideally, the most desirable and efficient location for all the functions and the people of a city would be at the single point at which the maximum possible interchange could be achieved. Such total coalescence of activity is obviously impossible.

Because uses must therefore arrange themselves spatially, the attractiveness of a parcel is rated by its relative accessibility to all other land uses of the city. Store owners wish to locate where they can easily be reached by potential customers; factories need a convenient assembling of their workers and materials; residents desire easy connection with jobs, stores, and schools. Within the older central city, the radiating mass transit lines established the elements of the urban land use structure by freezing in the landscape a clear-cut pattern of differential accessibility. The convergence of that system on the city core gave that location the highest accessibility, the highest desirability, and hence, the highest land values of the entire built-up area. Similarly, transit junction points were accessible to larger segments of the city than locations along single traffic routes; the latter were more desirable than parcels lying between the radiating lines (Figure 8.21).

Society deems certain functions desirable without regard to their economic competitiveness. Schools, parks, and public buildings are assigned space without being participants in the auction for land. Other uses, through the process of that auction, are granted spaces by market forces. The merchants with the widest variety and highest order of goods and the largest threshold requirements bid most for and occupy parcels within the

FIGURE 8.20 Duplexes, apartment buildings, and row houses like these in the Crown Heights district of Brooklyn were characteristic 19th-century residential responses to the price and scarcity of developable urban land. Where detached single-family dwellings were built, they were usually placed on far smaller lots than became the rule during the middle 20th century.

central business district (CBD), which became localized at the convergence of mass transit lines. The successful bidders for slightly less accessible CBD parcels were the developers of tall office buildings of major cities, the principal hotels, and similar land uses that help produce the distinctive *skylines* of high-order commercial centres.

Comparable, but lower-order, commercial aggregations developed at the outlying intersections—transfer points—of the mass transit system. With time, a distinctive retailing hierarchy emerged within the urban settlement, an intra-city central place pattern based on the purchasing-power thresholds and complementary regions of city populations themselves. Industry took control of parcels adjacent to essential cargo routes: rail lines, waterfronts, rivers, or canals. Strings of stores, light industries, and high-density apartment structures could afford and benefit from location along high-volume transit routes. The least accessible locations within the city were left for the least competitive uses: low-density residences. A diagrammatic summary of this repetitive allocation of space among competitors for urban sites in American mass transit cities is shown in Figure 8.22. Compare it to the generalized land use map of Calgary, Alberta, in Figure 8.26.

The land use regularities of the older, eastern mass transit central cities were not fully replicated in the 20th-century urban centres of western United States and Canada. The density and land use structures of those newer cities have been influenced more by the automobile than by mass transit systems. They spread more readily, evolved at lower densities, and therefore display less tightly structured and standardized land use patterns than their eastern predecessors.

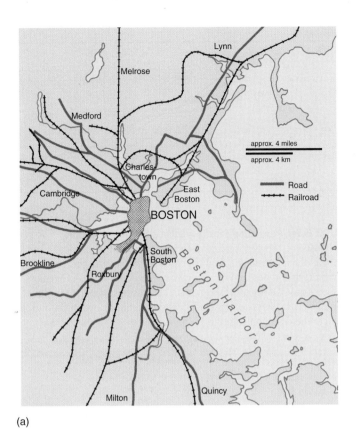

(a)

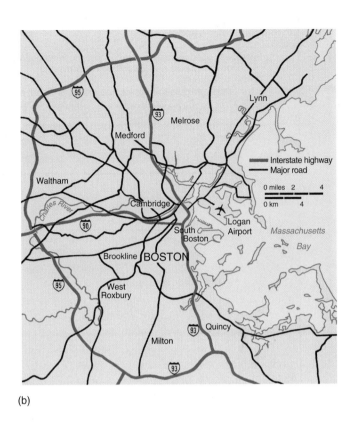

(b)

FIGURE 8.21 Major access lines in Boston in 1872 and 1994. (*a*) The convergence of mass transit lines in the 19th century gave to the central city and its downtown core a centrality that has been reduced or lost with (*b*) the freeway pattern and motor vehicle dominance in Boston of the 1990s. See also Figure 8.37.

Land Values and Population Density

Theoretically, the open land auction should yield two separate although interconnected distance decay patterns, one related to land values and the other to population density (as distance increases away from the CBD, population density decreases). If one thinks of the land value surface of the older central city as a topographic map with hills representing high valuations and depressions showing low prices, a series of peaks, ridges, and valleys would reflect the differentials in accessibility marked by the pattern of mass transit lines, their intersections, and the unserved interstitial areas.

Dominating these local variations, however, is an overall decline of valuations with increasing distance away from the *peak land value intersection*, the most accessible (by mass transit) and costly location of the central business district. As would be expected in a distance-decay pattern, the drop in valuation is precipitous within a short linear distance from that point, and then the valuation declines at a lesser rate to the margins of the built-up area.

With one important variation, the population density pattern of the central city shows a comparable distance decay arrangement, as suggested by Figure 8.23. The exception is the

tendency to form a hollow *at the centre*, the CBD. The city, always changing, has shown both declines and increases in population at its core. For many years, as cities experienced industrialization, city centres were filled with retail functions, offices, and some housing for the well-to-do. As transportation improvements made lower-priced and larger lots available on the fringes of cities, the wealthy and middle class moved away from the centre city, leaving the poorest residents behind in obsolescent slum-tenements near the urban core. In recent years, however, some middle-and upper-class urbanites are returning to the city centre, attracted by the convenience of the central location, cultural opportunities, and new and redeveloped upscale apartment buildings. Many U.S. cities have fostered this return by creating new parks, building stadiums and sports arenas, and trying to reinvigorate their downtowns. Columbus, Ohio, for example, built a hockey arena downtown and a soccer stadium north of the CBD, promoted rehabilitation of several neighbourhoods near the city centre, and aided the development of a stretch of art galleries that now dominate the northern part of the main street of the CBD.

Generalizations about central city population density change over time are demonstrated in Figure 8.24, a time series graph of population density patterns for Cleveland, Ohio, over a 50-year period. The peak density was 4.5 kilometres (2.8 m) from the

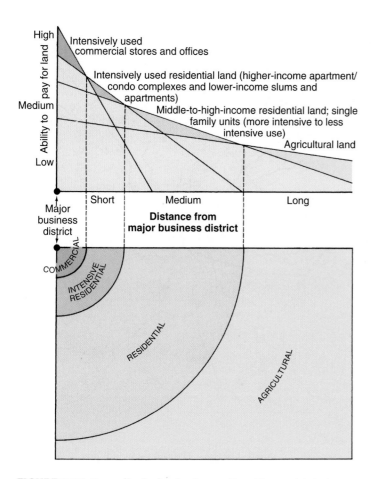

FIGURE 8.22 Generalized urban land use pattern. The model depicts the location of various land uses in an idealized city where the highest bidder gets the most accessible land.

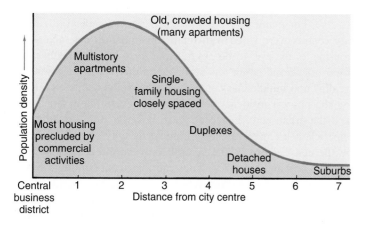

FIGURE 8.23 A summary population density curve. As distance from the area of multi-storey apartment buildings increases, the population density declines.

CBD in 1940, but by 1990 it was at 9.5 kilometres (5.8 m). As the city expanded, density close to the centre decreased. By 2000, however, that pattern was reversing as affluent younger people opted for housing in more accessible central locations.

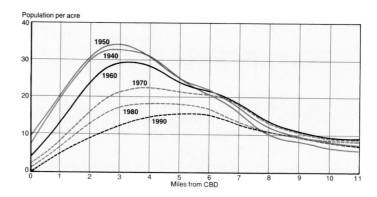

FIGURE 8.24 Population density gradients for Cleveland, Ohio, 1940–1990. The progressive depopulation of the central core and flattening of the density gradient over time to the city margin is clearly seen as Cleveland passed from mass transit to automobile domination. The Cleveland pattern is consistent with conclusions drawn from other urban density studies: density gradients tend to flatten over time, and the larger the city, the flatter the gradient.

Source: Anupa Mukhopadhyay and Ashok K. Dutt, "Population Density Gradient Changes of a Post-industrial City—Cleveland, Ohio 1940–1990," GeoJournal 34:517, no. 4, 1994. Redrawn by permission of Kluwer Academic Publishers and Ashok K. Dutt.

Models of Urban Land Use Structure

Generalized models of urban growth and land use patterns were proposed during the 1920s and 1930s describing the results of these controls on the observed structure of the central city. The models were simplified graphic summaries of U.S. mass transit city growth processes as interpreted by different observers. Although the culture, society, economy, and technology they summarized have now been superseded, the physical patterns they explained or summarized still remain as vestiges and controls on the current landscape. A review of their propositions and conclusions still helps our understanding of the modern North American urban complex.

The common starting point of the classical models is the distinctive central business district found in every older central city. The core of this area displays intensive land development: tall buildings, many stores and offices, and crowded streets. Framing the core is a fringe area of wholesaling activities, transportation terminals, warehouses, new car dealers, furniture stores, and even light industries. Just beyond the central business district frame is the beginning of residential land uses.

The land use models shown in Figure 8.25 differ in their explanation of patterns outside the CBD. The **concentric zone** (or **zonal**) **model** (Figure 8.25a), developed to explain the sociological patterning of American cities in the 1920s, sees the urban community as a set of nested rings. It recognizes four concentric circles of mostly residential diversity at increasing distance in all directions from the wholesaling, warehousing, and light industry border of the high-density CBD core:

- A zone in transition marked by the deterioration of old residential structures abandoned, as the city expanded, by the former wealthier occupants and now containing high-density,

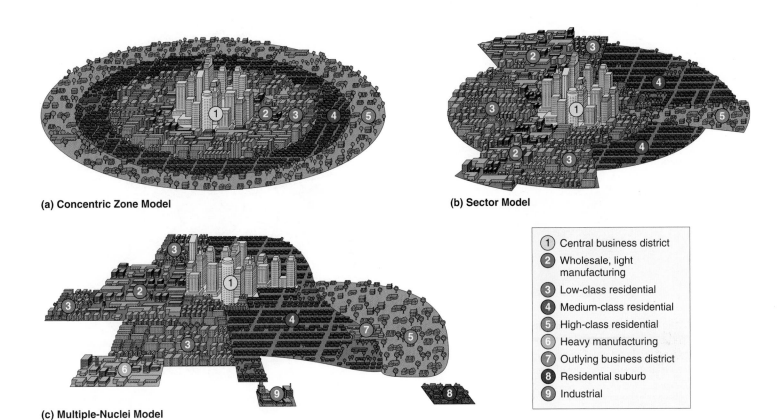

(a) Concentric Zone Model

(b) Sector Model

(c) Multiple-Nuclei Model

1. Central business district
2. Wholesale, light manufacturing
3. Low-class residential
4. Medium-class residential
5. High-class residential
6. Heavy manufacturing
7. Outlying business district
8. Residential suburb
9. Industrial

FIGURE 8.25 **Three classic models of the internal structure of cities.**

Source: Redrawn from "The Nature of Cities" by C. D. Harris and E. L. Ullman in volume no. 242 of The Annals of the American Academy of Political and Social Science. © 1945 The *American Academy of Political and Social Science, Philadelphia, PA.*

low-income slums, rooming houses, and, perhaps in the U.S., ethnic ghettos.

- A zone of "independent working people's homes" occupied by industrial workers, perhaps second-generation Americans able to afford modest but older homes on small lots.
- A zone of better residences, single-family homes, or high-rent apartments occupied by those wealthy enough to exercise choice in housing location and to afford the longer, more costly journey to CBD employment.
- A commuters' zone of low-density, isolated residential suburbs, just beginning to emerge when this model was proposed.

The model is dynamic; it imagines the continuous expansion of inner zones at the expense of the next outer developed circles and suggests a ceaseless process of *invasion* and *succession* that yields a restructured land use pattern and population segregation by income level.

The **sector model** (Figure 8.25b) also concerns itself with patterns of housing and wealth, but it arrives at the conclusion that high-rent residential areas are dominant in city expansion and grow outward from the centre of the city along major arterials. New housing for the wealthy, the model concludes, is added in an outward extension of existing high-rent axes as the city grows. Middle-income housing sectors lie adjacent to the high-rent areas, and low-income residents occupy the

remaining sectors of growth. There tends to be a *filtering down* process as older areas are abandoned by the outward movement of their original inhabitants, with the lowest-income populations (closest to the centre of the city and farthest from the current location of the wealthy) becoming the dubious beneficiaries of the least desirable vacated areas. The accordance of the sector model with the actual pattern that developed in Calgary, Canada, is suggested in Figure 8.26 and for Chicago in Figure 8.29.

The concentric circle and sector models assume urban growth and development outward from a single central core, the site of original urban settlement that later developed into the central business district. These "single-node" models are countered by a **multiple-nuclei model** (see Figure 8.25c), which maintains that large cities develop by peripheral spread from several nodes of growth, not just one. Individual nodes of special function—commercial, industrial, port, residential—are originally developed in response to the benefits accruing from the spatial association of like activities. Peripheral expansion of the separate nuclei eventually leads to coalescence and the meeting of incompatible land uses along the lines of juncture. The urban land use pattern, therefore, is not regularly structured from a single centre in a sequence of circles or a series of sectors but based on separately expanding clusters of contrasting activities. The metropolitan consequences of that pattern may be glimpsed in Figures 8.27 and 8.32.

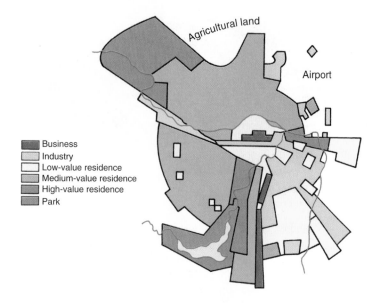

FIGURE 8.26 The land use pattern in and around Calgary, Alberta, in 1981. Physical and cultural barriers and the evolution of cities over time tend to result in a sectoral pattern of similar land uses. Calgary's central business district was the focus for many of the sectors.

Source: Revised and redrawn with permission from P. J. Smith, "Calgary: A Study in Urban Patterns" in Economic Geography *vol. 38, p. 328. © 1962 Clark University, Worcester, MA.*

Legend:
- Business
- Industry
- Low-value residence
- Medium-value residence
- High-value residence
- Park

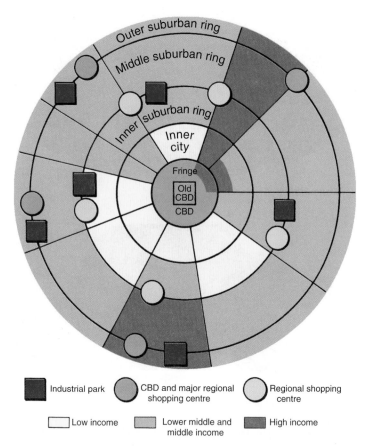

Legend:
- Industrial park
- CBD and major regional shopping centre
- Regional shopping centre
- Low income
- Lower middle and middle income
- High income

FIGURE 8.27 A diagram of the present-day United States metropolitan area. Note that aspects of the concentric zone, sector, and multiple-nuclei patterns are evident and carried out into the suburban fringe. The "major regional shopping centres" of this earlier, mid-1970s model are increasingly the cores of newly developing "outer cities."

Source: Figure 4.10 (redrawn) from The North American City, *4th ed. by Maurice Yeates. © 1990 by Harper & Rowe, Publishers, Inc.*

Social Areas of Cities

Vestiges of these classical models of North American city layout can be seen in modern interpretations of urban structure based on observed social segregation within urban areas. The larger and more economically and socially complex cities are, the stronger is the tendency for their residents to segregate themselves into groups based on *social status*, *family status*, and *ethnicity*. In a large metropolitan region with a diversified population, this territorial behaviour may be a defence against the unknown or the unwanted, a desire to be among similar kinds of people, a response to income constraints, or a result of social and institutional barriers. Most people feel more at ease when they are near those with whom they can easily identify. In traditional societies, these groups are the families and tribes. In modern society, people group according to income or occupation (social status), stages in the life cycle (family status), and language or ethnic characteristics. Awareness of such social and economic clustering is important in the commercial world (see "Birds of a Feather").

Many of these social area groupings are fostered by the size and the value of available housing. Land developers, especially in cities, produce homes of similar quality in specific areas. The social sorting process, then, takes place in relation to existing land uses, themselves the product of older generations of urban growth. Of course, as time elapses, there is a change in the condition and quality of that housing, and new groups may replace previous tenants. In any case, neighbourhoods of similar social characteristics evolve.

Social Status

The social status or 'class' (see Chapter 5, p. 156) of an individual or a family is determined by income, education, occupation, and home value, though it may be measured differently in different cultures. In Canada and the United States, high income, a university or college education, a professional or managerial position, and high home value constitute high status. High home value can mean an expensive rental apartment as well as a large house with extensive grounds.

A good housing indicator of social status is persons per room. A low number of persons per room tends to indicate high status. Low status characterizes people with low-income jobs living in low-value housing. There are many levels of status, and people tend to filter out into neighbourhoods where most of the heads of households and household incomes are of similar rank. Social status patterning agrees with the sector model, and in most cities, people of similar status are grouped in sectors which fan out from the innermost urban residential

Birds of a Feather ... or, Who are the People in Your Neighbourhood?

How does a McDonald's or a Burger King decide which 99-cent menu items to promote at a certain site, or whether it can profitably offer salads at that franchise? Are there enough families with children to justify building a play area? On what basis does a Starbucks or a Jiffy Lube determine in what neighbourhood to seek a new store location?

Many businesses, large and small, base their sales and locational decisions on a marketing analysis system. The system is based on census data and postal codes to categorize Americans and Canadians by the social and economic characteristics they share with their neighbourhoods. People tend to cluster together in roughly homogeneous areas based on social status, family status, ethnicity, and other cultural markers. People in any one cluster tend to have or adopt similar lifestyles. As one analyst put it, "You are where you live." Residents of a cluster tend to read the same kinds of books, subscribe to the same magazines and newspapers, watch the same movies and television shows. They exhibit similar preferences in food and drink, clothes, furniture, cars, and all the other goods a consumer society offers.

Marketing analysts use a number of variables to classify areas of the country: household density per square kilometre; area type (city, suburb, town, farm); degree of ethnic diversity; family type (married with children, single, and so on); predominant age group; extent of education; type of employment; housing type; and neighbourhood quality. After analyzing the data, the firm characterizes each postal code as belonging to from one to five of 62 possible neighbourhood lifestyle categories. Catchy names have been assigned to these clusters, ranging from "Blueblood Estates" (elite, super-rich families) to "Hard Scrabble" (older families in poor, isolated areas). Some of the others: "Winner's Circle" (executive suburban families); "Pools and Patios" (established empty nesters); "Upward Bound" (young, upscale white collar families); and "Big City Blend" (middle income immigrant families).

Marketing companies realize that the designations don't define the tastes and habits of every single person in a community. But despite critical commentary from some social science researchers, it maintains that the identified clusters summarize the behaviour that most people within them are apt to follow. In the "Towns and Gowns" (university and college-town singles aged 18–34) postal code area, for example, residents are likely to be U.S. college basketball fans, own a computer, have a school loan, watch television shows advertisers gear to their age and income group, and read magazines similarly focused. But in the "Money and Brains" (older, sophisticated married couples with few children, living in town houses or fashionable homes, predominantly employed in white-collar jobs) postal code, residents are most likely to have a passport, have advanced degrees, own bonds, shop up-market, and watch educational television shows.

areas (Figure 8.28). The pattern in Chicago is illustrated in Figure 8.29. If the number of people within a given social group increases, they tend to move away from the central city along an arterial connecting them with the old neighbourhood. Major transport routes leading to the city centre are the usual migration routes out from the centre.

Family Status

As the distance from the city centre increases, the average age of the adult residents declines, or the size of their family increases, or both. Within a particular sector—say, that of high status—older people whose children do not live with them or young professionals, unmarried or without families, tend to live close to the city centre. Between these are the older families who lived at the outskirts of the city in an earlier period before expansion moved beyond them. The young families seek space for child rearing, and older people may covet more the accessibility of the cultural and business life of the city. However, where inner-city life is unpleasant, there is a tendency for older people to migrate to the suburbs or to retirement communities.

Within lower-status sectors, the same pattern tends to emerge. Transients and single people are housed in the inner city, and families, if they find it possible or desirable, live farther from the centre. The arrangement that emerges is a concentric circle patterning according to family status, as Figure 8.29 suggests. In general, there is a concentric zone pattern wherein inner-city areas house older people and outer-city areas house younger populations.

Ethnicity

The durability of "Little Italys" and "Chinatowns," and of Polish, Greek, Armenian, and other ethnic neighbourhoods in many Canadian and U.S. cities is evidence of the persistence of self-maintained ethnic concentrations. But why do some members of some ethnic groups locate in the same neighbourhoods? Are they forced into ghettos, due to prejudice from the host cultural groups or economic limitations? Or are they feely chosen enclaves, where people locate amidst those with whom they share an ethnic heritage and practice? (See Chapter 6, Ethnic Enclaves and Ghettos, p. 169.)

In Canadian cities there are an increasing number of neighbourhoods with concentrations of visible minority groups, but as Adams (2007: 49–60) points out, there is much evidence to suggest that is not a function of ghettoization or racism, but rather a result of the increasing number of visible minority populations over the past two to three decades who, understandably so, choose to live in neighbourhoods with others who share their language and national origin. This has been a long

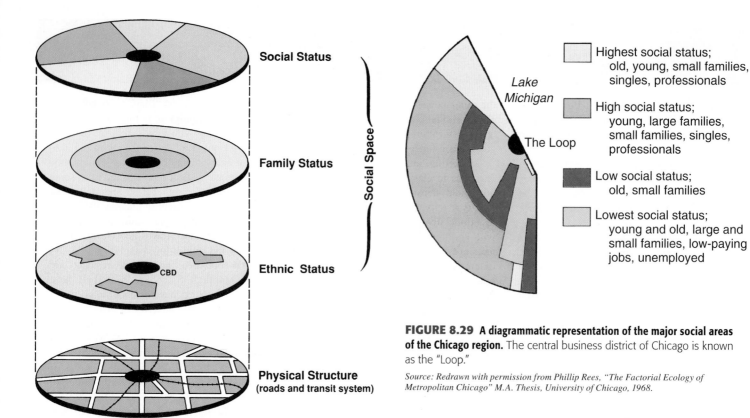

FIGURE 8.28 The social geography of Canadian and American cities.

Source: Redrawn with permission from Robert A. Murdie, Factorial Ecology of Metropolitan Toronto. *Research Paper 116. Department of Geography Research Series, University of Chicago, 1969.*

FIGURE 8.29 **A diagrammatic representation of the major social areas of the Chicago region.** The central business district of Chicago is known as the "Loop."

Source: Redrawn with permission from Phillip Rees, "The Factorial Ecology of Metropolitan Chicago" M.A. Thesis, University of Chicago, 1968.

standing settlement pattern in Canada which has resulted in some quite renowned neighbourhoods: Montreal's Mile End, Vancouver's Chinatown, and Toronto's Kensington Market. In a city such a Toronto, for example, where many residents were born outside the country, ethnic neighbourhoods are to be expected. Increasing ethnic concentrations in our cities, therefore, is a function of having more newcomers than ever before, doing what their immigrant predecessors have always done: move to the most familiar neighbourhoods in a new and different world.

Certain ethnic groups living elsewhere, specifically African Americans in the U.S., have had segregation in nuclear communities forced on them. Every city in the United States has one or more "black" areas that in many respects may be considered cities within a city, with their own self-contained social geographies of social status, income, and housing quality. Social and economic barriers to movement outside the area have always been high, as they also have been for Hispanics and other non-English-speaking minorities. Although U.S. segregation in 2000 was slightly lower nationally than in 1990, at the start of the 21st century the average U.S. city "black" lived in a census tract that was more than 75% minority and three-fifths "black" in composition.

Of the three social geographic patterns depicted on Figure 8.29, family status has undergone the most widespread change in recent years. Today, the suburbs in both Canada and the U.S. house large numbers of singles and childless couples, as well as two-parent families. Areas near the central business district have become popular for young professionals. Gay couples and families often choose to live in urban centres as well. The city structure is constantly changing, reflecting changes in family and employment makeup. For example, there are now large numbers of new jobs for professionals in the suburbs and central business districts, but not in between. With more women in the workforce than ever before, and as a result of multiple-earner families, residential site selection has become a more complex undertaking.

Institutional Controls

Over the past century, and particularly since World War II, institutional controls have strongly influenced the land use arrangements and growth patterns of most U.S. and Canadian cities. Indeed, the governments—local and national—of most Western urbanized societies have instituted a myriad of laws to control all aspects of urban life with particular emphasis on the ways in which individual property and city areas can be developed and used. In both the United States and Canada, emphasis has been on land use planning, subdivision control and zoning by-laws, and building, health, and safety codes. All have been designed to assure a legally acceptable manner and pattern of urban development, and all are based on broad applications of the police powers of municipalities to assure public health, safety, and well-being even when private property rights are infringed.

These non-market controls on land use are designed to minimize incompatibilities (residences adjacent to heavy industry, for example), and provide for the creation in appropriate locations of public uses (the transportation system, waste disposal facilities, government buildings, parks), and private uses (shopping centres, housing) needed for and conducive to a balanced, orderly community. In theory, such careful planning should prevent the emergence of slums, so often the result of undesirable adjacent uses, and should stabilize neighbourhoods by reducing market-induced pressures for land use change.

Zoning by-laws and land use planning have sometimes been criticized as being unduly restrictive and unresponsive to changing land use needs and patterns of economic development. Zoning and subdivision control regulations that specify large lot sizes for residential buildings and large house-floor areas have been particularly criticized as devices to exclude from upper-income areas lower-income populations or those who would choose to build or occupy other forms of residences: apartments, special housing for the aged, and so forth. Bitter court battles have been waged, with mixed results, over "exclusionary" zoning practices that in the view of some serve to separate rather than to unify the total urban structure and to maintain or increase diseconomies of land use development. All institutional controls, of course, interfere with the market allocation of urban land, as do the actions of real estate agents who "steer" people of certain ethnic groups into neighbourhoods that the agent thinks are appropriate.

In most of Asia, there is no zoning, and it is quite common to have small-scale industrial activities operating in residential areas. Even in Japan, a house may contain living space and several people doing piecework for a local industry. In both Europe and Japan, neighbourhoods have been built and rebuilt gradually over time to contain a wide variety of building types from several eras intermixed on the same street. In North America, such mixing is much rarer and is often viewed as a temporary condition in a process of transition to total redevelopment.

Suburbanization in Canada

At the dawn of the last century, only 37% of Canadians lived in cities and towns: today it is some 80%. The 20th century saw Canada transformed from a nation of rural to urban dwellers, and suburbanization played a vital role in this transition. Although this process has been the single most important factor altering our cities since World War II (1939–45), suburbs, as we know them today, did exist prior to 1946.

Suburbanization is a process that has been underway in what is now Canada for three centuries. During the 18th century, Quebec City and Montreal urbanized areas lying outside their city walls, and by the second half of the 19th century, suburbs were present in a number of Canadian towns and cities (Linteau, 1987). These emerged due to the overpowering forces of population growth, the rise of industrialization, and its increasingly affluent working class, and technological

innovations that made suburban living possible for large segments of the population (Smith, 2000). More people and people with more income both needed and demanded more housing, and only new developments beyond the inner city could accommodate them. Advances in construction design, cheaper house styles, and successive improvements in public and private transportation—horse-drawn buses, electric streetcars, passenger rail, and eventually subways and the automobile—helped to spread suburban development in Canada, the United States, and Britain (see "Suburbanization in the United States").

Well into the early 20th century, however, Canadian suburbs tended to be built at a relatively slow pace, with houses built in small batches, often one at a time, by individual small-scale house builders. This changed dramatically in the mid-20th century. Since then urban growth has been essentially *sub*urban growth. In the last five decades, Canada's urban population has tripled the number of urban residents to some 15 million: they comprise over 90% of the country's entire population growth. Most of this growth transpired on the fringe of existing cities in the form of suburbs, overtaking surrounding countryside and existing towns and villages.

Much like the initial phase of suburbanization, the factors fuelling this growth were demographic, economic, and technological, but added to this mix was the emergence of two other important factors, one governmental and public, the other organizational and private (Smith, 2000). The end of World War II saw an unprecedented population growth. Returning troops and immigrants from Europe embraced domestic life and generated the "baby boom" (1946–1965). Peace time and an expanding population demanding more goods, services, and housing brought economic prosperity as well. New technological inventions, particularly electrical appliances for the home, and new and improved physical structures—water and sewage infrastructures, hydroelectric generators, expansive road networks and highways—introduced massive changes to Canada's urban form and way of life. The private automobile and the skyscraper, for example, made it possible for people to easily commute great distances from low density residential suburbs to high density inner-city workplaces. Canada's modern city had emerged.

This massive suburbanization would not have occurred on such a grand scale had it not been for government assistance. Not only were planning boards and building regulations introduced across the country at various levels of government to help orchestrate this growth and to establish and ensure health, safety, and building standards; individual homebuyers were assisted in a variety of ways. The creation in 1946 of the Canadian (formerly Central) Mortgage and Housing Corporation (CMHC) remains Canada's national housing agency. It is a government owned, public corporation that allows the federal government to play a leading role in housing programs. Initially formed to address the country's post-war housing shortage, it has grown into a major national institution impacting almost every community. CMHC provides mortgage loan insurance—making home ownership more accessible—implements housing policy and programs (e.g., urban renewal projects, public housing, historic preservation of neighbourhoods and buildings), and housing research (e.g., indoor

As was the case in Canada, the decades after World War II saw the creation of a technological, physical, and institutional structure that resulted in a sudden and massive alteration of past urban forms. Demand for housing, pent up by years of economic depression and wartime restrictions, was loosed in a flood after 1945, and a massive suburbanization of people and functions altered the existing pattern of urban America. Between 1950 and 1970, the two most prominent patterns of population growth were the *metropolitanization* of people and, within metropolitan areas, their *suburbanization*. During the 1970s, the interstate highway system was substantially completed and major metropolitan expressways put in place, allowing sites 30 to 45 or more kilometres (20 to 30 or more miles) from workplaces to be within acceptable commuting distance from home. The major metropolitan areas rapidly expanded in area and population. Growth patterns for the Chicago area, reflecting those developments, are shown in Figure 8.30.

Suburban expansion reached its maximum pace during the decade of the 1970s when developers were converting open land to urban uses at the rate of 80 hectares (200 acres) an hour. High energy prices of the 1970s slowed the rush to the suburbs, but during the 1980s, suburbanization again proceeded apace. In much of the recent outward flow, the tendency has been as much for "filling in" as for continued sprawl.

Indeed, by the 1990s, a new urban America had emerged on the perimeters of the major metropolitan areas. With increasing sprawl and the rising costs implicit in the ever-greater spatial separation of the functional segments of the fringe, peripheral expansion slowed, the supply of developable land was reduced (with corresponding increases in its price), and the intensity of land development grew. No longer dependent on the central city, the suburbs were reborn as vast, collectively self-sufficient outer cities, marked by landscapes of skyscraper office parks, massive retailing complexes, established industrial parks, and a proliferation of apartment and condominium districts and gated communities.

The new suburbia began to rival older central business districts in size and complexity. Collectively, the new centres surpassed the central cities as generators of employment and income. Individually, each of the major suburban complexes established its own particular role in the metropolitan economy. Together with the older CBDs, the suburbs perform the many tertiary and quaternary services that mark the post-industrial metropolis. Regional and national headquarters of leading corporations, banking, professional services of all kinds, major hotel complexes and recreational centres—all formerly considered immovable keystones of central business districts—became parts of the new outer cities. And these outer cities themselves filled in and made more continuous the urban landscape of all North American conurbations. Recognized as **edge cities**, they are defined by their large nodes of concentrated office and commercial structures, and characterized by having more jobs than residents within their boundaries.

Edge cities now exist in all regions of urbanized North America, and are most prevalent in less compact cities that developed during the automobile age. The metropolis has become polynucleated, and urban regions are increasingly "galactic"— that is, galaxies of economic activity nodes organized primarily around the freeway systems (Figure 8.31). Commuting across the galaxy is far more common than journeys-to-work between suburbs and central cities. In recent years, suburban outliers and edge cities are coalescing, creating continuous metropolitan belts on the pattern shown in Figure 8.6.

air quality, ventilation, construction techniques, energy efficiency) for the country. Public regulation has been a primary agent in Canada's urbanization.

Private developers have been the other driving force. Suburbs built since the later half of the past century have been primarily constructed by big developers and builders—private corporations—who build not individual housing or commercial units per se, but entire "suburban communities." They have the necessary organizational and technological skills, and the financial capital, to undertake such mass-produced, large-scale projects, and to complete them quickly. The average house built in the 1940s took 2400 site-person hours and seven months; by the mid-1960s the average house took only 950 site-person hours and eight weeks.

The creation of Don Mills in the early 1950s, a suburb on the eastern fringes of Toronto, is considered a landmark event, both for the novelty and sheer scale of the development itself and the birth of the Canadian land development industry (Evenden and Walker, 1993; Smith, 2000). E.P. Taylor, one of the most important Canadian financiers of the day, controlled a development company that launched a planned suburban community on 810 hectares (2000 acres) of land. The plan was unique for its day and became a leading example of suburban development: a focus on neighbourhoods composed of single-family units, wide residential lots with low densities, the separation of vehicles and pedestrians, green spaces, and the provision for industrial workplaces. The plan was deemed a success, perhaps more so for developers than urban planners, and set a new standard that was replicated across Canada. Its landscape became the quintessential image of the typical Canadian suburb (Figure 8.32).

And yet today's suburbs are in fact quite diverse. They come in a variety of patterns, sizes, and ages, differ in municipal status and dominant function, and house and/or employ a diversity of people (Smith, 2000). Some suburbs are *contiguous* and merge with other suburbs or the inner-city, as is the case in Calgary, while others are physically *detached* unto themselves, as are many in Vancouver and Toronto. They can comprise hundreds of thousands of residents, with a mixture of residential, commercial, and industrial land uses (e.g., Mississauga: population 668,549), or only a few hundred households in a homogeneous residential subdivision. They have differing forms of municipal government

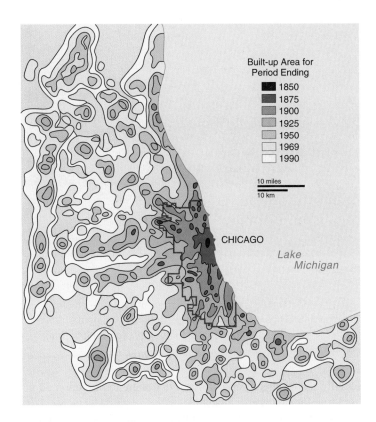

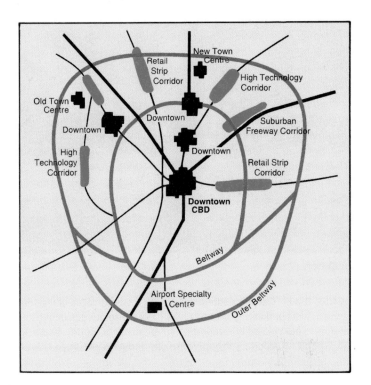

FIGURE 8.30 A history of urban sprawl. In Chicago, as in most larger and older U.S. cities, the slow peripheral expansion recorded during the late 19th and early 20th centuries suddenly accelerated as the automobile suburbs began developing after 1945. The red line marks the Chicago city boundary.

Source: Revised with permission from B. J. L. Berry, Chicago: Transformation of an Urban System, *1976, with additions from other sources.*

status: *unincorporated* suburbs are under the jurisdiction of rural municipalities; *incorporated* suburbs are those large enough to warrant city status; and still others are governed by the larger municipality—*central city jurisdiction*—of which they are a part. Their function has remained primarily *residential* but that may be one of several functions. A suburb located immediately adjacent or within a central city is likely to be exclusively residential because of land use zoning regulations, whereas a suburb outside the central city may be *mixed-use* and include commercial properties, and high and low density housing. Some may function as *resort/ retirement* communities that offer special amenities to residents (see "The Gated Community"). Others may be termed *industrial suburbs* because they employ large numbers of workers, many of whom live outside the suburb and commute. And finally, there are *multifunctional suburbs:* those relatively large developments that have broadly based economies and often city status, places like Burnaby and Mississauga.

Diverse, too, are the Canadians who reside in them. Income levels, occupations, educational attainment, ethnicities, religions, and place of origin vary immensely among and even within suburbs: this is a function of Canada's multiculturalism (Chapter 5). Nevertheless, some suburbs are more socially and economically

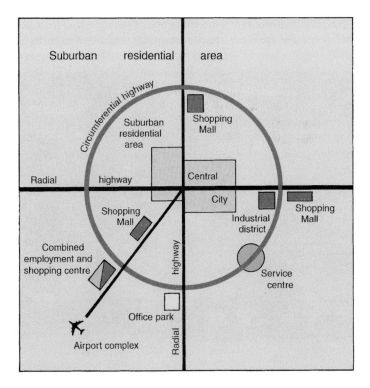

FIGURE 8.31 The galactic city's multiple downtowns and special function nodes and corridors are linked by the metropolitan expressway systems in these conceptualizations proposed by (*a*) Truman Hartshorn and Peter Muller and (*b*) Chauncy Harris.

Source: (a) Redrawn with permission from V. H. Winston and Son, Inc., "Suburban Downtowns and the Transformation of Atlanta's Business Landscape," Urban Geography, *10: 382 (Silver Springs, Md.: V. H. Winston and Son, Inc., 1989); (b) Redrawn with permission from Winston and Son, Inc., "'The Nature of Cities' and Urban Geography in the Last Half Century."* Urban Geography, *18: 17 (Silver Springs, Md.: Winston and Son, Inc., 1997).*

(a) Guelph, Ontario

(b) Calgary, Alberta

FIGURE 8.32 "Creeping Conformity" Among the advantages of residential suburban development is the relatively fast, efficient, and inexpensive way vast tracts of housing can be built to meet consumer demands. Conversely, the replication of housing and landscape designs by corporate developers has created a "creeping conformity" (Harris, 2004). Two neighbourhoods in different parts of the country, for example (*a*) Guelph, Ontario, and (*b*) Calgary, Alberta, can appear like one and the same place.

uniform than others, housing prices themselves do serve to segregate households by income, and there is evidence indicating "creeping conformity" in the landscape of suburbia (Figure 8.32), but generally speaking the stereotypical notions of suburbs as socially homogeneous and uniform in design and function do not hold true for suburban Canada.

Neither does the utopian ideal that suburbia constitutes a "middle landscape" where the best of both urbanism and the

(a)

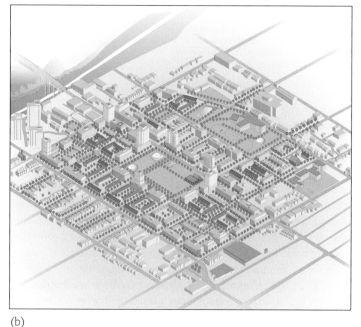

(b)

FIGURE 8.33 (a) Regent Park is Canada's oldest and largest public housing project. Opened in several phases first commencing in 1949, this 28-hectare (69-acre) development, just east of Toronto's downtown district, was intended as a break from the nearby slums of Cabbagetown. High-rise apartments such as these offered much improved living standards, but critics maintain they remained physically and socially isolating. By the late 1990s, Regent Park was home to some 12,000 people of numerous ethnicities. The vast majority of residents were immigrants, visible minorities, with a first language other than English: half were 18 years of age or younger. The community suffered from higher than average unemployment rates and lower than average incomes. (b) In July, 2003, Toronto City Council approved the revitalization of Regent Park. The new neighbourhoods are designed according to new urbanist ideas: mid-rise and tall-rise buildings are both used, for example, as are mixed-income and mixed-use neighbourhoods. Of the total 28-hectare (69-acre), 21% is open space with 22% allocated to streets. Some 4,500 units of apartment buildings and townhouses were built compared to the 2,087 that were previously there: more people on the same amount of space.

Houses, condominiums, and apartments have long had some measure of security inherent in their design, if only a lock on the door. A more recent urban phenomenon involves not just securing entrances to homes, but access to entire neighbourhoods and communities. A **gated community** is a residential area with restricted access such that normally public spaces open to all—streets, sidewalk, and parks—have been privatized, open to a relative few who own homes within. They are intentionally designed security communities with designated and landscapes perimeters, usually with walls and fences and sometimes guarded checkpoints, that are designed to prevent access by non-residents.

Although long prevalent in other parts of the world, most notably South and Central America, and more recently Western Europe and China, their route to Canada over the past two decades comes from the United States, where some 9 million people currently live in gated communities. First emerging in the American Southwest in the 1950s and 1960s, they spread across that country, and by the early 1990s, into Canada. Here their presence is much less pronounced, but it is growing. Estimates place the number of these communities between 600 to 900 with British Columbia and Ontario leading the way (see "Want to Learn More?" on p. 293).

Those people who choose to live in these exclusive enclaves tend to be from middle and upper economic classes, but this, too, appears to be changing. The elite and famous have

long resided in such communities, but residents now include executives with families, affluent singles, and particularly retirees. Homes are marketed to this demographic cohort based on safety, lifestyle, and class. Indeed with private security forces and 24/7 surveillance systems atop individual home security systems, these partitioned communities provide a sense of safety from the

perceived crime, drugs, and related social problems of 'big cities,' particularly in the United States. In Canada, the marketing emphasis is directed more toward lifestyle, one accentuating leisure amenities and activities, especially golf. A shared sense of values, leisure pursuits, and similar income levels are also features attracting like-minded people to these communities. There is evidence indicating that since the 9/11 terrorist attacks on the U.S, and the ensuing concerns over security, the demand for gated communities there have trickled down to lower economic classes, who

in turn, find appealing the sense of safety perceived by gated communities. Such a trickle down is much less so in Canada.

The emergence of such segregated residential developments presents urban planners, developers and geographers with a set of contradictory values. On the one hand, gated communities do support several prevalent planning values: the high density and compact form minimizes transportation costs while providing immediate access to local shops and services; there is an emphasis on community amenities, such as parkland; they are pedestrian friendly and vehicular traffic calming; and they create a sense of place attachment, belonging, and community for residents. These are all positive attributes, often highlighted by building developers and residents alike.

However, there are numerous drawbacks: there is a uniformity of both building and people rather than mixed land use and social diversity; housing choice is limited to one or only several designs and often come with strict codes of aesthetics (e.g., only certain exterior colours are allowed); connectivity to other parts of the city, and passage through the community to other parts of the city, are interrupted if not entirely negated; they target specific income levels, effectively censuring a diversity of residents from differing economic classes; and they are the opposite of an open, inclusive community by their very exclusive design.

How to reconcile these differences remains a problem.

rural idyll live harmoniously. There are challenges facing suburban growth and development now and in the decades to come (Smith, 2000). Among the more geographically noteworthy issues involve questions about long-term sustainability. Growth has its limits: where will the suburbs be built for a Toronto of 10 million or a Vancouver of 5 million? What are the long-term implications for agricultural production as adjacent farmland continues to be suburbanized? Should low-density housing continue to be built at current scales given the transportation costs incurred by commuters, and the environmental costs born by us all? The challenge presented by these and other questions is to adapt our

suburbs to the changing needs, circumstances, and expectations of Canadian society.

Central City Change

Continuing growth in suburbia has altered Canada's central cities such that downtowns have experienced a relative decline over time. However, this change has not diminished their prominence. Generally speaking, our central cities are important nodes within their immediate and even regional urban environs. The inner cities remain livable, with a broad range of activities and people, well served by public transport, and supported by government planning and funding. These strengths suggest that Canadian downtowns are in a more favourable position in comparison to U.S. central cities (Charney, 2005).

Constricted Central Cities

Suburbanization in the U.S. has grievously damaged the economic base and the financial stability of central cities unable to absorb new growth areas, especially in the eastern United States. In earlier periods of growth, as new settlement areas developed beyond the political margins of the city, annexation absorbed new growth within the corporate boundaries of the expanding older city. The additional tax base and employment centres became part of the municipal whole. But in states that recognized the right of separate incorporation for the new growth areas, the ability of the city to continue to expand was restricted. Where possible, suburbanites opted for a separation from the central city and for aloofness from the costs, the deterioration, and the adversities associated with it. Their homes, jobs, shopping, schools, and recreation all existed outside the confines of the city from which they had divorced themselves.

The redistribution of population caused by suburbanization resulted not only in the spatial but also in the political segregation of social groups of the metropolitan area. The upwardly mobile resident of the city—younger, wealthier, and better educated—took advantage of the automobile and the highway to leave the central city. The poorer, older, least-advantaged urbanites were left behind. The central cities and the suburbs became increasingly differentiated. Large areas within those cities now contain only the poor and minority groups, including women (see "Women in the City"), a population little able to pay the rising costs of the social services that their numbers, neighbourhoods, and condition require.

The services needed to support the poor include welfare payments, social workers, extra police and fire protection, health delivery systems, and subsidized housing. Central cities, by themselves, are unable to support such an array and intensity of social services since they have lost the tax bases represented by suburbanized commerce, industry, and upper-income residential uses. Lost, too, are the job opportunities that were formerly a part of the central city structure. Increasingly, the poor and minorities are trapped in a central city without the possibility of nearby employment, and are isolated by distance, immobility, and unawareness—by *spatial mismatch*—from the few remaining low-skill jobs, which are now largely in the suburbs.

Population shift and the abandonment of the central city by commercial and industrial functions has nearly destroyed the traditional active, open auction of urban land, which led to the replacement of obsolescent uses and inefficient structures in a continuing process of urban modernization. In the vacuum left by the departure of private investors, the U.S. government, particularly after the landmark Housing Act of 1949, initiated urban renewal programs with or without provisions for a partnership with private housing and redevelopment investment. Under a wide array of programs, slum areas were cleared; public housing was built; cultural complexes and industrial parks were created; and city centres have been reconstructed.

With the continuing erosion of the urban economic base and the disadvantageous restructuring of the central city population mix, however, the hard-fought governmental battle in the U.S. to maintain or revive the central city is frequently judged to be a losing one. Public assistance programs have not reduced the central city burden of thousands of homeless people, and central city economies, with their high land and housing values, limited unskilled job opportunities, and inadequate resources for social services, appeared to many observers to offer few or no prospects for change.

In Canada, urban renewal projects are not as numerous or as necessary, but as in the U.S., the federal government did become formally involved in housing, particularly in the city core. Various legislation in the 1930s and 1940s lead eventually to the federal government instituting its first public housing project in Toronto's Regent Park in 1949 (Figures 8.33a and 8.33b). Public housing refers to federally owned units designated for the very poor and managed by public housing authorities. 'Cooperative housing' commenced in 1973 and refers to units owned and operated by non-profit cooperatives outside the control of the state or private sectors. Together, public housing and cooperative housing funded in part or in whole by the government constitute **social housing** (DeJong, 2000).

The largest proportion of public housing construction occurred in the early to mid-1970s and remained strong well into the 1980s. Canada was a model of social housing for other countries. The St. Lawrence neighbourhood in Toronto, for example, was visited by governments and policy makers from around the world who sought to emulate the success of the thriving mixed-income neighbourhood of public and private housing. Federal government support for social housing over the past two decades, however, has lessened in favour of allowing the private sector and lower levels of government to address the housing needs of low income people. As of 2000, there were approximately 205,000 public housing units and 400,000 third-sector housing units to serve Canada. Critics argue these numbers are insufficient to combat the problem of affordable housing (see "Geography and Public Policy: The Homeless").

Revitalized Central Cities

The pessimistic outlook in the U.S., however, began to change dramatically in the 1990s. Although their death was widely reported, central cities by 2000 were showing many positive signs of revival and renewed centrality both in the expanded metropolitan districts they anchored and in the larger national economy. That revival reflects at least two rediscovered attractions of core cities: as centres of economic opportunity and employment and as competitive and attractive residential locations for educated and affluent home-seekers.

Women in the City

Urban space is not identically viewed or uniformly accessible to men and women; fear of rape and sexual harassment, for example, may restrict women's mobility within some areas and times of urban movement, and deny them the same access to public space enjoyed by men. Maurice Yeates has noted that women have quite different needs, problems, and patterns than men with respect to urban social space.

In the first place, women are more numerous in large central cities than are men. Washington, D.C. probably is the most female-dominant (numerically) of any city in North America, with a "sex ratio" of 87 (or 115 females for every 100 males). In Minneapolis it is 84. The preponderance of women in central cities is related to an above-average number of household units headed by women, and to the larger numbers of women among the elderly.

A second characteristic is that women, along with their children, constitute the bulk of the poor. This feminization of poverty is a consequence of the low wage rates, part-time work, and lack of security of employment in many "women's jobs." Central cities, with their low-cost but often low-quality rental housing units, house the vast majority of poor women.

A third spatial characteristic of women in urban areas is that they have shorter journeys to work and rely more heavily upon public transportation than do men, a reflection of the lower incomes received by women, the differences in location of "female jobs," and the concentration of women in the central cities. Women on the whole simply cannot afford to spend as much on travel costs as men and make greater use of public transportation, which in the United States is usually inferior and often dangerous. The concentration of employment of women in clerical, sales, service jobs, and nursing also influences travel distances because these "women's jobs" are spread around the metropolitan area more than "men's jobs," which tend to be concentrated. It might well be argued that the more widespread location of "women's jobs" helps maintain the relative inaccessibility of many higher-paid "men's jobs" to a large number of women.

Given the allocation of roles, the resulting inequities, and the persistence of these inequities, there are spatial issues that impinge directly upon women. One is that many women find that their spatial range of employment opportunities is limited as a result of the inadequate availability of childcare facilities within urban areas. A second spatial issue relates to the structure of North American metropolitan areas and to the design of housing in general. North American cities are the outcome of male-dominant traits. Suburbs, in particular, reflect a male-paid work and female-home/children ethos. The suburban structure mitigates against women by confining them to a place and role in which there are very few meaningful choices. It has been argued that suburban women really desire a greater level of accessibility to a variety of conveniences and services, more efficient housing units, and a range of public and private transportation that will assure higher levels of mobility. These requirements imply higher-density urban areas.

Text excerpt from *The North American City,* 4th ed., by Maurice Yeates. Copyright @ 1997. Reprinted by permission of Pearson Education, Inc., Upper Saddle River, NJ, 07458.

Central cities were often dismissed in the 1980s as anachronisms in the coming age of fax machines, the Internet, mobile phones, and the like, that would eliminate the need for the face-to-face interaction intrinsic to cities. Instead, communications have become centralizing concerns of knowledge-based industries and activities such as finance, entertainment, health care, and corporate management that depend on dense, capital-intensive information technologies concentrated in geographically centralized markets. Cities—particularly large metropolitan cores—provide the first-rate telecommunications and fibre optics infrastructures and the access to skilled workers, customers, investors, research, educational, and cultural institutions needed by the modern, post-industrial economy.

As a reflection of cities' renewed attractions, employment and gross domestic product in the United States' 50 largest urban areas grew significantly in the 1990s, reversing stagnation and decline in the preceding decade. Demand for downtown office space was met by extensive new construction and urban renewal, and even manufacturing revived in the form of small and midsize companies providing high-tech equipment and processes. These, in turn, supported a growing network of suppliers and specialized services, with "circular and cumulative" growth the result.

Part of the new vigour of central cities comes from its new residents. Between 1980 and 2000, some 15 million immigrants arrived in the United States, most concentrating in "gateway" cities where they have become deeply rooted in their new communities by buying and renovating homes in inner-city areas, spending money in neighbourhood stores, and most importantly establishing their own businesses (Figure 8.34a). They also are important additions to the general urban labour force, providing the skilled and unskilled workers needed in expanding office-work, service, and manufacturing sectors.

Another part of central city residential revival is found in **gentrification**, the rehabilitation of housing in the oldest and now deteriorated inner-city areas by middle- and high-income groups (Figure 8.34b). Welcomed by many as a positive, privately financed projects promote the renewal of depressed urban neighbourhoods.

Geography and Public Policy

The Homeless

If the homeless lack housing, then the solution appears simple: build housing. But homelessness is a much more complicated issue than simply a lack of shelter. To have a home is to have a place of one's own—a centre of felt value—a site that is charged with personal and important emotional, social, and geographical meanings for the occupant. Home is arguably the most important place in the lives of human beings. It provides us with roots, a sense of order and security, self-identity, and cultural expression. Those who lack a home suffer not only an absence of adequate shelter, but control, privacy, and security.

Precisely who are the homeless depends upon how homelessness is defined. If conceived as a continuum, there are degrees of homelessness. If one is living in an apartment, for example, that is emotionally distressing—the roommate is difficult, the plumbing is sporadic, family members are far away—this is an unsatisfactory living arrangement, and does constitute a form of homelessness. However, resources combating the issue are targeted at the other extreme of this continuum—the *absolute homeless*—those using emergency shelters and/or sleeping on the streets (Murphy, 2000).

Today's absolute homeless are not the stereotypical, middle-aged, alcoholic male many Canadians imagine. The majority is a lone male, and the average age of a homeless person in Canada is 29, but others include adolescents, children, entire families, and single-parent families. The recently unemployed are the fastest growing sector (50%), followed by substance abusers (30%), and those deinstitutionalized with psychiatric problems (20%). The number of homeless is difficult to determine, but it was estimated in 2000 that there are between 35,000 to 40,000 homeless in Canada, with Montreal and Toronto having 10,000 each, Vancouver 5000, and Edmonton, Calgary, Ottawa, Winnipeg, Hamilton, Saskatoon, and Regina having 1000 to 2000 each. In 2001, over 14,000 homeless were counted in Canada's shelters. The numbers aside, it is clear that their size has steadily increased since the 1980s, and there is no sign of abatement.

The causes of homelessness are numerous. Personal events are responsible for many of the people being on the street or in shelters. Divorce, abuse, illness, eviction, and deinstitutionalization are among the more prevalent paths to homelessness. Many social scientists argue, however, that the majority find themselves homeless due to structural conditions in Canadian society: changes in the economy resulting in loss of employment, and the loss or reform of the social safety net, namely the removal or reduction of welfare and a minimum wage that has failed to keep pace with the cost of living.

There is no single, quick-fix solution to a problem as complex and large as homelessness, but solutions are possible. A spokesperson for the Canadian Council on Social Development maintains that in such a rich society as Canada, all it would take to eradicate the problem is the right amount of funding and political will. One thing is certain: until there is affordable housing made accessible to all, homelessness will persist.

Questions to Consider

1. What is the nature of the homeless problem in the community where you live or with which you are most familiar?

2. Where should responsibility for the homeless lie: at the federal, provincial, or local governmental level? Is it best left to private groups such as churches and charities? Or is it ultimately best recognized as a personal matter to be handled by homeless individuals themselves? What reasons form or support your response?

3. Some people argue that giving money, food, or housing but no therapy to street people makes one an "enabler" or accomplice of addicts. Do you agree? Why or why not?

4. Assuming you had the "political will" of governments, the support of Canadians, an unlimited budget, and the power to implement your plan, what one action would you take to combat the country's problem of homelessness? In other words, how would you spend the money and why? Exchange ideas with your classmates.

A homeless person finds temporary shelter and some assistance from an emergency outreach worker, along a Downtown East Side Vancouver street.

Gentrification has also sometimes caused serious negative social and housing impacts, such as the displacement of low-income, minority families. Gentrification, it is argued, is simply another expression of the continuous remaking of urban land use and social

(a)

(b)

FIGURE 8.34 Revitalized central cities. (*a*) New entrepreneurs in New York City. Many Latin American and Asian immigrants have established their own businesses fixing, making, or selling things, adding to the vitality of central cities. Some work out of sidewalk stalls, others have stores. According to the U.S. Census Bureau, 36% of New York City residents were born abroad. (*b*) Gentrified housing in the Georgetown section of Washington, D.C. Gentrification is especially active in the major urban centres of the eastern United States, from Boston south along the Atlantic Coast to Charleston, South Carolina, and Savannah, Georgia; it is also increasingly a part of the regeneration of older, deteriorated, first-generation residential districts in major central cities across the country.

patterns in accordance with the rent-paying abilities of alternate potential occupants. Yet the rehabilitation and replacement of housing stock that it implies yield inflated rents and prices that may push out established residents, disrupt the social networks they have created, and totally alter the characteristics and services of their home areas.

The city districts usually targeted for gentrification are those close to downtown jobs, with easy access to transit, and often of interesting older architecture. The replacement population of younger, wealthier professionals has helped revitalize and repopulate inner city zones already the destination of growing numbers of urbanites. A study of 26 U.S. cities found each expecting its downtown population to grow by 2010, some by double-digit percentages.

The reason for that expected growth lies in demographics. Young professionals are marrying and having children later or, often, are divorced, never-married, or same-sex couples. For them—a growing proportion of Americans—suburban life and shopping malls hold few attractions, while central city residence offers high-tech and executive jobs within walking or biking distance, and cultural, entertainment, and boutique shopping opportunities close at hand. The younger group has been joined by "empty-nesters," couples who no longer have children living at home and who find big houses on suburban lots no longer desirable. By their interests and efforts, these two groups have largely or completely remade and upgraded such old city neighbourhoods as the Mill District of Minneapolis; the Armory District of Providence, Rhode Island; the Denny Regrade and Belltown of Seattle; Main St./Market Square district of Houston; and many others throughout the country.

Gentrification is a particularly important process in the Canadian context (Ley, 2000). Since the 1970s onwards, living in the central city has been attractive to a minority of well-educated, middle class professional and administrative workers. This social group has played a key role in the revitalization of parts of Canada's larger cities. Renovation of older housing stock in districts such as Toronto's Cabbagetown, Ottawa's New Edinburgh, and the Plateau Mont-Royal in Montreal clearly exemplify this process. And yet gentrification alone does not explain the vitality of Canada's central cities. There are districts in decline in most cities, but they have yet to take on the scale of inner city decay experienced in larger American cities. The rapid influx of immigrants to cities such as Toronto and Vancouver, the stability of existing inner city neighbourhoods, the role of government regulation in housing and urban planning, the renewal of de-industrialized urban waterfronts, and the rise of entertainment districts in the central city, all contribute to a city's social and economic vibrancy.

Expanding Central Cities

During the latter part of the 20th century, the most dynamic U.S. urban growth areas were in the 13 states of the Mountain and Pacific West. In 1940, little more than half of all Westerners lived in cities; by 2000, nearly 90% were urbanites. Arizona, California, Nevada, and Utah all have a higher percentage of city dwellers than New York, and six of the 10 U.S. metropolitan areas with the biggest population gains from 1990 to 2000 were in the West (see Tables 8.3 and 8.4). For the most part, these newer "automobile" metropolises were able to expand physically to keep within the central city boundaries the new growth areas on their peripheries. Nearly without exception they placed few restrictions on physical expansion. That unrestricted growth has often resulted in the coalescence of separate cities into ever-larger metropolitan complexes.

The speed and volume of growth has spawned a complex of concerns, some reminiscent of older eastern cities and others specific to areas of rapid urban expansion like in the West. As in the East, the oldest parts of western central cities tend to be pockets of poverty, ethnic conflict, and abandonment. In addition, western central city governments face all the economic, social, and environmental consequences of unrestricted marginal expansion. Scottsdale, Arizona, for example, covered only 2.5 square kilometres in 1950; by 2000, it grew to nearly 517 square kilometres (200 sq m), four times the physical size of San Francisco. Phoenix, with which Scottsdale has now coalesced, surpasses in sprawl Los Angeles, which has three times as many people. The phenomenal growth of Las Vegas, Nevada, has similarly converted vast areas of desert landscape to low-density urban use (Figure 8.35).

Such unrestricted central city expansion has introduced its own fiscal crises. In many instances limited by state law from raising taxes, central cities have been unable to provide the infrastructural improvements and social services their far-flung new populations require. Schools remain unbuilt and underfunded, water supplies are increasingly difficult and expensive to obtain, open space requirements for parkland are ignored, and street and highway improvements and repairs are inadequate

even as demand for them increases. In short, each additional unit of unrestricted growth costs the municipality more than the additional development generates in tax revenue.

Increasingly, central cities and metropolitan areas of both East and West are seeking to restrain rather than encourage physical growth. Portland, Oregon, drew a "do not pass" line around itself in the late 1970s, prohibiting urban conversion of surrounding forests, farmlands, and open space. Even with its vigorously enforced "Smart growth" policies, however, Portland has been unable to stop some suburbanization of rural land in the face of continuing population growth, although at least part of that growth was accommodated by higher densities per square mile rather than by low-density sprawl.

Faced with the realization that the United States loses 1 hectare of mostly prime farmland every minute to development, other cities, metropolitan areas, and states are also beginning to resist and restrict urban expansion. "Smart growth" programs have been adopted by such states as Colorado, Delaware, Minnesota, and Washington. Resisting plans for expansion or extension of highways and other roadways in order to prevent further traffic generation and urban construction, cities of both the West and East are beginning to tighten controls on unrestricted and uneconomic expansion.

Sustainable Cities in Canada

According to Mark Roseland, a geographer at Simon Fraser University, the origins of sustainable cities emerged in the 1970s and can be benchmarked to the founding of Urban Ecology in Berkley (1975), a non-profit organization with the purpose to "rebuild cities in balance with nature." That organization published *Eco-City Berkley* (1987), a book dedicated to explaining how that city could be ecologically rebuilt, and continues to publish the journal *Urban Ecologist*. Seven international Eco-City Conferences have been held: Berkley (1990); Adelaide, Australia (1992); Yoff, Senegal (1996); Curitaba, Brazil (2000); Shenzhen, China (2002); Bangalore, India (2006); and San Francisco (2008).

There is no single correct definition of **urban sustainability**. However, its essential elements, which are reflected in the quotes below, suggest the integration of economic, social, and environmental considerations into decision making processes that directly and indirectly influence urban quality of life over the long term. Some definitions include:

- A sustainable city enhances the economic, social, cultural, and environmental well-being of current and future generations (International Centre for Sustainable Cities (ICSC), http://SustainableCities.net/).
- Long-term urban sustainability involves planning cities and regions to exist in harmony with the natural environment, while sustaining their human populations and economic base for current and future generations. Long-term integrated planning looks out 50-100 years and treats the city as a complex system, addressing environmental, economic, social and

FIGURE 8.35 Urban sprawl in the Las Vegas, Nevada, metropolitan area. Like many western U.S. cities, Las Vegas has spread out over great expanses of desert in order to keep pace with its rapidly growing population. The fastest growing metropolitan area of the United States in the 1990s, Las Vegas increased from a little more than 850,000 people in 1990 to more than 1.5 million by 2000, an increase of over 83%.

cultural well-being, as well as governance and infrastructure (PLUS Network, http://sustainablecities.net/plusnetwork).

- The enhanced well-being of cities or urban regions, including integrated economic, ecological and social components which maintain the quality of life for future generations (National Roundtable on the Environment and Economy (NTREE, http://www.nrtee-trnee.com/).

Much of the literature suggests a decentralized decision-making structure and local participation in planning are important in order that communities can define sustainability from their perspective. It calls for social equity between current and future generations, between urban residents and those in the surrounding regions, and through improved governance and adequate housing.

Implementing the concept of urban sustainability will require making difficult choices, such as decisions about production and consumption patterns in urban areas (see Chapter 12). Other hard choices include balancing regional versus urban demands, development versus non-development, the abilities of ecosystems to support human and non-human needs, and the nature of how we define the quality of life.

Governments must play a fundamental role in being active agents of positive change. New administrative arrangements, at national, provincial, regional, and local levels must be carefully considered. Some of these alternatives may include increased application of user fees, entering into public/private partnerships, establishing competitive but regulated land markets, providing housing finance and building materials, restructuring production regulations, improving urban and regional planning, and reforming tax systems that support rather than detract from urban sustainability.

Urban sustainability issues are interdependent. Urban traffic congestions and air pollution reflect the geography, land use patterns, and structure of cities. In the context of improving environmental quality in cities, NTREE suggested that Canada's efforts should focus on urban form, urban transportation, and energy use in buildings. In considering urban form, there are two competing perspectives. On the one hand, there is a view that compact cities—large, high density, and concentrated urban centres—best support the principles of sustainable development. This approach offers the advantage of promoting intensive and efficient patterns of activity, which would assist in reducing greenhouse gas emissions (see Chapter 12). On the other hand, green cities, which have more open structure and a landscape mosaic comprised of buildings, agricultural fields, and open spaces, also support the principles of urban sustainability.

In its second annual ranking of sustainable cities in Canada, Corporate Knights and others (2008) characterized a "sustainable city" as having a viable economy fuelled by a healthy population and leaving the smallest environmental footprint possible. For them, "the bottom-line indicator of sustainability for a city is the ability to maintain its population. A sustainable city must be a place where people want to live, work, play, and build their lives." Using municipal boundaries (i.e., not CMA, regional governments, or urban agglomerations), they classified urban areas according

to size—large (>750,000 population), medium (>250,000 and <749,999 population) and small (<249,999)—and examined five categories of indicators:

- *Ecological Integrity* measures the environmental viability of a city, and associated indicators look at pollution, smog, and waste diversion. The integrity of the land upon which citizens live is absolutely crucial to a long-lasting city and a healthy population.
- *Green Mobility* indicators include car dependency, bike lanes, car-pool lanes, and median commuting distance.
- *Economic Security* indicators include employment rate, home ownership, municipal debt level, and income levels, and are meant to measure the economic viability of a city. Citizens cannot make environmental or social aspects a priority if their economy is faltering.
- *Empowerment* refers to how active and educated a city is. Indicators include voter turnout at the most recent municipal election, and city council diversity. An informed city is a city that cares about its future prospects.
- *Social Well-Being* category highlights a city's internal interactions. Indicators such as crime rate, obesity rate, and number of community gardens show how citizens relate to their communities.

Each category was graded out of 10, and the final score reflected the average of each category (Table 8.6). Ottawa, Quebec, and Yellowknife were viewed as the most sustainable cities in Canada for their respective size categories. Note that the Ecological Integrity, Economic Security, Social Well-being, and Final Score declined as one moves from the largest to the smallest centres. This has implications for capacity of local governments to deliver programs in a sustainable manner and urban form.

World Urban Diversity

The city, as Figure 8.3 reminds us, is a global phenomenon. It is also a regional and cultural variable. The descriptions and models that we have used to study the functions, land use arrangements, suburbanization trends, and other aspects of Canadian and U.S. cities would not in all—or even many—instances help us understand the structures and patterns of cities in other parts of the world. Those cities have been created under different historical, cultural, and technological circumstances. They have developed different functional and structural patterns, some so radically different from our North American model that we would find them unfamiliar and uncharted landscapes indeed. The city is universal; its characteristics are cultural and regional.

Canadian and U.S. Cities

The seemingly homogeneous culture realm of Canada and the United States has given rise to the concept of 'the North American City': because urban expression is similar in the two countries, differences are largely superficial. A suburban ranch house, with a

TABLE 8.6

Sustainable City Rankings in Canada (2008)

City	Ecological Integrity	Green Mobility	Economic Security	Empowerment	Social Well-being	Final Score
Large Centres						
Ottawa	5.95	7.26	9.30	7.72	8.26	7.70
Toronto	7.66	6.33	7.79	7.33	8.37	7.50
Montreal	7.26	6.66	6.99	7.14	7.86	7.19
Edmonton	5.10	7.74	7.91	6.57	8.27	7.11
Calgary	4.79	8.36	6.71	7.14	7.52	6.90
AVERAGE	6.16	7.27	7.74	7.18	8.06	7.28
Medium Centres						
Quebec	7.55	7.18	7.44	7.22	7.69	7.41
Halifax	6.08	6.70	7.65	7.13	8.11	7.13
Vancouver	4.47	7.41	8.44	6.88	7.79	7.00
Winnipeg	4.95	7.46	7.57	6.97	7.02	6.79
Mississauga	5.56	5.89	6.07	6.53	7.80	6.37
Hamilton	5.00	6.16	6.07	6.14	5.82	5.84
AVERAGE	5.61	6.98	7.43	6.87	7.28	6.84
Small Centres						
Yellowknife	4.16	2.60	6.88	8.39	10.00	6.41
Saskatoon	5.10	7.84	6.89	6.65	5.54	6.39
Iqaluit	2.55	5.00	6.83	9.28	5.00	5.73
Whitehorse	4.51	1.20	7.22	7.31	7.00	5.45
Saint John	3.72	6.21	8.37	6.40	1.88	5.32
St. John's	2.00	5.61	5.75	6.56	3.53	4.69
Charlottetown	3.68	1.17	6.50	6.45	1.15	3.79
AVERAGE	3.72	3.24	7.16	7.57	5.01	5.34

Adapted from: *static.corporateknights.ca/Cities2008.pdf*.

Ford parked in the driveway, situated not far from a McDonald's, a Starbucks or a Wal-Mart could be in Canada or the U.S. And yet, our respective cities are not identical: place matters because local and national contexts do make a difference. Mercer and England (2000) make a convincing argument that there are several essential Canadian-U.S. differences with respect to urban form: population and households, housing stock, urban transportation systems, level of investment in public transit provision (higher in Canada), the planning process, and the role of government. These dimensions, along with a host of global processes that are playing out in ways unique to each country—specifically economic restructuring and immigration—indicate that 'the North American City' is not homogeneous: it is a 'myth' (Goldberg and Mercer, 1986).

Population and household composition are useful indicators of urban form. Low or decreasing numbers of both people and household size in a central city, for example, may indicate economic, social, and urban decay. Whereas American cities over the past two decades vary considerably in terms of population and household size loss, and stability or growth at the central city or overall metropolitan region, there are virtually no Canadian instances where both the central city and the overall metropolitan region lost population. This points to the continued overall vitality of Canadian central cities relative to American ones. Canadian central city households are also much more likely to include children: they are more family oriented.

The housing stock itself differs, too. There are certainly overarching similarities in that housing is dominated by owner-occupied, single detached units, and home-ownership is typically in the 60 to 65 per cent range in both countries. However, Canadians do not share the various tax advantages used to promote home ownership that Americans enjoy, nor do they have the same proportion of single-family units in Canadian cities: there are proportionally-speaking slightly more multi-unit dwellings, and this is reflected in urban densities. Canadian cities are, on average, twice as dense as American ones, with 28.5 persons per hectare in Canada compared to 14.2 persons per hectare south of the border (Condon, 2004).

The size, density, and form of a city dictates the urban transportation systems that can be effectively provided, and once established, the transportation systems impact on-going urban growth and decay. Automobiles and trucks play an enormous role in the daily mobility of individuals and the movement of goods in North America. The personal car is a deeply embedded cultural practice across both countries. Per capita, Canadians own nearly as many cars as Americans, but they drive about half as much per year (Condon, 2004). Canadian commuters are significantly less likely to use automobiles in their daily commute to work than Americans, and are more likely to use public mass transit: the Canadian city is better served by and more dependent on mass transportation than is the U.S. city. Since Canadian metropolitan areas have only one-quarter the number of kilometres of highway lanes per capita as U.S. metropolises—and at least as much resistance to constructing more—urban sprawl of people and functions is less extensive north of the border than south (Figure 8.36).

The compactness and liveability of Canadian cities is in no small way a function of the greater acceptance of planning policies and a larger degree of government regulation. Urban and regional planning has a more wide-ranging and acceptable role in Canada, whereas local planning autonomy prevails in the U.S. The extent of local government fragmentation differs considerably, too. In the U.S., metropolitan areas tend to be comprised of numerous politically distinct governments—each 'city' within a contiguous urban region has its own government—and the central city is commonly the loser in the struggle for investment, taxable lands, and residents. Canada tends to govern large urban areas, such at the Greater Toronto Area, as a single administrative unit, wherein local autonomy is given less weight so resources are more likely to be dispersed throughout the metropolitan area.

In addition to these cross-border differences, there are several large-scale or global processes working on both countries, and once again, the differing cultural contexts means they manifest themselves in slightly differing ways. Both economies are increasingly linked to a common global market place and are integrated under free trade agreements. However, the historically greater role of government—the public sector—in economic development and the stronger commitment to social services, such as education and health, continue to differentiate Canada from the U.S. The economic restructuring from manufacturing and industry to more service and information sectors has, for example, had more dire impact for some U.S. cities in the North and West manufacturing belts than in Canada. The ensuing economic decline experienced in some U.S. cities, such as Flint, Michigan, for example, has not yet been experienced on a similar scale in Canadian cities for reasons outlined above. Even something as ordinary as shopping mall development has evolved differently. Canada has a lower per capita of shopping malls and our suburban malls tend to be surrounded primarily by residential tracts rather than other retail and commercial facilities. Canada also has ten times the relative

FIGURE 8.36 The central and outlying business districts of Toronto, easily visible in this photo, are still rooted firmly by mass transit convergence and mass transit usage. On average, Canadian metropolitan areas are almost twice as densely populated as are those of the United States. On a per capita basis, Canadian urbanites are two and a half times more dependent on public transportation than are American city dwellers. That reliance gives form, structure, and coherence to the Canadian central city, qualities now irretrievably lost in the sprawled and fragmented U.S. metropolis.

proportion of downtown or central city malls, in part, because city governments have been successful in persuading developers to locate in the core. More government regulation and active engagement in the economy has thus impacted Canada's cities in ways that differentiate them from the U.S.

Immigration has also changed the very face of our respective cities. Both countries are nations of predominantly immigrants, but Canada has been admitting immigrants at the twice the rate of the U.S. since 1960, and as of 2007, at four times the rate. As with shifts in the global economy, there have been shifts in the source countries of immigrants from Europe to elsewhere. In the U.S., the principle sources are now Mexico and other Central American and Caribbean countries; in Canada, the single largest source—and one comprising almost half of all new immigrants—is Asia. The impact in cultural and ethnic terms on the cities to which the immigrants have migrated has been major. Perhaps the most striking difference between U.S. and Canadian cities is the relative scale of ethnically concentrated and defined neighbourhoods. Latino, Black, and White neighbourhoods are quite common in the U.S., but geographers Walks and Bourne (2006) found that it is not the case in Canada that particular ethnic groups are isolated and marginalized in homogeneous neighbourhoods due to economic ghettoization.

Admittedly, Canadian and U.S. cities are similar, particularly when compared to European or Asian urban forms, but there cannot be a single 'North American City' simply because there is too much diversity between and within each country. Canadian cities do have a higher proportion of foreign born, more multi-family dwellings, greater government regulation, higher densities, fewer freeways, more mass transit, more retention of inner city shopping facilities, more employment opportunities, and more urban amenities than its U.S. central city counterpart. In particular, it does not have the rivalry from well-defined competitive "edge cities" of suburbia that sprawl and fragment U.S. metropolitan complexes.

The West European City

If such significant urban differences are found even within the tightly knit Anglo-American region, we can only expect still greater divergences from the U.S. model at greater linear and cultural distance, and in countries with long urban traditions and mature cities of their own. The political history of France, for example, has given to Paris an overwhelmingly primate position in its system of cities. Political, economic, and colonial history has done the same for London in the United Kingdom. On the other hand, Germany and Italy came late to nationhood, and no overwhelmingly dominant cities developed in their systems.

Nonetheless, a generally common heritage of medieval origins, Renaissance restructurings, and industrial period growth has given distinctive features to the cities of Western Europe. Despite wartime destructions and postwar redevelopments, many still bear the impress of past occupants and technologies, even back to Roman times in some cases. An irregular system of narrow streets may be retained from the random street pattern developed in medieval times of pedestrian and pack-animal movement. Main streets radiating from the city centre and cut by circumferential "ring roads" tell us the location of primary roads leading into town through the gates in city walls now gone and replaced by circular boulevards. Broad thoroughfares, public parks, and plazas mark Renaissance ideals of city beautification and the aesthetic need felt for processional avenues and promenades.

Although each is unique historically and culturally, West European cities as a group share certain common features that set them off from the U.S. model, though they are less removed from the Canadian norm. Cities of Western Europe have, for example, a much more compact form and occupy less total area than American cities of comparable population; most of their residents are apartment dwellers. Residential streets of the older sections tend to be narrow, and front, side, or rear yards or gardens are rare.

European cities were developed for pedestrians and still retain the compactness appropriate to walking distances. The sprawl of American peripheral or suburban zones is generally absent. At the same time, compactness and high density do not mean skyscraper skylines. Much of urban Europe predates the steel frame building and the elevator. City skylines tend to be low, three to five stories in height, sometimes (as in central Paris) held down by building ordinance (Figure 8.37), or by prohibitions on private structures exceeding the height of a major public building, often the central cathedral. Those older restrictions are increasingly relaxed as taller office buildings and blocks are developed in London and other commercial centres.

Compactness, high densities, and apartment dwelling encouraged the development and continued importance of public transportation, including well-developed subway systems. The

FIGURE 8.37 Even in their central areas, many European cities show a low profile, like that of Paris seen here. Although taller buildings—20, 30, even 50 or more stories in height—have become more common in major European cities since World War II, they are not the universal mark of central business districts that they have become in the United States, nor are they generally welcomed symbols of city progress and pride.

private automobile has become much more common of late, though most central city areas have not yet been significantly restructured with wider streets and parking facilities to accommodate it. The automobile is not the universal need in Europe that it has become in American cities. Home and work are generally more closely spaced in Europe—often within walking or bicycling distance—while most sections of towns have first-floor retail and business establishments below upper-storey apartments, bringing both places of employment and retail shops within convenient distance of residences.

A very generalized model of the social geography of the West European city has been proposed (Figure 8.38). Its exact counterpart can be found nowhere, but many of its general features are part of the spatial social structure of most major European cities. In the historic core, now increasingly gentrified, residential units for the middle class, the self-employed, and the older generation of skilled artisans share limited space with preserved historic buildings, monuments, and tourist attractions.

The old city fortifications may mark the boundary between the core and the surrounding transitional zone of substandard housing, 19th-century industry, and recent immigrants. The waterfront has similar older industry; newer plants are found on the periphery. Public housing and some immigrant concentrations may be near that newer industry, while other urban socio-economic groups aggregate themselves in distinctive social areas within the body of the city.

The West European city is not characterized by inner-city deterioration and out-migration. Its core areas tend to be stable in population and attract, rather than repel, the successful middle class and upwardly mobile. Nor does it always feature the ethnic

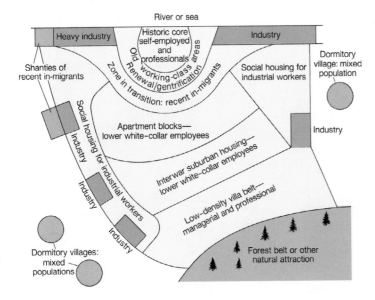

FIGURE 8.38 A diagrammatic representation of the West European city.

Source: Redrawn from Paul White, The West European City: A Social Geography. *© 1984 Longman Group UK Limited. Used by permission.*

neighbourhoods of U.S. cities although some, like London, do, particularly for immigrants of non-European origin. Similar segregation, though there in suburban apartment clusters, is found on the margins of French cities, particularly for North African ethnics.

The East European City

Cities of Eastern Europe, including Russia and the former European republics of the Soviet Union, make up a separate urban class—the East European city. It is an urban form that shares many of the traditions and practices of West European cities, but it differs from them in the centrally administered planning principles that were in the communist period (1945–1990) designed to shape and control both new and older settlements. For reasons both ideological and practical, the particular concerns were, first, limitation on size of cities to avoid supercity growth and metropolitan sprawl; second, assurance of an internal structure of neighbourhood equality and self-sufficiency; and third, strict land use segregation. The planned East European city fully achieved none of these objectives, but by attempting them it emerged as a distinctive urban form.

In general structural terms, the city is compact, with relatively high building and population densities reflecting the nearly universal apartment dwelling, and with a sharp break between urban and rural land uses on its margins. Like the older generation West European city, the East European city depended nearly exclusively on public transportation.

During the communist period, it differed from its Western counterpart in its purely governmental rather than market control of land use and functional patterns. That control dictated that the central area of cities (the Central Cultural District or CCD) should be reserved for public use, not occupied by retail establishments or office buildings on the Western, capitalist model. A large central square ringed by administrative and cultural buildings was the preferred pattern.

Nearby, space was provided for a large recreational and commemorative park. In the Russian prototype, neither a central business district nor major outlying business districts were required or provided. Residential areas were expected to be largely self-contained in the provision of at least low-order goods and services, minimizing the need for a journey to centralized shopping locations.

Residential areas are made up of *microdistricts*, assemblages of uniform apartment blocks housing perhaps 10,000 to 15,000 persons, surrounded by broad boulevards, and containing centrally sited nursery and grade schools, grocery and department stores, theatres, clinics, and similar neighbourhood necessities and amenities (Figure 8.39a). Plans called for effective separation of residential quarters from industrial districts by landscaped buffer zones, but in practice many microdistricts were built by factories for their own workers and were located immediately adjacent to the workplace. Since microdistricts were most easily and rapidly constructed on open land at the margins of expanding cities, high residential densities have been carried to the outskirts of town (Figure 8.39b).

These characteristic patterns will change in the decades to come as market principles of land allocation are adopted. Now that private interests can own land and buildings, the urban areas may take on forms more similar to those of the West European city. In Moscow, the prototypical communist-era East European city, a recent spate of building is rapidly remaking a landscape and skyline dominated by Soviet-style drab grey concrete monoliths. Glass and metal apartment buildings, modernistic Western-style shopping malls, gated communities of luxury apartments and individual houses, and commercial and residential redesign and redevelopment within existing older structures are the 21st-century trend experienced as well in other major Russian and East European cities. Currently, a prominent trend in all principal East European cities is to construct more spacious privately owned apartments and single-family houses for the newly rich.

Cities in the Developing World

Still farther removed from the Canadian urban model are the cities of Africa, Asia, the Middle East, and Latin America. Industrialization has come to them only recently. Modern technologies in transportation and public facilities are sparsely available, and the structures of cities and the cultures of their inhabitants are far different from the urban world familiar to North Americans. The developing world is vast in extent and diverse in physical and social content; generalizations about it or its urban landscapes lack certainty and universality. Islamic cities of North Africa, for example, are entities sharply distinct from the sub-Saharan African, the Southeast Asian, or the Latin American city.

The backgrounds, histories, and current economies of developing world cities vary greatly. Some are ancient, having been established as early as (or even earlier than) the 21st century B.C.E., not A.C.E. Some are still pre-industrial, with only a modest central commercial core; they lack industrial districts, public transportation, or any meaningful degree of land use separation. Others, though increasingly Western in form, are only beginning to industrialize. And some have taken on industrial, commercial,

(a)

(b)

FIGURE 8.39 (*a*) This scene from Bucharest, Romania, clearly shows important recurring characteristics of the East European socialist-era city design: mass transit service to boulevard-bordered "superblocks" of self-contained apartment-house microdistricts with their own shopping, schools, and other facilities. (*b*) High-density apartment houses bordered by wheat fields mark the urban margin of Poprad, Slovakia; the Tatra Mountains are in the background.

and administrative functions on the Western model and, at least in their central areas, assumed as well the appearance of fully modern urban centres (Figure 8.40).

Some developing-world cities are the product of colonialism, established as ports or outposts of administration and exploitation, built by Europeans on a Western model current at the time of their development. For example, the British built Kolkata (Calcutta), New Delhi, and Mumbai (Bombay) in India and Nairobi and Harare (formerly Salisbury) in Africa. The French developed

FIGURE 8.40 Downtown Nairobi, Kenya, is a busy, modern urban core, complete with high-rise commercial buildings.

Hanoi and Ho Chi Minh City (Saigon) in Vietnam, Dakar in Senegal, and Bangui in the Central African Republic. The Dutch planned Jakarta (former Batavia) in Indonesia as their main outpost, Belgium placed Kinshasa (formerly Leopoldville) in what is now the Democratic Republic of the Congo, and the Portuguese founded a number of cities in Angola and Mozambique.

Just as socialist planning principles shaped cities in Eastern Europe in the latter half of the 20th century, a number of Asian cities also bear their imprint. Examples include Pyongyang (North Korea), Phnom Penh (Cambodia), and Hanoi (Vietnam). Finally, some cities in the developing world are relatively new, having been built to serve as capital cities, among them Brasilia, Brazil; Abuja, Nigeria; and Islamabad, Pakistan. And still others were newly created as industrial and transportation centres.

Urban structure is a product not just of the time at which a city was founded, and by whom, but also of the role it plays in its own cultural setting. Land use patterns in capital cities reflect the centralization of government functions and the concentration of wealth and power in a single city of a country (Figure 8.41a). The physical layout of a religious centre is conditioned by the religion it serves, whether Hinduism, Buddhism, Islam, Christianity, or other faith. Typically, a monumental structure—a temple, mosque, or cathedral—and associated buildings rather than government or commercial offices occupy the city centre (Figure 8.41b). Traditional market centres for a wide area (Timbuktu in Mali and Lahore in Pakistan) or cultural capitals (Addis Ababa in Ethiopia and Cuzco in Peru) have land use patterns that reflect their special functions. Similarly, port cities such as Dubai (United Arab Emirates), Haifa (Israel), or Shanghai (China) have a land use structure different from that of an industrial or mining centre such as Johannesburg (South Africa). Adding to the complexity is the

(a)

(b)

FIGURE 8.41 Developing-world cities vary greatly in structure and appearance, reflecting their differing culture regions, histories, and functions. (*a*) Monumental government buildings mark single-function Brasilia, capital city of Brazil, whereas (*b*) the central area of multifunctional Guanajuato, Mexico, is dominated by religious structures.

fact that cities with a long history reflect the changes wrought by successive rulers or colonial powers, and that as some of the megacities in the developing world have grown, they have engulfed nearby towns and cities.

Even within a single culture realm, then, urban forms display significant variation. For example, for South Asia, which includes Afghanistan, Pakistan, India, Nepal, Bhutan, and Bangladesh, geographers have developed different models to characterize colonial cities, traditional bazaar cities, planned cities, and cities that are intermixtures of these. Still other models describe land use patterns in smaller cities that developed originally as hill stations (resorts), railway colonies, or military encampments.

Yet, by observation and consensus, some common features of developing-world cities are recognizable. For example, wherever the automobile or modern transport systems are an integral part of the modernizing city, the metropolis begins to take on Western characteristics. All the large cities have modern centres of commerce, not unlike their North American counterparts (see Figure 8.40). In places where the public transit system is limited, however, the result has been overcrowded cities centred on a single major business district. Examples include Mumbai, India; Lagos, Nigeria; Jakarta, Indonesia; and Bangkok, Thailand.

All, too, wherever located, have experienced massive in-migrations from rural areas. Many, particularly in sub-Saharan Africa, have absorbed large numbers of foreign immigrants seeking asylum or economic opportunity. Most have had even faster

rates of natural increase than of immigration. The predicted consequences, according to the UN, will be the concentration of nearly all the global population increase between 2000 and 2030 within the urban areas of the world's least developed countries. Many of those populations are and will continue to be impacted by the negative effects of a globalizing world economy that features massive transfers of money and jobs to cities and countries, which, at least temporarily, are able to offer the cheapest labour for the "footloose" operations of transnational corporations. UN-Habitat has termed the economic consequences a "race to the bottom" that yields widespread urbanization of poverty as jobs gained by temporary local advantages are lost to other locales offering superior—if transitory—inducements. Increased urban poverty and greater social and economic inequality and segregation are the foreseen consequences for much of the urbanizing developing countries. In all their cities, large numbers of people support themselves in the "informal" sector—as food vendors, peddlers of cigarettes or trinkets, street-side barbers or tailors, errand runners or package carriers—outside the usual forms of wage labour (Table 8.7).

The developing countries, emerging from formerly dominant subsistence economies, have experienced disproportionate population concentrations, particularly in their national and regional capitals. Lacking or relatively undeveloped is the substructure of maturing, functionally complex smaller and medium-sized centres characteristic of more advanced and diversified economies. The primate city dominates their urban systems (Figure 8.17).

TABLE 8.7		
Relative Importance of the Informal Economy in Employment (percent)		
	AFRICA	**ASIA**	**LATIN AMERICA AND CARIBBEAN**
Non-agricultural employment	78	45–85	57
Urban employment	61	40–60	40
Total new job creation	93	–	83

Source: Cities alliance, 2004 *Annual Report*, Table 1, p. 7.

TABLE 8.8	
Slum Dwellers' Share of Total Urban Population	
REGION	**PERCENTAGE**
Sub-Saharan Africa	72
South Central Asia	58
East Asia	36
Western Asia	33
Latin America and Caribbean	32
North Africa	28
South-western Asia	28
Developing Regions	*43*
Developed Regions	*6*

Source: UN-Habitat, *The Challenge of Slums*, 2003.

Nearly a quarter of all Nicaraguans live in metropolitan Managua, and Libreville contains 40% of the populace of Gabon. Vast numbers of surplus, low-income rural populations have been attracted to these developed seats of wealth and political centrality in the hope of finding a job.

Whatever their relative or absolute size within their respective states, large cities of the developing world typically produce a significant share of the gross domestic income (GDI) of their countries. Within Latin America, for example, Lima contributes 44% of Peru's GDI and São Paulo yields 37% of Brazil's. Major cities of Asia show comparable relative economic importance: Bangkok is credited with 38% of Thailand's gross domestic income, and Manila, Philippines; Karachi, Pakistan; and Shanghai, China, contributed 25%, 18%, and 12%, respectively, to the GDI of their countries, as reported by the UN in 2001. Despite its inadequate infrastructure, Mumbai generates one-sixth of the GDI of India.

Most cities of the developing world are now and seem likely to continue to be ringed by vast squatter settlements high in density and low in public facilities and services (see "The Informal Housing Problem"). With regional variations (Table 8.8), slum dwellers account for about 43% of the urban population in developing regions, and squatter slums in 2001 held just under a billion people—about a third of the world's city dwellers. The UN predicts that these areas will house some 2 billion people by 2030. Then, as now, their most vulnerable and deprived residents will be women and children as the urban "feminization of poverty" expresses itself in large parts of the developing world.

As many as half of the 3 million residents in Nairobi, Kenya, live in slums, most without electricity, running water, or sewers; in that city's sprawling slum district of Mathare Valley, some 250,000 people are squeezed into 15 square kilometres (6 sq mi) and are increasing by 10,000 inhabitants per year. Such impoverished squatter districts exist around most major cities in Africa, Asia, and Latin America, housing approximately one-fourth of the population of such Asian cities as Bangkok (Thailand), Kuala Lumpur (Malaysia), and Jakarta (Indonesia). The percentage is even higher in a number of major Indian cities, including Chennai (Madras) and Kolkata (Calcutta). The land use result has frequently been the creation of an *inverse concentric zone* pattern

in which the elite and upper class reside in central areas and social status declines with increasing distance from the centre. These generalizations, though valid and revealing, tend to mask real differences in urbanization patterns and trends in different world regions.

Asia, for example, the major beneficiary of economic globalization and outsourcing of transnational corporate production, is experiencing a rate and extent of urbanization never before seen. The continent had only 9% urban population in 1920, but had amassed 48% by 2000 and, the UN predicts, will rise to 53% by 2030. Increasingly, that growing urban component is concentrated in a series of *extended urban regions* (EURs), each extending 50 to 100 kilometres (30 to 60+ miles) from a megacity centre. And those megacities (more than 10 million inhabitants) are themselves growing in number and size. Asia contained six of them in the late 1990s; it is forecast to have 11 more by 2020.

Urban development is not, of course, uniform across the continent or within single countries. The concentration of economic advantage has similarly concentrated massive urbanization in a small number of *mega-urban-regions* (MURs). The UN anticipates, for example, that by 2020, two-thirds of Southeast Asia's urban population will live in only five MURs, led by the Java MUR with 100 million in population and by the Bangkok and Manila MURs, each with 30 million inhabitants. The Southeast Asian MURs (except for Java) will be dwarfed by developments anticipated for East Asia, such as the Tokyo–Osaka–Kyoto–Kobe–Nagoya MUR (60 million), the Hong Kong–Shenzen–Guangdong MUR (120 million), and the Greater Shanghai MUR (83 million). As the UN notes, "with the Shanghai MUR extending over 6340 square kilometres (2500 sq mi) and the Beijing MUR covering an area of 16,870 square kilometres (6512 sq mi), East Asia MURs are introducing urban issues on geographic scales never before experienced."

Indeed, China must confront similar problems experienced by other urbanizing countries, but the vast numbers of people and quantity of area involved is staggering. Canada's 31 million people may be 80% urban, but when 40.5% of China's population

Between one-third and two-thirds of the population of most developing world cities is crowded into shantytowns and squatter settlements built by the inhabitants, often in defiance of officialdom. These unofficial communities—*favela* in Brazil, *barrio* in Mexico, *kampung* in Indonesia, *gecekondu* in Turkey, or *katchiabadi* in Pakistan—usually have little or no access to publicly provided services such as water supply, sewerage and drainage, paved roads, and garbage removal. In such megacities as Rio de Janeiro, São Paulo, Mexico City, Bangkok, Chennai (Madras), Cairo, or Lagos, millions find refuge in the shacks and slums of the "informal housing sector." Crumbling tenements house additional tens of thousands, many of whom are eventually forced into shantytowns by the conversion of tenements into commercial property or high-income apartments.

No more than 20% of the new housing in Third World cities is produced by the formal housing sector; the rest develops informally, ignoring building codes, zoning restrictions, property rights, and infrastructure standards. Informal settlements house varying percentages of these populations, but for low-income developing countries as a whole

during the 1980s and 1990s, only one formal housing unit was added for every nine new households, and between 70% and 90% of all new households found shelter in shanties or slums. Peripheral squatter settlements, though densely built, may provide adequate household space and even water, sewers, and defined traffic lanes through the efforts of the residents. More usually, however, overcrowding transforms these settlements into vast zones of disease and squalor subject to constant danger from landslides, fire, and flooding. The informality and often illegality of the squatter housing solution means that those who improvise and build their own shelters lack registration and recognized ownership of their domiciles or the land on which they stand. Without such legal documentation, no capital accumulation based on housing assets is possible, and no collateral for home improvement loans or other purposes is created. The remedy, it has long been advocated, is to give formal title deeds to the poorest slum dwellers. In 2003, Brazil announced such a program, promising millions of residents in more than 4000 squatter communities, including 1.5 million in Rio's *favelas,* not only property ownership but also such basic services as access to

credit, mail delivery, and utilities. Actions such as there *can* reduce the problem, but there is no single-step solution.

For an in-depth and highly informative overview of this global problem of slums and informal housing, see Mike Davis's (2006) *Planet of Slums.*

A *favela* in Rio de Janeiro. These homes are built out of scrap wood and metal and have no city services such as sewers, running water, electricity, or street maintenance.

is urbanized, that translates into well over 500 million people. If the projections that China's urbanization rate will raise to 57% by 2020, this means 300 million more people—the equivalent of 10 more Canadas—with be living in cities. Urban sprawl will overtake agricultural land, and rapid growth in the form of large-scale developments will threaten both existing settlements and local ways of living. Environmental pollution and traffic congestion will worsen, as will issues of public health and safety. Administering such growth is a challenge in itself. All of these are classic problems of rapid urbanization, but the scale of the solutions required is unprecedented. How China will address the problems of rapid urbanization is arguably the biggest challenge facing that country as it moves into the 21st century.

Sub-Saharan Africa is the most rapidly urbanizing world region and is expected to have an urban majority by about 2030. Only five of its mainland countries (Botswana, Congo, Djibouti, Gabon, and South Africa) were more than 50% urban in 2004, but by 2010, the UN anticipates, no less than nine will have urban majorities. With urban growth rates exceeding 4 to 5% per year, some sub-Saharan African countries are matching the expansion rates characteristic of Western states at their peak growth

periods of the end of the 19th century. Unfortunately, in the current African situation, Western-style economic growth is not accompanying or driving that population growth, which for some sub-Saharan African main cities is exceeding 10% per annum, implying a doubling of residents every decade.

That kind of urban expansion—reflecting rural-to-urban and international migration as well as rapid rates of natural increase—without commensurate economic expansion, has made sub-Saharan African cities case studies of slum development and poverty to accompany the skyscraper modernization of many capital city cores. Early in the 21st century, 72% of the region's urbanites were slum dwellers; they were, in addition, afflicted with low life expectancies, high levels of infant and child mortality, HIV/AIDS prevalence, and illiteracy, particularly among women and girls. Although improvements in sanitary conditions are occurring (83% of sub-Saharan urban people have access to improved drinking water supplies and 73% use adequate sanitary facilities), the UN anticipates continuing pressure on city infrastructure as some 400 million additional people are added to city populations by 2020. It also expects that slum populations, at present rates of increase, are likely to double every 15 years.

The *Middle East and North Africa* is, like sub-Saharan Africa, only recently sharing in the global urban transition, with all the region's countries in the early 21st century experiencing pronounced urban population increases. With Bahrain, Israel, Kuwait, Lebanon, Libya, Qatar, and Saudi Arabia already (2004) more than 85% urban, only Egypt, Sudan, and Yemen are expected to be less than 50% urbanized by 2015. Throughout the region, cities contend with a host of problems that hinder the achievement of economic growth and social stability: deterioration of the urban environment, uncontrolled sprawl, discrepancies in access to services, and insufficient and inadequate housing for the poor. Some 12 million Egyptians live in unhygienic slums, and young married couples often wait for years before they can afford a place of their own.

The region's rapidly growing urban population puts increased but differential pressures on the existing current city structure. Rehabilitation and reconstruction are pressing needs in Lebanon and the West Bank/Gaza; poverty alleviation in Egypt, Jordan, and Morocco; and urban housing in Egypt and Jordan. In nearly all the countries of the Near East and North Africa, more than half the population is under 20 years old, and in all, the youthful population increasingly makes its way from the rural to urban areas, where high unemployment rates are the rule, and much of the youthful labour force lacks the technical skills required for economic growth.

In *Latin America and the Caribbean*, "city life" is the cultural norm. The vast majority of the residents of Mexico, Venezuela, Brazil, Argentina, Chile, and other countries live in cities, and very often in the primate city. The urbanization process is rapidly making Latin American cities among the largest in the world. Analysts predict that by the year 2015, 6 of the largest 28 cities will be in Latin America, and Rio de Janeiro and São Paulo, Brazil, will have merged into a continuous megalopolis 350 miles long.

Latin American cities (Figure 8.42) still retain the focus on their central areas which has been so largely lost in their U.S. counterparts. The entire transportation system converges on the downtown, where the vast majority of jobs are found. The city centres are lively and modern with many tall office buildings, clubs, restaurants, and stores of every variety. Condominium apartments house the well-to-do who prefer living in the centre because of its convenience to workplaces, theatres, museums, friends, specialty shops, and restaurants (Figure 8.43). Thousands of commuters pour into the urban core each day, some coming from the outer edge of the city (perhaps an hour or two commuting time) where the poorest people live. The mixed usages of the city centre are reflected in its increasing segregation into two parts: the modernizing CBD of self-contained newer high-rise office, hotel, and department store buildings, and the older traditional "market" segment of small, street-oriented businesses and shops.

Two features of the Latin American city pattern are noteworthy. One is the *spine*, which is a continuation of the features of the city centre outward along the main wide boulevard. Here one finds the upper-middle-class housing stock, which is again apartments and town houses. A mall or developing competitive major suburban business node often lies at the end of the elite commercial spine. A ring highway (*periférico*) is becoming common in most large Latin American cities, serving to connect the mall and developing industrial parks and to ensure access for the growing number of outlying elite residential communities and middle-class housing tracts. It

LATIN AMERICAN CITY

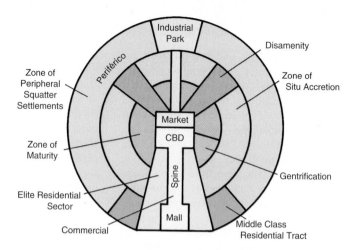

FIGURE 8.42 This model of the Latin American city does not suggest the growing number of wealthy suburbs on the fringes of many Latin American cities, often very close to poor barrios or favelas. Many older colonial cities, no longer functionally vibrant, are now deteriorating in their centres, with working class and poor families dividing up and sharing old colonial mansions.

Source: Redrawn by permission from Larry Ford, "A New and Improved Model of Latin American City Structure," in Geographical Review 86 (1996) American Geographical Society.

FIGURE 8.43 Buildings along the Paseo de la Reforma in Mexico City. Part of the central business district, this "spine" area contains apartment houses, theatres and nightclubs, and commercial high rises.

also marks the separation of the better inner-city residential areas and the peripheral squatter settlements and slums.

The second feature is the residential districts arranged in concentric rings around the core and housing ever poorer people as distance increases from the centre. This social patterning is just the opposite of many U.S. cities. The slums and squatter settlements (*barrios, favelas*) are on the outskirts of the city. In rapidly growing centres like Mexico City, the barrios are found in the farthest concentric ring, which is several kilometres wide. Many people within these areas find a meagre living in the informal sector, selling goods and services to other slum dwellers.

Each of the world's developing regions displays variants of their collective urban dilemma: an urban structure not fully capable of housing the peoples so rapidly thrust upon it. The great increases in city populations exceed urban support capabilities, and unemployment rates are disastrously high nearly everywhere. There is little chance to reduce them as additional millions continue to swell cities already overwhelmed by poverty. The problems, cultures, environments, and economies of developing-world cities are tragically unique to them. The urban models that give us understanding of U.S. and Canadian cities are of little assistance or guidance in such vastly different culture realms.

Want to Learn More?

Gated Communities

Life at the Ranch
Explore the promotional material of a gated community in Kelowna, B.C., and the greater Okanagan Valley.
http://www.acornhomes.com/sunsetranch/index.php

Security Gate Systems
Residential and commercial security is a big industry. This site provides one example of the kinds of security services, gates, and controlled access devices available to gated community builders and individual home and business owners.
http://www.simplygates.com/gated.html

Planning Responses to Gated Communities in Canada
This article by Jill Grant, School of Planning, Dalhousie University, examines municipal planning responses to gated communities and considers ways in which local planners can deal effectively with developers to maintain a balance in conflicting planning principals.
http://www.bristol.ac.uk/sps/cnrpapersword/gated/grant.doc

Urban Social Issues

Social Housing
Investigate the development, changes, and people of Canada's first major social housing project: Toronto's Regent Park.
http://www.catchdaflava.com/History_5fof_5fRegent_5fPark

See how Toronto's Regent Park has been revitalized.
http://www.regentparkplan.ca/pdfs/revitalization/revitalization_study_full.pdf

Homelessness
Read a report, "Homelessness in Canada: From Housing to Shelters to Blankets," which examines the role of insufficient housing as a cause of absolute homelessness.
http://www.share-international.org/archives/homelessness/hl-ch_Canada.htm

Gentrification
See what geography students in Vancouver have to say about gentrification in their city, in their project, "Gentrification in Vancouver: A Study of Changing Urban Dynamics."
http://www.geog.ubc.ca/courses/geog471/classof05/gentrification/Vangents-AboutUs.htm

Cities and Suburbs

City Profiles
From Abidjan to Tokyo, this site provides profiles of numerous cities around the world.
http://www.un.org/cyberschoolbus/habitat/profiles/index.asp

Suburbia
"So Long City: Hello Suburbs" is a CBC news retrospective clip examining Don Mills 50 years after its initial construction. There are links to other news story about suburbia.
http://archives.cbc.ca/IDCC-1-69-1464-9955/life_society/suburbs/

Canadian / U.S. Cities
Read about the similarities and differences of Canadian and U.S. cities.
http://www.fundersnetwork.org/usr_doc/Patrick_Condon_Primer.pdf

Urban Planning and Principles

Smart Growth
See how cities can be designed and used in more intelligent and ecologically friendly ways.
http://www.smartgrowth.bc.ca/index.cfm

New Urbanism
Learn about the philosophy and planning practices of "new" urbanism.
http://www.cnu.org/

The Urban Land Institute (ULI)
ULI is a non-profit research and education organization devoted to urban issues. Explore some of these issues at their website.
http://www.uli.org/

Sustainable Cities
PLUS is a network of over 30 cities and communities from around the world who share their learning and best practices about integrated long-term planning for sustainability.
http://SustainableCities.net/

Summary

The city is the essential activity focus of every society advanced beyond the subsistence level. Although they are among the oldest marks of civilization, only in the past century have cities become the home of the majority of the people in the industrialized countries and both the commercial crossroads and place of refuge for uncounted millions in the developing world.

All settlements growing beyond their village origins take on functions uniting them to the countryside and to a larger system of settlements. As they grow, they become functionally complex. Their economic base, composed of both *basic* and *service* activities, may become diverse. Basic activities represent the functions performed for the larger economy and urban system, while service (non-basic) activities satisfy the needs of the urban residents themselves. Functional classifications distinguish the economic roles of urban centres, while simple classification of them as transportation and special-function cities or as central places helps define and explain their functional and size hierarchies and the spatial patterns they display within a system of cities.

As North American urban centres expanded in population size and diversity, they developed structured land use and social patterns based on market allocations of urban space, channelization of traffic, socio-economic aggregation, and government regulation. The observed regularity of land use arrangements has been summarized for cities by the concentric circle, sector, and multiple-nuclei models. Social area counterparts of land use specializations are based on social status, family status, and ethnicity. Since 1945, these older models of land uses and social areas have been modified by the suburbanization of people and functions that

has led to the creation of new and complex urban areas. In the United States, "edge" cities and the deterioration of the older central city itself have altered urban form. Recent economic trends and gentrification, particularly in Canadian cities, have enhanced the employment and residential importance of central city downtown areas.

Urbanization is a global phenomenon, and the North American models of city systems, land use, and social area patterns are not necessarily or usually applicable to other cultural contexts. In Europe, stringent land use regulations have brought about a compact urban form ringed by greenbelts. Although rapidly changing, the East European urban areas still show a pattern of density and land use reflecting recent communist principles of city structure. Cities in the developing world are currently growing in population faster than it is possible to provide employment, housing, safe water, sanitation, and other minimally essential services and facilities.

KEY WORDS

basic sector 258
census metropolitan area (CMA) 256
central business district (CBD) 266
central city 256
central place 263
central place theory 263
Christaller, Walter 263

city 256
concentric zone (zonal) model 268
conurbation 252
economic base 258
edge city 274
gated community 277
gentrification 279
metropolitan area 256

multiple-nuclei model 269
multiplier effect 259
network city 265
non-basic (service) sector 258
primate city 262
rank-size rule 262
sector model 269

service (non-basic) sector 258
social housing 278
suburb 256
town 256
urban hierarchy 261
urban sustainability 282
urbanized area 256
world city 261

FOR REVIEW

1. Consider the city or town in which you live, attend school, or with which you are most familiar. In a brief paragraph, discuss that community's *site* and *situation*. Point out the connection, if any, between its site and situation and the basic functions that it earlier or now performs.

2. Why do urban slums form in developing countries? Are there any solutions to the problem?

3. What area does a *central place* serve, and what kinds of functions does it perform? If an urban system were composed solely of central places, what summary statements could you make about the spatial distribution and the urban size hierarchy of that system?

4. Is there a hierarchy of retailing activities in the community with which you are most familiar? Of how many and of what kinds of levels is that hierarchy

composed? What localizing forces affect the distributional pattern of retailing within that community?

5. Briefly describe the urban land use patterns predicted by the *concentric circle*, the *sector*, and the *multiple-nuclei* models of urban development. Which one, if any, best corresponds to the growth and land use pattern of the community most familiar to you? How well does Figure 8.28 or 8.32 depict the land use patterns in the metropolitan area with which you are most familiar?

6. In what ways do *social status*, *family status*, and *ethnicity* affect the residential choices of households? What expected distributional patterns of urban social areas are associated with each? Does the social geography of your community conform to the predicted pattern?

7. How has suburbanization damaged the economic base and the financial stability of the U.S. central city?

8. In what ways does the Canadian city differ from the pattern of its U.S. counterpart?

9. What are *primate cities*? Why are primate cities so prevalent in the developing world? How are some governments attempting to reduce their relative importance in their national systems of cities?

10. Why are metropolitan areas in developing countries expected to grow larger than Western metropolises by 2020?

11. Examine Table 8.6. Do you think it is appropriate to weight each of the five indicators of sustainability equally or not? If not what weightings should be applied? Explain your thinking.

FOCUS FOLLOW-UP

1. **What common features define the origin, nature, and locations of cities?** pp. 249–258.

   Cities arose 4000–6000 years ago as distinctive evidence of the growing cultural and economic complexity of early civilizations. Distinct from the farm villages of subsistence economies, true cities provided an increasing range of functions—religious, military, trade, production, etc.—for their developing societies. Their functions and importance were affected by the sites and situations chosen for them. The massive recent increase in number and size of cities worldwide reflects the universality of economic development and total population growth in the latter 20th century.

2. **How are cities structured economically, and how are systems of cities organized?** pp. 258–265.

   The economic base of a city—the functions it performs—is divided between basic and non-basic (or service) activities. Through a multiplier effect, adding basic workers increases both the number of service workers and the total population of a city. The amount of growth reflects the base ratio characteristic of the city. Cities may be hierarchically ranked by their size and functional complexity. Rank-size, primate, and central place hierarchies are commonly cited but distinctly different.

3. **How are cities structured internally, and how do people distribute themselves within them?** pp. 265–283.

   Cities are themselves distinctive land use and cultural area landscapes. In North America, older cities show repetitive land use patterns that are largely determined by land value and accessibility considerations. Classical land use models include the concentric circle, sector, and multiple nuclei patterns. Distinct social area arrangements have been equated with those land use models. Newer cities and growing metropolitan areas have created different land use and social area structures with suburbs.

4. **Are there world regional and cultural differences in the land use and population patterns of major cities?** pp. 283–293.

   Cities are regional and cultural variables; their internal land use and social area patterns reflect the differing historical, technological, political, and cultural conditions under which they developed. Although the North American city is the familiar U.S.–Canadian model, we can easily recognize differences among it and West European, East European, Asian, African, and Latin American city types.

 ## ONLINE LEARNING CENTRE

The World Wide Web has a tremendous number and variety of sites pertaining to geography. To access Web sites, Internet exercises, self-quizzes, videos, and additional study tools relevant to this chapter's content, visit the *Human Geography* Online Learning Centre at **www.mcgrawhill.ca/olc/fellmann**.

9 LIVELIHOOD AND ECONOMY: PRIMARY ACTIVITIES

Aims

- To identify the structure and categories of economic organization
- To identify and clarify primary economic activities
- To introduce and discuss a geography of agriculture
- To introduce and discuss a geography of resource exploitation

Some Specific Considerations for Review:

*T*he crop bloomed luxuriantly that summer of 1846. The disaster of the preceding year seemed over, and the potato, the sole sustenance of some 8 million Irish peasants, would again yield in the bounty needed. Yet within a week, wrote Father Mathew, "I beheld one wide waste of putrefying vegetation. The wretched people were seated on the fences of their decaying gardens . . . bewailing bitterly the destruction that had left them foodless." Colonel Gore found that "every field was black," and Father O'Sullivan noted that "the fields . . . appeared blasted, withered, blackened, and . . . sprinkled with vitriol. . . ." The potato was irretrievably gone for a second year; famine and pestilence were inevitable.

Within five years, the settlement geography of the most densely populated country in Europe was forever altered. The United States and Canada received hundreds of thousands of immigrants, who provided the cheap labour needed for the canals, railroads, and mines that they were creating in their rush to economic development. New patterns of commodity flows were initiated as North American maize for the first time found an Anglo-Irish market—as part of Poor Relief—and then entered a wider European market, which had also suffered general crop failure in that bitter year. Within days, a microscopic organism, the cause of the potato blight, had altered the economic and human geography of two continents.

FIGURE 9.1 These Japanese cars unloading at Seattle were forerunners of a continuing flow of imported goods capturing an important share of the domestic market traditionally held by American manufacturers. Canadian manufacturers face this same challenge. Established patterns of production and exchange are constantly subject to change in a world of increasing economic and cultural interdependence and of changing relative competitive strengths.

Although the Irish famine of the 1840s was a spatially localized tragedy, it dramatically demonstrated how widespread and intricate are the interrelations between widely separated peoples and areas of the earth. It made vividly clear how fundamental to all human activity patterns are those rooted in economy and subsistence. These are the patterns that, within the broader context of human geography, economic geography isolates for special study.

Simply stated, **economic geography** is the study of how people earn their living, how livelihood systems vary by area, and how economic activities are spatially interrelated and linked. It applies geography's general concern with spatial variation to the special circumstances of the production, exchange, and consumption of goods and services. In reality, of course, we cannot really comprehend the totality of the economic pursuits of more than 6 billion human beings. We cannot examine the infinite variety of productive and service activities found everywhere on the earth's surface, nor can we trace all their innumerable interrelationships, linkages, and flows. Even if that level of understanding were possible, it would be valid for only a fleeting instant of time, for economic activities are constantly undergoing change.

Economic geographers seek consistencies. They attempt to develop generalizations that will aid in the comprehension of the maze of economic variations characterizing human existence. From their studies emerges a deeper awareness of the dynamic, interlocking diversity of human enterprise and of the impact of economic activity on all other facets of human life and culture. From them, too, comes appreciation of the increasing interdependence of differing national and regional economic systems. The potato blight, although it struck only one small island, ultimately affected the economies of continents. In like fashion, the depletion of North America's natural resources and the "de-industrialization" of its economy and conversion to post-industrial service and knowledge

activities are altering the relative wealth of countries, flows of international trade, domestic employment and income patterns, and more (Figure 9.1).

The Classification of Economic Activity and Economies

The search for understanding of livelihood patterns is made more difficult by the complex environmental and cultural realities controlling the economic activities of humans. Many production patterns are rooted in the spatially variable circumstances of the *physical environment*. The staple crops of the humid tropics, for example, are not part of the agricultural systems of the mid-latitudes; livestock types that thrive in Canadian feedlots or on western ranges are not adapted to the Arctic tundra or to the margins of the Saharan desert. The unequal distribution of useful mineral deposits gives some regions and countries economic prospects and employment opportunities that are denied to others. Forestry and fishing depend on still other natural resources unequal in occurrence, type, and value.

Within the bounds of the environmentally possible, *cultural considerations* may condition economic or production decisions. For example, culturally based food preferences rather than environmental limitations may dictate the choice of crops or livestock. Maize is a preferred grain in Africa and the Americas; wheat in North America, Australia, Argentina, southern Europe, and Ukraine; and rice in much of Asia. Pigs are not produced in Muslim areas, where religious belief prohibits pork consumption.

Level of *technological development* of a culture will affect its recognition of resources or its ability to exploit them. **Technology**

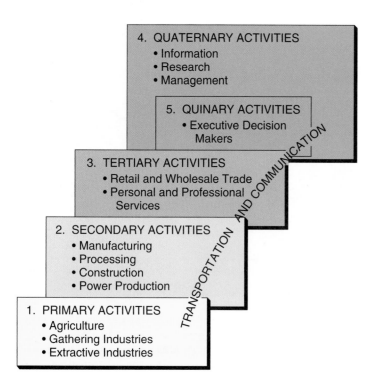

FIGURE 9.2 The categories of economic activity. The five main sectors of the economy do not stand alone. They are connected and integrated by transportation and communication services and facilities not assigned to any single sector but common to all.

FIGURE 9.3 These logs entering a lumber mill are products of *primary production*. Processing them into boards, plywood, or prefabricated houses is a *secondary activity* that increases their value by altering their form. The products of many secondary industries—sheet steel from steel mills, for example—constitute "raw materials" for other manufacturers.

refers to the totality of tools and methods available to and used by a culture group in producing items essential to its subsistence and comfort. Pre-industrial societies have no knowledge of or need for the iron ore or coking coal underlying their hunting, gathering, or gardening grounds. *Political decisions* may encourage or discourage—through subsidies, protective tariffs, or production restrictions—patterns of economic activity. And, ultimately, production is controlled by *economic factors* of demand, whether that demand is expressed through a free market mechanism, government instruction, or the consumption requirements of a single family producing for its own needs.

Categories of Activity

Regionally varying environmental, cultural, technological, political, and market conditions add spatial details to more generalized ways of classifying the world's productive work (see 'possibilism,' Chapter 1, page 9). One approach to that categorization is to view economic activity as ranged along a continuum of both increasing complexity of product or service and increasing distance from the natural environment. Seen from that perspective, a small number of distinctive stages of production and service activities may be distinguished (Figure 9.2).

Primary activities are those that harvest or extract something from the earth. They are at the beginning of the production cycle, where humans are in closest contact with the resources and potentialities of the environment. Such activities involve basic foodstuff and raw material production. Hunting and gathering,

grazing, agriculture, fishing, forestry, and mining and quarrying are examples. **Secondary activities** are those that add value to materials by changing their form or combining them into more useful—therefore more valuable—commodities. That provision of *form utility* may range from simple handicraft production of pottery or woodenware to the delicate assembly of electronic goods or space vehicles (Figure 9.3). Copper smelting, steel making, metalworking, automobile production, textile and chemical industries—indeed, the full array of *manufacturing and processing industries*—are included in this phase of the production process. Also included are the production of *energy* (the "power company") and the *construction* industry.

Tertiary activities consist of those business and labour specializations that provide *services* to the primary and secondary sectors and *goods* and *services* to the general community and to the individual. These include financial, business, professional, clerical, and personal services. They constitute the vital link between producer and consumer, for tertiary occupations importantly include the wholesale and retail *trade* activities—including "dot-com" Internet sales—necessary in highly interdependent societies. Tertiary activities also provide essential information to manufacturers: the knowledge of market demand without which economically justifiable production decisions are impossible.

In economically advanced societies, a growing number of individuals and organizations are engaged in the processing and dissemination of information and in the administration and control of their own or other enterprises. The term **quaternary** is applied to this fourth class of economic activities, which is composed entirely of services rendered by "white collar" professionals working in education, government, management, information processing, and research. Sometimes, a subdivision of these management functions—**quinary activities**—is distinguished to recognize high-level decision-making roles in all types of large organizations, public or private. (The distinctions between tertiary, quaternary, and quinary activities are more fully developed in Chapter 10.) As Figure 9.2 suggests, transportation and communication services cut across the general categories of economic activity, unite them, and make possible the spatial interactions that all human enterprise requires (discussed in Chapter 3).

The term *industry*—in addition to its common meaning as a branch of manufacturing activity—is frequently employed as a substitute identical in meaning to *activity* as a designation of these categories of economic enterprise. That is, we can speak of the steel, or automobile, or textile "industry" with all the impressions of factories, mills, raw materials, and products each type of enterprise implies. But with equal logic, we can refer in a more generalized way to the "entertainment" or the "travel" industries or, in the present context, to "primary," "secondary," and "tertiary" industries.

These categories of production and service activities or industries help us see an underlying structure to the nearly infinite variety of things people do to earn a living and to sustain themselves. But by themselves they tell us little about the organization of the larger economy of which the individual worker or establishment is a part. For that broader organizational understanding, we look to *systems* rather than *components* of economies.

Types of Economic Systems

Broadly viewed, national economies in the early 21st century fall into one of three major types of system: *subsistence*, *commercial*, or *planned*. None of these economic systems is "pure." That is, none exists in isolation in an increasingly interdependent world. Each, however, displays certain underlying characteristics based on its distinctive forms of resource management and economic control.

In a **subsistence economy**, goods and services are created for the use of the producers and their kinship groups. Therefore, there is little exchange of goods and only limited need for markets. In the **commercial economies** that have become dominant in nearly all parts of the world, producers or their agents, in theory, freely market their goods and services, the laws of supply and demand determine price and quantity, and market competition is the primary force shaping production decisions and distributions. In the extreme form of **planned economies** associated with the communist-controlled societies that have now collapsed in nearly every country where they were formerly created or imposed, producers or their agents disposed of goods and services through government agencies that controlled both supply and price. The quantities produced and the locational patterns of production were strictly programmed by central planning departments.

With a few exceptions—for example, Cuba and North Korea—rigidly planned economies no longer exist in their classical form; they have been modified or dismantled in favour of free market structures or only partially retained in a lesser degree of economic control associated with governmental supervision or ownership of selected sectors of increasingly market-oriented economies. Nevertheless, their landscape evidence lives on. The physical structures, patterns of production, and imposed regional interdependencies they created remain to influence the economic decisions of successor societies.

In actuality, few people are members of only one of these systems, although one may be dominant. A farmer in India may produce rice and vegetables privately for the family's consumption but also save some of the produce to sell. In addition, members of the family may market cloth or other handicrafts they make. With the money derived from those sales, the Indian peasant is able to buy, among other things, clothes for the family, tools, and fuel. Thus, that Indian farmer is a member of at least two systems: subsistence and commercial.

In Canada and the United States, government controls on the production of various types of goods and services (such as growing wheat or tobacco, producing alcohol, constructing and operating nuclear power plants, and engaging in licensed personal and professional services) mean that these countries do not have a purely commercial economy. To a limited extent, citizens participate in a controlled and planned as well as free market environment. Many African, Asian, and Latin American market economies have been decisively shaped by governmental policies encouraging or demanding production of export commodities rather than domestic foodstuffs, or promoting through import restrictions the development of domestic industries not readily supported by the national market alone. Example after example would show that there are very few people in the world who are members of only one type of economic system.

Inevitably, spatial patterns, including those of economic activities and systems, are subject to change. For example, the commercial economies of Western European countries, some with sizeable infusions of planned economy controls, are being restructured by both increased free market competition and supranational regulation under the World Trade Organization and the European Union (see pp. 238–239). Many of the countries of Latin America, Africa, Asia, and the Middle East that traditionally were dominated by subsistence economies are now benefiting from technology transfer from advanced economies and integration into expanding global production and exchange patterns.

No matter what economic system prevails locally, in all systems transportation is a key variable. No advanced economy can flourish without a well-connected transport network. All subsistence societies—or subsistence areas of developing countries—are characterized by their isolation from regional and world routeways (Figure 9.4). That isolation restricts their progression to more advanced forms of economic structure.

Former sharp contrasts in economic organization are becoming blurred and national economic orientations are changing as globalization reduces structural contrasts in national economies. Still, both approaches to economic classification—by type of activity and by organization of economies—help us to visualize and understand changing world economic geographic patterns. In the remainder of this chapter, we will centre our attention on the primary industries. In Chapter 10, we will consider secondary through quinary activity patterns.

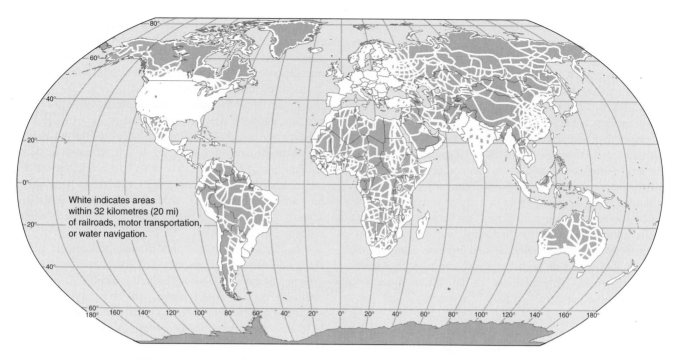

White indicates areas
within 32 kilometres (20 mi)
of railroads, motor transportation,
or water navigation.

FIGURE 9.4 Patterns of access and isolation. Accessibility is a key measure of economic development and of the degree to which a world region can participate in interconnected market activities. Isolated areas of countries with advanced economies suffer a price disadvantage because of high transportation costs. Lack of accessibility in subsistence economic areas slows their modernization and hinders their participation in the world market.

Source: Copyright permission: Hammond Inc., Maplewood, N.J. 07040.

Primary Activities: Agriculture

Humankind's basic economic concern is producing or securing food resources sufficient in caloric content to meet individual daily energy requirements, and so balanced as to satisfy normal nutritional needs. Those supplies may be acquired by the consumer directly through the primary economic activities of hunting, gathering, farming, and fishing (a form of "gathering"), or indirectly through performance of other primary, secondary, or higher level economic endeavours that yield income sufficient to provide the earner and earner's family with income to obtain needed daily sustenance.

Since the middle of the 20th century, a recurring but unrealized fear has been that the world's steadily increasing population would inevitably and quickly exceed available or potential food supplies. Instead, although global population has more than doubled since 1950, the total amount of human food produced worldwide since then has also more than doubled. The Food and Agriculture Organization of the United Nations has set the minimum daily requirement for caloric intake per person at 2350. By that measure, annual food supplies are more than sufficient to meet world needs. That is, if total food resources were evenly distributed, everyone would have access to amounts sufficient for adequate daily nourishment. In reality, however, some one-eighth of the world's population—and one-sixth of the population of less developed countries—are inadequately supplied with food and nutrients. Conservatively, 54 countries fall below achieving the FAO minimum per capita requirement; they do not produce enough food to supply their populations nor have the economic means to close the gap through imports.

This stark contradiction between sufficient worldwide food supplies and widespread malnutrition reflects, among other reasons, inequalities in national and personal incomes; population growth rates; lack of access to fertile soils, credit, and education; local climatic conditions or catastrophes; and lack of transportation and storage facilities. By mid-century, the increasingly interconnected world population will expand to at least 9 billion, and concerns with individual states' food supplies will inevitably continue and remain, as well, a persistent international issue. World and regional issues of food supply and nutrition are explored in Chapter 11 (pp. 395–397).

Before there was farming, *hunting* and *gathering* were the universal forms of primary production. These pre-agricultural pursuits are now practised by at most a few thousands of persons worldwide, primarily in isolated and remote pockets within the low latitudes and among the sparse populations of very high latitudes. The interior of New Guinea, rugged areas of interior Southeast Asia, diminishing segments of the Amazon rain forest, and a few districts of tropical Africa and northern Australia still contain such pre-agricultural people. Much of the Arctic region, of course, is ill-suited for any form of food crop production. Hunter-gatherer numbers are few and declining, and wherever they are brought into contact with technologically more advanced cultures, their way of life is eroded or lost.

Agriculture, defined as the growing of crops and the tending of livestock whether for the subsistence of the producers or for sale or exchange, has replaced hunting and gathering as economically the most significant of the primary activities. It is spatially the most widespread, found in all world regions where environmental

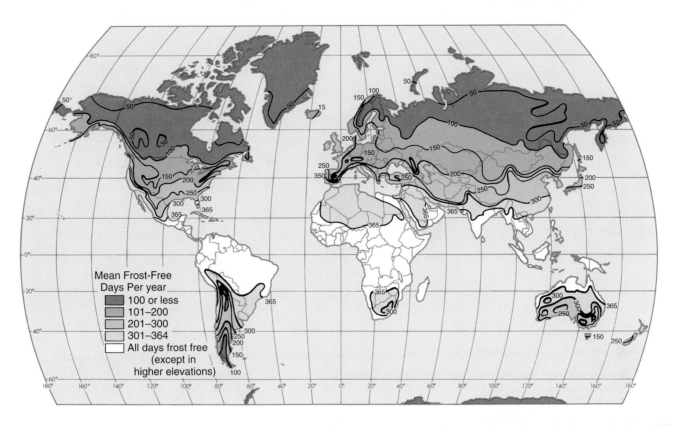

FIGURE 9.5 **Average length of growing season.** The number of frost-free days is an important environmental control on agriculture, as is the availability of precipitation sufficient in amount and reliability for crop production. Since agriculture is not usually practicable with less than a 90-day growing season, large parts of Russia and Canada have only limited cropping potential. Except where irrigation water is available, arid regions are similarly outside of the margins of regular crop production.

Source: Wayne M. Wendland.

circumstances—including adequate moisture, good growing season length, and productive soils—permit (Figure 9.5). The United Nations estimates that more than one-third of the world's land area (excluding Greenland and Antarctica) is in some form of agricultural use, including permanent pastureland. Crop farming alone covers some 15 million square kilometres (5.8 million sq mi) worldwide, about 10% of the earth's total land area. In many developing economies, at least two-thirds of the labour force is directly involved in farming and herding. In some, such as Bhutan in Asia or Burkina Faso and Burundi in Africa, the figure is more than 90%. Overall, however, employment in agriculture is steadily declining in developing economies, echoing but trailing the trend in commercial economies, in which direct employment in agriculture involves only a small fraction of the labour force (Figure 9.6). (For the world pattern of the agricultural labour force early in this century, see Figure 11.8.) Indeed, a declining number or proportion of farm workers, along with farm consolidation and increasing output, are typical in all present-day highly developed commercial agricultural systems. On the other hand, agriculture remains a major component in the economies of many of the world's developing countries, producing for domestic markets and providing a major source of national income through exports (Figure 9.7).

It has been customary to classify agricultural societies on the twin bases of the importance of off-farm sales and the level

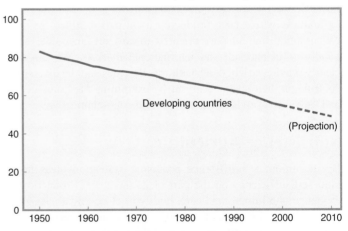

FIGURE 9.6 In the developing economies worldwide, the percentage of the labour force in agriculture has been steadily declining—and is projected to decrease to even lower levels.

Sources: FAO and World Bank.

of mechanization and technological advancement. *Subsistence*, *traditional* (or *intermediate*), and *advanced* (or *modern*) are usual terms employed to recognize both aspects. These are not mutually

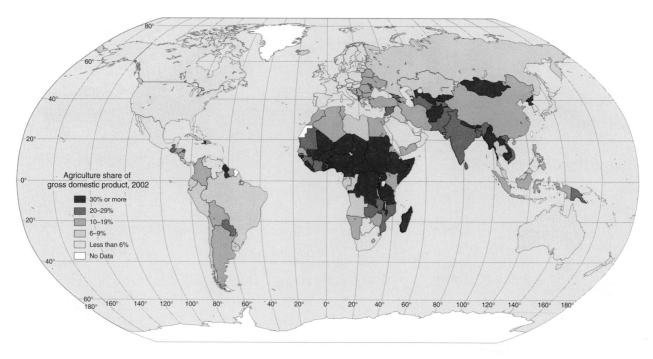

FIGURE 9.7 Share of agriculture in gross domestic product, 2002. Agriculture contributed 30% or more of gross domestic product (the total monetary output of goods and services of an economy) of more than 30 countries in 2002. Most were small, developing economies with less than US $500 in annual per capita income. Together, they held 11% of world population.

Sources: The World Bank, World Development Indicators 2004, *and CIA*, The World Factbook 2004.

exclusive but rather are recognized stages along a continuum of farm economy variants. At one end lies production solely for family sustenance, using rudimentary tools and native plants. At the other is the specialized, highly capitalized, near-industrialized agriculture for off-farm delivery that marks advanced economies. Between these extremes is the middle ground of traditional agriculture, where farm production is in part destined for home consumption and in part oriented toward off-farm sale, either locally or in national and international markets. We can most clearly see the variety of agricultural activities and the diversity of controls on their spatial patterns by examining the "subsistence" and "advanced" ends of the agricultural continuum.

Subsistence Agriculture

By definition, a *subsistence* economic system involves nearly total self-sufficiency on the part of its members. Production for exchange is minimal, and each family or close-knit social group relies on itself for its food and other most essential requirements. Farming for the immediate needs of the family is, even today, the predominant occupation of humankind. In most of Africa, South and East Asia, and much of Latin America, a large percentage of people are primarily concerned with feeding themselves from their own land and livestock.

Two chief types of subsistence agriculture may be recognized: *extensive* and *intensive*. Although each type has several variants, the essential contrast between them is realizable yield per unit of area used and, therefore, population-supporting potential. **Extensive** (subsistence) **agriculture** involves large areas of land and

minimal labor input per hectare. Both product per land unit and population densities are low. **Intensive** (subsistence) **agriculture** involves the cultivation of small landholdings through the expenditure of great amounts of labour per acre. Yields per unit area and population densities are both high (Figure 9.8).

Extensive Subsistence Agriculture

Of the several types of *extensive subsistence* agriculture—varying one from another in their intensities of land use—two are of particular interest: nomadic herding and shifting cultivation.

Nomadic herding, the wandering but controlled movement of livestock solely dependent on natural forage, is the most extensive type of land use system (Figure 9.8). That is, it requires the greatest amount of land area per person sustained. Over large portions of the Asian semi-desert and desert areas, in certain highland zones, and on the fringes of and within the Sahara, a relatively small number of people graze animals for consumption by the herder group, not for market sale. Sheep, goats, and camels are most common, while cattle, horses, and yaks are locally important. The reindeer of Lapland were formerly part of the same system.

Whatever the animals involved, their common characteristics are hardiness, mobility, and an ability to subsist on sparse forage. The animals provide a variety of products: milk, cheese, blood and meat for food; hair, wool, and skins for clothing; skins for shelter; and excrement for fuel. For the herder, they represent primary subsistence. Nomadic movement is tied to sparse and seasonal rainfall or to cold temperature regimes, and to the

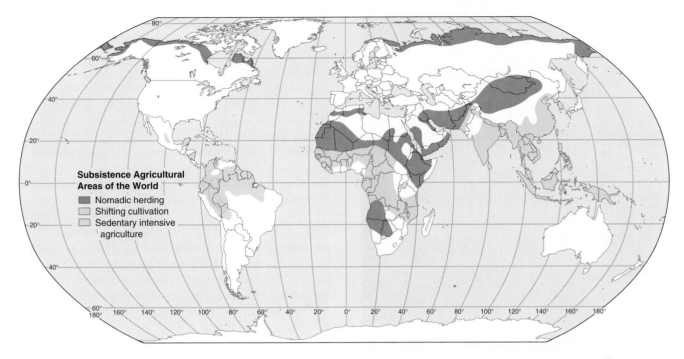

FIGURE 9.8 Subsistence agricultural areas of the world. Nomadic herding, supporting relatively few people, was the age-old way of life in large parts of the dry and cold world. Shifting or swidden agriculture maintains soil fertility by tested traditional practices in tropical wet and wet-and-dry climates. Large parts of Asia support millions of people engaged in sedentary intensive cultivation, with rice and wheat the chief crops.

areally varying appearance and exhaustion of forage. Extended stays in a given location are neither desirable nor possible. *Transhumance* is a special form of seasonal movement of livestock to exploit specific locally varying pasture conditions. Used by permanently or seasonally sedentary pastoralists and pastoral farmers, transhumance involves either the regular vertical alteration from mountain to valley pastures between summer and winter months, or horizontal movement between established lowland grazing areas to reach pastures temporarily lush from monsoonal (seasonal) rains.

As a type of economic system, nomadic herding is declining. Many economic, social, and cultural changes are causing nomadic groups to alter their way of life or to disappear entirely. On the Arctic fringe of Russia, herders under Communism were made members of state or collective herding enterprises; in post-Soviet years, extensive oil and natural gas exploration and extraction are damaging or destroying large portions of tundra habitat. In northern Scandinavia, Lapps (Saami) are engaged in commercial more than in subsistence livestock farming. In the Sahel region of Africa on the margins of the Sahara, oases formerly controlled by herders have been taken over by farmers, and the great droughts of recent decades have forever altered the formerly nomadic way of life of thousands.

A much differently based and distributed form of extensive subsistence agriculture is found in all warm, moist, low-latitude areas of the world. There, many people engage in a kind of nomadic farming. Through clearing and use, the soils of those areas lose many of their nutrients (as soil chemicals are dissolved and removed by surface and groundwater—*leaching*—or nutrients are removed from the land in the vegetables picked

and eaten), and farmers cultivating them need to move on after harvesting several crops. In a sense, they rotate fields rather than crops to maintain productivity. This type of **shifting cultivation** has a number of names, the most common of which are *swidden* (an English localism for "burned clearing") and *slash-and-burn*. Each region of its practice has its own name—for example, *milpa* in Middle and South America, *chitemene* in Africa, and *ladang* in Southeast Asia.

Characteristically, the farmers hack down the natural vegetation, burn the cuttings, and then plant such crops as maize (corn), millet (a cereal grain), rice, manioc or cassava, yams, and sugarcane (Figure 9.9). Increasingly included in many of the crop combinations are such high-value, labour-intensive commercial crops as coffee, which provide the cash income that is evidence of the growing integration of all peoples into exchange economies. Initial yields—the first and second crops—may be very high, but they quickly become lower with each successive planting on the same plot. As that occurs, cropping ceases, native vegetation is allowed to reclaim the clearing, and gardening shifts to another newly prepared site. The first clearing will ideally not be used again for crops until, after many years, natural fallowing replenishes its fertility (see "Swidden Agriculture").

Less than 3% of the world's people are still predominantly engaged in tropical shifting cultivation on about one-seventh of the world's land area (Figure 9.8). Because the essential characteristic of the system is the intermittent cultivation of the land, each family requires a total occupance area equivalent to the garden plot in current use plus all land left fallow for regeneration. Population densities are traditionally low, for much land is needed

FIGURE 9.9 An African swidden plot being fired. Stumps and trees left in the clearing will remain after the burn.

to support few people. Here as elsewhere, however, population density must be considered a relative term. In actuality, although crude (arithmetic) density is low, people per unit area of *cultivated* land may be high.

Shifting cultivation is one of the oldest and most widely spread agricultural systems of the world. It is found on the islands of Borneo, New Guinea, and Sumatra but is now retained only in small parts of the uplands of Southeast Asia in Vietnam, Thailand, Myanmar, and the Philippines. Nearly the whole of Central and West Africa away from the coasts, Brazil's Amazon basin, and large portions of Central America were formerly all known for this type of extensive subsistence agriculture.

It may be argued that shifting cultivation is a highly efficient cultural adaptation where land is abundant in relation to population, and levels of technology and capital availability are low. As those conditions change, the system becomes less viable. The basic change, as noted in Chapter 4, is that land is no longer abundant in relation to population in many of the less developed, wet, tropical countries. Their growing populations have cleared and settled the forestlands formerly only intermittently used in swidden cultivation. The **Boserup thesis**, proposed by the economist Ester Boserup, is based on the observation that population increases necessitate increased inputs of labour and technology to compensate for reductions in the natural yields of swidden farming. It holds that population growth independently forces an increased use of technology in farming and—in a reversal of the Malthusian idea (see Chapter 4) that the supply of essential foodstuffs is basically fixed or only

Swidden Agriculture

The following account describes shifting cultivation among the Hanunóo people of the Philippines. Nearly identical procedures are followed in all swidden farming regions.

When a garden site of about one-half hectare (a little over one acre) has been selected, the swidden farmer begins to remove unwanted vegetation. The first phase of this process consists of slashing and cutting the undergrowth and smaller trees with bush knives. The principal aim is to cover the entire site with highly inflammable dead vegetation so that the later stage of burning will be most effective. Because of the threat of soil erosion, the ground must not be exposed directly to the elements at any time during the cutting stage. During the first months of the agricultural year, activities connected with cutting take priority over all others. It is estimated that the time required ranges from 25 to 100 hours for the average-sized swidden plot.

Once most of the undergrowth has been slashed, chopped to hasten drying, and spread to protect the soil and assure an even burn, the larger trees must be felled or killed by

girdling (cutting a complete ring of bark) so that unwanted shade will be removed. The successful felling of a real forest giant is a dangerous activity and requires great skill. Felling in second growth is usually less dangerous and less arduous. Some trees are merely trimmed but not killed or cut, both to reduce the amount of labour and to leave trees to reseed the swidden during the subsequent fallow period.

The crucial and most important single event in the agricultural cycle is swidden burning. The main firing of a swidden is the culmination of many weeks of preparation in spreading and leveling chopped vegetation, preparing firebreaks to prevent flames escaping into the jungle, and allowing time for the drying process. An ideal burn rapidly consumes every bit of litter; in no more than an hour or an hour and a half, only smoldering remains are left.

The Hanunóo, swidden farmers of the Philippines, note the following as the benefits of a good burn: 1) removal of unwanted vegetation, resulting in a cleared swidden;

2) extermination of many animal and some weed pests; 3) preparation of the soil for dibble (any small hand tool or stick to make a hole) planting by making it softer and more friable; 4) provision of an evenly distributed cover of wood ashes, good for young crop plants and protective of newly-planted grain seed. Within the first year of the swidden cycle, an average of between 40 and 50 different types of crop plants have been planted and harvested.

The most critical feature of swidden agriculture is the maintenance of soil fertility and structure. The solution is to pursue a system of rotation of 1 to 3 years in crop and 10 to 20 in woody or bush fallow regeneration.

When population pressures mandate a reduction in the length of fallow period, productivity of the region tends to drop as soil fertility is lowered, marginal land is utilized, and environmental degradation occurs. The balance is delicate.

Source: Based on Harold C. Conklin, *Hanunóo Agriculture,* FAO Forestry Development Paper No. 12.

FIGURE 9.10 Transplanting rice seedlings requires arduous hand labour by all members of the family. The newly flooded diked fields, previously ploughed and fertilized, will have their water level maintained until the grain is ripe. This photograph was taken in Indonesia. The scene is repeated wherever subsistence wet-rice agriculture is practised.

slowly expandable—requires a conversion from extensive to intensive subsistence agriculture.

Intensive Subsistence Systems

About 45% of the people of the world are engaged in intensive subsistence agriculture, which predominates in the areas shown in Figure 9.8. As a descriptive term, *intensive subsistence* is no longer fully applicable to a changing way of life and economy in which the distinction between subsistence and commercial is decreasingly valid. Although families may still be fed primarily with the produce of their individual plots, the exchange of farm commodities within the system is considerable. Production of foodstuffs for sale in rapidly growing urban markets is increasingly vital for the rural economies of subsistence farming areas and for the sustenance of the growing proportion of national and regional populations no longer themselves engaged in farming. Nevertheless, hundreds of millions of Indians, Chinese, Pakistanis, Bangladeshis, and Indonesians, plus further millions in other Asian, African, and Latin American countries remain small-plot, mainly subsistence producers of rice, wheat, maize, millet, or pulses (peas, beans, and other legumes). Most live in monsoon Asia, and we will devote our attention to that area.

Intensive subsistence farmers are concentrated in such major river valleys and deltas as the Ganges and the Chang Jiang (Yangtze) and in smaller valleys close to coasts—level areas with fertile alluvial soils. These warm, moist districts are well suited to the production of rice, a crop that under ideal conditions can provide large amounts of food per unit of land. Rice also requires a great deal of time and attention, for planting rice shoots by hand in standing fresh water is a tedious art (Figure 9.10). In the cooler and drier portions of Asia, wheat is grown intensively, along with millet and, less commonly, upland rice.

Rice is known to have been cultivated in parts of China and India for more than 7000 years. Today, wet, or lowland, rice is the mainstay of subsistence agriculture and diets of populations from Sri Lanka and India to Taiwan, Japan, and Korea. It is grown on more than 80% of the planted area in Bangladesh, Thailand, and Malaysia and on more than 50% in six other Asian countries. Almost exclusively used as a human food, rice provides 25% to 80% of the calories in the daily diet of some 3 billion Asians, or half the world's population. Its successful cultivation depends on the controlled management of water, relatively easy in humid tropical river valleys with heavy, impermeable, water-retaining soils, though more difficult in upland and seasonally dry districts. Throughout Asia, the necessary water management

The Economy of a Chinese Village

The village of Nanching is in subtropical southern China on the Zhu River delta near Guangzhou (Canton). Its traditional subsistence agricultural system was described by a field investigator in the late 1950s, whose account is here condensed. The system is still followed in its essentials in other rice-oriented societies today.

In this double-crop region, rice was planted in March and August and harvested in late June or July and again in November. March to November was the major farming season. Early in March the earth was turned with an iron-tipped wooden plow pulled by a water buffalo. The very poor who could not afford a buffalo used a large iron-tipped wooden hoe for the same purpose.

The ploughed soil was raked smooth, fertilizer was applied, and water was let into the field, which was then ready for the transplanting of rice seedlings. Seedlings were raised in a seedbed, a tiny patch fenced off on the side or corner of the field. Beginning from the middle of March, the transplanting of seedlings took place. The whole family was on the scene. Each took the seedlings by the bunch, ten to fifteen plants, and pushed them into the soft inundated soil. For the first thirty or forty days the emerald green crop demanded

little attention except keeping the water at a proper level. But after this period came the first weeding; the second weeding followed a month later. This was done by hand, and everyone old enough for such work participated. With the second weeding went the job of adding fertilizer. The grain was now allowed to stand to "draw starch" to fill the hull of the kernels. When the kernels had "drawn enough starch," water was let out of the field, and both the soil and the stalks were allowed to dry under the hot sun.

Then came the harvest, when all the rice plants were cut off a few inches above the ground with a sickle. Threshing was done on a threshing board. Then the grain and the stalks and leaves were taken home with a carrying pole on the peasant's shoulder. The plant was used as fuel at home.

As soon as the exhausting harvest work was done, no time could be lost before starting the chores of ploughing, fertilizing, pumping water into the fields, and transplanting seedlings for the second crop. The slack season of the rice crop was taken up by chores required for the vegetables which demanded continuous attention, since every peasant family devoted a part of the farm to vegetable gardening. In the hot and damp period of late spring and

summer, eggplant and several varieties of squash and beans were grown. The green-leafed vegetables thrived in the cooler and drier period of fall, winter, and early spring. Leeks grew the year round.

When one crop of vegetables was harvested, the soil was turned and the clods broken up by a digging hoe and levelled with an iron rake. Fertilizer was applied, and seeds or seedlings of a new crop were planted. Hand weeding was a constant job; watering with the long-handled wooden dipper had to be done an average of three times a day, and in the very hot season when evaporation was rapid, as frequently as six times a day. The soil had to be cultivated with the hoe frequently, as the heavy tropical rains packed the earth continuously. Instead of the two applications of fertilizer common with the rice crop, fertilizing was much more frequent for vegetables. Besides the heavy fertilizing of the soil at the beginning of a crop, usually with city garbage, additional fertilizer, usually diluted urine or a mixture of diluted urine and excreta, was given every ten days or so to most vegetables.

Source: Adapted from C. K. Yang, *A Chinese Village in Early Communist Transition* (Cambridge, Mass.: Massachusetts Institute of Technology, 1959).

---

systems have left their distinctive marks on the landscape. Permanently diked fields to contain and control water, levees against unwanted water, and reservoirs, canals, and drainage channels to control its availability and flow are common sights. Terraces to extend level land to valley slopes are occasionally encountered as well (see Figure 4.4).

Intensive subsistence farming is characterized by large inputs of labour per unit of land, by small plots, by the intensive use of fertilizers, mostly animal manure, and by the promise of high yields in good years (see "The Economy of a Chinese Village"). For food security and dietary custom, *polyculture*—production of several different crops, often in the same field—is practised. Vegetables and some livestock are part of the agricultural system, and fish may be reared in rice paddies and ponds. Cattle are a source of labour and of food. Food animals include swine, ducks, and chickens, but since Muslims eat no pork, hogs are absent in their areas of settlement. Hindus generally eat little meat, mainly goat and lamb but not pork or beef. The large number of cattle in India are vital for labour, as a source of milk and cheese, and as producers of fertilizer and fuel.

Urban Subsistence Farming

Not all of the world's subsistence farming is based in rural areas. Urban agriculture is a rapidly growing activity, with some 800 million city farmers worldwide providing, according to United Nations figures, one-seventh of the world's total food production. Occurring in all regions of the world, developed and underdeveloped, but most prevalent in Asia, urban agricultural activities range from small garden plots, to backyard livestock breeding, to fish raised in ponds and streams. Using the garbage dumps of Jakarta, the rooftops of Mexico City, and meagre dirt strips along roadways in Kolkata (Calcutta) or Kinshasa, millions of people are feeding their own families and supplying local markets with vegetables, fruit, fish, and even meat—all produced within the cities themselves and all without the expense and spoilage of storage or long-distance transportation.

In Africa where, for example, two of three Kenyan and Tanzanian urban families engage in farming, a reported 20% of urban nutritional requirement is produced in the towns and cities; in Accra, Ghana's capital, urban farming provides the city with 90%

of its fresh vegetables. Early in the 21st century, city farming in Cuba produced 65% of the country's rice, 43% of its fruits and vegetables, and 12% of roots and fibres; altogether, some 165,000 urban Cubans annually produced 800,000 tonnes of fresh produce in 1999.

Urban agriculture occupies city land as well as city residents: in Bangkok, Thailand for example, some 60% of the metropolitan area is cultivated. A similar inclusion of adjacent rural land within urban boundaries is characteristic of China. There, based on an earlier mandate that socialist cities be self-sufficient, municipal boundaries were set to include large areas of rural land now worked intensively to supply the fruits, vegetables, fish and the like consumed within the city proper. Chinese urban agriculture—by UN estimates providing 90% of the vegetable supply of cities—is, in reality, periurban (suburban) farming within city administrative control. Little or no backyard (or rooftop) land is available for food production within the densely developed Chinese city proper. In whatever form urban farming efforts are expressed, not all its area or yield is solely for local subsistence. An estimated 200 million global urban dwellers also produce food for sale to others.

In all parts of the developing world, urban-origin foodstuffs have reduced the incidence of adult and child malnutrition in cities rapidly expanding by their own birth rates and by the growing influx of displaced rural folk. City farming is, as well, a significant outlet for underemployed residents. In some cities, as many as one-fifth to two-thirds of all families are engaged in agriculture, a United Nations Development Program study reports, with as many as one-third of them having no other source of income.

There are both positive and negative environmental consequences of urban agricultural activities. On the plus side, urban farming helps convert waste from a problem to a resource by reducing runoff and erosion from open dumps, and by avoiding costs of wastewater treatment and solid waste disposal. In Khartoum, Sudan, for example, about 25% of the city's garbage is consumed by farm animals; in Kolkata (Calcutta), India, city sewage is used to feed some 3000 hectares (7400 acres) of lagoons which, in turn, produce some 6000 tonnes of fish annually. Additionally, some 20,000 Kolkata residents diligently farm on the city's garbage dumps, converting waste area and rotting refuse to nutrition. Nearly everywhere, human and animal wastes, vegetable debris, and table scraps are composted or applied to garden areas, and nearly everywhere, vegetable gardens and interspersed fruit trees, ornamental plants, and flowers enhance the often drab urban scene.

Negative consequences also attend urban agriculture and frequently evoke restrictive governmental regulations and prohibitions. The widespread use of untreated human waste as fertilizers exposes both producers and consumers to infectious diseases such as cholera and hepatitis. When pesticides and chemical fertilizers are available and indiscriminately used by untrained gardeners, local water supplies may become contaminated. In some instances, limited supplies of drinking water may be severely depleted through diversion for illegal irrigation or watering of subsistence gardens and livestock. In response to its estimate of 35% of fresh drinking water lost through leakage

and illegal tapping by urban farmers, Tanzania's National Urban Water Agency imposed severe penalty fees and prohibitions on urban agricultural use. Other municipal water agencies elsewhere have reacted similarly.

Expanding Crop Production

Continuing population pressures on existing resources are a constant spur for ways to increase the food supply available both to the subsistence farmers of the developing economies and to the wider world as well. Two paths to promoting increased food production are apparent: (1) expand the land area under cultivation, and (2) increase crop yields from existing farmlands.

The first approach—increasing cropland area—is not a promising strategy. Approximately 70% of the world's land area is agriculturally unsuitable, being too cold, too dry, too steep, or totally infertile. Of the remaining 30%, most of the area well suited for farming is already under cultivation, and of that area, millions of hectares annually are being lost through soil erosion, salinization, desertification, and the conversion of farm land to urban, industrial, and transportation uses in all developed and developing countries. In Canada and the United States, land is being withdrawn from—rather than added to—the cultivated total in response primarily to individual decisions that continued farming of some lands is no longer economically attractive. Only the rain forests of Africa and the Amazon Basin of South America retain sizeable areas of potentially farmable land. The soils of those regions, however, are fragile, are low in nutrients, have poor water retention, and are easily eroded or destroyed following deforestation.

When population pressures dictate land conversion, serious environmental deterioration may result. Clearing of wet tropical forests in the Philippines, the Amazon Basin, and Indonesia has converted dense woodland to barren desolation within a very few years as soil erosion and nutrient loss have followed forest destruction. In Southeast Asia, some 10 million hectares (25 million acres) of former forestland are now wasteland, covered by useless sawgrasses that supply neither forage, food, nor fuel. By most measures, world food output cannot reasonably be increased by simple expansion of cultivated areas.

Intensification and the Green Revolution

Increased productivity of existing cropland rather than expansion of cultivated area has been the key to the growth of agricultural production over the past few decades. Between 1974 and 2004, world total grain production rose 68%. Crop output, however, varies considerably from year to year, adversely or favourably affected by weather, insect damage, plant diseases, and other growing season conditions. That variability plus growing world population has resulted in an average per capita grain availability picture less favourable than single-year output comparisons might suggest. Indeed, for the 1990s and early years of the 21st century, per capita grain output was regularly lower than it had been during most of the 1980s. Nevertheless, gross tonnage increases of grain since the mid-1970s have been impressive, and the vast majority of that production growth was due to increases in yields rather

Index of Total and Per Capita Food Production, 1961–2001

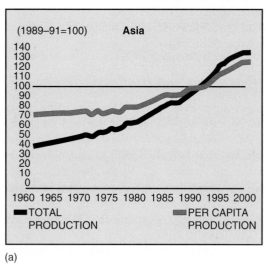

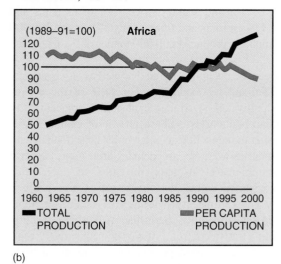

(a)

(b)

FIGURE 9.11 Trends in food production, 1961–2001. Globally, production of food crops increased over the 40-year span shown, but the average annual increase dropped from 3% during the 1960s to 2.4% in the 1970s, 2.2% in the 1980s, and to 1% or less in the 1990s. Although *total* food production expanded in nearly all world regions (the area of the former Soviet Union was a notable exception), that expansion has not in all cases been reflected in improved *per capita* availability. (*a*) Intensification and expansion of farming in Asia resulted both in greatly increased food production and, despite continuing population growth, in expanding per capita availability. Asia's total food production and population both increased by 1.2% in 2002, leaving per person food availability unchanged. (*b*) Population growth presented a different picture in Africa, where total production of food steadily grew over the graphed period, but per capita food supplies persistently declined. The nutrition problem there continued in 2002 with stagnant food production levels but continuing (2.7%) population growth.

Source: Data from Food and Agriculture Organization.

than expansions in cropland. Two interrelated approaches to those yield increases mark recent farming practices.

First, throughout much of the developing world, production inputs such as water, fertilizer, pesticides, and labour have been increased to expand yields on a relatively constant supply of cultivable land. Irrigated area, for example, nearly doubled between 1960 and 2004 to comprise by the latter year some 17% of the world's cropland. Global consumption of fertilizers has dramatically increased since the 1950s, and inputs of pesticides and herbicides have similarly grown. Traditional practices of leaving land fallow (uncultivated) to renew its fertility have been largely abandoned, and double and triple cropping of land where climate permits has increased in Asia and even in Africa, where marginal land is put to near-continuous use to meet growing food demands.

Many of these intensification practices are part of the second approach, linked to the **Green Revolution**—the shorthand reference to a complex of seed and management innovations adapted to the needs of intensive agriculture and designed to bring larger harvests from a given area of farmland. Largely through the application of Green Revolution techniques, cereal yields for Asia as a whole grew by more than 40% between 1980 and 2000, accounted for largely by increases in China and India; they increased by over 35% in South America. Such yield increases and the improved food supplies they represent have been particularly important in densely populated, subsistence farming areas heavily dependent on rice and wheat cultivation. Chinese rice harvests grew by two-thirds, and India's wheat yields doubled between 1970 and the start of the 21st century.

Genetic improvements in rice and wheat have formed the basis of the Green Revolution. Dwarfed varieties have been developed that respond dramatically to heavy applications of fertilizer, that resist plant diseases, and that can tolerate much shorter growing seasons than traditional native varieties can. Adopting the new varieties and applying the irrigation, mechanization, fertilization, and pesticide practices they require have created a new "high-input, high-yield" agriculture. Most poor farmers on marginal and rain-fed (non-irrigated) lands, however, have not benefited from the new plant varieties requiring irrigation and high chemical inputs.

Expanded food production made possible through the Green Revolution has helped alleviate some of the shortages and famines predicted for subsistence agricultural regions since the early 1960s (Figure 9.11), saving an estimated one billion people from starvation. According to World Bank calculations, more than 80% of people in developing countries now have adequate diets, versus 55% in 1950. Although the *number* of undernourished people remains near the 900 million mark because of population growth, total world food supply has increased even faster than population and will continue to do so, the UN predicts, through at least 2030. However, a series of years beginning in 2000 in which production of all major grains fell substantially below consumption levels, materially reducing carryover stocks and, therefore, endangering world food security, called the UN's prediction into question. Further, global warming threatens the expanding food base necessary to supply the still-growing world population. A common observation is that world rice production must increase by about 1% every year to meet growing demand. Long-term studies in the Philippines,

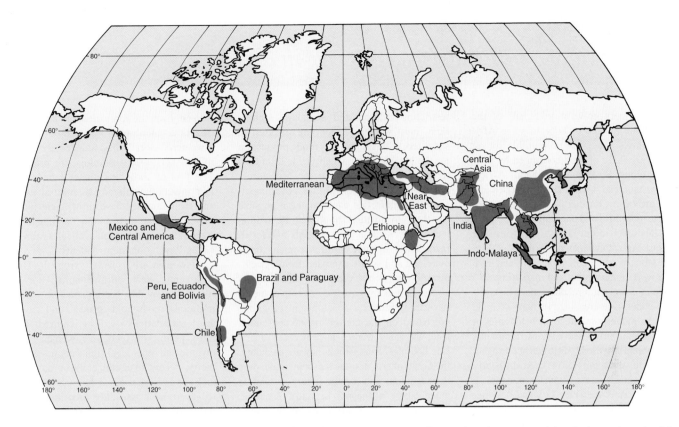

FIGURE 9.12 Areas with high current genetic diversity of crop varieties. Loss of crop varieties characterizes the commercial agriculture of much of the developed world. In place of the many thousands of species and subspecies (varieties) of food plants grown since the development of agriculture 15,000 or more years ago, fewer than 100 species now provide most of the world's food supply. Most of the diversity loss has occurred in the last 100 years. In the United States, for example, 96% of commercial vegetable varieties listed by the Department of Agriculture in 1903 are now extinct. Crop breeders, however, require genetic diversity to develop new varieties that are resistant to evolving plant pest and disease perils. That need necessitates the protection of plant stocks and environments in those temperate and subtropical zones where food plants were first domesticated and are home to the wild relatives of our current food crops. Comparable losses of species diversity are being felt in livestock as well. Half the livestock breeds that existed in Europe in 1900 are already extinct, and almost half the remainder are at risk or endangered.

Sources: J. G. Hawkes, The Diversity of Crop Plants, *(Cambridge, Mass.: Harvard University Press, 1983); and Walter V. Reid and Kenton R. Miller,* Keeping Options Alive: The Scientific Basis for Conserving Biodiversity *(Washington, D.C.: World Resources Institute, 1989), fig. 5, p. 24.*

however, show rice yields there dropped by 10% for each degree Centigrade (1.8° F) of nighttime temperature rise. In the tropical and subtropical regions of major subsistence rice production, night temperatures from 1980 to 2004 registered a 1.1° C increase.

But a price has been paid for Green Revolution successes. Irrigation, responsible for an important part of increased crop yields, has destroyed large tracts of land; excessive salinity of soils resulting from poor irrigation practices is estimated to have a serious effect on the productivity of 20 million to 30 million hectares (80,000–120,000 sq mi) of land around the world, out of a world total of some 270 million hectares of irrigated land. And the huge amount of water required for Green Revolution irrigation has led to serious groundwater depletion, conflict between agricultural and growing urban and industrial water needs in developing countries—many of which are in subhumid climates—and to worries about scarcity and future wars over water.

And very serious genetic consequences are feared from the loss of traditional and subsistence agriculture. With it is lost the food security that distinctive locally adapted native crop varieties (*land races*) provided, and the nutritional diversity and balance that multiple-crop intensive gardening assured. Subsistence farming,

wherever practised, was oriented toward risk minimization. Many differentially hardy varieties of a single crop guaranteed some yield whatever adverse weather, disease, or pest problems might occur.

Commercial agriculture, however, aims at profit maximization, not minimal food security. Poor farmers unable to afford the capital investment the Green Revolution demands have been displaced by a commercial monoculture, one often oriented toward specialty and industrial crops designed for export rather than to food production for a domestic market. Traditional rural society has been disrupted, and landless peasants have been added to the urbanizing populations of affected countries. To the extent that land races are lost to monoculture, varietal distinction in food crops is reduced. "Seed banks" rather than native cultivation are increasingly needed to preserve genetic diversity for future plant breeding and as insurance against catastrophic pest or disease susceptibility of inbred varieties (Figure 9.12).

The presumed benefits of the Green Revolution are not available to all subsistence agricultural areas or advantageous to everyone engaged in farming (see "Women and the Green Revolution"). Africa is a case in point (see Figure 9.11). Green Revolution

Women and the Green Revolution

Women farmers grow at least half of the world's food and up to 80% in some African countries. They are responsible for an even larger share of food consumed by their own families: 80% in sub-Saharan Africa, 65% in Asia, and 45% in Latin America and the Caribbean. Further, women comprise between one-third and one-half of all agricultural labourers in developing countries. For example, African women perform about 90% of the work of processing food crops and 80% of the work of harvesting and marketing.

Women's agricultural dominance in developing states is increasing, in fact, as male family members continue to leave for cities in search of paid urban work. In Mozambique, for example, for every 100 men working in agriculture, there are 153 women. In nearly all other sub-Saharan countries the female component runs between 120 and 150 per 100 men. The departure of men for near or distant cities means, in addition, that women must assume effective management of their families' total farm operations.

Despite their fundamental role, however, women do not share equally with men in the rewards from agriculture, nor are they always beneficiaries of presumed improvements in agricultural technologies and practices. Often, they cannot own or inherit the land on which they work, and they frequently have difficulty in obtaining improved seeds or fertilizers available to male farmers.

As a rule, women farmers work longer hours and have lower incomes than do male farmers. This is not because they are less educated or competent. Rather, it is due to restricting cultural and economic factors. First, most women farmers are involved in subsistence farming and food production for the local market, which yields little cash return. Second, they have far less access than men to credit at bank or government-subsidized rates that would make it possible for them to acquire the Green Revolution technology, such as hybrid seeds and fertilizers. Third, in some cultures women cannot own land and so are excluded from agricultural improvement programs and projects aimed at landowners. For example, many African agricultural development programs are based on the conversion of communal land, to which women have access, to private holdings, from which they are excluded. In Asia, inheritance laws favour male over female heirs, and female-inherited land is managed by husbands; in Latin America, discrimination results from the more limited status held by women under the law.

At the same time, the Green Revolution and its greater commercialization of crops has generally required an increase in labour per hectare, particularly in tasks typically reserved for women, such as weeding, harvesting, and pos-tharvest work. If women are provided no relief from their other daily tasks, the Green Revolution for them may be more burden than blessing. But when mechanization is added to the new farming system, women tend to be losers. Frequently, such predominantly female tasks as harvesting or dehusking and polishing of grain—all traditionally done by hand—are given over to machinery, displacing rather than employing women. Even the application of chemical fertilizers (a "man's task") instead of cow dung ("women's work") has reduced the female role in agricultural development programs. The loss of those traditional female wage jobs means that already poor rural women and their families have insufficient income to improve their diets even in the light of substantial increases in food availability through Green Revolution improvements.

If women are to benefit from the Green Revolution, new cultural norms—or culturally acceptable accommodations within traditional household, gender, and customary legal relations—will be required. These must permit or recognize women's land-owning and other legal rights not now clearly theirs, access to credit at favourable rates, and admission on equal footing with males to government assistance programs. Recognition of those realities fostered the Food and Agriculture Organization of the United Nations' "FAO Plan of Action for Women in Development (1996–2001)" and its "Gender and Development Plan (2002–2007)." Both were aimed at stimulating and facilitating efforts to enhance the role of women as contributors and beneficiaries of economic, social, and political development. Objectives of the plan included promoting gender-based equity in access to, and control of, productive resources; enhancing women's participation in decision- and policy-making processes at all levels, local and national; and encouraging actions to reduce rural women's workload while enhancing their opportunities for paid employment and income.

---

crop improvements have concentrated on wheat, rice, and maize. Of these, only maize is important in Africa, where principal food crops include millet, sorghum, cassava, manioc, yams, cowpeas, and peanuts. Although new varieties of maize resistant to the drought and acidic soils common in Africa were announced in the middle 1990s, belated research efforts directed to other African crops, the continent's great range of growing conditions, and its abundance of yield-destroying pests and viruses have denied it the dramatic regionwide increases in food production experienced elsewhere in the developing world.

Cassava is a hopeful early exception. The most widely cultivated tuber and second most important food staple in sub-Saharan Africa, cassava has been transformed from a low-yielding subsistence hedge against famine to a high-yielding cash crop. Between 1980 and 2003, total output more than doubled to 103 million tonnes thanks to the introduction of new varieties developed by the International Institute of Tropical Agriculture. More recent experimental successes with a variety of genetically modified (GM) crops promise other important yield improvements. Virus-resistant varieties of sweet potatoes and both white and yellow maize, and faster-growing bananas are already available though not yet widespread, and other food and fibre crops are receiving attention from African biotechnology scientists in Kenya, South Africa, and Egypt, with contributions from American and other Western investigators.

In many areas showing the greatest past successes, Green Revolution gains are falling off. Recent cereal yields in Asia, for example, are growing at only two-thirds of their 1970s rate; the

UN's Food and Agriculture Organization now considers Green Revolution technologies "almost exhausted" of any further productivity gains in Asian rice cultivation. Little prime land and even less water remain to expand farming in many developing countries, and the adverse ecological and social consequences of industrial farming techniques arouse growing resistance. Nor does biotechnology—which many have hailed as a promising new Green Revolution approach—seem likely to fill the gap. Consumer resistance to the genetic modification of food crops, fear of the ecological consequences of such modification, the partial rejection of GM foods in the European Union market, and the high cost and restrictions on the new biotechnologies imposed by their corporate developers all conspire to inhibit the universal adoption of the new technologies in the developing world.

Nevertheless, the production of engineered crops is spreading rapidly. In 1996, the first year genetically modified crops were commercially available, about 1.7 million hectares (4.3 million acres) were placed in biotechnology cultivation. In 2004, a reported 81 million hectares (more than 200 million acres) were planted with GM crops, an increase of 20% over 2003. Almost one-third (30%) of the global GM crop area in that year was located in developing countries; indeed, the percentage growth of GM acreage in the developing countries—notably Argentina, Brazil, China, India, and South Africa—was twice as high as in the industrial countries in the first years of this century. Globally, the principal GM crops have been GM soybeans, GM corn (including white corn for food in South Africa), transgenic cotton, and GM canola. Herbicide resistance (Roundup Ready soybeans) and insect resistance (Bt corn and cotton) have been the most important of the genetic crop modifications introduced and the ones responsible for the significant increase in productivity and reduction in costs of the crops involved.

Even in those world regions favourable for Green Revolution introductions, its advent has not always improved diets or reduced dependency on imported basic foodstuffs. Often, the displacement of native agriculture involves a net loss of domestic food availability. In many instances, through governmental directive, foreign ownership or management, or domestic market realities, the new commercial agriculture is oriented toward food and industrial crops for the export market, or toward specialty crop and livestock production for the expanding urban market, rather than food production for the rural population.

Commercial Agriculture

Few people or areas still retain the isolation and self-containment characteristic of pure subsistence economies. Nearly all have been touched by a modern world of trade and exchange, and have adjusted their traditional economies in response. Modifications of subsistence agricultural systems have inevitably made them more complex by imparting to them at least some of the diversity and linkages of activity that mark the advanced economic systems of the more developed world. Farmers in those systems produce not for their own subsistence but primarily for a market off the farm itself. They are part of integrated exchange economies in which agriculture is but one element in a complex structure that includes mining, manufacturing, processing, and the service activities

of the tertiary, quaternary, and quinary sectors. In those economies, farming activities presumably mark production responses to market demand expressed through price, and are related to the consumption requirements of the larger society rather than to the immediate needs of farmers themselves.

Production Controls

Agriculture within modern, developed economies is characterized by *specialization*—by enterprise (farm), by area, and even by country; by *off-farm sale* rather than subsistence production; and by *interdependence* of producers and buyers linked through markets. Farmers in a free market economy supposedly produce those crops that their estimates of market price and production cost indicate will yield the greatest return. Theoretically, farm products in short supply will command an increased market price. That, in turn, should induce increased production to meet the demand with a consequent reduction of market price to a level of equilibrium with production costs. In some developing countries, that equation between production costs and market price is broken, and the farm economy distorted, when government policy requires uneconomically low food prices for urban workers. It may also suffer material distortion under governmental programs protecting local producers by inhibiting farm product imports, or subsidizing production by guaranteeing prices for selected commodities.

Where free market conditions prevail, however, the crop or the mix of crops and livestock that individual commercial farmers produce is a result of an appraisal of profit possibilities. Farmers must assess and predict prices, evaluate the physical nature of farmland, and factor in the possible weather conditions. The costs of production (fuel, fertilizer, capital equipment, labour) must be reckoned. A number of unpredictable conditions may thwart farmers' aspirations for profit. Among them are the uncertainties of growing season conditions that follow the original planting decision, the total volume of output that will be achieved (and therefore the unit cost of production), and the supply and price situation that will exist months or years in the future, when crops are ready for market.

Beginning in the 1950s in Canada and the United States, specialist farmers and corporate purchasers developed strategies for minimizing those uncertainties. Processors sought uniformity of product quality and timing of delivery. Vegetable canners—of tomatoes, sweet corn, and the like—required volume delivery of raw products of uniform size, colour, and ingredient content on dates that accorded with cannery and labour schedules. And farmers wanted the support of a guaranteed market at an assured price to minimize the uncertainties of their specialization and stabilize the return on their investment.

The solution was contractual arrangements or vertical integrations uniting contracted farmer with purchaser-processor. Broiler chickens of specified age and weight, cattle fed to an exact weight and finish, wheat with a minimum protein content, popping corn with prescribed characteristics, potatoes of the kind and quality demanded by particular fast-food chains, and similar product specification became part of production contracts between farmer and buyer-processor. In the United States, the percentage of total farm output produced under contractual arrangements or by vertical integration (where production, processing, and sales are all coordinated within one firm) rose from 19% in 1960 to well over one-third during the 1990s. This trend is evident in Canada as well, where the number of family owned and operated farms dropped 13.3% between 1996 and 2001, leaving only 187,770 farm families (Statistics Canada, 2001a). The term *agribusiness* is applied to the growing merging of the older, farm-centred crop economy and newer patterns of more integrated production and marketing systems.

Contract farming is spreading to developing countries as well, though it is often criticized as another adverse expression of globalization subjecting small-size farmers to exploitation by powerful Western agribusiness. The UN's FAO, however, argues that well-managed contract arrangements are effective in linking the small farmers of emerging economies with both foreign and local sources of advanced extension advice, seeds, fertilizers, machinery, and profitable markets at stable prices. The agency cites successful examples of contract farming in northern India, Sri Lanka, Nepal, Indonesia, Thailand, and the Philippines, and sees in the arrangements a most promising approach to market-oriented production in areas still dominated by subsistence agriculture.

Even for family farmers not bound by contractual arrangements to suppliers and purchasers, the older assumption that supply, demand, and the market price mechanism are the effective controls on agricultural production is not wholly valid. In reality, those theoretical controls are joined by a number of non-market governmental influences that may be as decisive as market forces in shaping farmers' options and spatial production patterns. If there is a glut of wheat on the market, for example, the price per tonne will come down and the area sown to it should diminish. It will also diminish regardless of supply if governments, responding to economic or political considerations, impose acreage controls.

Distortions of market control may also be introduced to favour certain crops or commodities through subsidies, price supports, market protections, and the like. The political power of farmers in the European Union (EU), for example, secured for them generous product subsidies and for the EU immense unsold stores of butter, wine, and grains until 1992, when reforms began to reduce the unsold stockpiles even while increasing total farm spending. In Japan, the home market for rice is largely protected and reserved for Japanese rice farmers even though their production efficiencies are low and their selling price is high by world market standards. In the United States, programs of farm price supports, acreage controls, financial assistance, and other governmental involvements in agriculture have been of recurring and equally distorting effect (Figure 9.13).

A Model of Agricultural Location

Early in the 19th century, before such governmental influences were the norm, Johann Heinrich von Thünen (1783–1850) observed that lands of apparently identical physical properties were utilized for different agricultural purposes. Around each major urban market centre, he noted, there developed a set of concentric land use rings of different farm products (Figure 9.14). The ring closest to the market specialized in perishable commodities that were both

FIGURE 9.13 Open storage of 1 million bushels of Iowa corn. In the world of commercial agriculture, supply and demand are not always in balance. Both the bounty of nature in favourable crop years and the intervention of governmental programs that distort production decisions can create surpluses for which no market is readily available.

expensive to ship and in high demand. The high prices they could command in the urban market made their production an appropriate use of high-valued land near the city. Surrounding rings of farmlands farther away from the city were used for less perishable commodities with lower transport costs, reduced demand, and lower market prices. General farming and grain farming replaced the market gardening of the inner ring. At the outer margins of profitable agriculture, farthest from the single central market, livestock grazing and similar extensive land uses were found.

To explain why this should be so, von Thünen constructed a formal spatial model—the **von Thünen model**—perhaps the first developed to analyze human activity patterns. He concluded that the uses to which parcels were put was a function of the differing "rent" values placed on seemingly identical lands. Those differences, he claimed, reflected the cost of overcoming the distance separating a given farm from a central market town ("A portion of each crop is eaten by the wheels," he observed). The greater the distance, the higher was the operating cost to the farmer, since transport charges had to be added to other expenses. When a commodity's production costs plus its transport costs just equalled its value at the market, a farmer was at the economic margin of its cultivation. A simple exchange relationship ensued: the greater the transportation costs, the lower the rent that could be paid for land if the crop produced was to remain competitive in the market.

Since, in the simplest form of the model, transport costs are the only variable, the relationship between land rent and distance from market can be easily calculated by reference to each competing crop's *transport gradient*. Perishable commodities, such as fruits and vegetables, would encounter high transport rates per unit of distance; other items such as grain would have lower rates. Land rent for any farm commodity decreases with increasing distance from the central market, and the rate of decline is determined by the transport gradient for that commodity. Crops that

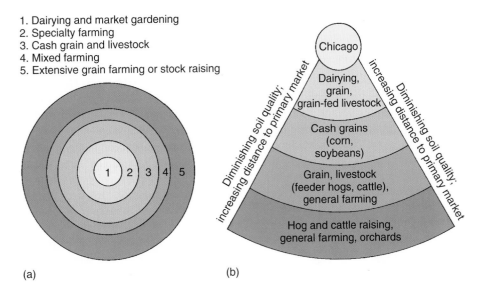

1. Dairying and market gardening
2. Specialty farming
3. Cash grain and livestock
4. Mixed farming
5. Extensive grain farming or stock raising

(a)

(b)

FIGURE 9.14 (*a*) **von Thünen's model.** Recognizing that as distance from the market increases, the value of land decreases, von Thünen developed a descriptive model of intensity of land use that holds up reasonably well in practice. The most intensively produced crops are found on land close to the market; the less intensively produced commodities are located at more distant points. The numbered zones of the diagram represent modern equivalents of the theoretical land use sequence von Thünen suggested over 175 years ago. As the metropolitan area at the centre increases in size, the agricultural specialty areas are displaced outward, but the relative position of each is retained. Compare this diagram with Figure 9.18. (*b*) **A schematic view of the von Thünen zones** in the sector south of Chicago. There, farmland quality decreases southward as the boundary of recent glaciation is passed and hill lands are encountered in southern Illinois. On the margins of the city near the market, dairying competes for space with livestock feeding and suburbanization. Southward into flat, fertile central Illinois, cash grains dominate. In southern Illinois, livestock rearing and fattening, general farming, and some orchard crops are the rule.

Source: (b) Modified with permission from Bernd Andreae, Farming Development and Space: A World Agricultural Geography, *trans. Howard F. Gregor (Berlin; Hawthorne, N.Y.: Walter de Gruyter and Co., 1981).*

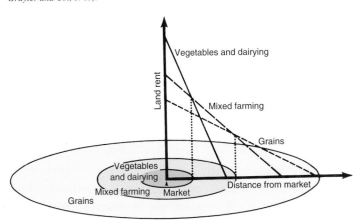

FIGURE 9.15 Transport gradients and agricultural zones.

have both the highest market price and the highest transport costs will be grown nearest to the market. Less perishable crops with lower production and transport costs will be grown at greater distances away (Figure 9.15). Since in this model transport costs are uniform in all directions away from the centre, a concentric zonal pattern of land use called the *von Thünen rings* results.

The von Thünen model may be modified by introducing ideas of differential transport costs (Figure 9.16), variations in topography or soil fertility, or changes in commodity demand and market price. With or without such modifications, von Thünen's analysis helps explain the changing crop patterns and farm sizes evident on the landscape at increasing distance from major cities, particularly

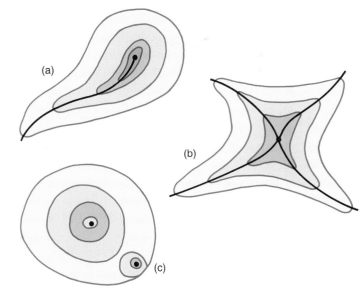

FIGURE 9.16 Ring modifications. Modifications of controlling conditions will alter the details but not change the underlying pattern of the von Thünen rings. For example, a growth in demand and therefore market price of a commodity would merely expand its ring of production. An increase in transport costs would contract the production area, while reductions in freight rates would extend it. (*a*) If transport costs are reduced in one direction, the circularity—but not the sequence—of the rings will be affected. (*b*) If several roads are constructed or improved, land use sequences assume a star-shaped or digitate outline. (*c*) The addition of a smaller outlying market results in the emergence of a set of von Thünen rings subordinate to it.

Livelihood and Economy: Primary Activities   313

in regions dominantly agricultural in economy. Farmland close to markets takes on high value, is used *intensively* for high-value crops, and is subdivided into relatively small units. Land far from markets is used *extensively* and in larger units.

In dominantly industrial and post-industrial economies, it has been suggested, the basic forces determining agricultural land use near cities are those associated with urban expansion itself, and von Thünen regularities are less predictable. Rather, irregularities and uncertainties of peripheral city growth, the encroachment on agricultural land by expansion from two or more cities, and the withholding of land from farming in anticipation of subdivision may locally reverse or invert the von Thünen intensity rings. Where those urbanizing forces dominate, the agricultural pattern often may be one of increasing—rather than decreasing—intensity with distance from the city.

Intensive Commercial Agriculture

Following World War II, agriculture in the developed world's market economies turned increasingly to concentrated methods of production. Machinery, chemicals, irrigation, and dependence on a restricted range of carefully selected and bred plant varieties and animal breeds all were employed in a concerted effort to wring more production from each unit of farmland. In that sense, all modern commercial agriculture is "intensive." There are, however, significant differences among the several types of farm specializations and practices in the relative ratios of capital inputs per hectare of farmed land. Those differences underlie generalized distinctions made between intensive and extensive commercial agriculture.

Farmers who apply large amounts of capital (for machinery and fertilizers, for example) and/or labour per unit of land engage in **intensive** (commercial) **agriculture**. (Figure 9.17.) The crops that justify such costly inputs are characterized by high yields and high market value per unit of land. They include fruits, vegetables, and dairy products, all of which are highly perishable. Near most medium-sized and large cities, dairy farms and **truck farms** (horticultural or "market garden" farms) produce a wide range of vegetables and fruits. Since the produce is perishable, transport costs increase because of the required special handling, such as use of refrigerated trucks and custom packaging. This is another reason for locations close to market. Note the distribution of truck and fruit farming in Figure 9.17.

Livestock-grain farming involves the growing of grain to be fed on the producing farm to livestock, which constitute the farm's cash product. In Western Europe, three-fourths of cropland is devoted to production for animal consumption; in Denmark, 90% of all grains are fed to livestock for conversion not only into meat but also into butter, cheese, and milk. Although livestock-grain farmers work their land intensively, the value of their product per unit of land is usually less than that of the truck farm. Consequently, in North America at least, livestock-grain farms are farther from the main markets than are horticultural and dairy farms.

Normally the profits for marketing livestock (particularly beef cattle in Canada) are greater per kilogram than those for selling corn or other feed, such as alfalfa and clover. As a result, farmers convert their corn into meat on the farm by feeding it to the livestock, efficiently avoiding the cost of buying grain. They may also convert farm grain at local feed mills to the more balanced feed modern livestock rearing requires. Where land is too expensive to be used to grow feed, especially near cities, feed must be shipped to the farm. The grain-livestock belts of the world are close to the great coastal and industrial zone markets. The prarie grain belt of Canada and the livestock region of Western Europe are two examples.

In Canada—and commonly in all other developed countries—traditional small or family farm livestock-grain operations have been largely supplanted by very large-scale concentrated animal feeding operations or "livestock factory farms" involving thousands and tens of thousands of closely quartered animals. From its inception in the 1920s, the intensive, industrialized rearing of livestock, particularly beef and dairy cattle, hogs, and poultry, has grown to dominate meat, dairy, and egg production. To achieve their objective of producing a marketable product in volume at the lowest possible unit cost, operators of livestock factory farms confine animals to pens or cages, treat them with antibiotics and vitamins to maintain health and speed growth, provide processed feeds often containing low-cost animal by-products or crop residue, and deliver them under contract to processors, packers, or their parent company. Although serious concerns have been voiced about animal waste management and groundwater, stream, and atmospheric pollution, contract-based concentrated feeding operations now provide almost all supermarket meat and dairy supplies.

Extensive Commercial Agriculture

Farther from the market, on less expensive land, there is less need to use the land intensively. Cheaper land gives rise to larger farm units. **Extensive** (commercial) **agriculture** is typified by large wheat farms and livestock ranching.

There are, of course, limits to the land use explanations attributable to von Thünen's model. While it is evident from Figure 9.18 that farmland values decline westward with increasing distance from, for example, the northeastern market of the United States, they show no corresponding increase with increasing proximity to the massive West Coast market region until the specialty agricultural areas of the coastal states themselves are reached. The western states are characterized by extensive agriculture, but as a consequence of environmental, not distance, considerations. Climatic conditions obviously affect the productivity and the potential agricultural use of an area, as do associated soils regions and topography. In North America, of course, increasing distance westward from eastern markets is by chance associated with increasing aridity and the beginning of mountainous terrain. In general, rough terrain and subhumid climates rather than simple distance from market underlie the widespread occurrence of extensive agriculture.

Large-scale wheat farming requires sizeable capital inputs for planting and harvesting machinery, but the inputs per unit of land are low; wheat farms are very large. Nearly half the farms in Saskatchewan, for example, are more than 400 hectares (1000 acres). The average farm in Kansas is larger than 400 hectares, and in North Dakota, more than 525 hectares (1300 acres). In North America, the spring wheat (planted in spring, harvested

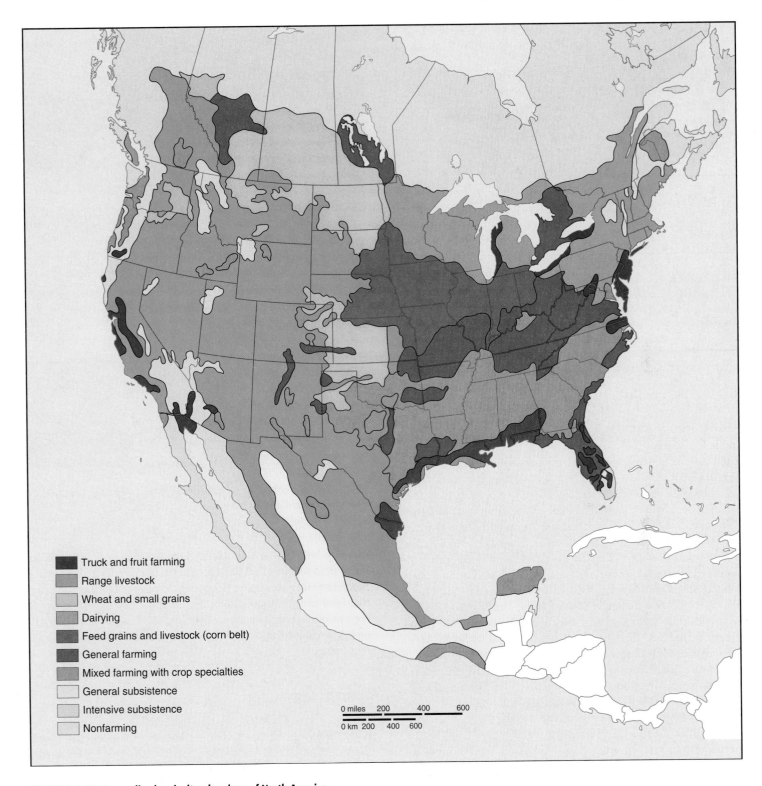

FIGURE 9.17 Generalized agricultural regions of North America.

Sources: U.S. Bureau of Agricultural Economics; Agriculture Canada; and Secretaría de Agricultura y Recursos Hidráulicos, Mexico.

Legend:
- Truck and fruit farming
- Range livestock
- Wheat and small grains
- Dairying
- Feed grains and livestock (corn belt)
- General farming
- Mixed farming with crop specialties
- General subsistence
- Intensive subsistence
- Nonfarming

Scale:
0 miles 200 400 600
0 km 200 400 600

in autumn) region includes the Dakotas, eastern Montana, and the southern parts of the Prairie Provinces of Canada. The winter wheat (planted in fall, harvested in midsummer) belt focuses on Kansas and includes adjacent sections of neighbouring states (Figure 9.19). Argentina is the only South American country to have comparable large-scale wheat farming. In the Eastern Hemisphere, the system is fully developed only east of the Volga River in northern Kazakhstan and the southern part of Western Siberia, and in southeastern and western Australia. Because wheat is an important crop in many agricultural systems—today, wheat ranks first in total production among all the world's grains and accounts for more than 20% of the total calories consumed by

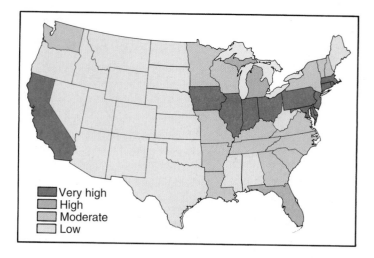

FIGURE 9.18 Relative value per hectare/acre of farmland and buildings.
In a generalized way, per hectare/acre valuations support von Thünen's model. The major metropolitan markets of the Northeast, the Midwest, and California are in part reflected by high rural property valuations, and fruit and vegetable production along the Gulf Coast increases land values there. National and international markets for agricultural goods, soil productivity, climate, and terrain characteristics are also reflected in the map patterns.

Source: Statistical Abstract of the United States.

FIGURE 9.19 Contract harvesters follow the ripening wheat northward through the plains of the United States and Canada.

humans collectively—large-scale wheat farms face competition from commercial and subsistence producers throughout the world (Figure 9.20).

Livestock ranching differs significantly from livestock-grain farming and, by its commercial orientation and distribution, from the nomadism it superficially resembles. A product of the 19th century growth of urban markets for beef and wool in Western Europe and the northeastern United States, ranching has been primarily confined to areas of European settlement. It is found in the western United States and adjacent sections of Mexico and Canada (see Figure 9.17); the grasslands of Argentina, Brazil, Uruguay, and Venezuela; the interior of Australia; the uplands of South Island, New Zealand; and the Karoo and adjacent areas of South Africa (Figure 9.20). All except New Zealand and the humid pampas of South America have semi-arid climates. All, even the most remote from markets, were a product of improvements in transportation by land and sea, refrigeration of carriers, and of meat-canning technology.

In all of the ranching regions, livestock range (and the area exclusively in ranching) has been reduced as crop farming has encroached on their more humid margins, as pasture improvement has replaced less nutritious native grasses, and as grain fattening has supplemented traditional grazing. Recently, the mid-latitude demand for beef has been blamed for expanded cattle ranching and extensive destruction of tropical rain forests in Central America and the Amazon basin, although in recent years Amazon Basin deforestation has reflected more the expansion of soybean farming than of beef production.

In areas of livestock ranching, young cattle or sheep are allowed to graze over thousands of acres. In the United States, when the cattle have gained enough weight so that weight loss in shipping will not be a problem, they are sent to livestock-grain farms or to feedlots near slaughterhouses for accelerated fattening. Since ranching can be an economic activity only where alternative land uses are nonexistent and land quality is low, ranching regions of the world characteristically have low population densities, low capitalizations per land unit, and relatively low labour requirements.

Special Crops

Proximity to the market does not guarantee the intensive production of high-value crops should terrain or climatic circumstances hinder it. Nor does great distance from the market inevitably determine that extensive farming on low-priced land will be the sole agricultural option. Special circumstances, most often climatic, make some places far from markets intensively developed agricultural areas. Two special cases are agriculture in Mediterranean climates and in plantation areas (Figure 9.21).

Most of the arable land in the Mediterranean basin itself is planted to grains, and much of the agricultural area is used for grazing. *Mediterranean agriculture* as a specialized farming economy, however, is known for grapes, olives, oranges, figs, vegetables, and similar commodities. These crops need warm temperatures all year round and a great deal of sunshine in the

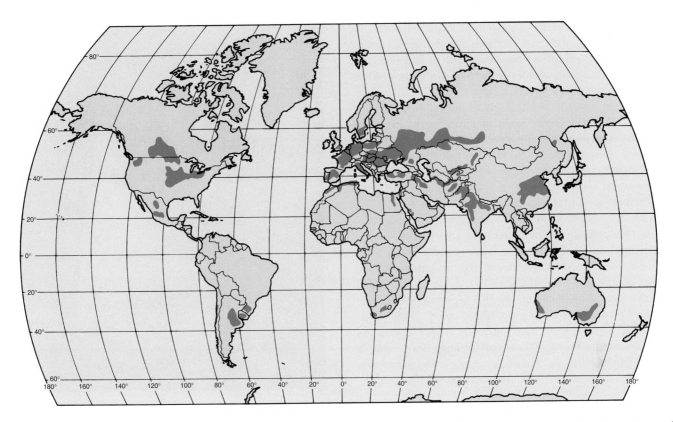

FIGURE 9.20 Principal wheat-growing areas. Only part of the world's wheat production comes from large-scale farming enterprises. In western and southern Europe, eastern and southern Asia, and North Africa, wheat growing is part of general or intensive subsistence farming. Recently, developing country successes with the Green Revolution and subsidized surpluses of the grain in Europe have altered traditional patterns of production and world trade in wheat.

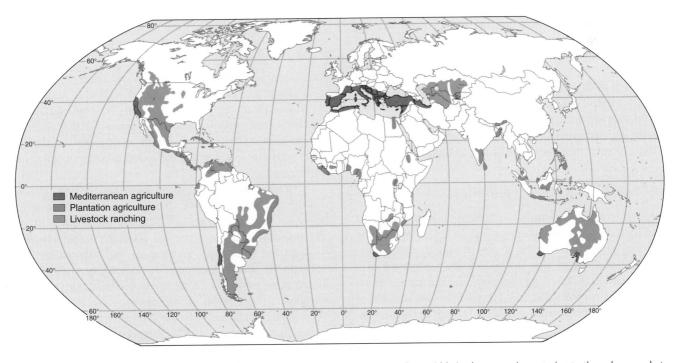

Mediterranean agriculture
Plantation agriculture
Livestock ranching

FIGURE 9.21 Livestock ranching and special crop agriculture. Livestock ranching is primarily a mid-latitude enterprise catering to the urban markets of industrialized countries. Mediterranean and plantation agriculture are similarly oriented to the markets provided by advanced economies of western Europe and North America. Areas of Mediterranean agriculture—all of roughly comparable climatic conditions—specialize in similar commodities, such as grapes, oranges, olives, peaches, and vegetables. The specialized crops of plantation agriculture are influenced by both physical geographic conditions and present or, particularly, former colonial control of the area.

summer. The Mediterranean agricultural lands indicated in Figure 9.21 are among the most productive in the world. Farmers can regulate their output in sunny areas such as these because storms and other inclement weather problems are infrequent. Also, the precipitation regime of Mediterranean climate areas—winter rain and summer drought—lends itself to the controlled use of water. Of course, much capital must be spent for the irrigation systems. This is another reason for the intensive use of the land for high-value crops that are, for the most part, destined for export to industrialized countries or areas outside the Mediterranean climatic zone and even, in the case of Southern Hemisphere locations, to markets north of the equator.

Climate is also considered the vital element in the production of what are commonly, but imprecisely, known as *plantation crops*. The implication of **plantation** is the introduction of a foreign element—investment, management, and marketing—into an indigenous culture and economy, often employing an introduced alien labour force. The plantation itself is an estate whose resident workers produce one or two specialized crops. Those crops, although native to the tropics, were frequently foreign to the areas of plantation establishment: African coffee and Asian sugar in the Western Hemisphere and American cacao, tobacco, and rubber in Southeast Asia and Africa are examples (Figure 9.22). Entrepreneurs in Western countries such as England, France, the Netherlands, and the United States became interested in the tropics partly because they afforded them the opportunity to satisfy a demand in temperate lands for agricultural commodities not producible in the market areas. Custom and convenience usually retain the term "plantation" even where native producers of local crops dominate, as they do in cola nut production in Guinea, spice growing in India or Sri Lanka, or sisal production in the Yucatán.

The major plantation crops and the areas where they are produced include tea (India and Sri Lanka), jute (India and Bangladesh), rubber (Malaysia and Indonesia), cacao (Ghana and Nigeria), cane sugar (Cuba and the Caribbean area, Brazil, Mexico, India, and the Philippines), coffee (Brazil and Colombia), and bananas (Central America). As Figure 9.21 suggests, for ease of access to shipping, most plantation crops are cultivated along or near coasts, since production for export rather than for local consumption is the rule (see "Organic Farming in Canada").

Agriculture in Planned Economies

As their name implies, planned economies have a degree of centrally directed control of resources and of key sectors of the economy that permits the pursuit of governmentally determined objectives. When that control is extended to the agricultural sector, state and collective farms and agricultural communes replace private farms, crop production is divorced from market control or family need, and prices are established by plan rather than by demand or production cost. Although such extremes of rural control have in recent years been relaxed or abandoned in most formerly strictly planned economies, wherever past centralized control of agriculture was imposed, traditional rural landscapes were altered. Before the former Soviet Union's collapse in 1991, its rural landscape had been transformed from millions of pre-revolutionary

FIGURE 9.22 An Indonesian rubber plantation worker collects latex in a small cup attached to the tree and cuts a new tap just above the previous one. The scene typifies classical plantation agriculture in general. The plantation was established by foreign capital (Dutch) to produce a non-native (American) commercial crop for a distant, mid-latitude market using non-native (Chinese) labour supervised by foreign (Dutch) managers. Present-day ownership, management, and labour may have changed, but the nature and market orientation of the enterprise remain.

small farm holdings to a consolidated pattern of fewer than 50,000 centrally controlled operating units. Even today, because of inadequacies in farm registry and boundary descriptions, and because of clouded ownership rights, the remnants of the old Soviet collective farm system still operate more than 90% of the country's farmlands but now respond to market conditions, not centralized directives.

An incomplete progression from private and peasant agriculture, through collectivization, and back to what is virtually a private farming system took place in the planned economy of the People's Republic of China. After its assumption of power in 1949, the communist government redistributed all farmlands to some 350 million peasants in inefficiently small (0.2 hectare, or 0.5 acre) subsistence holdings that were totally inadequate for the growing food needs of the country. Later, by the end of 1957, 90% of peasant households were collectivized into about 700,000 communes, a number further reduced in the 1970s to 50,000 communes averaging some 13,000 members. After the death of Chairman Mao Zedong in 1976, what became effectively a private farming system was reintroduced when 180 million new farms were allocated for unrestricted use to peasant families under rent-free leases. Farmland still remains owned and controlled by the

Organic farming is based on a simple principle, namely, strict respect for the links and natural balances among soil, plants and animals (animals nourish the soil, which nourishes plants). To this is added the constraint of a prohibition on synthetic chemicals. Supporters of organic farming add a social and ethical aspect to the definition of organic farming, because they see in it a means of preserving a human dimension in agriculture, one that is respectful of the environment and in touch with the consumer. Because it is virtually impossible to distinguish a product produced by organic farming from one produced by conventional farming, organic farms must be certified by appropriate regulatory bodies. Certification allows the producer to sell his or her products under the designation "organic." In 2000, Canada had more than 40 such certification bodies.

The organic farming movement in Canada emerged in the 1950s, but has significantly developed since then. By 2000, the number of certified organic producers in Canada had plateaued, after nearly tripling between 1990 and 2000. In 2003, the country had 3,100 organic producers—1.3% of Canada's farmers—farming just over 390,000 hectares. Saskatchewan is home to the largest number of organic farmers (34%). Though organic farming is commonly thought of as primarily market gardening, it is actually field crops such as buckwheat, barley, and wheat that currently dominate in Canada. Canadian consumption of organic products remains modest, about 1-2% of total food consumption, but it is growing steadily at a rate of 20% a year—an unusual phenomenon in the food industry, where growth usually averages 2-3% a year. Canadian organic products account for about 90% of the organic dairy products consumed in this country, 22% of organic fruits and vegetables, and 10% of organic grocery items.

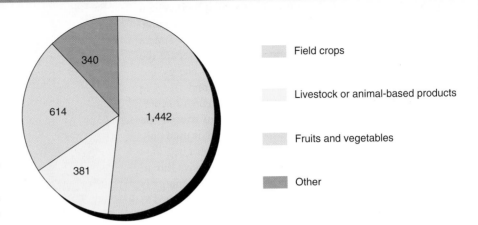

Certified Organic Farms in Canada, 2001

Source: Statistics Canada, Census of Agriculture, 2001.

Because conventional agriculture has been marked by several crises or controversies, organic farming has often been advocated by some as a desirable model for sustainable agriculture. It is now recognized that organic farming has a generally positive environmental impact. First of all, organic farming differs from conventional farming in that it releases a smaller volume of pollutants into the environment.

Many surveys show that consumers buy organic food products because they believe them to be better for their health. Not surprisingly, the organic products industry supports this argument and asserts that organic products contain fewer harmful elements (such as pesticides) and more healthful elements (such as vitamins and minerals).

Despite a strong growth in the market for organic products in Canada, the number of organic farms has been stagnant for several years. A number of reasons may explain this phenomenon: the difficulty farmers experience trying to learn and adapt to new, more labour-intensive techniques; the lack of services designed to make new techniques comprehensible and accessible; uncertainty over premiums; lower yields; and the absence of regulations that would make it possible to standardize the designation "organic" in Canada and to ensure long-term access to export markets.

It is difficult to say that a phasing out of conventional farming and a wholesale conversion to organic farming could guarantee the same level of income for farmers and a stable and adequate food supply. To many, organic farming is a niche that must remain a niche if it is to retain its economic advantage. Moreover, it is a more demanding form of agriculture as far as operating a farm is concerned, one that tends to attract only the more technically proficient. This is the basis for the argument that some people have put forward: that it is the prototype of a more rational approach to agriculture, one that can develop options that are compatible with sustainable development.

Source: Text adapted from *Organic Farming in Canada: An Overview,* by Frédéric Forge, Science and Technology Division, revised 5 October 2004. http://www.parl.gc.ca/information/library/PRBpubs/prb0029-e.htm.

state, and most staple crops are still sold under enforced contracts at fixed prices to government purchasers. Increasingly, however, vegetables and meat are sold on the open market (Figure 9.23), and per capita food production and availability have increased dramatically.

Food and Energy Consumption

Contemporary agriculture, whether practised in a capitalist or centrally planned economy, is heavily dependent upon energy consumption, in particular oil and electricity (Brown 2006). Gasoline and diesel fuel are used in tractors for plowing, planting, cultivating, and harvesting, and electricity is needed for operating irrigation pumps. Fertilizer production, such as phosphates and potash, is also energy-intensive in its mining, manufacturing, and transportation to market. But farms consume a relatively small proportion of the energy consumed in the total food system energy used in Canada and the U.S. Food processing, packaging, marketing, transport, and kitchen preparation account for almost four-fifths of the energy used to create, deliver and prepare the foods we eat. Some 16 per cent of the food system energy use is expended during processing—canning, drying, and freezing food—be it frozen orange juice or canned corn. It is not uncommon for the energy invested in packaging food to exceed the energy contained in the food itself, and the packaging is used only once, and then is discarded as waste, which in turn must be transported elsewhere. And of course the most energy-intensive link in the food chain is the individual household kitchen. More energy is consumed to refrigerate and cook food in the home than is used to produce the food itself.

Whereas oil dominates the production of food, electricity—often produced from gas or coal—dominates the consumption of food. As energy prices rise—as they already have—the food system currently in place will become less tenable. For example, the average number of 'food miles'—the distance food travels from producer to consumer—for one kilogram of chocolate in Canada is 8,598 kilometres! This is an immense about of energy expenditure, particularly for a non-essential food stuff, that simply cannot endure unless cheap oil and electricity continue. With increased energy costs, more local food production will necessarily grow in importance.

FIGURE 9.23 Independent street merchants, shop owners, and peddlers in modern China are members of both a planned and a market system. Free markets and private vendors multiplied after government price controls on most food items were removed in May 1985. Increasingly, non-food trade and manufacturing, too, are being freed of central government control and thriving in the private sector. As state-run companies shrank and laid-off workers, privately owned businesses in 2004 accounted for over half of China's gross domestic product, and the private sector was growing twice as fast as the rest of the economy. The photo shows a row of outdoor poultry merchants in Wanxian, Sichuan Province.

Primary Activities: Resource Exploitation

In addition to agriculture, primary economic activities include fishing, forestry, and the mining and quarrying of minerals. These industries involve the direct exploitation of natural resources that are unequally available in the environment and differentially evaluated by different societies. Their development, therefore, depends on the occurrence of perceived resources, the technology to exploit their natural availability, and the cultural awareness of their value.

Fishing, forestry, and fur trapping are **gathering industries** based on harvesting the natural bounty of renewable resources that are in serious danger of depletion through overexploitation. Livelihoods based on these resources are areally widespread and involve both subsistence and market-oriented components. Mining and quarrying are **extractive industries**, removing non-renewable metallic and non-metallic minerals, including the mineral fuels, from the earth's crust. They are the initial raw material phase of modern industrial economies.

Resource Terminology

Resources or **natural resources** are the naturally occurring materials that a human population, at any given state of economic development and technological awareness, perceives to be necessary and useful to its economic and material well-being. Their occurrence and distribution in the environment are the result of physical processes over which people have little or no direct control. The fact that things exist, however, does not mean that they are resources. To be considered such, a given substance must be *understood* to be a resource—and this is a cultural, not purely a physical, circumstance. Native Americans may have viewed the resource base of Pennsylvania, West Virginia, or Kentucky as composed of forests for shelter and fuel and as the habitat of the game animals (another resource) on which they depended for food. European settlers viewed the forests as the unwanted covering of the resource that *they* perceived to be of value: soil for agriculture. Still later, industrialists appraised the underlying coal deposits, ignored or unrecognized as a resource by earlier occupants, as the item of value for exploitation (Figure 9.24).

Resources may be classified as *renewable* or *non-renewable*. **Renewable resources** are materials that can be consumed and then replenished relatively quickly by natural or by human-assisted processes. Food crops are renewable resources, for example, as are forests, grasslands, animals and fish, and other living things. Even renewable resources can be exhausted if exploited to extinction or destruction; soils can be totally eroded, or an animal species may be completely eliminated. That is, some resources are renewable

FIGURE 9.24 The original hardwood forest covering these West Virginia hills was removed by settlers who saw greater resource value in the underlying soils. The soils, in their turn, were selectively stripped away for access to the still more valuable coal deposits below. Resources are as a culture perceives them, though their exploitation may consume them and, as coal refuse does here near Racine, destroy the potential of an area for alternate uses.

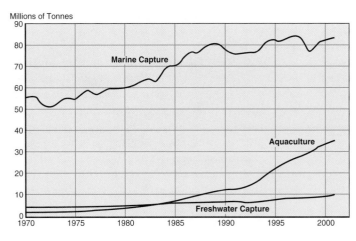

FIGURE 9.25 Officially recorded annual fish harvests, 1970–2001 rose irregularly from 57 million tonnes in 1970 to 131 million tonnes in 2001. On the basis of individual country reports, the FAO recorded fluctuating but slowly growing harvest totals up to 2003, when the world total production was a reported 132.2 million tonnes; the 1993 and 1998 dips are associated with El Niño-produced ocean temperature changes. Chinese admission of regular over-reporting of, particularly, their marine capture suggests that world marine catch and composite harvest totals actually registered an irregular downward trend each year since 1988. A compensating adjustment to this graph would reduce 2001 total harvest and marine catch figures by some 9 million tonnes. The FAO estimates that 20 to 40 million tonnes per year of unintended marine capture of juvenile or undersized fish and non-target species are discarded each year.

Source: Food and Agriculture Organization (FAO).

only if carefully managed. The **maximum sustainable yield** of a resource is the maximum volume or rate of use that will not impair its ability to be renewed or to maintain the same future productivity. For fishing and forestry, for example, that level is marked by a catch or harvest equal to the net growth of the replacement stock. If that maximum exploitation level is exceeded, the renewable resource becomes a non-renewable one—an outcome increasingly likely in the case of Atlantic cod and some other food fish species. **Non-renewable resources** exist in finite amounts and either are not replaced by natural processes—at least not within any time frame of interest to the exploiting society—or are replaced at a rate slower than the rate of use.

Both types of resource are exploited by the non-agricultural primary industries. Fish as a food resource and forests as a source for building materials, cellulose, and fuel are heavily exploited renewable resources. Mining and quarrying extract from nature the non-renewable minerals essential to industrialized economies.

Fishing

Although fish and shellfish account for less than 20% of all human animal protein consumption, an estimated one billion people—primarily in developing countries of eastern and southeastern Asia, Africa, and parts of Latin America—depend on fish as their primary source of protein. Fish are also very important in the diets of most advanced states, both those with and those without major domestic fishing fleets. Although about 75% of the world annual fish harvest is consumed by humans, up to 25% is processed into fish meal to be fed to livestock or used as fertilizer. Those two quite different markets have increased both the demand for and the annual harvest of fish. Indeed, so rapidly have pressures on the world's fish stocks expanded that evidence is unmistakable that at least locally, their *maximum sustainable yield* is actually or potentially being exceeded. The annual fish supply comes from three sources:

1. the *inland catch,* from ponds, lakes, and rivers;
2. *fish farming,* in which fish are produced in a controlled and contained environment; and
3. the *marine catch,* all wild fish harvested in coastal waters or on the high seas.

Inland waters supply less than 7% of the global fish catch (capture), and yet this translates into substantive dollars. The Great Lakes fisheries alone are collectively valued at more than 4 billion dollars annually. Fish farming, both inland and marine, accounts for some 32%. The other 61% or more of the total harvest comes from the world's ocean catch (Figure 9.25). And most of that catch is made in coastal wetlands, estuaries, and the relatively shallow coastal waters above the *continental shelf*—the gently sloping extension of submerged land bordering most coastlines and reaching seaward for varying distances up to 150 kilometres (about 100 miles) or more. Near shore, shallow embayments and marshes provide spawning grounds and river waters supply nutrients to an environment highly productive of fish. Increasingly, these areas are also seriously affected by pollution from runoff and ocean dumping, an environmental assault so devastating in some areas that fish and shellfish stocks have been destroyed with little hope of revival.

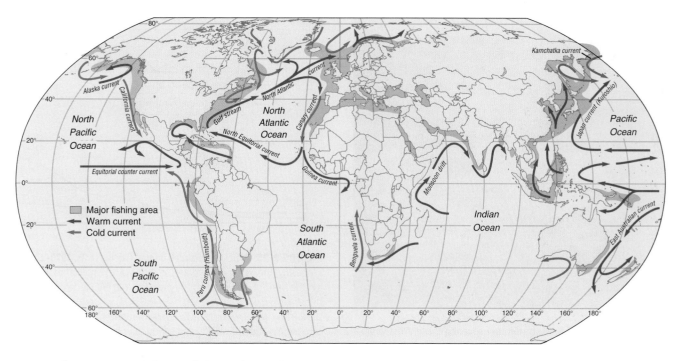

FIGURE 9.26 The major commercial marine fisheries of the world. With approximately 244,000 kilometres of coastline—the longest in the world—Canada's shoreline is an integral part of the country's fishing and related economic sectors, as well as its social, cultural, and recreational constitution. Overfishing, urban development, and the contamination of bays, estuaries, and wetlands have contributed to the depletion of the fish stocks in those coastal waters.

Commercial marine fishing is largely concentrated in northern waters, where warm and cold currents join and mix and where such familiar food species as herring, cod, mackerel, haddock, and flounder congregate or "school" on the broad continental shelves and *banks*—extensive elevated portions of the shelf where environmental conditions are most favourable for fish production (Figure 9.26). Two of the most heavily fished regions are the Northeast Pacific and Northwest Atlantic, which together yield about 40% of the marine catch total. Tropical fish species tend not to school and, because of their high oil content and unfamiliarity, are less acceptable in the commercial market. They are, however, of great importance for local consumption. Traditional or "artisan" fishermen, nearly all working in inshore waters within sight of land, are estimated to number between 8 and 10 million worldwide. Their annual harvest of some 24 million tonnes of fish and shellfish is usually not included in world fishery totals. Only a very small percentage of total marine catch comes from the open seas that make up more than 90% of the world's oceans.

Modern technology and more aggressive fishing fleets of more countries greatly increased annual marine capture in the years after 1950. That technology included use of sonar, radar, helicopters, and satellite communications to locate schools of fish; more efficient nets and tackle; and factory trawlers to follow fishing fleets to prepare and freeze the catch. In addition, more nations granted ever-larger subsidies to expand and reward their marine trawler operations. The rapid rate of increase led to inflated projections of continuing or growing fisheries productivity, and to optimism that the resources of the oceans were inexhaustible.

Quite the opposite has proved to be true. In fact, in recent years, the productivity of marine fisheries has declined because *overfishing* (catches above reproduction rates) and pollution of coastal waters have seriously endangered the supplies of traditional and desirable food species. Adjusted world total catch figures indicate that rather than the steady increase in capture rates shown on Figure 9.25, there has really been a decline of more than 660,000 tonnes per year since the late 1980s. This decline, coupled with growing world population, has caused a serious drop in the average per capita marine catch. The UN reports that all 17 of the world's major oceanic fishing areas are being fished at or beyond capacity; 13 are in decline. The plundering of North American coastal waters has imperiled a number of the most desirable fish species. In 1993, Canada shut down its cod industry to allow stocks to recover—with disasterous economic consequences for Newfoundland—but recovery has yet to occur, although the value of the fishery has increased significantly. U.S. authorities report that 67 North American species are overfished and 61 harvested to capacity.

Overfishing is partly the result of the accepted view that the world's oceans are common property, a resource open to anyone's use with no one responsible for its maintenance, protection, or improvement. The result of this "open seas" principle is but one expression of the so-called **tragedy of the commons**[1]—the economic reality that when a resource is available to all, each user, in the absence of collective controls, thinks he or she is best served by exploiting the resource to the maximum even though this exploitation means its eventual depletion. In 1995, more than 100 countries adopted a treaty—to become legally binding when

---

[1] The *commons* refers to undivided land available for the use of everyone; usually, it meant the open land of a village that all used as pasture. The *Boston Common* originally had this meaning.

ratified by 30 nations—to regulate fishing on the open oceans outside territorial waters. Applying to such species as cod, pollock, and tuna—that is, to migratory and high-seas species—the treaty requires fishers to report the size of their catches to regional organizations that would set quotas and subject vessels to boarding to check for violations. These and other fishing control measures could provide the framework for the future sustainability of important food fish stocks.

One approach to increasing the fish supply is through fish farming or **aquaculture**, the breeding of fish in freshwater ponds, lakes, and canals, or in fenced-off coastal bays and estuaries or enclosures (Figure 9.27). Aquaculture production has provided about 30% of the total fish harvest in recent years; its contribution to the human food supply is even greater than raw production figures suggest. Whereas one-third of the conventional fish catch is used to make fishmeal and fish oil, virtually all farmed fish are used as human food. Fish farming has long been practised in Asia, where fish are a major source of protein, but now takes place on every continent. Its rapid and continuing production increase makes aquaculture the fastest-growing sector of the world food economy, with promise of overtaking cattle ranching as a human food source by 2010.

Forestry

After the retreat of continental glaciers some 12,000 years ago and before the rise of agriculture, the world's forests and woodlands probably covered some 45% of the earth's land area exclusive of Antarctica. They were a sheltered and productive environment for earlier societies that subsisted on gathered fruits, nuts, berries, leaves, roots, and fibres collected from trees and woody plants. Few such cultures remain, though the gathering of forest products is still an important supplemental activity, particularly among subsistence agricultural societies.

Even after millennia of land clearance for agriculture and, more recently, commercial lumbering, cattle ranching, and fuelwood gathering, forests still cover roughly 30% of the world's land area excluding Greenland and Antarctica. As an industrial raw material source, however, forests are more restricted in area. Although forests of some type reach discontinuously from the equator northward to beyond the Arctic Circle and southward to the tips of the southern continents, *commercial forests* are restricted to two very large global belts. One, nearly continuous, is found in upper-middle latitudes of the Northern Hemisphere; the second is located in the equatorial zones of South and Central America, Central Africa, and Southeast Asia (Figure 9.28). These forest belts differ in the types of trees they contain and in the type of market or use they serve.

The northern coniferous, or softwood, forest is the largest and most continuous stand, extending around the globe from Scandinavia across Siberia to North America, then eastward to the Atlantic and southward along the Pacific Coast. The pine, spruce, fir, and other conifers are used for construction lumber and to produce pulp for paper, rayon, and other cellulose products. On the south side of the northern mid-latitude forest region are the deciduous hardwoods: oak, hickory, maple, birch, and the like. These and the trees of the mixed forest lying between the

FIGURE 9.27 Harvesting fish at an aquaculture farm in Thailand. Fish farming is one of the fastest-growing sectors in world food production, with Asian countries supplying the vast majority of total aquaculture harvest.

hardwood and softwood belts have been greatly reduced in areal extent by centuries of agricultural and urban settlement and development. In both Europe and North America, however, although they—like northern softwoods—have lately been seriously threatened by acid rain and atmospheric pollution, their area has been held constant through conservation, protection, and reforestation. They still are commercially important for hardwood applications: furniture, veneers, railroad ties, and the like.

The tropical lowland hardwood forests are exploited primarily for fuelwood and charcoal, although an increasing quantity of special quality woods are cut for export as lumber. In fact, developing —particularly tropical—countries account for 90% of the world's hardwood log exports (Figure 9.29); some two-thirds of these in the 1990s came from Malaysia alone, with the Malaysian state of Sarawak (on the island of Borneo slightly larger than Newfoundland) the source then of one-half of the world's hardwood logs.

These contrasting uses document *roundwood* (log) production as a primary economic activity. About 47% of the world's annual logging harvest is for industrial consumption, some 73% of it the output of industrialized countries from the temporal and boreal forest belt. Half of all production of industrial wood is from the United States, Canada, and Russia. Chiefly because of their distance from major industrial wood markets, the developing countries as a group accounted for less than one-quarter of industrial wood production in 2000. The logic of von Thünen's analysis of transportation costs and market accessibility helps explain the pattern.

The other half (53%) of roundwood production is for fuelwood and charcoal; 90% of world fuelwood production comes from the forests of Africa, Asia, Oceania, and Latin America, and demand for fuelwood grows by more than 1.2% per year. Since the populations of developing countries are heavily dependent on fuelwood and charcoal, their growing numbers have resulted in serious depletion of tropical forest stands. Indeed, about 60% (some 1.5 billion people) of those who depend upon fuelwood as their principal energy source are cutting wood at a rate well above the maximum sustainable yield. In tropical areas as a whole,

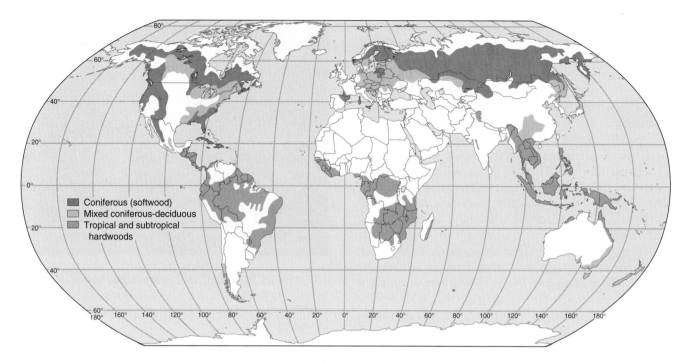

FIGURE 9.28a Major commercial forest regions. Much of the original forest, particularly in mid-latitude regions, has been cut over. Many treed lands-capes that remain do not contain commercial stands. Significant portions of the northern forest are not readily accessible and at current prices cannot be considered commercial. Deforestation of tropical hardwood stands involves more clearing for agriculture and firewood than for roundwood production.

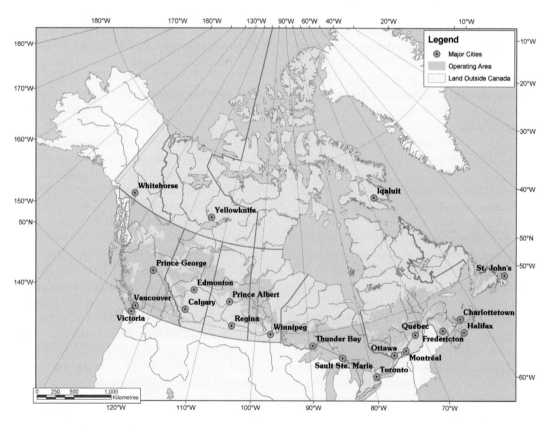

FIGURE 9.28b Major Commercial Forest Operating Areas in Canada. Some 94 per cent of Canada's forested land is publicly owned, with 71 percent under provincial jurisdiction, and 23 percent under federal or territorial jurisdiction. These forests are most commonly harvested and managed by commercial forest companies under a diverse variety of logging concessions or 'forest tenures': the agreements whereby the Crown has transferred the rights to harvest timber in public forests to private forest companies under certain conditions, while retaining the underlying title to the land.

Source: Global Forest Watch Canada, 2003. http://www.globalforestwatch.ca/tenure/maps/Maps01.png (from Global Forest Watch Canada, http://globalforestwatch.ca/tenure/download.htm).

FIGURE 9.29 Teak logs for export stacked near Mandalay, Myanmar.

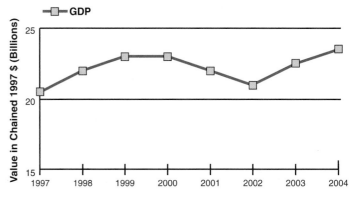

(a) **Canadian agriculture, forestry, fishing, and hunting sectors.**

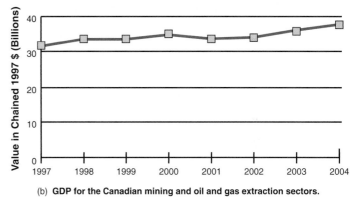

(b) **GDP for the Canadian mining and oil and gas extraction sectors.**

FIGURE 9.30 (*a*) The GDP of the agriculture, forestry, fishing, and hunting sectors grew by a compounded annual growth rate of 2.3%, from $20.4 billion to $23.9 billion, between 1997 and 2004.
(*b*) The GDP of the mining and oil and gas extraction sectors grew by a compounded annual growth rate of 1.6%, from $33.9 billion to $37.8 billion, between 1997 and 2004.

Source: (a) http://strategis.ic.gc.ca/canadian_industry_statistics/cis.nsf/IDE/cis11gdpe.html.
(b) http://strategis.ic.gc.ca/canadian_industry_statistics/cis.nsf/IDE/cis21gdpe.html.

deforestation rates exceed reforestation by 10 to 15 times. During the 1990s, tropical forest and woodlands were converted to agricultural lands at a rate of 10 to 12 million hectares (25 to 30 million acres) annually. Additional millions of hectares, particularly in South and Central America, have been cleared for pasture for beef cattle destined primarily for the North American market.

These uses and conversions have serious implications not only ecologically but also economically. Forest removal without replenishment for whatever reason converts the renewable resource of a gathering industry into a destructively exploited non-renewable one. Regional economies, patterns of international trade, and prospects of industrial development are all adversely affected.

Fur Trapping and Trade

The fur trade is ancient, with references and records dating to early Mediterranean and Far Eastern civilizations. In more recent centuries, demand for fine skins (including sable) lay behind Russia's 17th- and 18th-century expansion eastward to Siberia, Alaska, and down to northern California. Elsewhere in North America, early history was closely tied to a commercial need to satisfy European demand, initially for beaver. Worldwide, the fur trade was and is one of the few sectors of the European and Western economy in which Aboriginal people could and can participate and still retain their traditional lifestyles, values, and skills. Ardent anti-fur campaigns that began in the late 1960s led to European Union bans on imported seal pelts and on furs originating in countries permitting leg-hold traps. The annual seal hunt, for example, is a highly charged moral and economic issue in Canada, and one that is not likely to dissipate in the near future. Protestors argue that the seal hunt is inhumane, unnecessary, constitutes a relatively small sector of the Canadian economy, the profits of which could be surpassed through seal sightseeing tourism rather than slaughter, and are opposed by the vast majority of Canadians (Humane Society of Canada, 2006). Supporters counter otherwise: seals are "harvested" in humane ways, providing not simply fur but leather, handcrafts, oil, and meat for human and animal consumption; the

$16.5 million generated annually provides 25% to 35% of annual income for sealers, who experience a 30% higher than average unemployment rate; and, they argue, most Canadians support a "responsible" hunt (Fisheries and Oceans Canada, 2006). Much of the furor over the annual seal hunt, however, is directed toward the commercial seal hunt by non-Aboriginal sealers, not those who use seals for subsistence. Nevertheless, fur protests have hurt Canadian trapping communities in general. Those restrictions have materially reduced traditional fur trade income opportunities for First Nations People of Canada and Alaska. Elsewhere, however, fur trapping and hunting are still important or essential in the livelihoods of many people in Siberia and South America, and support thousands of others worldwide from Mongolia to Australia.

Trapping and hunting are currently only minor parts of the fur trade scene, and a traditional gathering economy is now largely lost, replaced by fur farming as the primary supplier of market demand. Farmed furs—often produced as an income supplement to other farming activities—now account for some 85% of the industry's income generation. Most fur farming takes place in northern Europe (64%) and North America (11%), with the remainder found widely spread, from Argentina to Ukraine, European Russia, and Siberia (see Figure 9.30a.)

Mining and Quarrying

Societies at all stages of economic development can and do engage in agriculture, fishing, forestry, and trapping. The extractive industries—mining and drilling for non-renewable mineral wealth—emerged only when cultural advancement and economic necessity made possible a broader understanding of the earth's resources. Now those industries provide the raw material and energy base for the way of life experienced by people in the advanced economies, and are the basis for a major part of the international trade connecting the developed and developing countries of the world (see Figure 9.30b.)

The extractive industries depend on the exploitation of minerals unevenly distributed in amounts and concentrations determined by past geologic events, not by contemporary market demand. In physically workable and economically usable deposits, minerals constitute only a tiny fraction of the earth's crust—far less than 1%. That industrialization has proceeded so rapidly and so cheaply is the direct result of an earlier ready availability of rich and accessible deposits of the requisite materials. Economies grew fat by skimming the cream. It has been suggested that should some catastrophe occur to return human cultural levels to a pre-agricultural state, it would be extremely unlikely that humankind ever again could move along the road of industrialization with the resources available for its use.

Our successes in exploiting mineral resources have been achieved, that is, at the expense of depleting the most easily extractable world reserves and with the penalty of increasing monetary costs as the highest-grade deposits are removed (Figure 9.31). Costs increase as more advanced energy-consuming technologies must be applied to extract the desired materials from ever greater depths in the earth's crust or from new deposits of smaller mineral content. That observation states a physical and economic reality relevant particularly to the exploitation of both the *metallic minerals* and the *mineral fuels*. It is less applicable to the third main category of extractive industry, the *non-metallic minerals*. In few cases, however, does the observation imply that natural scarcity is a limit on resource availability. In fact, as a consequence of modern exploration technologies and extraction efficiencies, known reserves of all fossil fuels and of most commercially important metals are now larger than they were in the middle of the 20th century. That increasing abundance of at least non-fuel resources is reflected in the steady decrease in raw material prices since the 1950s that has so adversely affected some export-oriented developing world economies.

Metallic Minerals

Because usable mineral deposits are the result of geologic accident, it follows that the larger the country, the more probable it is that such accidents will have occurred within the national territory. And in fact, Russia, Canada, China, the United States, Brazil, and Australia possess abundant and diverse mineral resources. It is also true, however, that many smaller developing countries are major sources of one or more critical raw materials and become, therefore, important participants in the growing international trade in minerals.

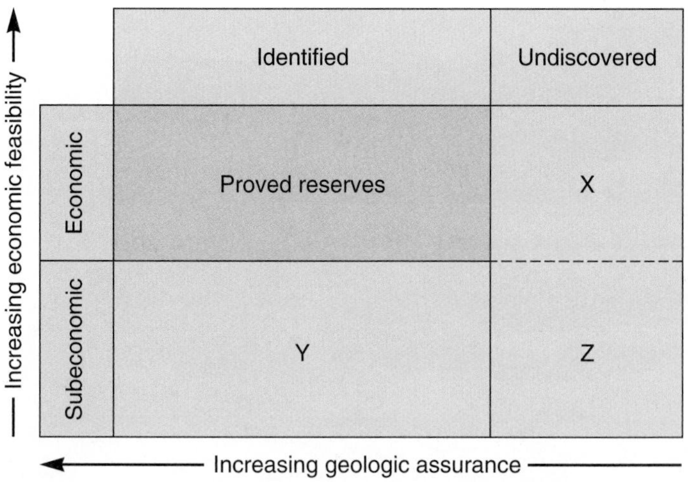

FIGURE 9.31 The variable definition of reserves. Assume the large rectangle includes the total world stock of a particular resource. Some deposits of that resource have been discovered and are shown in the left column as "identified." Deposits not yet known are "undiscovered reserves." Deposits that are economically recoverable with current technology are at the top of the diagram. Those below, labelled "sub-economic" reserves, are not attractive for any of several reasons of mineral content, accessibility, cost of extraction, and so on. Only the pink area can be properly referred to as **usable reserves**. These are deposits that have been identified and can be recovered at current prices and with current technology. X denotes reserves that would be attractive economically but are not yet discovered. Identified but not economically attractive reserves are labelled Y. Z represents undiscovered deposits that would not now be attractive even if they were known.

Source: U.S. Geological Survey.

The production of most metallic minerals, such as copper, lead, and iron ore, is affected by a balance of three forces: the quantity available, the richness of the ore, and the distance to markets. A fourth factor, land acquisition and royalty costs, may equal or exceed other considerations in mine development decisions. Even if these conditions are favourable, mines may not be developed or even remain operating if supplies from competing sources are more cheaply available in the market. In the 1980s, more than 25 million tonnes of iron ore-producing capacity was permanently shut down in the United States and Canada (see "Reclamation of Mines in Canada's North"). Similar declines occurred in North American copper, nickel, zinc, lead, and molybdenum mining as market prices fell below domestic production costs. Beginning in the early 1990s, as a result of both resource depletion and low cost imports, the United States became a net importer of non-fuel minerals for the first time. Of course, increases in mineral prices may be reflected in opening or re-opening mines that, at lower returns, were deemed unprofitable. However, the developed industrial countries of market economies, whatever their former or even present mineral endowment, find themselves at a competitive disadvantage against developing country producers with lower-cost labour and state-owned mines with abundant, rich reserves.

When the ore is rich in metallic content (in the case of iron and aluminum ores), it is profitable to ship it directly to the market for refining. But, of course, the highest-grade ores tend to be mined first. Consequently, the demand for low-grade ores

Geography and Public Policy

Reclamation of Mines in Canada's North

The mining of Canada's North has a long history, and its legacy is mixed. From the earliest explorations of what is now Nunavut for gold in the late 1500s by England's Martin Frobisher, through to the great Klondike gold rush of the Yukon in the late 1890s, to the extraction of uranium from the Northwest Territories (NWT) in the 1940s for the atomic bombs dropped on Japan, to the 1998 opening of Canada's first diamond mine 300 kilometres (185 miles) northeast of Yellowknife, mining has generated both economic prosperity and a host of political, legal, and environmental issues (Mining Watch Canada, 2002).

Obtaining mining rights is surprisingly simple in Canada, while the responsibility for regulating mines is a complex political and legal matter. Under the law of "free entry," individuals and companies alike may acquire exclusive rights from the government to mine virtually any portion of Crown-owned land—virtually all land in Canada—to an unlimited depth. These rights take privilege over private property rights, Aboriginal land claims, and resource management and land use plans. The costs to obtain a prospector's licence and to register a land claim should minerals be found and mining conducted are not entirely "free" per se and do vary across Canada, but the costs are minimal. In Ontario, for example, a prospector's licence costs about $25 and fees for registering a land claim vary with land size, roughly $20 to $65 (Campbell, 2004).

Who regulates the mines and their eventual closure and clean up is not so simple a process. The federal government manages mineral resources in the Yukon, NWT, and Nunavut, but does so through a variety of federal agencies. The Department of Indian Affairs and Northern Development (DIAND) is perhaps the most important of these agencies because it is responsible for Aboriginal peoples and the environmental protection of the North. Territorial and Aboriginal governments, however, are playing larger leadership roles due to their increasing political autonomy and as part of land ownership transfers as land claims are settled. Nevertheless, Canada has no national program to address abandoned and contaminated mine sites, although some provinces do hold mining companies legally responsible.

A geographical study of abandoned mining exploration sites in Nunavik, Northern Quebec, illustrates this point well (Duhaime, Bernard, and Comtois, 2005). Prior to 1976, mining companies were not obliged to clean up their excavation sites, and materials remain there today that pose dangers to the environment and human health. Entire mining sites were simply abandoned when mining ceased, leaving behind various chemical products, gasoline tanks, oil cans, entire buildings (tents, garages, laboratories, cabins), vehicles, machinery and assorted scrap (mattresses, debris, tools). There are some 595 known and documented abandoned mining sites with varying degrees of residual toxins and waste remaining in Nunavut today.

Who should clean up and restore such abandoned sites? Who should pay for this reclamation? And who should enforce these measures? Some argue that DIAND should legislate and enforce reclamation standards, and compel mining companies to contribute financially to the clean up of sites their industry has damaged while amassing huge profits. Still others maintain that the Canadian federal, provincial, and territorial governments must coordinate their positions and laws to ensure effective action is taken to clean up toxic mine sites from coast to coast. Clearly there is a policy gap in need of closure. Between the variety of governmental agencies and levels involved in overseeing mines and the mining industry, and the sweeping privileges granted through "free entry" law, the issue of mine abandonment has fallen through the cracks.

Questions to Consider

1. If the house you live in has minerals underneath the surface, someone else can register a claim and literally mine beneath your house. Should this be permissible? And if so, should you get a portion of the profits? Why or why not?

2. "Free entry" law is intrinsically tied to the "right to explore," which was a driving force in the economic development of what is now Canada by European interests and settlers of centuries past. Has such a law outlived its original intent, or would any modification to this law hinder the mining industry in Canada? First consider the point of view of a miner, and then consider the position of someone displaced by a mining operation.

3. Are toxic sites in the North simply the cost Canadian society must pay to enjoy the material and economic benefits accrued from mining? If so, does the fact that profits from mining public land go to private interests alter your initial position?

4. Who do *you* think should clean up and restore abandoned mine sites? Who do *you* think should pay for mine clean up and reclamation? And who do *you* think should enforce these measures? Why?

---

has been increasing in recent years as richer deposits have been depleted (Figure 9.32). Low-grade ores are often upgraded by various types of separation treatments at the mine site to avoid the cost of transporting waste materials not wanted at the market. Concentration of copper is nearly always mine oriented (Figure 9.33); refining takes place near areas of consumption. The large amount of waste in copper (98% to 99% or more of the ore) and in most other industrially significant ores should not be considered the mark of an unattractive deposit. Indeed, the opposite may be true. Because of the cost of extraction or the smallness of the reserves, many higher-content ores are left unexploited in favour of the utilization of large deposits of even very low-grade ore. The attraction of the latter is a size of reserve sufficient to justify the long-term commitment of development capital and, simultaneously, to assure a long-term source of supply.

At one time, high-grade magnetite iron ore was mined and shipped from the Mesabi area of Minnesota. Those deposits are now exhausted. However, immense amounts of capital have been

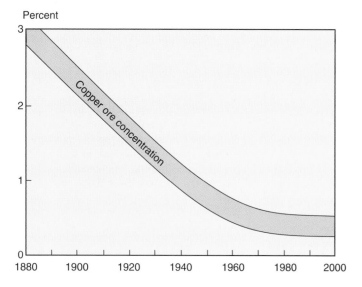

FIGURE 9.32 Needed metal content of copper ore for profitable mining.
In 1830, 3% copper ore rock was needed to justify its mining; today, rock with 0.5% ore content is mined. As the supply of a metal decreases and its price increases, the concentration needed for economic recovery goes down. It also goes down as improved and more cost-effective technologies of rock mining and ore extraction come into play.

Source: Data from the U.S. Bureau of Mines.

FIGURE 9.33 Copper ore concentrating and smelting facilities at the Phelps-Dodge mine in Morenci, Arizona. Concentrating mills crush the ore, separating copper-bearing material from the rocky mass containing it. The great volume of waste material removed assures that most concentrating operations are found near the ore bodies. Smelters separate concentrated copper from other, unwanted, materials such as oxygen and sulphur. Because smelting is also a "weight-reducing" (and, therefore, transportation-cost reducing) activity, it is frequently—though not invariably—located close to the mine as well.

invested in the mining and processing into high-grade iron ore pellets of the virtually unlimited supplies of low-grade iron-bearing rock (taconite) still remaining. Such investments do not assure the profitable exploitation of the resource. The metals market is highly volatile. Rapidly and widely fluctuating prices can quickly change profitable mining and refining ventures to losing undertakings. Marginal gold and silver deposits are opened or closed in reaction to trends in precious metals prices. Taconite *beneficiation* (waste material removal) in the Lake Superior region has virtually ceased in response to the decline of the U.S. steel industry. In commercial economies, cost and market controls dominate economic decisions. In planned economies, cost may be a less important consideration than other concerns such as goals of national development and resources independence.

The mined *fertilizer* minerals include potash and phosphate, which do move in international trade because of their unequal distribution and market value. *Precious* and *semiprecious* stones are also important in the trade of some countries, including South Africa and Sri Lanka.

Non-metallic Minerals

From the standpoint of volume and weight of material removed, the extraction of non-metallic earth materials is the most important branch of the extractive industries. The minerals mined are usually classified by their end use. Of widest distribution, greatest use, and least long-distance movement are those used for *construction*: sand and gravel, building stone, and the gypsum and limestone that are the ingredients of cement. Transportation costs play a great role in determining where low-value minerals will be mined. Minerals such as gravel, limestone for cement, and aggregate are found in such abundance that they have value only when they are near the site where they are to be used. For example, gravel for road building has value if it is at or near the road-building project, not otherwise. Transporting gravel hundreds of miles is an unprofitable activity (Figure 9.34).

FIGURE 9.34 The Vancouver, British Columbia, municipal gravel quarry and storage yard. Proximity to market gives utility to low-value minerals unable to bear high transportation charges.

Mineral Fuels

The advanced economies have reached that status through their control and use of energy. By the application of energy, the conversion of materials into commodities and the performance of services far beyond the capabilities of any single individual are made possible. Energy consumption goes hand-in-hand with industrial production and with increases in personal wealth. In general, the greater the level of energy consumption, the higher the gross national income per capita. Further, the application of energy can overcome deficiencies in the material world that humans exploit. High-quality iron ore may be depleted, but by massive applications of energy, the iron contained in rocks of very low iron content, such as taconite, can be extracted and concentrated for industrial uses.

Because of the association of energy and economic development, a basic disparity between societies is made clear. Countries that can afford high levels of energy consumption through production or purchase continue to expand their economies and to increase their levels of living. Those without access to energy, or those unable to afford it, see the gap between their economic prospects and those of the developed states growing ever greater.

Except for the brief and localized importance of waterpower at the outset of the Industrial Revolution, modern economic advancement has been heavily dependent on the *mineral fuels*: coal, petroleum, and natural gas. Also known as *fossil fuels*, these non-renewable energy sources represent the capture of the sun's energy by plants and animals in earlier geologic time and its storage in the form of hydrocarbon compounds in sedimentary rocks within the earth's crust.

Coal was the earliest in importance and is still the most plentiful of the mineral fuels. As the first of the major industrial energy sources, coal deposits—as we shall see in Chapter 10—were formerly very important in attracting manufacturing and urbanization in industrializing countries. Although coal is a nonrenewable resource, world supplies are so great—on the order of 10,000 billion (10^{13}) tonnes—that its resource life expectancy is measured in centuries, not in the much shorter spans usually cited for oil and natural gas. Worldwide, the most extensive deposits are concentrated in the industrialized middle latitudes of the Northern Hemisphere (Table 9.1). Two countries, China and the United States, accounted for over 55% of total world coal output in 2003; industrializing China alone yielded one-third of world production. Russia and Germany, both with large domestic reserves, together produced only 7%.

Coal is not a resource of constant quality, varying in *rank* (a measure—from lignite to anthracite—of increasing carbon content and fuel quality) and *grade* (a measure of its waste material content, particularly ash and sulphur). The value of a coal deposit depends on these measures and on its accessibility, which is a function of the thickness, depth, and continuity of the coal seam. Much coal can be mined relatively cheaply by open-pit (surface) techniques, in which huge shovels strip off surface material and remove the exposed coal (see Figure 9.35). Much coal, however, is available only by expensive and more dangerous shaft mining, as in Appalachia and most of Europe. In spite of their generally lower heating value, some North American coals are attractive because of their low sulphur content. They do, however, require expensive

FIGURE 9.35 About 400 square kilometres (some 150 sq mi) of land surface in the United States are lost each year to the strip-mining of coal and other minerals; far more is chewed up worldwide. On flat or rolling terrain, strip-mining leaves a landscape of parallel ridges and trenches, the result of stripping away the unwanted surface material. That material—*overburden*—taken from one trench to reach the underlying mineral is placed in an adjacent one, leaving the wavelike terrain shown here. Besides altering the topography, strip-mining interrupts surface and subsurface drainage patterns, destroys vegetation, and places sterile and frequently highly acidic subsoil and rock on top of the new ground surface. Current law is not always successful in requiring stripped areas to be returned to their original contours.

transportation to market or high-cost transmission lines if they are used to generate electricity for distant consumers (Figure 9.36).

Petroleum, first extracted commercially in the 1860s in both North America and Azerbaijan, became a major power source and a primary component of the extractive industries only early in the 20th century. The rapidity of its adoption as both a favoured energy resource and a raw material important in a number of industries from plastics to fertilizers, along with the limited size and the speed of depletion of known and probable reserves, promise that petroleum cannot continually retain its present position of importance in the energy budget of countries. No one has more than a vague notion of how much oil (or natural gas) remains in the world or how long it will last. Optimistic year 2004 estimates were that world production of conventional (easily extracted) oil will peak about 2016 and decline after that date. The U.S. Geological Survey, more optimistic still, projects that world production will peak around 2040: still others suggest that the world has already reached 'peak oil production' and that increasing demand, coupled with decreasing supplies, will wreak global economic havoc. Industry analysts tend to agree that some 95% of the world's major oil reserves have been found, and that locating the remaining 5% will be expensive and time consuming (Brown 2006). Estimates that demand for global oil consumption will increase by half over the next twenty years, assuming oil production can meet such demands, means prices will rise considerably.

Others are convinced that price volatility marked by the sharp run-up in oil prices since late 2004, carbon dioxide emissions concerns, and the steady drop in price of solar and other alternative energy sources, will reduce oil demand long before price and supply become issues.

Petroleum is among the most unevenly distributed of the major resources, and Canada is among those fortunate to possess substantial deposits. Seventy-five percent of proved reserves are concentrated in just seven countries, and 82% in only 10. Iran and the Arab states of the Middle East alone control nearly two-thirds of the world total (Table 9.1). The Alberta oil sands deposits in Canada are second only to the oil reserves of Saudi Arabia. Some 140,800 square kilometres (54,350 sq m) of northeastern Alberta contain bitumen—thick, solidified oil that liquefies with heat. Estimates suggest that in 2005 oil sands production accounted for one-half of Canada's total crude oil output and 10% of North American production (Alberta Department of Energy, 2006). Newfoundland is also fortunate to possess an estimated 2.75 billion barrels of oil in the Hibernia oil fields, situated 350 kilometres (218 miles) southeast of St. John's under 90 metres (295 feet) of water. Canadian oil production is only likely to increase as the industry and oil demand grows.

FIGURE 9.36 Long-distance transportation to eastern markets adds significantly to the cost of the low-sulphur western coal useful in meeting government environmental protection standards. To minimize these costs, unit trains carrying only coal engage in a continuous shuttle movement between western strip mines and eastern utility companies.

TABLE 9.1
Proved Petroleum, Natural Gas, and Coal Reserves, January 1, 2004

	SHARE OF WORLD TOTAL PETROLEUM (%)	SHARE OF WORLD TOTAL NATURAL GAS (%)	SHARE OF WORLD TOTAL COAL (%)
North America[a]	5.5	4.2	26.2
Europe	1.7	3.5	11.8
Former Soviet Union	7.5	31.9	23.9
of which: Russian Federation	6.0	26.7	15.9
Others	1.5	5.2	8.0
Central and South America	8.9	4.1	2.2
Africa	8.9	7.8	5.6
Middle East[b]	63.3	40.8	0.2
Australia/New Zealand	0.4	1.4	8.4
Japan	—	—	0.1
China	2.1	1.0	11.6
Other Asia Pacific	1.7	5.3	10.0
Total World	100.0	100.0	100.0
of which OPEC[c]	76.9	49.8	NA

[a] Includes Canada, Mexico, U.S.A.
[b] Incl udes Arabian Peninsula, Iran, Iraq, Israel, Jordan, Lebanon, Syria.
[c] OPEC: Organization of Petroleum Exporting Countries. Member nations are, by world region:
    South America: Venezuela
    Middle East: Iran, Iraq, Kuwait, Qatar, Saudi Arabia, United Arab Emirates (Abu Dhabi, Dubai, Ras-al-Khaimah, and Sharjah)
    North Africa: Algeria, Libya
    West Africa: Nigeria
    Asia Pacific: Indonesia

Source: BP Statistical Review of World Energy (2004).

A Costly Habit

The United States is a crude oil junkie, dependent on daily fixes of petroleum. On average, America in 2003 consumed 18.3 million barrels per day. That was the equivalent of 9.8 litres (2.6 U.S. gallons) per person per day, or nearly 3,786 litres (1000 U.S. gallons) per person per year. What are some of the implications of this dependence? Consider the data in the table.

Notice the imbalance between production and consumption for the United States. In contrast to its hemispheric neighbours, Canada and Mexico, the United States consumes far more oil than it produces. At 2003 rates of consumption, assuming no imports, and barring new discoveries or increased recovery rates from existing fields, the proved reserves would meet domestic demand for less than five years. Americans continue to drive their cars, and their manufacturing plants continue to turn out a wide range of petroleum-based products, only because the country imports between 11 and 12 million barrels a day. That is, the United States relies on foreign sources to meet more than 60% of its crude-oil needs.

American dependence on imports should ease, and U.S. proved reserves increase significantly as deepwater fields in the Gulf of Mexico are tapped. They are estimated to hold about 15 billion barrels of oil, considerably more oil than the giant Prudhoe Bay fields in Alaska, which are currently among

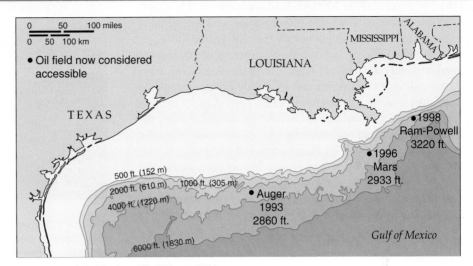

Source: PB Statistical Review of World Energy, *2004.*

the largest sources of domestic oil. The Gulf fields lie beyond the continental shelf and until recently were considered too deep—deeper than 456 metres (1500 feet)—to reach economically. New deep and lateral drilling techniques, coupled with vastly enhanced computerized seismic mapping to reveal geologic structures at great depth and underneath thick salt deposits, have improved discovery and recovery prospects for Gulf and other oil fields.

Several petroleum companies have built oil production platforms anchored 0.8 kilometre

(0.5 mile) or more below the surface of the water. One company, Shell Oil, has produced from two of these platforms in its Auger and Mars fields since the early and mid-1990s. Two additional fields—Ram-Powell and Ursa—began producing in the late 1990s. Unlike oil rigs in shallower water, which are rigid towers built on fixed platforms attached to the sea bottom, the new platforms float on the surface, tethered by steel tendons to enormous anchors. Each platform cost between $1 billion and $2 billion, reflecting the high price of dependence on oil.

COUNTRY	2003 PROVED RESERVES (BILLION BARRELS)	2003 PRODUCTION (BILLION BBLS)	2003 CONSUMPTION (BILLION BBLS)
United States	30.7	2.5	6.7
Canada	16.9	1.0	.7
Mexico	16.0	1.4	.6

Table source: BP Statistical Review of World Energy, 2004.

The distribution of petroleum supplies differs markedly from that of the coal deposits on which the urban-industrial markets developed, but the substitution of petroleum for coal did little to alter earlier patterns of manufacturing and population concentration. Because oil is easier and cheaper to transport than coal, it was moved in enormous volumes to the existing centres of consumption via intricate and extensive national and international systems of transportation, a textbook example of spatial interaction, complementarity, and transferability (see Chapter 3 and Figure 3.6).

The uninterrupted international flow of oil is particularly vital to the economic health of Canada and the United States, and such other advanced industrial economies as those of Europe and Japan (see "A Costly Habit"). That dependence on imported oil gives the oil-exporting states tremendous power, as reflected in the periodic oil "shocks" that reflect the supply and selling-price control exerted by the Organization of Petroleum Exporting Countries (OPEC). Their expressions can be worldwide recessions and large net trade deficits for some importers, and a reorientation of international monetary wealth.

Natural gas has been called the nearly perfect energy resource. It is a highly efficient, versatile fuel that requires little processing and is environmentally benign. Geologists estimate that world recoverable gas reserves are sufficient to last to near the last third of the century at 2000 levels of consumption. *Ultimately recoverable reserves*, those that may be found and recovered at very much higher prices, might last another 200 years.

As we saw for coal and petroleum, reserves of natural gas are very unevenly distributed (Table 9.1). In the case of gas, however, inequalities of supply are not so readily accommodated by massive international movements. Like oil, natural gas flows easily and cheaply by pipeline, but unlike petroleum it does not move freely in international trade by sea. Transoceanic shipment involves costly equipment for liquefaction and for special vessels to contain the liquid under appropriate temperature conditions. Where the fuel can be moved, even internationally, by pipeline, its consumption has increased dramatically. For the world as a whole, gas consumption rose more than 60% between 1974 and 2002, to almost 25% of global energy consumption.

Trade in Primary Products

International trade expanded eleven-fold between 1980 and 2004 to account for about 20% of all economic activity, though the sluggish world economy through 2003 temporarily slowed that growth. Primary commodities—agricultural goods, minerals, and fuels—made up one-quarter of the total dollar value of that international trade. In the past, the world distribution of supply and demand for those items in general resulted in an understandable pattern of commodity flow: from raw material producers located within less developed countries to processors, manufacturers, and consumers of the more developed ones (Figure 9.37). The reverse flow carried manufactured goods processed in the industrialized states back to the developing countries. That two-way trade presumably benefited the developed states by providing access to a continuing supply of industrial raw materials and foodstuffs not available domestically, and gave less developed countries needed capital to invest in their own development or to expend on the importation of manufactured goods, food supplies, or commodities—such as petroleum—they did not themselves produce.

By the end of the century, however, world trade flows and export patterns of the emerging economies were radically changing. Raw materials greatly decreased, and manufactured goods correspondingly increased in the export flows from developing states as a group. In 1992, non-manufactured (unprocessed) goods accounted for 60% of their exports; a decade later, that share had been cut in half, and in a reversal, manufactured goods made up 60% of the export flows from the developing to the industrialized world. Even with that overall decline in raw material exports, however, trade in unprocessed goods remains dominant in the economic well-being of many of the world's poorer economies. Increasingly, the terms of the traditional trade flows on which they depend have been criticized as unequal and damaging to commodity-exporting countries.

Commodity prices are volatile; they may rise sharply in periods of product shortage or international economic growth.

FIGURE 9.37 Sugar being loaded for export at the port of Cebu in the Philippines. Much of the developing world depends on exports of mineral and agricultural products to the developed economies for the major portion of its income. Fluctuations in market demand and price of some of those commodities can have serious and unexpected consequences.

During much of the 1980s and 1990s, however, commodity price movements were downward, to the great detriment of material-exporting economies. Prices for agricultural raw materials, for example, dropped by 30% between 1975 and 2000, and those for metals and minerals decreased by almost 40%. Such price declines cut deeply into the export earnings of many emerging economies. Many of those same economies, however, benefited from the sudden increase—beginning in early 2002—in world price levels for fuels, metals, and other minerals, and for basic food and feed commodities. Commodity prices increased 27% in 2004 alone.

Whatever the current world prices of raw materials may be, raw material exporting states as a group have long expressed resentment at what they perceive as commodity price manipulation by rich countries and corporations to ensure low-cost supplies. Although collusive price-fixing has not been demonstrated, other price-depressing agencies are evident. Technology, for example, has provided industries in advanced countries with a vast array of materials that now can and do substitute for the ores and metals produced by developing states. Glass fibres replace copper wire in telecommunication applications; synthetic rubber replaces natural rubber; glass and carbon fibres provide the raw material for rods, tubes, sheet panels, and other products superior in performance and strength to the metals they replace; and a vast and enlarging array of plastics become the accepted raw materials for commodities and uses for which natural rivals are not even considered. That is, even as the world industrial economy expands, demands and prices for traditional raw materials remain depressed.

Whereas prices paid for developing country commodities tend to be low, prices charged for the manufactured goods offered in exchange by the developed countries tend to be high. To capture processing and manufacturing profits for themselves, some developing states have placed restrictions on the export of unprocessed commodities. Malaysia, the Philippines, and Cameroon, for example, have limited the export of logs in favour of increased domestic processing of sawlogs and exports of lumber. Some developing countries have also encouraged domestic manufacturing to reduce imports and to diversify their exports. Frequently, however, such exports meet with tariffs and quotas protecting the home markets of the industrialized states.

Many developing regions heavily dependent on commodity sales saw their share of global trade fall materially between 1970 and the early 21st century: sub-Saharan Africa from 3.8% to 1%, Latin America from 5.6% to 3.3%, and the least developed states as a group from 0.8% to 0.4%. Those relative declines are understandable in the light of greatly expanding international trade in manufactured goods from China, Korea, Mexico, and other rapidly industrializing states and from the expansion of trade in both manufactured goods and primary products between the industrialized countries themselves within newly established regional free-trade zones. For example, the developed countries acquire some three-quarters by value of their agricultural imports, and 70% of their industrial raw materials from one another, diminishing the prospects for developing country exports.

In 1964, in reaction to the whole range of perceived trade inequities, developing states promoted the establishment of the United Nations Conference on Trade and Development (UNCTAD). Its central constituency—the "Group of 77," expanded by 2004 to 135 developing states—continues to press for a new world economic order based in part on an increase in the prices and values of exports from developing countries, a system of import preferences for their manufactured goods, and a restructuring of international cooperation to stress trade promotion and recognition of the special needs of poor countries. The Word Trade Organization, established in 1995, was designed in part to reduce trade barriers and inequities.

It has, however, been judged by its detractors as ineffective on issues of importance to developing countries. Chief among the complaints is the continuing failure of the industrial countries significantly (or at all) to reduce protections for their own agricultural and mineral industries, though in the 2004 world trade negotiations, the advanced states promised the eventual elimination of all their domestic agricultural subsidies, the scrapping of their export subsidies, and the reduction or elimination of some or all of the protested trade barriers. The World Bank has calculated, for example, that agricultural trade barriers and subsidies in rich countries have reduced incomes in developing countries by at least $20 billion a year. Despite early 21st century progress, solutions are yet to be achieved to debated questions of the fair treatment of international trade in primary products.

Want to Learn More?

Fishing, Farming and Forestry Issues

Canada's Only Land-Based Salmon Farm
How are fish raised out of water?
http://www.canadiangeographic.ca
/Magazine/so04/indepth/portrait.asp

Canada's Seal Hunt
How do other countries view Canada's annual seal hunt?
http://www.hsus.org/index-seals.html

The Problems for Family Farms
CBC television has several news bites about the problems facing family farms available for viewing.
http://archives.cbc.ca/IDD-1-69-1720/
life_society/family_farm/

Managing Canada's Commercial Forests
Review the development activities of Canada's forests and their environmental impacts.
http://www.globalforestwatch.ca/tenure/
forest_tenure_2003.pdf

Canada–US Lumber Trade Disputes
Review the history and key issues of these high profile resource disputes.
http://www.for.gov.bc.ca/HET/Softwood/
disputes.htm

Mining Matters

Mining and Women
The impact of mining on the environment and its effect on women's health is a national and international matter garnering increased attention. Explore several articles on this issue at the website of Mining Watch Canada.
http://www.miningwatch.ca/index.php?/
Women

Canada's First Diamond Mine
The Ekati Diamond Mine in the Northwest Territories is Canada's first surface and underground diamond mine. Explore that operation and Canada's diamond mining

industry in general at the following sites.
http://www.nrcan.gc.ca/ms/diam/
index_e.htm
http://noconflictdiamonds.com/index.
php?tag=conflict-free-diamonds

Alternative Energies to Oil

Zero Emissions No Noise Cars
A Canadian company has developed an alternative to oil-dependent automobiles. Curious?
http://www.feelgoodcars.com/index.html

Green Energies
For the latest news on alternative energies and technologies visit *Green Energy News*.
http://www.nrglink.com/

Energy Solutions and Technologies
Natural Resources Canada provides information and advice on how individuals can use energy efficiently.
http://www.canren.gc.ca/default_en.asp

Summary

How people earn their living and how the diversified resources of the earth are employed by different peoples and cultures are of fundamental concern in human geography. The economic activities that support us and our society are constant preoccupations that colour our perception of the world and its opportunities. At the same time, the totality of our culture—technology, religion, customary behaviour—and the circumstances of our natural environment influence the economic choices we discern and the livelihood decisions we make.

In seeking spatial and activity regularities in the nearly infinite diversity of human economic activity, it is useful to generalize about systems of economic organization and control and about classes of productive effort and labour specialization. We can observe, for example, that, broadly speaking, there are three types of economic systems: subsistence, commercial, and planned. The first is concerned with production for the immediate consumption of individual producers and family members. In the second, economic decisions ideally respond to impersonal market forces and reasoned assessments of monetary gain. In the third, at least some non-monetary social rather than personal goals influence production decisions. The three system forms are not mutually exclusive; all societies contain some intermixture of features of at least two of the three pure types, and some economies have elements of all three. Recognition of each type's respective features and controls, however, helps us to understand the forces shaping economic decisions and patterns in different cultural and regional settings.

Our search for regularities is furthered by a classification of economic activities according to the stages of production and the degree of specialization they represent. We can, for example, decide all productive activity is arranged along a continuum of increasing technology, labour specialization, value of product, or sophistication of service. With that assumption, we can divide our continuum into primary activities (food and raw material production), secondary production (processing and manufacturing), tertiary activities (distribution and general professional and personal service), and the quaternary and quinary activities (administrative, informational, and technical specializations) that mark highly advanced societies of either planned or commercial systems.

Agriculture, the most extensively practised of the primary industries, is part of the spatial economy of both subsistence and advanced societies. In the first instance—whether it takes the form of extensive or intensive, shifting or sedentary production—it is responsive to the immediate consumption needs of the producer group and reflective of the environmental conditions under which it is practised. Agriculture in advanced economies involves the application of capital and technology to the productive enterprises; as one sector of an integrated economy, it is responsive to consumption requirements expressed through free or controlled markets. Its spatial expression reflects assessments of profitability and the dictates of social and economic planning.

Agriculture, fishing, forestry, trapping, and the extractive industries are closely tied to the uneven distribution of earth resources. Their spatial patterns reflect those resource potentials, but they are influenced as well by the integration of all societies and economies through the medium of international trade and mutual dependence. The flows of primary products and of manufactured goods suggest the hierarchy of production, marketing, and service activities, which will be the subject of Chapter 10.

KEY WORDS

FOR REVIEW

1. What are the distinguishing characteristics of the economic systems labeled *subsistence*, *commercial*, and *planned*? Are they mutually exclusive, or can they coexist within a single political unit?

2. What are the ecological consequences of the different forms of *extensive subsistence* land use? In what world regions are such systems found? What, in your opinion, are the prospects for these land uses and for the way of life they embody?

3. How is *intensive subsistence* agriculture distinguished from *extensive subsistence* cropping? Why, in your opinion, have such different land use forms developed in separate areas of the warm, moist tropics?

4. Briefly summarize the assumptions and dictates of von Thünen's agricultural model. How might the land use patterns predicted by the model be altered by an increase in the market price of a single crop? A decrease in the transportation costs of one crop but not of all crops?

5. What is the basic distinction between a *renewable* and a *nonrenewable* resource? What are the long term environmental and economic consequences of each?

6. What economic and ecological problems can you cite that do or might affect the viability and productivity of the *gathering industries* of forestry and fishing? What is meant by the *tragedy of the commons*? How is that concept related to the problems you discerned?

7. Why have the mineral fuels been so important in economic development? What are the mineral fuels, and what are the prospects for their continued availability? What economic and social consequences might you anticipate if the price of mineral fuels should double? If it should be cut in half?

FOCUS FOLLOW-UP

1. **How are economic activities and national economies classified?** pp. 297–302.

The innumerable economically productive activities of humans are influenced by regionally varying environmental, cultural, technological, political, and market conditions. Understanding the world's work is simplified by thinking of economic activity as arranged along a continuum of increasing complexity of product or service and increasing distance from nature. Primary industries (activities) harvest or extract something from the earth. Secondary industries change the form of those harvested items. Tertiary activities render services, and quaternary efforts reflect professional or managerial talents. Those activity stages are carried out within national economies grouped as subsistence, commercial, or planned.

2. **What are the types and prospects of subsistence agriculture?** pp. 302–311.

Subsistence farming—food production primarily or exclusively for the producers' family needs—still remains the predominant occupation of humans on a worldwide basis. Nomadic herding and shifting ("swidden") cultivation are extensive subsistence systems. Intensive subsistence farming involves large inputs of labour and fertilizer on small plots of land. Both rural and urban subsistence efforts are increasingly marked by some production for market; they have also benefited from Green Revolution crop improvements.

3. **What characterizes commercial agriculture, and what are its controls and special forms?** pp. 311–320.

The modern integrated world of exchange and trade increasingly implies farming efforts that reflect broader market requirements, not purely local or family needs. Commercial agriculture is characterized by specialization, off-farm sale, and interdependence of farmers and buyers linked through complex markets. The von Thünen model of agricultural location suggests that intensive forms of commercial farming—fruits, vegetables, dairy products, and livestock-grain production—should be located close to markets. More extensive commercial agriculture, including large-scale wheat farms and livestock ranches, are by model and reality at more distant locations. Special crops may by value or uniqueness defy these spatial determinants; Mediterranean and plantation agriculture are examples.

4. **What are the special characteristics and problems of non-agricultural primary industries?** pp. 320–332.

The "gathering" industries of fishing, forestry, and trapping, and the "extractive" industries of mining and quarrying, involve the direct exploitation of areally variable natural resources. Resources are natural materials that humans perceive as necessary and useful. They may be renewable—replenished—by natural processes or non-renewable once extracted and used. Overexploitation can exceed the maximum sustainable yield of fisheries and forests and eventually destroy the resource. Such destruction is assured in the case of non-renewable minerals and fuels when their total or economically feasible supply is exhausted.

5. **What is the status and nature of world trade in primary products?** pp. 332–333.

The primary commodities of agricultural goods, fish, forest products, furs, minerals, and fuels account for nearly one-third of the dollar value of international trade. Traditional exchange flows of raw materials outward from developing states that then imported manufactured goods from advanced economies have changed in recent years. Increasingly, the share of manufactured goods in developing world exports is growing, and dependence on income from raw material sales is dropping. However, material-exporting states argue that current international trade agreements are unfavourable to exporters of agricultural products and ores and minerals.

ONLINE LEARNING CENTRE

The World Wide Web has a tremendous number and variety of sites pertaining to geography. To access Web sites, Internet exercises, self-quizzes, videos, and additional study tools relevant to this chapter's content, visit the *Human Geography* Online Learning Centre at **www.mcgrawhill.ca/olc/fellmann.**

LIVELIHOOD AND ECONOMY: FROM BLUE COLLAR TO GOLD COLLAR

Aims

- To explain and illustrate the manufacturing sector and its spatial patterns
- To introduce factors and theories of manufacturing locational decision-making
- To explain and illustrate the service sectors and their spatial patterns
- To illustrate the global scale of the world economy

Some specific considerations for review:

1. The principles or considerations guiding manufacturing locational decisions, pp. 339–347, and how those considerations have been selectively incorporated in different industrial location theories, pp. 347–349.

2. How other non-theoretical considerations including transnational ownership affect, distort, or reinforce classical locational controls, pp. 349–355.

3. The older world patterns of manufacturing regions, pp. 356–362, and how they have been affected by the special locational characteristics of high-tech industries, pp. 362–365.

4. Identify the characteristics of tertiary, quaternary, and quinary service activities, pp. 365–370, and how their recent development impacts world economic patterns and international trade, pp. 370–372.

When Italian explorer John Cabot first encountered the rocky shores of Newfoundland in 1497, the cod were so plentiful that they virtually blocked his ship. For the next 400 years, the vast fish stocks of the northwest Atlantic were a resource harvested by fishers from North America, Europe, and as far away as Asia. The economies and much of the regional cultures of Canada's Maritime Provinces, and Newfoundland and Labrador, were premised on fishing and fish processing. Today, Cabot's ship would sail unhindered through those same waters: fish stocks have been seriously depleted. Some 250,000 tonnes or more of "northern cod" had been harvested annually for decades, and yet by 1995 estimates placed the entire northern cod population at just 1700 tonnes.

In 1992, the Canadian government was forced to take drastic steps and close the cod fishery. Both fishers and fish plant processors in the primary and secondary economic sectors, respectively, were devastated by unemployment: the region suffered the ensuing economic ripple effects throughout their communities. In response, the federal government provided nearly $1 billion in social welfare payments and retraining to those affected. Dependence on the cod industry has dropped considerably since then, with most cod fishers and plant employees primarily catching and processing other species, particularly shellfish, but the hard times have persisted.

Fish processing plants have continued to close in the early 21st century, others have been plagued by labour disputes, and unemployment: the need for government relief remains. In 2003 another $50 million was directed toward fishers, plant workers, and communities affected by the closure of still more fisheries. Some of those who remain employed are subject to wage rollbacks as plant managers seek ways of reducing operating costs, resulting in picket lines and lockouts at processing plants. As of 2006, cod stocks had yet to recover sufficiently such that cod fishing could commence again.

The collapse of the cod industry has consequences well beyond the fishing sector, affecting other parts of the economy and all Canadians. As unemployment numbers rise and incomes drop on the Atlantic coast, spending drops, retail and service sectors slow, and federal government aid—provided through taxes collected across the country—is needed. Historically speaking, industries come and go, and economies boom and bust, but this is little consolation to those for whom fishing and fish related businesses have provided livelihoods for generations.

The transformation of the Atlantic fisheries symbolizes the ever-changing nature and structure of the North American space economy. The smokestack industries of the 19th and early 20th centuries have also declined, replaced by research park industries, shopping centres, and office building complexes that in their turn experience variable prosperity and adversity. The continent's economic landscape and employment structure are inconstant at best (Figure 10.1). And North America is not alone. Change is the ever-present condition of contemporary economies, whether of the already industrialized, advanced countries or

(a) 1922

(b) 2005

FIGURE 10.1 (*a*) Vancouver's Granville Island was originally called *Industrial Island* when it was first developed as a manufacturing site in 1915. Factories produced goods and machinery for the construction, forestry, mining, and shipping sectors. With the decline of manufacturing and the rise in service industries—indicative of postindustrial economies such as Canada's—the island has been restructured. (*b*) Since the 1970s, it has become a site of parkland, housing, numerous arts and crafts studios, boutiques, and a farmer's market. It is now a highly successful public place and tourist destination.

of those newly developing in an integrated world marketplace. Resources are exploited and exhausted; markets grow and decline; patterns of economic advantage, of labour skills, of industrial investment and productive capacity undergo alteration as countries and regions differentially develop, prosper, or experience reversals and decline. Such changes have profound impact on the spatial structure and processes of economic activity.

Components of the Space Economy

All human activity has spatial expression. In the economic sphere, we recognize regions of industrial concentration, areas of employment and functional specialization, and specific factory sites and store locations. As geographers, we assume an underlying logic to those spatial economic patterns and seek, through observation and theory, an understanding and explanation of them. In a very preliminary fashion, that understanding has begun through classification of economic activity into *primary*, *secondary*, *tertiary*, *quaternary*, and *quinary* industries. (Remember, the term *industry* may be used in the narrow sense of type of manufacturing activity or enterprise, as well as in the broader meaning of category of economic orientation.)

Primary industries, you will recall from Chapter 9, are tied to the natural resources they gather or exploit. Location is therefore predetermined by the distribution of minerals, fuels, forests, fisheries, or natural conditions affecting agriculture and herding. The later (beyond primary) stages of economic activity, however, are increasingly divorced from the conditions of the physical environment. In them, processing, distribution, communication, and management permit enterprise location in response to cultural and economic rather than physical influences. They are movable, rather than spatially tied activities. The locational decisions made and the economic patternings that result differ with the type or level of economic activity in question. Secondary industries involved in material processing and goods production have different spatial constraints than do the retailing activities of tertiary industry or the research parks or office complexes of quaternary and quinary activities. At every industrial or activity level, however, it is assumed that a recurring set of economic controls may be identified.

Concepts and Controls

The controls that are assumed to exist are rooted in observations about human spatial behaviour in general and economic behaviour in particular. We have already explored some of those assumptions in earlier discussions. We noted, for example, that the intensity of spatial interaction decreases with increasing separation of places—distance decay, we called it (Chapter 3). We observed the importance of complementarity and transferability in the assessment of resource value and trade potential. Von Thünen's model of agricultural land use, you will recall, was rooted in conjectures about transportation cost and land value relationships (Chapter 9).

Such simplifying assumptions help us to understand a presumed common set of controls and motivations guiding human economic behaviour. We assume, for example, that people are *economically rational*; that is, given the information at their disposal, they make locational, production, or purchasing decisions in light of a perception of what is most cost-effective and advantageous. Behavioural research concludes that while people are not truly rational in the theoretical economic sense, neither are they insane

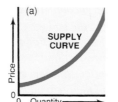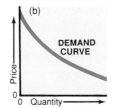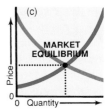

FIGURE 10.2 Supply, demand, and market equilibrium. The regulating mechanism of the market may be visualized graphically. (*a*) The *supply curve* tells us that as the price of a good increases, more of that good will be made available for sale. Countering any tendency for prices to rise to infinity is the market reality that the higher the price, the smaller the demand as potential customers find other purchases or products more cost-effective. (*b*) The *demand curve* shows how the market will expand as prices are lowered and goods are made more affordable and attractive to more customers. (*c*) *Market equilibrium* is marked by the point of intersection of the supply and demand curves and determines the price of goods, the total demand, and the quantity bought and sold.

or incompetent. The acceptance of rationality, they conclude, is proper if one also accepts the reality that individuals respond to behavioural traits—envy, rivalry, impulsiveness, forgetfulness of past mistakes, positive wishful thinking, and the like—at odds with purely rational actions or decisions. With those appreciations of behavioural human nature, economic rationality is still the accepted theoretical starting point.

From the standpoint of producers or sellers of goods or services, it is assumed each is intent on *maximizing profit*. To reach that objective, each may consider a host of production and marketing costs, and political, competitive, and other limiting factors—and, perhaps, respond to individual behavioural quirks—but the ultimate goal of profit-seeking remains clear. Finally, we assume that in commercial economies, the best measure of the correctness of economic decisions is afforded by the *market mechanism*.

At root, that market control mechanism is measured by *price*— the price of land (rent), of labour (wages), of a university program (tuition), or of goods at the store. In turn, price is seen as a function of *supply* and *demand*. In large, complex economies where there are many producers, sellers, and buyers, and many alternative products competing in the marketplace, price is the neutral measure of comparative value and profitability. The theoretical relationship among supply, demand, and price is simple. If demand for a good or service exceeds its available supply, scarcity will drive up the price it can command in the marketplace. That increased price will enhance the profitability of the sale, which will encourage existing producers to increase output or induce new producers or sellers to enter the market (Figure 10.2a). That is, *the higher the price of a good, the more of it will be offered in the market.*

When the price is very high, however, relatively few people are inclined to buy. To dispose of their increased output, old and new producers of the commodity are forced to reduce prices to enlarge the market by making the good affordable to a larger number of potential customers. That is, *at a lower price, more of a good will be purchased* (Figure 10.2b). If the price falls too low, production or sale becomes unprofitable, and inefficient suppliers are forced out of business, reducing supply. **Market equilibrium** is marked by the price at which supply equals demand, satisfying the needs of consumers and the profit motivation of suppliers (Figure 10.2c).

These and other modifying concepts and controls of the economist treat supply, demand, and price as if all production, buying, and selling occurred at a single point. But as geographers, we know that human activities have specific locational settings and that neither people, nor resources, nor opportunities are uniformly distributed over the earth. We appreciate that the place or places of production may differ from the locations of demand. We understand that there are spatial relations and interactions based on supply, demand, and equilibrium price. We realize there is a *geography* of supply, a *geography* of demand, and a *geography* of cost.

Secondary Activities: Manufacturing

If we assume free markets, rational producers, and informed consumers exist, then locational production and marketing decisions should be based on careful consideration of spatially differing costs and opportunities. In the case of primary industries—those tied to the environment—points or areas of possible production are naturally fixed. The only decision is whether or not to exploit known resources. In the instance of secondary and higher levels of economic activity, however, the locational decision is more complex. It involves the weighing of the locational "pulls" of a number of cost considerations and profit prospects.

On the *demand* side, the distribution of populations and of purchasing power defines general areas of marketing opportunities. The regional location of tertiary—sales and service—activities may be nearly as fixed as are primary industries, though specific site decisions are more complex. On the *supply* side, decision making for manufacturers involves a more intricate set of equations. Manufacturers must consider costs of raw materials, distance from them and from markets, wages of labour, outlays for fuel, capital availability and rates, and a host of other inputs to the production and distribution process. It is assumed that the nature and the spatial variability of those myriad costs are known and that rational location decisions leading to profit maximization are based on that knowledge. For market economies, both observation and theory tend to support that assumption.

Locational Decisions in Manufacturing

Secondary activities involve transforming raw materials into usable products, giving them *form utility*. Dominant among them is manufacturing in all of its aspects, from pouring iron and steel to stamping out plastic toys, assembling computer components, or sewing dresses. In every case, the common characteristics are the application of power and specialized labour to the production of standardized commodities in factory settings: in short, the characteristics of industrialization.

Manufacturing poses a different locational problem than does the gathering of primary commodities. It involves the assembly and the processing of inputs and the distribution of the output to other points, and therefore presents the question of where the processing should take place. The answer may require multiple spatial levels of consideration. The first is regional and addresses the comparative attractions for different types of industry of different sections of the country or even of different countries at the international scale. Later decision stages become more focused, localized, and specific to an individual enterprise. They involve assessment of the special production and marketing requirements of particular industrialists and of the degree to which those requirements can or will be met at different subregional scales—at the provincial, community, and individual site levels. That is, we can ask at one level why southeastern Canada–northeastern United States exerted an earlier pull on industry in general and, at other decision stages, why specific sites along the western shores of Lake Ontario, southwest of Toronto, were chosen by steel industries for their mills.

In framing responses, one needs to consider a wide range of industrial pulls and attractions and the modifying influence of a number of physical, political, economic, and cultural constraints. For a great many searches, two or several alternate locations would be equally satisfactory. In very practical financial terms, locational decisions at the state, community, and site levels may ultimately be based on the value of inducements that are offered by rival areas and agencies competing for the new or relocated manufacturing plant (see "Investment Competition and Questionable Incentives"). In both practice and theory, locational factors recognized and analyzed are complexly interrelated, change over time in their relative significance, and differ between industries and regions. But all of them are tied to *principles of location* that are assumed to operate under all economic systems, though to be determinant, perhaps, only in free market, or commercial, economies.

Principles of Location

The principles, or "ground rules," of location are simply stated.

1. Certain input costs of manufacturing are **spatially fixed costs**, that is, are relatively unaffected in their amount or relative importance no matter where the industry is located within a generalized regional or national setting. Wage rates set by national or areawide labour contracts are an example. Fixed costs have no implication for comparative locational advantage.

2. Other input costs of manufacturing are **spatially variable costs**; that is, they show significant differences from place to place in both their amount and their relative contribution to the total cost of manufacturing (Figure 10.3). These will influence locational choices.

3. The ultimate aim of the economic activity is *profit maximization*. In an economic environment of full and perfect competition, the profit objective is most likely to be achieved if the manufacturing enterprise is situated at the *least total cost* location. Under conditions of imperfect competition, considerations of sales and market may be more important than production costs in fixing "best" locations.

Geography and Public Policy

Investment Competition and Questionable Incentives

To promote economic growth and fuel both local and national economies, various levels of government compete among and between each other for businesses to locate within their political boundaries. Entire countries, provinces, states, counties, and cities encourage investors to locate in their areas. New businesses, be they managerial, retail, service, or manufacturing, mean new jobs, more income for workers, and more tax revenues for governments: the economy diversifies and grows. Like most any business, governments advertise to attract potential "customers," in this case, business investors. Potential investors are encouraged by the government of Halifax to "excel in Halifax Regional Municipality," Edmonton declares their city is "open for business," Manitoba "brings the entrepreneurial spirit to life," Prince Edward Island asserts that "doing business on P.E.I. has never been easier. . .or more rewarding?" and Canada announces to investors around the world that "They come, they see, they expand." Catchy slogans are merely the tip of the iceberg.

The real tool used to attract investors comes in the form of financial incentives. Businesses are more likely to locate wherever costs to conduct business are lowest, or at least competitive, relative to other potential locations. Financial advantages come in many forms, but the most prevalent involve tax breaks, grants, and loans. The government of Newfoundland and Labrador,

for example, provides numerous tax breaks if a new business meets certain criteria: creates and maintains at least 10 new jobs; generates annuals sales of $500,000; will not compete directly with an existing business; and other such stipulations. If these conditions are met, incentives and benefits are numerous: access to unserviced Crown land for $1.00; a 100% rebate on provincial corporate income tax, a 50% rebate on federal corporate tax, and a 100% rebate on municipal property, all for 10 years. Alberta boasts that they have business grants available through 57 different programs ranging in value from $1,500 to $500,000, and between $1,500 and $10 million worth of low or no-interest loans. In effect, governments compete and pay to create jobs, believing that the economic returns far outweigh the costs.

Not everyone is convinced that those investments are wise, however. A poll of Minnesotans showed a majority opposed the generous offer made by the state to Northwest Airlines. In the late 1980s, the governor of Indiana, a candidate for Kentucky's governorship, and the mayor of Flat Rock, Michigan, were all defeated by challengers who charged that too much had been spent in luring the Suburu-Isuzu, Toyota, and Mazda plants, respectively. Established businesses resent what often seems neglect of their interests in favour of spending their tax money on favours to newcomers. The U.S. Council for Urban Economic Development, surveying the escalating bidding wars in the U.S., has actively lobbied against incentives, and many academic observers in both Canada and the U.S. note that industrial attraction amounts

to a zero-sum game: unless the attracted newcomer is a foreign firm, whatever one province or state achieves in attracting an expanding domestic company comes at the expense of another part of the country.

Some doubt that inducements matter much, anyway. Although, sensibly, companies seeking new locations will shop around and solicit the lowest-cost, best deal possible, their site choices are apt to be determined by more realistic business considerations: access to labour, suppliers, and markets; transportation and utility costs; weather; the nature of the workforce; and overall costs of living. Only when two or more similarly attractive locations have essentially equal cost structures might such special inducements as tax reductions or abatements be determinants in a locational decision.

Questions to Consider

1. As citizen and taxpayer, do you think it is appropriate to spend public money to attract new employment to your province or community? If not, why not? If yes, what kinds of inducements and what total amount offered per job seem appropriate to you? What reasons support your opinion?

2. If you believe that "best locations" for the economy as a whole are those determined by pure location theory, what arguments would you propose to discourage locales and provinces from making financial offers designed to circumvent decisions clearly justified on abstract theoretical grounds?

---

4. Since among the totality of production costs some inputs are approximately the same irrespective of location, fixed costs are not of major importance in determining optimum, or least-cost, locations. Rather, the industrialist bases the locational search on the minimization of variable costs. The locational determinant is apt to be the cost that is both an important component of total costs and shows the greatest spatial variation.

5. Transportation charges—the costs of accumulating inputs and of distributing products—are highly variable costs. As such, they (rather than the commodity transported) may become the locational determinant, imparting an unmistakable

orientation—a term describing locational tendencies—to the plant siting decision.

6. Individual establishments rarely stand alone; they are part of integrated manufacturing sequences and environments in which *interdependence* increases as the complexity of industrial processes increases. The economies of structural and spatial interdependence may be decisive locational determinants for some industries. *Linkages* between firms may localize manufacturing in areas of industrial agglomeration where common resources—such as skilled labour—or multiple suppliers of product inputs—such as automobile component manufacturers—are found.

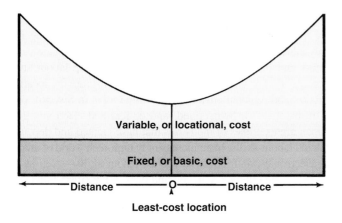

FIGURE 10.3 The spatial implications of fixed and variable costs.
Spatially fixed (or *basic*) costs represent the minimum price that must be paid at any location for the necessary inputs of production of a given item. Here, for simplicity, a single raw material is assumed and priced at its cheapest source. *Spatially variable* (*locational*) costs are the additional costs incurred at alternate locations in overcoming distance, attracting labour, purchasing the plant site, and so forth. In the example, only the transportation cost of the single material away from its cheapest (source) location is diagrammed to determine O, the optimal or least-cost location.

These principles are generalized statements about locational tendencies of industries. Their relative weight, of course, varies among industries and firms. Their significance also varies depending on the extent to which purely economic considerations—as opposed, say, to political or environmental constraints—dictate locational decisions.

Raw Materials

All manufactured goods have their origins in the processing of raw materials, but only a few industries at the early stages of the production cycle use raw materials directly from farms or mines. Most manufacturing is based on the further processing and shaping of materials already treated in some fashion by an earlier stage of manufacturing located elsewhere. In general, the more advanced the industrial economy of a nation, the smaller is the role played by truly *raw* materials in its economic structure.

For those industries in which unprocessed commodities are a primary input, however, the source and characteristics of the raw materials upon which they are based are important indeed. The quality, amount, or ease of mining or gathering of a resource may be a locational determinant if cost of raw material is the major variable, and multiple sources of the primary material are available. Raw materials may attract the industries that process them when they are bulky, undergo great weight loss in the processing, or are highly perishable. Copper smelting and iron ore beneficiation are examples of weight- (impurity-) reducing industries localized by their ore supplies (see pp. 326 to 328). Pulp, paper, and sawmills are, logically, found in areas within or accessible to timber. Lumber mills in British Columbia, meat

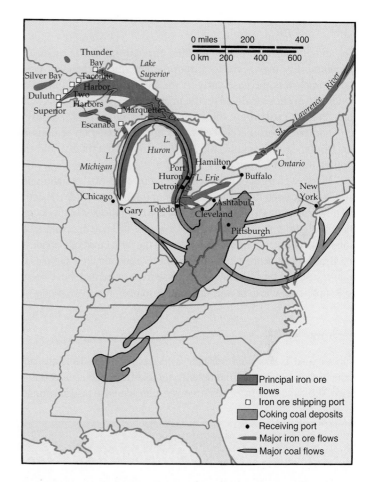

FIGURE 10.4 Material flows in the steel industry. When an industrial process requires the combination of several heavy or bulky ingredients, an intermediate point of assembly of materials is often a least-cost location. In the earlier 20th century, the iron and steel industry of the eastern United States showed this kind of localization—not at the source of any single input but where coking coal, iron ore, and limestone could be brought together at the lowest price.

packing in Alberta, and corn growing in Ontario, are different but comparable examples of raw **material orientation**. The reason is simple; it is cheaper and easier to transport to market a refined or stabilized product than one filled with waste material or subject to spoilage and loss.

Multiple raw materials might dictate an intermediate plant location. Least cost may be determined not by a single raw material input but by the spatially differing costs of accumulating several inputs. Steel mills at Gary, Indiana, or Hamilton, Ontario, for example, were not based on local raw material sources but on the minimization of the total cost of collecting at a point the necessary ore, coking coal, and fluxing material inputs for the production process (Figure 10.4). Steel mills along the U.S. East Coast—at Sparrows Point, Maryland, or the Fairless Works near Philadelphia—were localized where imported ores were unloaded from ocean carriers, avoiding expensive trans-shipment costs. In this latter avoidance, both the Great Lakes and the coastal locations are similar.

Power Supply

For some industries, power supplies that are immobile or of low transferability may serve to attract the activities dependent upon them. Such was the case early in the Industrial Revolution when water power sites localized textile mills and fuel (initially charcoal, later coking coal) drew the iron and steel industry. Metallurgical industries became concentrated in such coal-rich regions as the Midlands of England, the Ruhr district of Germany, and the Donets Basin of Ukraine.

Massive charges of electricity are required to extract aluminum from its processed raw material, *alumina* (aluminum oxide). Electrical power accounts for between 30% and 40% of the cost of producing the aluminum and is the major variable cost influencing plant location in the industry. The Kitimat plant on the west coast of Canada or the Bratsk plant near Lake Baikal in eastern Siberia are examples of industry placed far from raw material sources or market, but close to vast supplies of cheap power—in these instances, hydroelectricity.

Labour

Labour also is a spatial variable affecting location decisions and industrial development. Traditionally, three different considerations—price, skill, and amount of labour—were considered to be determinant singly or in combination. For many manufacturers today, an increasingly important consideration is *labour flexibility*, implying more highly educated workers able to apply themselves to a wide variety of tasks and functions. For some activities, a cheap labour supply is a necessity. For others, labour skills may constitute the locational attraction and regional advantage. Machine tools in Sweden, precision instruments in Switzerland, and optical and electronic goods in Japan are examples of industries that have created and depend on localized labour skills. In an increasingly high-tech world of automation, electronics, and industrial robots, labour skills—even at high unit costs—are often more in demand than an unskilled, uneducated workforce.

In some world areas, of course, labour of any skill level may be poorly distributed to satisfy the developmental objectives of government planners or private entrepreneurs (see "Global Employment Trends for Women"). In the former Soviet Union, for example, longstanding economic plans called for the fuller exploitation of the vast resources of sparsely populated Siberia, an area generally unattractive to a labour force more attuned to the milder climates and greater amenities of the settled European portion of the country. At the same time, labour surpluses were growing in Soviet Central Asia, where resources were few and rates of natural population increase were high, but whose Muslim populations resisted resettlement outside of their homeland areas.

Global Employment Trends for Women

More women are working than ever before, but they are also more likely than men to get low-productivity, low-paid, and vulnerable jobs, with no social protection, basic rights, or voice at work according to a new report by the *International Labour Office* (ILO). The number of employed women grew by almost 200 million over the last decade, to reach 1.2 billion in 2007 compared to 1.8 billion men. However, the number of unemployed women also grew from 70.2 to 81.6 million over the same period.

Women continue to enter the world's workforce in great numbers, but this progress must not obscure the glaring inequities that still exist in workplaces throughout the world (see Table 10.1). The workplace and the world of work are at the centre of global solutions to address gender equality and the advancement of women in society. By promoting decent work for women, we are empowering societies and advancing the cause of economic and social development for all.

The report shows that improvements in the status of women in labour markets throughout the world have not substantially narrowed gender gaps in the workplace. The share of women in vulnerable employment—either unpaid contributing family workers or piece-workers, rather than wage and salaried work—decreased from 56.1 to 51.7 percent since 1997. However the burden of vulnerability is still greater for women than men, especially in the world's poorest regions:

- Worldwide, the female unemployment rate stood at 6.4 percent compared to the male rate of 5.7 percent.

- Less than 70 women are economically active for every 100 men globally. Remaining outside of the labour force is often not a choice but an imposition. It is likely that women would opt for remunerated work outside the home if it became acceptable to do so.

- Over the past decade, the service sector has overtaken agriculture as the prime employer of women. In 2007, 36.1 percent of employed women worked in agriculture and 46.3 percent in services. In comparison, male sectoral shares were 34.0 per cent in agriculture and 40.4 per cent in services (see table below).

- More women are gaining access to education, but equality in education is still far from reality in some regions.

The report points out that for many women, moving away from vulnerable employment into wage and salaried work can be a major step toward economic freedom and self-determination. Access to labour markets and to decent and productive employment is crucial in the process of creating greater equality between men and women. Overall, the report found that policies to enhance women's chances to participate equally in labour markets are starting to pay off, but the sluggish pace of change means that disparities are still significant in most regions of the world. Society's ability to accept new economic roles for women, and the economy's ability to create decent jobs to accommodate them are the key prerequisites to improving labour market outcomes for women, as well as for economic development on the whole. Societies cannot afford to ignore the potential of female labour in reducing poverty, and need to search for innovative ways of lowering economic, social, and political barriers. Providing women an equal footing in the workplace is not just right, but smart.

TABLE 10.1

Male and Female Employment by Sector (as Share of Total Employment), 1997 and 2007

	EMPLOYMENT IN AGRICULTURE (%)		EMPLOYMENT IN INDUSTRY (%)		EMPLOYMENT IN SERVICES (%)	
Female	**1997**	**2007**	**1997**	**2007**	**1997**	**2007**
World	43.5	36.1	16.8	17.6	39.6	46.3
Developed Economies & European Union	5.3	3.2	16.7	12.5	78.1	84.3
Central & South-Eastern Europe (non-EU) & CIS	26.9	19.2	22.2	17.9	50.8	62.8
East Asia	51.9	41.0	22.8	25.5	25.3	33.5
South-East Asia & The Pacific	50.3	43.4	13.9	16.3	35.8	40.3
South Asia	74.0	60.5	11.2	18.4	14.7	21.1
Latin America & the Caribbean	14.6	10.7	13.6	14.5	71.9	74.8
Middle East	28.4	31.0	20.0	18.8	51.6	50.2
Sub-Saharan Africa	74.8	67.9	5.9	5.8	19.2	26.4
North Africa	31.2	32.6	19.1	15.2	49.7	52.2
Male						
World	40.0	34.0	24.0	25.6	36.1	40.4
Developed Economies & European Union	6.7	4.6	37.1	34.3	56.1	61.1
Central & South-Eastern Europe (non-EU) & CIS	27.0	19.8	33.2	32.6	39.8	47.6
East Asia	44.6	36.3	25.6	28.0	29.8	35.7
South-East Asia & The Pacific	47.7	44.3	19.4	21.0	32.9	34.7
South Asia	53.5	42.9	17.0	23.0	29.5	34.1
Latin America & the Caribbean	28.6	24.7	24.8	27.1	46.5	48.2
Middle East	19.6	12.5	27.2	28.0	53.3	59.4
Sub-Saharan Africa	70.0	62.4	10.4	12.4	19.6	25.2
North Africa	36.6	32.9	20.1	22.3	43.3	44.8

Source: http://www.oit.org/public/english/employment/strat/download/getw08.pdf.

Market

Goods are produced to supply a market demand. Therefore, the size, nature, and distribution of markets may be as important in industrial location decisions as are raw material, energy, labour, or other inputs. Market pull, like raw material attraction, is at root an expression of the cost of commodity movement. When the transportation charges for sending finished goods to market are a relatively high proportion of the total value of the good (or can be significantly reduced by proximity to market), then the attraction of location near to the consumer is obvious and **market orientation** results.

The consumer may be either another firm or the general public. When a factory is but one stage in a larger manufacturing process—firms making wheels, tires, windshields, bumpers, and the like in the assembly of automobiles, for example—location near the next stage of production is an obvious advantage. The advantage is increased if that final stage of production is also near the ultimate consumer market. To continue our example, automobile assembly plants have been scattered throughout the North American realm in response to the existence of large regional markets and the cost of distribution of the finished automobile. This market orientation is further reflected by the location in North America of auto manufacturing or assembly plants of Asian and European motor vehicle companies, although both foreign and domestic firms again appear to be reconcentrating the industry in the southeastern part of the United States.

People themselves, of course, are the ultimate consumers. Large urban concentrations represent markets, and major cities have always attracted producers of goods consumed by city dwellers. Admittedly, it is impossible to distinguish clearly between urbanites as market and urbanites as labour force. In either case, many manufacturing activities are drawn to major metropolitan centers. Certain producers are, in fact, inseparable from the immediate markets they serve and are so widely distributed that they are known as **ubiquitous industries**. Newspaper publishing, bakeries, and dairies, all of which produce a highly perishable commodity designed for immediate consumption, are examples.

Transportation

Transportation has been so much the unifying thread of all of these references to "factors" of industrial location that it is difficult to isolate its separate role. In fact, some of the earlier observations about manufacturing plant orientations can be restated in purely transportation cost terms. For example, copper smelting or iron ore beneficiation—described earlier as examples of raw material orientation—may also be seen as industries engaged in *weight reduction* designed to minimize transportation costs by removal of waste material prior to shipment. Some market orientation is of the opposite nature, reflecting *weight-gaining* production. Soft drink bottlers, for example, add large amounts of water to small amounts of concentrated syrup to produce a bulky product of relatively low value. All transport costs are reduced if only the concentrate is shipped to local bottlers, who add the water that is available everywhere, and distribute only to local dealers. The frequency of this practice suggests the inclusion of soft drink bottlers among the ubiquitous industries.

No matter the specific characterization of attraction, modern industry is intimately and inseparably tied to transportation systems. The Industrial Revolution is usefully seen as initially and simultaneously a transportation revolution as successive improvements in the technology of movement of peoples and commodities enlarged the effective areas of spatial interaction and made integrated economic development and areal specialization possible. All advanced economies are well served by a diversity of transport media (see Figure 10.5); without them, all that is possible is local subsistence activity. All major industrial agglomerations are simultaneously important nodes of different transportation media, each with its own characteristic advantages and limitations.

Water transportation is the cheapest means of long-distance freight movement (Figure 10.5), with low operating and right-of-way costs. Inland waterway improvement and canal construction marked the first phase of the Industrial Revolution in Europe and was the first stage of modern transport development in Canada and the United States. Even today, river ports and seaports have locational attractiveness for industry unmatched by alternative centres not served by water carriers, and where water routes are in place, as in northwestern Europe or the Great Lakes–St. Lawrence Seaway of Canada, they are vital elements in regional industrial economies.

Railroads efficiently move large volumes of freight over long distances at low fuel and labour costs (Figure 9.36). They are, however, inflexible in route, slow to respond to changing industrial locational patterns, and expensive to construct and maintain. When for any reason traffic declines below minimum revenue levels, rail service may be considered uneconomic and the lines abandoned—a response of American railroads, which abandoned over 201,168 km of line between 1930 and 2000: the equivalent of just under three times the total length of freight and passenger lines operating in Canada today (71,547 km).

High-volume, high-speed *motor trucks* operating on modern roadway and highway systems have altered the competitive picture to favour highways over railways in many intercity movements in modern economies. Road systems provide great flexibility of service and are more quickly responsive than railroads to new traffic

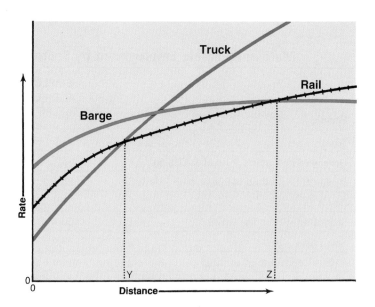

FIGURE 10.5 The pattern of carrier efficiency. Different transport media have cost advantages over differing distances. The usual generalization is that when all three media are available for a given shipment, trucks are most efficient and economical over short hauls of up to about 500 kilometres (about 300 miles), railroads have the cost advantage over intermediate hauls of 500 to 3200 kilometres (about 300 to 2000 miles), and water (ship or barge) movement over longer distances (and, often, over shorter distances where speed of delivery of non-perishable commodities is not a consideration). The differing cost curves represent the differing amounts of fixed or variable costs incurred by each transport medium, as further illustrated in Figure 10.8.

demands and changing origin and destination points. Intervening opportunities are more easily created and regional integration more cheaply achieved by highway than by railroad (or waterway systems).

Increasingly in North America and elsewhere, greater transport cost efficiencies are achieved by combining short-haul motor carriage with longer-haul rail or ship movement of the same freight containers. Hauling a truck trailer on a railroad flatcar ("piggybacking") or on ship deck serves to minimize total freight rates and transport times. Such *multimodal* freight movements seek the advantages of the most efficient carrier for each stage of the journey from cargo origin point to final destination through the use of prepacked internationally standardized shipping containers. The containers with undisturbed content may be transferred to ships for international ocean carriage, to railroads for long-haul land movement, and to truck trailers for shorter-haul distances and pickup and delivery. Their use is increasingly common: on long "trailer-on-flat-car" trains and in the growing volume of international ocean trade (Figure 10.6). Such flexibility resulted in 90% of all consumer products and foodstuffs within Canada being transported at some point between production and consumption by trucks.

Pipelines provide efficient, speedy, and dependable transportation specifically suited to the movement of a variety of liquids and gases. They serve to localize along their routes the industries—particularly fertilizer and petrochemical plants—that

FIGURE 10.6 The Kwai Chung container port, Hong Kong, China. In 2004, containerization accounted for more than 75% of all international shipments, and newer, larger, and more efficient ships able to carry over 8000 containers were entering service.

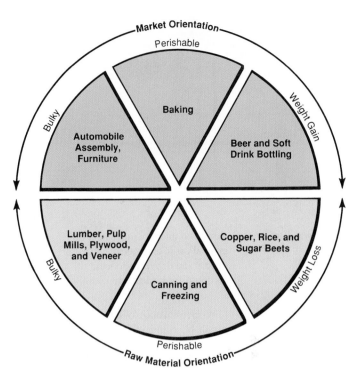

FIGURE 10.7 Spatial orientation tendencies. *Raw material orientation* is presumed to exist when there are limited alternative material sources, when the material is perishable, or when—in its natural state—it contains a large proportion of impurities or non-marketable components. *Market orientation* represents the least-cost solution when manufacturing uses commonly available materials that add weight to the finished product, when the manufacturing process produces a commodity much bulkier or more expensive to ship than its separate components, or when the perishable nature of the product demands processing at individual market points.

Source: Adapted with permission from Truman A. Hartshorn, Interpreting the City. *© 1980 John Wiley & Sons, Inc.*

use the transported commodity as raw material. In contrast, *air transport* has little locational significance for most industries despite its growing importance in long-distance passenger and high-value package freight movement. It contributes, of course, to the range of transport alternatives available to large population centres in industrially advanced nations and may increase the attractiveness of airport sites for high-tech and other industries shipping or receiving high-value, low-bulk commodities. It is not, however, an effective competitor in the usual patterns of freight flow (see "A Comparison of Transport Media").

Transportation and Location

Figure 10.7 indicates the general pattern of industrial orientation related to variable transportation costs. In their turn, those costs are more than a simple function of the distance that goods are carried. Rather, they represent the application of differing **freight rates**, charges made for loading, transporting, and unloading of goods. Freight rates are said to *discriminate* between commodities on the basis of their assumed ability to bear transport costs in relation to their value. In general, manufactured goods have higher value, greater fragility, require more special handling, and can bear higher freight charges than can unprocessed bulk commodities. The higher transport costs for finished goods are therefore seen as a major reason for the increasing market orientation of industry in advanced economies with high-value manufacturing.

In addition to these forms of rate discrimination, each shipment of whatever nature must bear a share of the **fixed costs** of the company's investment in land, plant, and equipment, and the assigned *terminal* and *line-haul* costs of the shipment. **Terminal costs** are charges associated with loading, packing,

and unloading of a shipment and of the paperwork and shipping documents it entails. **Line-haul** or *over-the-road* **costs** vary with the individual shipments and are the expenses involved in the actual movement of commodities once they have been loaded. They are allocated to each shipment according to equipment used and distance travelled. Total transport costs represent a combination of all pertinent charges and are curvilinear rather than linear functions of distance. That is, carrier costs have a tendency to decline as the length of haul increases because scale economies in long-haul movement permit the averaging of total costs over a greater number of miles. The result is the *tapering principle* diagrammed in Figure 10.8.

One consequence of the necessary assignment of fixed and terminal costs to *every* shipment regardless of distance moved is that factory locations intermediate between sources of materials and final markets are less attractive than location at either end of a single long haul. That is, two short hauls cost more than a single continuous haul over the same distance (Figure 10.9).

Two exceptions to this locational generalization are of practical interest. **Break-of-bulk points** are sites where goods have to

A Comparison of Transport Media

Mode	Uses	Advantages	Disadvantages
Railroad	Intercity medium- to long-haul bulk and general cargo transport.	Fast, reliable service on separate rights-of-way; essentially non-polluting; energy efficient; adapted to steady flow of single commodities between two points; routes and nodes provide intervening development opportunities.	High construction and operating costs; inflexibility of routes; underutilized lines cause economic drain.
Highway carrier	Local and intercity movement of general cargo and merchandise; pickup and delivery services; feeder to other carriers.	Highly flexible in routes, origins, and destinations; individualized service; maximum accessibility; unlimited intervening opportunity; high speed and low terminal costs.	Low energy efficiency; contributes to air pollution; adds congestion to public roads; high maintenance costs; inefficient for large-volume freight.
Inland waterway	Low-speed haulage of bulk, non-perishable commodities.	High energy efficiency; low per-mile costs; large cargo capacity.	High terminal costs; low route flexibility; not suited for short haul; possible delays from ice or low water levels.
Pipelines	Continuous flows of liquids, gases, or suspended solids where volumes are high and continuity is required.	Fast, efficient, dependable; low per-mile costs over long distances; maximum safety.	Highly inflexible in route and cargo type; high development cost.
Airways	Medium- and long-haul of high-value, low-bulk cargo where delivery speed is important.	High speed and efficiency; adapted to goods that are perishable, packaged, of a size and quantity unsuited to other modes; high route flexibility; access to areas otherwise inaccessible.	Very expensive; high mileage costs; some weather-related unreliability; inconvenient terminal locations; no intervening opportunities between airports.
Intermodal containerization	Employs standardized closed containers to move a shipment by any combination of water, rail, and truck without unpacking between origin and final destination.	Speed and efficiency of transit and lower shipping costs when multiple carriers are needed; reduced labour charges and pilferage losses.	Requires special terminals and handling machinery to load, off-load, and transfer containers.

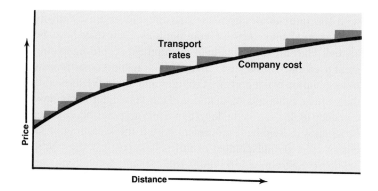

FIGURE 10.8 The tapering principle. The actual costs of transport, including terminal charges and line costs, increase at a decreasing rate as fixed costs are spread over longer hauls. The "tapering" of company cost is differently expressed among media because their mixes of fixed and variable costs are different, as Figure 10.5 diagrams. Note that actual rates charged move in stepwise increments to match the general pattern and level of company costs.

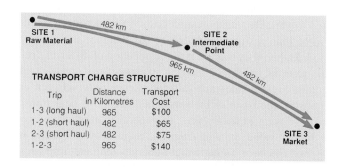

FIGURE 10.9 The short-haul penalty. Plant locations intermediate between material and market are generally avoided because of the realities of transportation pricing that are shown here. Two short hauls simply cost more than a single long haul because two sets of fixed costs must be assigned to the interrupted movement.

be transferred or trans-shipped from one carrier to another—at ports, for example, where barge or ocean vessel must be unloaded and cargo reloaded to railcar or truck, or between railroad and truck line. When such transfer occurs, an additional fixed or terminal cost is levied against the shipment, perhaps significantly increasing its total transport costs (piggyback transfers reduce, but do not eliminate, those handling charges). There is a tendency for manufacturing to concentrate at such points to avoid the additional charges. As a traffic-generating inducement, **in-transit privilege** may be granted to a manufacturer by a transportation agency through the quotation of a special single rate from material source to market for a movement that may be interrupted for processing or manufacturing *en route*. Such a special rate obviously removes the cost disadvantage of two short hauls and, by equalizing shipping costs between locations, tends to reduce the otherwise dominant attractions of either material or market locations.

Industrial Location Theories

In practice, enterprise locational decisions are based not on the impact of a single selected industrial factor but on the interplay and balance of a number of considerations. Implicit in our review has been the understanding that each type or branch of industry has its own specific set of significant plant siting conditions. For secondary activities as a whole, therefore, a truly bewildering complex of locational determinants exists. Theorists beginning in the first third of the 20th century set themselves the task of sorting through that complex in the attempt to define its underlying structure. The economic world they surveyed at that time, dominated by railroads, based on heavy industry and ideas of national industrial self-sufficiency, no longer is fully consistent with a globalized economy reflecting political, competitive, and social decisions of, for example, the World Trade Organization, transnational corporations, environmental protection agencies, and the like. Nevertheless, the logical systems and concepts they developed and the spatial conclusions they reached still are relevant in understanding present-day industrial locational decisions. Although a full review of all of their contributions is beyond our scope and interest, it is useful to survey briefly the three fundamental approaches to the problem of plant location those theorists proposed—*least-cost theory, locational interdependence theory,* and *profit-maximization approaches*—and the different conclusions they reach. Each of these following three theories has a different focus or independent variable: cost, revenue, and profit.

Least-Cost Theory

The classical model of industrial location theory, the **least-cost theory**, is based on the work of Alfred Weber (1868–1958) and sometimes called **Weberian analysis**. It explains the optimum location of a manufacturing establishment in terms of minimization of three basic expenses: relative transport costs, labour costs, and agglomeration costs. **Agglomeration** refers to the clustering of productive activities and people for mutual advantage. Such clustering can produce "agglomeration economies" through shared facilities and services. Diseconomies such as

higher rents or wage levels resulting from competition for these resources may also occur.

Weber concluded that transport costs are the major consideration determining location. That is, the optimum location will be found where the costs of transporting raw materials to the factory and finished goods to the market are at their lowest. He noted, however, if variations in labour or agglomeration costs are sufficiently great, a location determined solely on the basis of transportation costs may not in fact be the optimum one.

Weber made five controlling assumptions: (1) An area is completely uniform physically, politically, culturally, and technologically. This is known as the **uniform**, or **isotropic**, **plain** assumption. (2) Manufacturing involves a single product to be shipped to a single market whose location is known. (3) Inputs involve raw materials from more than one known source location. (4) Labour is infinitely available but immobile in location. (5) Transportation routes are not fixed but connect origin and destination by the shortest path; and transport costs directly reflect the weight of items shipped and the distance they are moved.

Given these assumptions, Weber derived the least transport cost location by means of the *locational triangle* (Figure 10.10). It diagrams the cost consequences of fixed locations of materials and market, and of movement in any direction of a given weight of commodity at a uniform cost per unit of distance. In Figure 10.10a, *S1* and *S2* are the two material sources for a product consumed at *M*. The problem is to locate the *optimum point of production* where the total tonne-distance involved in assembling materials and distributing the product is at a minimum. Each corner of the triangle exerts its pull; each has a defined cost of production should it be chosen as the plant site. If we assume that the material weights are cut in half during manufacturing (so that the finished product weighs the same as each of the original raw materials), then location at either S_1 or S_2 on the diagram would involve a \$3 shipping charge from the other raw material source plus \$3 to move the product, for a total delivered cost at market of \$6. If the market were selected as the plant site, two raw material shipments—again totalling \$6—would be involved.

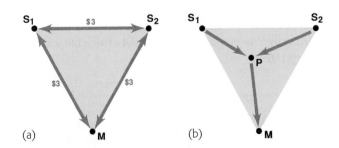

(a)   (b)

FIGURE 10.10 Weber's locational triangle with differing assumptions. (*a*) With one market, two raw material sources, and a finished product reflecting a 50% material weight loss, production could appropriately be located at S_1, S_2, or *M* since each length of haul is the same. In (*b*) the optimum production point, *P*, is seen to lie within the triangle, where total transport costs would be less than at corner locations. The exact location of *P* would depend on the weight-loss characteristics of the two material inputs if only transport charges were involved. *P* would, of course, be pulled toward the material whose weight is most reduced.

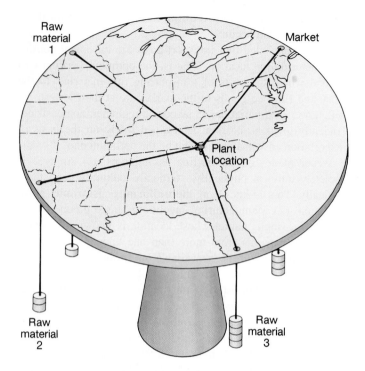

FIGURE 10.11 Plane table solution to a plant location problem.
This mechanical model, suggested by Alfred Weber, uses weights to demonstrate the least transport cost point where there are several sources of raw materials. When a weight is allowed to represent the "pull" of raw material and market locations, an equilibrium point is found on the plane table. That point is the location at which all forces balance each other and represents the least-cost plant location.

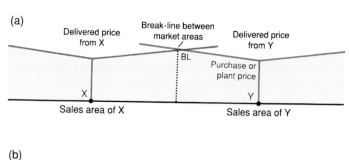

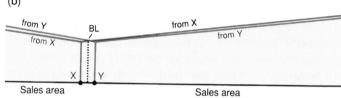

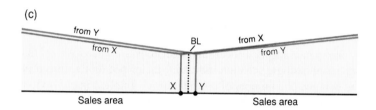

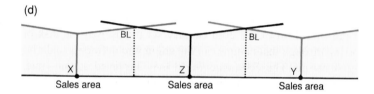

FIGURE 10.12 Competitive locations in a linear market (Hotelling model). The initial *socially optimal* locations (*a*) that minimize total distribution costs will be vacated in the search for market advantage (*b*), eventually resulting in *competitive equilibrium* at the center of the market (*c*). Spatial dispersion will again occur if two or more competitors either encounter elasticity of demand or subdivide the market by agreement (*d*).

Weberian analysis, however, aims at the least transport cost location, which most likely will be an intermediate point somewhere within the locational triangle. Its exact position will depend on distances, the respective weights of the raw material inputs, and the final weight of the finished product, and may be either material or market oriented (Figure 10.10b). Material orientation reflects a sizable weight loss during the production process; market orientation indicates a weight gain. The optimum placement of *P* can be found by different analytical means, but the easiest to visualize is by way of a mechanical model of weights and strings (Figure 10.11).

Locational Interdependence Theory

When the locational decision of one firm is influenced by locations chosen by its competitors, a condition of **locational interdependence** exists. It influences the manner in which competitive firms with identical cost structures arrange themselves in space to assure themselves a measure of *spatial monopoly* in their combined market. In locational interdependence theory, the concern is with *variable revenue analysis* rather than, as in the Weber model, with variable costs.

The simplest case concerns the locational decisions of two firms in competition with each other to supply identical goods to customers evenly spaced along a linear market. The usual example

cited is of two ice cream vendors, each selling the same brand at the same price along a stretch of beach having a uniform distribution of people. All will purchase the same amount of ice cream (that is, demand is *inelastic*—is not sensitive to a change in the price) and will patronize the seller nearer to them. Figure 10.12 suggests that the two sellers would eventually cluster at the midpoint of the linear market (the beach) so that each vendor could supply customers at the extremities of the market without yielding locational advantage to the single competitor.

This is a spatial solution that maximizes return but does not minimize costs. The lowest total cost location for each of the two vendors would be at the midpoint of his or her half of the beach, as shown at the top of Figure 10.12, where the total effort expended by customers walking to the ice cream stands (or cost by sellers delivering the product) is least. To maximize market share, however, one seller might decide to relocate immediately next to the competitor (Figure 10.12b), dominating now three-fourths of the entire beach market. The logical retaliation would be for the second vendor to jump back over the first to recapture market share. Ultimately, side-by-side location at the centre line of the beach is inevitable and a stable placement is achieved since neither seller can gain any further advantage from moving. But now the customers collectively have to walk farther to satisfy their ice cream hunger than they did initially; that is, total acquisition cost or delivered price (ice cream purchase plus effort expended) has increased.

The economist Harold Hotelling (1895–1973), who is usually associated with the locational interdependence approach, expanded the conclusion about clustered ice cream sellers to a more generalized statement explaining industrial concentration by multiple producers under conditions of identical production costs and inelastic market demand. However, if the market becomes sensitive to price, sales to more distant customers will be discouraged and producers seeking to maximize sales will again separate rather than aggregate. The conclusion then is that price sensitivity (elasticity of demand) will encourage industrial dispersion.

Profit-Maximization Approaches

For many theorists, the simplicities and rigidities of the least-cost and the locational interdependence explanations are unrealistically restrictive. Ultimately, they maintain, the correct location of a production facility is where the net profit is greatest. They propose employing a **substitution principle** that recognizes that in many industrial processes it is possible to replace a declining amount of one input (e.g., labour) with an increase in another (e.g., capital for automated equipment) or to increase transportation costs while simultaneously reducing land rent. With substitution, a number of different points may be appropriate manufacturing locations. Further, they suggest, a whole series of points may exist where total revenue of an enterprise just equals its total cost of producing a given output. These points, connected, mark the **spatial margin of profitability** and define the larger area within which profitable operation is possible (Figure 10.13). Location anywhere within the margin assures some profit and tolerates both imperfect knowledge and personal (rather than economic) considerations. Such less-than-optimal, but still acceptable, sites are considered **satisfying locations**.

For some firms, spatial margins may be very broad because transport costs are a negligible factor in production and marketing. Such firms are said to be **footloose**—that is, neither resource nor market oriented. For example, both the raw materials and the finished product in the manufacture of computers are so valuable, light, and compact that transportation costs have little bearing on where production takes place.

Other Locational Considerations and Controls

The behaviour of individual firms seeking specific production sites under competitive commercial conditions forms the basis of most classical industrial location theory. But such theory no longer fully explains world or regional patterns of industrial localization or specialization. Moreover, it does not account for locational behaviour that is uncontrolled by objective "factors,"

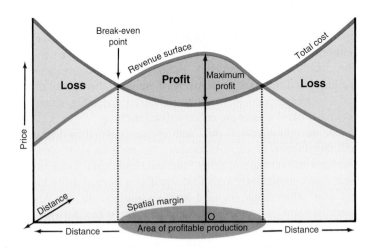

FIGURE 10.13 The spatial margin of profitability. In the diagram, *O* is the single optimal profit-maximizing location, but location anywhere within the area defined by the intersects of the total cost and total revenue surfaces will permit profitable operation. Some industries will have wide margins; others will be more spatially constricted. Skilled entrepreneurs may be able to expand the margins farther than less able industrialists. Importantly, a *satisfying* location may be selected by reasonable estimate even in the absence of the totality of information required for an *optimal* decision.

influenced by new production technologies and corporate structures, or directed by non-capitalistic planning goals.

Traditional theories (including many variants not reviewed here) sought to explain location decisions for plants engaged in mass production for mass markets where transportation lines were fixed and transport costs relatively high. Both conditions began to change significantly during the last years of the 20th century. Assembly line production of identical commodities by a rigidly controlled and specialized labour force for generalized mass markets—known as "**Fordism**" to recognize Henry Ford's pioneering development of the system—became less realistic in both market and technology terms. In its place, post-Fordist *flexible manufacturing* processes based on smaller production runs of a greater variety of goods aimed at smaller, niche markets than were catered to by traditional manufacturing have become common. At the same time, information technology applied to machines and operations, increasing flexibility of labour, and declining costs for transportation services that were increasingly viewed from a cost-time rather than a cost-distance standpoint have materially altered underlying assumptions of the classical theories.

Agglomeration Economies

Geographical concentration of economic, including industrial, activities is the norm at the local or regional scale. The cumulative and reinforcing attractions of industrial concentration and urban growth are recognized locational factors, but ones not easily quantified. Both cost-minimizing and profit-maximizing theories, as we have seen, make provision for *agglomeration*, the spatial concentration of people and activities for mutual benefit. That is, both recognize that areal grouping of industrial activities may produce benefits for individual firms that they could not experience in isolation. Those benefits—**agglomeration economies**, or **external economies**—accrue in the form of savings from shared transport facilities, social services, public utilities, communication facilities, and the like. Collectively, these and other installations and services needed to facilitate industrial and other forms of economic development are called **infrastructure**.

Areal concentration may also create pools of skilled and ordinary labour, of capital, ancillary business services, and, of course, a market built of other industries and urban populations. New firms, particularly, may find significant advantages in locating near other firms engaged in the same activity, for labour specializations and support services specific to that activity are already in place. Some may find profit in being near other firms with which they are linked either as customers or suppliers.

A concentration of capital, labour, management skills, customer base, and all that is implied by the term *infrastructure* will tend to attract still more industries from other locations to the agglomeration. In Weber's terms, that is, economies of association distort or alter locational decisions that otherwise would be based solely on transportation and labour costs, and once in existence, agglomerations will tend to grow (Figure 10.14). Through a **multiplier effect**, each new firm added to the agglomeration will lead to the further development of infrastructure and linkages. As we saw in Chapter 8, the "multiplier effect" also implies total (urban) population growth and thus the expansion of the labour pool and the localized market that are part of agglomeration economies.

Agglomeration—concentration—of like industries in small areas dates from the early industrial age and continues with many of the newest industries. Familiar examples include the town of

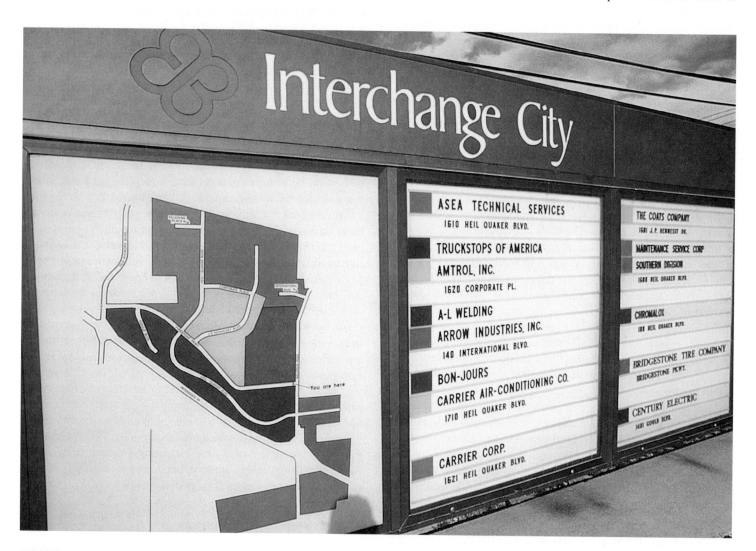

FIGURE 10.14 On a small scale, the planned industrial park furnishes its tenants external agglomeration economies similar to those offered by large urban concentrations to industry in general. An industrial park provides a subdivided tract of land developed according to a comprehensive plan for the use of (frequently) otherwise unconnected firms. Since the park developers, whether private companies or public agencies, supply the basic infrastructure of streets, water, sewage, power, transport facilities, and perhaps private police and fire protection, park tenants are spared the additional cost of providing these services themselves. In some instances, factory buildings are available for rent, still further reducing firm capital outlays. Counterparts of industrial parks for manufacturers are the office parks, research parks, science parks, and the like for "high-tech" firms and for enterprises in tertiary and quaternary services.

Dalton, Georgia, in or near which were found all but one of the top 20 United States carpet makers, and Akron, Ohio, which, before 1930, held almost the entire 100 or so tire manufacturers in the United States. Silicon Valley dating from the 1960s and other more recent high-tech specialized concentrations simply continue the tradition.

Admittedly, agglomeration can yield disadvantages as well as benefits. Overconcentration can result in diseconomies of congestion, high land values, pollution, increased governmental regulation, and the like. When the costs of aggregation exceed the benefits, a firm will actually profit by relocating to a more isolated position, a process called **deglomeration**. It is a process expressed in the suburbanization of industry within metropolitan areas or the relocation of firms to non-metropolitan locations.

Just-in-Time and Flexible Production

Agglomeration economies and tendencies are also encouraged by newer manufacturing policies practised by both *older*, established industries and by newer post-Fordist plants.

Traditional Fordist industries required the on-site storage of large lots of materials and supplies ordered and delivered well in advance of their actual need in production. That practice permitted cost savings through infrequent ordering and reduced transportation charges and made allowances for delayed deliveries and for inspection of received goods and components. The assurance of supplies on hand for long production runs of standardized outputs was achieved at high inventory and storage costs.

Just-in-time (JIT) manufacturing, in contrast, seeks to reduce inventories for the production process by purchasing inputs for arrival just in time to use and producing output just in time to sell. Rather than costly accumulation and storage of supplies, JIT requires frequent ordering of small lots of goods for precisely timed arrival and immediate deployment to the factory floor. Such "lean manufacturing" based on frequent purchasing of immediately needed goods demands rapid delivery by suppliers and encourages them to locate near the buyer. Recent manufacturing innovations thus reinforce and augment the spatial agglomeration tendencies evident in the older industrial landscape, and de-emphasize the applicability of older single-plant location theories.

JIT is one expression of a transition from mass-production Fordism to more *flexible production systems*. That flexibility is designed to allow producers to shift quickly and easily between different levels of output and, importantly, to move from one factory process or product to another as market demand dictates. Flexibility of that type is made possible by new technologies of easily reprogrammed computerized machine tools, and by computer-aided design and computer-aided manufacturing systems. These technologies permit small-batch, just-in-time production and distribution responsive to current market demand as monitored by computer-based information systems.

Flexible production to a large extent requires significant acquisition of components and services from outside suppliers rather than from in-house production. For example, modular assembly, where many subsystems of a complex final product enter the plant already assembled, reduces factory space and worker requirements. The premium that flexibility places on proximity to component suppliers adds still another dimension to industrial agglomeration tendencies. "Flexible production regions" have, according to some observers, emerged in response to the new flexible production strategies and interfirm dependencies. Those regions, it is claimed, are usually some distance—spatially or socially—from established concentrations of Fordist industrialization (e.g., Southwestern Ontario's auto industry).

Comparative Advantage, Outsourcing, and Offshoring

The principle of *comparative advantage* and the practices of *outsourcing* and *offshoring* are of growing international importance in industrial location and specialization decisions. They are interconnected in that each reflects cost advantages of specialization and each is dependent on free trade and flow of information. **Comparative advantage** tells us that areas and countries can best improve their economies and living standards through specialization and trade. These benefits will follow if each area or country concentrates on the production of those items for which it has the greatest relative advantage over other areas, or for which it has the least relative disadvantage, and imports all other goods. This principle, basic to the understanding of regional specializations, applies as long as areas have different relative advantages for two or more goods and free trade exists between them.

Assume that two countries have a need for and are domestically able to produce two commodities. Further assume that there is no transport cost consideration—no matter what its cost of production of either commodity, Country A will choose to specialize in only one of them if, by that specialization and through exchange with Country B for the other, Country A stands to gain more than it loses. The key to comparative advantage is the utilization of resources in such a fashion as to gain, by specialization, a volume of production and a selling price that permit exchange for a needed commodity at a cost level that is below that of the domestic production of both.

The logic of comparative advantage was recognized by economists in the 19th century when specialization and exchange involved shipments of grain, coal, or manufactured goods whose relative costs of production in different areas were clearly evident. When other countries' comparative advantages reflect lower labour, land, and capital costs, however, the application of the principle is, by some observers, seen in a much less favourable light. They observe that manufacturing activities may relocate from higher-cost market country locations to lower-cost foreign production sites, taking with them the employment and income formerly housed in the consuming country—to the apparent detriment of that country's prosperity. For others, such voluntary **outsourcing**—producing parts or products abroad for domestic sale—by Canadian manufacturers has employment and areal economic consequences no different from those resulting from successful competition by foreign companies or from industrial locational decisions favouring one section of the country over others.

Outsourcing has also assumed the meaning of subcontracting production and service sector work to outside, often non-union, domestic companies. In 2004, U.S. companies outsourced an estimated $4 trillion in goods and services, a 50% increase since the start of the century; outsourcing in the American context is growing at an estimated 15% to 20% yearly pace. Roughly one-half of the 2004 total value of outsourcing related to manufacturing, with about one-third of that involving foreign suppliers. The other half was domestic, involving purchases—including service sector activities—from American suppliers. In manufacturing, outsourcing has become an important element in just-in-time acquisition of preassembled components for snap-together fabrication of finished products, often built only to fill orders actually received from customers. Reducing parts inventories and introducing build-to-order production demands a high level of flexible freight movement increasingly supplied by "logistics" firms that themselves may become involved in packaging, labelling, and even manufacturing products for client companies. When comparative advantage and outsourcing are exploited by individual corporations, one expression of flexible production systems is evident in the erosion of the rigid spatial concentration of manufacturing assumed by classical location theory.

A clear example of that impact is evident in the changing nature of automobile manufacturing. Formerly, motor vehicle companies were largely self-contained production entities controlling raw material inputs through their own steel and glass plants, and producing themselves all parts and components required in the assembly of their products. Since late 1992, that self-containment has been abandoned because car companies have divested themselves of raw material production facilities and have in large part sold off their in-house parts production. Increasingly, they are purchasing parts and sub-assemblies from independent, often distant, suppliers. In fact, some observers of the changing vehicle production scene predict that established automobile companies will eventually convert themselves into "vehicle brand owners," retaining for themselves only such essential tasks as vehicle design, engineering, and marketing. All else, including final product assembly, is projected to be done through outsourcing to parts suppliers. Similar trends are already evident in consumer electronics, where a third of manufacturing (2004) is estimated to be outsourced.

A distinctive regional illustration of more diversified industrial deconcentration through outsourcing is found along the northern border of Mexico. In the 1960s, Mexico enacted legislation permitting foreign (specifically, American) companies to establish "sister" plants, called *maquiladoras*, within 20 kilometres (12 miles) of the U.S. border for the duty-free assembly of products destined for re-export. By 2003, more than 3000 such assembly and manufacturing plants had been established to produce a diversity of goods, including electronic products, textiles, furniture, leather goods, toys, and automotive parts. The plants generated direct and indirect employment for more than one million Mexican workers (Figure 10.15) and for large numbers of U.S. citizens, employees of growing numbers of American-side *maquila* suppliers and of diverse service-oriented businesses spawned by the "multiplier effect." The

FIGURE 10.15 American manufacturers, seeking lower labour costs, began in the 1960s to establish light manufacturing, component production, and assembly operations along the international border in Mexico. *Outsourcing* to such plants as this Converse Sport Shoe factory at Reynosa has moved a large proportion of American electronics, small appliance, toy, and garment industries to offshore subsidiaries or contractors in Asia and Latin America. More than a quarter-million Mexican *maquilador* jobs and 350 plants were lost between 2000 and 2004, however, largely to competition from lower-cost, more-efficient Chinese and other Asian producers. Comparative advantage is not a permanent condition.

North American Free Trade Agreement (NAFTA), which created a single Canadian–United States–Mexican production and marketing community, turns outsourcing in the North American context from a search abroad for low-cost production sites to a review of best locations within a broadened unified economic environment.

On the international scene, outsourcing often involves production of commodities by developing countries that have benefited from the transfer of technology and capital from industrialized states, and that use their new facilities and skills to improve productivity in areas formerly dominated by the profitable home products and exports of a rich world state. Electrical and electronic goods from China and Southeast Asia competing with and replacing in the market similar goods formerly produced by Western firms are examples. Such replacements, multiplied by numerous new country origins of the whole range of producer and consumer goods in world trade, have resulted in new global patterns of industrial regions and specializations. They have, as well, produced a strikingly changed picture of the developing world's share of gross global income: from an estimated 20% in the mid-20th century to almost one-half in 2004. That improvement reflected, in part, the growth of manufactures' share of their exports, from less than half in 1990 to more than 75% in 2003. For some observers, that change is ample proof of the beneficial impact of comparative advantage on the world economy.

Outsourcing not only involves manufacturing activity and blue-collar jobs but also, as we shall see later in this chapter, may be used by companies to reduce their service worker costs as well. When that reduction involves janitorial and similar services spatially tied to the home establishment, no adverse domestic employment consequences are felt. When, however, lower-paid foreign workers can satisfactorily replace technical, professional, and white-collar workers, the outsourcing action is known as service *offshoring* and has the immediate effect of exporting the jobs of highly paid skilled workers. **Offshoring** is the practice of either hiring foreign workers or, commonly, contracting with a foreign third-party service provider to take over and run particular business processes or operations. It has become an increasingly standard response to cost-containment strategies, reflecting the drastic lowering of communication costs, the ease of Internet use, and the growing technical proficiency for foreign labour pools. With an ever-increasing portion of the developing world acquiring the education and experience to provide skilled professional services of almost every kind at a level comparable to that formerly available only in advanced countries, traditional notions of comparative advantage are disappearing in the face of a new era of *hypercompetition*, at least in business and professional services. Software development, paralegal services, call centres, and back-office activities are among the many, now readily transferable clerical and skilled white-collar tasks, the performance of which is swelling the service component of developing countries' economies. India in particular has emerged as the dominant competitor and beneficiary of services offshoring, echoing China's position as the preferred destination of production outsourcing.

The exploitation of comparative advantage and utilization of outsourcing and offshoring, by transferring technology from economically advanced to underdeveloped economies is transforming the world economy by introducing a New International Division of Labor (NIDL). In the 19th and first half of the 20th centuries, the division invariably involved exports of manufactured goods from the "industrial" countries and of raw materials from the "colonial" or "undeveloped" economies. Roles have now altered. Manufacturing no longer is the mainstay of the economy and employment structure of Europe or North America, and as the NAFTA example showed, the world pattern of industrial production is shifting to reflect the growing dominance of countries formerly regarded as subsistence peasant societies but now emerging as the source areas for manufactured goods of all types produced competitively for the world market. In recognition of that shift, the NIDL builds on the current trend toward the increased subdivision of manufacturing process into smaller and smaller steps (and a similar fragmentation of stages of professional services). That subdivision permits multiple outsourcing and offshoring opportunities based on differential land and capital costs and skill levels available in the globalized world economy.

Imposed Considerations

Locational theories dictate that in a pure, competitive economy, the costs of material, transportation, labour, and plant should be controlling in locational decisions. Obviously, neither in Canada nor in any other market economy do the idealized conditions exist. Other constraints—some representing cost considerations, others political or social impositions—also affect, perhaps decisively, the locational decision process. Land use and zoning controls, environmental quality standards and regulations, governmental area-development inducements, local tax abatement provisions or developmental bond authorizations, non-economic pressures on quasi-governmental corporations, and other considerations constitute attractions or repulsions for industry outside of the context and consideration of pure theory (see "Investment Competition and Questionable Incentives"). If these non-economic forces become compelling, the assumptions of the commercial economy classification no longer apply, and locational controls reminiscent of those enforced by centrally planned economies become determining.

No other imposed considerations were as pervasive as those governing industrial location in planned economies. The theoretical controls on plant location decisions that apply in commercial economies were not, by definition, determinant in the centrally planned Marxist economies of Eastern Europe and the former Soviet Union. In those economies, plant locational decisions were made by government agencies rather than by individual firms.

Governmental rather than company decision making did not mean that location assessments based on factor cost were ignored; it meant that central planners were more concerned with other than purely economic profit in the creation of new industrial plants and concentrations. Important in the former Soviet Union, for example, was a controlling policy of the *rationalization* of industry through full development of the resources of the country wherever they were found and without regard to the cost or competitiveness of such development. Inevitably, although the factors of industrial production are identical in capitalist and non-capitalist economies, the philosophies and patterns of industrial location and areal development will differ between them. Since major capital investments are relatively permanent additions to the landscape, the results of their often non-economic-driven decisions are fixed and will long remain to influence industrial regionalism and competitive efficiencies into the post-Communist present and future. Those same decisions and rigidities continue to inhibit the transition by the formerly fully planned economies to modern capitalist industrial techniques and flexibilities.

Transnational Corporations

Outsourcing is but one small expression of the growing international structure of modern manufacturing and service enterprises. Business and industry are increasingly stateless and economies borderless as giant **transnational corporations (TNCs)**—private firms that have established branch operations in nations foreign to their headquarters' country—become ever-more important in the globalizing world space economy (see Chapter 3). Early in the 21st century, about 62,000 transnational (or *multinational*) companies controlled over 900,000 foreign affiliates employing about 56 million workers. Excluding the parent companies themselves, the TNC affiliates accounted for almost $19 trillion in sales, one-tenth of world GDP, and one-third of world exports.

Measured by value added (not total sales), 29 of the world's top 100 economic entities in 2003 were corporations, not countries. The country with the single largest economy is the United States, while Wal-Mart—an American company—is the single largest private enterprise. The great majority of these economies, and all of the TNCs, are engaged in secondary industries. That is, except for a few resource-based firms, they are principally involved in producing and selling manufactured goods. Although as we shall see, tertiary and quaternary activities have also become international in scope and transnational in corporate structure, the locational and operational advantages of multicountry operation were first discerned and exploited by manufacturers. Because of their outsourced purchases of raw materials, parts and components, and services, the total number of worldwide jobs associated with TNCs in 2003 reached 150 million or more.

TNCs are increasingly international in origin and administrative home, based primarily in a growing number of economically advanced countries. In the early 21st century, about 90% of the world's 100 largest TNCs had home offices in the European Union, United States, and Japan; only three developing country firms were on the list. Increasingly, however, cash-rich multinationals of the developing world are appearing and actively investing around the world; investment outflows from companies from India, Brazil, South Africa, Malaysia, and China (among others) have swelled, rising from $3 billion in 1991 to $40 billion in 2004, with one-third of that latter total going to other developing countries.

The direct impact of TNCs is limited to relatively few countries and regions. **Foreign direct investment (FDI)**—the purchase or construction of factories and other fixed assets by TNCs—has been an engine of globalization. At the start of the 21st century, however, less than 30% of FDI flows went to developing countries and the majority of that share was concentrated in 10 to 15 states, mainly in South, Southeast, and East Asia (China was the largest developing country recipient) and in Latin America and the Caribbean. In 2004, however, an estimated 42% of world FDI inflows went to developing countries, suggesting their increasing attractiveness for TNC investment. The portion of FDI going to the 50 least developed countries as a group—including nearly all African states—has been small but steadily increasing, from a low of 1% in 1994 to almost 5% in 2004. Nevertheless, despite poor countries' hopes for foreign investment to spur their economic growth, the vast majority of FDI still flows not to the poor or developing worlds but to the rich.

The advanced-country destination of those capital flows is understandable: TNCs are actively engaged in merging with or purchasing competitive established firms in already developed foreign market areas, and cross-border mergers and acquisitions have been the main stimuli behind FDI. Between 1980 and 2000, more than 225,000 mergers or purchases were announced worldwide; foreign investment activity continued but at a markedly slower pace and lower level during the worldwide economic slowdown beginning in 2001. According to the United Nations Conference on Trade and Development (UNCTAD), FDI in 2004 amounted to less than half the peak reached in 2000, and most of the decline reflected reduced inward investment into the developed world. However, FDI into the developing world—especially into Asia—rose by more than 6%.

Because most transnational corporations operate in only a few industries—computers, electronics, petroleum and mining, motor vehicles, chemicals, and pharmaceuticals—the worldwide impact of their consolidations is significant. Some dominate the marketing and distribution of basic and specialized commodities. In raw materials, a few TNCs account for 85% or more of world trade in wheat, maize, coffee, cotton, iron ore, and timber, for example. In manufactures, the highly concentrated world pharmaceutical industry is dominated by just six firms, and the world's 15 major automobile producers at the start of the 21st century, it has been predicted, will fall to five or 10 by 2015.

Because they are international in operation with multiple markets, plants, and raw material sources, TNCs actively exploit the principle of comparative advantage. In manufacturing, they have internationalized the plant-siting decision process and multiplied the number of locationally separated operations that must be assessed. TNCs produce in that country or region where costs of materials, labour, or other production inputs are minimized, while maintaining operational control and declaring taxes in localities where the economic climate is most favourable. Research and development, accounting, and other corporate activities are placed wherever economical and convenient.

TNCs have become global entities because global communications make it possible (Figure 10.16). Many have lost their original national identities and are no longer closely associated with or controlled by the cultures, societies, and legal systems of a nominal home country. At the same time, their multiplication of economic activities has reduced any earlier identifications with single products or processes, and given rise to "transnational integral conglomerates" spanning a large spectrum of both service and industrial sectors.

Nokia—Finland (Pakistan)

Ford—United States (China)

IBM—United States (Vietnam)

Nestlé—Switzerland (Egypt)

Sony—Japan (Vietnam)

British Petroleum—U.K. (China)

FIGURE 10.16 The world's transnational corporations increased in number from some 7000 in 1970 to about 62,000 in 2004. Ninety of the top 100 TNCs are headquartered in the *Triad*—the European Union, the United States, and Japan. Their recognition and impact, however, are global, as suggested by these billboards advertising just a sample of leading TNCs in distant settings. Corporate names and headquarters countries are followed by billboard locations in parentheses.

World Manufacturing Patterns and Trends

Whether locational decisions are made by private entrepreneurs or central planners—and on whatever considerations those decisions are based—the results over many years have produced a distinctive world pattern of manufacturing. Figure 10.17 suggests the striking prominence of a relatively small number of major industrial concentrations localized within relatively few countries, primarily but not exclusively parts of the "industrialized" or "developed" world. These may be roughly grouped into four commonly recognized major manufacturing regions: *Northeastern America*, *Western and Central Europe*, *Eastern Europe*, and *Eastern Asia*. Together, the industrial plants within these established regional clusters account for an estimated three-fifths of the world's manufacturing output by volume and value. Nevertheless, the developing world, those regions with emerging manufacturing economies, such *Africa*, do contribute the remaining two-fifths.

Their continuing dominance is by no means assured. The first three—those of northeastern America and Europe—were the beneficiaries of an earlier phase in the development and spread of manufacturing following the Industrial Revolution of the 18th century and lasting until after World War II. The countries within them now are increasingly "post-industrial" and traditional manufacturing and processing are of declining relative importance.

The fourth—the East Asian district—is part of the wider, newer pattern of world industrialization that has emerged in recent years, the result of massive international *cultural convergence* (see Chapter 5) and technology transfers in the latter half of the 20th century and early in the 21st. The older rigid economic split between the developed and developing worlds has rapidly weakened as the full range of industrial activities, from primary metal processing (e.g., the iron and steel industries) through advanced electronic assembly, has been dispersed from, or separately established within, an ever-expanding list of countries.

Such states as Mexico, Brazil, China, and others of the developing world have created industrial regions of international significance, and the contribution to world manufacturing activity of the smaller newly industrializing countries (NICs) has been growing significantly. The spreading use of efficient and secure containerized shipment of high-value goods to North American and European markets has been a major contributor to their competitive success. Even economies that, until recently, were overwhelmingly subsistence or dominated by agricultural or mineral exports have become important players in the changing world manufacturing scene. Foreign branch plant investment in low-wage Asian, African, and Latin American states has not only created an industrial infrastructure there, but has increased their gross national incomes and per capita incomes sufficiently to permit expanded production for growing domestic—not just export—markets.

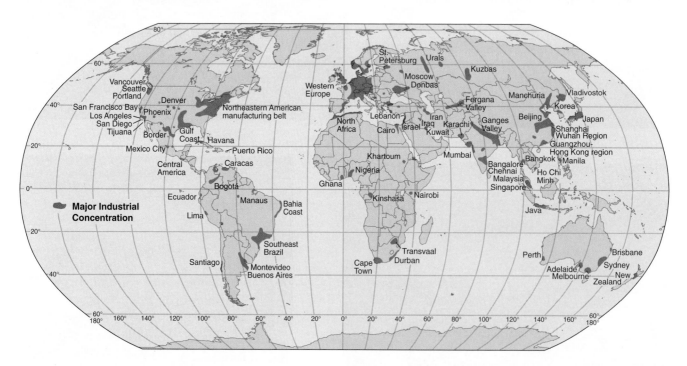

FIGURE 10.17 World industrial regions. Industrial districts are not as continuous or "solid" as the map suggests. Manufacturing is a relatively minor user of land even in areas of greatest concentration. There is a loose spatial association of major industrial districts in an "industrial belt" extending from Western Europe eastward to the Ural Mountains and, through outliers in Siberia, to the rapidly expanding factories of the Far East, particularly in China, which is now the world's sixth largest trading partner. The belt picks up again on the west coast of North America, though its major northeastern North American concentration lies east of the Mississippi River and along the eastern shoreline of Lake Ontario. North America's former overwhelming production dominance is being steadily and increasingly eroded by the expanding industrialization of countries throughout the developing world where labour costs are substantially lower.

Much of that new plant investment and expanded developing country industrial production has concentrated within the great number of *export processing zones* (EPZs) recently created within those countries. An EPZ may be either a delimited geographical area or, frequently, an export-oriented manufacturing enterprise located anywhere within a host country that benefits from special investment incentives. These incentives usually include exemptions from customs duties, preferential treatment from various regulatory and financial regulations, and the provision of high quality infrastructure—airports, highways, telecommunications, and electric and water facilities—usually provided by the local or national governments. Enterprises operating within or as an EPZ usually enjoy preferential conditions under which they can import equipment, components, and raw materials duty-free to produce goods mainly for export. And exports from those zones generally are afforded tariff reductions or duty-free entry into receiving European and North American markets. Because of their obvious production-site advantages, therefore, EPZs are both favoured locations for transnational corporation outsourcing and the promoted device with which developing countries compete for TNC foreign investment.

Nevertheless, those smaller Asian, African, and Latin American countries separately and collectively figure less prominently in world manufacturing volumes and values than do the North American and European industrial regions that still remain major components on the world economic landscape, and are now matched by the Eastern Asian region of more recent origin. Because of either their traditional or newly emerging world significance, each of those Western and Eastern Hemisphere industrial regions warrants a closer look.

Northeastern America

The importance of manufacturing in North America has been steadily declining. In 1960, the 28% of the labour force engaged in manufacturing generated nearly one-third of the region's wealth. In the early 21st century, manufacturing employment had dropped to about 16% of a much larger labour force, and manufacturing contributed less than a fifth of the gross domestic product of the Anglo-American realm.

Manufacturing is found particularly in the urbanized sections of North America, but is not uniformly distributed. Its primary concentration is in the northeastern part of the United States and adjacent sections of southeastern Canada, the *Northeastern American Manufacturing Belt* (Figure 10.18). That district contains the majority of the urban population of the two countries, their densest and best-developed transportation network, the largest number of their manufacturing establishments, and the preponderance of heavy industry.

North American manufacturing began early in the 19th century in southern New England, where waterpowered textile mills, iron plants, and other small-scale industries began to free Canada and the new United States from total dependence on European—particularly English—sources. The eastern portion of the manufacturing belt contained early population centres, a growing canal and railroad network, a steady influx of immigrant skilled and unskilled labour, and concentrations of investment capital to invest in new manufacturing enterprises. The U.S. eastern seaboard remains an important producer of consumer goods, light industrial, and high-technology products on the basis of its market and developed labour skills. Its core is *Megalopolis*,[1] a 1000-kilometre- (600-mile-) long city system stretching from southern Maine to Norfolk, Virginia, with a great array of market-oriented industries and thousands of individual industrial plants.

The heart of the North American manufacturing belt developed across the Appalachians in the interior of the continent. The Ohio River system and the Great Lakes provided the early—and still important—"highways" of the interior, supplemented later by canals and, after the 1850s, by the railroads that tied together the agricultural and industrial raw materials, the growing cities, and multiplying manufacturing plants of the interior with markets and materials throughout the country. The early heavy metallurgical emphasis—the U.S. Steel plants of the Monongahela Valley are an example—has declined and been succeeded early in the 21st century by advanced material processing and fabrication plus high-tech manufacturing, creating a renewed and modernized diversified industrial base.

The Canadian portion of the northeastern American manufacturing belt lies close to neighbouring U.S. industrial districts. About one-half of Canada's manufacturing labour force is localized in southern Ontario. With Toronto as the hub, the industrial belt extends westward to Windsor, across from Detroit. Another third of Canadian manufacturing employment is found in Quebec, with Montreal as the obvious core, but with energy-intensive industries—particularly aluminum plants and paper mills—along the St. Lawrence River (Figure 10.19).

By the 1990s, manufacturing employment and volume was declining everywhere in the Anglo-American economy. What remained showed a pattern of relocation to western and southern zones, reflecting national population shifts and changing material and product orientations.

In the *Southeast*, textiles, tobacco, food processing, wood products, furniture, and a Birmingham-based iron and steel industry became important users of local resources. In the *Gulf Coast–Texas district*, petroleum and natural gas provide wealth, energy, and raw materials for a vast petrochemical industry; sulphur and salt support other branches of chemical production. Farther west, *Denver* and *Salt Lake City* have become major, though isolated, industrial centres with important "high-tech" orientations. On the West Coast, three distinctive industrial subregions have emerged. In the *Northwest*, from Vancouver to Portland, orientation to both a regional and a broader Asian-Pacific market is of greater significance than are the primary domestic markets of Canada and the United States. Seattle's aircraft production and the software industry of the Northwest are, by their high-value products, largely unaffected by transport costs to world markets. The *San Francisco Bay district* is home to Silicon Valley and the electronics/computer/high-tech manufacturing that name implies. Food specializations there (wine, for example) for a national market have their counterpart farther south in the *Los Angeles–San Diego corridor*, where fruits and vegetables are grown and packed. More important, however, is diversified, particularly consumer-goods, production for the rapidly growing California and western market.

---

[1] *Megalopolis* or *conurbation* is an extended urbanized area formed by the gradual merger of several individual cities.

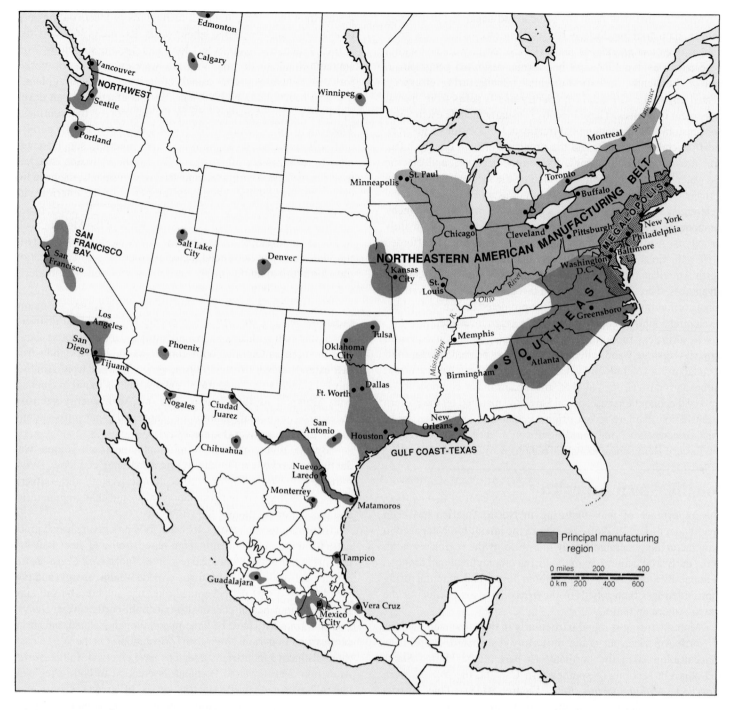

FIGURE 10.18 North American manufacturing districts. Although the preponderance of North American industry is still concentrated in northeastern America, Mexican manufacturing activity is rapidly growing and diversifying—for both expanding domestic and export markets. While Mexico City alone yields nearly half of the country's manufacturing output volume, industrial plants are also localized in the Central Plateau area and along the northern border with the United States, where most *maquiladoras* have been established.

North America's fastest growing industrial region lies along the U.S.–Mexican border. Called *la frontera* by its Mexican workers and extending 3380 kilometres (100 miles) from the Pacific Ocean to the Gulf of Mexico, this subregion served us earlier as an example of "outsourcing" and comparative advantage (p. 351).

Western and Central Europe

The Industrial Revolution that began in England in the late 1700s and spread to the continent during the 19th century established Western and Central Europe as the world's premier manufacturing region, and the source area for the diffusion of industrialization

Port de Montréal
Port of Montreal

FIGURE 10.19 The St. Lawrence Seaway (SLS) links Canada with more than 100 countries around the globe. Opened in 1959, it remains one of the world's largest navigable waterways. From its most western inland port of Deluth, Minnesota, on Lake Superior, eastern to the Atlantic Ocean, it extends some 3700 kilometres and covers some 245,750 square kilometres. Of the 4,361,000 tonnes of commodities transported annually (2005), 40% are agricultural products, 40% are mined materials, and 10% are oil and petroleum products, forest and animal products, and chemicals. Such high levels of freight traffic makes the port at Montreal, pictured above, one of the busiest inland ports in the world.

across the globe. By 1900, Europe accounted for 80% of the world's industrial output though, of course, its relative position has since eroded, particularly after World War II. Although industry is part of the economic structure of every section and every metropolitan complex of Europe, the majority of manufacturing output is concentrated in a set of distinctive districts stretching from the Midlands of England in the west to the Ural Mountains in the east (Figure 10.20).

Water-powered mechanical spinning and weaving in the textile industry of England began the Industrial Revolution, but it was steam power, not waterpower, that provided the impetus for the full industrialization of that country and of Europe. Consequently, coal fields, not rivers, were the sites of the new manufacturing districts in England. London, although remote from coal deposits, became the largest single manufacturing centre of the United Kingdom, its consumers and labour force potent magnets for new industry.

Technologies developed in Britain spread to the continent. The coal fields, distributed in a band across northern France, Belgium, central Germany, the northern Czech Republic, southern Poland, and eastward to southern Ukraine, along with iron ore deposits, localize the metallurgical industries to the present day. Other pronounced industrial concentrations focus on the major metropolitan districts and capital cities of the countries of Europe.

The largest and most important single industrial area of Europe extends from the French–Belgian border to western Germany. Its core is Germany's Ruhr, a compact, highly urbanized industrial

FIGURE 10.20 The industrial regions of Europe.

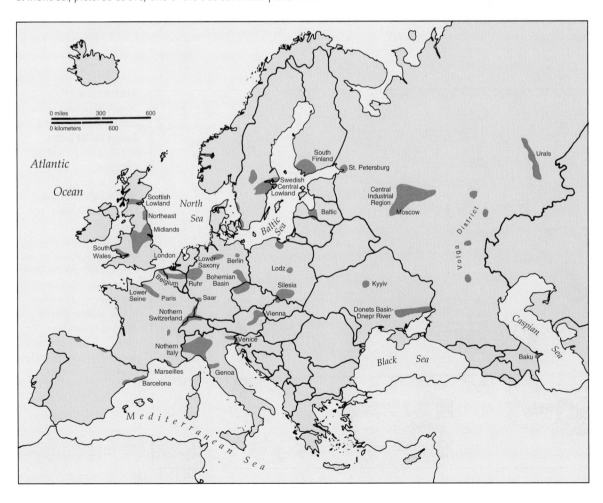

concentration of more than 50 major cities housing iron and steel, textiles, automobiles, chemicals, and all the metal-forming and metal-using industries of modern economies. In France, heavy industry located near the iron ore of Nancy and the coal of Lille also specialized in textile production. Like London, Paris lacks raw materials, but with easy access to the sea and to the domestic market, it became the major manufacturing centre of France. Farther east, the Saxony district began to industrialize as early as the 1600s, in part benefiting from labour skills brought by immigrant artisans from France and Holland. Those skills have been preserved in a district noted for the quality of its manufactured goods.

Western Europe is experiencing a de-industrialization accompanied by massive layoffs of workers in coal mining because of declining demand, and in iron mining because of ore depletion. Iron and steel, textiles, and shipbuilding—the core industries of the Industrial Revolution—have been particularly hard hit. As in the Northeastern American Manufacturing Belt, a restructuring of the Western European economy is introducing new industrial and service orientations and employment patterns.

Eastern Europe

Between the end of World War II and 1990, Eastern European industrial concentrations, such as that of Silesia in Poland and the Czech portion of the Bohemian Basin (Figure 10.20), were largely cut off from their earlier connections with the larger European market and economy. Instead, they were controlled by centralized industrial planning and tied to the regional economic plans imposed by the Soviet Union. Since its fall, Eastern European states have struggled with a generally poorly conceived, technologically antiquated, uneconomic industrial structure that, in its creation and operation, was unresponsive to market realities.

Farther east, in Russia and Ukraine, two distinctly different industrial orientations predominate, both dating from Czarist times and strengthened under Soviet-era planning. One emphasis is on light industrial, market-oriented production primarily focused on Russia's Central Industrial Region of Greater Moscow and surrounding areas (Figure 10.21). The other orientation is heavy industrial. Its Czarist beginnings were localized in the southern Ukrainian Donets Basin-Dnepr River district where coking coal, iron ore, fluxing materials, and iron alloys are found near at hand. Under the Stalinist Five-year Plans, with their emphasis on creation of multiple sources of supply of essential industrial goods, heavy industry was also developed elsewhere in the Soviet Union. The industrial districts of Russia's Volga, Urals, Kuznetsk Basin, Baikal, and Far East regions, and the industrial complexes of the Caucasus, Kazakhstan, and Central Asia resulted from those Soviet programs first launched in 1928.

Eastern Asia

The Eastern Asian sphere is rapidly becoming the most productive of the world's industrial regions (Figure 10.22). Japan has emerged as the overall second-ranked manufacturing nation. China—building on a rich resource base, massive labour force, and nearly insatiable market demand—is industrializing rapidly and ranks among the top 10 producers of a number of major industrial commodities. South Korea, Taiwan, Singapore, and (before its inclusion in China's mainland economy in 1997) Hong Kong,

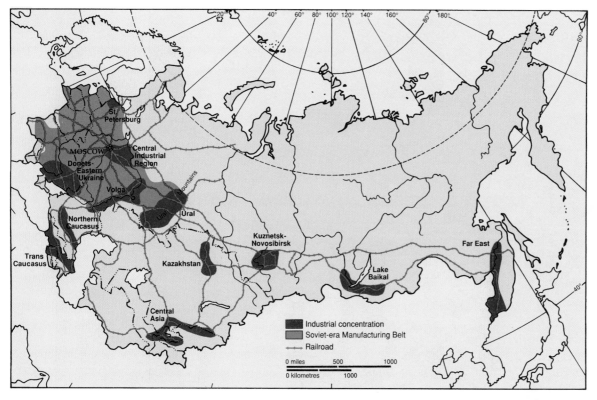

FIGURE 10.21

Industrial regions under central planning in the former Soviet Union. The Volga, the Central Industrial, and the St. Petersburg (Leningrad) concentrations within the former Soviet manufacturing belt were dependent on transportation, labour, and market pulls. All the other planned industrial regions had a strong orientation to materials and were developed despite their distance from the population centres and markets of the west.

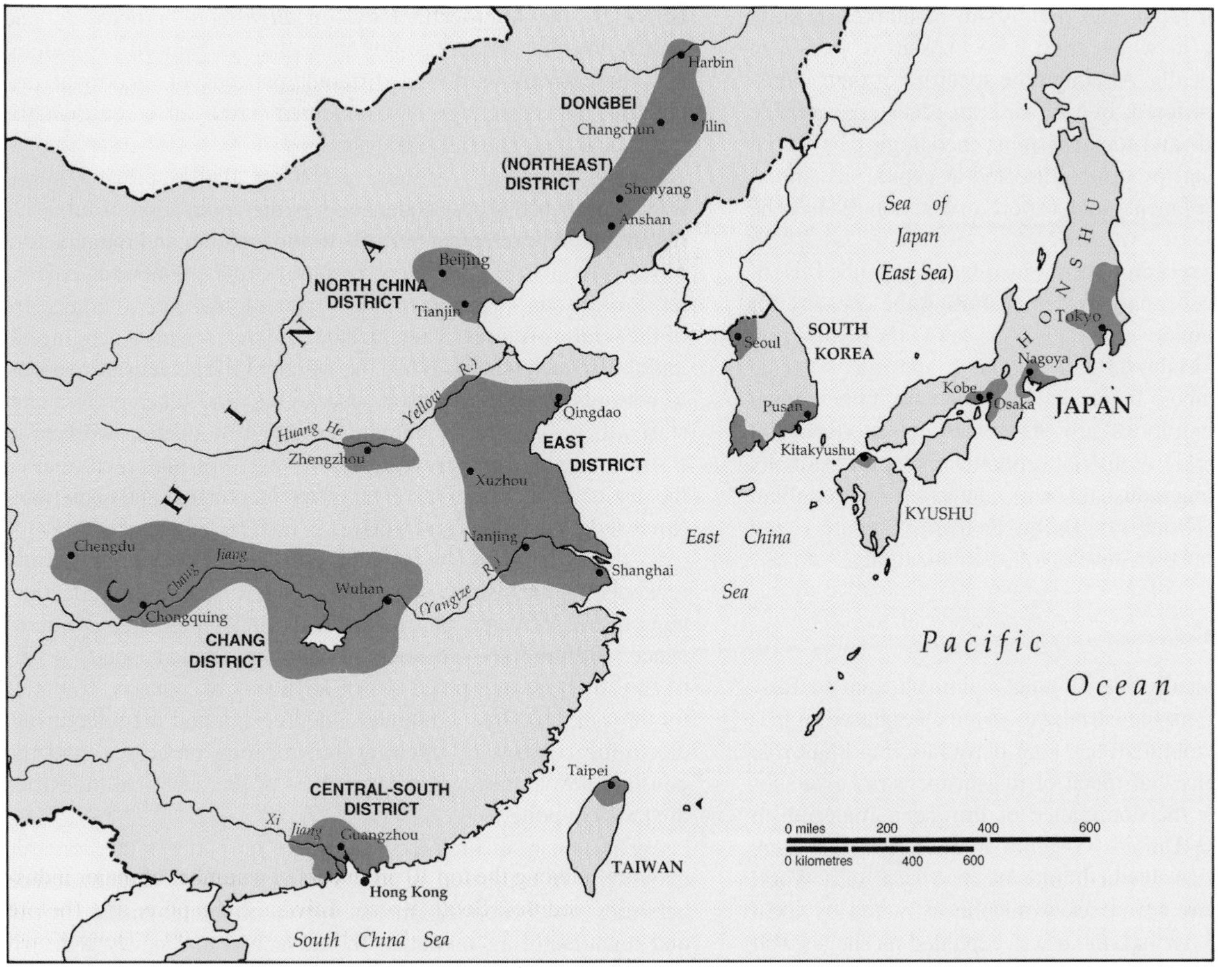

FIGURE 10.22 The industrial districts of Eastern Asia.

were recognized as "the four tigers," swiftly industrializing Asian economies that have become major presences in markets around the world.

Japanese industry was rebuilt from near total destruction during World War II to its present leading position in some areas of electronics and other high-tech production. That recovery was accomplished largely without a domestic raw material base, and primarily with the export market in mind. Dependence on imports of materials and exports of product has encouraged a coastal location for most factories. The industrial core of modern Japan is the heavily urbanized belt from Tokyo to northern Kyushu (Figure 10.22).

When the communists assumed control of China's still war-damaged economy in 1949, that country was essentially unindustrialized. Most manufacturing was small-scale production geared to local subsistence needs. A massive industrialization program initiated by the new regime greatly increased the volume, diversity, and dispersion of manufacturing in China. Until 1976, domestic needs rather than foreign markets were the principal concern of an industrial development totally controlled by the state and the communist party. From the late 1970s, manufacturing activities were freed from absolute state control, and industrial output grew rapidly with most dramatic gains coming not from state enterprises but from quickly multiplying rural collectives.

By the start of the 21st century, however, it was foreign direct investment, foreign firm outsourcing of production to low-cost Chinese suppliers, and relocation to China of manufacturing and assemblage of a host of consumer electronics, clothing, toys, and industrial equipment from other Asian countries that propelled China to the forefront among East Asian and developing countries worldwide as an industrial powerhouse. Simultaneously, China's economic planners actively shuttered inefficient and uneconomic state-owned enterprises (SOEs) that had been the mandated industrial units of the Communist past. Between 1997 and 2002, 27 million workers in SOEs were laid off, and further plant closings followed. China's admission in 2001 to the World Trade Organization (see Chapter 7) further enhanced the competitive position of an economy already accounting for 9.6% of total world exports of manufactured goods in 2002, a share predicted to grow to 14% by 2007.

Unlike Japan, China possesses a relatively rich and diversified domestic raw material base of ores and fuels. The pattern of resource distribution in part accounts for the spatial pattern of industry, though coastal locations, urban agglomerations, and market orientations are equally important (Figure 10.22).

Three smaller East Asian economies—Taiwan, South Korea, and Singapore—have outgrown their former "developing country" status to become advanced industrialized states. Their rise to prominence has been rapid, and their share of market in those branches of industry in which they have chosen to specialize has increased dramatically. Although the specifics of their industrial successes have differed, in each case an educated, trainable labour force; economic and social systems encouraging industrial enterprise; and national programs directed at capital accumulation, industrial development, and export orientation fueled the programs.

Their ranks have recently been joined by an expanded list of other industrial "tigers"—nations demonstrating the capacity for rapid, sustained economic growth. At the least, the new Asian tiger group includes Malaysia and Thailand, and may soon be joined by the Philippines, Indonesia, and Vietnam. Other Asian manufacturing concentrations are also emerging as important participants in the world's industrial economy. India, for example, benefits from expanding industrial bases centered in metropolitan Bangalore, Mumbai (Bombay), Delhi, Kolkata (Calcutta), and elsewhere, each with its own developing specializations.

Africa

Africa is an economically 'developing' continent, and to fully appreciate this status, its industrialization must be placed in historical context. This continent has long played an important role in the world's economy, but much of that history was as a subordinate player under the dominance of European Imperialism (See Figure 7.7). The United Kingdom, France, and Germany had particularly well established colonies in Africa until World War I (1914–18), where resources would be extracted by local workers and exported north. Labour was exploited on site, as well as in the form of export slaves. Since the end of World War II (1945–present), some forty-nine colonies have become independent states (e.g., Egypt, Kenya, Angola, Namibia). Colonialism, then, has been a fundamental force in making the 'developing' economy of Africa: industrialization is thus still in its infancy.

The continent's most valuable exports are minerals and petroleum, but these resources are concentrated in a few countries (e.g., Nigeria, Libya). Only North Africa, Egypt, and South Africa have substantial manufacturing sectors. The latter contributes two-fifths of the continent's industrial output with less than seven percent of the population. South Africa has a wealth of natural resources, is the world's leading producer of both diamonds and gold, and other than Swaziland, is the only state that produces pulp and paper. Generally speaking, the rest of Africa has a total industrial output of less than a single developed country, such as Sweden. This is not surprising, given nearly all of Africa's natural resources are exported to other continents for secondary refining and manufacturing.

High-Tech Patterns

Major industrial districts of the world developed over time as entrepreneurs and planners established traditional secondary industries according to the pulls and orientations predicted by classical location theories. Those theories are less applicable in explaining the location of the latest generation of manufacturing activities: the high-technology—or *high-tech*—processing and production that is increasingly part of the advanced economies. For these firms, new and different patterns of locational orientation and advantage have emerged based on other than the traditional regional and site attractions.

High technology is more a concept than a precise definition. It probably is best understood as the application of intensive research and development efforts to the creation and manufacture of new products of an advanced scientific and engineering character. Professional—"white collar"—workers make up a large share of the total workforce. They include research scientists, engineers, and skilled technicians. When these high-skill specialists are added to administrative, supervisory, marketing, and other professional staffs, they may greatly outnumber actual production workers in a firm's employment structure. In the world of high-tech, that is, the distinction between secondary (manufacturing) and quaternary (knowledge) activities and workers is increasingly blurred.

Although only a few types of industrial activity are generally reckoned as exclusively high-tech—electronics, communication, computers, software, pharmaceuticals and biotechnology, aerospace, and the like—advanced technology is increasingly a part of the structure and processes of all forms of industry. Robotics on the assembly line, computer-aided design and manufacturing, electronic controls of smelting and refining processes, and the constant development of new products of the chemical industries are cases in point.

The impact of high-tech industries on patterns of economic geography is expressed in at least three ways. First, high-tech activities are becoming major factors in employment growth and manufacturing output in the advanced and newly industrializing economies. In the United States, for example, between 1986 and 2000, the largest five high-tech industry groups alone added more than 8 million new jobs to the secondary sector of the economy, helping replace many thousands of other workers who lost jobs to outsourcing, foreign competition, changing markets, and deindustrialization. In 2000, total U.S. high-technology employment equalled more than 16% of all non-farm workers, while even workers in more strictly defined "high-technology industries" totalled 7% of all employment. In Canada, the industrial sector is becoming increasingly technology-intensive and knowledge-based: computers and office equipment, communication equipment, semi-conductors, and communication services are "engines" of economic growth. The United Kingdom, Germany, Japan, and other advanced countries—though not yet those of Eastern Europe—have had similar employment and sector shifts, while many of the newly industrializing economies of East and Southeast Asia have registered high-tech employment growth of similar or greater proportions.

Many of the confident generalizations concerning, particularly, the computer and software segments of high-technology industry and employment and the prospects for their continuing expansion were called into question by the abrupt dot-com bubble collapse of the first years of the century. Tens of thousands of software jobs lost, scores of innovative, visionary, or simply hopeful software and hardware ventures bankrupt, billions of dollars of venture capital and stock valuations erased, and lavish offices and plants left vacant marked the end of a period of exuberant growth and expectations that shaped high-tech locational patterns and bolstered national economies throughout the world. Within the United States alone, high-tech employment dropped by an estimated 15% from 2001 through 2004. Although first-of-the-century details of the computer software and hardware distributions, specializations, and employment structures were severely disturbed or destroyed during the subsequent dot-com depression, there was both a continuation of high-technology applications to established general manufacturing activities, and a gradual revival of investment and employment in software development. Locational concentrations and specializations may change, but high-tech's fundamental alteration of older economic structures and patterns endures.

The products of high-technology activity represent an increasing share of total industrial output of individual countries and of the trade between them. As early as 1995, high-tech manufactures represented 15% of manufacturing output in the United States; by 2001, that share had risen to 21%. Over that same span, the United Kingdom high-tech component increased from 14% to 17%. Gains were even more impressive in some newly industrializing economies. In 1989, high-tech manufactures accounted for 12.4% of Taiwan's total manufacturing output; that proportion jumped to 29.2% by 2001. Similarly, the high-tech share of manufacturing in South Korea—10% in 1989—grew to 31% in 2001. Both the post-2000 economic slowdown and the increase in outsourcing have, to different degrees, affected various countries' high-tech manufacturing component, but in all cases the high-tech industries continue to claim a prominent, but variable, place in national manufacturing structures. Global data are incomplete, but Figure 10.23 suggests the great disparity between countries in the importance of high-tech products in their exports of manufactured goods.

A second impact is more clearly spatial. High-tech industries have tended to become regionally concentrated in their countries of development, and within those regions, they frequently form self-sustaining, highly specialized agglomerations. California, for example, has a share of U.S. high-tech employment far in excess of its share of American population. Along with California, the Pacific Northwest (including British Columbia), New England, New Jersey, Texas, and Colorado all have proportions of their workers in high-tech industries above the national average. And within these and other states or regions of high-tech concentration, specific locales have achieved prominence: "Silicon Valley" of Santa Clara County near San Francisco; Irvine and Orange County south of Los Angeles; the "Silicon Forest" near Seattle; North Carolina's Research Triangle; Utah's "Software Valley"; Routes 128 and 495 around Boston; "Silicon Swamp" of the Washington, D.C. area; Ottawa, Canada's "Silicon Valley North"; or the Canadian Technology Triangle west of Toronto are familiar North American examples (see "Canada's Technology Triangle").

Within such concentrations, specialization is often the rule: medical technologies in Minneapolis and Philadelphia; biotechnology around San Antonio; computers and semiconductors in eastern Virginia and at Austin, Texas; biotechnology and telecommunications in New Jersey's Princeton Corridor; telecommunications and Internet industries near Washington, D.C. Elsewhere, Scotland's Silicon Glen, England's Sunrise Strip and Silicon Fen, Wireless Valley in Stockholm, Zhong Guancum in suburban Beijing, and

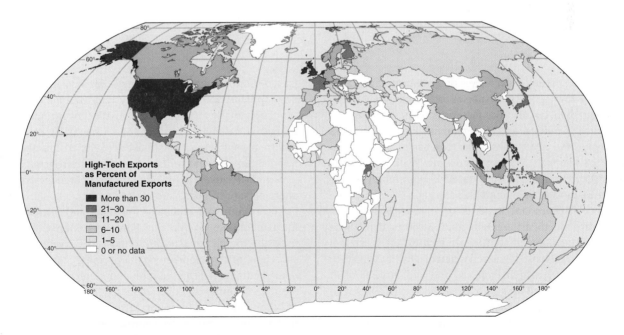

FIGURE 10.23 This map of **high-tech exports** clearly suggests the importance of the industrialized countries—particularly the United States and Western Europe—in high-tech manufacturing and exports in 2002. Less evident is the relative role of high-tech in the manufactured exports of a few smaller, developing states: 60% for Singapore; 58% for Malaysia; 65% for the Philippines; and 37% for Costa Rica in 2002. By the early 21st century, in fact, high-tech goods made up a larger proportion of the exports of developing countries than of advanced industrial ones, and the disparity continues to grow. The map, of course, does not report a country's ranking in volumes or values of high-tech manufactured goods exports.

Source: The World Bank, World Development Indicators 2006.

Canada's Technology Triangle

Anchored by the three cities of Kitchener, Cambridge, and Waterloo, "Canada's Technology Triangle" (CTT) is located in the Waterloo Region of southwestern Ontario, just west of Toronto. Herein lays a rapidly growing cluster of businesses and manufacturers on the cutting edge of research, development and production. Between 1996 and 2001, CTT grew by over 8.2%, with a gross domestic product larger than several Canadian provinces: $18.6 billion. In 2002 alone, there were some 260,000 people employed, producing $10.8 billion in product exports shipped throughout the world.

The business base is diverse and may be categorized into seven key sectors: *high tech* includes more than 400 companies producing goods and services, including information technologies such as wireless and Internet hardware and software; *automotive* comprises more than 450 automotive-related companies, both car manufacturers and auto parts suppliers; *advanced manufacturing* consists of engineering and robotic designers and producers, which provide still other businesses and manufacturers with the latest means of accelerating their own methods of production; similarly the *business process*

outsourcing sector provides telecommunication and technical services; *business and financial services* are diverse and numerous, and include several large insurance companies; *biotech and life sciences* is an emerging cluster of research institutes producing medical and biological technologies; and finally, *other sectors* are comprised of such manufacturing and services as food processing, furniture manufacturing, transportation, and warehousing. There are also more than 150 research centres within the CTT, as well as The University of Waterloo, Wilfrid Laurier University, The University of Guelph, and Conestoga College Institute of Technology and Advanced Learning.

The businesses and services here are truly global in constitution and market. A 2005 survey of the CTT revealed that 247 of the firms are foreign-owned, meaning investment in this area extends outside of Canada and included much of the rest of the world: 68% were U.S., 26% were European—Germany, United Kingdom, France, The Netherlands, Ireland, Switzerland, Italy—others were Asian—China, Japan and Taiwan—and still others Brazilian and Australian. This is not by chance but design.

CTT is more than simply an organizing label designated to an economic region, it is a not-for-profit, private-public economic development organization formed to market, grow, and develop the Waterloo region. Its goals include the attraction and retention of investment and businesses from around the country and the world, and to create and sustain a highly skilled and educated workforce, with high incomes and low unemployment rates. The project is successful: Waterloo Region has become an important part of the postindustrial global, Canadian, and Ontarian economies.

Bangalore, India, are other examples of industrial landscapes characterized by low, modern, dispersed office-plant-laboratory buildings rather than by massive factories, mills, or assembly structures, freight facilities, and storage areas. Planned business parks catering to the needs of smaller companies are increasingly a part of regional and local economic planning. Irvine, California's Spectrum, for example, housed 44,000 employees and 2200 companies, most of them high-tech start-ups.

The older distributional patterns of high-tech industries suggest they respond to different localizing forces than those controlling traditional manufacturing industries. At least five locational tendencies have been recognized: (1) Proximity to major universities or research facilities and to a large pool of scientific and technical labour skills; (2) avoidance of areas with strong labour unionization where contract rigidities might slow process innovation and workforce flexibility; (3) locally available venture capital and entrepreneurial daring; (4) location in regions and major metropolitan areas with favourable "quality of life" reputations—climate, scenery, recreation, good universities, and an employment base sufficiently large to supply needed workers and provide job opportunities for professionally trained spouses; (5) availability of top-quality communication and

transportation facilities to unite separated stages of research, development, and manufacturing and to connect the firm with suppliers, markets, finances, and the government agencies so important in supporting research. Essentially all of the major high-tech agglomerations have developed on the semi-rural peripheries of metropolitan areas but far from inner-city problems and disadvantages. Many have emerged as self-sufficient areas of subdivisions, shopping centres, schools, and parks in close proximity to company locations and business parks that form their core. While the New York metropolitan area is a major high-tech concentration, most of the technology jobs are suburban, not in Manhattan; the periphery's share of computer-related employment in the region amounted to 80% at the end of the 20th century.

Agglomerating forces are also important in this new industrial locational model. The formation of new firms is frequent, and rapid in industries where discoveries are constant and innovation is continuous. Since many are "spin-off" firms founded by employees leaving established local companies, areas of existing high-tech concentration tend to spawn new entrants and to provide necessary labour skills. Agglomeration, therefore, is both a product and a cause of spatial associations.

Not all phases of high-tech production must be concentrated, however. The spatial attractions affecting the professional, scientific, and knowledge-intensive aspects of high tech have little meaning for many of the component manufacturing and assembly operations, which may be highly automated or require little in the way of labour skills. These tasks, in our earlier locational terminology, are "footloose"; they require highly mobile capital and technology investments but may be advantageously performed by young women in low-wage areas at home or—more likely—in countries such as Taiwan, Singapore, Malaysia, or Mexico. Contract manufacturers totally divorced spatially and managerially from the companies whose products they produce accounted for an estimated 15% to 20% of the output of electronics hardware. Most often the same factory produces similar or identical products under a number of different brand names. Through such manufacturing transfers of technology and outsourcing, high-tech activities are spread to newly industrializing countries—from the centre to the periphery, in the developmental terms we will explore in Chapter 11. This globalization through areal transfer and dispersion represents a third impact of high-tech activities on world economic geographic patterns already undergoing significant but variable change in response to the new technologies.

Tertiary and Beyond

Primary activities, you will recall, gather, extract, or grow things. *Secondary* industries, we have seen in this chapter, give form utility to the products of primary industry through manufacturing and processing efforts. A major and growing segment of both domestic and international economic activity, however, involves *services* rather than the production of commodities. These **tertiary activities** consist of business and labour specializations that provide services to the primary and secondary sectors, to the general community, and to the individual. They imply pursuits other than the actual production of tangible commodities.

As we have seen in these last two chapters, regional and national economies undergo fundamental changes in emphasis in the course of their development. Subsistence societies exclusively dependent on primary industries may progress to secondary stage processing and manufacturing activities. In that progression, the importance of agriculture, for example, as an employer of labour or contributor to national income declines as that of manufacturing expands. Many parts of the formerly underdeveloped world have made or are making that developmental transition, as we shall review in Chapter 11.

The advanced countries that originally dominated the world manufacturing scene, in contrast, saw their former industrial primacy reduced or lost during the last third of the 20th century. Rising energy and labour costs, the growth of transnational corporations, transfer of technology to developing countries, and outsourcing of processing or assembly have all changed the structure and pattern of the world economy. The earlier competitive manufacturing advantages of the developed countries could no longer be maintained, and new economic orientations emphasizing service and information activities became the replacement.

Advanced economies that have most completely made that transition are often referred to as "post-industrial."

Among only a handful of countries in the world, Canada has reached post-industrial status. Its primary sector—agriculture, forestry, mining, oil, and gas—employs only 4% of Canadians, manufacturing employs another 13.7%, while the vast majority, 75.2%, work in the service sectors (Table 10.2). Between 65% and 80% of all jobs currently created in Canada, Japan, Australia, Israel, and all major Western European countries are in the service sector; Russia and Eastern Europe averaged rather less.

The significance of tertiary activities to national economies and the contrast between more developed and less developed states are made clear not just by employment but also by the differential contribution of services to the gross domestic products of states. The relative importance of services displayed in Figure 10.24 shows a marked contrast between advanced and subsistence societies. The greater the service share of an economy, the greater is the integration and interdependence of that society. That share has grown over time among most regions, and all national income categories as all economies have shared, to some degree, in world developmental growth (Table 10.3). Indeed, the expansion of the tertiary sector in modernizing East Asia, South Asia, and the Pacific was three times the world average in the 1990s. In Latin America and the Caribbean, services accounted for 67% of total output in 2002. Canada is one of the "high income" countries with a high percentage of its GDP generated in the service sector. Some 68% of the country's 2005 GDP was created through service-producing industries (see Table 10.4).

Tertiary and *service*, however, are broad and imprecise terms that cover a range of activities from neighbourhood barber to World Bank president. The designations are equally applicable both to traditional low-order personal and retail activities, and to higher-order, knowledge-based professional services performed primarily for other businesses, not for individual consumption.

Logically, the composite tertiary category should be subdivided to distinguish between those activities answering to the daily living and support needs of individuals and local communities, and those involving professional, administrative, or financial management tasks at regional, national, and international scales. Those differing levels and scope of activity represent different locational principles and quite different roles in their contribution to domestic and world economies (see Table 10.4).

To recognize such fundamental contrasts, we can usefully restrict the term "tertiary" specifically to those lower-level services largely related to day-to-day needs of people and to the usual range of functions found in smaller towns and cities worldwide. We can then assign higher-level, more specialized information research, and management activities to distinctive "quaternary" and "quinary" categories (see Figure 9.2) with quite different and distinctive characteristics and significance.

Tertiary Services

Some services are concerned with the wholesaling or retailing of goods, providing what economists call *place utility* to items produced elsewhere. They fulfill the exchange function of advanced economies and provide the market transactions necessary in

TABLE 10.2

Distribution of Employed Canadians by Industry and Province (2005)

PERCENTAGES OF CANADA'S TOTAL EMPLOYMENT

	Canada	B.C.	Alberta	Sask.	Man.	Ont.	Que.	N.B.	N.S.	P.E.I.	Nfld
All industries	100	13.1	11	3	3.6	39.5	22.9	2.2	2.7	0.4	1.3
Goods-producing sector	24.8	2.8	3	0.8	0.9	10.1	5.7	0.5	0.6	0.1	0.3
Agriculture	2.1	0.2	0.3	0.3	0.2	0.6	0.4	<0.1	<0.1	<0.1	<0.1
Forestry, fishing, mining, oil and gas	1.9	0.2	0.8	0.1	<0.1	0.2	0.2	<0.1	0.1	<0.1	0.1
Utilities	0.8	0.1	0.1	<0.1	<0.1	0.3	0.2	<0.1	<0.1	<0.1	<0.1
Construction	6.3	1.1	1	0.2	0.2	2.4	1.1	0.1	0.2	<0.1	<0.1
Manufacturing	13.7	1.2	0.8	0.2	0.4	6.6	3.8	0.2	0.2	<0.1	0.1
Service-producing sector	75.2	10.3	8	2.2	2.7	29.4	17.2	1.7	2.1	0.3	1
Trade	15.9	2	1.7	0.5	0.5	6.1	3.8	0.4	0.5	<0.1	0.2
Transportation and warehousing	4.9	0.7	0.7	0.2	0.2	1.8	1	0.1	0.1	<0.1	0.1
Finance, insurance, real estate, and leasing	6.1	0.8	0.6	0.2	0.2	2.8	1.3	0.1	0.1	<0.1	<0.1
Professional, scientific, and technical services	6.5	1	0.8	0.1	0.2	2.7	1.4	0.1	0.1	<0.1	<0.1
Business, building, and other support services	4	0.6	0.4	0.1	0.1	1.7	0.8	0.1	0.2	<0.1	<0.1
Educational services	6.8	0.9	0.7	0.2	0.3	2.6	1.5	0.2	0.2	<0.1	0.1
Health care and social assistance	10.7	1.3	1.1	0.4	0.5	3.9	2.8	0.3	0.3	<0.1	0.2
Information, culture, and recreation	4.6	0.7	0.4	0.1	0.1	1.9	1	0.1	0.1	<0.1	<0.1
Accommodation and food services	6.2	1.1	0.7	0.2	0.2	2.3	1.3	0.1	0.2	<0.1	0.1
Other services	4.3	0.6	0.5	0.1	0.2	1.6	1	0.1	0.1	<0.1	0.1
Public administration	5.2	0.6	0.4	0.1	0.2	2	1.3	0.1	0.2	<0.1	0.1

Source: Statistics Canada, http://www40.statcan.ca/l01/cst01/labour21b.htm.

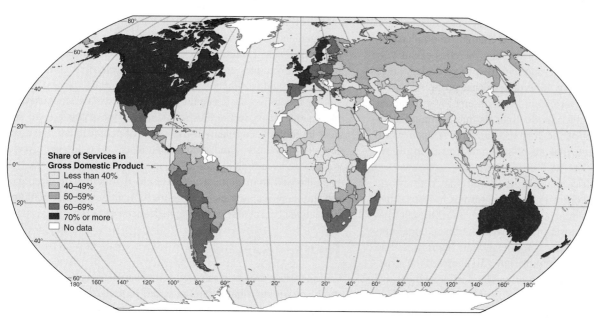

FIGURE 10.24
Services accounted for nearly two-thirds of global GDP early in the 21st century, up sharply from about 50% in the 1980s. As the map documents, the contribution of services to individual national economies varied greatly, whereas Table 10.3 indicates all national income categories shared to some degree in the expansion of service activities.

Share of Services in Gross Domestic Product
- Less than 40%
- 40–49%
- 50–59%
- 60–69%
- 70% or more
- No data

Source: World Bank, World Development Indicators.

TABLE 10.3

Contribution of the Service Sector to Gross Domestic Product

PERCENTAGE OF GDP

COUNTRY GROUP	1960	1980	2000
Low income	32	30	44
Middle income	47	46	55
High income	54	59	64
World	–	55	63

Source: World Bank.

TABLE 10.4

Canadian Gross Domestic Product by Industries (2005)

PERCENT OF CANADA'S TOTAL GDP

Services-producing industries	**68.3**
Finance and insurance, real estate, renting, leasing, management of companies and enterprises	19.7
Wholesale trade	6.4
Retail trade	5.9
Health care and social assistance	5.7
Public administration	5.5
Transportation and warehousing	4.8
Educational services	4.4
Professional, scientific, and technical services	4.3
Information and cultural industries	4.1
Other services	2.4
Administrative and support, waste management and remediation services	2.2
Accommodation and food services	2.1
Arts, entertainment, and recreation	0.8
Goods-producing industries	**31.7**
Manufacturing	17.2
Construction industries	5.9
Mining and oil and gas extraction	3.8
Utilities	2.6
Agriculture, forestry, fishing, and hunting	2.2
All industries	**100.0**

Source: World Bank.

highly interdependent societies. In commercial economies, tertiary activities also provide vitally needed information about market demand, without which economically justifiable production decisions are impossible.

The locational controls for tertiary enterprises are rather simpler than those for the manufacturing sector. Service activities are by definition market oriented. Those dealing with transportation and communication are concerned with the placements of people and commodities to be connected or moved; their locational determinants are therefore the patterns of population distribution and the spatial structure of production and consumption.

Most tertiary activities, however, are concerned with personal and business services performed in shops, restaurants, and company and governmental offices that cluster in cities large and small. The supply of those kinds of low-level services of necessity must be identical to the spatial distribution of *effective demand*—that is, wants made meaningful through purchasing power. Retail and personal services are localized by their markets, because the production of the service and its consumption are simultaneous occurrences. Retailers and personal service providers tend to locate, therefore, where market density is greatest and multiple service demands are concentrated (Figure 10.25). Their locational patterns and the employment support they imply are important aspects of urban economic structure and were dealt with in Chapter 8.

In all of the world's increasingly interdependent post-industrial societies, the growth of the service component reflects not only the development of ever more complex social, economic, and administrative structures, it also indicates changes made possible by growing personal incomes and alterations in family structure and individual lifestyle. For example, in subsistence economies families produce, prepare, and consume food within the household. Urbanizing industrial societies have increasing dependence on specialized farmers growing food and wholesalers and retailers selling food to households that largely prepare and consume it at home. Post-industrial North America increasingly opts to purchase prepared foods in restaurants, fast-food, or carry-out establishments with accelerating growth of the tertiary food service workers that change demands. People are still fed, but the employment structure has altered (see "Women and the Workplace").

Part of the growth in the tertiary component is statistical, rather than functional. We saw in our discussion of modern industry that "outsourcing" was increasingly employed as a device to reduce costs and enhance manufacturing and assembly efficiencies. In the same way, outsourcing of services formerly provided in-house is also characteristic of current business practice. Cleaning and maintenance of factories, shops, and offices—formerly done by the company itself as part of internal operations—now are subcontracted to specialized service providers. The jobs are still done, perhaps even by the same personnel, but worker status has changed from "secondary" (as employees of a manufacturing plant, for example) to "tertiary" (as employees of a service company).

Special note should be made of *tourism*—travel undertaken for purposes of recreation rather than business. It has become not only the most important single tertiary sector activity but is, as well, the world's largest industry in jobs and total value generated. On a worldwide basis, tourism accounts for some 250 million recorded jobs and untold additional numbers in the informal economy. Altogether, 15% or more of the world's workforce is

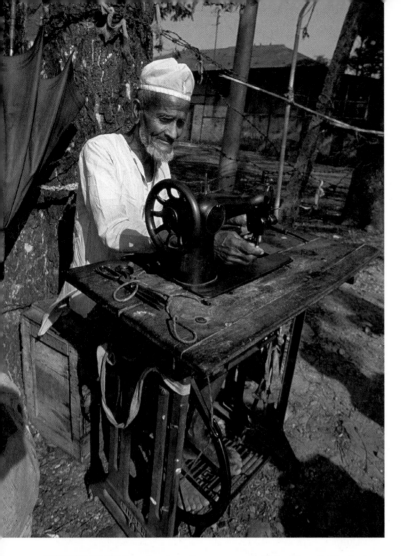

FIGURE 10.25 Low-level services are most efficiently and effectively performed where demand and purchasing power are concentrated, as this garment repairman in a Bangladesh city marketplace demonstrates. Such informal sector employment—street vendors, odd-job handypeople, open-air dispensers of such personal services as barbering, shoe shining, clothes mending, and the like—usually escapes governmental registration and is not included in official service employment totals.

For half of the world's 50 poorest countries, tourism had become by 2002 the leading service export sector.

Whatever the origins of tertiary employment growth, the social and structural consequences are comparable. The process of development leads to increasing labour specialization and economic interdependence within a country. That was true during the latter part of the 20th century for all economies, as Table 10.3 attests. Carried to the postindustrial stage of advanced technology-based economies and high per capita income, the service component of both the gross domestic product (see Figure 10.24) and the employed labour force rises to dominance.

Beyond Tertiary

Available statistics unfortunately do not always permit a clear distinction between *tertiary* service employment that is a reflection of daily lifestyle or corporate structural changes and the more specialized, higher-level *quaternary* and *quinary* activities.

The **quaternary** sector may be seen realistically as an advanced form of services involving specialized knowledge, technical skills, communication ability, or administrative competence. These are the tasks carried on in office buildings, elementary and university classrooms, hospitals and doctors' offices, theatres, accounting and brokerage firms, and the like. With the explosive growth in demand for and consumption of information-based services—mutual fund managers, tax consultants, software developers, statisticians, and more at near-infinite length—the quaternary sector in the most highly developed economies has replaced all primary and secondary employment as the basis for economic growth. In fact, over half of all workers in rich economies are in the "knowledge sector" alone—in the production, storage, retrieval, or distribution of information.

Quaternary activities performed for other business organizations often embody "externalization" of specialized services similar to the outsourcing of low-level tertiary functions. The distinction between them lies in the fact that knowledge and skill-based free-standing quaternary service establishments can be spatially divorced from their clients; they are not tied to resources, affected by the environment, or necessarily localized by market. They can realize cost reductions through serving multiple clients in highly technical areas, and permit client firms to utilize specialized skills and efficiencies to achieve competitive advantage without the expense of adding to their own labour force.

Often, of course, when high-level personal contacts are required, the close functional association of client and service firms within a country encourages quaternary locations and employment patterns similar to those of the headquarters distribution of the primary and secondary industries served. But the transportability of quaternary services also means that many of them can be spatially isolated from their client base. In Canada and the United States, at least, these combined trends have resulted both in the concentration of certain specialized services—merchant banking or bond underwriting, for example—in major metropolitan areas and, as well, in a regional diffusion of the quaternary sector to accompany a growing regional deconcentration of the client firm base. Similar locational tendencies have been noted even for the spatially more restricted advanced economies of, for example, England and France.

engaged in providing services to recreational travellers, and the total economic value of tourism goods and services at the start of the 21st century reached about $4 trillion, or some 14% of the world's gross domestic product. In middle- and high-income countries, tourism supports a diversified share of domestic expenditures through transportation-related costs, roadside services, entertainment, national park visits, and the like. International tourism, on the other hand, generates new income and jobs of growing importance in developing states since one-fifth of all international tourists now travel from an industrial country to a developing one. Altogether, worldwide international tourist visits numbered about 700 million in 2002, more than a quarter of them destined for the less developed low- and middle-income countries. That inbound flow produced over 8% of all foreign earnings of developing states in 2000 and—in the form of goods and services such as meals, lodging, and transport consumed by foreign travellers—comprised about 44% of their total "service exports."

Women and the Workplace

Precisely what constitutes "work" and the spaces where it occurs has varied over time within and between societies. As noted previously, prior to the Industrial Revolution and the rise of capitalism, industries in the Western world were geographically dispersed into "cottage industries": small operations with low, time-consuming outputs of a unique product, run by craftspeople out of their own home. Like those who farmed, the place of home and work were closely tied, if not blurred entirely, together. Childrearing and earning a livelihood took place often in or immediately adjacent the home. Only with the rise of centralized energy sources, mechanized methods of mass production, large-scale manufacturing plants, and the shift to industrialized, urban economies did the organization and division of labour come to resemble what is now taken by some as the "natural" order of things: work—the *public sphere*—and home—the *private sphere*—are separate places in distinct spaces. Accordingly, labour is divided along the lines of gender: men work at some jobs, mostly in the public sphere, while women work at others, mostly in the private sphere.

Since the 1970s, feminists have challenged both the myth of work as limited to waged labour (*employment*) in the production of goods or services for the market, and the myth of the work/home dualism (Klahr, 1999). If work is narrowly equated with paid labour, it makes unpaid labour at home invisible. Anyone who has performed domestic chores or childcare knows that they demand time, effort, and a great deal of energy. If work is more broadly conceived as the exertion of physical or mental energy directed toward chores that serve human needs, homework becomes recognized for the essential role it performs in socializing and sustaining household members and the current and

future workforce. Unfortunately, such recognition is far from universal. Even today when the number of women employed in the formal paid economy continues to grow across the globe, and in Canada where almost half of all employees are female (46%), women's work is often not given the same status and respect as that of men's (Statistics Canada, 2005b).

Part of the explanation for this difference is a function of the myth of "separate worlds" wherein work and home—the public and the private—are considered distinct and separate spaces (Kobayashi, Peake, Beneson, and Pickles, 1994). As part of this work/home duality, the former has become equated with masculine identity and the later with feminine identity. Women's place

in the workforce was—and to a large extent remains—secondary to their domestic chores. Indeed, two out of three part-time employees in Canada are female, and males tend to spend less time performing domestic chores than do women (Statistics Canada, 2005b). The problem for many women in Canada and elsewhere is not their exclusion from the so-called public sphere of work, but that their inclusion is in addition to their domestic responsibilities in the so-called private sphere of home: they have too much "work" in the geographies of their everyday lives. For geographers the task is to identify, document, explain, critique, and challenge the unquestioned gender roles and experiences of working women in the places and spaces where they labour.

Information, administration, and the "knowledge" activities in their broadest sense are dependent on communication. Their spatial dispersion has been facilitated by the underlying technological base of most quaternary activities: electronic digital processing and telecommunication transfer of data. That technology permits many "back-office" tasks to be spatially far distant from the home office locations of either the service or client firms. Insurance claims, credit card charges, mutual fund and stock market transactions, and the like, are more efficiently and

economically recorded or processed in low-rent, low-labour cost locations—often in suburbs or small towns and in rural states—than in the financial districts of major cities. Production and consumption of such services can be spatially separated in a way not feasible for tertiary, face-to-face activities.

Finally, there are the **quinary activities**, the "gold collar" professions of the chapter title, another separately recognized subdivision of the tertiary sector representing the special and highly paid skills of top business executives, government officials, research scientists, financial and legal consultants, and the like. These people find their place of business in major metropolitan centres, in and near major universities and research parks, at first-rank medical centres, and in cabinet and department-level offices of political capitals. Within their cities of concentration, they may be highly localized by prestigious street addresses (Bay Street) or post offices (Montreal, Quebec), or by notable "signature" office buildings (BCE Place). Their importance in the structure of advanced economies far outweighs their numbers.

The list of tertiary, quaternary, and quinary employment is long. Its diversity and familiarity remind us of the complexity of modern life and of how far removed we are from the subsistence economies. As societies advance economically, the share of employment and national income generated by the primary, secondary, and composite tertiary sectors continually changes; the spatial patterns of human activity reflect those changes. The shift is steadily away from production and processing, and toward the trade, personal, and professional services of the tertiary sector and the information and control activities of the quaternary and quinary. That transition is the essence of the now-familiar term *post-industrial*.

Services in World Trade

Just as service activities have been major engines of national economic growth, so too have they become an increasing factor in international trade flows and economic interdependence. Between 1980 and 2002, services increased from 15% of total world trade to nearly 25%. The fastest growing segment of that increase was in such private services as financial, brokerage, and leasing activities, which had grown to 50% of all commercial services trade by the early 21st century. As in the domestic arena, rapid advances and reduced costs in information technology and electronic data transmission have been central elements in the internationalization of services, as wired and wireless communication costs have been reduced to negligible levels. Many services considered non-tradable even late in the 1990s are now actively exchanged at long distance, as the growth of services offshoring clearly shows.

Developing countries have been particular beneficiaries of the new technologies. Their exports of services—valued at nearly $267 billion in 2002—grew at an annual 15% rate in the 1990s, twice as fast as service exports from industrial regions. The increasing tradability of services has expanded the international comparative advantage of developing states in relatively labour-intensive long-distance service activities such as mass data processing, computer software development, and the like. At the same time, they have benefited from increased access to efficient, state-of-the-art equipment and techniques transferred from advanced economies.

That integration has increasingly moved to higher levels of economic and professional services. The cost and efficiency advantages of outsourcing skilled functions—such as para-legal and legal services, accountancy, medical analysis and technical services, and research and development work in a nearly unlimited range of businesses—are now widely understood and appreciated. Wired and wireless transmission of

data, documents, medical and technical records, charts, X-rays, and the like, make distant quaternary and higher-level services immediately and efficiently accessible. Further, many higher-level services are easily subdivided and performable in sequence or simultaneously in multiple locations. The well-known "follow the sun" practices of software developers who finish a day's tasks only to pass on work to colleagues elsewhere in the world are now increasingly used by professionals in many other fields. When the practice involves highly educated and talented specialists receiving developing world compensation levels, the cost attractions for developed country companies are irresistible. The necessary levels of education and technical expertise themselves are, to an ever greater extent, more apt to have been acquired not by expensive training in European or North American universities, but rather through distant learning programs and professional school contacts through the Internet.

The concentration of computer software development around Bangalore and Hyderabad has made India a major world player in software innovation, for example, whereas there and elsewhere in that country, increasing volumes of back-office work for Western insurance, financial and accounting companies, and airlines are being performed. Customer interaction services ("call centres") formerly based in North America are now increasingly relocated to India, employing workers trained to speak to callers in perfect

TABLE 10.5

Shares of World Trade in Commercial Services (Exports plus Imports, 2002)

COUNTRY OR CATEGORY	% OF WORLD
United States	16.1
United Kingdom	7.5
Japan	5.7
France	5.2
China (with Hong Kong)	5.1
Germany	5.0
Italy	4.0
Netherlands	3.7
Spain	3.3
Belgium/Luxembourg	3.1
Canada	2.6
Austria	2.4
Ireland	2.3
Korea (Rep)	2.1
Total	**68.1**
High-income states	81.3
Low-income states	3.1
Sub-Saharan Africa	1.0
European Monetary Union	32.4

Source: Data from International Monetary Fund and World Bank.

English. Claims processing for life and health insurance firms have become concentrated in English-speaking Caribbean states to take advantage of the lower wages and availability of a large pool of educated workers there. In all such cases, the result is an acceleration of the transfer rate of technology in such expanding areas as information and telecommunications services and an increase in the rate of developing-country integration in the world economy.

Many of the current developing-country gains in international quaternary services are the result of increased foreign direct investment (FDI) in the services sector. Those flows accounted for three-fifths of all FDI in the early years of the 21st century. The majority of such investment, however, is transferred among the advanced countries themselves rather than between industrial and developing states. In either case, as transnational corporations use mainframe computers around the clock for data processing, they can exploit or eliminate time zone differences between home office countries and host countries of their affiliates. Such cross-border intrafirm service transactions are not usually recorded in

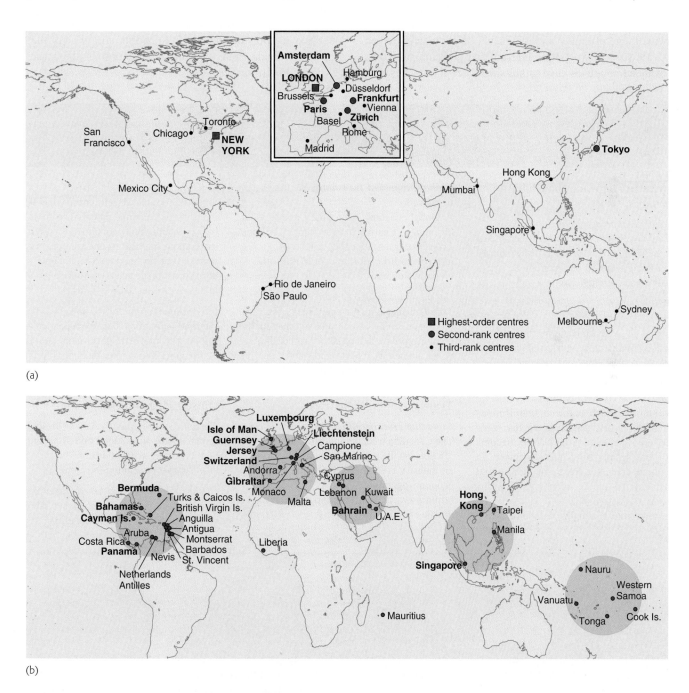

FIGURE 10.26 (*a*) **The hierarchy of international financial centres,** topped by New York and London, indicates the tendency of highest-order quaternary activities to concentrate in a few world and national centres. (*b*) At the same time, the multiplication of offshore locations where "furtive money" avoiding regulatory control and national taxes finds refuge suggests that dispersed convenience sites also serve the international financial community. In 2002, under international pressure, most of the tax havens agreed to greater openness and less protective secrecy.

Source: Peter Dicken, Global Shift, *4th ed., Guilford Press, 2003, Figures 13.8 and 13.10.*

balance of payment or trade statistics, but materially increase the volume of international services flows.

Despite the increasing share of global services trade held by developing countries, world trade—imports plus exports—in services is still overwhelmingly dominated by a very few of the most advanced states (Table 10.5). The country and category contrasts are great, as a comparison of the "high-income" and "low-income" groups documents. At a different level, the single small island state of Singapore had nearly twice the 2002 share (1.9%) of world services trade as all of sub-Saharan Africa (1.0%).

The same cost and skill advantages that enhance the growth and service range of quaternary firms and quinary activities on the domestic scene also operate internationally. Principal banks of all advanced countries have established foreign branches, and the world's leading banks have become major presences in the primary financial capitals. In turn, a relatively few world cities have emerged as international business and financial centres whose operations and influence are continuous and borderless, while a host of offshore banking havens have emerged to exploit gaps in regulatory controls and tax laws (Figure 10.26). Accounting firms, advertising agencies, management consulting companies, and similar establishments of primarily North American or European origin have increasingly established their international presence, with main branches located in principal business centres worldwide. Those advanced and specialized service components help swell the dominating role of the United States, Canada, and the European Union in the structure of world trade in services.

 Want to Learn More?

High Technology and the Global Economy

Canada's Technology Triangle
Learn more about Canada's high-tech industries and kinds of businesses that comprise this growing sector of our economy.
http://www.techtriangle.com/

Markham, Ontario: Canada's High-Tech Capital?
The city of Markham promotes itself as Canada's "high-tech capital": find out why.
http://www.markham.ca/Markham/
Departments/EDO/HiTech_Capital.htm

Canada in the Global Economy
New industries such as telecommunications equipment, lasers, pharmaceuticals, aerospace, and biotechnologies have become important sectors of Canada's place in the global economy. To learn more about Canada in the global economy, visit this website:
http://www.international.gc.ca/commerce/
strategy-strategie/details.aspx

Globalization and Transnational Corporations
A global economy is premised upon global businesses. Learn what the United Nations says about transnational corporations.
http://www.hri.ca/fortherecord2001/vol1/
globalization.htm

International Labour Organization
This United Nations agency seeks the promotion of social justice and internationally recognized human and labour rights. It generates numerous reports and data bases on employment issues around the world.
http://www.ilo.org/

Transportation Industries

Canadian Trucking Alliance
The Canadian trucking industry has a slogan: "If you got it, a truck brought it." Explore an industry crucial to keeping the Canadian economy operating.
http://www.cantruck.com/industry/
profile.php

Rail Transport
Since 1836 Canada's rail industry has served industry and remains essential to the country's prosperity and economic growth. Learn more about the history and role of this vital form of transporting goods and people.
http://www.hrsdc.gc.ca/en/hip/hrp/sp/
industry_profiles/railway_transport.shtml

International Shipping
International trade is largely dependent upon shipping to move freight around the globe. Learn more about international shipping at this website:
http://www.shipping-international.com/?google

Outsourcing and Offshoring

Outsourcing: Frequently Asked Questions
Explanations, advantages, and disadvantages of outsourcing are found here:
http://www.outsourcing-faq.com/

Offshoring: Frequently Asked Questions
Visit this website for answers about offshoring:
http://www.epinet.org/content.cfm/
issueguide_offshoring_faq

Summary

The spatial patterns of the world's manufacturing regions represent the landscape evidence of industrial location theories. Those theories are based on assumed regularities of human economic behaviour that is responsive to profit and price motivations and on simplifying assumptions about fixed and variable costs of manufacturing and distribution. In commercial economies, market mechanisms and market prices guide investment and production decisions.

Industrial cost components considered theoretically important are raw materials, power, labour, market accessibility, and transportation. Weberian analysis argues that least-cost locations are optimal and are strongly or exclusively influenced by transportation charges. Locational interdependence theory suggests that firms situate themselves to assure a degree of market monopoly in response to the location of competitors. Profit maximization concepts accept the possibility of multiple satisfactory locations within a spatial margin of profitability. Agglomeration economies and the multiplier effect may make attractive locations not otherwise predicted for individual firms, while comparative advantage may dictate production, if not location, decisions of entrepreneurs. Location concepts developed to explain industrial distributions under Fordist production constraints have been challenged as new just-in-time and flexible production systems introduce different locational considerations.

Major industrial districts of Eastern North America, Western and Central Europe, Eastern Europe, and Eastern Asia are part of a world-girdling "industrial belt" in which the vast majority of global secondary industrial activity occurs. The most advanced countries within that belt, however, are undergoing deindustrialization as newly industrializing countries with more favourable cost structures compete for markets. In the advanced economies, tertiary, quaternary, and quinary activities become more important as secondary-sector employment and share of gross

national income decline. The new high-tech and postindustrial spatial patterns are not necessarily identical to those developed in response to theoretical and practical determinants of manufacturing success.

The demise of the Atlantic cod fisheries and the crowded highways of high-tech and office park corridors are symbols of those changes in North America. As economic activity becomes less concerned with raw materials and freight rates, it becomes freer of the locational constraints of an older industrial society. Increasingly, skills, knowledge, communication, and population concentrations are what attract and hold the newer economic sectors in the most advanced economies. At the same time, much of the less developed world is striving for the transfer of manufacturing technology from developed economies and for the industrial growth seen as the path to their future prosperity.

Those aspirations for economic development and the contrasts they imply in the technological subsystems of the countries of the world are topics of concern in Chapter 11.

KEY WORDS

agglomeration   347
agglomeration (external)
    economies   350
break-of-bulk point   345
comparative advantage   351
deglomeration   351
fixed cost   345
footloose   349
Fordism   349
foreign direct investment
    (FDI)   354

freight rates   345
infrastructure   350
in-transit privilege   347
least-cost theory   347
line-haul (over-the-road)
    costs   345
locational
    interdependence   348
market equilibrium   339
market orientation   343
material orientation   341

multiplier effect   350
offshoring   353
outsourcing   351
quaternary activities   368
quinary activities   369
satisficing location   349
secondary activities   339
spatially fixed costs   339
spatially variable costs   339
spatial margin of
    profitability   349

substitution principle   349
terminal costs   345
tertiary activities   365
transnational
    (multinational)
    corporation
    (TNC)   354
ubiquitous industry   343
uniform (isotropic)
    plain   347
Weberian analysis   347

FOR REVIEW

1. What are the six *principles of location* outlined in this chapter? Briefly explain each and note its contribution to an entrepreneur's spatial search.

2. What is the difference between *fixed* and *variable* costs? Which of the two is of interest in the plant locational decision? What kinds of variable costs are generally reckoned as most important in locational theory?

3. What role do prices play in the allocation of resources in commercial economies? Are prices a factor in resource allocation in planned economies? What differences in locational patterns of industry are

implicit in the different treatment of costs in the two economies?

4. *Raw materials*, *power*, *labour*, *market*, and *transportation* are "factors of location" usually considered important in industrial placement decisions. Summarize the role of each, and cite examples of where each could be decisive in a firm's location.

5. What were Weber's controlling assumptions in his theory of plant location? What "distortions" did he recognize that might alter the locational decision?

6. With respect to plant siting, in what ways do the concepts and conclusions of *locational interdependence theory* differ from those of *least-cost theory*?

7. What is the *spatial margin of profitability*? What is its significance in plant location practice?

8. How have the concepts or practices of *comparative advantage* and *outsourcing* affected the industrial structure of advanced and developing countries?

9. In what ways are the locational constraints for *high-tech* industries significantly different from those of more basic secondary activities?

10. As high-tech industries and *quaternary* and *quinary* employment become more important in the economic structure of advanced nations, what consequences for economic geographic patterns do you anticipate? Explain.

FOCUS FOLLOW-UP

1. **What are the principal elements of locational theory, and how do different classical theories employ them?** pp. 339–349.

   Costs of raw materials, power, labour, market access, and transportation are the assumed controls governing industrial location decisions. They receive different emphases and imply different conclusions in the theories considered here. *Least-cost* (Weber) analysis concludes transport costs are the fundamental consideration; *locational interdependence* (Hotelling) considers that location of competitors determines a firm's siting decision; *profit maximization* maintains a firm should locate where profit is maximized by utilizing the substitution principle.

2. **How do agglomeration, just-in-time, comparative advantage, and TNC control affect traditional location theory outcomes?** pp. 349–355.

   By sharing infrastructure, agglomerating companies may reduce their individual total costs, while JIT supply flows reduce their inventory capital and storage charges. Comparative advantage recognizes that different regions or nations have different industrial cost structures. Companies utilize *outsourcing* of part of their production to exploit those differences. Transnational corporations distribute their operations based on comparative advantage: manufacturing in countries where production costs are lowest; performing research, accounting, and other service components where economical or convenient; and maintaining headquarters in locations that minimize taxes. Outsourcing and TNC practices evade the single location implications of classical location theories.

3. **What influences high-tech activity location, and what is the impact of high-tech growth on established world manufacturing regions?** pp. 356–365.

   Long-established industrial regions of Northeastern America and of Western, Central, and Eastern Europe developed over time in response to predications of classical location analysis. Eastern Asia, the most recently developed major industrial region, has been influenced by both classical locational pulls and outsourcing and high-tech locational needs. High-tech industries tend to create regionally specialized agglomerations reflecting proximity to scientific research centres, technically skilled labour pools, venture capital availability, quality of life environments, and superior transport and communication facilities. Their emergence has altered traditional industrial emphases and distributional patterns.

4. **What are the functional and locational characteristics of tertiary, quaternary, and quinary service activities** (pp. 365–370), **and how are they reflected in world trade patterns?** (pp. 370–372).

   Tertiary industries include all non-goods production activities, and provide services to goods producers, the general community, and individuals. Subdivided for easier recognition, the general tertiary category contains: (*a*) low-level personal and professional services, retailing of goods, and the like involved in daily life and market-oriented functions. This subcategory is also called *tertiary*. (*b*) The *quaternary* sector comprises advanced forms of services suggested by the term "knowledge industries" that are performed in classrooms, hospitals, accounting and brokerage firms, corporate office buildings, etc. (*c*) *Quinary* activities include highly specialized and advanced services of research scientists, highest-level corporate executives and governmental officials, and the like. The growing world trade in services, made possible by plummeting costs of information transmission, has altered international economic relations and encouraged cultural and functional integration.

ONLINE LEARNING CENTRE

The World Wide Web has a tremendous number and variety of sites pertaining to geography. To access Web sites, Internet exercises, self-quizzes, videos, and additional study tools relevant to this chapter's content, visit the *Human Geography* Online Learning Centre at **www.mcgrawhill.ca/olc/fellmann**.

PATTERNS OF DEVELOPMENT AND CHANGE

Aims

- To understand the differences among economic growth, economic development, and human development measures of development
- To understand how concepts, such as the core-periphery model and gender, can assist in explaining why development varies among nations

Some Specific Considerations for Review

1. Definitions and explanations of development and underdevelopment, pp. 376–384.

2. Economic measures and models of development: income, energy, farming and food, and stages of growth, pp. 384–394.

3. Non-economic measures of development: education, services, health, and cultural satisfaction, and their relationship to economic indices, pp. 394–401.

4. Women's roles and rewards: the determinants of the pattern of gender relationships, pp. 401–407.

*T*he Hindu funeral pyres burned day and night; Muslims were buried five and more together in common graves. Countless dead cattle, buffalo, and dogs were hastily gathered and dumped in pits. In a sense, on that unseasonably cold December night in central India, all had died for economic development (Figure 11.1). Some 40% of the Indian population exists in poverty. Eager to attract modern industry to its less developed states, to create additional industrial and urban employment, and to produce domestically the chemicals essential to its drive for agricultural self-sufficiency, the Indian government in 1969 granted Union Carbide Corporation a licence to manufacture pesticides at a new plant built on vacant land on the outskirts of Bhopal. A principal ingredient was deadly methyl isocyanate gas, the silent killer that escaped from its storage tank that winter night of 1984 after a sudden and unexplained build-up of its temperature and pressure.

To assure the plant's success, Union Carbide had been exempted from many local taxes, and land, water, and power costs were heavily subsidized. To yield maximum benefit to the local economy and maximum transfer of technology and skills, 50% ownership in the enterprise was retained for Indian investors along with total local control of construction and operation of the plant. The 1000 jobs were considered so important by the state and local governments that despite six accidents and one death in the years before the night of disaster, reports critical of plant safety and operation were shelved and ignored. A local official who had called for the removal of the factory to a more isolated area was himself removed from office.

By the time of the fatal accident, Bhopal had grown from 300,000 to over 900,000 people. More than 130,000 residents lived in the slums and shantytowns they built for themselves just across the street from a factory they thought produced "plant medicine" to keep crops healthy; they were the principal victims. Before the week was over, almost 3000 people had died. Another 300,000 had been affected by exposure to the deadly poison, and perhaps 150,000 of those suffer long-term permanent disabilities—blindness, sterility, kidney and liver infections, and brain damage.

Development as a Cultural Variable

Whatever its immediate cause of equipment failure or operator error, the tragedy of Bhopal—seen by opponents of globalization as an emblem of the evils of multinationalism—is witness to the lure of economic development so eagerly sought that safety and caution are sacrificed to achieve it. That lure is nearly irresistible for those countries and regions that look to industrialization and urban employment as their deliverance from traditional economies no longer able to support their growing populations or to satisfy their hopes for an improved quality of life.

Any view of the contemporary world quickly shows great—almost unbelievable—contrasts from place to place in levels of economic development and people's material well-being. Variations in these are indicative of the tools, energy sources, and other *artifacts* (see Chapter 5) differing societies employ in production and the kinds of economic activities in which they engage, and underlie the social organizations and behaviour patterns they have developed. A look around tells us that these interrelated economic and social structures are not shared by all societies; they vary between cultures and countries. The ready distinction that we make between the "Gold Coast" and the "slum" indicates that different groups have differential access to the wealth, tools, and resources of the global and national societies of which they are a part.

At an international scale, we distinguish between "advanced" or "rich" nations, such as Canada or Switzerland, and "less developed" or "poor" countries, like Bangladesh or Burkina Faso, though neither class of states may wish those adjectives applied to its circumstances. Hunter-gatherers of southwest Africa or Papua New Guinea, shifting gardeners of Amazonia, or subsistence farmers of southeastern Asia may be largely untouched by the modernization, industrialization, or urbanization of society commonplace elsewhere.

These general statements tend to hide other truths. For instance, while Canada is a "rich" nation, poverty within its First Nation people is a particular public policy problem. Development differentials exist within other countries, too. The poverty of drought- and hunger-plagued northeastern Brazil stands in sharp contrast to the prosperous, industrialized modernity of São Paulo state or city (Figure 11.2), while in Canada, fishers in the Atlantic region and people who reside in northern Canada live in a very different economic and cultural reality than do urban dwellers in such cities as Montreal, Toronto, Calgary, and Vancouver.

Dividing the Continuum: Definitions of Development

Countries display different levels of development. **Development** in that comparative sense means simply the extent to which the human and natural resources of an area or country have been brought into full productive use. It may also carry in common usage the implications of economic growth, modernization, and improvement in levels of material production and consumption. For some, it also suggests changes in traditional social, cultural, and political structures to resemble more nearly those displayed in countries and economies deemed "advanced." For others, "development" and "underdevelopment" as concepts and measurable conditions were post–World War II inventions of Western cultural thought and economic institutions. Their creation presumably permitted viewing the global scene as an orderly structure or system, parts of which did not conform to Western standards of wealth, well-being, and achievement. Once visualized in this manner, the perceived conditions of underdevelopment could be addressed by international institutions, such as the World Bank, and accepted as valid by the non-Western societies to which they were applied. Those who view development theory in this negative light see it as a conscious and effective means of exerting Western influence and control over postcolonial societies.

Whatever the philosophical merits of the two viewpoints, many of the attributes of development under its usual economic

FIGURE 11.1 Burning the dead at Bhopal. At the time of the tragedy, India was more prepared than many developing countries to accept the transfer of advanced technology. In 1984, it ranked among the top 15 countries in manufacturing output and supplied most basic domestic needs from its own industry. India still sought modern plants and processes and, particularly, industry supporting agricultural improvement and expansion.

(a)

(b)

FIGURE 11.2 The modern high-rise office and apartment buildings of prosperous São Paulo (*a*), a city that generates over one-third of Brazil's national income, stand a world apart from the poverty and peasant housing of north-eastern Brazil (*b*). The evidences and benefits of "development" are not equally shared by all segments of any country or society.

definition can be quantified by reference to statistics of national production, per capita income, energy consumption, nutritional levels, labour force characteristics, and the like. Taken together, such variables might calibrate a scale of achievement against which the level of development of a single country may be compared.

Such a scale would reveal that countries lie along a continuum from the least advanced in technology or industrialization to the most developed in those and similar characteristics. Geographers (and others) attempt to classify and group countries along the continuum in ways that are conceptually revealing and spatially informative. The extremes are easy; the middle ground is less clear-cut, and the terminology referring to it is mixed.

The concept of development has been around for centuries. However, the period between the end of World War II, which saw the dismantling of the colonial empires, and the present has been termed "the era of development." The inaugural address by U.S.

President Harry S. Truman to the United Nations Assembly in 1949 is often identified as a defining moment in launching this era when he stated:

> We must embark on a bold new program for making the benefits of our scientific advances and industrial progress available for the improvement and growth of underdeveloped areas. The old imperialism— exploitation for foreign profit—has no place in our plans. What we envisage is a program of development on the concepts of democratic fair dealing (as cited by Cowen and Shenton, 1996: 7).

Truman indicated that industrial progress was to be the engine to promote development in underdeveloped areas. **Underdevelopment** from a strictly economic point of view suggests the possibility or desirability of applying additional capital, labour, or technology to the resource base of an area to permit the present population to improve its material well-being or to allow populations to increase without a deterioration in their quality of life.

The catch-all category of *underdeveloped*, however, does not tell us in which countries such efforts at improvement have occurred or been effective. With time, therefore, more refined subdivisions of development have been introduced, including such indistinctly relative terms as *moderately*, *less*, or *least developed* countries.[1] Since development is commonly understood to imply industrialization and to be reflected in improvements in national and personal income, the additional terms *newly industrializing countries* (NICs) (which we encountered in Chapter 10) and *middle income countries* have been employed. More recently, *emerging economy* has become a common designation, providing a more positive image than "underdeveloped." In a corruption of its original meaning, the term *Third World* is often applied to the developing countries as a group, though when first used that designation was a purely political reference to nations not formally aligned with a "First World" of industrialized free market (capitalist) nations or a "Second World" of centrally controlled (communist bloc) economies. And increasingly, the name *Fourth World* has been attached to the UN-recognized group of least developed states.

Because all these terms and categories are in common usage and clearly suggest the possibility of a country progressing from a lower to a higher developmental status, one would expect agreement on which category is applicable to a specific country and when a state can be seen to have advanced from a lesser to a greater degree of development. Unfortunately, neither conclusion is valid. Different international agencies reach different conclusions: for the United Nations, the countries of Singapore, South Korea, and Taiwan are "developing" or "emerging" economies; for

the International Monetary Fund, they are "advanced economies." On the reasonable basis of per capita income, Singapore ("emerging") surpasses Italy ("advanced"), and Taiwan and South Korea ("developing") equal Portugal and Greece ("developed"). And to equate "advanced" with "industrialized" economies, which is commonly done, seems meaningless because, for example, industry accounts for only 13% of the labour force in Canada, much less than in poorer countries.

In 1980 the contrasting terms *North* and *South* were introduced (by the Independent Commission on International Development Issues, commonly called the Brandt Report[2]) as a broad and not wholly accurate generalization to emphasize the distinctions between the rich, advanced, developed countries of the Northern Hemisphere (to which Southern Hemisphere Australia and New Zealand are added)—the *North*—and, roughly, all the rest of the world—the *South* (Figure 11.3). This split agreed with the United Nations classification that placed all of Europe and North America, plus Australia, Japan, New Zealand, and the former USSR in a *more developed country* category, with all other states classed as *less developed countries* (LDCs).

The variety of terms devised—not all of them accurately descriptive or acceptable to those countries designated—represent honest efforts to categorize countries whose developmental circumstances are defined by a variety of economic and social measures along a continuum of specific or composite characteristics. In the remainder of this chapter, broad developmental contrasts between countries or regions will conform to the "North-South" and the UN "more developed-less developed" categorizations. Our primary attention in maps and text, however, will be given to the developing countries of the "South."

The terminology of development is usually applied to country units, but it is equally meaningful at the regional and local levels within them, for few countries are uniformly highly developed or totally undeveloped. Many emerging economies contain pockets— frequently the major urban centres—of productivity, wealth, and modernity not shared by the rest of the state. For example, Mexico is a leading NIC, but more than 50% of its industrial workers and over 60% of value of manufacturing are located in metropolitan Mexico City. Many other parts of the country and, particularly, its Indian population, remain untouched by the development concentrated in the capital city. Even within the most advanced societies, some areas and populations remain outside the mainstream of progress and prosperity enjoyed by the majority. Fourth World deprivation is not just a whole country concept.

Explanations of Underdevelopment

It is one thing to devise categories of relative development and to assign countries to them; it is quite another to see in those

---

[1] In 1971, the General Assembly of the UN listed 24 "least developed" countries identified by per capita gross domestic product, share of manufacturing in GDP, and adult literacy. In later years the criteria were changed to reflect: low national income (per capita GDP under $900); weak human assets (a composite index based on health, nutrition, and educational measures); and high economic vulnerability (a composite index based on instability of agricultural production and inadequate diversification of a small economy). In addition, population of a "least developed country" had to be below 75 million. The list of those countries—also recognized as "poorest" countries has grown over the years and reached 50 in 2004. Only one country, Botswana, has ever "graduated" from the list. See Figure 11.3.

[2] *North–South: A Programme for Survival.* The Commission was established in 1977 at the suggestion of the chairman of the World Bank. Under its charge, "global issues arising from economic and social disparities of the world community" were to be studied and "ways of promoting adequate solutions to the problems involved in development" were to be proposed. The former Soviet Union was at that time included within the North, and its successor states retain that association.

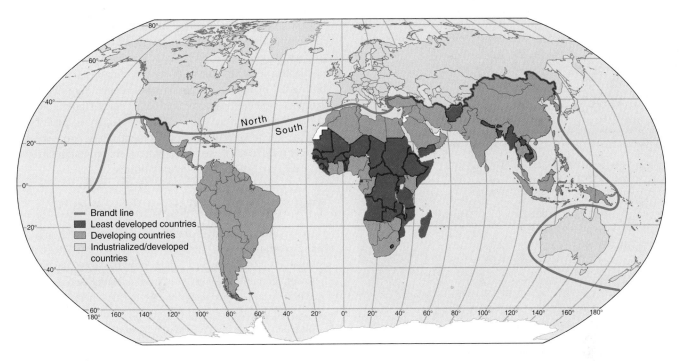

FIGURE 11.3 Comparative development levels. The "North–South" line of the 1980 *Brandt Report* suggested a simplified world contrast of development and underdevelopment based largely on degree of industrialization and per capita wealth recorded then. In 2004, the United Nations Economic and Social Council and the UN Conference and Trade and Development (UNCTAD) expanded to 50 the list of "least developed countries." The inclusive category of "developing countries" ignores recent significant economic and social gains in several Asian and Latin American states that raises them now to "industrialized/developed" status. Some "least developed" states are small island countries not shown at this map scale.

Sources: UNCTAD and United Nations Development Program.

categories an explanation of their spatial pattern. Why are different countries arranged as they are along the continuum of advancement? What conditions underlie their relative degrees of development? Are those conditions common to all countries at the same level of technology? And do those conditions have spatial expression and spatial explanation?

The Brandt Report hints at one frequent but simplistic spatial explanation based on ideas of environmental determinism (Chapter 1)–development is a characteristic of the rich "North"— the mid-latitudes, more precisely; poverty and underdevelopment are tropical conditions. Proponents of the latitudinal explanation support their conviction not only by reference to such topical maps as Figure 11.3, 11.7, or 11.8, but by noting that rich countries—some 30 in number—have 93% of their population resident in temperate or "snow belt" zones; 42 of the world's poorest states have 56% of their people in tropical latitudes and 18% in arid zones. They also note that observable differences in development and wealth exist within individual countries. Brazilians of the south-eastern temperate highlands, for example, have average incomes several times higher than their compatriots of tropical Amazonia. Annual average incomes of Mexicans of the temperate north far exceed those of southern Yucatán. Australians of the tropical north are poorer than Australians of the temperate south. Unfortunately for the search for easy explanation, many of the poorer nations of the "South" lie partially or wholly within the mid-latitudes or at temperate elevations—Afghanistan, North Korea, and Mongolia are examples—while equatorial Singapore and Malaysia prosper. Geography, many argue forcefully, is not destiny, although tropi-

cal regions admittedly face the major ecological handicaps of low agricultural productivity and high incidence of plant, animal, and human disease.

Other generalizations seem similarly inconclusive: (1) Resource poverty is cited as a limit to developmental possibilities. Although some developing countries are deficient in raw materials, others are major world suppliers of both industrial minerals and agricultural goods—bauxite, cacao, and coffee, for example. Admittedly, a Third World complaint is that their materials are under-priced in the developed world markets to which they flow or are restricted in that flow by tariffs and subsidized destination country competitors. Those, however, are matters of marketing, politics, and economics, not of resources. Further, economists have long held that reliance on natural resource wealth and exports by less developed countries undermines their prospects for growth by interfering with their development of industry and export-oriented manufacturing. (2) Overpopulation and overcrowding are frequently noted as common denominators of national underdevelopment, but Singapore prospers with 6757 per square kilometre (17,500 per sq mi) while impoverished Mali is empty with 11 per square kilometre (28 per sq mi) (Figure 11.4). (3) Former colonial status is often blamed for present underdevelopment. The accusation is arguably valid for countries where—as in sub-Saharan Africa and southern Asia—colonizers left largely intact the indigenous populations but created political structures and physical infrastructures suited more for exploitation for mother country profit than for balanced economic, social, and political development for the long-term benefit of the colony itself.

FIGURE 11.4 Landlocked and subject to severe droughts, Mali is one of the poorest of the "least developed" countries. Low densities of population are not necessarily related to prosperity, or high densities to poverty. Mali has only 11 people per square kilometre (28 per sq mi); Japan has 338 per square kilometre (875 per sq mi). These Dogon women crossing a parched millet field near Sanga are on their way to get water—a time- and energy-consuming daily task for many least developed country women. Even in more humid South Africa, rural women on average spend 3 hours and 10 minutes each day fetching water, according to a government survey.

In cases in which the colonists were expatriates of an already advanced state and largely replaced the original inhabitants—as in the ex-colonies of Australia, New Zealand, Canada, or the United States—the association of colonial past with present underdevelopment is, of course, inapplicable.

Although there appears to be no single, simple explanation of Third World status, just as there is no single measure of underdevelopment that accounts for every Third World case, the Harvard Institute for International Development did attempt to quantify differences in national economic development. It argued that "physical geography" is one of four factors influencing global patterns of growth; the least developed countries are almost without exception located in ecological zones that pose serious health conditions—including much shorter life spans—not found in the mid-latitudes, and have agricultural limitations that are very different from those of wealthy states. The other three factors are initial economic level, government policy, and demographic change. The Institute's conclusions were that landlocked countries grew more slowly than coastal economies, that—because of poor health and unproductive farming—tropical states were slower to develop than temperate zone ones, and that sparse natural resources and transport isolation inhibited growth possibilities and rates.

These physical differences and environmental limitations, the Institute found, were far less explanatory of national growth rates than were market economies, prudent fiscal policies, and the rule of laws prohibiting corruption, breach of contract, expropriation of property, and the like. These are circumstances and controls independent of locational or resource differentials. That conclusion is buttressed by a United Nations report concluding that "good government," including protection of property rights under a stable political and legal system, is the top priority in poverty-fighting and the key to sustainable development. These are, however, conditions reflective of western market economy standards that are not necessarily acceptable to all cultures.

The Core-Periphery Argument

Core-periphery models are based on the observation that within many spatial systems, sharp territorial contrasts exist in wealth, economic advancement, and growth—in "development"—between economic heartlands and outlying subordinate zones. Wealthy urban cores and depressed rural peripheries, or prospering "high-tech" concentrations and declining "rust belts," are contrasts found in many developed countries. On the international scene, core-periphery contrasts are discerned between, particularly, Western Europe, Japan, and the United States as prosperous cores and the Fourth World as underdeveloped periphery. At all spatial scales, the models assume that at least partially and temporarily the growth and prosperity of core regions is at the expense of exploited peripheral zones (see Chapter 3).

That conclusion is drawn from the observation that linkages and interactions exist between the contrasting parts of the system. As one variant of the model suggests, if for any reason (perhaps a new industrial process or product) one section of a country experiences accelerated economic development, that section by its expanding prosperity becomes increasingly attractive for investors and other entrepreneurs. Assuming national investment capital is limited, growth in the developing core must come at the expense of the peripheries of the country.

A process of **circular and cumulative causation**, thus set in motion, continues to polarize development and, according to economist Gunnar Myrdal, leads to a permanent division between prosperous (and dominating) cores and depressed (and exploited) peripheral districts that are milked of surplus labour, raw materials, and profits. In its *dependency theory* form, this version of the core-periphery argument sees the developing world as effectively held captive by the leading industrial nations. It is drained of wealth and deprived of growth by remaining largely a food and raw material exporter and an importer of manufactured commodities—and frequently suffering price discrimination in both their sales and purchases. A condition of *neocolonialism* is said to exist in which economic and even political control is exercised by developed states over the economies and societies of legally independent countries of the underdeveloped world.

A more hopeful variant of the model observes that regional income inequalities exist within all countries but that they tend to be greater in less developed countries than in the developed ones. That is, within market economies, income disparities tend to be reduced as developmental levels increase. Eventually, it is argued, income convergence will occur as **trickle-down effects**, or **spread effects**, work to diffuse benefits outward from the center in the form of higher prices paid for needed materials, or through the dispersion of technology to branch plants or contract suppliers in lower-cost regions of production. On the international scale, such spread effects should work to reduce the dominance of formerly exploitative cores and equalize incomes between world regions. The increasing wealth of the newly industrializing economies and the penetration of European and American markets by, for example, Asian-produced goods ranging from cheap textiles to expensive automobiles and high-technology electronics, are cited in support of this model variant.

Core-periphery models stress economic relationships and spatial patterns of control over production and trade. Indeed, the usual measures and comparisons of development are stated in economic terms. As we shall see later in this chapter, non-economic measures may also be employed, though usually not without reference to their relationships to national or per capita income, or to other measures of wealth and productivity. We shall also see that composite measures of developmental level are perhaps more useful and meaningful than those restricted to single factors or solely to matters of either economy or social welfare.

And finally, we should remember that "development" is a culturally relative term. It is usually interpreted in western, democratic, market economy terms that presumably can be generalized to apply to all societies. Others insist that it must be seen against the background of diverse social, material, and environmental conditions that differently shape cultural and economic aspirations of different peoples, many of whom specifically reject those western cultural and economic standards.

Core-Periphery Model in Canada

At a global scale, Canada has been always on the periphery. Between the 16th and 19th centuries, Canada provided staple goods—fish, fur, and lumber—to Britain (Figure 3.2). This is the essence of Harold Innis' Heartland–Hinterland model that describes Canada's economic development (Chapter 1). Within the nation, the Great Lakes–St. Lawrence region emerged as Canada's core region. The opportunity to exploit resources and access to water transport attracted initial interest from people who invested and settled in the area. Improvements to transportation in the form of canals, roads, rail, and later, air, reinforced the importance of the region. Most of Canada's large urban centres are located in the region. On the basis of its population, this region contains significant political power within the House of Commons (Table 7.2). Those people living in the periphery region of Canada are frequently on the receiving end of political and corporate decisions that are made in central Canada, or in boardrooms located in the United States, western Europe, or Japan. This situation has contributed to tension between core and periphery regions. A political response to the lack of influence western Canada had in the development of national policies was seen with the formation of the Reform Party of Canada in 1987. At a provincial level, core and periphery regions are also evident. Cities such as Halifax, St. John's, Winnipeg, and Saskatoon serve as core centres within their respective provinces. Today, Canada is a relatively small economic player compared to the United States, western Europe, and Japan. China is an emerging economic force at the global scale.

The core-periphery model is one concept that guides our thinking about why the pattern of development varies around the globe. It is also important to consider what we mean by development and how we measure it. The following sections identify how development can be measured. Three key perspectives provide the foundation for this discussion: (i) economic growth indicators, (ii) economic development indicators, and (iii) social indicators. In this discussion you should note the use of single indicators versus composite indexes.

Development Theory

In his book, *Development Theory: An Introduction*, P. W. Preston identifies seven contemporary theories of development. To provide a sense of the importance of development theory in guiding our research and influencing how we solve development problems, three general theories are briefly described below. These serve to illustrate important lessons related to clarifying the problem implied in Chapter 2—the selection of a theory can directly influence how we study and solve problems. Notice this relationship in the following discussion.

Modernization Theory: assumes that if the conditions in the First World were replicated in the Third World, development would occur. In other words, it maintains that underdeveloped economies can break out of their poverty trap by coordinated investment in both basic—but higher wage—industries and infrastructure. This would simultaneously expand the consumer base for products. The cost for products would steadily decline as the volume of production increased. These outcomes, in turn, would encourage the creation of backward- and forward-linked industries, which would further reduce costs, increase economic growth, and perhaps foster industrial agglomeration economies and trade expansion (see Chapter 10, pages 338–339; 349–351). These types of findings imply that if developed countries, such as Canada, provided the 'right' assistance or if the right investments were made by the private sector, the development process would be accelerated.

Applying this type of logic and based on the historical development of the economies in western Europe (i.e., inductive reasoning see Chapter 2), W. W. Rostow (1916–2003) theorized that all developing economies may pass through five successive stages of growth and advancement. *Traditional societies* of subsistence agriculture, low technology levels, and poorly developed commercial economies can have only low productivity per capita. The *preconditions for takeoff* are established when those societies, led by an enterprising elite, begin to organize as political rather than kinship units and to invest in transportation systems and other productive and supportive infrastructure. The *takeoff* to sustained growth is the critical developmental stage, lasting perhaps 20 to 30 years, during which rates of investment increase, new industries are established, resources are exploited, and growth becomes the expected norm. The *drive to maturity* sees the application of modern technology to all phases of economic activity; diversification carries the economy beyond the industrial emphases first triggering growth, and the economy becomes increasingly self-sufficient. Finally, when consumer goods and services begin to rival heavy industry as leading economic sectors, and most of

Geography and Public Policy

Does Foreign Aid Help?

A 1998 World Bank report on "Assessing Aid" concluded that the raw correlation between rich country aid and developing country growth is near zero. Simply put, more aid does not mean more growth, certainly not for countries with "bad" economic policies (high inflation, large budget deficits, and corrupt bureaucracy); for them, the report claims, aid actually retards growth and does nothing to reduce poverty. Other studies similarly have found no clear link between aid and faster economic development. The $1 trillion that rich countries and international agencies gave and loaned to poor ones between 1950 and 2002 did not have the hoped-for result of eliminating poverty and reducing economic and social disparities between the rich and poor countries of the world.

In part, that was because economic growth was not necessarily a donor country's first priority. During the Cold War, billions flowed from both the Soviet Union and the United States to prop up countries whose leaders favoured the donor state agendas. Even today, strategic considerations may outweigh charitable or developmental aims. Israel gets a major share of American aid for historical reasons; Egypt, Pakistan, and Colombia get sizeable portions for political and strategic reasons; and Afghanistan and Iraq, after 2003, received billions for humanitarian efforts—rehabilitation and restructuring— as well as in military spending. America, in fact, spends only 40% of its modest foreign aid budget on assistance to poorer states.

About one-quarter of all aid from whatever source has been tied to purchases that must be made in the donor country, and additional large shares flow, regardless of need or merit, to former colonies of donor countries. In part, a World Bank report admits, aid failures reflect the fact that the Bank and its sister agencies have wasted billions on ill-conceived projects.

More optimistic conclusions are drawn by other observers who note that (*a*) foreign aid tends to reduce poverty in countries with market-based economic policies but is ineffective where those policies do not exist; (*b*) aid is most effective in lowering poverty if it is given to poor, rather than less poor, countries; and (*c*) aid targeted to specific objectives—eradication of disease or Green Revolution crop improvement, for example— is often remarkably successful, though spending on food aid or on aid tied to purchases from donor countries is of little use.

Although some countries—Botswana, the Republic of Korea, China, different southeast Asian states—made great progress thanks to development assistance, a large number of others have seen their prospects worsen and their economies decline. Slow growth and rising populations have lowered per capita incomes; poor use of aid and loans has failed to improve their infrastructures and social service levels. Most critically for the economic and social development prospects of those countries is that the financing offered to them over the years in the hopes of stimulating new growth has become a burden of unmanageable debt.

So great and intractable has their debt problem become that the international community has now recognized a whole class of countries distinguished by their high-debt condition: Heavily Indebted Poor Countries (HIPCs) that are so far in debt that many of them are paying more in interest and loan payments to industrialized countries and international agencies than they are receiving in exports to or aid from those sources. Gradually, the rich world has accepted that debt relief, not lectures on capitalism, is the correct approach to helping the world's poor countries and people. In 1996, the World Bank, International Monetary Fund, and other agencies launched the first HIPC initiative, identifying 41 very poor countries and acknowledging that their total debt burden (including the share owed to international institutions) must be reduced to sustainable levels. In the years since, differing definitions of "sustainable" and criteria for debt relief have been adopted but remain rooted in the requirement that benefiting countries must face an unsustainable debt burden, maintain good economic policies, and prepare a "Poverty Reduction Strategy Paper," which is a blueprint laying out how a country will fight poverty and promote health and educational programs and how savings from debt relief will help.

Official donor country development assistance increased by $12 billion from 2000 to 2004. By the end of 2004, 27 of the 38 eligible countries had been accepted into the HIPC debt relief program. The debt reduction packages approved for the 27 states—23 of them in Africa—aimed to remove over $40 billion in debt, about half of what the countries owed. Funds freed from debt service were to be spent on social services and other Millennium Development Goal-related projects (see below) by the beneficiary states.

---

the population has consumption levels far above basic needs, the economy has completed its transition to the *age of mass consumption*. More recently—and referring to most advanced economies (and discussed in Chapter 10)—a sixth stage, the *post-industrial*, has been recognized. Services replace industry as the principal sector of the economy, professional and technical skills assume pre-eminence in the labour force, and information replaces energy as the key productive resource.

Rostow's expectations of an inevitable progression of development have often proved illusory. Many LDCs remain locked in one of the first two stages of his model, unable to achieve the takeoff to self-sustained growth despite importation of technology and of foreign aid investment funds from the more developed world (see "Geography and Public Policy: Does Foreign Aid Help?"). Indeed, it has become apparent to many observers that despite the efforts of the world community, the development gap between the most and the least advanced countries widens rather than narrows over time. A case in point is sub-Saharan Africa; between 1975 and 2000, per capita income declined by almost 1% a year, leaving all but a tiny elite significantly poorer at the

[Continued]

In a dramatic new approach, in 2004 Britain's prime minister Tony Blair offered a plan to cancel 100% of the foreign debts owed by the world's poorest states, freeing them to spend on social and infrastructure improvements rather than on interest payments on their massive loans. To pay for that cancellation, Mr. Blair's suggestion was to revalue upward to current market prices of about $400 per ounce the 103 million ounces of gold held by the World Bank and valued by it at only $40 an ounce. Part of the hoard, the Blair plan proposed, could be sold for perhaps $40 billion for poor country debt erasure. The rest of the funds needed for the proposed 100% debt forgiveness would come, the plan envisioned, from donations from the rich countries and the sale of $100 billion of bonds. Although the Blair plan was not then adopted, its serious discussion and agreement in principle led many observers to believe that it, or a similar total debt forgiveness scenario, should receive international endorsement.

The expressed hope of the international community now is that the answer to the question "Does foreign aid help?" will finally be "Yes." In a reconsideration of its former pessimism, the World Bank now concludes that, indeed, the answer is affirmative. It feels that foreign aid has been instrumental in increasing life expectancy at birth in developing countries by 20 years since 1960, cutting adult illiteracy in half since 1970, reducing the number of people in abject poverty by 200 million since 1980 even as world population increased by 2 billion, and more than doubling the per capita income in developing countries since 1965. The expectation

now is that massive debt forgiveness will be reflected in accelerating social and economic improvements that further reduces the disparities between their conditions and those in the more affluent developed states.

Since 1968, the Canadian International Development Agency (CIDA) is Canada's lead development agency. It has a mandate to reduce poverty and to contribute to a more secure, equitable, and prosperous world by working around the globe to promote sustainable development (see page 373). The following aims are to be achieved through the implementation of CIDA's policies and programs:

- advance Canadian values of global citizenship, equity, and environmental sustainability, as well as Canadian interests regarding security, prosperity, and governance;

- deliver a visible, durable impact on the world's key development challenges as identified in the Millennium Development Goals;

- focus on reducing poverty through an effective and focused approach that matches Canadian resources and expertise to developing countries' needs in coordination with other donors;

- recognize and promote sustainable solutions to address the critical linkages between environmental degradation, poverty, and social inequity; and

- mobilize Canadians in dialogue and participation to build our society's capacity to contribute effectively to global poverty reduction.

Questions to Consider

1. In light of World Bank and other studies concluding aid does not always correlate with development or poverty reduction in recipient countries, do you think the rich world and international agencies should halt all further monetary assistance to developing states? Why or why not?

2. Do you think donor countries such as the United States should completely ignore all self-interest including, for example, extra generosity toward friendly or politically compatible states, in making aid decisions? Why or why not?

3. Do you think international programs of forgiveness of debts contracted by sovereign states are appropriate or fair to lending countries and their citizens? Why or why not?

4. One widely held opinion is that money now spent on direct and indirect foreign aid more properly should be spent on domestic programs dealing with poverty, unemployment, homelessness, inner-city decay, inequality, and the like. An equally strongly held contrary view is that foreign aid should take priority, for it is needed to address world and regional problems of overpopulation, hunger, disease, destruction of the environment, and civil and ethnic strife those conditions foster. Assuming you had to choose one of the two polar positions, which view would you support, and why?

5. Explain why you think CIDA's policies and program aims can promote development.

end of the period. Over the same years, income per head in the industrial market economies grew at a 1.8% annual rate. The 1960s, 1970s, and 1980s were all proclaimed by United Nations resolutions as "Development Decades." They proved instead to be decades of disappointment, at least by economic measures. Between 1990 and 2004, however, the picture brightened for the developing world as a whole. Average per capital income growth in developing countries in the 1990s was 1.5%, about three times the rate of the 1980s; between 2000 and 2004 their average rate of growth was 3.4%, double the rate for high-income states. Even

sub-Saharan Africa posted an increase of 1.2% a year between 2000–2004. For many, faith in the likelihood of growth—even if not in definable stages of development—was renewed.

A number of factors have been identified that are problematic in achieving development through the type of investments advocated by Rostow and other Modernization theorists. Lack of access to the capital required for investment in infrastructure and technology is sometimes problematic. Another explanation for the differential in national growth rates pertains to the necessary investments in "human capital"—that is, the ill-defined composite of skills, habits, schooling, and knowledge that can contribute to successful economic development and sustained growth. In this regard, recent technological progress has required a more educated workforce. An absence of the 'right' values, such as profit motivation and risk-taking, has been identified as problematic in some studies.

Dependency Theory: Evidence suggests that those countries where the poorest 20% of the world's people live were, at the start of the century, 60 times worse off than those where the richest fifth live, and the gap between the two groups had doubled since the early 1960s. Dependency theory holds that these differentials are not accidental but the logical result of the ability and necessity of developed countries and power elites to exploit and subjugate other populations and regions to secure for themselves a continual source of new capital. Transnational corporations, the theory contends, tend to dominate, through their investments, key areas of developing state economies (see Chapter 10). They introduce technologies and production facilities to further their own corporate goals, not to further the balanced development of the recipient economies. However, since research and development operations remain in the developed world, the Third World industry is often dependent upon the second-best production technologies. These technologies are often owned by entities outside the developing world through the patent system. This hoarding of ideas can stifle innovation. Since there would be few linkages between other industries in the developed nation, relatively few people in the developed nation would benefit from this industrialization. The implication arising from this theory is related to the need to dramatically change (or sever) the relationship between developing and developed nations. Development aid where proffered, dependency theory holds, involves a forced economic reliance on donor countries and economies that continues an imposed cycle of selective industrialization that leads not to independent growth but to further dependent underdevelopment—a negative consequence of circular and cumulative causation (see p. 380).

World Systems Theory: Wallerstein's World Systems Theory (Chapter 2) is a third development theory. As noted in Chapter 3, it divided the world into three regions—core, periphery, and semi-periphery which reflect their different roles in the global economy. For many countries in the periphery, this role was initially started with colonialization. It also focuses attention on a country's role in the global economy—the international division of labour. It differs from Dependency Theory in two ways. First, World Systems Theory identifies three regions—core, semi-periphery, and periphery—rather than two (core and periphery). Second, dependency theory focuses attention on a country's reliance on the world system—its vulnerability to changes and extent of foreign control. As noted in Chapter 3, World Systems Theory is, in part, based on Marxist philosophy. This orientation contributes to a general distrust in the state because it viewed as a group of elites, who benefits from the current exploitation of labour. In order to promote development, change must occur in the division of labour that would be best achieved through labour movements (e.g., Unions) and social-democratic reforms. In practice, for the least developed or newly industrializing countries, this has meant providing incentives that encourage foreign direct investment and technology transfer. When imported ideas and technology that

help create "human capital" labour and intellectual skills are combined with domestic industrial control, encouragement of education, and local research and development, there will certainly follow industrial specializations, massive exports, and rising levels of living—as presumably they did for Taiwan, Singapore, and the other Asian "tigers" (see Chapter 10).

In shifting from theory to the real-world, it is clear that there is no single correct theory or world-reality. For instance, there is some evidence that economic growth for developing countries as a group is increasing. This evidence, which supports Rostow's model, indicates that they are collectively generating nearly one-half of world output and 25% of world trade. Based on this evidence, some people believe that the best stimulus for economic development has been the widespread relaxation of restrictive economic and political controls on all economies and on international trade flows in the past generation. Transnational corporations, technology transfer, pro-development national policies, trade restriction relaxations, and selective foreign aid and lending have all played a part. On the other hand, the economies of many eastern European countries that shifted from communist to market-based economies are in shambles after implementing these same economic measures. Many Latin American and African countries have refused to adopt the neo-liberal economic policies associated with modernization theory because of the negative impacts on their people (e.g., increased costs for water and food).

In reality, there is no single 'best' development theory to explain development and assist in promoting it. The internal socio-economic, political, and legal contexts are different within countries, as are its role with other nations. With respect to research, note that the development theories (and all theories in general) are built on a series of assumptions and/or focus attention on important but selected aspects of the development process. Selecting the 'best theory' to suit one's project is an important aspect of defining the problem (Chapter 2 "The Research Process"). Measurement was also identified as an important element of the research process. How we measure development is the focus of the next section.

Economic Growth Measures of Development

The developing countries as a group have made significant progress along the continuum of economic development. Between 1990 and 2003, their economies collectively grew at an average annual rate of 3.7% compared to 2.6% per year for the industrial states. As a result of those growth differentials and of overall changes in the composition of their gross domestic products, the less developed states were in a decisively different relative position at the end of the 20th century than they were at its start. In 1913, on the eve of World War I, the 20 or so countries now known as the rich industrial economies produced almost 80% of world manufacturing. In 1950, the United States alone accounted for around half of world output, about the share produced by all the developed economies together in 2002.

The last half of the 20th and early years of the 21st century, indeed, witnessed a remarkable expansion of the "core" of economically advanced states and a substantial reordering of world economic power and national rankings. Income of countries and individuals may be either measured by *purchasing power parity* (which allows for lower prices in poorer countries, see Figure 11.6) or by *market rates of exchange* (using U.S. dollar equivalents). By the purchasing power measure, the emerging world—the South—now accounts for over 50% of global economic output; even by current exchange rates, the former "underdeveloped" world now contributes nearly 30% of world production and accounted for half the growth in global output in 2006. By a variety of measures, economic power is shifting away from the more developed economies of the North (North America, Western Europe, Japan, Australasia basically) toward the emerging or semi-periphery states, particularly in Asia. By 2006, developing countries held the majority of the world's foreign exchange reserves, consumed over half the world's energy, and accounted for nearly 45% of all exports (up from 20% in 1970). That growing world prosperity is rather broadly spread. Africa lags seriously behind the widely recognized new powerhouses of China, Brazil, India, and Russia, which combined for 40% of the world's output in 2006.

Impressive as the shifts in global economic balance between the industrial and developing countries may be, they do little to reduce the contrasts that remain between the richest of the North and the poorest of the South. While as a group the developing countries—187 of them by UN definition—are catching up to the developed world in total productivity, a good part of the aggregate gain is lost in per capita terms (see "Poverty and Development"). With the South's (excluding China) population increasing at nearly a 2% per annum rate, growing national prosperity has to be—at least statistically—divided among an increasing number of claimants. In the early 1990s, the South had to apportion its recalculated one-third share of *gross global product* (the total value of goods and services produced by the world economy) among more than three-fourths of world population.

Not all of the employment shifts and structural changes within developing countries, however, are accounted for by official statistics. In all countries, at least a portion of goods and services is produced and workers supported by the **informal** (shadow, grey, underground) **economy.** The informal economy in developing countries as a group, a 2002 World Bank study estimated, was equivalent to 41% of their official gross domestic product. Even in the rich West European countries, the share of the informal economy reached 18%. The proportion of economic activity escaping official notice and thus not part of published gross national income (GNI) totals varies greatly among regions and states. In Africa, the average size of the informal economy was 42% of GNI. Zimbabwe, Tanzania, and Nigeria had by far the largest informal sector with between 58% and 59% of GNI; the figure dropped to 28% in South Africa. In Asia, Thailand at 53% of GNI is the developing country most affected by informal sector activity; China (13%) and Vietnam (16%) are the least impacted. Bolivia, at 67% of GNI, is the grey economy leader in Latin America, where the informal sector accounted on average for 41% of gross national income. Whether undertaken to avoid taxes or to hide illegal enterprises, or whether it simply reflects the efforts and employment of those unable to find jobs with registered businesses, informal economic activity obviously distorts government statistics on total employment and GDP and their agricultural, industrial, and service components (Figure 11.5).

Development and the Standard of Living

The terms *level of living* and *standard of living* bring to mind some of the ways in which economic advancement implies both technological and societal change, including amount of personal income, levels of education, food consumption, life expectancy, and the availability of health care. The complexity of the occupational structure, the degree of specialization in jobs, the ways in which natural resources are used, and the level of industrialization are also measures of development and of the innovation or adoption of technology within a society.

Income is but one measure of the standard of living. Since Truman's 1949 address, the outcomes of development efforts have been mixed. Rigg (1997) suggested that positive aspects of development include:

- economic growth;
- overall national progress;
- provision of basic needs (e.g., food, clothing, housing, basic education, and health care);
- creation of sustainable growth; and
- support of improved governance.

Negative outcomes are also present and include:

- increased dependency of developing nations on developed nations;
- widening of inequalities between rich and poor;
- undermining of local cultures and values;
- promotion of environmental degradation; and
- infringement on human rights and undermining of democracy.

These contradictions highlight some of the implications and attributes of development. It also makes it clear why no single measure or indicator is sufficient to assess the comparative stage of economic development or level of living in a society. We might, for example, simplistically assume that national contrasts in average per capita income would serve to measure the level of living in all of its aspects; but personal income figures are particularly hard to compare across national borders. An income of $50,000 in Canada is taxed at a much higher rate than a similar income in the United States. But social welfare programs, higher education, and medicine receive greater government support in Canada; the American family must set aside a larger portion of their income for such services.

Further, identical incomes will be spent on different amounts and types of goods and services in different countries. Americans, because of lower prices, spend a smaller proportion of their personal income on food than do the residents of most European states or Japan; those living in upper latitudes must buy fuel and heavy clothing not necessary in tropical household budgets; and price levels may vary widely in different economies for similar essential goods. Of course, national average personal income figures do not indicate how earnings are distributed among the citizenry. In some countries, the wealthiest 5% of the population control over 50% of the income, whereas in others, revenues are more uniformly distributed.

According to the World Bank and the United Nations Development Programme (UNDP), of the world's start of-century 6.2 billion people (2006), 2.6 billion—some 42%—lived on less than $2 per day. Over 1 billion—about a sixth of the world total—experienced "absolute poverty: These folk exist on an income of less than $1 per day ($440 per year in purchasing power parity), a figure below which, it is usually believed, people are unable to buy adequate food, shelter, and other necessities. As a hopeful measure of progress, this is a smaller number and a smaller percentage of the world's population than were abjectly poor in 1990. About 43% of the very poor live in South Asia and another 29% in sub-Saharan Africa. East Asia and the Pacific account for 21% of those in absolute poverty, and Latin America and the Caribbean add another 5%.

Although the dollar definition of poverty is applied as if it were a worldwide constant, in reality poverty is comprised of two separate elements that are regional variables. One of these is the reasonably objective observation that you are impoverished if you can't afford a minimum standard of nutrition. The other element is more subjective and equates poverty with inability to buy basic goods that other citizens of your country regard as necessities. The UNDP has attempted to combine these separate elements in devising a human poverty index (HPI) that, first, identifies poverty populations by the simple income test, and then concentrates on measuring deprivation in three essential dimensions of human life: longevity (percentage of people not expected to live to age 40); knowledge (percentage of adults who are illiterate); and deprivation in living standards (measured by access to safe water, access to health services, and percentage of malnourished children under 5).

By these standards, the world made significant progress in reducing human poverty in the 1990s. In developing countries, the percentage of newly born people not expected to survive to age 40 declined from 20% to 14% during the decade. Adult illiteracy dropped from 35% to 28%, and access to safe water increased from 68% to 78%. The purchasing power income poverty rate, even at the $1-a-day standard, dropped from 17% of world population in 1970 to about 7% in 2000. Income poverty declined during the 1990s in every developing region, though the decline was not uniform and ranged from 11 percentage points in East Asia to only 0.3 percentage points in sub-Saharan Africa.

The UNDP reports that some countries have made notable progress. Malaysia reduced income absolute poverty (the $1-per-day level) from 50% in 1960 to 2% in 2003, China from 33% in 1978 to 17%, and India from 54% in 1974 to 35% in 2002. In contrast, in Niger, the African country lowest on the human poverty index scale in 2003, more than 60% of residents live in conditions of absolute poverty, the highest figure for any of the world's developing countries, though Mali held the record that year with 72.3% of its population living on less than $1 a day and 90.6% below the $2 as day level. In the Western Hemisphere, Haiti has the highest HPI, and Guatemala is the Latin American poverty leader. In Asia, Bangladesh is worst off among South Asian states and Yemen leads the Arab world.

Poverty is an areal variable within countries. In Burkina Faso and Zambia, rural poverty fell and urban poverty rose during the 1990s. In Mexico between 1989 and 1994, overall poverty declined modestly, but there were large variations across regions within the country. In Thailand, the incidence of poverty in the rural northeast was almost double the national average in 1992. The World Bank notes that, in general, poverty tends to be associated with distance from cities and the seacoast.

Africa is a continuing problem region. Because of its rapid population growth, stagnation or decline in per capita food production, weakness in infrastructure and facilities systems, periodic drought, and devastating civil wars, in sub-Saharan Africa the number of poor people increased from 217 million in 1987 to more than 300 million in 2002. The World Bank projects that the sub-Saharan region will have 360 million people or 40% of its population in poverty in 2010.

One key to improving both the economic and social lot of the "poorest of the poor," the World Bank and United Nations argue, is to target public spending on their special needs of education and health care and to pursue patterns of investment and economic growth that can productively employ that underutilized and growing labour force so abundant in the least developed countries. These identified socio-economic needs are important elements of the UN's interlocked Millennium Development Goals (see p. 403). Another needed solution, many argue, is for rich creditor countries and international lending agencies to provide relief from the massive burden of interest and principal repayments owed by the group of 38 or more highly indebted poor countries (HIPCs).[a] Some steps to that goal have been taken by the International Monetary Fund, the World Bank and the finance ministers of large donor countries. In 2005, they reached agreement on plans to erase as much as $55 billion in debt owed by impoverished nations based on their per capital incomes, and adherence to 'sound" economic policies and standards of good government.

[a] See "Does Foreign Aid Help?" p. 386.

To broaden the limited view afforded by per capita income figures, therefore, a variety of more specific and descriptive measures has been employed to suggest national levels of development. Each such measure can present only part of a total picture of developmental status. Taken together, however, the comparative criteria tend to show a high, but not perfect, correlation that collectively supports the accepted North-South global split. The primarily economic measures discussed here illustrate two commonly accepted as most revealing of the relative progress of countries of the "South" along the scale of development. They are (1) gross national income and purchasing power parity (PPP) per capita, (2) percent of the workforce engaged in agriculture, and (3) the diffusion and availability of technology.

FIGURE 11.5 "Informal sector" initiative by street typists for hire in Huancayo, Peru. Between 1965 and 2000, the percentage of the labour force in agriculture dropped precipitously in all countries of Latin America. That decline was not matched by a proportional increase in jobs in manufacturing and other industries. In Peru, employment in agriculture fell from 50% to less than 8% of the total, but the share of workers in industry remained constant at about 20%. Many of the former rural workers found urban work in the informal or shadow economy sector, the generator of 60% of all new Latin American jobs in the 1990s. They became errand runners, street vendors, odd-job handymen, open-air dispensers of such personal services as barbering, shoe shining, clothes mending, letter-writing, and the like, as well as unregistered workers in small-scale construction and repair shops. For Latin America as a whole, the UN reports, 74% of the female and 55% of the male labour force worked in the informal economy at the start of the century. For developing countries as a group, informal sector employment made up 37% of total jobs; it reached 45% in Africa and 33% in Asia. See also Figure 10.25.

Gross National Income and Purchasing Power Parity

Gross National Income (GNI) is a commonly available statistic (formerly known as gross national product) that reports the total market value of goods and services[3] produced within an economy within a given time period, usually a year. Expressed in per capita terms (see Appendix A), GNI is a frequently used indicator of a country's economic performance (Figure 11.6). Like any other single index of development, gross national income tells only part of a complex story. Indeed, its concept, and that of the related gross domestic product, is under increasing attack for its assumed distortions of reality. One group, including environmentalists, argues that the GNI overstates the wealth of a society by ignoring the cost of ecological damage and the drain modern economies place on natural resources. An opposing group holds that GNI understates the strength of economic growth by overlooking much of the quality and productivity improvements brought by technology (safer automobiles; faster, more powerful computers, etc.).

Of course, gross national income per capita is not a personal income figure, but simply a calculated assignment of each individual's share of a national total. Change in total population or in total national income will alter the average per capita figure but need have no impact on the personal finances of any individual citizen. Nor is per capita GNI a totally realistic summary of developmental status. It tends to distort a more inclusive picture of underdevelopment by overemphasizing the purely monetary circumstances of countries and not accurately representing the economic circumstances of countries with dominantly subsistence economies, for example, many of the nations of Asia and Africa with low income figures.

As expected, the countries with the highest GNI per capita are those in north-western Europe, where the Industrial Revolution began, and in the mid-latitude colonial areas—North America, Australia, and New Zealand—to which the new technologies were

---

[3] Adjusted by deducting income earned by foreign interests and adding income accruing to residents from foreign investments or remittances. Without these adjustments, the statistic is called **gross domestic product**, itself subject to different adjustments.

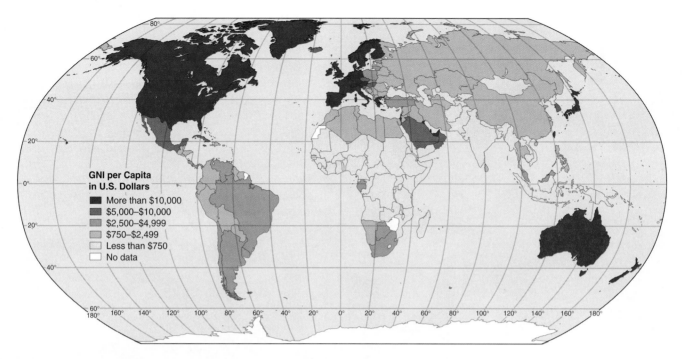

FIGURE 11.6 Gross national income per capita, 2003. GNI per capita is a frequently employed summary of degree of economic advancement, though high incomes in sparsely populated, oil-rich countries may not have the same meaning in developmental terms as do comparable per capita values in industrially advanced states. The map implies an unrealistic precision. For many states, when uncertain GNI is divided by unreliable population totals, the resulting GNI per capita is at best a rough approximation that varies between reporting agencies. A comparison of this map and Figure 11.8 presents an interesting study in regional contrasts.

Source: Data from World Bank and Population Reference Bureau.

first transplanted. In the middle position are found many of the countries of Latin America and of southern and eastern Europe. Large sections of Africa and Asia, in contrast, are at the low end of average income figures, since the money value of the non-traded goods and services that subsistence farmers provide for themselves and their communities goes unrecorded in the GNI. That problem is partly resolved, by calculating what are sometimes called "real per capita gross domestic products," but more usually summarized as *purchasing power parities.*

The world and regional impacts of continuing shifts in global economic balance are obscured by traditional market exchange rate estimates of the relative size of national economies. Those estimates measure gross national income or per capita share of gross domestic product in U.S. dollar equivalents, making no assessment of relative price levels in different countries or of the value of non-traded goods and services. Seeking a more realistic measure of national economies, the International Monetary Fund and the World Bank now use **purchasing power parity (PPP)**, which takes account of what money actually buys in each country. PPP is based on the idea that an identical basket of traded goods should cost the same in all countries (Figure 11.7). If, for example, a loaf of bread costs $1 in Canada but only 50 cents in Thailand, the Thai citizen's assigned per capita dollar income should be adjusted upward to reflect what can actually be bought with a dollar's equivalent in Thai currency. When the new PPP measure was introduced in 1993, it gave a clearer picture of the world economy and radically changed traditional assessments of it (see "PPP as Burgernomics").

Immediately, the relative economic importance of the emerging economies doubled. Using purchasing power parity, East Asia's share of world 2000 output jumped from 6% to 17%, and the revised 2003 weight for all developing states vaulted from less than one-quarter to almost one-half of global output. That is, the rich industrial economies in 2003 accounted for just 53% of total global output using PPPs, a marked come-down from their assumed 80% contribution under the old exchange rate system. If present trends hold, the World Bank forecasts, by 2020 the current "rich world's" share of global output could shrink to less than two-fifths.

Poverty in Canada

It can be confusing listening to media reports about poverty in Canada. First, it seems contradictory that a country that has often been identified as the most developed country in the world, as measured by the Human Development Index, would have a poverty problem. Unlike poverty in the Third World where people starve, poverty in Canada often consists of lining up for food at food banks and shelters. This suggests that in Canada, part of the poverty problem reflects an unequal distribution of this country's wealth, as measured by per capita income, rather than an absolute lack of it. Second, after recognizing that a poverty problem exists in Canada, there is no agreement on its extent, in large part, because definitions and measures of poverty are varied. There are at least two perspectives on the nature of the definition—absolute and relative. *Absolute poverty* focuses attention on a person's ability to meet basic needs, while the latter is related to inadequacy

In 1986, *The Economist* introduced the "Big Mac index," which is essentially a form of purchasing power parity(PPP) and gave rise to the term *burgernomics*. The popularity of this index reflects an aspect of the globalization of the economy. The Big Mac index is obtained by dividing the price of a Big Mac in one country (in its currency) by the price of a Big Mac in another country (in its currency). The exchange rate between the two currencies is then compared to the actual exchange rate in order to determine over and under valuations of currency.

While this form of measurement is not perfect, it is easily communicated to those people familiar with 'Big Macs.' Since the Big Mac can be purchased in about 120 countries, it is relevant to many people. In 2007, a person buying a Big Mac in the United States paid $3.22. In Canada, this burger cost $3.08.

The most expensive Big Mac was found in Iceland at $7.44. The least expensive Big Mac was found in China—$1.41. Can you think of any shortcomings with this form of PPP measurement?

A Feast of Burgernomics
THE BIG MAC INDEX

	Big Mac Prices		Implied PPP* of the dollar	Actual dollar exchange rate Jan. 31st	Under(−)/over(+) valuation against the dollar, %
	In local currency	In dollars			
United States†	$3.22	3.22			
Canada	C$3.63	3.08	1.13	1.18	−4
China	Yuan 11.0	1.41	3.42	7.77	−56
Iceland	Kronur 509	7.44	158	68.4	+131
Indonesia	Rupiah 15,900	1.75	4,938	9,100	−46
Mexico	Peso 29.0	2.66	9.01	10.9	−17
Pakistan	Rupee 140	2.31	43.5	60.7	−28
Peru	New Sol 9.50	2.97	2.95	3.20	−8
Russia	Rouble 49.0	1.85	15.2	26.5	−43
South Africa	Rand 15.5	2.14	4.81	7.25	−34

Sources: Wodall, Pam. "On the Hamburger Standard." *The Economist*. p. 83. September 1986.

* Purchasing-power parity: local price divided by price in United States
† Average of New York, Atlanta, Chicago, and San Francisco

relative to average living standards or incomes. *Relative poverty* takes into consideration both being able to meet basic needs as well as participate in everyday activities of society. Canadian definitions and measures of poverty include:

• Low-income cut-offs, which are calculating by estimating the percentage of gross income spent by a household on

food, shelter, and clothing, which is then arbitrarily marked up by 20%. If a household spends 20 percentage points or more of its income on these three essentials than the average Canadian spends, it is a low income household. In 1995, the cut-off for a household of four ranged from about $22,000 in rural areas to about $32,000 in urban areas over 500,000 in population.

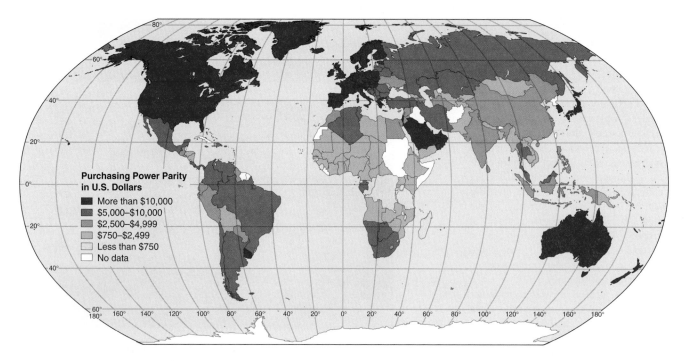

FIGURE 11.7 Purchasing power parity (PPP), 2003. When local currency measures of gross national income or gross domestic product are converted into purchasing power parities, there is a twofold revision of the usual view of world economic status. The first result is a sharp increase in developing countries' share of total world output. By the PPP calculation, in 2005 China had the world's second largest economy and India its fourth largest; Russia and Mexico emerged as bigger than Canada. Second, the abject poverty suggested by per capita gross national income or goss domestic product is seen to be much reduced in many developing countries. India, for example, showed a 2004 gross national income per capita at market exchange rates of $620; in purchasing power parity, the figure rose to $3120, and the Central African Republic's people jumped from $250 to $1340. Compare this map with Figure 11.8 to see how PPP changes our impressions of some countries' economic status.

Source: Data from World Bank and United Nations.

- Distribution of wealth among Canadians, which often suggests that "the rich get richer and the poor get poorer." One study focused on British Columbia and found that families from the richest 10% of the province had a combined wealth of more than $231 billion, or 54.6% of all personal wealth. Average wealth in the group was $1,378,534. In contrast, the poorest 10% of families had debts that were larger than their assets. They collectively owed nearly $1.4 billion, which represented an average net wealth of negative $8,126.

Can you think of other economic and non-economic definitions and measures of poverty for Canada? What are the strengths and weaknesses of those offered above and the ones you suggest?

In 2007, the Canadian Council on Social Development published a study of urban poverty in Canada. Poverty is measured using Statistics Canada's "before-tax Low-Income Cut-offs" (see Table 11.1). It found that while Canada enjoyed significant economic growth in the 1990s, there was virtually no progress on reducing its comparatively high level of poverty—about 1 in 6 Canadians continue to live in poverty. During the 1990s, the number of Canadians living in poverty increased by 10.1% to 4.7 million people, and almost all of this growth occurred in Canada's largest urban areas (CMAs). In terms of its spatial distribution, poverty rates were highest within CMAs (17.5%) (see Chapter 2 regarding CMAs), followed by urban areas outside CMAs (14.9%), and in rural areas (12.6%). This pattern is true for all provinces except Newfoundland, Nova Scotia, and Saskatchewan,

where rural poverty rates are higher than those in urban areas (Table 11.1). In these provinces, the majority of residents and the majority of poor residents live outside the CMAs. Quebec had the highest poverty rate within CMAs (21.1%), while Alberta (15.1%) had the lowest rate. The narrow range between these two figures indicates that poverty within CMAs is a significant national public policy problem. The highest poverty rate for urban areas outside CMAs was in Nova Scotia (20.1%), with the lowest in Alberta (12.0%). At 19.7%, Newfoundland had the highest poverty rate in rural areas (Table 11.1).

In the same study, the Canadian Council on Social Development found that over 3.1 million people who lived in poverty in Canada in 1995 were residents of the country's large CMAs (over 500,000 population) (Table 11.1). Almost 70% of these people lived in Montreal, Vancouver, and Toronto, with Montreal having the highest number of poor residents at about 891,000 persons and a 27.3% rate of poverty. Ottawa–Hull had the lowest poverty rate among the large CMAs at 18.9%. Collectively, the large CMAs had a poverty rate of 22.7%, which was higher than the rate experienced by small CMAs (17.3%) (Table 11.1). Poverty rates among the smaller CMAs were higher in the Atlantic Provinces and Quebec than the rest of Canada. Without exception, poverty rates between 1990 and 1995 have increased among all large and small CMAs. Poverty grew at a faster rate in large CMAs (4.7%) relative to the smaller CMAs (2.9%). Visible minorities, immigrants, and Aboriginal peoples living in urban areas were most frequently among the poorer populations.

Percentage of the Workforce Engaged in Agriculture

A high percentage of employment in agriculture (Figure 11.8) is almost invariably associated with low per capita gross national income and low energy consumption, that is, with underdevelopment. Economic development always means a range of occupational choices far greater than those available in a subsistence agricultural society. Mechanization of agriculture increases the productivity of a decreasing farm labour force; surplus rural workers are made available for urban industrial and service employment, and if jobs are found, national and personal prosperity increases. When a labour force is primarily engaged in agriculture, on the other hand, subsistence farming, low capital accumulation, and limited national economic development are usually indicated.

Landlessness

Developing region economies devoid of adequate urban industrial or service employment opportunities can no longer accommodate population growth by bringing new agricultural land into cultivation. In the most densely settled portions of the developing world, rural population expansion increasingly means that new entrants to the labour force are denied access to land either through ownership or tenancy. The problem is most acute in southern Asia, particularly on the Indian subcontinent, where the landless rural population is estimated to number some 290 million. Additional millions have access to parcels too small to adequately feed the average household. A landless agricultural labour force is also of increasing concern in Africa and Latin America (Figure 11.9).

Landlessness is in part a function of an imbalance between the size of the agricultural labour force and the arable land resource. It is also frequently a reflection of concentration of ownership by a few and consequent landlessness for many. Restricted ownership of large tracts of rural land appears to affect not just the economic fortunes of the agricultural labour force itself but also to depress national economic growth through inefficient utilization of a valuable but limited resource. Large estates are often farmed carelessly, are devoted to production of crops for export with little benefit for low-paid farm workers, or even left idle. In some societies, governments concerned about undue concentration of ownership have imposed restrictions on total farm size—though not always effectively.

In Latin America, where farms are often huge and most peasants landless, land reform—that is, redistribution of arable land to farm workers—has had limited effect. The Mexican revolution early in the 20th century resulted in the redistribution of nearly half the country's agricultural land over the succeeding 60 years, but the rural discord in Chiapas beginning in the 1990s reflects the persistence there of underutilized large estates and peasant landlessness. The Bolivian revolution of 1952 was followed by a redivision of 83% of the land. Some 40% of Peru's farming area was redistributed by the government during the 1970s. In other Latin American countries, however, land reform movements have been less successful. In Guatemala, for example, 85% of rural households are landless or nearly so, and the top 1% of landowners control 34% of arable land; in Brazil, data from 2000 indicate

TABLE 11.1

Canada's Poor by Province and CMA Location (population in '000s)

| | WITHIN CMAs | | | OUTSIDE CMAs | | | | | |
| | | | | Urban Areas | | | Rural Areas | | |
	Total population	Poor population	Poverty Rate (%)	Total population	Poor population	Poverty Rate (%)	Total population	Poor population	Poverty Rate (%)
Newfoundland & Labrador	170	30	17.4	78	15	19.0	258	51	19.7
PEI	na	na	na	52	8	17.1	81	8	9.8
Nova Scotia	354	55	15.5	241	49	20.1	291	43	14.9
New Brunswick	120	22	17.8	242	38	15.5	347	52	15.0
Quebec	4,723	1,000	21.1	921	160	17.4	1,414	190	13.4
Ontario	8,293	1,285	15.5	1,889	239	12.7	1,021	88	8.6
Manitoba	657	126	19.2	122	21	17.1	257	34	13.2
Saskatchewan	411	69	16.8	145	26	18.3	356	49	13.7
Alberta	1,858	280	15.1	516	62	12.0	502	53	10.6
B.C.	2,399	470	19.6	874	137	15.7	512	65	12.7
Canada	18.987	3,332	17.5	5,079	756	14.9	5,039	663	12.6

Source: Canadian Council on Social Development, 2000, http://www.ccsd.ca/pubs/2007/upp/.

that ownership of more than 60% of the country's arable area was held by just 3% of its population.

In India, where two-thirds of rural families either have no land at all or own less than 2 hectares (5 acres), a government regulation limits ownership of "good" land to 7 hectares (18 acres). That limitation has been effectively circumvented by owners distributing title to the excess land to their relatives. Population growth has reduced the amount of land available to the average farmer on the Indonesian island of Java to only 0.3 hectares (three-quarters of an acre), and the central government reports that over half of Java's farmers now work plots too small to support them.

The rural landless are the most disadvantaged segment of the poorest countries of the least developed regions of the world. They have far higher levels of malnutrition and incidence of disease, and lower life expectancies than other segments of their societies. In Bangladesh, for example, the rural landless consume only some 80% of the daily caloric intake of their landholding neighbours. To survive, many there and in other countries where landlessness is a growing rural problem leave the agricultural labour force and migrate to urban areas, swelling the number of shantytown residents but not necessarily improving their fortunes.

The Diffusion of Technology

Composite figures mask the disparities that exist within the ranks of developing countries. The world's 50 "least developed" states in 2003 produced less than 0.6% of global wealth, measured at market exchange rates. In contrast, the small, industrialized "four tigers"—Hong Kong, Singapore, South Korea, and Taiwan—alone contributed more than 3% to gross world product. Obviously, there are differences within the developing world in the successful application of technology to the creation of wealth.

Technology refers to the totality of tools and methods available to and used by a culture group in producing items essential to its subsistence and comfort. We saw in Chapter 5 how in antiquity there emerged *culture hearths*—centres of technological innovation, of new ideas and techniques that diffused or were carried out from the core region. Innovation is rarely a single event; as cultures advance, needs multiply and different solutions develop to meet expanding requirements. The ancient hearths (See Figure 5.19) were locales of such multiple invention and innovation. Their modern counterparts are the highly urbanized, industrialized advanced nations whose creativity is recorded by patent registrations and product and process introductions. The changing rate of innovation over time is suggested by Figure 5.7.

In all periods, there has existed between hearths and outlying regions a **technology gap**, a contrast in the range and productivity of artifacts introduced at the core and those known or employed at the periphery. That gap widened at an accelerating rate as technology moved farther away from the shared knowledge of earlier periods. During the Industrial Revolution, the technological distance between cottage hand looms of 18th-century English

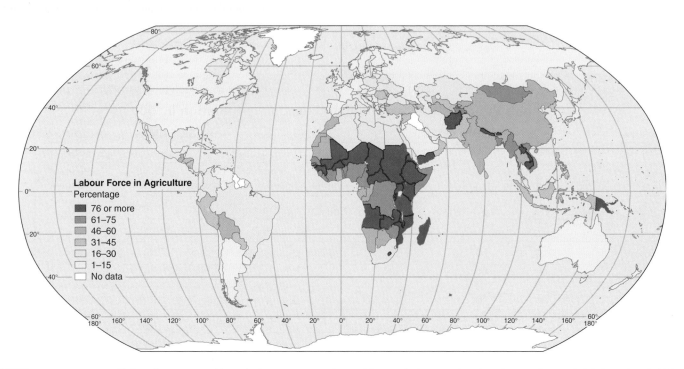

FIGURE 11.8 Percentage of labour force engaged in agriculture, 2002. For the world as a whole, agricultural workers make up slightly less than half the total labour force. Highly developed economies usually have relatively low proportions of their labour forces in the agricultural sector, but the contrast between advanced and underdeveloped countries in the agricultural labour force measure is diminishing. Rapid Third World population growth has resulted in increased rural landlessness and poverty from which escape is sought by migration to cities. The resulting reduction in the agricultural labour force percentage is an expression of relocation of poverty and unemployment, not of economic advancement.

Sources: Data from C.I.A., The World Factbook 2005, *and* FAO 2004.

FIGURE 11.9 Throughout much of the developing world, growing numbers and proportions of rural populations are either landless agricultural labourers with, at best, tiny garden plots to provide basic food needs, or independent holders of parcels inadequate in size or quality to provide food security for the family. In either case, size of land holding and poverty of farmer restrict the operator to rudimentary agricultural implements and practices. In this photo, a Nuer woman of Sudan cultivates corn with a simple hand tool.

villagers and the power looms of their neighbouring factories was one of only moderate degree (Figure 11.10). Far greater is the gap between the range of traditional crafts known throughout the world and the modern technologies of the most advanced societies. It is much more difficult now for a less developed society to advance to the "state of the art" by its own efforts than it was for British colonies or the rest of Europe to recreate the textile or iron-making industries first developed in England.

The persistence and expansion of the technology gap suggest that the idea of **cultural convergence**—the increasing similarity in technologies and ways of life among societies at the same levels of development—does not as well unite the most and the least advanced economies. In the modern world, as we saw in Chapter 5, there is a widespread sharing of technologies, organizational forms, and developed cultural traits. But not all countries are at the same developmental state. Not all are equally able to draw on advanced technology to create the same products with identical efficiency and quality, although there is increasing awareness of the existence of those products and the benefits of their use.

The technology gap matters. At any given level of technology, the resources of an area will have a limited population supporting capacity. As population growth approaches or exceeds those limits, as it has in many less developed areas of the globe, poverty, famine, and political and social upheaval can result. Understandably, all countries aspire to expand their resource base, increase its support levels through application of improved technologies, or enter more fully into an income-producing exchange relationship with other

world regions through economic development. Their objective is a **technology transfer**, placing in their own territory and under their own controls the productive manufacturing plants and processes that are enjoyed by the more advanced countries. The chemical plant of Bhopal was one item in a technology transfer sought by the state of Madhya Pradesh and the government of India, one step in the process of moving the region and country further along the continuum from less developed to more developed status.

Not all technology, of course, is equally transferable. Computers, information management techniques, cell phones, and the like easily make the move between advanced and emerging economies. Other technologies, particularly in the life sciences, materials innovation, and energy, are more specific to the markets, monetary resources, and needs of the rich countries and not adapted to those of the less developed states. Even where transfer is feasible, imported innovations may require domestic markets sufficient to justify their costs, markets that poor countries will not possess at their current national income levels. And the purchase of technology presumes recipient country export earnings sufficient to pay for it, again a condition not met by the poorest states.

Developing countries have, in a form of reverse flow, contributed to scientific and engineering innovation. Advanced technologies and scientific breakthroughs depend on public and private research institutions and corporate research and development departments common in the rich states. Many of the advances produced by those agencies have been made by poor-country scientists working in the rich-country laboratories. Indian and Chinese technologists and engineers, for example, are major components in the workforce of all the high-tech concentrations discussed in Chapter 10, though many are increasingly contributing to innovative research and development in their home countries.

Bioprospecting and biodiversity illustrate some of the issues related to technology transfer. By 2007, almost 80 nations have ratified the Convention on Biological Diversity (CBD)—a legally binding treaty that requires governments to establish laws and regulations to meet the following objectives: 1) the conservation of biodiversity, 2) the sustainable use of its components, and 3) the fair and equitable sharing of the benefits arising out of the utilization of genetic resources. The CBD establishes that source countries (largely developing nations) have ownership over the genetic resources found within their borders. Prior to 1992, when the CBD was established, there were no restrictions. Within the new regime, pharmaceutical companies are a very important group of participants who undertake bioprospecting (or biodiversity prospecting). This involves searching for and collecting plants that are screened for their medically beneficial components. Bioprospectors are particularly attracted to the biologically diverse tropical areas. It is coincident that more than two thirds of all plant species are also located in the Third World. Ideally, bioprospecting could benefit both the host nation and bioprospectors through capacity building and the transfer of research facilities. However, this transfer does not always occur and the major benefits accrue to firms often located in the developed world.

Per capita energy consumption is another common measure of technological advancement of nations because it loosely

FIGURE 11.10 Early in the Industrial Revolution, new techniques that diffused most readily from the English hearth were those close to handicraft production processes. In some industries, the important innovation was the adoption of power and volume production, not radically new machines or products. For textiles and similar light industries, capital requirements were low and workers required little training in new skills. The picture shows carding, drawing, and spinning machinery built by memory in the United States in 1790 by Samuel Slater, an Englishman who introduced the new technology despite British prohibitions on exports of drawings or models of it.

correlates with per capita income, degree of industrialization, and use of advanced technology. In fact, the industrialized countries use about 10 times more energy on a per capita basis than developing economies do. The consumption rather than the production of energy is the concern. Many of the highly developed countries consume large amounts of energy but produce relatively little of it. Japan, for example, must import from abroad the energy supplies its domestic resource base lacks. In contrast, many less developed countries have very high per capita or total energy production figures but primarily export the resource (petroleum). Libya, Nigeria, and Brunei are cases in point. Most of the less and least developed countries depend less on commercial forms of inanimate energy (petroleum, coal, lignite, natural gas, hydropower, etc.) than they do on animate energy (human and animal labour) and the firewood, crop residues, dung, peat, and other domestic fuels on which subsistence populations must depend. Both rudimentary and some advanced technologies are locally and gradually improving that picture as solar stoves, waste matter converters (Figure 11.11), solar photovoltaic panels, and the like, come into use.

The advanced countries developed their economic strength through the use of cheap energy and its application to industrial processes. But energy is cheap only if immense capital investment is made to produce it at a low cost per unit. The less advanced nations, unable to make those necessary investments or lacking domestic energy resources, use expensive animate energy or such decreasingly available fuels as firewood, and they must forgo energy-intensive industrial development. Anything that increases

the cost of energy further removes it from easy acquisition by less developed countries. Periodic surges in petroleum prices beginning in the 1970s and the consequent increase in the price of all purchased energy supplies served to widen further the gulf between the technological subsystems of the rich and the poor countries of the world.

Non-economic Measures of Development

Development is measured by more than economic standards, though income and national wealth strongly affect the degree to which societies can invest in education, sanitation, health services, and other components of individual and group well-being. Indeed, the relationship between economic and social measures of development is direct and proportional. The higher the per capita gross national income is, for example, the higher the national ranking tends to be in such matters as access to safe drinking water, prevalence of sanitary waste treatment, availability of physicians and hospital beds, and educational and literacy levels.

In contrast, the relationship between social-economic and demographic variables is usually inverse. Higher educational or income levels, that is, are usually associated with lower infant mortality rates, birth and death rates, rates of natural increase, and the like. However it is measured, the gap between the most and least developed countries in non-economic characteristics is at least as great as it is in their economic-technological circumstances. Table 11.2 suggests that the South as a whole has made progress in reducing its disadvantages in some human well-being measures. In others, however, the gap between rich and poor remains or is increasing, and disparities still persist after the three UN "development decades."

Education

A literate, educated labour force is essential for the effective transfer of advanced technology from the developed to developing countries. Yet in the poorest societies half or more of adults are illiterate; for the richest, the figure is 1% or less (Figure 11.12). The problem in part stems from a national poverty that denies funds sufficient for teachers, school buildings, books, and other necessities of the educational program. In part it reflects the lack of a trained pool of teachers and the inability to expand their number rapidly enough to keep up with the ever-increasing size of school-age populations. In African countries worst hit by the AIDS epidemic, deaths among established teachers exceeded the supply of new teachers entering the profession beginning in the late 1990s. For the same number of potential pupils, the richest countries may have 20 to 25 times as many teachers as do the poorest countries. In Norway in 2004, there was one teacher for every 10 primary school children; in Congo Republic there was 1 to 83. Commitment appears as important as wealth in determining student–teacher ratios; Israel had more teachers per 1000 students than did richer Canada and the United Kingdom.

FIGURE 11.11 A biogas generator in Nepal. Human, animal, and vegetable wastes are significant energy sources in developing economies such as Pakistan, India, Thailand, and China where such wastes are fermented to produce methane gas (*biogas*) as a fuel for cooking, lighting, and heating. The simple technology involves only a stone fermentation tank (foreground) fed with wastes: straw and other crop residues, manure, human waste, kitchen scraps, and the like. These are left to decompose and ferment; the emitted methane gas passes into a large collection chamber (left background tank) and later is drawn through a tube into the farm kitchen. After the gas is spent, the remaining waste is pumped out and used for fertilizer in the fields.

Lack of facilities and teachers, family poverty that makes tuition fees prohibitive and keeps millions of school-age children in full-time work, and national poverty that under funds all levels of education, together combine to restrict school enrolment in poor countries to a fraction of normal rich country expectations. In the least developed states in 2000–2002, only 55% of primary-age children and 20% of secondary school-age students were actually in school. Whatever the enrolment percentages were in individual countries, girls were less apt to be in school than were boys. In 2004, the UN estimated that 121 million children world-wide were being denied formal education; 54% of them were girls. More than 50 million primary-school-age girls were out of school in sub-Saharan Africa and South Asia alone. And the disparity in many countries increases with age, because girls are less likely than boys to progress to secondary school. The implicit economic and social development consequences are evident in the correlations that have been established between levels of female education and, for example, birth rates and family size preferences, family nutrition practices and health maintenance, and life expectancies.

Poverty, Calories, and Nutrition

Poverty is the most apparent common characteristic of countries, regions, communities, or households afflicted by malnourishment. Availability of urban employment or rural access to arable land is far more important in determining national levels of under nourishment than is a country's aggregate per capita food production. During the Bangladesh famine of 1974, for example, total food availability per capita was at a long-term peak; starvation, according to World Bank reports, was the result of declines in real wages and employment in the rural sector and short-term speculative increases in the price of rice. In India in 2002, huge stockpiles of government-owned wheat purchased at high subsidy costs rot-

ted in storage while held for sale at prices beyond the reach of malnourished or starving but impoverished citizens.

Nourishment levels, therefore, are as truly an indicator of economic development of a country as are any of the dollar-indexed measures of production and income or summary statements about the structure of national employment. Indeed, no other economic measure of national prosperity or development level can be as meaningful as the availability of food supplies sufficient in caloric content to meet individual daily energy requirements and so balanced as to satisfy normal nutritional needs. Food, as the essential universal consumption necessity and the objective of the majority of human productive activity, is the ultimate indicator of economic well-being.

Calorie requirements to maintain moderate activity vary according to a person's type of occupation, age, sex, and size, and to climate conditions. The Food and Agriculture Organization (FAO) of the UN specifies 2350 calories as the minimum necessary daily consumption level, but that figure has doubtful universal applicability. By way of a benchmark, per capita daily calorie availability in the United States is nearly 3700. Despite the limitations of the FAO standards, Figure 11.13 uses them to assess the degree of under nourishment of countries' populations.

Like other national indicators, caloric intake figures must be viewed with suspicion; the dietary levels reported by some states may more reflect self-serving estimates or fervent hopes than actual food availability. Even if accurate, of course, they report national averages, which may seriously obscure the food deprivation of large segments of a population. But the data in Figure 11.12 support FAO's 2003 estimate that 842 million people were undernourished, including 10 million in the industrialized countries. Despite that sobering world total, a number of developing countries have succeeded in reducing hunger levels. In 19 states, including China, the FAO reports, the number of chronically hungry people declined by over 80 million between 1990

TABLE 11.2

The Narrowing North–South Disparity in Human Development, 1960 to 2004

	NORTH		SOUTH		ABSOLUTE DISPARITY	
	1960	2004	1960	2004	1960	2004
Life expectancy (years)	69	78	46	62	23	16
Adult literacy (%)	95	97	46	67	49	30
Nutrition (daily calorie supply as % of requirement)	124	141	90	114	34	27
Infant mortality (per 1000 live births)	37	7	149	62	112	55
Child mortality (under age 5 deaths per 1000 per year)	46	7	216	90	170	83
Access to safe water (% of population)	100	100	40	78	60	22

Sources: United Nations Development Programme, World Bank, and UNICEF.

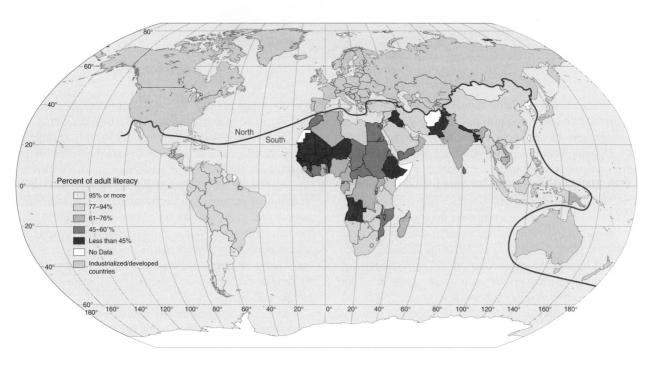

FIGURE 11.12 The South: Adult literacy rate, 2003, as a percentage of the adult population (over 15 years of age) able to read and write short, simple statements relating to their everyday life. With almost no exceptions, adult literacy is 95% or more in countries of the North. With only a few exceptions, literacy rates in all countries of the South improved dramatically during the 1990s. For developing countries as a group, 80% of adults were literate in 2003 compared to 64% in 1990; for least developed countries the improvement was from 45% literate at the start of the 1990s to 54% literate in 2003.

Sources: Data from United Nations Development Programme, Human Development Report 2005.

and 2003. In contrast, 26 countries showed a 60-million increase in the number of undernourished people over the same period. On the basis of those mixed and discouraging trends, the FAO concludes, the goals of the UN World Food Summit of 1996 (to reduce the number of undernourished people by half by the year 2015) cannot be reached and the tragic reality of inadequate supplies of food energy will persist (Figure 11.14).

Another way to measure poverty and the adequacy of a person's diet is to ask their opinions. A recent study by Statistics Canada confirmed that poverty is a widespread problem in Canada. Based on survey data of 131,535 adults in private households between September 2000 and October 2001, Statistics Canada estimated that 3.7 million Canadians (15% of the population) experienced food insecurity. *Food insecurity* was defined as someone who has been unable to obtain the quality or variety of food desired, has worried about getting enough food to eat, or has not had enough to eat. Since the study focused on private households, the findings likely underestimate the extent of the problem because it fails to consider homeless or Aboriginals living on reserves.

Low caloric intake is usually coupled with lack of dietary balance, reflecting an inadequate supply of the range and amounts of carbohydrates, proteins, fats, vitamins, and minerals needed for optimum physical and mental development and maintenance

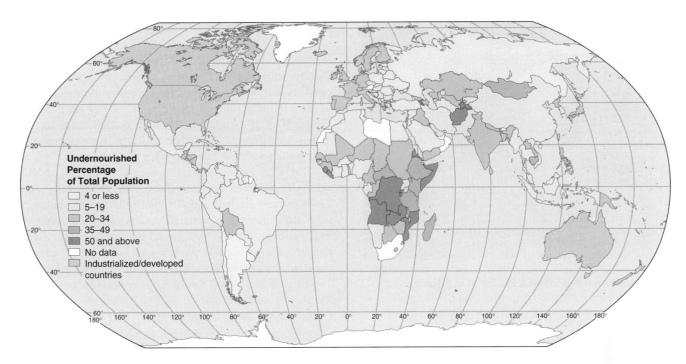

FIGURE 11.13 Percent of national population that is undernourished, 2003. Early in the 21st century, according to the FAO, there were about 850 million undernourished people worldwide facing chronic hunger or starvation, under nutrition, and deficiencies of essential iron, iodine, Vitamin A, and other micronutrients. For many, sickness and parasites take the nutritive value from what little food is eaten. The world's nutritional levels have proportionally improved in the past several decades. More than one-third of people living in poor countries in 1970 were undernourished; by 2003 that figure had fallen to 24%. Numerically, however, the number of malnourished people across the developing world grew by an average of 4.5 million a year between 1995 and 2003. Sub-Saharan Africa's incidence of under nourishment has remained constant, a reflection of the region's continuing poverty and progressive drop in per capita food production since the 1960s. In contrast, the FAO indicates that all industrialized countries have average daily per capita caloric intake above 110% of physiological requirements, although that generalization masks troubling incidences of areal and household hunger and malnutrition.

Sources: Data from World Bank, World Development Indicators 2006.

of health. The World Health Organization estimates that more than 2 billion people worldwide suffer from some form of micronutrient malnutrition that leads to high infant and child mortality, impaired physical and mental development, and weakened immune responses. As Figure 11.14 indicates, dietary insufficiencies—with inevitable adverse consequences for life expectancy, physical vigour, and intellectual acuity—are most likely to be encountered in those developing countries that have large proportions of their populations in the young age groups (see Figure 4.15). Indeed, under nourishment is damaging and widespread throughout the developing world where, collectively, 30% of children under 5 years are moderately to severely underweight and one-third are stunted. South Asia shows the highest incidence of childhood nutritional problems measured by standardized weight-for-age and weight-for-height measures. There, of the under-5 age group, 46% are moderately or severely underweight, 44% show stunting, and half the world's undernourished children are found. Malnutrition among young Indians, for example, is proportionately nearly twice as high as in sub-Saharan Africa.

Public Services

Development implies more than industrial expansion or agricultural improvement. The quality of public services and the creation of facilities to assure the health of the labour force are equally significant evidences of national advancement. Safe drinking water and the sanitary disposal of human waste are particularly important in maintaining human health. As Table 11.2 notes, disparities in access to safe water are being steadily reduced between developed and developing countries. Similar improvements have been registered for access to improved sanitation. Even in the least developed countries, more than one-third of the population had basic hygienic sanitation in 2002, up from less than one-quarter in 1990. But worldwide, more than 40% of all people—2.6 billion in 2002—lacked that access.

The accepted presence of pure water and sanitary toilets in the North and their general absence in, particularly, rural areas and urban slums in the less developed world present a profound contrast between the two realms. Only half of the rural populations of the predominantly rural least developed states have access in 2002 to water safe to drink. Within the expanding cities of the developing countries, nearly a quarter-billion people live in shantytowns and slums devoid of adequate water supply or sanitary disposal facilities (Figure 11.15). Worldwide, more than 1 billion people in the developing countries lack a dependable sanitary supply of water (Figure 11.16) and water-related diseases kill approximately 10 million people every year. Yet, significant progress has been made; during the 1980s (the UN designated it

FIGURE 11.14 Malnourished Sudanese children at an aid centre. The FAO estimates that early in the 21st century, some 200 million children under 10 years of age were among the more than 840 million people chronically undernourished in the developing world alone. As a result of hunger, 6 million children under the age of 5 die each year. The occasional and uncertain supplies of food dispensed by foreign aid programs and private charities are not sufficient to assure them of life, health, vigour, or normal development.

the International Drinking Water Supply and Sanitation Decade), 1.2 billion people worldwide were added to the ranks of those with access to potable water; nearly another 1 billion were supplied during the 1990s. By 2002, the UN reported, some 83% of all people had access to clean water, up from 77% in 1990, though more than 40% of sub-Saharan Africans still relied on unsafe drinking water supplies.

Health

Access to medical facilities and personnel is another spatial variable with profound implications for the health and well-being of populations. Within the less developed world, vast numbers of people are effectively denied the services of physicians. While in industrial countries, on average (2005), one physician served 270 people, the figure for developing countries is over 2,500. For sub-Saharan Africa as a whole, the ratio is about 10,000 to 1. In the developing world, there are simply too few trained health professionals to serve the needs of expanding populations. Those few who are in practice tend to congregate in urban areas, particularly in the capital cities. Rural clinics are few in number and the distance to them so great that many rural populations are effectively denied medical treatment of even the most rudimentary nature.

Increasingly, those sorts of health-related contrasts between advanced and developing countries have become matters of international concern and attention (see "Poverty and Development," p. 386). We saw in Chapter 4 how important for developing states population growth is the transfer of advanced technologies of medicine and public health: insecticides, antibiotics, and immunization, for example. Most recently, childhood diseases and deaths in developing countries have come under coordinated attack by the World Health Organization under the Task Force for

Child Survival program (Figure 11.17). Gains have been impressive. If the 1960 worldwide infant mortality rate had remained in 2000, 15 million more children would have died than in fact did. Yet stark contrasts between most developed and least developed societies remain. Based on the mortality levels for children under 5 in industrialized countries in 2004 (7 per thousand), the United Nations estimated that more than 90% of the approximately 11 million infant and child deaths in developing countries (122 per thousand) in that year were preventable.

Taken at their extremes, advanced and developing countries occupy two distinct worlds of disease and health. One is affluent; its death rates are low, and the chief killers of its mature populations are cancers, heart attacks, and strokes. The other world is impoverished, often crowded, and prone to disease. The deadly dangers of its youthful populations are infectious, respiratory, and parasitic diseases made more serious by malnutrition.

In 1978, the World Health Organization endorsed preventive health care as an attainable goal and adopted "health for all by the year 2000" as its official target. It was to be reached through primary health care: low technologies aimed at disease prevention in poorer nations. Although substantial improvements in global health were made by the target year, and disparities between the developed and developing worlds had been reduced, gaps had actually widened between the developing world as a whole and its "least developed" components, and health gains have actually been reversed in some states. The World Health Assembly of 1998, recognizing the continuing challenges, renewed the global commitment to "health for all" and established new targets for the early 21st century.

The general determinants of health are well known: enough purchasing power to secure the food, housing, and medical care essential to it; a healthful physical environment that is both sanitary and free from infectious disease; and a (particularly female) educational level sufficient to comprehend the essentials of nutrition and hygiene. Family planning, health, and infrastructure and economic developmental programs have begun to increase the numbers in the developing world that now have access to at least rudimentary health services.

Unfortunately, resurgence of old diseases and emergence of new ones may disrupt or reverse the hoped-for transition to better health in many world areas (see "Our Delicate State of Health," Chapter 4). Almost 10% of world population now suffer from one or more tropical diseases, many of which—malaria, affecting 200 to 300 million people with up to 3 million deaths annually, is an example—were formerly thought to be eradicable but now are spreading in drug-resistant form. One such scourge, tuberculosis, is appearing as a major concern among particularly poorer populations outside tropical regions. Low income countries are also hard hit by the spread of AIDS (acquired immune deficiency syndrome). In 2005, the UNAIDS/WHO reported over 90% of a worldwide estimated 40 to 45 million adult and 2–3 million child cases of HIV infection were found in the developing world (see "Mapping Diseases").

The high and rising costs of modern medications place unbearable burdens on strained budgets of developing states. Those costs increasingly must include health care for the rapidly growing number of their elderly citizens and for those exposed to

FIGURE 11.15 Because they have no access to safe drinking water or sanitary waste disposal, impoverished populations of a developing country's unserved rural districts and urban slums—like this one in Capetown, South Africa—are subject to water-borne and sanitation-related diseases: 900 million annual cases of diarrhea including 2 million childhood deaths, 900 million cases of roundworm, 200 million of schistosomiasis, and additional millions of other similarly related infections and deaths.

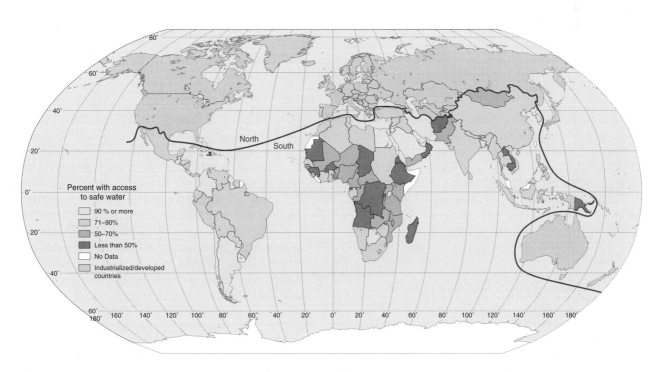

FIGURE 11.16 Percentage of population with access to safe drinking water, 2002. Between 1975 and 2002, access to safe water increased by more than two-thirds to make potable water available to 92% of urban residents in developing countries and 70% of rural folk (though only to 58% of total populations in the least developed states). By the start of the 21st century, thanks to WHO, United Nations, and World Bank programs and to targeted foreign aid, much of the developing world was approaching the levels of safe water availability formerly found only in industrialized states of the North.

Source: Data from UNICEF, State of the World's Children 2004.

FIGURE 11.17 The World Health Organization (WHO) is the agency of the United Nations that helps bring modern preventive health care, safe water, and sanitation to the less developed world. WHO workers help to fight certain diseases, advise on nutrition and living conditions, and aid developing countries in strengthening their health services. When the organization launched its Expanded Programme on Immunization in 1974, only 5% of the world's children were immunized against measles, diphtheria, polio, tetanus, whooping cough, and tuberculosis, diseases claiming 7 million young lives annually. In the early 1990s, more than 70% of children in developing countries were vaccinated against basic childhood diseases following an accelerated campaign by Unicef and WHO. But by 2002, poor countries reported that only 56% of their children received such immunization because of a fall-off in financial support from wealthy nations. In response to the slowdown, in 1999, a Global Alliance for Vaccines and Immunization was formed by national and international agencies, philanthropies, and pharmaceutical companies to revive the earlier efforts. The UN Children's Fund reported at the start of this century that more than 90% of the children of the developing world lived in countries again making significant progress toward reducing malnutrition and preventing diseases. Pictured is preventive health care in a Micronesian clinic.

the health risks that come with economic development and industrialization: higher consumption of alcohol, tobacco, and fatty foods; pollution; motor vehicle accidents; and the like. The World Health Organization is concerned that health services in poor developing countries may be overwhelmed by the twin burdens of poverty-related illness and health problems of industrialization and urbanization; heart disease and cancer now claim as many developing world lives as industrial world ones.

Sustainable Development and the Millennium Development Goals

In 1987, the concept of sustainable development was popularized by the Brundtland Commission (also referred to as the World Commission on Environment and Development) in its report "Our Common Future." Chaired by Gro Harlem Brundtland, then prime minister of Norway, it defined sustainable development as "development which meets the needs of present generations without compromising the ability of future generations to meet their own needs." This definition was both praised and criticized. Supporters found in the concept a way of focusing attention on the needs of current and future generations (termed intergenerational and intragenerational equity), and, at the same time, be concerned about the need to maintain or enhance environmental quality. Thus, development was not seen in economic terms, but rather as socio-cultural and ecological objectives such as social justice, democracy, and biodiversity. From this perspective, attention is focused on linkages between society, which includes the economy and the environment. Critics believed that the definition of sustainable development was vague and an oxymoron (a basic contradiction in terms—that is to have development that was sustainable). They would often suggest that governments view development in economic terms (e.g., gross national income (GNI)) and have relatively little regard for environmental and socio-cultural considerations. Thus, one of the attractive features about the concept is that it allows all people to use the term to express how they view environment–economy–society interactions.

While there is some ambiguity in defining the concept, some aspects of the Brundtland Report are very clear. First, basic human needs (e.g., shelter, food, water, energy) must be met. Second, poverty must be alleviated. Third, a "bottom-up" versus a "top-down" decision-making structure should be applied. Fourth, the environment must be considered alongside economic considerations rather than as an afterthought. Thus, sustainable development is an overarching concept that embraces many themes including development (current chapter), resource management, and health and well-being (Chapter 12). There are also concerns about if the achievement of sustainable development is even possible. Achieving sufficient commitment within the developed world to support the investments required to achieve the goals of sustainable development in the developing world appears lacking. Governments and people in the developed world may not support sustainable development if it means reducing their economic and non-economic qualities of life.

In 2000, it was realized that significant progress had been made in living conditions by many countries. However, this progress had been very uneven and extremely slow in many developing nations. It was within this context that eight **millennium development goals** (**MDGs**) were agreed at the United Nations Millennium Summit by 189 countries in September 2000. The eight MDGs are quantified targets to be met by 2015 to address key dimensions of poverty and basic needs that, in many ways, were the heart of the Brundtland Report. These include hunger, disease, and lack of adequate shelter. At the same time, the MDGs promote gender equality, education, and environmental sustainability. The specific goals and targets are provided in Table 11.4.

There is a belief that while progress has been made to achieve the MDGs, it is at a very slow pace. A World Bank report entitled "Partnerships in Development: Progress in the Fight Against Poverty" concluded that the goal for eradicating extreme income poverty by 2015 is within reach. However, this view is likely overly-optimistic. Political commitment to achieve development on a global basis has been generally lacking since Truman's 1949 inaugural address.

Aggregate Measures of Development and Well-Being

As we have seen, no single measure adequately summarizes the different facets of national development or gives a definitive comparison of countries on the continuum of development. Composite measures to achieve that summary aim can, of course, be devised from the growing body of comparative statistics regularly published by United Nations agencies, the World Bank, and other sources. Many of those—Figure 11.3 is an example—have been criticized for being based too strongly on economic and infrastructural indicators: gross national income, per capita income, sectoral structure of national economies, import and export data, miles of railroad or paved highways, and the like.

Development, it is maintained, is more than the purely economic and physical, and personal development may have little or nothing to do with objective statistical measures. The achievement of development must also be seen in terms of individual and collective well-being: a safe environment, freedom from want, opportunity for personal growth and enrichment, and access to goods and services beyond the absolute minimum to sustain life. Health, safety, educational and cultural development, security in old age, political freedom, and similar non-economic criteria are among the evidences of comparative developmental levels that are sought in composite statistics. Also sought is a summary statistic of development that is value free; that is, the input data should not measure development by expenditure patterns or performance standards that are ethnocentric or coloured by political agendas.

One such ranking gaining increasing recognition is employed by the United Nations Development Programme. Its "human development index" (HDI) combines purchasing power (not just dollar amount of per capita, GNI), life expectancy, and literacy (Figure 11.19). The HDI reflects the Programme's conviction that the important human aspirations are leading a long and healthy life, receiving adequate education, and having access to assets and income sufficient for a decent quality of life. The arbitrary weighting of the three input variables—longevity (measured by life expectancy at birth), knowledge (indicated by weighted measures of adult literacy and mean years of schooling), and income (based on a poverty-adjusted statistic of gross domestic product per capita)—makes the derived national rankings subjective rather than fully objective. The HDI, like all attempts at measuring developmental levels of countries and categorizing their variations in qualities of life and human welfare, is a recognition both of the complexity of the economic and social structures involved and of the need to focus developmental efforts.

The UN Development Programme has also developed a reverse image of poverty in its Human Poverty Index (HPI). While the HDI measures average *achievement*, the HPI measures *deprivation* in the same three measures of development underlying the HDI. For the poverty index, the benchmarks of concern are probability of not surviving to age 40; exclusion from full social intercourse because of illiteracy; and deprivation of a decent level of living as measured by lack of safe water access and percentage of underweight small children. The Human Poverty Index was discussed in more detail in "Poverty and Development" (p. 386).

Gender Roles

Many of the common measures of development and change within and between countries take no account of the gender and age structures of the societies examined. Gross national income per capita, literacy rates, percentage of labour force in agriculture, and the like are statistics that treat all members (or all adult members) of the society uniformly. Yet among the most prominent strands in the fabric of culture are the social structures (*sociofacts*) and relationships that establish distinctions between males and females in the duties assigned and the rewards afforded to each.

Geographers and their use of maps are like a hand and glove. Geographers have contributed to the study of one of the most widespread epidemics of modern times—acquired immunodeficiency syndrome (AIDS). A virus, called human immunodeficiency virus (HIV), causes AIDS by attacking a person's immune system. The immune system begins to reproduce the virus rather than fight diseases. With a lower ability to fight disease, people with AIDS are more vulnerable to infectious diseases, such as tuberculosis and pneumonia. AIDS victims are also more susceptible to certain forms of cancer. HIV is transmitted via bodily fluids and often spreads undetected because it does not have immediate and visible symptoms. Thus, HIV can spread undetected for many years, resulting in widespread diffusion.

There are two strains of HIV, both originating in Africa. HIV-1 originated in East Central Africa and HIV-2 in West Africa. In 1980, AIDS first appeared in East Africa, and spread rapidly in Tanzania, the Democratic Republic of Congo, and Uganda. It soon reached Kenya and southern Africa. In these areas, the disease spread through the entire population (male, female, heterosexuals). Infants born to women with HIV have high infection rates. Its discovery in major American urban centres—New York, San Francisco, Los Angeles, and southern Florida—shattered the illusion that major infectious diseases were a thing of the past in developed countries. Soon AIDS was a worldwide pandemic. Worldwide, over 20 million people have died from AIDS since 1981, and in 2004, about 40 million people have been infected by HIV (Table 11.3 and Figure 11.18). About 95% of those people are located in the developing world, and approximately 75% of the total number of people who are infected with AIDS live in sub-Saharan Africa, where the disease is transmitted heterosexually. There, the average life expectancy has fallen to 47 years. It is believed that it would be 62 years without the effect of AIDS. Each day about 14,000 people worldwide become infected with HIV. If there is not a cure found by 2015, geographer Harold Foster (2004) maintains that the "AIDS pandemic will have become by far the greatest catastrophe in human history, far worse than the Black Death and the Second World War combined, the equivalent of eight First World Wars."

Geographers have made at least two contributions to the study of AIDS. First, they have studied its diffusion. Although AIDS is present in every region of the United States and Canada, it has been particularly concentrated in the inner-city regions of urban areas. In the developed world, it is prevalent among male homosexuals and drug users who shared needles, and haemophiliacs who received blood transfusions before blood was screened for HIV. These trends made some people homophobic and very nervous about entering a hospital for any type of blood transfusion. It is now increasingly appearing in male and female heterosexual populations. In Africa, the diffusion of AIDS has been very different. There, heterosexual males and females, and non-drug users have always been part of the victimized population. The spread of AIDS in Africa has occurred along transportation networks (e.g., roads, rivers).

Second, Harold Foster has helped to promote the idea that incidence of AIDS may be related to the presence of selenium. Those African countries, such as Zaire, Uganda, Tanzania, Kenya, and South Africa, where AIDS is now the number one cause of death, have soils that are deficient in selenium. In contrast, Senegal, which has soils that are enriched with selenium, has a much slower rate of AIDS diffusion. In appropriate concentrations, selenium is vital for human health. Research now suggests that it helps block HIV replication. This finding opens alternative approaches to solving the AIDS problem in the selenium-deficient regions of the developing world.

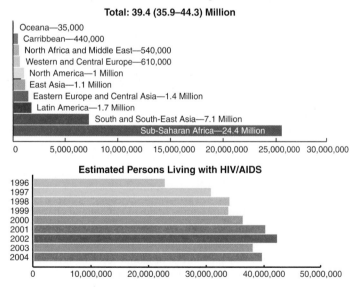

FIGURE 11.18 Adults and children estimated to be living with HIV (2004).

Source: http://unaids.org/bangkok.

TABLE 11.3	
Estimated Persons Living with HIV/AIDS	
Year	World
1996	22,600,000
1997	30,600,000
1998	33,800,000
1999	33,600,000
2000	36,100,000
2001	40,000,000
2002	42,000,000
2003	37,800,000
2004	39,400,000

Source: http://www.unaids.org/bangkok.

TABLE 11.4

Millennium Development Goals

Goal 1. Eradicate extreme poverty and hunger

Halve, between 1990 and 2015, the proportion of people whose income is less than one dollar a day.

Halve, between 1990 and 2015, the proportion of people who suffer from hunger.

Goal 2. Achieve universal primary education

Ensure that, by 2015, children everywhere, boys and girls alike, will be able to complete a full course of primary schooling.

Goal 3. Promote gender equality and empower women

Eliminate gender disparity in primary and secondary education, preferably by 2005, and to all levels of education no later than 2015.

Goal 4. Reduce child mortality

Reduce by two thirds, between 1990 and 2015, the under-five mortality rate

Goal 5. Improve maternal health

Reduce by three-quarters, between 1990 and 2015, the maternal mortality ratio.

Goal 6. Combat HIV/AIDS, malaria, and other diseases

Have halted by 2015 and begun to reverse the spread of HIV/AIDS.

Have halted by 2015 and begun to reverse the incidence of malaria and other major diseases.

Goal 7. Ensure environmental sustainability

Integrate the principles of sustainable development into country policies and programs, and reverse the losses of environmental resources.

Halve, by 2015, the proportion of people without sustainable access to safe drinking water.

By 2020 to have achieved a significant improvement in the lives of at least 100 million slum dwellers.

Goal 8. Develop a global partnership for development

Develop further an open, rule-based, predictable, non-discriminatory trading and financial system

Address the special needs of the least developed countries

Address the special needs of landlocked countries and small island developing states.

Deal comprehensively with the debt problems of developing countries through national and international measures in order to make debt sustainable in the long term.

In cooperation with developing countries, develop and implement strategies for decent and productive work for youth

In cooperation with pharmaceutical companies, provide access to affordable essential drugs in developing countries

In cooperation with the private sector, make available the benefits of new technologies, especially information and communications.

Source: www.undp.org.

Since gender relationships and role assignments vary among societies, the status of women is a cultural spatial variable. Because so much of that variation is related to the way economic roles and production and reward assignments are allocated by gender, we might well assume a close tie between the status of women in different societies and their level and type of economic development. Further, it would be logical to believe that advancement in the technological sense would be reflected in an enhancement of the status and rewards of both men and women in developing countries. Should that prove true, it would logically follow that contrasts between the developed and developing world in gender relationships and role assignments would steadily diminish.

The pattern that we actually observe is not quite that simple or straightforward, for gender relationships and role assignments are only partially under the control of the technological subsystem. **Gender** in the cultural sense refers to socially created—not biologically based—distinctions between femininity and masculinity (see Chapter 5). Therefore, religion and custom play their own important roles. Further, it appears that at least in the earlier phases of technological change and development, women generally lose rather than gain in status and rewards. Only recently and only in the most developed countries have gender-related contrasts been reduced within and between societies.

Hunting and gathering cultures observed a general egalitarianism; each sex had a respected, productive role in the kinship group (see Figure 5.24). Gender is more involved and changeable in agricultural societies (see "Women and the Green Revolution," p. 310). The Agricultural Revolution—a major change in the technological subsystem—altered the earlier structure of gender-related responsibilities. In the hoe agriculture found in much of sub-Saharan Africa and in South and Southeast Asia, women became responsible for most of the actual field work, while still retaining their traditional duties in child rearing, food preparation, and the like. In some places, such as Latin America, and, increasingly, in sub-Saharan Africa, women are becoming more visibly productive in the market than in the field (Figure 11.20). As women's agricultural productive role declined, they were afforded less domestic authority, less control over their own lives, and few if any property rights independent of male family members.

Western industrial—"developed"—society emerged directly from the agricultural tradition of the subordinate female who was not considered an important element in the economically active population, no matter how arduous or essential the domestic tasks assigned, and who was not afforded full access to education or similar amenities of an advancing society. Only within the later 20th century, and then largely in the more developed countries, has that subordinate role pattern changed.

The rate and extent of women's participation in the labour force has expanded everywhere in recent years. Between 1970 and 1997, both the percentage of the total labour force who are women, and the percentage of women who are economically active[4] increased in nearly every world region—developed and

---

[4] The International Labour Office defines "economically active" work as that "producing significant amounts of 'economic' (that is, marketable) goods, or of visible income." Included in the "economically active population" are all employed and unemployed persons seeking employment and all wage earners, unpaid family workers, and members of producers' cooperatives.

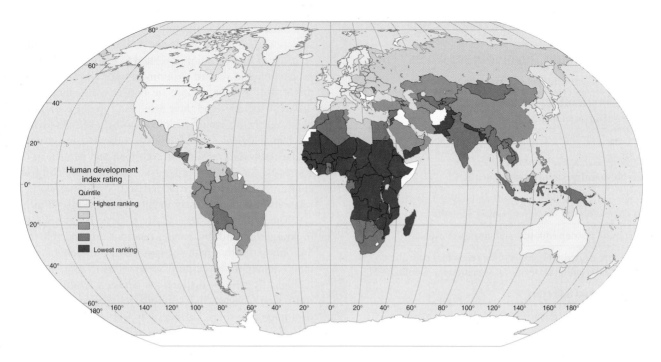

FIGURE 11.19 Country rankings according to the Human Development Index, 2003 of the United Nations Development Programme. Since the index is intended to measure the absence of deprivation, it discounts incomes higher than needed to achieve an acceptable level of living and therefore is uninformative in comparing the levels of development of the richest countries. The four measures that are used by the UNDP—life expectancy, adult literacy, combined school enrolment ratios, and real (PPP) income—are highly correlated with one another. For that reason, it has been noted, the rankings derived by the HDI differ only slightly from income rankings adjusted for purchasing power parity; the Indian minister for human resources in 2002 objected that the HDI ignored "spiritual happiness" and "intellectual advances." Fifth quintile countries, at the bottom of the Human Development Index, closely match the "least developed" countries recognized by the UN and shown on Figure 11.3.

Source: "Human Development Index," country rankings are made and reported by United Nations Development Programme in its annual Human Development Report.

developing (Figure 11.21). Women's increased participation in the workforce reflects several changing conditions. Women have gained greater control over their fertility, thus increasing their opportunities for education and employment. Further, attitudes toward employed women have changed and public policies on, for example, child care, maternity benefits, and the like, are more favourable. Economic growth, including the expansion of service sector jobs open to women, was also important in many regions. Permissive attitudes and policies with regard to micro and small enterprises, including financing and credit programs, have in some areas played a major role in encouraging women entrepreneurs (see "Empowering Women Financially").

Considering all work—paid and unpaid economic activity and unpaid housework—women spend more hours per day working than do men in all developing and developed regions except Anglo-America and Australia. In developing countries, the UN estimates, when unpaid agricultural work and housework are considered along with wage labour, women's work hours exceed men's by 30% and may involve at least as arduous—or heavier—physical labour. The FAO reports "rural women in the developing world carry 80 tonnes or more of fuel, water, and farm produce for a distance of 1 km during the course of a year. Men carry much less . . ." Everywhere women are paid less than men

for comparable employment, but in most world regions the percentage of economically active women holding wage or salaried positions is about equal to the rate for men. Exceptions are Latin America, where a higher proportion of active women than men are wage earners, and Africa, where wage-earning opportunities for women are few; in several African states, less than 10% of economically active women are wage earners.

Despite these and similar widely applicable generalizations, the present world pattern of gender-related institutional and economic role assignments is varied. It is influenced by a country's level of economic development, by the persistence of the religious and customary restrictions its culture imposes on women, and by the specific nature of its economic—particularly agricultural—base. The first control is reflected in contrasts between the developed and developing world; the second and third are evidenced in variations within the developing world itself.

The differential impact of these and other conditions is evident in Figure 11.22. The pattern shows a distinct gender-specific regionalization among the countries of the developing world. Among the Arab or Arab-influenced Muslim areas of western Asia and North Africa, the recorded proportion of the female population that is economically active is low. Religious tradition restricts women's acceptance in economic activities outside of the

FIGURE 11.20 Women dominate the once-a-week periodic markets in nearly all developing countries. Here they sell produce from their gardens or the family farm and often offer processed goods for sale (to which their labour has added value)—oil pressed from seeds or, in Niger, for example, from peanuts grown on their own fields; cooked, dried, or preserved foods; simple pottery and baskets; or decorated gourds. In West Africa, the Caribbean, and Asia, between 70% and 90% of all farm and marine produce is traded by women. The market shown here is in the West African country of Ghana. More than half of the economically active women in sub-Saharan Africa and southern Asia and about one-third in northern Africa and the rest of Asia are self-employed, working primarily in the informal sector. In the developed world, only about 14% of active women are self-employed.

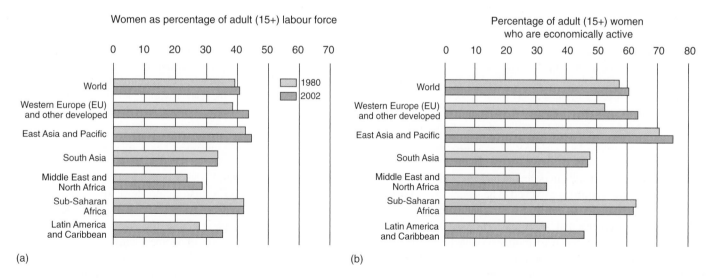

FIGURE 11.21 (*a*) **Women's share of the labour force** increased in almost all world regions between 1980 and 2002. Worldwide, women were recorded by the World Bank at 41% of the total labour force in 2002 and comprised at least one-third of the workers in all areas except the Middle East and North Africa. (*b*) **Women's economic activity rates** showed a mixed pattern of change between and within many world regions. More than half the world's female labour force lived in Asia and the Pacific area in 2002. Although the regional share of economically active women varies widely, the UN estimates that women now make up half the labour force in most countries and regions.

Source: (a) *World Bank*, World Development Indicators 2004. (b) *International Labour Office and World Bank*, World Development Indicators, 2004.

The Fourth World Conference on Women held in Beijing during September, 1995, called on all governments to formulate strategies, programs, and laws designed to assure women their full human rights to equality and development. The Conference's final declaration, reinforced at the "Beijing Plus Five" Conference held at The United Nations in June, 2000, detailed recommended policies in the areas of sexuality and child-bearing, violence against women, discrimination against girls, female inheritance rights, and family protection. Its particular emphasis, however, focused on efforts to "ensure women's equal access to economic resources including land, credit, and markets as a means to further advancement and empowerment of women and girls."

That special economic emphasis was reinforced by the UN Food and Agriculture Organization's "Gender and Development Plan (2000–2007)," which aimed at stimulating efforts to enhance gender-based equity in the control of productive resources and providing women with access to credit to enable them to engage as creators and owners of small-scale manufacturing, trade, or service businesses. Still later, the UN General Assembly designated 2005 as the "International Year of Microcredit" to further the same objectives.

Two-thirds of the total amount of work women do is unpaid, but that unpaid work amounts to an \$11 trillion addition to the total world economy. The Beijing Conference declaration was a recognition that women's economic contribution would be even greater—and of more social and personal benefit—were governments to grant them equal opportunity through financial support to engage as owners in small-scale manufacturing, trade, or service enterprises. In fact, both the model and proof of success in granting women access to credit were already in place.

In 1976, a Bangladeshi economist, Muhammad Yunus, wandered into a poor village and got an idea that has captured international interest and changed accepted beliefs and practices of banking in developing countries. The concept behind the Grameen Bank he established is simple: if individual borrowers are given access to credit, they will be able to identify and engage in viable income-producing activities such as pottery making, weaving, sewing, buying and marketing simple consumer goods, or providing transportation and other basic services.

Declaring that "access to credit should be a human right," Mr. Yunus was a pioneer in extending "microcredit" for "microenterprises" with women emerging as the primary borrowers and beneficiaries of Grameen Bank's practice of lending money without collateral and at low rates of interest. Under the original Grameen concept, to be eligible for the average loan of about U.S. \$160, women without assets must join or form a "cell" of five unrelated women, of whom only two can borrow at first though all five are responsible for repayment. When the first two begin to repay, two more can borrow, and so on. As a condition of the loan, clients must also agree to increase their savings, observe sound nutritional practices, and educate their children.

By 2000, the bank had made over 2 million loans in 40,000 villages in Bangladesh alone. More than 94% of the borrowers are women, and repayment rates reach above 95%. The average household income of Grameen Bank members has risen to about 59% higher than that of non-members in the same villages, with the landless benefiting most and marginal landowner families following closely. Because of enterprise incomes resulting from the lending program, there has been a sharp reduction in the number of Grameen Bank members living below the poverty line—to 20% compared to nearly 60% for non-members. There has also been a marked shift from low-status agricultural labour to self-employment in simple manufacturing and trading. That shift has encouraged a borrower and lender recognition that larger loans are needed to enable increasingly entrepreneurial women to build small businesses, hire employees, acquire office and manufacturing equipment, and the like. In consequence, some lenders now approve loans of several thousand dollars, though such larger loans are still very much in the minority.

The Grameen concept has spread from its Bangladesh origins to elsewhere in Asia and to Latin America, eastern Europe, and Africa. Figures for worldwide microloans vary widely; in 2005, the UN guessed total loan numbers ranged from 70 million to 200 million or more, granted to some of the world's poorest people. But the women recipients still represent only a faction of the estimated 500 to 600 million women worldwide who have virtually no access to credit—or to the economic, social, educational, and nutritional benefits that come from its availability. It is that globally enormous number of women now effectively denied credit equality that the resolutions of the Fourth World Conference on Women and the FAO and UN General Assembly plans and programs seek to benefit.

home, a tradition that results in probable underreporting of female employment by the countries involved. The same cultural limitations do not apply under the different rural economic conditions of Muslims in southern and south-eastern Asia, where labour force participation by women in Indonesia and Bangladesh, for example, is much higher than it is among the western Muslims.

In Latin America, women have been overcoming cultural restrictions on their employment outside the home and their active economic participation has been increasing. That participation is occurring almost entirely outside of the agricultural realm, where the high degree of farm labour tenancy as well as custom limits the role of females. Sub-Saharan Africa, highly diverse culturally and economically, in general is very dependent on female farm labour and market income. The historical role of strongly independent, property-owning females formerly encountered under traditional agricultural and village systems, however, has increasingly been replaced by subordination of women with the modernization of agricultural techniques and the introduction of formal, male-dominated financial and administrative farm-sector institutions.

A "gender empowerment measure" devised by the United Nations Development Programme emphasizes female participation in national economic, political, and professional affairs and clearly displays areal differentials in the position of women in different cultures and world regions (Figure 11.23).

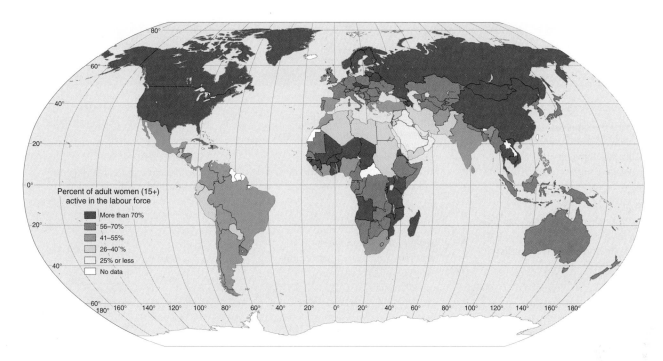

FIGURE 11.22 Economically active women, 2004. Since female participation in the labour force is reported by individual countries with differing definitions of "economically active," international comparisons may be misleading. The International Labour Office definition is given as a footnote on page 410. Because a higher proportion of the female than the male labour force is engaged in the "informal" sector, their recorded presence in the workplace is officially understated. The ILO maintains that "in many developing areas . . . the number of women in the labour force . . . is much larger than that given in official statistics."

Source: International Labour Office and World Bank, World Development Indicators 2004.

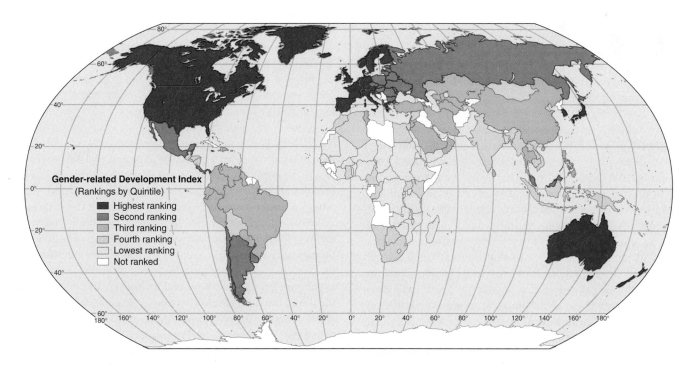

FIGURE 11.23 The gender-related development index (GDI) is a composite index that attempts to measure inequalities of achievements between men and women through differences in their life expectancies at birth, literacy levels and educational attainments, and female and male earned income shares. The greater the gender achievement disparities, the lower is a country's GDI. Analysis of the measured achievements and resulting rankings suggests that, first, no society treats its women as well as its men and, second, gender equality does not depend on the overall income level of a country.

Source: 2003 rankings from United Nations Development Programme, Human Development Report 2005. *Rankings are adjusted for each annual edition.*

Want to Learn More?

Definitions of Development

Sustainable Development
Explore some of the various perspectives on sustainable development at:
http://www.gdrc.org/sustdev/definitions.html

Social and Economic Statistics
Statistics to further some of the data found in Appendix A is found here:
http://www.un.org/special-rep/ohrlls/ldc/statistics.htm

Economic Development
http://en.wikipedia.org/wiki/Economic_development

Underdevelopment
http://en.wikipedia.org/wiki/Underdevelopment

Human Development Index
http://hdr.undp.org/

Gender and Development
http://www.tgnp.co.tz/gender.htm

Core Periphery Model
See how the core-periphery model is relevant at the city scale.

Within Cities
http://geographyfieldwork.com/CorePeriphery.htm

Summary

Development as a concept and process implies change and improvement. It suggests the fuller and more productive use of the resources of an area through the application of advanced levels of technology. The result is presumed to be improved conditions of life and well-being for constant or growing populations and, for the society undergoing development, a fuller integration into—and more equal share of—the world space economy.

Development in that light can be seen as a cultural variable with a distinctive spatial patterning. No two countries have exactly the same position on the continuum of development in all of its many different possible economic and no economic measures. For this reason, precise classification of countries by developmental level is impossible, and a variety of general descriptive terms have been introduced, including the following: developed, developing, underdeveloped, least (or less) developed, Third and Fourth World, and the like. Whatever the terms, the overall world pattern of development is clear: the advanced and relatively wealthy countries of the economic core are those of Europe, North America, Japan, Australia, and New Zealand, and a small but growing number of newly industrialized countries with high incomes and quality of life—Taiwan, South Korea, Singapore, and the like. The rest of the world is considered to be "developing" on the economic periphery, where individual countries are progressing at different rates and with different degrees of success. These general statements hide other truths. For instance, while Canada has consistently ranked very highly as a developed nation through the HDI, many Aboriginal peoples live in poverty.

A variety of comparative economic and non-economic data are available to help identify the relative position of individual countries. *Gross national income* and *purchasing power parity per capita* document the basic core-periphery pattern while making clear the diversity among the developing countries in the monetary success of their economies. *Per capita consumption of commercial energy* reveals the immense size of the technology gap between most and least developed states, for energy use may be loosely equated with modern industrial plant and transportation facilities. A high percentage of a country's *workforce in agriculture* is associated with less developed subsistence economies with low labour productivity and low levels of national wealth. The price of underdevelopment—and of the relative poverty it implies—is malnutrition. Although the correlation is not exact, countries registering *average caloric intake* below daily requirements are also countries registering poorly on all purely economic measures of development.

Earlier hopes that underdevelopment was simply the common starting point in a series of expected and inevitable stages of advancement have been dashed. Many countries appear unable to accumulate the capital, develop the skills, or achieve the technology transfer necessary to carry them along the path to fuller economic development and prosperity. Without that development, countries score poorly on non-economic measures such as literacy, safe water, and conditions of health. With it, they can—as the experience of newly industrializing countries demonstrates—experience growing cultural and technological convergence with the most advanced states. That convergence, in fact, is increasing, and the share of the *gross world product* attributable to what is still called the "developing" world continues to grow and amounted to over 45% at the start of the 21st century.

Development implies pervasive changes in the organizational and institutional structuring of peoples and space. Urbanization of populations and employment has invariably accompanied economic development, as has a more complete and rigorous political organization of space.

KEY WORDS

FOR REVIEW

1. How does the *core-periphery* model help us understand observed contrasts between developed and developing countries? In what way is *circular and cumulative causation* linked either to the perpetuation or the reduction of those contrasts? How does the concept of *trickle-down effects*, or *spread effects*, explain the equalization of development and incomes on a regional or international scale?

2. What are some of the reasons that have been given to explain why some countries are *developed* and others are *underdeveloped*?

3. What different ways and measures do we have to indicate degrees of development of particular countries or regions? Do you think these measures can be used to place countries or regions into uniform *stages of development*?

4. Why should any country or society concern itself with *technology transfer* or with the *technology gap*? What do these concepts have to do with either development or societal well-being?

5. What kinds of material and non-material economic and non-economic contrasts can you cite that differentiate more developed from less developed societies?

6. Assume you are requested to devise a composite index of national development and well-being. What *kinds* of characteristics would you like to include in your composite?

Why? What specific *measures* of those characteristics would you like to cite?

7. Why is energy *consumption* per capita considered a reliable measure of level of national economic development? If a country has a large per capita *production* of energy, can we assume that it also has a high level of development? Why or why not?

8. Have both males and females shared equally in the benefits of economic development in its early stages? What are the principal contrasts in the status of women between the developed and developing worlds? What regional contrasts within the developing world are evident in the economic roles assigned to women?

FOCUS FOLLOW-UP

1. **How do we define development and explain the occurrence or persistence of underdevelopment?** pp. 376–384.

Development implies improvement in economic and quality-of-life aspects of a society. It presumably results from technology transfer from advanced to developing states and, through consequent cultural convergence, promises the full integration of the developing society into the larger modern world order. When that stage of advancement is reached, transition from the world economic and social "periphery" to its "core" has been achieved. Persistence of underdevelopment is usually attributed to failure of a culture or region to accumulate capital, develop skills, or achieve technology transfers to improve its prosperity or quality of life.

2. **What economic measures mark a country's stage of development or its progress from underdevelopment?** pp. 384–394.

Gross national income and purchasing power parity per capita, per capita commercial energy consumption, percentage of labour force in agriculture, and average daily caloric intake are common, accepted measures of development. Attempts to model the process of development have led to inconclusive and contrasting theories of inevitable "stages of growth," optimistic "Big Push" ideas of coordinated investment, and pessimistic "dependency theory" concepts of perpetual exploitation of underdeveloped regions.

3. **What are non-economic aspects of development, and how are they related to measures of economic growth?** pp. 394–401.

Education, sanitation, and health services are among many non-economic indices of development that are strongly related to income and national wealth.

FOCUS FOLLOW-UP continued

The higher a country's ranking on purely economic measures, the more it can and does spend on improvement of quality-of-life conditions for its citizens. Similarly, the higher those expenditures are, the lower on average are national rates of infant mortality, births and deaths, rates of natural increase, and the like. "Happiness" or satisfaction of such cultural wants as social support, aesthetic and sensory needs, creativity outlets, etc., also figure as importantly into well-being assessments as do gross domestic product or energy consumption.

4. **What conditions underlie the varying world pattern of women's roles, status, and rewards?** pp. 401–407.

The status of women is a cultural spatial variable reflecting gender relationships characteristic of different societies. The world pattern of gender-related institutional and economic role assignments and rewards appears strongly influenced by national levels of economic development and by the persistence of customary and religious restrictions on women. With few exceptions, women worldwide spend more hours per day working than do men; everywhere they are paid less for comparable work. A general world trend is toward greater equality for women in political and economic opportunities and status.

ONLINE LEARNING CENTRE

The World Wide Web has a tremendous number and variety of sites pertaining to geography. To access Web sites,

Internet exercises, self-quizzes, videos, and additional study tools relevant to this chapter's content, visit the *Human*

Geography Online Learning Centre at **www. mcgrawhill.ca/olc/fellmann.**

Alberta, Canada: Oil Sands.
Dragline scooping sand at Syncrude project at Fort McMurray, Alberta in order
to extract the oil in the sand.

HUMAN–ENVIRONMENT
INTERACTIONS

The final chapter of our study of human geography brings to the fore an important geographic theme: human activities and physical environments in interaction. In previous chapters, we have come to understand how over the past several thousand years people in their increasing numbers and growing technological skills have placed their mark on the natural landscape, altering it to conform to their needs. In some instances, such as that of modern cities, the human imprint may be so complete that the original landscape of nature has been totally wiped away and replaced by a created cultural environment. People, we now understand, are the dominant agents in the continuing drama of human–environmental interaction. Ecological alteration, damage, or destruction may be the unplanned and unwanted consequences of the power they possess. In the end, we not only degrade the environment, but our own health. This linkage between the environment and health is also considered in this last chapter.

We need that understanding, for increasingly evident environmental deterioration has become an ever-present and growing concern of people and governments throughout the world. Ecological damage or change is no longer occasional and localized; it has now become permanent and generalized. Climatic modification, air and water pollution, soil erosion, natural vegetation destruction, and loss of productive lands to advancing deserts are just part of the testimony of destructive cultural pressures that has aroused widespread public and private discussion. Increasingly, the inseparable interplay of the cultural and physical environments—seen in the imprint of humans on the endowment of nature—is apparent and accepted.

For convenience and focus, geographers may arbitrarily separate the physical and human systems that together comprise the reality of the earth's surface we occupy. We have made such a separation in our study of human geography, for our primary concern has been with the processes and patterns of human spatial organization. In addition to exploring the structure and logic of social spatial systems, that focus has also prepared us to evaluate the relationship of these systems to the physical environment humans occupy and alter. With the insights we have gained, we can now bring a more informed voice to discussion of the interaction of human cause and environmental consequence. Further background for that discussion is offered in our concluding chapter, "Human Impacts on Natural Systems and Human Health." Its subject matter bridges our temporarily convenient subdivision of the discipline and brings back into focus the inseparable unity of human and physical geography.

These Mauitanian villages hope to stabilize advancing sand set in motion by desertification at the margin of the Sahara.

12 HUMAN IMPACTS ON NATURAL SYSTEMS AND HUMAN HEALTH

Aims

- To understand how humans adjust to hazards, particularly climate change
- To appreciate the human dimensions of a range of environmental issues
- To appreciate the roles geographers can play in solving environmental problems

Some specific considerations for review:

Environment–Human–Health Interactions

"There was once a town in the heart of America where all life seemed to live in harmony with its surroundings...a pastoral Eden of hardwood forests and bountiful wildlife...then a strange blight crept over the area and everything began to change. Some evil spell had settled on the community; mysterious maladies swept the flocks of chickens; the cattle and sheep sickened and died. Everywhere was a shadow of death...It was a spring without voices. On the mornings that had once throbbed with the dawn chorus of robins, catbirds, doves, jays, wrens, and scores of other bird voices there was now no sound; only silence lay over the fields and woods and marsh...Even the streams were now lifeless...No witchcraft, no enemy action had silenced the rebirth of new life in this stricken world. The people had done it themselves...

The most alarming of all man's assaults upon the environment is the contamination of air, earth, rivers, and sea with dangerous and even lethal materials...The poisons circulate mysteriously by underground streams until they emerge and, through the alchemy of air and sunlight, combine into new forms that kill vegetation, sicken cattle, and work unknown harm on those who drink from once pure wells...They travel from link to link of the food chain...." (Rachel Carson, Silent Spring, 1962).

Introduction

This final chapter considers two major themes in geography that are captured in the text above. First, it examines the environment, thus pursuing a long-standing interest for geographers: physical geography. Many people live with an immediate environmental contact that is not known to most of us in the highly developed, highly urbanized countries of the world. In fact, much of the content of the preceding chapters has detailed ways that humans isolate themselves from the physical environment and how they superimpose cultural landscapes on it to accommodate the growing needs of their growing numbers. Contemporary geographic studies of human–environment interactions extend beyond just "the environment," which was the focus of *Silent Spring* and many other environmental research efforts up to the 1990s. Since that time, there has been a realization that environmental quality affects human health. For instance, we know that certain diseases, such as malaria, occur in some places and not in others. We also are becoming more aware that potential changes to our climate system may result in the spread of malaria to places where it has not occurred previously. Human health is also adversely affected by poor air and water quality that are the result of human activities, such as driving and waste disposal. This type of environment–health link is the second focus of this chapter.

Human geography is also concerned with society–environment relationships at the full range of scales—local to global. Environmental problems and their solutions are part of our everyday life. In various news reports, the impacts of human activities are described, in part, informed by physical geographers and other natural scientists, who study environmental systems and processes and the effects of human activities. In response to these problems, the public is encouraged, among other things, to look to other forms of transport to our personal vehicles, to participate in recycling programs, and reduce energy use at home in order to reduce their ecological footprint. The study of human–environment interactions has been of longstanding interest to geographers. However, the focus of geographic research efforts has evolved in response to societal concerns. For instance, prior to the publication of Rachel Carson's book *Silent Spring* in 1962, there was little attention paid to the impacts that pesticides had on human and environmental health. Over 40 years later, most national governments have established an array of regulations aimed at ensuring pesticides are tested to ensure impacts are insignificant, and that standards for their safe application are established. Some municipalities in Canada are just now extending this regulatory approach and have applied or are considering mandatory or voluntary pesticide bans (e.g., Halifax, Calgary, and London). In the 1960s, major environmental problems also included nuclear proliferation, industrial emissions, endangered species, and energy use, and these remain ongoing challenges. This research has clear implications for public policy.

Not only do environmental problems reflect the concerns of people at specific times but of specific places and regions as well. A development proposal in those areas of the world with tropical rainforest would likely relate to developing those environmental resources (e.g., harvesting trees) and focus primary concern on maintaining ecological biodiversity and the way of life of indigenous peoples who live in the area. In contrast, it is very unlikely that the primary goal of a development project in Toronto would be aimed at developing its forest resources. It is more likely to be focused on locating more housing or manufacturing capacity in the region, which may result in the loss of some forests, agricultural, or green space. Scale is also important in defining environmental problems.

The **environment** and the concept of sustainable development are introduced in the next section.

The Environment

Evidence from physical geography, and life and natural sciences indicates that the earth has undergone many natural changes, as evidenced by periods of glaciation through much world. However, the role of humans in increasing the pace and magnitude of these changes and impacting on natural processes and human health has only recently been appreciated. Humans have responded to many environmental problems. For instance, in the 1960s, the media pronounced that Lake Erie was "dead"—the result of massive algal blooms that contributed to a reduced level of oxygen in the water. Research indicated that phosphorus from laundry detergents and agricultural activities had entered the waterways of the Great Lakes and increased the biological oxygen demand. Legislation was passed in Canada and the United States to reduce concentrations of phosphorus in laundry detergents, and funds were spent building sewage treatment plants to remove phosphorus and to reduce the amount of phosphorus entering waterways through non-point pollution sources.

Many of the environmental problems of the 1960s and 1970s were viewed as local or regional problems that required local and regional solutions. Phosphorus control in the Great Lakes and the Sudbury Superstack (p. 421) illustrate this scale of thinking. We realize the importance of local problems and actions (see "Greening University Campuses") we now realize that problems such as climate change have global impacts. By the late 1980s, many scientists and some governments became convinced that greenhouse gases (such as carbon dioxide) were causing increased temperatures at a global scale. As the evidence

Greening University Campuses

Closer to your current life experience, the 'greening' of university campuses has become a more popular undertaking over the past 10 years. In 2008, a *College Sustainability Report Card 2008* reported on the Canadian and American universities/colleges with the largest endowments. Alberta, UBC, Calgary, McGill, Queen's, and Toronto were the six Canadian universities which met this criterion. The assessment was based on activities related to the following eight areas: Administration, Climate Change & Energy, Food & Recycling, Green Building, Transportation, Endowment Transparency, Investment Priorities, and Shareholder Engagement. Some of the key findings include:

- **Climate Change & Energy:** Schools are taking on climate change through aggressive carbon reduction commitments. Half of schools have committed to reduce carbon emissions. In the United States, more than 25% schools have committed to achieving carbon neutrality in the long term by signing the American College and University Presidents Climate Commitment.

- **Food and Recycling:** 84% of schools report buying at least some food from local farms or producers.

- **Green Building:** Green building policies have been adopted by 69% of schools.

- **Endowment Transparency and Investment Priorities:** Endowment investments in renewable energy funds are being made by 31% of schools, and are an investment priority for 38%.

Overall Sustainability Leaders were all from the United States—Carleton College, Dartmouth College, Harvard University, Middlebury College, University of Vermont, and University of Washington. Some notable initiatives among the Canadian universities are as follows. The University of Calgary was awarded a "Sustainability Innovator Award" for its Comprehensive Sustainability Strategy. This initiative, which began in 2006, saw 13 interdisciplinary teams comprised of students,

University campuses should not be forgotten in our drive to become sustainable. UBC is among the Canada's leaders in this area.

staff and faculty, research, identify, implement, and report on initiatives that directly address priorities for campus sustainability. The teams addressed the following issues: governance and senior administration; curriculum and research; participation, collaboration, and communication; student clubs; procurement; transportation and mobility; energy and atmosphere; water management; land planning and new buildings; existing buildings; operations and maintenance; solid waste management; and health, safety, and wellness. UBC and U of T were identified as administrative leaders in sustainability.

UBC, McGill University, and the University of Toronto and received a higher grades than last year, UBC was identified as a sustainability leader for several of its initiatives. It has established a "Sustainability Office" with a dedicated staff and ongoing partnership with students. It has also reduced its energy use by 23% and its carbon emissions by 25% since 2000, despite a 46% increase in building area. UBC also plans to work with other institutions of higher education to set up a Canadian University and College Climate Alliance. The university also purchases some green energy certificates and has introduced alternative energy solutions, including geothermal at the Okanagan campus. The University of Toronto makes its proxy voting records and a list of endowment holdings available to the public on the website of the university's investment management subsidiary, the University of Toronto Asset Management Corporation. U of T has also partnered with an NGO that certifies local farmers and links them with purchasers. Dining services is currently putting a plan in place to offer as many sustainable and organic items as possible. Food waste from the dining hall is composted. The full report is available from: http://www.endowmentinstitute.org/sustainability/.

What sustainable policies does your college/university have in place? What might you do to support the adoption and implementation of more effective policies?

supporting this view increased and improved, the need for a global strategy emerged. In 1992, this recognition was formalized in the United Nations Framework Convention on Climate Change, which will be discussed later in this chapter.

It is the increased scale and complexity of environmental problems and its implications for nations that has, in part, prompted many people to suggest that the 'environment' is and will increasingly be an important issue in the 21st century. In this regard, the idea of sustainable development, which was mentioned in Chapter 11, has attracted considerable interest since it was identified by the Brundtland Commission as the driving force behind its 'global agenda for change.' A fundamental aspect of sustainable development is the belief that economic and ecological concerns must be seen as interdependent systems rather than opposing forces. In the words of the Brundtland Commission, "economy is not just about the production of wealth, and ecology is not just about the protection of nature; they are both equally relevant for improving the lot of humankind" (WCED, 1987: 38). Several principles associated with sustainable development are:

Balance—the need to integrate the environment into our decision making;

Ecosystem—environmental assessment should be completed; reduce and eliminate unsustainable patterns of production and consumption; conserve biodiversity;

Partnerships—access to information held by public authorities; opportunities to participate in decision making; and

Precautionary Principle—where there are threats of serious or irreversible damage, lack of full scientific certainty shall not be used as a reason for postponing cost-effective measures to prevent environmental degradation.

Although the concept of sustainable development is attractive, the Brundtland Commission believed it would be difficult to achieve because it required government leaders, the private sector, and the public to adopt a very different mindset that focused not only on how decisions were made about environment and development but about what was "needed" as opposed to wanted by societies. Part of this can be seen in the debate about what has caused environmental problems—human numbers or human consumption?

Another way to think about the environmental problem is to consider the role of human consumption. There are a variety of things we could measure on a gross and per capita basis, such as water, energy, and food consumption (Chapter 11), the production of wastes, and carbon footprints and ecological footprints. One way of measuring this consumption is through the "Ecological Footprint" (Figure 12.20). Whether the footprint should be equal or variable, a limitation on consumption would reflect the basic definition of sustainable development—meeting the needs of current generations without compromising the ability of future generations. It is, in part, our avoidance of thinking about, discussing, and resolving fundamental questions, such as these, that makes the achievement of sustainable development difficult.

We will now turn our attention to selected environmental issues in order to describe the nature of the problem, areas of progress and areas where further work is required.

Responding to Global Climate Change

Overview—The Science of Climate Change

To those who fear its reality, the evidence of global atmospheric warming seems compelling, and modern civilization's role in its occurrence appears easily traced. Humankind's massive assault on the atmosphere presumably began with the Industrial Revolution. First coal and then increasing amounts of petroleum and natural gas have been burned to power industry, heat and cool cities, and drive vehicles. Their burning has turned fuels into carbon dioxide and water vapour. At the same time, the world's forest lands—most recently its tropical rain forests—have been destroyed wholesale by logging, and to clear land for agriculture. With more carbon dioxide in the atmosphere and fewer trees to capture the carbon and produce oxygen, carbon dioxide levels have risen steadily.

The role of trees in managing the carbon cycle is simple: Probably more than half the carbon dioxide put into the atmosphere by burning fossil fuels is absorbed by the earth's oceans, plants, and soil. The rest of the carbon dioxide remains in the atmosphere where it traps earth heat radiation. In theory, atmospheric carbon dioxide could be reduced by expanding plant carbon reservoirs, or "sinks," on land. Under actual circumstances of expanded combustion of fuels and reduction of forest cover, atmospheric carbon dioxide levels now total well over 200% of their amounts at the start of the Industrial Revolution and continue to rise. Yearly carbon emissions that totalled 1.6 billion tonnes in 1950 reached more than 7 billion tonnes in 2006. The International Energy Agency predicts that annual carbon emissions will total more than 8.8 billion tonnes in 2010, 5.5 times their 1950 level.

That extra carbon dioxide makes the atmosphere just a bit less transparent to the long-wave heat energy radiated back into space from the earth. Along with three other partially man-made gases (methane, nitrous oxides, and chlorofluorocarbons), the carbon dioxide traps the heat before it can escape. That so-called **greenhouse effect** is a natural condition and a necessary element in earth's heat budget. Without the atmospheric heat absorption and retention provided by carbon dioxide and water vapour, energy reradiated by the globe would pass through the atmosphere and be lost in space; earth temperatures would fluctuate widely as they do on airless Mars, and plant and animal life as we know it could not exist. The "greenhouse effect" that is of recent concern is the *increased* absorption of long-wave radiation from the earth's surface induced by the apparent increase in atmospheric carbon dioxide concentrations. *That* greenhouse effect is far less benign and nurturing than the name implies (Figure 12.1). Slowly but inexorably, the retained heat raises the average temperature of the earth; slowly but unavoidably, if the process continues, new patterns of climates and biomes must result.

During the first century of the Industrial Revolution, from 1780 to 1880, mean global temperature rose 0.3° Celsius

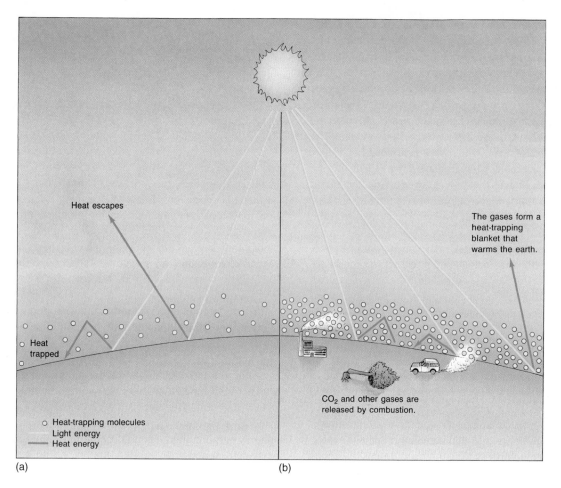

Heat escapes

The gases form a
heat-trapping
blanket that
warms the earth.

Heat
trapped

Heat
trapped

CO₂ and other gases are
released by combustion.

○ Heat-trapping molecules
── Light energy
── Heat energy

(a)   (b)

FIGURE 12.1 Creating the greenhouse effect. When the level of carbon dioxide (CO₂) in the air is low, as in (*a*), incoming solar radiation strikes the earth's surface, heating it up, and the earth radiates the energy back into space as heat. The greenhouse effect, depicted in (*b*), is the result of the more than 6 billion tonnes of CO₂ that the burning of fossil fuels adds to the atmosphere each year. The carbon dioxide molecules intercept some of the reradiated energy, deflecting it groundward and preventing it from escaping from the atmosphere.

(0.5° Fahrenheit). In the next hundred years—even allowing for a slight cooling between 1945 and 1975—average temperatures increased about 0.6° C (a bit over 1° F). They rose another half degree Celsius in the last half of the 1980s alone. Apparently the rate of heating was increasing. The 20th was the warmest century for the past 600 years, and most of its warmest years were concentrated near its end; the decade of the 1990s was the warmest on record before 2000. The pattern of high and increasing average global temperatures has continued into the 21st century.

Because of the time lag in developing the greenhouse effect, temperatures would continue to rise even if carbon dioxide amounts were stabilized at today's levels. If temperatures rise by the "best estimate" made in 2007 by the United Nation's Intergovernmental Panel on Climate Change (IPCC) of 1.8 to 4°C (3.2 to 7.2°F) over the 21st century, the effects upon world climates could be profound. The panel, a United Nations and World Meteorological Organization group of 2000 scientists from around the world, was established in 1988 to assess the science of climate change, determine the impact of any changes on the environment and society, and formulate strategies to respond.

Past IPCC assessments and predictions were received with scepticism by some who disputed the role of humans in global warming. Those doubters noted that nearly half the observed atmospheric warming occurred before 1940 even though almost all the increased production of carbon dioxide and other greenhouse gases came after that date. Sceptics further argued that every millennium since the end of the last Ice Age has had one or two centuries in which temperatures rose by at least as much as they have in the last 100 years. Those arguments appear now to have been effectively refuted by the IPCC's 2007 assertion in its Fourth Assessment Report that it was at least 90% certain that human emissions of greenhouse gases rather than natural variations are responsible for warming the earth's surface. A 2006 review of available evidence by the federal Climate Change Science Program reached the same conclusion: that there is "clear evidence" of climate change caused by human activities and that trends over the last 50 years "cannot be explained by natural processes alone."

As a high latitude country, the impacts of climate change will likely be more pronounced in Canada. The impacts will affect environment and human–environment interactions, and will vary across the country. Examples include: in northern Canada, winter snow cover may be reduced by up to 30 days and in western regions snow may be replaced by rain or freezing rain in early spring and autumn; climate models suggest that summer sea ice cover in the North will disappear by 2100; coastal areas of Canada will be impacted by flooding as a result of the expansion of ocean waters as they warm and the melting of the polar ice caps; the average sea level over the next 100 years is expected to be in the range of 15 cm to 95 cm, which would have significant impact on the Fraser Delta; water courses that originate in the Prairies have a highly variable annual range of flow and this variability may increase with climate change and with hotter and longer summers may place increased stresses on surface water resources; shortages of surface water could mean increased use of groundwater resources; the composition of Ontario's forests will likely be different with climate change, and affect ecosystems and logging and tourist operations.

Whatever the attributable causes of global heating, climatologists agree that the eventuality of certain consequences should it continue. Increases in sea temperatures would cause ocean waters to expand slightly and the polar ice caps to melt at least a bit. The reality of Arctic ice melt is already clearly evident. Using passive microwave data, a 2007 study concluded that the perennial ice cover was about 40% less than the previous 28-year average. The average thickness of Arctic ice has declined by 42%, from 3.1 to 1.8 metres, suggesting the possibility of its complete summertime disappearance by the middle of the 21st century (open water was already observed at the North Pole in August, 2000). More serious consequences would result from the simultaneously observed significant melting of the Greenland ice sheet, the accelerating disintegration of Antarctic ice shelves, and the rapid retreat or total melting of glaciers throughout the world. Melting sea ice would have no effect on sea levels; water melted from continental sources, however, is added to ocean volumes. Inevitably, sea levels would rise, perhaps 0.5 to 3 metres (1.5 to 10 feet) or more within a hundred years. Even a conservative 1-metre (3-foot) rise would be enough to cover the Maldives and other low-lying island countries. The homes of between 50 and 100 million people would be inundated and a fifth of Egypt's arable land in the Nile Delta would be flooded.

Other trends now also seem clear. The prolonged, crippling early 21st century droughts in Australia and the American Southwest emphasize the likelihood of the predicted desert advances. In all drought-prone areas of the world, aridity has become more intense and enduring since the 1970s. Earlier IPCC assessments warned that much of the continental interiors of middle latitudes would receive less precipitation than they do now and suffer at least periodic drought if not absolute aridity. Precipitation might decline by as much as 40% in the U.S. corn and wheat belts, drastically reducing agricultural productivity, bringing to near ruin the rural economy, and altering world patterns of food supply and trade (Figure 12.2). That same 40% reduction of rainfall would translate into significantly reduced flows of such western rivers as the Colorado, cutting back the water supply of major south-western cities and irrigated farming districts. In other world areas, the torrential rains and consequent destructive floods of the

FIGURE 12.2 Many climatologists noted that the parched cornfields in the U.S. Midwest during the summer of 1988 were a sample of what could be expected on a recurring basis if a worst-case scenario of global warming were to be realized. In actuality, the 1988 drought was a natural climatic fluctuation—much like the abundant rain and floods of 1993 and the varying wet and dry periods during following years—but an event whose probability of recurrence is increased by the long-term accumulation of greenhouse gases.

early 21st century are predicted to increase in severity and frequency. And in many regions, winters no longer get cold enough to kill off a variety of insect pests and diseases formerly kept at lower latitudes and elevations.

Not all the projected impacts of climate change are negative. The IPCC also observed that climate shifts could benefit some regions, though benefits will inevitably be balanced by penalties. It projected more rainfall and longer growing seasons in high latitudes, for example; Canada, Scandinavia, and Siberia will have improved agricultural prospects, even as precipitation is declining in already arid regions of lower latitudes. By 2005, the growing season north of 45°N was already more than 12 days longer than it had been in the mid-20th century, and summer temperatures in Siberia were their warmest in 1000 years. In North America, crop patterns could shift northward, making the northern Great Lakes states and Canada the favoured agricultural heartland climatically, though without the rich soil base supporting the present patterns and volumes of production will continue. On average, some climatologists conclude, established middle and upper middle latitude farm districts would be net beneficiaries of global warming through longer growing seasons and faster crop growth resulting from extra atmospheric carbon. Sceptics, however, remind us that a scientific rule of thumb is that a one degree centigrade (1.8°F) rise in temperature above the optimum reduces grain yields by 10%. Long-term studies clearly document the temperature rise and yield decline ratio for rice, the staple food for most of the world's expanding population. Greater summer warmth, that is, might reduce, not increase, farm productivity.

Certainly, global warming would tend to reduce latitudinal differences in temperature; higher latitudes would become relatively more heated than equatorial regions. In recent decades, average temperatures in the Arctic have increased almost twice as fast as they have in the rest of the world. Among the consequences of that poleward shift of warmth is an already observed 80 to 100 kilometre (50 to 60 mile) poleward shift of the ranges of many animal and bird species. Similar latitudinal shifts in plant associations can be assumed, though they will be slower to materialize. Shifts in structure and distribution of ecosystems and biomes would be inevitable. One 2005 study, for example, foresees the eventual disappearance of the Arctic tundra biome, the loss of Alaska's evergreen boreal forest, and the conversion of that state into a largely temperate zone. Arctic seaways will become more open, finally realizing the long-sought and economical Northwest Passage through the northern seas (see Chapter 7), though the economy and culture of the Inuit will at the same time be irreversibly altered or destroyed.

Global warming and climatic change would impact most severely, of course, on developing countries highly dependent on natural, unmanaged environments for their economic support. Agriculture, hunting and gathering, forestry, and coastal fishing have that dependency, but even in those economic sectors the impact of greenhouse warming is not certain. Studies suggest that warming would reduce yields in many crops, but also that the associated fertilization effect of higher carbon dioxide content would probably offset the negative impact of warming, at least for the next century. Indeed, the UN's Food and Agriculture Organization observes that global crop productivity could increase by up to 30% if the concentration of carbon dioxide doubles as they foresee over the next 50 years. But certainly, small and poor countries with great dependence on agriculture are potentially most at risk from projected climatic changes. The lower-latitude states would be most vulnerable as increased heat and higher evaporation rates would greatly stress wheat, maize, rice, and soybean crops. There is disagreement about the economic impacts of climate change. In a 2006 report, economist Sir Nicholas Stern, Head of Britain's the Government Economic Service, stated "our actions over the coming few decades could create risks of major disruption to economic and social activity, later in this century and in the next, on a scale similar to those associated with the great wars and the economic depression of the first half of the 20th century." Critics would suggest that Stern overestimated the present and future costs of climate change.

Nevertheless, on the world scene, any significant continuing deviation from the present norm would at the very least disrupt existing patterns of economy, productivity, and population-supporting potential. At the worst, severe and pervasive changes could result in a total restructuring of the landscapes of culture and the balances of human–environmental relationships presently established. Nothing, from population distributions to the relative strength of countries, would ever be quite the same again. Such grim predictions were the background for major international conferences and treaty proposals of the 1990s and early 2000s seeking to address and limit the dangers prophesied.

Those conferences culminated in the Kyoto Protocol of 1997 that set variable requirements for national reductions of greenhouse gas emissions below 1990 levels by 2012. For example, the European Union goal was set at an 8% reduction, the United States at 7%, Canada at 6% and Japan at 6%. To avoid inhibiting their industrial and economic growth, no goals were set for developing countries. The Protocol became a binding part of international law after Russia, the last of the required total of 55 countries, ratified the agreement in February 2005. The United States, however, has steadfastly refused to endorse the Protocol or consider itself bound by its emission goals and limitation. And the effectiveness of the Protocol has been questioned. A model by one of the Climate Change Panel's lead authors predicts that the Treaty, if fully implemented, would lower the temperature increase that it assumed of 2.1°C by 2100 to an increase of only 1.9°C instead—or, that is, to postpone anticipated 2094 temperatures by just 6 years, to 2100.

Adapting to Climate Change

Responses to climate change will in part be influenced by perceptions, legal requirements, finances, and the availability of new technologies. The International Panel on Climate Change (IPCC) has identified two general types of adjustment strategies that can be adopted in response to climate change (Figure 12.3). The first is termed mitigation, which calls for reductions in greenhouse gas emissions, and is best illustrated in the Kyoto Convention (see "Climate Change Summits"). However, a vocal opposition, including the United States, questions its adequacy and need, and/or is concerned about the adverse economic impacts. The second strategy is termed adaptive and considers how humans alter or adjust their activities in response to changing climates. For instance, coastal cities may build dykes to address rising ocean levels. Building codes may require structures to withstand greater wind velocities. Farmers may decide to install irrigation networks and/or change to other crops. Decisions about how to adapt to climate change will reflect, in part, the perception of governments, businesses, and individuals about the extent and nature of the problem, and net benefits achieved by that response.

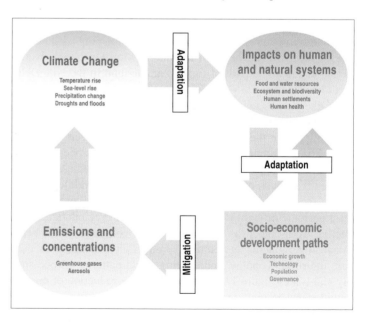

FIGURE 12.3 Climate change: An integrated framework and choice of adjustments.

Source: The Intergovernmental Panel on Climate Change.

Climate Change Summits

Accumulating evidence of global warming, projections about its long-term effect, and growing public and political determination to address its causes led during the 1990s to two high-level international conferences and treaty proposals.

The first, the "Earth Summit," was held in Rio de Janeiro in June, 1992. The Framework Convention on Climate Change signed by 166 nations called on industrialized countries to try to cap emissions of greenhouse gases at 1990 levels by the year 2000 as a necessary first step to prevent disruption of world agriculture and natural ecosystems. Small island countries, fearing their possible obliteration with rising seas, proposed even more stringent reductions.

Canada, the European Union, and the United States, agreeing with the overall emissions caps proposed, based their plans for voluntary compliance on hoped-for improved energy efficiencies. Unlike the industrialized countries collectively responsible for most of the present and past production of carbon dioxide, China and other developing economies were not to be bound by any precise targets or timetables; they successfully rejected being subject to treaty provisions that would lower their economic growth prospects by limiting industrialization and the increase in fossil fuel use such growth implies.

It became apparent in the years after the Rio Summit that most advanced economies were not going to meet the voluntary greenhouse gas reductions envisioned there, and that the production of such gases by developing states was increasing more rapidly than earlier projected. At subsequent lower-level conferences, notably Berlin in 1995, it was determined that a second Earth Summit was required and that the gas emission targets to be adopted there had to be made mandatory and binding on all parties concerned. The Kyoto (Japan) Climate Change Summit of 1997 was to be the stage for those binding treaty arrangements.

The world's nations came to Kyoto with different interests and bargaining positions. The European Union, for example, proposed that industrial nations—including its own members—reduce emissions of CO_2 and other heat-trapping gases to 85% of their 1990 levels within 12 years. The United States, in contrast, proposed that emissions be reduced no lower than 1990 levels and not until some time between 2008 and 2012. The developing countries demanded that industrialized countries collectively achieve a 35% emissions reduction by 2020. The Kyoto Protocol, the result of 10 days of intense discussion and bargaining, represents compromises among the various extreme positions originally held, and established at least an initial institutional framework and mechanism for addressing the global warming problem in future years.

By the variable goals it set, the adopted climate accord acknowledged the diversity of concerns among and between developed and developing economies. Thirty-eight industrial nations were required collectively to reduce greenhouse emissions by 5.2% below 1990 levels from 2008 through 2012—a 30% reduction below what they otherwise would likely be without the Protocol. The actual targets differ among them, however. Some industrial states would have smaller reductions and a few, such as Russia, would not face any cuts immediately. No specific goals were set on developing countries—though as a group they were asked to set voluntary reduction quotas—and no enforcement provisions for developed country compliance were agreed on.

The basic accord adopted at the Kyoto conference needed ratification by at least 55 countries representing over 55% of 1990 carbon dioxide emissions to take effect. The Protocol became a binding part of international law in February, 2005, following Russia's November, 2004, ratification. Canada ratified the treaty in 2002. The United States, however—responsible for nearly 23% of world carbon emissions in the mid-1990s—had earlier effectively refused to take part when, in March, 2001, President George W. Bush made clear his view that the Protocol was "fatally flawed," unequal in the obligations it placed on developed and developing states, and potentially unacceptably damaging to the U.S. economy.

The most recent International Conference occurred in Bali in 2007 and was attended by over 180 countries. It adopted the **Bali Road Map**, which is comprised of several initiatives: (1) the Bali Action Plan which outlines a new negotiation process and a 2009 deadline to complete the required negotiations; (2) the ad-hoc Working Group—Kyoto Protocol negotiations and their 2009 deadline, (3) the launch of the Adaptation Fund, the scope and content of the Article 9 review of the Kyoto Protocol, as well as decisions on technology transfer and on reducing emissions from deforestation.

The election of Stephen Harper's Conservative government in 2006 saw a reversal of Canada's climate change policy. In April, the government indicated that Canada's emission reduction targets under the Kyoto Protocol would be abandoned. In its place, the government pledged $2 billion over five years to develop a "made-in-Canada" solution. Beyond a new $370-million tax credit program to those Canadians who buy monthly bus passes, no further details have been announced as of June 2008.

The acceptance of "emissions trading" was among the adopted weakening compromises. Emissions trading works by allowing countries to buy and sell their agreed allowance of greenhouse gas emissions. That is, highly polluting countries can buy unused credits from those countries allowed to emit more than they actually do. Further, countries can gain credits for activities such as tree planting and soil conservation that increase the environment's capacity to absorb carbon; those activities can be carried out in the country itself or by that country working in a developing state. At present, Canada will not participate in this market. We will have to wait for 2009 to better determine what Canada and other countries intend to do about implementing the Bali Road Map and Kyoto Protocol.

The Province of British Columbia is seen as a Canadian leader in reducing the emission of greenhouse gases. On July 1, 2008, it began phasing in a carbon tax, which will be applied to gasoline, diesel, natural gas, coal, propane, and home heating fuel. The starting rate will be based on $10 per tonne of carbon emissions, and rise $5 a year to $30 per tonne by 2012. Over $1.8 billion is expected to be generated from the carbon tax. This money will be returned to residents in the form of personal and business tax cuts. At the time of writing, we have yet to see if federal and other provincial/territorial governments are committed to follow and further this approach.

Geographers are one of the few people to study climate change and adaptation from a range of perspectives: climate change impact assessment, natural hazards, agrarian political economy, innovation adoption, agricultural systems and farm decision making, risk management, and agricultural vulnerability and adaptation. This variety of research perspectives operating at a range of scales reflects geography's integrative nature. The study of human adaptation to climate change impact and vulnerability assessment reflects how the discipline can make practical contributions to public policy.

Most people are familiar with the portion of the Kyoto Protocol pertaining to reducing greenhouse gas emissions. From a hazards research perspective, this is a strategy based on the premise that if greenhouse gas emissions are reduced, the rate of climate change and its associated impacts will decrease. A second important but lesser known aspect of the Kyoto Protocol is contained in Article 10, which promotes adaptation and deployment of adaptation technologies to address climate change. Geographers Barry Smit and Mark Skinner considered the nature of adaptation in the agricultural sector. Rather than being a simple issue of focusing on the decisions made by individual farmers in response to climate adaptation, agricultural activities also reflect non-climatic factors such as economic conditions, politics, environment, society, and technology. They suggested that agricultural adaptations reflect the following mix of characteristics:

- Intent and purposefulness: they are not part of a spontaneous, automatic, or unconscious decision-making process. People have a clear sense of what they wish to achieve in making certain adaptations.
- Timing and duration: Adaptations can be considered according to when they are made—anticipatory (proactive), concurrent (during), and responsive (reactive)—and how long they apply—tactical (short-term) or strategic (long-term). For instance, a farmer may delay planting a crop (tactical) or purchase irrigation equipment (strategic) in response to a drought.
- Scale and responsibility: Scale includes individual seeds/plants, plot, field, farm, region, and nation. Responsibility for action can lie with producers (farmers), agribusiness (private industries), and governments (public agencies). The responsibility (role) of each participant is crucial to a single adaptation. Drought resistant crops likely require research from government, development and marketing from agribusiness, and adoption by farmers.
- Form: adaptation can take many forms—administrative, financial, technical, institutional, legal.

On this basis, Smit and Skinner developed the following four-part typology of adaptation options in Canadian agriculture:

1. Technological developments
- Crop development—new varieties to increase plant tolerance to climatic factors
- Weather and climate information systems—develop early warning systems to detect seasonal and daily forecasts
- Resource management innovations—water management innovations (e.g., irrigation, frost protection measures)

2. Government programs and insurance
- Agricultural subsidy and support programs—government provided climate-related crop insurance
- Private insurance
- Resource management programs—implement programs that influence farm-level land and water-based resource use and management practices

3. Farm production practices
- Farm production—diversify crops and/or livestock, change intensification of operations
- Land use—change location of production
- Land topography—change land topography
- Irrigation—install irrigation equipment
- Timing of operation—changing timing of planting, tilling, harvesting

4. Farm financial management
- Crop insurance
- Crop shares and futures
- Income stabilization program

This typology identifies the range of decisions that might be made in the agricultural sector to adjust to climate change, and improve the development of climate assessments and policies that will support us to more effectively adapt to climate change.

Long-Range Transboundary Air Pollution (LRTAP)—Acid Rain

On a daily basis, humans emit large quantities of natural and synthetic chemicals into the atmosphere. Once released, these substances are dispersed throughout the globe by air currents that know no boundaries—local, provincial, state, national, or continental—and deposit them either as dry particulates or as a solution in precipitation. This phenomenon is referred to as **long-range transboundary air pollution (LRTAP).**

Acid rain is one of the most publicized conflicts between Canada and the United States, and reflects an LRTAP. LRTAPs are problematic in other parts of the world, such as Europe and Asia. Like global warming, acid rain is a current environmental concern that is, in part, traceable to actions taken in previous decades to alleviate a widespread source of atmospheric pollution dangerous to public health and damaging to public and private property. Smoke and soot that poured into the skies from the chimneys of power plants, mills, and factories in industrial areas of all countries were increasingly blamed for high incidences of respiratory disease, lowered life expectancies, and vast damage to property. Urban smoke abatement and clean air programs usually incorporated prohibitions against the discharge of atmospheric pollutants damaging to areas near the discharge point.

The response was to raise chimneys to such a height that smoke, soot, and gases were carried far from their origin points by higher elevation winds.

But when power plants, smelters, and factories were fitted with tall smokestacks to free local areas from pollution, the sulphur dioxide and nitrogen oxides in the smoke were pumped high into the atmosphere instead of being deposited locally. There they mixed with water and other chemicals and turned into sulphuric and nitric acid that was carried to distant areas (Figure 12.4a). They were joined in their impact by other sources of acid gases. Motor vehicles are particularly prolific producers of nitrogen oxides in their exhausts, and volcanoes can add immense amounts of acidic gases, as the Tambora eruption demonstrated (see "Sudbury Superstack").

When acids from all sources are washed out of the air by rain, snow, or fog, the result is **acid rain**, though *acid precipitation* is a more precise designation. Acidity levels are described by the *pH factor,* the measure of acidity/alkalinity on a scale of 0 to 14. The average pH of normal rainfall is 5.6, slightly acidic, but acid rainfalls with a pH of 2.4—approximately the acidity of vinegar and lemon juice—have been recorded. Primarily occurring in developed nations, acid rain has become a serious problem in many parts of Europe, North America, and Japan. It expresses itself in several forms, though the most visible are its corrosive effects on marble and limestone sculptures and buildings, on metals such as iron and bronze (Figure 12.4b), and in the destruction of forests. Trees at higher elevations are particularly susceptible, with widespread forest loss clearly apparent on the hillsides and mountain tops of New England, Scandinavia, and Germany, where acid rain had apparently degraded much of that country's famous forests by the early 1990s.

Damage to lakes, fish, and soils is less immediately evident, but more widespread and equally serious. Acid rain has been linked to the disappearance of fish in thousands of streams and lakes in New England, Canada, and Scandinavia, and to a decline in fish populations elsewhere. It leaches toxic constituents such as aluminum salts from the soil, and kills soil micro-organisms that break down organic matter and recycle nutrients through the ecosystem.

Acid deposition can harm and decrease yields of many food crops and increase the content of poisonous heavy metals in drinking water supplies. The culprit acids are borne in the atmosphere and so may wreak their injury far from the power plants or cities (or volcanoes) that put them in the air (Figure 12.5). In North America, mid-western coal-burning power stations and industries are blamed for acid rain contamination in New England. They, along with other U.S. industries, power plants, and automobiles, are credited with the widespread acid rain damage in Canada (including almost 2000 lakes totally dead to fish life with another 150,000 in danger). Canada itself has major urban and industrial pollution sources contributing to its acid rain incidence.

Sudbury Superstack

Sudbury's "superstack" is a classic example of the "build it taller" approach to solving local air pollution problems. On the positive side, its construction has allowed for the rehabilitation of the previous "moonscape" landscape (see 1979 photo). This land reclamation program has been recognized as a "success story" by the United Nations (see 2001 photo). It has also won several international, national, and provincial awards for its successful environmental initiatives. Over the past two decades, more than 6 million trees have been planted under the Sudbury Regional Land Reclamation Program. Both Inco and Falconbridge mining companies have played very active roles in the re-greening of Sudbury. On the negative side, until the installation of proper cleaning technologies, the superstack promoted the long range transport of pollutants. Acid deposition can harm and decrease yields of many food crops and increase the content of poisonous heavy metals in drinking water supplies. The culprit acids are borne in the atmosphere and so may wreak their injury far from the power plants or cities (or volcanoes) that put them in the air (Figure 12.4a). In North America, mid-western coal-burning power stations and industries are blamed for acid rain contamination in New England.

They, along with other United States industries, power plants, and automobiles, are credited with the widespread acid rain damage in Canada (including some 2000 lakes totally dead to fish life, and another 150,000 in danger). According to Environment Canada, the major sources of sulphur dioxide emissions, which are a major constituent of acid rain, are non-ferrous metal smelters, followed by coal-fired generators. About 50% of the wet sulphate deposition in eastern Canada is believed to come from the United States, while about 10% of the deposition in the north-eastern United States comes from Canada.

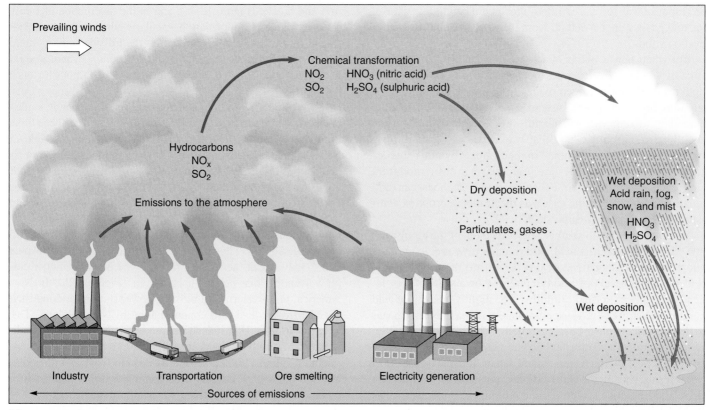

(a)

(b)

Land Use and Land Cover

Human-induced alterations in land use and vegetative cover affect the radiation balance of the earth and, therefore, contribute to climatic change. Since the beginning of the 19th century, vast portions

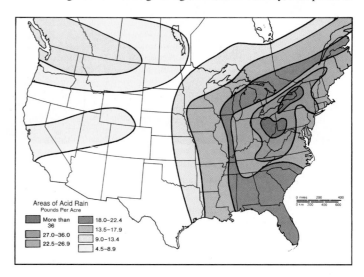

FIGURE 12.5 Where acid rain falls. In general, the areas that receive the most acid rain in the eastern United States and Canada are those that are least able to tolerate it. Their surface waters tend to be acidic rather than alkaline and are unable to neutralize the acids deposited by rain or snow. Ironically, the highly industrialized Ohio Valley and southern Great Lakes districts have high natural resistance to soil and water acidification.

Source: Data from Canadian Government.

FIGURE 12.4 The formation and effects of acid precipitation. (*a*) Sulphur dioxide and nitrogen oxides produced by the combustion of fossil fuels are transformed into sulphate and nitrate particles; when the particles react with water vapour, they form sulphuric and nitric acids, which then fall to earth. (*b*) The destructive effect of acid rain is evident on this limestone statuary at the cathedral in Reims, France.

of the earth's surface have been modified, whole ecosystems destroyed, and global biomes altered or eliminated. North American and European native forests have largely vanished; the grasslands of interior United States, Canada, and Ukraine have been converted into farmland. Marshes and wetlands have been drained, dams built, and major water impoundments created. Steppe lands have become deserts; deserts have blossomed under irrigation.

At least locally, every such change alters surface reflectivity for solar radiation, land and air temperature conditions, and water balances. In turn, these changes in surface conditions affect the climates of both the local area and of areas downwind. On a global basis, their cumulative impact is less clear, but certain generalizations are agreed upon. The generation of methane gas, an important contributor to the greenhouse effect, is almost certainly reduced by the drainage of swamps, but it is also greatly increased as a by-product of expanding paddy rice production and of growing herds of cattle on pastureland. Heavy applications of nitrogen fertilizers are thought to be important in increasing the nitrous oxide content of the atmosphere. When they enter streams and lakes through farm runoff, the fertilizers encourage the algal growth that alters water surface reflectivity and evaporation rates.

But unquestionably the most important of the land surface changes has been that of clearing of forests and ploughing of grasslands. Both effect drastic environmental changes that alter temperature conditions and water balances and release—through vegetative decomposition—large quantities of carbon dioxide and other gases to the atmosphere. The destruction of both biomes represents, as well, the loss of major "sinks" that extract carbon dioxide from the atmosphere and hold it in plant tissue.

Tropical Deforestation

Forests, we saw in Chapter 9, still cover some 30% of the earth's land surface, though the forest biomes have suffered mightily as human pressures on them have increased. Forest clearing accompanied the development of agriculture and spread of people throughout Europe, Central Asia, the Middle East, and India. European colonization had much the same impact on the temperate forests of eastern North America and Australasia. In most mid-latitude developed countries, although original forest cover is largely gone, replanting and reversion of cropland to timber has tended to replenish woodlands at about their rate of cutting.

Now it is the tropical rain forest—also known as the tropical moist forest—biome that is feeling the pressure of growing population numbers, the need for more agricultural land, particularly for soy bean cultivation, expanded demand for fuel and commercial wood, and a mid-latitude market for beef that can be satisfied profitably by replacing tropical forest with cleared grazing land. These disappearing forests—covering no more than 6% of the planet's land surface—extend across parts of Asia, Africa, and Latin America, and are the world's most diverse and least understood biome. About 45% of their original expanse has already been cleared or degraded. Africa has lost more than half of its original rain forest; nearly half of Asia's is gone; 70% of the moist forests of Central America and some 40% of those of South America have disappeared. Every year additional thousands of

square kilometres are lost, though recent satellite surveys indicate the overall rate of tropical forest cutting is not as great as estimates of the 1980s and 1990s feared. Even so, FAO data of 2003 suggest tropical deforestation still exceeds 130,000 square kilometres (50,000 sq mi) annually. Tropical forest removal raises three principal global concerns and a host of local ones.

First, on a worldwide basis, all forests play a major role in maintaining the oxygen and carbon balance of the earth. This is particularly true of tropical forests because of their total area and volume. Humans and their industries consume oxygen; vegetation replenishes it through photosynthesis and the release of oxygen back into the atmosphere as a by-product. At the same time, plants extract the carbon from atmospheric carbon dioxide, acting as natural retaining sponges for the gas so important in the greenhouse effect. Each year, each hectare (2.47 acres) of Amazon rain forest absorbs a tonne of carbon dioxide. When the tropical rain forest is cleared, not only is its role as a carbon sink lost but the act of destruction itself through decomposition or burning releases as carbon dioxide the vast quantities of carbon the forest had stored.

A second global concern is also climate related. Forest destruction changes surface and air temperatures, moisture content, and reflectivity. Conversion of forest to grassland, for example, increases surface temperature, raises air temperatures above the treeless ground, and therefore increases the water-holding capacity of the warmer air. As winds move the hotter, drier air, it tends to exert a drying effect on adjacent forest and agricultural lands. Trees and crops outside the denuded area experience heat and aridity stresses not normal to their geographical locations. It is calculated that cutting the forests of South America on a wide scale should raise regional temperatures from $3°$ C to $5°$ C ($5.5–9°$ F), which in turn would extend the dry season and greatly disrupt not only regional but global climates.

In some ways, the most serious long-term global consequence of the eradication of tropical rain forests will be the loss of a major part of the biological diversity of the planet. Of the estimated 5–10 million plant and animal species believed to exist on earth, a minimum of 40% to 50%—and possibly 70% or more—are native to the tropical rain forest biome. Many of the plants have become important world staple food crops: rice, millet, cassava, yam, taro, banana, coconut, pineapple, and sugarcane to name but a very few well-known ones. Unknown additional potential food species remain as yet unexploited. Reports from Indonesia suggest that in that country's forests alone, some 4000 plant species have proved useful to native peoples as foodstuffs of one sort or another, though less than one-tenth have come into wide use. The rain forests are, in addition, the world's main storehouse of drug-yielding plants and insects, including thousands with proven or prospective anticancer properties and many widely used as sources of antibiotics, antivirals, analgesics, tranquilizers, diuretics, and laxatives, among a host of other items (see "Tropical Forests and Medical Resources"). The loss of the zoological and botanical storehouse that the rain forests represent would deprive humans of untold potential benefits that might never be realized.

On a more local basis, tropical forests play for their inhabitants and neighbours the same role taken by forests everywhere. They protect watersheds and regulate water flow. After forest cutting, unregulated flow accentuates the problems of high and low water variations, increases the severity of valley flooding,

Tropical forests are biological cornucopias, possessing a stunning array of plant and animal life. Costa Rica, about the size of South Carolina, contains as many bird species as all of North America, more species of insects, and nearly half the number of plant species. One stand of rain forest in Kalimantan (Borneo) contains more than 700 species of tree, as many as exist in North America, and half a square kilometre of Malaysia's forest can feature as many tree and shrub species as the whole of the United States and Canada. Forty-three species of ant inhabit a single tree variety in Peru, dependent on it for food and shelter and providing in return protection from other insects.

The tropical forests yield an abundance of chemical products used to manufacture alkaloids, steroids, anaesthetics, and other medicinal agents. Indeed, one quarter to one half of all modern drugs, including strychnine, quinine, curare, and ipecac, come from the tropical forests. A single flower, the Madagascar periwinkle, produces two drugs used to treat leukemia and Hodgkin's disease.

As significant as these and other modern drugs derived from tropical plants are, scientists believe that the medical potential of the tropical forests remains virtually untapped. They fear that deforestation will eradicate medicinal plants and traditional formulas before their uses become known, depriving humans of untold potential benefits that may never be realized. Indigenous peoples make free use of plants of the rain forest for such purposes as treating stings and snakebites, relieving burns and skin fungi, reducing fevers, and curing earaches. Yet botanists have only recently begun to identify tropical plants and study traditional herbal medicines to discover which plants might contain pharmaceutically important compounds.

A second concern is that forest destruction will create shortages of drugs already derived from those plants. Reportedly, as many as 60,000 plants with valuable medical properties are likely to become extinct by 2050. Already endangered is reserpine, an ingredient in certain tranquilizers that is derived from the *Rauwolfia serpentina* plant found in India. Also threatened are cinchona, whose bark produces quinine, and foxglove varieties that are used to make the heart medications digitoxin and acetyldigitoxin.

---

and makes more serious and prolonged the impact of low water flow on irrigation agriculture, navigation, and urban and rural water supply. Accelerated **soil erosion**—the process of removal of soil particles from the ecosystem, usually by wind or running water—quickly removes the always thin, infertile tropical forest soils from deforested areas. Lands cleared for agriculture almost immediately become unsuitable for that use partially because of soil loss (Figure 12.6). The surface material removed is transported and deposited downstream, changing valley contours, extending the area subject to flooding, and filling irrigation and drainage channels. Or it may be deposited in the reservoirs behind the increasing number of major dams on rivers within the tropical rain forests or rising there (see "Dam Trouble in the Tropics").

Soil Erosion

Over much of the earth's surface, the thin layer of topsoil upon which life depends is only a few inches deep, usually less than 30 centimetres (1 ft). Below it, the lithosphere is as lifeless as the surface of the moon. A **soil** is a complex mixture of rock particles, inorganic mineral matter, organic material, living organisms, air, and water. Under natural conditions, soil is constantly being formed by the physical and chemical decomposition of rock material and by the decay of organic matter. It is simultaneously being eroded, for soil erosion is as natural a process as soil formation and occurs even when land is totally covered by forests or grass. Under most natural conditions, however, the rate of soil formation equals or exceeds the rate of soil erosion, so soil depth and fertility tend to increase with time.

FIGURE 12.6 Wholesale destruction of the tropical rain forest guarantees environmental degradation so severe that the forest can never naturally regenerate itself. Exposed soils quickly deteriorate in structure and fertility and are easily eroded, as this growing gully in Amazonia clearly shows.

The great tropical river systems have a sizeable percentage of the world's undeveloped power potential. The lure of that power and its promise for economic development and national modernization have proved nearly irresistible. But the tropical rain forests have been a particularly difficult environment for dam builders. The dams (and their reservoirs) often carry a heavy ecological price, and the clearing and development of the areas they are meant to serve often assure the destruction of the dam projects themselves.

The creation of Brokopondo in Suriname in 1964 marked the first large reservoir in a rain forest locale. Without being cleared of their potentially valuable timber, 1480 square kilometres (570 sq mi) of dense tropical forest disappeared underwater. As the trees decomposed, producing hydrogen sulphide, an intolerable stench polluted the atmosphere for scores of miles downwind. For more than two years, employees at the dam wore gas masks at work. Decomposition of vegetation produced acids that corroded the dam's cooling system, leading to costly continuing repairs and upkeep. Identical problems have occurred at the Tucuruí dam and reservoir in Brazil, started in 1984 and covering 2850 sq. km (1100 sq mi) of uncleared rain forest.

Water hyacinth spreads rapidly in tropical impoundments, its growth hastened by the rich nutrients released by tree decomposition. Within a year of the reservoir's completion, a 130-square-kilometre (50-sq-mi) blanket of the weed was afloat on Lake Brokopondo, and after another year almost half the reservoir was covered. Another 440 square kilometres (170 sq mi) were claimed by a floating fern, *Ceratopteris*. Identical problems plague most rain forest hydropower projects.

The expense, the disruption of the lives of valley residents whose homes are to be flooded, and the environmental damage of dam projects in the rain forest all may be in vain. Deforestation of river banks and clearing of vegetation for permanent agriculture usually results in accelerated erosion, rapid sedimentation of reservoirs, and drastic reduction of electrical generating capacity. The Ambuklao Reservoir in the Philippines, built with an expected payback period of 60 years, now appears certain to silt up in half that time. The Anchicaya Reservoir in Colombia lost 25% of its storage capacity only two years after it was completed and was almost totally filled with silt within 10 years. The Peligre Dam in Haiti was completed in 1956 with a life expectancy of at least 50 years; siltation reduced its usefulness by some 15 years. El Cajon Dam in Honduras, Arenal in Costa Rica, Chixoy in Guatemala and many others—all built to last decades or even centuries—have, because of premature siltation, failed to repay their costs or fulfill their promise. The price of deforestation in wet tropics is high indeed.

When land is cleared and planted to crops or when the vegetative cover is broken by overgrazing, deforestation, or other disturbances, the process of erosion inevitably accelerates. When its rate exceeds that of soil formation, the life-sustaining veneer of topsoil becomes thinner and eventually disappears, leaving behind only sterile subsoil or barren rock. At that point, the renewable soil resource has been converted through human impact into a non-renewable and dissipated asset. Carried to the extreme of bare rock hillsides or wind-denuded plains, erosion spells the total end of agricultural use of the land. Throughout history, such extreme human-induced destruction has occurred and been observed with dismay.

Any massive destruction of the soil resource could spell the end of the civilization it had supported. For the most part, however, farmers—even those in difficult climatic and topographic circumstances—devised ingenious ways to preserve and even improve the soil resource on which their lives and livelihoods depended. Particularly when farming was carried on outside of fertile, level valley lands, farmers' practices were routinely based on some combination of crop rotation, fallowing, and terracing.

Rotation involves the planting of two or more crops simultaneously or successively on the same area to preserve fertility or to provide a plant cover to protect the soil. **Fallowing** leaves a field idle (uncropped) for one or more years to achieve one of two outcomes. In semi-arid areas, the purpose is to accumulate soil moisture from one year to apply to the next year's crop; in tropical wet regions, as we saw in Chapter 9, the purpose is to renew soil fertility of the swidden plot. **Terracing** (see Figure 4.4) replaces steep slopes with a series of narrow layered, level fields, providing cropland where little or none existed previously. In addition, because water moving rapidly down-slope has great erosive power, breaking the speed of flow by terracing reduces the amount of soil lost. Field trials in Nigeria indicate that cultivation on a 1% slope (a drop of .3 metre (1 ft) in elevation over 30 metres (100 ft) of horizontal distance) results in soil loss at or below the rate of soil formation; farming there on a 15% slope would totally strip a field of its soil cover in only 10 years.

Farming skills have not declined in recent years. Rather, pressures on farmlands have increased with population growth and the intensification of agriculture and clearing of land for the commercial cropping that is increasingly part of the developing countries' economies. Farming has been forced higher up on steeper slopes, more forest land has been converted to cultivation, grazing and crops have been pushed farther and more intensively into semi-arid areas, and existing fields have had to be worked more intensively and less carefully. Many traditional agricultural systems and areas that were ecologically stable and secure as recently as 1950, when world population stood at 2.5 billion and subsistence agriculture was the rule, are disintegrating under the pressures of more than 6 billion people and a changing global economy.

The evidence of that deterioration is found in all parts of the world (Figure 12.7). The International Food Policy Research Institute reports that each year some 10 million hectares

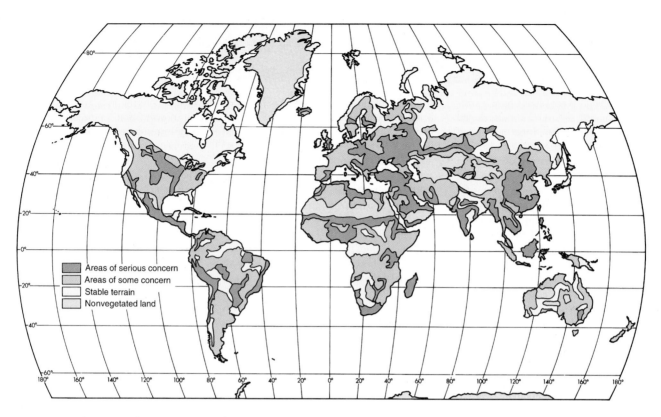

FIGURE 12.7 The world pattern of soil degradation concern. Between 1945 and 2000, nearly 2 billion hectares (almost 5 billion acres) of the world's 8.7 billion hectares (21.5 billion acres) of cropland, pastures, and forests used in agriculture—an area as large as Russia and India combined—were added to the existing total of degraded soils. Globally, about 18% of forest area, 21% of pastures, and 37% of cropland have undergone moderate to severe degradation. Water erosion accounted for 56% of that recorded deterioration, wind erosion for 28%, chemical deterioration (salinization and nutrient loss) for 12%, and physical degradation (e.g., compaction and waterlogging) for 4%.

Sources: World Resources Institute and International Soil Reference and Information Center.

(25 million acres) of cropland worldwide are abandoned because of soil erosion and diminished production caused by erosion. Nearly 40% of the world's agricultural land is seriously degraded, though the percentages differ by region. Almost 75% of cropland in Central America shows serious degradation, as does 11% in Asia. In Africa, some 500 million hectares (1.2 billion acres) have been affected by soil erosion since the mid-1950s, including as much as 65% of agricultural land, a major factor limiting food production in that continent to, at most, an inadequate 2% annual increase.

Soil deterioration expresses itself in two ways: through decreasing yields of cultivated fields themselves and in increased stream sediment loads and downstream deposition of silt. In Guatemala, for example, some 40% of the productive capacity of the land has been lost through erosion, and several areas of the country have been abandoned because agriculture has become economically impracticable; the figure is 50% in El Salvador. In Turkey, a reported 75% of the land is affected, and 54% is severely or very severely eroded. Haiti has no high-value soil left at all. A full one-quarter of India's total land area has been significantly eroded: some 13 million hectares (32 million acres) by wind and nearly 74 million hectares (183 million acres) by water. Between 1960 and 2000, China lost over 15% of its total arable land to erosion, desertification, or conversion to non-agricultural use; some 700,000 hectares

(1.7 million acres) of cultivated land annually are taken by construction. Its Huang River is the most sediment laden of any waterway on earth; in its middle course it is about 50% silt by weight, just under the point of liquid mud. The world's rivers deliver about 24 billion tonnes of sediment to the oceans each year, while additional billions of tons settle along stream valleys or are deposited in reservoirs (see "Dam Trouble in the Tropics" on page 425).

Agricultural soil depletion through erosion—and through salt accumulation and desertification—has been called "the quiet crisis." It continues inexorably and unfolds gradually, without the abrupt attention attracted by an earthquake or volcanic explosion. Unfortunately, silent or not, productive soil loss is a crisis of growing importance and immediacy, not just in the countries of its occurrence but—because of international markets and relief programs—throughout the world.

In contrast, Canada has relatively minor problems with erosion. A national summary estimated that 63% of cultivated land in Canada is at negligible-to-low risk of water erosion, and about 20% is at high-to-severe risk. Agriculture Canada states that the Maritime Provinces are at the highest risk of water erosion with more than 80% of the cultivated land in the high-to-severe risk categories, followed by British Columbia (75%), and Central Canada (about 50%). The Prairie Provinces are at a much lower risk of water erosion because of their relatively flat terrain and low rainfall.

Water Supply and Water Quality

Solar energy and water are the indispensable ingredients of life on Earth. The supply of both is essentially constant and beyond the scope of humans to increase or alter although, as we saw with aerosols and atmospheric gases, humans can affect the quality and utility of an otherwise fixed resource. Any threat of reduction in availability or lessening of quality of a material so basic to our very lives as water is certain to arouse strong emotions and deep concerns. In many parts of the world and for many competitors for limited freshwater supplies, those emotions and concerns are already real.

The problem is not with the global amount of water, but with its distribution, its availability, and its quality. The total amount of water on the earth is enormous, though only a small part of the hydrosphere is suitable or available for use by humans, plants, or animals (Figure 12.8). And the total amount remains constant. Water is a renewable resource; the **hydrologic cycle** assures that water, no matter how often used or how much abused, will return over and over to the earth for further exploitation (Figure 12.9). Enough rain and snow fall on the continents each year to cover the earth's total land area with 83 centimetres (33 in.) of water. It has usually been reckoned that the volume of fresh water annually renewed by the hydrologic cycle would meet the needs of the growing world population. Yet, over the past 75 years, as world population has tripled—with growth particularly rapid in regions of low and variable rainfall—total water demand has increased six fold. Even now, it is generally agreed, a little more than half of the world's available fresh water is being used each year. Based on current population growth trends alone, that fraction could well rise to 74% by 2025—and to 90% should people everywhere then consume water in the current daily amount used by the average American or Canadian.

In many parts of the world water supplies are inadequate and dwindling. Insufficient water for irrigation periodically endangers crops and threatens famine; permanent streams have become intermittent in flow; fresh- and saltwater lakes are shrinking; and from throughout the world come reports of rapidly falling water tables and wells that have gone dry. Reduced availability and reliability of supply are echoed in a reduced quality of the world's freshwater inventory. Increased silt loads of streams, pollution of surface and groundwater supplies, and lakes acidified and biologically dead or prematurely filled by siltation and algal growth are evidences of adverse human impact on an indispensable component of the biosphere.

Patterns of Availability

Observations about global supplies and renewal cycles of fresh water ignore the ever-present geographic reality: things are not uniformly distributed over the surface of the earth. There is no necessary relationship between the earth's pattern of freshwater availability and the distribution of consuming populations and activities. For example, the Middle East and North Africa is home to 6.3% of the World's population but contains only 1.4% of the world's renewable fresh water. Three different world maps help us to understand why. The first, Figure 12.10, shows the spatially variable world pattern of precipitation. The second, Figure 12.11, reminds us that, as a rule, the lower the average amount of precipitation received in an area, the greater is the variability of precipitation from year to year. The recurring droughts and famines of the Sahel region of Africa are witness to the deadly impact of those expected fluctuations in areas of already low rainfall. Finally, Figure 12.12 takes account of the relationship between precipitation receipts and losses through *evapotranspiration*, the return of water from the land to the atmosphere through evaporation from soil and plants and by transpiration through plant leaves. These losses are higher in the tropics than in middle and upper latitudes, where lower rainfall amounts under cooler conditions may be more effective and useful than higher amounts received closer to the equator.

The distribution and vegetative adequacy of precipitation are givens and, except for human impact on climatic conditions, are largely independent of cultural influences. Regional water sufficiency, however, is also a function of the size of the population using the resource, its pattern of water use, and the amount of deterioration in quantity and quality the water supply experiences in the process of its use and return to the system. These are circumstances under human, not natural, control.

At first glance, Canadians would appear to have little cause for concern over the availability of water. The needs of a population of only 34 million are served by a mean annual discharge of 105,000 cubic metres per second, which represents nearly 9% of the global runoff. These characteristics of low population and high supply have led some people to classify Canada as a water rich nation. However, although Canada is known for its abundant water resources, this is, in fact, a myth.

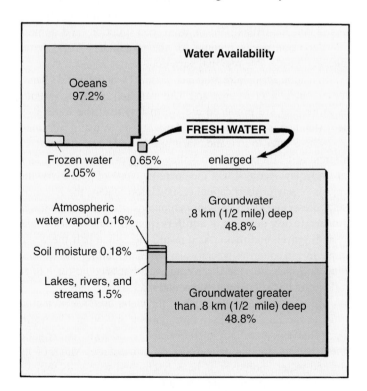

FIGURE 12.8 Less than 1% of the world's water supply is available for human use in fresh water lakes and rivers and from wells. An additional 2% is effectively locked in glaciers and polar ice caps.

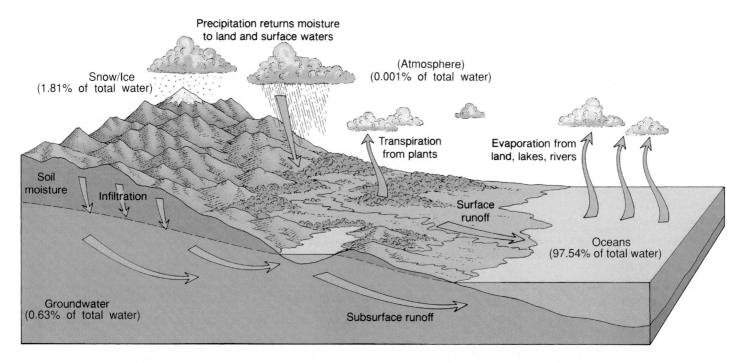

FIGURE 12.9 The hydrologic cycle. Water may change form and composition, but under natural environmental circumstances, it is marvellously purified in the recycling process and is again made available with appropriate properties and purity to the ecosystems of the earth. The sun provides energy for the evaporation of fresh and ocean water. The water is held as vapour until the air becomes supersaturated. Atmospheric moisture is returned to the earth's surface as solid or liquid precipitation to complete the cycle. Precipitation is not uniformly distributed, and moisture is not necessarily returned to areas in the same quantity as it has evaporated from them. The continents receive more water than they lose; the excess returns to the seas as surface water or groundwater. A global water balance, however, is always maintained.

The application of averages is meaningless since supply and demand are not evenly distributed over time and space. Over 60% of the rivers drain to the north while 90% of Canada's population and industry are concentrated within 300 km of its southern border. Mean annual precipitation ranges from over 2000 mm on the west coast of British Columbia to less than 500 mm in Saskatchewan. Physical stresses on water resources are evident in Canada; between 1994 and 1999, one in four Canadian municipalities experienced water shortages due to increased consumption, drought, or infrastructure constraints (Environment Canada, 2002). The Federal Commissioner of the Environment and Sustainable Development (2001) found that fresh water in southern Canada was heavily used and overly stressed. Specific areas under stress included the Great Lakes, Okanagan Valley, the South Saskatchewan River Basin, and Assiniboine–Red River Basin (Brandes *et al.*, 2005). Evidence of physical stress includes falling water tables and lower water levels as well as degraded water quality. In other situations, water is not returned to its original source but transferred to another water body (see "Water Diversions in Canada"). Cumulatively, both types of change produce direct and indirect consequences (Brookes *et al.*, 2004): for instance, ecosystems may be altered and water that supports instream uses may be diminished.

Water Use and Abuse

For the world as a whole, irrigated agriculture accounts for nearly three-quarters (73%) of freshwater use; in the poorest countries, the proportion is 90%. The irrigation share continues to grow worldwide as irrigation farming expands by between 5 and 6 million additional hectares (12 to 15 million acres) annually. Industry uses about one-fifth (21%) of water consumption, and domestic and recreation needs account for the remainder. World figures conceal considerable regional variation.

Irrigation agriculture produces some 40% of the world's harvest from about 17% of its cropland. Unfortunately, in many instances the crops that are produced are worth less than the water itself; the difference is made up in the huge subsidies that governments everywhere offer to irrigation farming. In areas and economies as different as California's Napa Valley or Egypt's Nile Valley, farmers rarely pay over a fifth of the operating costs of public irrigation projects or any of their capital costs. Unfortunately, the increasing use of diesel and electrically driven pumps since the 1950s has led to extensive over pumping of **aquifers** (porous, water-bearing layers of sand, gravel, and rock). As a result, more than half the world's people live in countries where water tables are falling and wells are going dry, including the three countries that account for half the world grain harvest: China, India, and the United States.

Unfortunately as well, much of the water used for agriculture is lost to the regional supply through evaporation and transpiration; often less than half of the water withdrawn for irrigation is returned to streams or aquifers for further use. Much of that returned water, moreover, is heavily charged with salts removed from irrigated soils, making it unfit for reuse.

On the other hand, most of the water used for manufacturing processes and power production is returned to streams, lakes, or aquifers, but often in a state of pollution that renders it unsuitable for alternate and subsequent uses. Industrial water use rises

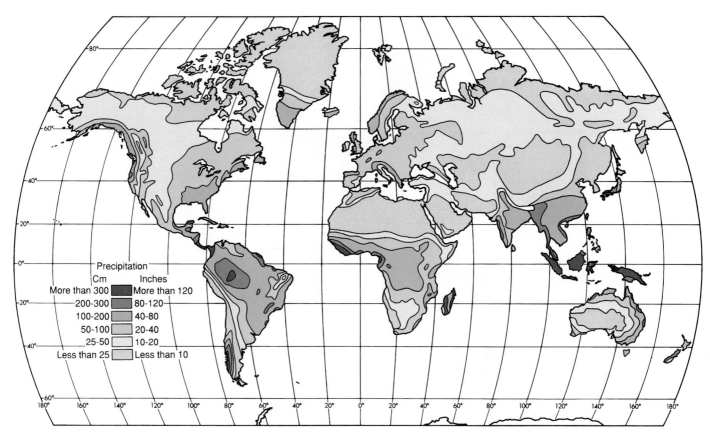

FIGURE 12.10 Mean annual precipitation. Regional contrasts of precipitation receipts clearly demonstrate the truism that natural phenomena are unequally distributed over the surface of the earth. High and very high rainfall amounts are recorded in equatorial and tropical areas of Central and South America, Africa, and South and Southeast Asia. Productive agricultural regions of North America and Europe have lower moisture receipts. The world's desert regions—in North Africa, Inner Asia, the south-western United States, and interior Australia—are clearly marked by low precipitation totals. But not all areas of low moisture receipt are arid, as Figure 12.12 makes clear.

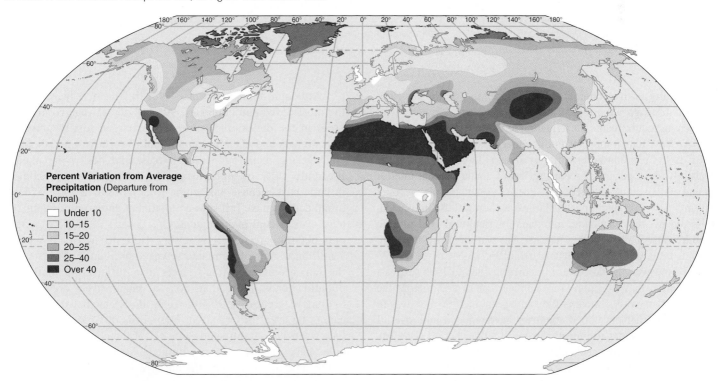

FIGURE 12.11 The pattern of precipitation variability. Note that regions of low total precipitation tend to have high variability. In general, the lower the amount of long-term annual precipitation, the lower is the probability that the "average" will be recorded in any single year. Short-run variability and long-term progressive change in climatic conditions are the rule of nature and occur independent of any human influence.

Human Impacts on Natural Systems and Human Health   429

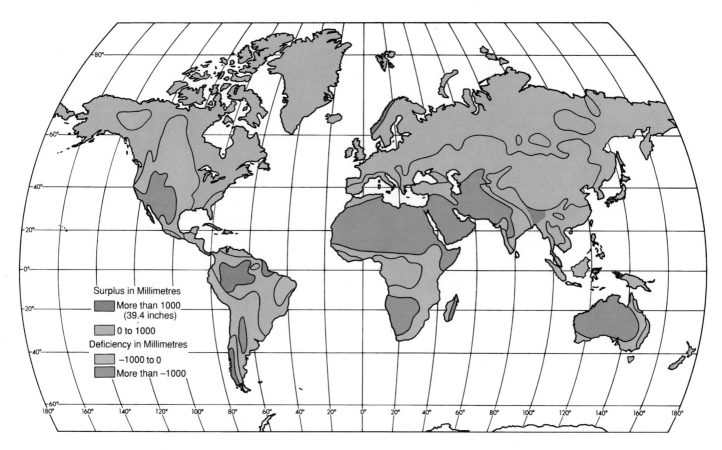

FIGURE 12.12 World water supplies. The pattern of surplus and deficit is seen in relation to the demands of the vegetation cover. Water is in surplus when precipitation is sufficient to satisfy or exceed the demands of the vegetation cover. When precipitation is lower than this potential demand, a water deficit occurs. By this measure, most of Africa (except the tropical rain forest areas of West Africa), much of the Middle East, the south-western United States, and almost all of Australia are areas of extreme moisture deficit.

A comparison of this map with Figure 12.11 helps demonstrate the **limiting factor principle**, which notes that the single factor that is most deficient in an ecosystem is the one that determines what kind of plant and animal associations will exist there. Moisture surplus or deficit is the limiting factor that dictates whether desert, grassland, or forest will develop under natural, undisturbed conditions.

Source: Redrawn with permission from Malin Falkenmark, "Water and Mankind—A Complex System of Mutual Interaction," Ambio 6 (1977): 5.

dramatically with economic development, and in the developing countries, growing industrial demands compete directly with increasing requirements for irrigation and urban water supply.

At least four important points emerge from considering the 1981–1996 Canadian water withdrawal data (Table 12.1). First, the relatively short period of record reflects Canada's recent interest in and perceived need to record water use systematically. Second, thermal power production is the largest withdrawal use in Canada, followed by manufacturing, municipal, agricultural, and mining withdrawals. Third, total water use has varied. For the entire period, total water use increased from 36,717 MCM to 44,873 MCM. However, the downward trend from 1986 to 1996 suggests the situation may be improving. Our per capita use mirrors the same trends, and is almost at the same point in 1996 as it was in 1981. Most other developed countries have reduced both overall and per capita water use levels during this time period (Brookes *et al.*, 2004). Fourth, each Canadian uses about 1.50 MCM of water (about 4400 litres per capita per day) to support our lifestyle. This far exceeds the amount of water used by Europeans who have a similar standard of living (Brookes *et al.*, 2004).

Although municipal wastewater treatment is increasing in the most developed countries, 90% of raw sewage from urban areas in the developing world is discharged totally untreated into streams and oceans, contaminating surface water supplies, endangering drinking water sources, and destroying aquatic life. Fully 70% of total surface waters in India are polluted, in large part because only eight of its more than 3000 sizeable urban centres have full sewage treatment and no more than 200 have even partial management. Of Taiwan's 22 million people, only 600,000 are served by sewers. Hong Kong each day pours 1 million tonnes of untreated sewage and industrial waste into the sea. Mainland China's rivers also suffer from increasing pollution loads. More than 80% of major rivers are polluted to some degree, over 20% to such an extent that their waters cannot be used for irrigation. Four-fifths of China's urban surface water is contaminated, only six of the country's 27 largest cities have drinking water within the state standards, and the water to be impounded by the massive Three Gorges Dam project, it is predicted, will be seriously contaminated by untreated raw sewage from the dozens of cities along the new reservoir.

Water Diversions in Canada

The pressure to dam and divert water in response to water shortages and the need for hydroelectric energy could result in increased demand for large-scale water projects. Like the beaver on the back of the nickel, Canada diverts more water than any other nation—over 4400 cubic metres per second. Most of the diversions are associated with hydro projects the largest being the La Grande (James Bay) diversion in Quebec, the Churchill–Nelson diversion in Manitoba, and the Churchill Falls project in Labrador. The experience of the Kemano Diversion in British Columbia is an instructive example of the issues associated with water diversions.

The smelting of aluminum requires an abundant and secure supply of electricity, and Canada's physical geography provides many opportunities to develop hydroelectric generating facilities. In 1950, the Government of British Columbia permitted the Aluminum Company of Canada (Alcan) to develop a hydroelectric generating facility and to divert water from the Nechako River in order to develop one of the largest smelters in the world at Kitimat. Unlike most diversions in Canada that are funded by some type of public agency (e.g., hydro company), the cost of the project, which is estimated to be over $3.3 billion in today's currency, was provided by a private company—Alcan. The project involved several phases including the construction of Kenney Dam on the Nechako River, which created the Nechako Reservoir and diverting 115 m³/s towards Kitimat through a tunnel. Phase I of the project saw 800 km² (200,000 acres) of land flooded, displacing the entire Cheslatta Indian Band

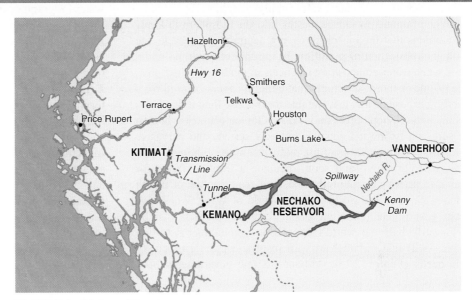

The Nechako–Kemano Diversion

who lived in the area. Indeed, the Cheslatta's land was flooded for seven months before the federal minister of Indian Affairs approved the sale of the land to Alcan for $125,000.

During the late 1970s, decreased flows on the Nechako River were particularly detrimental to fish populations as Alcan diverted more water in order to increase electrical production, and secure its water rights. This prompted the federal Department of Fisheries and Oceans, which has jurisdiction over fisheries, to seek and obtain a court injunction. An agreement was negotiated that allowed Alcan to increase its diversion and leave 13% of the original flow in the Nechako River, which is the migratory route of about 20% of the Fraser River sockeye salmon run.

The agreement was contingent upon Alcan mitigating the loss of fish by producing an equal number of fish elsewhere. Since ecosystems are complex and our knowledge incomplete, this number is unknown. It is also unclear if fish from a hatchery are equivalent to fish produced from a wild run. Phase II of the project, which would increase the diversion to 202 m³/s was rejected following an intense and controversial debate. A watershed council has now been formed to settle disputes between Alcan and other interests.

Want to learn more about water diversions in Canada? See *Water Allocation, Diversion and Export* at www.nwri.ca/threats2full/ch1-1-e.html.

TABLE 12.1

Major Withdrawal Uses of Water and Per Capita Water Use in Canada: 1981, 1986, 1991, 1996

YEAR	MAJOR WITHDRAWAL USES (MCM)						PER CAPITA WATER USE
	Municipal	Agriculture	Thermal	Manufacturing	Mining	Total Water Use	(MCM/ capita)
1981	3760	3125	18,166	11,042	624	36,717	1.48
1986	3719	3559	24,963	9298	544	42,083	1.61
1991	3802	3991	28,288	8410	489	44,980	1.60
1996	3922	4098	28,664	7508	681	44,873	1.50

Source: http://www40.statcan.ca/101/cst01/envir05a.htm?sdi.

In Malaysia, more than 40 major rivers are so polluted that they are nearly devoid of fish and aquatic mammals. And even in developed countries of formerly communist Eastern Europe and Russia, sewage and, particularly, industrial waste seriously pollute much of the surface water supply.

When humans introduce wastes into the biosphere in kinds and amounts that the biosphere cannot neutralize or recycle, the result is **environmental pollution**. In the case of water, pollution exists when water composition has been so modified by the presence of one or more substances that either it cannot be used for a specific purpose or it is less suitable for that use than it was in its natural state. In both developed and developing countries, human pressures on freshwater supplies are now serious and pervasive concerns. If current trends of use and water abuse continue, fresh water will certainly—and soon—become a limiting factor for economic activity, food production, and maintenance of health in many parts of the world (see "A World of Water Woes"). A recent government report on global resources predicts that by 2015 nearly half the world's population—more than 3 billion people—will live in countries with insufficient water to satisfy their needs (Figure 12.13). Although a few governments have

begun to face the water problem—potentially one every bit as serious as atmospheric pollution, soil erosion, deforestation, and desertification—much remains to be done.

Canadians have often taken their access to safe drinking water for granted, and as a right. However, the quality of this most precious of water resource uses and the utilities that provide for its treatment have received considerable attention following the events of spring 2000 when the small agricultural community of Walkerton, Ontario, found its water supply contaminated by *E. coli O157:H7*. This lethal strain of the usually harmless bacterium caused the deaths of seven people and sent over 2500 individuals to hospital. In April 2001, *Cryptosporidium parvum* contaminated the water supply in North Battleford, Saskatchewan, inflicting over 5800 residents with gastrointestinal illnesses and symptoms including diarrhoea, abdominal cramps, fever, nausea, and headaches. One lesson from these incidents is the need to manage our drinking water supplies "from the source to the tap" rather than only at treatment plants. Effective disposal of our wastewater also is of primary concern.

Environment Canada (2001) identified 13 key threats to our drinking water sources: nutrients, acidification, endocrine

A World of Water Woes

Water covers almost three-quarters of the surface of the globe, yet "scarcity" is the word increasingly used to describe water-related concerns in both the developed and developing world. Globally, fresh water is abundant. Each year, an average of over 7000 cubic metres (some 250,000 cubic feet) per person enters rivers and underground reserves. But rainfall does not always occur when or where it is needed. Already, 80 countries with 40% of the world's population have serious water shortages that threaten to cripple agriculture and industry; 22 of them have renewable water resources of less than 1000 cubic metres (35,000 cubic feet) per person—a level generally understood to mean that water scarcity is a severe constraint on the economy and public health. Another 18 countries have less than 2000 cubic metres per capita on average, a dangerously low figure in years of rainfall shortage. Most of the water-short countries are in the Middle East, North Africa, and sub-Saharan Africa, the regions where populations (and consumption demands) are growing fastest. By 2025, two-thirds of the world's population is likely to be living in areas of acute water stress.

In several major crop-producing regions, water use exceeds sustainable levels, threatening future food supplies. America's largest underground water reserve, stretching from

west Texas northward into South Dakota, is drying up, partially depleted by more than 150,000 wells pumping water for irrigation, city supply, and industry. In parts of Texas, Oklahoma, and Kansas, the underground water table has dropped by more than 30 metres (100 feet). In some areas, the wells no longer yield enough to permit irrigation, and farmed land is decreasing; in others, water levels have fallen so far that it is uneconomical to pump it to the surface for any use.

In many agricultural districts of northern China, western and southern India, and Mexico, water scarcity limits agriculture even though national supplies are adequate. In Uzbekistan and adjacent sections of Central Asia and Kazakhstan, virtually the entire flow of the area's two primary rivers—the Amu Darya and the Syr Darya—is used for often wasteful irrigation, with none left to maintain the Aral Sea or supply growing urban populations. In Poland, the draining of bogs that formerly stored rainfall, combined with unimaginable pollution of streams and groundwater, has created a water shortage as great as that of any Middle Eastern desert country. And salinity now seriously affects productivity—or prohibits farming completely—on nearly 10% of the world's irrigated lands.

Water scarcity is often a region-wide concern. More than 200 river systems draining

over half the earth's land surface are shared by two or more countries. Egypt draws on the Nile for 86% of its domestic consumption, but virtually all of that water originates in eight upstream countries. Turkey, Iraq, and Syria have frequently been in dispute over the management of the Tigris and Euphrates rivers, and the downstream states fear the effect on them of Turkish impoundments and diversions. Mexico is angered at American depletion of the Colorado before it reaches the international border.

Many coastal communities face saltwater intrusions into their drinking water supplies as they draw down their underlying freshwater aquifers, while both coastal and inland cities dependent on groundwater may be seriously depleting their underground supplies. In China, 110 mostly large cities face acute water shortages; for at least 50 of them, the problem is groundwater levels dropping on average 1 to 2 metres (3 to 6 ft) each year. In Mexico City, groundwater is pumped at rates 40% faster than natural recharge; the city has responded to those withdrawals by sinking 9 metres (30 ft) during the 20th century. Millions of citizens of major cities throughout the world have had their water rationed as underground and surface supplies are used beyond recharge or storage capacity.

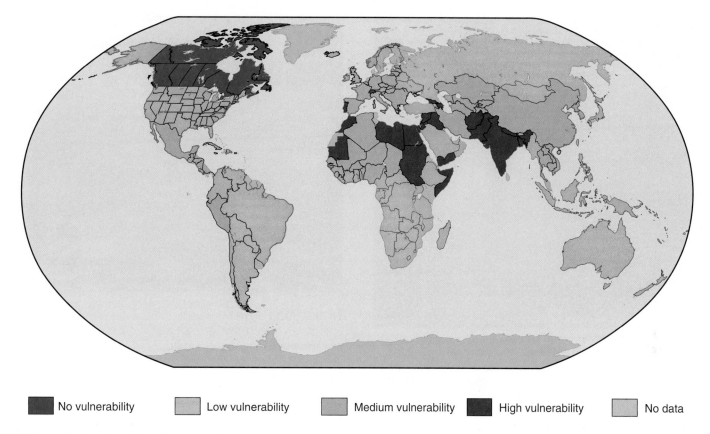

| ■ No vulnerability | ▢ Low vulnerability | ▢ Medium vulnerability | ■ High vulnerability | ▢ No data |

FIGURE 12.13 Countries vulnerable to water shortage. Water consumption rises with population growth, increases in the standard of living, expansion of irrigation farming, and the enlarged demands of industry and municipalities that come with development. In a growing number of world areas—many where water is already scarce—limited freshwater resources severely constrain sustainable development, requiring hard choices in the allocation of water among competing users.

Source: From Environmental Science *9th ed., by E. Enger and B. Smith. Reprinted by permission of The McGraw-Hill Companies, Inc.*

disrupting substances (EDS) and genetically modified organisms (GMOs), pathogens, algal toxins, pesticides, long-range atmospherically transported pollutants, municipal wastewater effluents, industrial wastewater discharges, urban runoff, solid waste management practices, and water quantity changes that result from climate change and diversions, and extreme events. Some of these threats, such as nutrients and acidification from agricultural and industrial activities, have been persistent problems during the past 50 years. Others, such as endocrine disrupting substances and GMOs are new technological risks emerging from actual food sources and lifestyle choices. Threats posed by climate change reinforce a longstanding and fundamental principle of water management—water quality and water quantity are interconnected and must be managed on an integrated basis.

Garbage Heaps and Toxic Wastes

Humans have always managed to leave their mark on the landscapes they occupy. The search for minerals, for example, has altered whole landscapes, beginning with the pockmarks and pits marking Neolithic diggings into chalk cliffs to obtain flints, or early Bronze Age excavations for tin and culminating with mod-

ern open-pit and strip-mining operations that tear minerals from the earth and create massive new landforms of depressions and rubble. Ancient irrigation systems still visible on the landscape document both the engineering skills and the environmental alterations of early hydraulic civilizations in the Near East, North Africa, and elsewhere. The raised fields built by the Mayas of Yucatán are still traceable 1000 years after they were abandoned, and aerial photography reveals the sites of villages and patterns of fields of medieval England.

Among the most enduring of landscape evidences of human occupancy, however, are not the holes deliberately dug or the structures built but the garbage produced and discarded by all societies everywhere. Prehistoric dwelling sites are located and analyzed by their *middens*, the refuse piles containing the kitchen wastes, broken tools, and other debris of human settlement. We have learned much about Roman and medieval European urban life and lifestyles by examination of the refuse mounds that grew as man-made hills in their vicinities. In the Near East, whole cities gradually rose on the mounds of debris accumulating under them (Figure 12.14).

Modern cultures differ from their predecessors by the volume and character of their wastes, not by their habits of discard. The greater the society's population and material wealth, the greater the amount and variety of its garbage. Developed countries of the

FIGURE 12.14 Aerial view of Erbil, Iraq. Here and elsewhere in the Middle East, the debris of millennia of human settlement gradually raised the level of the land surface, producing *tells*, or occupation mounds. The city—one of the oldest in the world—literally was constantly rebuilt at higher elevations on the accumulation of refuse of earlier occupants. In some cases, these striking landforms may rise scores of feet above the surrounding plains.

FIGURE 12.15 Some of the millions of tires Canadians replace each year. Some are retreaded, some are exported, and some are burned to generate electricity. But most remain unused and unwanted in growing dumps that remain both fire hazards and breeding grounds for insects and the diseases they carry.

late 20th century are increasingly discovering that their material wealth and technological advancements are submerging them in a volume and variety of wastes—solid and liquid, harmless and toxic—that threaten both their environments and their established ways of life.

Solid Wastes and Rubbish

North Americans produce rubbish and garbage at a rate of 220 million tonnes per year, or about 2 kilograms (4.5 pounds) per person per day. As populations grow, incomes rise, and consumption patterns change, the volume of disposable materials continues to expand. Relatively little residue is created in subsistence societies that move food from garden to table, and wastes from table to farm animals or compost heaps. The problem comes with urban folk who purchase packaged foods, favour plastic wrappings and containers for every commodity, and seek (and can afford) an ever-broadening array of manufactured goods, both consumer durables such as refrigerators and automobiles, and many designed for single use and quick disposal.

The wastes that communities must somehow dispose of include newspapers and beer cans, toothpaste tubes and empty glass bottles, broken stoves and rusted cars (Figure 12.15). Such ordinary household and municipal trash does not meet the usual designation of *hazardous waste*: discarded material that may pose a substantial threat to human health or the environment when improperly stored or disposed of. Much of it, however, does have a component of danger to health or to the environment. Paints and paint removers, old

television sets and computer monitors, used motor oils, pesticides and herbicides, bleaches, many kinds of plastics, and the like pose problems significantly different from apple cores and waste paper.

Landfill Disposal

The supply of open land and a free-enterprise system of waste collection and disposal led most North American communities to opt for dumping urban refuse in *landfills*. In earlier periods, most of these were simply open dumps on the land, a menace to public health and an aesthetic blot on the landscape. Beginning in the 1960s, more stringent controls began to require waste disposal in what was considered a more environmentally sound manner: the *sanitary landfill*. This involves depositing refuse in a natural depression or excavated trench, compacting it, and then covering it each day with soil to seal it (Figure 12.16).

Most of the municipal waste in the United States and Canada is disposed of by landfill. In the 1970s and 80s, there was a real fear that the available, affordable, or permitted landfill sites were rapidly disappearing and the cost of solid waste disposal would soon greatly increase. Some two-thirds of all landfills in operation in the late 1970s were filled and closed by 1990, and more than half the cities on the U.S. East Coast were without any local landfill sites in the middle 1990s. Because of changes in garbage economics during the 1990s, however, those earlier fears proved unnecessary. First, large waste management companies have built efficient mega-landfills, replacing a great many small, local, and inefficient operations, increasing disposal capacity nationwide. Second, widespread adoption of municipal recycling programs—now diverting an estimated 20% of trash away from landfills—has extended the capacity and life span of

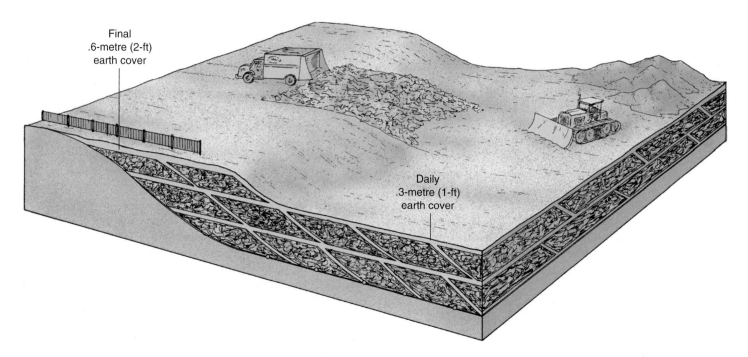

FIGURE 12.16 A sanitary landfill. Each day's deposit of refuse is compacted and isolated in a separate cell by a covering layer of soil or clay. Although far more desirable than open dumps, sanitary landfills pose environmental problems of their own, including potential groundwater contamination and seepage of methane and hydrogen sulphide, gaseous products of decomposition. By federal law, modern landfills must be lined with clay and plastic, equipped with leachate (chemically contaminated drainage from the landfill) collection systems to protect the groundwater, and monitored regularly for underground leaks—requirements that have increased significantly the cost of constructing and operating landfills.

Final
.6-metre (2-ft)
earth cover

Daily
.3-metre (1-ft)
earth cover

the remaining landfills. Lack of profitable (or any) market for recyclables, however, has caused some cities—New York in 2002 is an example—to suspend or curtail their recycling programs. These problems are also common in Canada.

Any such recycling program elimination, reduction, or suspension poses serious environmental contamination threats in light of the rapid increase and accumulation of *e-waste*—the refuse from discarded consumer electronic products: computers, cellular phones, televisions, digital cameras, camcorders, iPods, and the like. In addition to their frequently stripped and recycled steel, aluminum, and copper, they contain toxic chemicals and metals more difficult to separate that tend to remain: lead, arsenic, antimony trioxide, selenium, cadmium, mercury, and more.

The e-waste pile is growing around the world, running into millions of tons annually. More and more governments are drafting legislation for the environmentally friendly disposal of this waste; China, for example, instituted regulations in 2004 providing that old electronic devices must be sold to appliance distributors or to enterprises specifically engaged in appliance reclamation. Two European Union directives were issued in 2005 addressing e-waste recycling and toxic content problems; one puts recycling responsibilities on the manufacturers to whom electronic appliances may be returned; the other bans, after mid-2006, six toxic substances, including lead, cadmium, mercury, and chromium-6, present in almost all electronics products. In Edmonton, a $10 million facility has been built to disassemble lead from monitors, iron from CPUs, aluminum from printers, as well as platinum, silver, cadmium, copper, steel, and plastic. The Edmonton Waste Management Centre is seen as a leader in electronic waste recycling.

Other initiatives include composting and the production of biogas—enough to power 4,600 Edmonton households. Each year, all but 9% of the 40,000 tonnes of paper, glass, metals and plastic from residential sources are recovered for use in other products. The challenge is to expand the program to cover industrial and commercial sources of waste product.

Over the years, of course, many filled dumps have posed problems for the cities which gave rise to them. New York City, for example, for years placed all of its daily 14,000 tonnes of residential waste into the world's largest dump, Fresh Kills on Staten Island. Opened in 1947 as a three-year "temporary" 202-hectare (500-acre) facility, it became a malodorous 1,214 hectares (3000 acres) of decomposing garbage rising some 15 stories above former ground level. Generating 140,000 cubic metres (5 million cubic feet) of methane gas annually and illegally exuding contaminated water, Fresh Kills—finally closed in 2001 at a cost of more than $1 billion—symbolized the rising tide of refuse engulfing cities and endangering the environment.

It has sometimes been necessary for communities to send their garbage to distant communities, and in the case of Toronto, to the United States (see "Geography and Public Policy: Waste Management in Toronto").

Incineration

For cities and regions faced with growing volumes of solid waste, alternatives to local landfill are few, expensive, and strongly resisted. One possibility is *incineration*, a waste-to-energy option of burning refuse to produce steam or electricity that usually also involves sorting, recapturing, and recycling useful rubbish components, such as paper, glass, metals, and the like. Incinerators also produce air pollution, including highly toxic dioxin,[1] so control equipment is required. Acid gases and heavy metals are also released by waste burning. The gases add to atmospheric pollution and acid rain, although "scrubbers" and fabric filters on modern incinerators reduce emissions to very low levels; the metals contribute to the toxicity of the ash that is the inevitable product of incineration and that requires landfill disposal.

The likelihood of pollution from one or many incinerator by-products has sparked strong protest to their construction in the United States and Canada. The seriousness of the dioxin and toxic ash problem, however, has aroused concern everywhere. In Japan, where about three-quarters of municipal waste is incinerated in over 1850 municipal and 3300 private industrial incinerators, atmospheric dioxin levels triple those of the United States led the Ministry of Health in 1997 to strengthen earlier inadequate dioxin emission guidelines. Some European countries called at least temporary halts to incinerator construction while their safety was reconsidered, and increasingly landfills are refusing to take their residue.

Ocean Dumping

For coastal communities around the world the ocean has long been the preferred sink for not only municipal garbage, but for (frequently untreated) sewage, industrial waste, and all the detritus of an advanced urban society. The practice has been so common and long-standing that by the 1980s, the oceans were added to the list of great environmental concerns of the age. While the carcinogenic effect of ozone reduction had to be assumed from scientific report, the evidence of serious ocean pollution was increasingly apparent to even the most casual observer.

Along the Atlantic coast of North America from Massachusetts to Chesapeake Bay, reports of dead dolphins, raw sewage, tar balls, used syringes, vials of contaminated blood and hospital waste, diapers, plastic products in unimagined amounts and varieties, and other foul refuse kept swimmers from the beach, closed coastal shellfisheries, and elicited health warnings against wading or even breathing salt spray (Figure 12.17). The Gulf of Mexico coast is also tainted and polluted by accumulations of urban garbage, litter from ships and offshore oil rigs, and the toxic effluent of petrochemical plants. Long stretches of Pacific shoreline are in similar condition. Many Canadian municipalities, such as Montreal and Victoria, discharge their sewage into fresh or open water without full treatment.

Elsewhere, the Adriatic, Aegean, Baltic, and Irish seas and the Sea of Japan—indeed, all the world's coastal waters—are no better. Environmental surveys of the shores of the Mediterranean Sea show serious damage and pollution. Around Italy, the Mediterranean waters are cloudy with raw sewage and industrial waste, and some of the world's most beautiful beaches are fouled by garbage. The Bay of Guanabara, the grand entryway to Rio de Janeiro, Brazil, has been called a cesspool.

An international treaty to regulate ocean dumping of hazardous trash was drafted in 1972; another, the Ocean Dumping Ban to control marine disposal of wastes, was negotiated in 1988; and a "global program of action" for protection of the marine environment from land-based pollution was devised in 1995, but their effectiveness has yet to be demonstrated. In light of the length of the world's coastline, the number of countries sharing it, and the great growth of urban populations in the vicinity of the sea, serious doubt has been raised whether any international agreement can be fully effective or enforced. Many portents—from beach litter to massive fin- and shellfish kills—suggest that the oceans' troubled waters have reached the limit of the abuse they can absorb.

Whether the solution to solid waste disposal is sought by land, by fire, or by sea, humanity's rising tide of refuse threatens to overwhelm the environments that must deal with it. The problem is present, growing, and increasingly costly to manage. Solutions are still to be found, a constant reminder for the future of the threatening impact of the environments of culture upon those of nature.

Toxic Wastes

The problems of municipal and household solid-waste management are daunting; those of treatment and disposal of hazardous and toxic wastes seem overwhelming. The definitions of the terms are imprecise, and *hazardous* and *toxic* are frequently used interchangeably, as we shall do here. More strictly defined, **toxic waste** is a relatively limited concept, referring to materials that can cause death or serious injury to humans or animals. **Hazardous waste** is a broader term referring to all wastes, including toxic ones, that pose an immediate or long-term human health risk or that endanger the environment. About 23,000 substances are to

FIGURE 12.17 Warning signs and beaches littered with sewage, garbage, and medical debris are among the increasingly common and distressing evidences of ocean dumping of wastes.

---

[1] Any of several types of hydrocarbon compounds that are extremely toxic, persistent in the environment, and biologically magnified in the food chain. Dioxin is a frequently unavoidable trace contaminant in chemical processes and may also be formed during waste matter incineration or other combustion processes.

Geography and Public Policy

Waste Management in Toronto

Waste management (or garbage disposal) is a controversial issue in many communities, but has been a particularly intense issue in Toronto that has reached international dimensions. This reflects the fact that in 2004, 120 trucks a day left Toronto for Michigan. Over the year, these trucks left 1.25 million tonnes of garbage in Michigan. This level of activity is down from 2003 levels of 140 trucks a day. The origins of the story are complex but some highlights are provided below.

In the 1980s, Toronto used the Keele Valley dump as its major garbage site. While it was realized that it would not last forever, no other feasible sites were found. Potential sites in the Toronto region were resisted by local residents. Residents in Vaughn were also anxious to see the closure of the adjacent Keele Valley site. Mandatory recycling in the form of the "Blue Box" program saw plastics and bottles diverted, but the need for another garbage site was only modestly delayed. An exhaustive three-year environmental impact study was completed to review the desirability and feasibility of shipping garbage by rail to the Town of Kirkland Lake (population 10,000), located some 600 km north of Toronto. There, an abandoned open pit mine was believed adequate to accommodate Toronto's garbage. In 2000, Toronto Council confirmed this belief by voting to start shipping 1.3 million tonnes of garbage there for the period 2003–2023. However, the deal fell apart two months later due to concerns about who would be responsible for any cost overruns. One day later, Toronto announced that it had made arrangements to send its garbage to a 140-hectare (345-acre) landfill site called Carleton Farms, in Sumpter Township, Michigan, located immediately southwest of Detroit. Initially it was estimated that each day about 250 trucks would take Highway 401 from Toronto to Windsor and cross the border for the relatively short trip to Carleton Farms.

The garbage dilemma in general and the Carleton Farm decision specifically had mixed impacts. On the positive side, Toronto Council realized that it had to develop a more aggressive plan to divert waste from the garbage stream. It has established the goal of 60% diversion of residential garbage by 2006, and 100% by 2010. The fact that the number of trucks going to Michigan declined between 2003 and 2004 reflects some level of success. However, much work remains to be done by 2010 if the goal is to be met. On the other hand, there were many opponents to the Carleton Farm decision. There was resistance by mayors of communities along the 401 between Toronto and Windsor (Mitchell, 2004). For instance, the mayor of Cambridge indicated that, "This was irresponsible of Toronto Council. They gave no consideration to the communities dealing with the added traffic." In London, an official said, "We are scrambling to react. There was no consultation at all with the 401 communities at all. When the Adams Mine was an option, there were three years of consultations. There are environmental and transportation concerns. What environmental safeguards are there?" These concerns deal, in part, with the risk health of people.

Not all were opposed to the development. Sumpter Township, receives more than $3.4 million in royalties from the dump. This represents about 40% of the township's total revenues. However, other local residents are opposed to the importing of trash. They are concerned about the impacts that the burning and/or burying of wastes, including old computers, televisions, human sewage, and biomedical waste, pose to their health.

There have been attempts in Michigan to stop the import of garbage. In the 2003 campaign, Democratic U.S. presidential candidate John Kerry promised to close the U.S. border to Canadian waste. This will not be easily accomplished for at least two reasons. First, the waste-disposal industry is a multinational $10-billion per year activity in the United States. Second, under NAFTA it is not possible to close the border in this manner. NAFTA also makes it impossible to raise the disposal fee higher for imported versus domestic waste product. NAFTA guarantees equal treatment for all "goods," including garbage, which are covered by the treaty regardless of the country of origin.

On January 1, 2003, the decision was made to change the route in order that the trucks would avoid Windsor and use the 402 in Ontario and travel 90 miles along Interstate 94 in Michigan to Carleton Farms. Crossing into Port Huron adds eight miles to the 500-mile roundtrip, but it keeps trucks on highways and off residential streets in Windsor, where neighbours had complained, Wilson said. It also saves the company money: The Blue Water Bridge also calculates tolls by axle, rather than weight, so each truck pays $8.75 to enter the country rather than the $11 it costs to enter from the Ambassador Bridge. This has been resisted by some residents along Interstate 94 because of fears of increased accident levels and wear on their roads. In 2006, Toronto Council bought a landfill site outside London, Ontario, and will begin to use it rather than Michigan to handle its garbage.

Questions to Consider

1. Do you believe that a full environmental impact study, similar to the three-year study done on the Kirkland Lake site, should have been completed for the Carleton Farm site? Why or why not?

2. Should communities along the original and new route been consulted during the process? Why or why not?

3. Should the U.S. be able to charge Canadians a higher rate for disposing of their garbage than domestic garbage?

4. Should communities be forced to find local solutions to waste management problems? What if Toronto does not meet its 100% reduction limit; should it be allowed to use distant Canadian or American landfill sites to solve the problem?

Source: www.detnews.com/2003/metro/0301/14/a01-59739.htm; B. Mitchell (2004), "Incorporating Environmental Justice," *Resource and Environmental Management in Canada: Addressing Conflict and Uncertainty* (3rd. ed.). (Toronto: Oxford University Press), 555–578.

be categorized under the Canadian Environmental Protection Act for their potential for exposure to Canadians, or for their inherent toxicity and persistence or bioaccumulation. About 25 substances have been declared "toxic" under the Act. Forty-one substances have been identified under the Canada–Ontario Agreement respecting the Great Lakes Basin for virtual elimination.

Such wastes contaminate the environment in different ways and by different routes. Because most hazardous debris is disposed of by dumping or burial on land, groundwater is most at risk of contamination. In all, some 2% of North America's groundwater supply could have hazardous waste contamination. No comparable world figures exist, but in all industrial countries at least some drinking water contamination from highly toxic solvents, hydrocarbons, pesticides, trace metals, and polychlorinated biphenyls (PCBs) has been detected. Toxic waste impoundments are also a source of air pollutants through the evaporation of volatile organic compounds. Finally, careless or deliberate distribution of toxic materials outside of confinement areas can cause unexpected, but deadly, hazards. Although methods of disposal other than containment techniques have been developed—including incineration, infrared heating, and bacterial decomposition—none is fully satisfactory and none is as yet in wide use. A higher level of concern is associated with the release of toxic chemicals, which are a by-product of our industrial and manufacturing sector (Figure 12.18). Space perception studies reveal a small but measurable adverse assessment by people of places deemed "dangerous," no matter what the probability of the hazard occurring.

Canada's only integrated hazardous waste facility is located in Swan Hills, Alberta (Figure 12.19). Constructed in 1987, a plebiscite was held to determine if the community wanted the facility located there. It treats a variety of hazardous wastes, including PCBs, dioxins/furans, and ozone depleting substances (ODS), from across North America. Exceptions include pathological, explosive, mercury, and radioactive wastes.

Radioactive Wastes

Every facility that either uses or produces radioactive materials generates at least *low-level waste*, material whose radioactivity will decay to safe levels in 100 years or less. Nuclear power plants produce about half the total low-level waste in the form of used resins, filter sludges, lubricating oils, and detergent wastes. Industries that manufacture radiopharmaceuticals, smoke alarms, and other consumer goods produce such wastes in the form of machinery parts, plastics, and organic solvents. Research establishments, universities, and hospitals also produce radioactive waste materials.

High-level waste can remain radioactive for 10,000 years and more; plutonium stays dangerously radioactive for 240,000 years. It consists primarily of spent fuel assemblies of nuclear power-reactors—termed "civilian waste"—and such "military waste" as the by-products of nuclear weapons manufacture. The volume of civilian waste alone is not only great but increasing rapidly, because approximately one-third of a reactor's rods need to be disposed of every year.

By 2002, there were over 1.7 million spent fuel rods being "temporarily" stored in Canada. "Spent fuel" is a misleading term: the assemblies are removed from commercial reactors not because their radiation is spent, but because they have become too radioactive for further use. The assemblies will remain radioactively "hot" for thousands of years.

Unfortunately, no satisfactory method for disposing of any hazardous waste has yet been devised. Although sealing liquids with a radioactive life measured in the thousands of years within steel drums expected to last no more than 40 years seems an unlikely solution to the disposal problem, it is one that has been widely practiced. Some wastes have been sealed in protective tanks and dumped at sea, a practice that has now been banned worldwide. Several of these storage areas have experienced leakages, with seepage of waste into the surrounding soil and groundwater.

Because low-level waste is generated by so many sources, its disposal is particularly difficult to control. Evidence indicates that much of it has been placed in landfills, often the local municipal dump, where the waste chemicals may leach through the soil and into the groundwater.

An even less constructive response, according to increasing complaints, has been the export of radioactive materials—in common with other hazardous wastes—to willing or unwitting recipient countries with less restrictive or costly controls and its illegal and unrecorded dumping at sea—now banned by the legally binding London Convention of 1993.

Exporting Waste

Regulations, community resistance, and steeply rising costs of disposal of hazardous wastes in the developed countries encouraged producers of those unwanted commodities to seek alternate areas for their disposition. Transboundary shipments of dangerous wastes became an increasingly attractive option for producers. In total, such cross-border movement amounted to tens of thousands of shipments annually by the early 1990s, with destinations including debt-ridden Eastern European countries and impoverished developing ones outside of Europe that were willing to trade a hole in the ground for hard currency. It was a trade, however, that increasingly aroused the ire and resistance of destination countries and, ultimately, elicited international agreements among both generating and receiving countries to cease the practice.

The Organization of African Unity in 1988 adopted a resolution condemning the dumping of all foreign wastes on that continent. More broadly and under the sponsorship of the United Nations, 117 countries in March of 1989 adopted a treaty—the Basel Convention on the Control of Transboundary Movements of Hazardous Wastes and Their Disposal—aimed at regulating the international trade in wastes. That regulation was to be achieved by requiring exporters to obtain consent from receiving countries before shipping waste, and by requiring both exporter and importer countries to ensure that the waste would be disposed of in an environmentally sound manner.

A still more restrictive convention was reached in March, 1994, when—with the United States dissenting—most Western industrialized countries agreed to ban the export of all poisonous

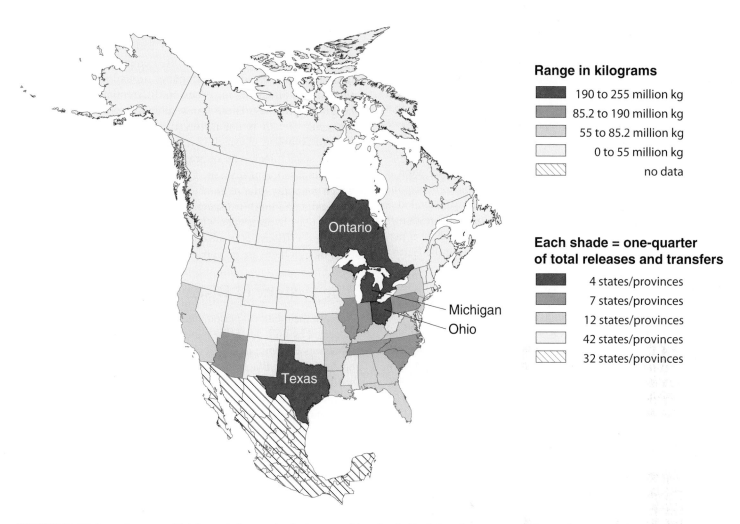

Range in kilograms

- 190 to 255 million kg
- 85.2 to 190 million kg
- 55 to 85.2 million kg
- 0 to 55 million kg
- no data

Each shade = one-quarter of total releases and transfers

- 4 states/provinces
- 7 states/provinces
- 12 states/provinces
- 42 states/provinces
- 32 states/provinces

Ontario

Michigan
Ohio

Texas

FIGURE 12.18 Largest sources of total reported amounts of releases and transfers in North America, 2002. According to the Commission on Environmental Cooperation, which was established under NAFTA, North Americans are concerned about the effects of chemicals on their health and environment. It annually publishes information documenting the extent and nature of pollutant releases throughout North America. In 2002, 3.25 million tonnes of toxic chemicals were released and transferred in North America. Texas, Ohio, Ontario, and Michigan accounted for over 25% of total releases and transfers.

FIGURE 12.19 The Swan Hills treatment facility. Located on 129 hectares (320 acres) of land, the site can store 700 cubic metres of bulk solids, 1,000,000 litres of bulk liquids and 17,000 drums.

or hazardous industrial wastes and residues to the developing world, the countries of Eastern Europe, and the former Soviet Union. United States' objections concerned the assumed prohibition on export of such materials as scrap metals for recycling within consenting receiving countries. Despite the agreement, a UN committee in 1998 identified the United States, Germany, Australia, Britain, and the Netherlands as continuing major toxic waste exporters, and even in 2005 an estimated 50% to 80% of e-waste collected in the United States for recycling is exported to areas such as China, India, and Pakistan. Investigating toxic wastes dumping as a violation of basic human rights, the UN committee reported that Africa still receives masses of developed country toxic waste in spite of its 1988 resolution. The bulk of European waste goes to the Baltic countries and to Eastern and Central Europe. Half of the United States' exports go to Latin America, and those of Britain go largely to Asia.

Measuring Human Consumption

Humans have been perhaps the most successful species in the history of the Earth. Chapter 4 indicated that between 1800 and 2000, our population increased from 1 billion to over 6 billion people. Our levels of consumption have also increased over that time, and in many ways, have outpaced our increase in numbers. As noted in Chapter 4, some people are concerned that we may reach a crash as a result of our numbers and consumption (e.g., Malthus). One way of measuring this consumption is through the "Ecological Footprint." It allows people to realize the impact of their lifestyle on ecosystems. It measures the total area of land and water (ecosystems) needed to provide all the resources consumed and to assimilate all the wastes discharged by a person or community. Collectively, we are overshooting the Earth's ecological capacity by about 20%. North Americans have the highest footprint in the world (Figure 12.20). Western Europeans, who have a reasonably comparable lifestyle to our own, use about 40% less in resources. Figure 12.20 also raises questions concerning the equitable distribution of resources at the present. You can calculate your own footprint at http://ecofoot.org/. How does your footprint compare to the average Canadian footprint of 8.6 hectares? Do you think it is too high, and if so on what basis do you believe this and what might you do to reduce it?

Environment and Health

A distinction is sometime made between medical and health geography. Health geography studies the effects of location and climate upon health in order to improve our understanding of various factors that affect the health of people and societies. Medical geographers often employ quantitative methodologies and focus on the incidence of disease. Health geographers address the spatial aspects of health care (i.e., health care planning, the provision and uptake of health care services). They will focus attention on illnesses and often employ qualitative methodologies. The precision of language around the terms health, illness, and disease is important in differentiating medical and health geographies. These terms, although related, are not synonymous. Health is not merely the absence of disease, but a state of complete physical, psychological and social well-being (WHO, 1947). However, in practice, health tends to be referred to as an absence of disease. There are many types of diseases, which generally refer to an objective "malfunction" (i.e., adverse physical condition) irrespective of whether the person feels unwell (e.g., hypertension—high blood pressure) (see "Types of Diseases"). Illness is a subjective feeling of unwell ("disease") even though there are no apparent symptoms.

The History of Disease

Up until the medieval period, human population growth was characterized by high death rates, low life expectancy (see Chapter 4), numerous endemic diseases, and frequent and often devastating epidemics. The Black Plague that ravaged Europe from 1348 to 1350 reduced the population by between 33% and 50%. It resulted in possibly the only set-back in the world's otherwise continuous population growth. As outlined in Chapter 4, population increased in the 18th century, although it is not clear whether the increase was due to an increase in the birth rate or a decline in the death rate, or both. Health and life expectancy probably improved. Over the 18th and 19th centuries, mortality "spikes" caused by epidemics and famine became less frequent.

During the early stages of the Industrial Revolution, it was diseases such as cholera, small pox, typhoid, typhus, and tuberculosis, not old age, that caused most deaths. Indeed, the life expectancy was much less than we are used to in the developed

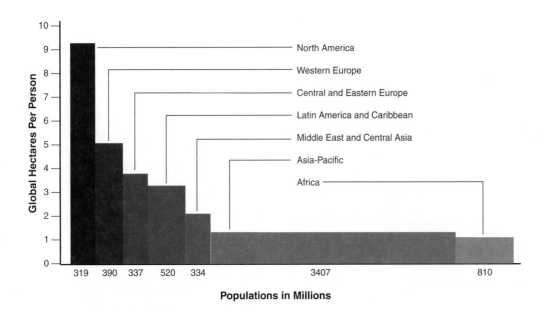

FIGURE 12.20 Ecological footprints around the world.

Types of Diseases

There are many ways of categorizing disease types (e.g., location on the body, and if and how it is transmitted). Meade and Earickson offer the following thoughts on disease types:

Acute: Symptoms are severe and the time duration is relatively short.

Chronic: Diseases present and that recurring over a long time.

Congenital: Diseases present at birth, e.g., a child born to a mother who has consumed excessive alcohol or drugs during pregnancy. May also be genetic in origin.

Contagion: The transmission of infectious disease agents between people, may be direct through person-to-person contact or indirect through the bites of insect vectors or pathways such as water, blankets, or money.

Degenerative: Diseases characterized by the deterioration or impairment of an organ or cell structure of cells or tissues of which they are a part. These are thought to be non-transmissible or non-communicable (e.g., the aging process).

Infectious: Diseases resulting from activities of living creatures, usually bacteria or viruses that invade the body. These diseases can be transmitted from person to person, or between species (e.g., avian flu), although transmission may be genetic. Also referred to as communicable, contagious, or transmissible (e.g., common cold, measles).

world because there was a lack of hygiene, little knowledge of sanitary care, little knowledge about the causes of diseases, and no effective treatments for them. At this time, diseases such as cholera, typhoid, and typhus devastated many communities. As cities became more populated, health problems became worse. At this time, cholera, which is caused by contaminated drinking water, was perhaps the most feared disease. Several major outbreaks occurred in Britain—1831–32, 1848–49, 1854, and 1867. In the 1849 outbreak, 15,000 Londoners died from cholera and another 30,000 Londoners became sick from it. The culprit proved to be sewage that was discharged near drinking water sources. As more people moved into cities and cities increasingly relied on surface waters for a secure supply, and these same surface waters were used to dispose of sewage, cholera spread easily. Air provided another pathway for the spread other infectious diseases such as tuberculosis and measles.

Like cholera, these diseases thrived in overcrowded urban areas. Since people often earned very low wages, many people could not afford a proper diet, which compromised their immune system. Although the rich did not escape having these diseases, it was the poor who were particularly vulnerable to disease. Even though there was a vaccine for small pox, many people, particularly the poor, were not aware of it and/or unable to afford it, and many people favoured traditional treatments. Tuberculosis, which is a degenerative lung disease, was the greatest killer to urban dwellers. In overcrowded dwellings, the disease was spread easily among people. The research suggests that tuberculosis accounted for up to one-third of all deaths in Britain between 1800 and 1850. At the time, doctors thought bad smells and gases caused these outbreaks. This view was justified because many industrial cities suffered from the bad smells emanating from raw sewage in water, garbage, and industrial pollutants. These problems were particularly evident in poorer neighbourhoods. However, these smells were only the symptom, not the problem.

A traditional approach to the practice of medical geography at this time (and still a popular and useful one) was to map the incidence of morbidity (illnesses and complications from a disease) and mortality (death). Often the spatial distribution of morbidity and mortality can be associated with natural and/or human factor(s) (see "John Snow's Map"). Mapping can also be done over time sequence in order to examine how a disease diffuses through the population. Until the 19th century, the practice of medicine in Europe and North America pertained to the study of the geographic variations in the physical (e.g., air, water, soil) and human environments (diet, clothing, house type). The difficult task for medical geographers is to explain the spatial patterns (i.e., clusters, dispersions) that are found on a map. This often requires further research and the participation of medical researchers, such as epidemiologists. Morbidity and mortality data can be obtained from hospitals, health care centres, and death records. This will be quantitative in nature and support what we have called health geography. Qualitative data to support current health geography research are often obtained from survey and interview data.

As our understanding of the causes of infectious disease increased, we began to treat the problem rather than the symptom. The provision of drinking water treatment, sewage treatment, and the increase use of vaccines resulted in increased life expectancies. Decreases in the poverty rate allowed more people to afford a proper diet. Thus, by the late 19th century, the relative importance of infectious diseases (e.g., cholera) to degenerative ones (e.g., heart disease, stroke) in causing sickness and death declined. We have responded in a number of ways to the impacts that human use of the environment has had on human health.

The 20th century has been characterized by the continued decline in the importance of infectious diseases as a cause of death, and an increase in life expectancy. This trend reflects several factors including:

One of the first uses of a map to show the pattern of disease was the dot map shown here, drawn by Dr. John Snow. In 1854, nearly 600 people from the Soho District, London England, died from cholera in a 10-day period. With no known cure, people feared for their lives because they believed that vapours from corpses that were buried in the cemetery upon which their homes were built were responsible for their sickness. (Nearly a century earlier, a pandemic had killed many people who were buried in the area.) Dr. John Snow, a London physician and anaesthesiologist, knew the only way to control the disease was to contain its source. He mapped two variables. First, he showed the homes of the people who had died. Second, he mapped the location of water pumps. The map showed that most people died in the vicinity of the Broad Street pump and not in the vicinity of the cemetery. Snow concluded that the water from the pump was the cause of the problem, and asked the water authorities to remove the handle from the pump. Shortly afterwards, the number of cholera victims declined dramatically. Snow's work is perhaps the most famous illustration of the power of geography and maps as an approach and tool to better understand diseases. Today, medical geographers continue to play an active role in studying the diffusion a wide range of diseases such as AIDS, cancer, and SARS.

- Improved medical treatment—The late 19th and early 20th century saw the refinement of the current practice of medicine to treat infectious diseases. Immunization for tuberculosis and polio became common practice, often supported by national government programs, which made them accessible to the entire population.
- Reduced exposure to infections—Improved housing stock and lower housing densities combined with the reduction of airborne and water-based pollutants saw people exposed to less concentrated pollutants. Water and sewage treatment technologies were developed and installed in most urban communities, often with government support.
- Improved diets and hygiene meant that people were healthier and better able to resist disease.

Degenerative, non-infectious diseases, such as heart disease, cancers, and respiratory diseases are now the primary causes of death in the developed world. For much of the late 20th century, there was little fear of widespread epidemics in the developed world. That has changed with the outbreak of AIDS, SARS, and the threat of a "pandemic" that has prompted the banking of large quantities of vaccines by nations such as Canada and the United States.

The situation in developing countries is very different from Canada. In fact, in many ways, the characterization of diseases there resembles the European experience during the Industrial period. Relative to Canada and other developed world countries, developing nations lack a high level of medical services and water treatment. The prevalence of absolute poverty in these countries contributes to poor health in many ways: (1) people cannot afford a proper diet; (2) funding is unavailable for medicines and water/sewage treatment; and (3) cities are often overcrowded due to high migration levels from rural areas. Solving the poverty problem is key to promoting development and health for the people of developing nations (Chapter 11).

Mapping and Determining the Environment–Health Link

The first portion of this chapter described selected human impacts of the environment. The following text describes how the natural environment and human impacts on it can influence human health. A variety of natural and human factors can influence people's health. These include climate, weather, and air pollution. Climate change can also have impacts on human health.

The human response to climate and weather as viewed from the perspective of "comfort" depends on temperature, as well as humidity and wind. Physiologically, humans will respond to changes in temperature, humidity, wind, solar radiation, and air pollution. In most of the world, people live comfortably in the temperature range of 17° C–31° C. Excessive heat and humidity will cause people to sweat. Exposure to more extreme temperatures may lead to heat stroke or frostbite. Seasonal variations in weather and mortality rates are significant in many countries. Since most developed countries are located in the mid-latitudes, they tend to have a winter peak. The tropically located developing countries often have a summer mortality peak due to the more rapid spread of infectious diseases.

Research has concluded that El Niño is linked to epidemics of certain diseases, such as malaria, Rift Valley Fever, and viral and other insect-borne diseases, which are more prevalent after heavy rains. Following the heavy rainfall caused by the 1997/1998 El Niño in north-eastern Kenya and southern Somalia, the associated outbreak of Rift Valley Fever, which had been effectively eradicated, killed large numbers of cattle, and even spread to humans. Future research might reduce these mortality peaks. For instance, if we could better predict the occurrence of El Niño, we might be able to establish a malaria warning and response system that would reduce the impact of this and other mosquito-transmitted disease.

At a local scale, urban populations are typically more vulnerable to changes in weather than their rural counterparts. Daily weather as well as the regular cycle of the seasons are known to be related to a number of diseases (Table 12.2). Geographers are well placed to consider these types of associations.

Historically, the main air pollutants of interest were smoke from factories and wood/coal heated households, and sulphur dioxide (SO_2). These continue to be problematic in many major urban areas. One of the worst smog episodes occurred in London, England in February 1952, due to a combination of natural and human factors. During a particular cold snap, homeowners stoked their coal-fired furnaces and smoke bellowed from the chimneys. The winds were calm, and the air near the ground was moist. These conditions were ideal for the formation of radiation fog for a five-day period. Visibility within central London was reduced to below 50 metres (170 feet), and below 10 metres (32 feet) at Heathrow Airport for two days. Road, rail, and air transport were brought to a standstill. Plays and concerts at theatres were cancelled when fog in the auditorium made conditions unbearable. Sadly, over 12,000 people were believed to have died and thousands of others became ill as a result of the smog. Most people died from pneumonia, bronchitis, tuberculosis, and heart failure. Eventually, winds picked up and the smog was dispersed. This event highlighted the need to clean up the air.

Earlier in this chapter a range of air pollution problems were noted. Many of these contribute to poor health. The exhaust fumes from motor vehicles emit several pollutants. Carbon monoxide interferes with the transfer of oxygen in the blood. Lead, which was found in gasoline in Canada up to the late 1970s and is still used in many other countries, can contribute to brain damage in children. At high enough concentrations, some nitrous oxides (NO and NO_2) can cause respiratory problems for some people. Volatile organic compounds (VOCs) combine in the presence of ultraviolet light (UV) to produce secondary pollutants such as low level ozone (O_3), and contribute to the formation of smog. Small air-borne particulates have been associated with heart attacks, respiratory diseases, and asthma.

Climate change is likely to affect the health of future human populations. Some potential impacts of climate change on health are well understood. For example, we know that certain insects play a vital role in transmitting malaria, sleeping sickness, and river blindness to people. Since climate can play a dominant role in determining the distribution and abundance of these insects, climate change could have an effect on the geographical range of many of these insects. As a result of a warmer climate, for example, the southern United States, Canada, and parts of Europe could be threatened with malaria. Geographic information systems allow us to establish potential habitat and the survival rate of insects, and identify potential human populations at risk. A report on climate change impacts in Canada indicates that communities in northern Canada would face additional health-related issues due to the impacts of climate change on the distribution and characteristics of permafrost, sea ice, and snow cover. In fact, it suggests that these impacts are already being experienced by northern communities. Some key concerns include the consequences of these changes on travel safety, ability to hunt traditional food, access to clean drinking water, and fish contamination.

Since there will be impacts on our ability to grow food and provide water, climate change can have a profound indirect influence on human health. A warmer world is expected to produce more severe flooding in some places and more severe droughts in others. Flooding, which is already a major problem in Canada and other parts of the world, can lead to increased contamination of water by human and animal waste and agricultural chemicals.

The Perception and Management of Hazards

How humans respond to hazards was initially applied to local floods. Now geographers investigate a wide range of hazards—droughts, hail, tornadoes, hurricanes, earthquakes, climate change, pesticide use, and smog. Distinction is made between chronic low-level hazards (health affecting mineral content of drinking water, for example) and high-consequence/low-probability events

TABLE 12.2
The Effects of Weather on Certain Diseases

Disease	Short Periodical Effects	Long Periodical Effects
Tuberculosis	More problematic in warm and humid weather, cold and foggy weather, and sudden heat waves	High sensitivity in winter, low in autumn
Asthma	Increases with sudden cooling, lowest during periods of high pressure	Low in winter, highest in late summer
Bronchitis	Worst during fog	High in winter, low in summer
Skin cancer	Increases with exposure to sun	
Rheumatic diseases	Associated with strong cooling	More common in autumn and early winter
Heart diseases	More frequent after strong cooling	Highest in January and February
Cold	Sudden changes in weather	Maximum in February and March
Influenza	Relative humidity <50%, low wind speeds	Maximum December to February

Source: Howe, 1972.

such as hurricanes, floods, earthquakes, and landslides. Remedial low-level hazards do not appear to create negative space perceptions. Distinction must also be made between natural hazards, which have been of long-standing interest to geographers (e.g., floods, tornadoes, frost, earthquakes) and technological hazards (e.g., pesticides, toxic chemicals).

Mental images of home areas do not generally include as an overriding concern an acknowledgment of potential dangers. On July 31, 1987, a devastating tornado struck Edmonton, Alberta killing 27 people, hospitalizing 53, injuring 250 other people, and destroying 133 homes (Figure 12.21). In the summer of 2003, tens of thousands of people living in British Columbia had to evacuate their homes to avoid forest fires that were burning near residential areas. Unfortunately, 2003 was one of many "bad fire years" over the past 20 years; others being 1985, 1990, and 1998. More recently, an earthquake in the Indian Ocean on December 26, 2004, triggered a series of tsunamis that spread throughout the Indian Ocean killing about 187,000 people, and displacing over 1.1 million people who lived in coastal areas (Figure 12.22). Over $7 billion was provided in humanitarian relief. Violent storms have struck the coasts of the United States, with the recent events in New Orleans being the most prominent. The human response to these types of major events often sees people decide to remain or return to these hazardous areas. Violent storms strike the Gulf

FIGURE 12.21 Tornado damage.

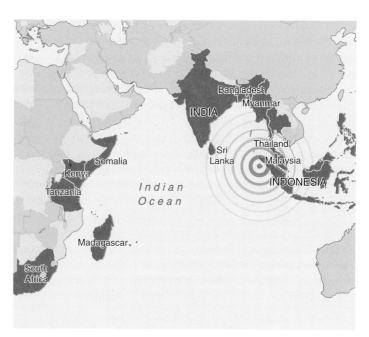

FIGURE 12.22 The 2004 Indian Ocean tsunami.

and East coasts of the United States, and people remain or return. Californians may be concerned about Kansas tornadoes if contemplating a move there but be unconcerned about earthquake dangers at home.

Why do people choose to settle in areas of high-consequence hazards in spite of the potential threat to their lives and property? Why do hundreds of thousands of people live along the San Andreas Fault in California, build houses in Pacific coastal areas known to experience severe erosion during storms, return to flood-prone river valleys in Europe or Asia, or avalanche-threatened Andean valleys? What is it that makes the risk worth taking? Ignorance of natural hazard danger is not necessarily a consideration. People in seismically active regions of Canada, the United States, and Europe, at least, do believe that damaging earthquakes are a possibility in their districts but, research indicates, are often reluctant to reduce the risk (Figure 12.23). Similar awareness and reticence accompanies other low-incidence/high-consequence natural dangers. Not many people move long distances to avoid natural hazards.

There are many reasons why natural-hazard risk does not deter settlement or adversely affect space–behavioural decisions. Of importance, of course, is the persistent belief that the likelihood of an earthquake or a flood or other natural calamity is sufficiently remote so that it is not reasonable or pressing to modify behaviour because of it. People are influenced by their innate optimism and the predictive uncertainty about timing or severity of a calamitous event and by their past experiences in high-hazard areas. If they have not suffered much damage in the past, they may be optimistic about the future. If, on the other hand, past damage has been great, they may think that the probability of repetition in the future is low (Table 12.3).

Perception of place as attractive or desirable may be quite divorced from any understanding of its hazard potential. Attachment to locale or region may be an expression of emotion and economic or cultural attraction, not just a rational assessment of risk. Indeed, high-hazard areas are often sought out because they possess desirable topography or scenic views, as do, for instance, coastal areas subject to storm damage. Once people have purchased property in a known hazard area, they may be unable to sell it for a reasonable price even if they so desire. They think that they have no choice but to remain and protect their investment. The cultural hazard—loss of livelihood and investment—appears more serious than whatever natural hazards there may be.

Carried further, it has been observed that spatial adjustment to perceived natural hazards is a luxury not affordable to impoverished people in general or to the urban and rural poor of developing countries in particular. Forced by population growth and economic necessity to exert ever-greater pressures upon fragile environments or to occupy at higher densities hazardous hillside and floodplain slums, their margin of safety in the face of both chronic and low-probability hazards is minimal to non-existent (Figure 12.24).

FIGURE 12.23 Destruction from the San Francisco earthquake and fire. The first shock struck San Francisco early on the morning of April 18, 1906, damaging the city's water system. Fire broke out and raged for three days. It was finally stopped by dynamiting buildings in its path. When it was over, some 700 people were dead or missing, and 25,000 buildings had been destroyed. Locally, the event is usually referred to as the Great Fire of 1906, suggesting a denial of the natural hazard in favour of assigning blame to correctable human error. Post-destruction reconstruction began at once. Rebuilding following earthquake damage is the rule, though the immediate return of population to northern Italian areas after a major quake in 1976 was followed by an abrupt longer-term exodus after a subsequent, much weaker shock.

TABLE 12.3
Common Responses to the Uncertainty of Natural Hazards

ELIMINATE THE HAZARD

Deny or Denigrate Its Existence	Deny or Denigrate Its Recurrence
"We have no floods here, only high water."	"Lightning never strikes twice in the same place."
"It can't happen here."	"It's a freak of nature."

ELIMINATE THE UNCERTAINTY

Make It Determinate and Knowable	Transfer Uncertainty to a Higher Power
"Seven years of great plenty. . . . After them seven years of famine."	"It's in the hands of God."
"Floods come every five years."	"The government is taking care of it."

Source: Barton and Kates, "The Perception of Natural Hazards in Resource Management," 3 *Natural Resources Journal* 435 (1964).

FIGURE 12.24 Many of the poor of Rio de Janeiro, Brazil, occupy steep hillside locations above the reach of sewer, water, and power lines that hold the more affluent at lower elevations. Frequent heavy rains cause mudflows from the saturated hillsides that wipe away the shacks and shelters that insecurely cling to them, and deposit the homes and hopes of the poor in richer neighbourhoods below.

Prospects and Perspectives

Not surprisingly, the realities of the human impacts upon the environment that we have looked at in this chapter bring us directly back to ideas first presented in Chapter 5, at the start of our examination of the meaning of culture and the development of human geographic patterns on the surface of the earth. We noted there and see more clearly now that humans, in their increasing numbers and technical sophistication, have been able since the end of the last glaciation to alter for their own needs the physical landscapes they occupy. Humans, it is often observed, are the ecological dominant in the human–environmental equation that is the continuing focus of geographic inquiry.

That dominance reflected itself in the growing divergence of human societies as they separated themselves from common hunting-gathering origins. In creating their differing cultural solutions to common concerns of sustenance and growth, societies altered the environments they occupied. Diverse systems of exploitation of the environment were developed in and diffused from distinctive culture hearths. They were modified by the ever-expanding numbers of people occupying earth areas of differing carrying capacities and available resources. Gradually developing patterns of spatial interaction and exchange did not halt the creation of areally distinctive subsystems of culture or assure common methods of utilization of unequally distributed earth resources or environments. Sharp contrasts in levels of economic development and well-being emerged and persisted even as cultural convergence through shared technology began increasingly to unite societies throughout the world.

Each culture separately placed its imprint on the environment it occupied. In many cases—Easter Island as our earlier example—that imprint was ultimately destructive of the resources and environments upon which the cultures developed and depended. For human society collectively or single cultures separately, environmental damage or destruction is the unplanned consequence of the ecological dominance of humans. Our perpetual dilemma lies in the reality that what we need and want in support and supply from the environments we occupy generally exceeds in form and degree what they are able to yield in an unaltered state. To satisfy their felt needs, humans have learned to manipulate their environment. The greater those needs and the larger the populations with both needs and technical skills to satisfy them, the greater is the manipulation of the natural landscape. For as long as humans have occupied the earth the implicit but seldom addressed question has not been should we exploit and alter the environment, but how can we extract our requirements from the natural endowment without dissipating and destroying the basis of our support?

This final chapter detailing a few of the damaging pressures placed upon the environment by today's economies and cultures is not meant as a litany of despair. Rather it is a reminder of the potentially destructive ecological dominance of humans. Against the background of our now fuller understanding of human geographic patterns and interactions, this chapter is also meant to remind us yet again of the often repeated truism that everything is connected to everything else; we can never do just *one* thing. The ecological crises defined in this chapter and the human geographic patterns of interaction, contrast, and—occasionally—conflict observed in the preceding chapters show clearly and repeatedly how close and complex are the connections within the cultural world and how intimately our created environment is joined to the physical landscape we all share.

There is growing awareness of those connections, of the adverse human impacts upon the natural world, and of the unity of all cultural and physical landscapes. Climatic change, air and water pollution, soil loss and desertification, refuse contamination, and a host of other environmental consequences and problems of intensifying human use of the earth are all matters of contemporary public debate and consideration. Awareness and concern of individuals are increasingly reflected by policies of environmental protection introduced by governments and supported or enforced by international conferences, compacts, and treaties. Acceptance of the interconnectedness and indivisibility of cultural and natural environments—the human creation and the physical endowment—is now more the rule than the exception. By looking at both the mistakes we have made and the opportunities to fix these as well as avoid future problems, is one way we can strive to understand our world and our place in it. This approach requires us to understand both biophysical processes and human interactions with these processes. Geographers are well-suited to meet this challenge.

Our understanding of those relationships is advanced by what we have learned of the human side of the human–environmental structure. We have seen that the seemingly infinitely complex diversity of human societies, economies, and inter-relations is in fact logical, explicable, and far from random or arbitrary. We now have developed both a mental map of the cultural patterns and content of areas and an appreciation of the dynamics of their creation and operation. We must have that human geographic background—that sense of spatial interaction and unity of cultural, economic, and political patterns—to understand fully the relationship between our cultural world and the physical environment on which it ultimately depends. Only with that degree of human geographic awareness can we individually participate in an informed way in preserving and improving the increasingly difficult and delicate balance between the endowment of nature and our landscapes of culture.

Want to Learn More?

Anyone interested in the geography of disease will need a good understanding of the basics of epidemiology, or at least of health statistics. The World Health Organization website is a good starting place. The WHO collects mortality and morbidity data from member countries, allowing international and inter-regional comparisons of health and disease. They publish the annual World Health Report, the Weekly Epidemiological Record, WHO Statistical Information System (WHOSIS), and a wealth of other useful publications. The Non-communicable Disease Division of WHO describes the global epidemiology of diseases such as cardiovascular diseases.

Data on the global epidemiology of cancer can be found at CANCER*Mondial*, a website of the International Agency for Research on Cancer (IARC), part of the WHO. The Atlas of Cancer Mortality in the United States (1950–1994) of the U.S. National Cancer Institute is another excellent site worth visiting. Projects are currently being developed to use this exciting resource as a catalyst for research in cancer aetiology and control.

A Canadian view on climate change can be found at www.ec.gc.ca/climate/home-e.html. The full report entitled *Climate Change Impacts and Adaptation: A Canadian Perspective* can be found at http://adaptation.nrcan.gc.ca/perspective/toc_e.asp. One section deals with health impacts.

An interactive map on flooding in Canada can be found at Natural Resources Canada's website: http://sts.gsc.nrcan.gc.ca/clf/geoserv_floods.asp and more general information at http://nher.nrcan.gc.ca/k02_supplement_e.php.

Information on A Range of Environmental Issues

United Nations Environment Program
www.unep.org/

Environment Canada
www.ec.gc.ca/envhome.html

Climate Change Summits
http://climate2005.greenpeace.ca/primer

Stockholm International Water Institute
www.siwi.org/

Convention on Long-Range Transboundary Air Pollution
www.unece.org/env/lrtap/

Tropical Deforestation
http://earthobservatory.nasa.gov/Library/Deforestation/

Soil Erosion
www.omafra.gov.on.ca/english/engineer/facts/87-040.htm

Waste Management
www.ec.gc.ca/wastes_e.html

Environment and Health
www.canadian-health-network.ca/servlet/ContentServer?cid=1047656077684&pagename=CHN-RCS%2FPage%2FGTPageTemplate&c=Page&lang=En

Summary

Cultural landscapes may buffer but cannot isolate societies from the physical environments they occupy. All human activities, from the simplest forms of agriculture to modern industry, have an impact upon the biosphere. Cumulatively, in both developed and developing countries, that impact is now evident in the form of serious and threatening environmental deterioration. The atmosphere unites us all, and its global problems of greenhouse heating, ozone depletion, and particulate pollution endanger us all. Desertification, soil erosion, and tropical deforestation may appear to be local or regional problems, but they have worldwide implications of both environmental degradation and reduced population-supporting capacity. Fresh water supplies are deteriorating in quality and decreasing in

sufficiency through contamination and competition. Finally, the inevitable end product of human use of the earth—the garbage and hazardous wastes of civilization—are beginning to overwhelm both sites and technologies of disposal. In some cases, we ignore these and other human-generated problems at the risk of our health.

We do not end our study of human geography on a note of despondency, however. We end with the conviction that the fuller knowledge we now have of the spatial patterns and structures of human cultural, economic, and political activities will aid in our understanding of the myriad ways in which human societies are bound to the physical landscapes they occupy—and which they have so substantially modified.

KEY WORDS

acid rain   421
aquifer   428
Bali Road Map   419
ecosystem   415
environment   413

environmental pollution   432
fallowing   425
greenhouse effect   415
hazardous waste   436
hydrologic cycle   427

limiting factor
    principle   430
long-range transboundary air
    pollution (LRTAP)   420
rotation   425

soil   424
soil erosion   424
terracing   425
toxic waste   436

FOR REVIEW

1. What lines of reasoning and evidence suggest that human activity is altering global climates? What kind of alteration has occurred or is expected to occur?

2. What is *desertification*? What types of areas are particularly susceptible to desertification? What kinds of land uses are associated with it? How easily can its effects be overcome or reversed?

3. What agricultural techniques have been traditionally employed to reduce or halt soil erosion? Since these are known techniques that have been practised throughout the world, why is there a current problem of soil erosion anywhere?

4. What effects has the increasing use of fossil fuels over the past 200 years had on the environment? What is *acid rain*, and where is it a problem? What factors affect the type and degree of air pollution found at a place? What is the relationship of *ozone* to *photochemical smog*?

5. Describe the chief sources of water pollution of which you are aware. How has the supply of fresh water been affected by pollution and human use? When water is used, is it forever lost to the environment? If so, where does it go? If not, why should there be water

shortages now in regions of formerly ample supply?

6. What methods do communities use to dispose of solid waste? Can *hazardous wastes* be treated in the same fashion? Since disposition of waste is a technical problem, why should there be any concern with waste disposal in modern advanced economies?

7. Suggest ways in which your study of human geography has increased your understanding of the relationship between the environments of culture and those of nature.

FOCUS FOLLOW-UP

1. **What human actions have contributed to tropical deforestation, desertification, and soil erosion? What are the consequences?** pp. 415–427.

   Current rapid destruction of tropical forests reflects human intentions to expand farming and grazing areas and harvest tropical wood. Their depletion endangers or destroys the world's richest, most diversified plant and animal biome, and adversely affects local, regional, and world patterns of temperature and rainfall. Their loss also diminishes a vital "carbon sink" needed to absorb excess carbon dioxide. Desertification—the expansion of areas of destroyed soil and plant cover in dry climates—results from both natural climatic fluctuations and human pressures from ploughing, woody plant removal, or livestock overgrazing. Those same human actions and pressures can accelerate the normal erosional loss of soil beyond natural soil regeneration potential. Such loss reduces total and per capita area of food production, diminishing the human carrying capacity of the land.

2. **How are emerging water supply and waste disposal problems related to human numbers and impacts?** pp. 427–433.

   The hydrologic cycle assures water will be continuously regenerated for further use. But growing demand for irrigation, industrial use, and individual and urban consumption means increasing lack of balance between natural water supplies and consumption demands. Pollution of those supplies by human actions further reduces water availability and utility.

3. **How are modern societies addressing the problems of solid and toxic waste disposal?** pp. 433–440.

   Increasingly, all societies are becoming more dependent on modern manufacturing and packaging of industrial, commercial, and personal consumption items. The easy recycling of waste materials found in subsistence cultures is no longer possible, and humans are presented with increasing needs for sites and facilities to safely dispose of solid wastes. Sanitary landfills and incineration are employed to handle nontoxic wastes. The former demands scarce and expensive land near cities or costly export to distant locations; the latter is often opposed because of unsafe emissions and ash residue. Disposal of toxic and hazardous wastes including nuclear wastes, products of modern societies and technologies, poses problems yet to be satisfactorily and safely solved.

ONLINE LEARNING CENTRE

The World Wide Web has a tremendous number and variety of sites pertaining to geography. To access Web sites, Internet exercises, self-quizzes, videos, and additional study tools relevant to this chapter's content, visit the *Human* *Geography* Online Learning Centre at **www. mcgrawhill.ca/olc/fellmann.**

Appendix A

WORLD POPULATION DATA (2007)

DEMOGRAPHIC DATA AND ESTIMATES FOR THE COUNTRIES AND REGIONS OF THE WORLD											
	Population mid-2007 (millions)	Births per 1,000 Population	Deaths per 1,000 Population	Rate of Natural Increase (%)	Net Migration Rate per 1,000 Population	Projected Population (millions) mid–2025	Projected Population (millions) mid–2050	Projected Population Change 2007–2050 (%)	Infant Mortality Rate[a]	Total Fertility Rate[b]	Percent of Population of Age < 15	65+
---	---	---	---	---	---	---	---	---	---	---	---	---
WORLD	**6,625**	**21**	**9**	**1.2**	**0**	**7,965**	**9,294**	**40**	**52**	**2.7**	**28**	**7**
MORE DEVELOPED	1,221	11	10	0.1	3	1,254	1,259	3	6	1.6	17	16
LESS DEVELOPED	5,404	23	8	1.5	−0	6,711	8,036	49	57	2.9	31	6
LESS DEVELOPED (Excl. China)	4,086	27	9	1.8	−0	5,235	6,599	61	61	3.3	34	5
AFRICA	**944**	**38**	**14**	**2.4**	**−0**	**1,359**	**1,953**	**107**	**86**	**5.0**	**41**	**3**
SUB-SAHARAN AFRICA	**788**	**41**	**16**	**2.5**	**−0**	**1,160**	**1,716**	**118**	**92**	**5.5**	**43**	**3**
NORTHERN AFRICA	**195**	**26**	**7**	**1.9**	**−1**	**253**	**310**	**59**	**42**	**3.1**	**33**	**5**
Algeria	34.1	21	4	1.7	−1	43.2	50.0	47	30	2.4	30	5
Egypt	73.4	27	6	2.1	−2	95.9	117.9	61	33	3.1	33	5
Libya	6.2	24	4	2.0	−0	8.1	9.7	57	21	3.0	30	4
Morocco	31.7	21	6	1.5	−2	38.9	45.3	43	38	2.4	30	5
Sudan	38.6	33	11	2.2	−1	54.3	73.0	89	69	4.5	41	4
Tunisia	10.2	17	6	1.1	−1	12.1	13.2	29	20	2.0	26	6
Western Sahara	0.5	28	8	2.0	6	0.8	0.9	95	49	2.9	31	2
WESTERN AFRICA	**283**	**42**	**15**	**2.7**	**−0**	**419**	**616**	**118**	**98**	**5.7**	**44**	**3**
Benin	9.0	42	12	3.0	2	14.5	22.5	149	98	5.7	44	3
Burkina Faso	14.8	45	15	3.0	1	23.7	37.5	154	81	6.2	47	3
Cape Verde	0.5	30	5	2.5	−6	0.7	0.9	87	28	3.5	38	6
Côte d'Ivoire	20.2	38	14	2.4	5	27.4	36.4	80	104	5.0	41	3
Gambia	1.5	38	11	2.7	3	2.2	3.2	114	75	5.1	42	3
Ghana	23.0	33	10	2.3	−0	33.1	47.8	108	59	4.4	40	4
Guinea	10.1	42	14	2.9	−8	15.7	24.5	142	113	5.7	46	3
Guinea-Bissau	1.7	50	19	3.1	−1	2.9	5.3	214	117	7.1	48	3
Liberia	3.8	50	19	3.1	3	6.8	12.5	232	138	6.8	47	2
Mali	12.3	48	16	3.3	−3	20.6	34.2	177	96	6.6	48	4
Mauritania	3.1	35	9	2.7	1	4.5	6.4	104	74	4.8	40	4
Niger	14.2	48	15	3.4	−0	26.3	53.2	274	126	7.1	48	3

	Population mid-2007 (millions)	Births per 1,000 Population	Deaths per 1,000 Population	Rate of Natural Increase (%)	Net Migration Rate per 1,000 Population	Projected Population (millions) mid–2025	Projected Population (millions) mid–2050	Projected Population Change 2007–2050 (%)	Infant Mortality Rate[a]	Total Fertility Rate[b]	Percent of Population of Age < 15	Percent of Population of Age 65+
WESTERN AFRICA (continued)												
Nigeria	144.4	43	18	2.5	−0	204.9	281.6	95	100	5.9	45	3
Senegal	12.4	39	10	3.0	−2	18.0	25.3	104	61	5.3	44	4
Sierra Leone	5.3	48	23	2.5	−4	7.6	10.9	103	158	6.1	42	4
Togo	6.6	38	10	2.8	−0	9.9	14.1	113	91	5.1	43	3
EASTERN AFRICA	**294**	**41**	**15**	**2.5**	**−0**	**438**	**650**	**121**	**83**	**5.5**	**44**	**3**
Burundi	8.5	46	16	3.0	6	15.0	28.3	233	107	6.8	45	3
Comoros	0.7	37	7	2.9	−3	1.0	1.5	104	59	4.9	42	3
Djibouti	0.8	30	12	1.8	0	1.1	1.5	78	67	4.2	39	3
Eritrea	4.9	40	10	3.0	7	7.7	11.5	136	59	5.3	43	2
Ethiopia	77.1	40	15	2.5	−0	108.7	145.9	89	77	5.4	43	3
Kenya	36.9	40	12	2.8	−0	51.3	65.2	77	77	4.9	42	2
Madagascar	18.3	40	12	2.7	0	28.2	41.8	129	79	5.2	45	3
Malawi	13.1	46	18	2.8	−0	20.6	30.9	136	96	6.3	46	3
Mauritius	1.3	14	7	0.7	−0	1.4	1.5	18	14.4	1.7	24	7
Mayotte	0.2	39	3	3.6	5	0.3	0.6	183	—	4.5	42	2
Mozambique	20.4	41	20	2.1	−0	27.5	37.2	83	108	5.4	43	3
Reunion	0.8	19	6	1.3	1	1.0	1.1	33	7	2.4	27	7
Rwanda	9.3	43	16	2.7	1	14.6	21.7	133	86	6.1	46	3
Seychelles	0.1	17	8	1.0	5	0.1	0.1	38	11	2.1	25	8
Somalia	9.1	46	17	2.9	5	14.9	25.5	180	117	6.8	45	3
Tanzania	38.7	40	15	2.6	−2	57.4	81.5	110	78	5.4	44	3
Uganda	28.5	48	16	3.1	−1	55.9	117.0	310	83	6.7	50	3
Zambia	11.5	41	22	1.9	−3	14.8	18.4	61	100	5.5	46	2
Zimbabwe	13.3	31	21	1.1	−1	16.0	19.1	43	60	3.8	41	3
MIDDLE AFRICA	**118**	**46**	**18**	**2.8**	**−0**	**191**	**315**	**167**	**113**	**6.3**	**46**	**3**
Angola	16.3	49	22	2.7	2	26.2	42.7	162	141	6.8	47	2
Cameroon	18.1	37	14	2.3	−0	25.5	34.9	93	74	4.9	42	3
Central African Republic	4.3	38	19	1.9	−1	5.8	7.6	75	102	5.0	43	4
Chad	10.8	47	16	3.1	2	17.5	29.4	173	102	6.5	46	3
Congo	3.8	41	14	2.7	−2	6.1	9.6	153	75	5.3	42	3
Congo, Dem. Rep. Of	62.6	50	19	3.0	−1	107.5	186.8	198	120	6.7	47	3
Equatorial Guinea	0.5	40	16	2.3	0	0.8	1.2	133	101	5.6	42	4
Gabon	1.3	28	12	1.6	1	1.7	2.1	56	62	3.4	26	5
Sao Tome and Principe	0.2	35	8	2.7	−9	0.2	0.3	88	77	4.1	42	4
SOUTHERN AFRICA	**55**	**24**	**16**	**0.8**	**0**	**58**	**62**	**13**	**46**	**2.8**	**33**	**4**
Botswana	1.8	26	27	−0.1	−1	1.7	1.7	−5	56	3.1	38	3
Lesotho	1.8	28	25	0.3	−4	1.7	1.6	−10	91	3.5	39	5
Namibia	2.1	27	13	1.5	−0	2.6	3.0	47	55	3.6	41	3

	Population mid-2007 (millions)	Births per 1,000 Population	Deaths per 1,000 Population	Rate of Natural Increase (%)	Net Migration Rate per 1,000 Population	Projected Population (millions) mid–2025	Projected Population (millions) mid–2050	Projected Population Change 2007–2050 (%)	Infant Mortality Rate[a]	Total Fertility Rate[b]	Percent of Population of Age < 15	Percent of Population of Age 65+
SOUTHERN AFRICA (continued)												
South Africa	47.9	23	15	0.8	0	51.5	54.8	14	43	2.7	32	4
Swaziland	1.1	28	29	−0.1	0	1.0	0.8	−34	73	3.6	41	4
NORTHERN AMERICA	**335**	**14**	**8**	**0.6**	**4**	**387**	**462**	**38**	**6**	**2.0**	**20**	**12**
Canada	32.9	11	7	0.3	7	37.6	41.6	26	5.3	1.5	18	13
United States	302.2	14	8	0.6	4	349.4	419.9	39	6.5	2.1	20	12
LATIN AMERICA/ CARIBBEAN	**569**	**21**	**6**	**1.5**	**−2**	**691**	**784**	**38**	**24**	**2.5**	**30**	**6**
CENTRAL AMERICA	**148**	**23**	**5**	**1.8**	**−5**	**181**	**205**	**39**	**23**	**2.7**	**33**	**5**
Belize	0.3	27	5	2.3	10	0.4	0.6	85	25	3.3	41	4
Costa Rica	4.5	16	4	1.2	4	5.6	6.3	41	10	1.9	28	6
El Salvador	6.9	25	6	1.9	−4	9.0	11.9	73	25	2.9	35	5
Guatemala	13.4	34	6	2.8	−4	19.9	27.5	106	34	4.4	43	4
Honduras	7.1	27	6	2.1	−4	9.7	12.1	70	23	3.3	38	4
Mexico	106.5	21	5	1.7	−6	124.7	132.3	24	21	2.4	32	6
Nicaragua	5.6	28	5	2.3	−7	7.5	9.8	75	26	3.2	39	4
Panama	3.3	20	4	1.5	0	4.2	5.0	50	15	2.4	30	6
CARIBBEAN	**40**	**19**	**8**	**1.1**	**−3**	**46**	**51**	**27**	**32**	**2.5**	**28**	**8**
Antigua and Barbuda	0.1	21	6	1.5	−6	0.1	0.1	0	20	2.3	28	7
Bahamas	0.3	16	7	1.0	1	0.4	0.5	36	12.7	1.9	28	6
Barbados	0.3	14	8	0.6	−1	0.3	0.3	−8	14.2	1.9	22	12
Cuba	11.2	11	8	0.3	−3	11.5	10.8	−4	6.2	1.5	19	11
Dominica	0.1	24	7	1.7	−12	0.1	0.1	20	22.2	3.0	29	10
Dominican Republic	9.4	24	5	1.8	−3	11.9	14.7	57	30	2.9	33	6
Grenada	0.1	19	7	1.2	−15	0.1	0.1	−12	17	2.1	32	5
Guadeloupe	0.5	16	6	1.0	2	0.5	0.5	4	6.9	2.2	26	8
Haiti	9.0	29	11	1.8	−3	11.5	14.3	59	57	4.0	39	4
Jamaica	2.7	17	6	1.1	−6	3.0	3.4	26	24	2.1	30	8
Martinique	0.4	13	7	0.7	1	0.4	0.4	−12	5	2.0	22	12
Netherlands Antilles	0.2	13	8	0.5	21	0.2	0.2	11	9	1.8	23	10
Puerto Rico	3.9	13	7	0.5	−2	4.1	3.8	−4	9	1.7	21	13
St. Kitts-Nevis	0.05	18	9	1.0	−6	0.1	0.1	34	14.5	2.3	28	8
Saint Lucia	0.2	15	7	0.8	7	0.2	0.2	31	19.4	1.7	28	7
St. Vincent and the Grenadines	0.1	18	7	1.1	−8	0.1	0.1	−12	18.1	2.0	29	7
Trinidad and Tobago	1.4	14	8	0.6	−3	1.5	1.4	−1	15	1.6	25	6
SOUTH AMERICA	**381**	**21**	**6**	**1.5**	**−1**	**463**	**528**	**38**	**24**	**2.4**	**29**	**6**
Argentina	39.4	19	8	1.2	−1	46.4	53.7	36	14.4	2.5	27	10
Bolivia	9.8	29	8	2.1	−1	13.3	16.0	63	51	3.7	38	4
Brazil	189.3	21	6	1.4	−0	228.9	259.8	37	27	2.3	28	6
Chile	16.6	15	5	1.0	2	19.1	20.2	22	8.4	2.0	25	8

	Population mid-2007 (millions)	Births per 1,000 Population	Deaths per 1,000 Population	Rate of Natural Increase (%)	Net Migration Rate per 1,000 Population	Projected Population (millions) mid–2025	Projected Population (millions) mid–2050	Projected Population Change 2007–2050 (%)	Infant Mortality Rate[a]	Total Fertility Rate[b]	Percent of Population of Age < 15	Percent of Population of Age 65+
SOUTH AMERICA												
(continued)												
Colombia	46.2	20	6	1.5	−1	55.6	61.9	34	19	2.4	30	5
Ecuador	13.5	26	6	2.0	−4	17.5	20.4	51	25	3.1	33	6
French Guiana	0.2	31	4	2.7	5	0.3	0.4	84	10	4.0	35	4
Guyana	0.8	21	9	1.2	−7	0.8	0.6	−15	48	2.7	32	5
Paraguay	6.1	27	6	2.1	−2	8.0	9.9	61	36	3.5	36	5
Peru	27.9	21	6	1.5	−4	34.1	39.0	40	24	2.5	32	6
Suriname	0.5	21	7	1.4	−7	0.5	0.5	−7	20	2.5	30	6
Uruguay	3.3	15	9	0.6	−3	3.5	3.6	9	14.5	2.1	24	13
Venezuela	27.5	22	5	1.7	0	35.2	41.8	52	17.5	2.7	31	5
ASIA	**4,010**	**19**	**7**	**1.2**	**−0**	**4,768**	**5,378**	**34**	**48**	**2.4**	**28**	**6**
ASIA (Excl. China)	**2,692**	**23**	**7**	**1.5**	**−0**	**3,292**	**3,941**	**46**	**53**	**2.8**	**31**	**6**
WESTERN ASIA	**223**	**26**	**6**	**2.0**	**2**	**292**	**367**	**65**	**41**	**3.4**	**34**	**5**
Armenia	3.0	15	9	0.6	−3	3.4	3.4	12	26	1.7	22	11
Azerbaijan	8.6	18	6	1.2	0	9.7	11.6	35	10	2.1	24	7
Bahrain	0.8	21	3	1.8	7	1.0	1.2	56	9	2.6	27	3
Cyprus	1.0	12	6	0.5	29	1.1	1.1	5	6	1.5	19	11
Georgia	4.5	11	10	0.1	18	4.1	3.2	−29	20	1.3	18	13
Iraq	29.0	36	11	2.5	−3	43.2	61.9	114	94	4.9	42	3
Israel	7.3	21	6	1.5	2	9.3	11.2	52	3.9	2.8	28	10
Jordan	5.7	28	4	2.4	7	7.7	9.8	71	24	3.5	37	3
Kuwait	2.8	21	2	1.9	15	3.9	5.1	84	8	2.6	26	2
Lebanon	3.9	19	5	1.5	−0	4.6	5.0	27	17	2.3	27	8
Oman	2.7	25	3	2.2	16	3.1	3.9	42	10	3.4	33	3
Palestinian Territory	4.0	33	4	2.9	—	6.2	8.8	120	25	4.6	44	3
Qatar	0.9	17	2	1.5	36	1.1	1.4	55	7	2.8	23	1
Saudi Arabia	27.6	30	3	2.7	0	35.7	49.7	80	16	4.1	38	2
Syria	19.9	28	4	2.5	2	27.5	34.9	75	19	3.5	37	3
Turkey	74.0	19	6	1.2	0	87.8	88.7	20	23	2.2	28	6
United Arab Emirates	4.4	17	2	1.5	35	6.2	8.4	90	9	2.7	20	1
Yemen	22.4	40	9	3.2	−1	36.6	58.0	159	75	6.2	47	2
SOUTH CENTRAL ASIA	**1,662**	**25**	**8**	**1.7**	**−0**	**2,080**	**2,601**	**56**	**64**	**3.0**	**34**	**5**
Afghanistan	31.9	47	21	2.6	0	50.3	81.9	157	166	6.8	45	2
Bangladesh	149.0	27	8	1.9	−1	190.0	231.0	55	65	3.0	33	4
Bhutan	0.9	20	7	1.3	3	1.1	1.3	42	40	2.9	33	5
India	1,131.9	24	8	1.6	−0	1,391.2	1,747.3	54	58	2.9	33	5
Iran	71.2	18	6	1.2	−3	88.2	100.2	41	32	2.0	29	5
Kazakhstan	15.5	20	10	0.9	2	17.1	17.4	13	29	2.5	27	8
Kyrgyzstan	5.2	23	7	1.6	−6	6.6	8.1	56	50	2.8	32	6
Maldives	0.3	19	3	1.6	0	0.4	0.5	77	15	2.8	34	4
Nepal	27.8	28	9	1.9	−1	36.1	42.6	53	51	3.1	41	4

	Population mid-2007 (millions)	Births per 1,000 Population	Deaths per 1,000 Population	Rate of Natural Increase (%)	Net Migration Rate per 1,000 Population	Projected Population (millions) mid–2025	Projected Population (millions) mid–2050	Projected Population Change 2007–2050 (%)	Infant Mortality Rate[a]	Total Fertility Rate[b]	Percent of Population of Age < 15	Percent of Population of Age 65+
SOUTH CENTRAL ASIA (continued)												
Pakistan	169.3	31	8	2.3	−1	228.8	295.0	74	78	4.1	40	4
Sri Lanka	20.1	18	7	1.2	−1	21.2	19.5	−3	11	2.0	27	6
Tajikistan	7.1	26	7	1.9	−1	9.4	11.4	59	65	3.4	32	3
Turkmenistan	5.4	25	8	1.6	−0	6.6	7.4	36	74	2.9	34	5
Uzbekistan	26.5	24	7	1.7	−2	32.9	37.2	40	58	2.7	35	5
SOUTHEAST ASIA	**574**	**21**	**7**	**1.4**	**−0**	**691**	**778**	**35**	**32**	**2.5**	**29**	**5**
Brunei	0.4	19	3	1.6	3	0.5	0.6	55	7	2.3	30	3
Cambodia	14.4	26	9	1.7	0	19.6	25.5	78	71	3.4	37	3
East Timor	1.0	44	11	3.3	0	1.7	3.0	188	98	7.0	45	3
Indonesia	231.6	21	7	1.4	−1	271.2	296.9	28	34	2.4	28	6
Laos	5.9	36	12	2.4	0	8.5	11.8	102	85	4.8	44	4
Malaysia	27.2	23	5	1.8	4	34.5	40.5	49	10	2.9	33	4
Myanmar	49.8	20	10	0.9	−0	55.4	58.7	18	75	2.3	27	6
Philippines	88.7	27	5	2.1	−2	120.2	149.8	69	27	3.4	35	4
Singapore	4.6	10	4	0.6	27	5.3	5.3	13	2.6	1.3	19	8
Thailand	65.7	14	7	0.7	−0	70.2	68.9	5	20	1.7	23	7
Vietnam	85.1	19	5	1.3	−0	103.6	116.9	37	18	2.1	29	7
EAST ASIA	**1,550**	**12**	**7**	**0.5**	**−0**	**1,705**	**1,632**	**5**	**25**	**1.6**	**19**	**9**
China	1,318.0	12	7	0.5	−0	1,476.0	1,437.0	9	27	1.6	20	8
China, Hong Kong SAR[d]	6.9	10	5	0.4	5	8.1	8.7	25	1.8	1.0	14	12
China, Macao SAR[d]	0.5	8	3	0.5	53	0.6	0.6	9	3	0.9	15	7
Japan	127.7	9	9	0.0	0	119.3	95.2	−26	2.8	1.3	14	21
Korea, North	23.3	16	7	0.9	0	25.8	26.4	13	21	2.0	27	8
Korea, South	48.5	9	5	0.4	−2	49.1	42.3	−13	5	1.1	18	10
Mongolia	2.6	18	6	1.2	0	3.1	3.4	29	41	2.0	29	4
Taiwan	22.9	9	6	0.3	1	23.1	18.9	−18	5.0	1.1	18	10
EUROPE	**733**	**10**	**11**	**−0.1**	**2**	**719**	**669**	**−9**	**6**	**1.5**	**16**	**16**
NORTHERN EUROPE	**98**	**12**	**10**	**0.2**	**4**	**104**	**108**	**11**	**5**	**1.8**	**18**	**16**
Channel Islands	0.2	12	9	0.2	—	0.2	0.1	−3	3.4	1.4	15	13
Denmark	5.5	12	10	0.2	2	5.6	5.5	1	3.9	1.9	19	15
Estonia	1.3	11	13	−0.2	−0	1.2	1.0	−23	4.4	1.6	15	17
Finland	5.3	11	9	0.2	2	5.6	5.7	9	3.0	1.8	17	16
Iceland	0.3	15	6	0.8	17	0.3	0.4	14	2.4	2.1	21	12
Ireland	4.4	15	7	0.9	16	4.9	5.1	16	3.8	1.9	20	11
Latvia	2.3	10	14	−0.5	−1	2.2	1.8	−22	7.6	1.4	14	17
Lithuania	3.4	9	13	−0.4	−1	3.1	2.9	−15	6.8	1.3	16	16
Norway	4.7	13	9	0.4	5	5.2	5.8	24	3.2	1.9	19	15
Sweden	9.1	12	10	0.2	6	9.9	10.5	15	2.8	1.9	17	17
United Kingdom	61.0	12	10	0.3	4	65.8	69.2	13	4.9	1.8	18	16

	Population mid-2007 (millions)	Births per 1,000 Population	Deaths per 1,000 Population	Rate of Natural Increase (%)	Net Migration Rate per 1,000 Population	Projected Population (millions) mid-2025	Projected Population (millions) mid-2050	Projected Population Change 2007–2050 (%)	Infant Mortality Rate[a]	Total Fertility Rate[b]	Percent of Population of Age < 15	Percent of Population of Age 65+
WESTERN EUROPE	**187**	**10**	**9**	**0.1**	**1**	**191**	**187**	**−0**	**4**	**1.6**	**16**	**17**
Austria	8.3	9	9	0.0	4	8.8	9.0	8	3.6	1.4	16	17
Belgium	10.6	11	10	0.1	3	10.8	11.0	3	4.4	1.7	17	17
France	61.7	13	9	0.4	2	66.1	70.0	13	3.7	2.0	18	16
Germany	82.3	8	10	−0.2	0	79.6	71.4	−13	3.8	1.3	14	19
Liechtenstein	0.04	11	6	0.5	4	0.04	0.04	19	2.9	1.4	17	12
Luxembourg	0.5	12	8	0.4	6	0.5	0.6	35	3.2	1.7	19	14
Monaco	0.03	25	16	0.9	8	0.04	0.04	12	—	—	13	22
Netherlands	16.4	11	8	0.3	−2	16.9	16.8	3	4.4	1.7	18	14
Switzerland	7.5	10	8	0.2	5	8.1	8.1	7	4.2	1.4	16	16
EASTERN EUROPE	**295**	**10**	**14**	**−0.4**	**1**	**271**	**229**	**−22**	**9**	**1.3**	**15**	**14**
Belarus	9.7	9	14	−0.5	0	9.0	7.8	−20	7	1.2	16	14
Bulgaria	7.7	10	15	−0.5	−0	6.6	5.0	−35	9.7	1.4	13	17
Czech Republic	10.3	10	10	0.0	3	10.2	9.4	−8	3.3	1.3	15	14
Hungary	10.1	10	13	−0.3	2	9.6	8.9	−11	5.7	1.3	15	16
Moldova	4.0	11	12	−0.2	1	3.7	3.0	−24	12	1.3	20	10
Poland	38.1	10	10	0.0	−1	36.7	30.5	−20	6.0	1.3	16	13
Romania	21.6	10	12	−0.2	−0	19.7	17.1	−21	14.0	1.3	16	15
Russia	141.7	10	15	−0.5	2	128.5	109.4	−23	10	1.3	15	14
Slovakia	5.4	10	10	0.0	1	5.2	4.7	−12	6.8	1.3	16	12
Ukraine	46.5	10	16	−0.6	0	41.7	33.4	−28	10	1.3	14	16
SOUTHERN EUROPE	**153**	**10**	**9**	**0.1**	**4**	**153**	**144**	**−5**	**5**	**1.4**	**15**	**18**
Albania	3.2	14	6	0.8	−3	3.5	3.5	12	8	1.8	27	8
Andorra	0.1	11	4	0.7	15	0.1	0.1	−4	2.5	1.3	15	12
Bosnia-Herzegovina	3.8	9	9	0.0	0	3.7	3.1	−20	7	1.2	18	13
Croatia	4.4	10	12	−0.2	2	4.3	3.8	−14	5.7	1.4	16	17
Greece	11.2	10	9	0.0	4	11.3	10.8	−4	3.8	1.3	14	19
Italy	59.3	10	9	0.0	4	58.7	55.9	−6	3.7	1.4	14	20
Macedonia[e]	2.0	11	9	0.2	−1	2.0	1.7	−15	13	1.4	20	11
Malta	0.4	10	8	0.2	2	0.4	0.3	−20	6.0	1.4	17	13
Montenegro	0.6	12	9	0.2	−1	0.6	0.6	−4	9.5	1.6	20	13
Portugal	10.7	10	10	0.0	5	10.4	9.3	−13	3.5	1.4	16	17
San Marino	0.03	10	6	0.4	11	0.04	0.04	13	3.3	1.2	15	16
Serbia	9.5	11	12	−0.0	1	9.6	9.3	−2	13	1.8	20	15
Slovenia	2.0	9	9	0.0	4	2.0	1.9	−6	3.3	1.3	14	16
Spain	45.3	11	8	0.3	7	46.2	43.9	−3	3.8	1.4	14	17
OCEANIA	**35**	**18**	**7**	**1.0**	**5**	**42**	**49**	**41**	**27**	**2.1**	**25**	**10**
Australia	21.0	13	6	0.6	7	24.7	28.1	34	5.0	1.8	20	13
Federated States of Micronesia	0.1	26	6	2.0	−17	0.1	0.1	21	40	4.1	39	3
Fiji	0.9	21	6	1.4	−5	0.9	0.9	8	16	2.5	31	4
French Polynesia	0.3	18	5	1.3	0	0.3	0.4	36	6.3	2.2	28	5

	Population mid-2007 (millions)	Births per 1,000 Population	Deaths per 1,000 Population	Rate of Natural Increase (%)	Net Migration Rate per 1,000 Population	Projected Population (millions) mid–2025	Projected Population (millions) mid–2050	Projected Population Change 2007–2050 (%)	Infant Mortality Rate[a]	Total Fertility Rate[b]	Percent of Population of Age < 15	Percent of Population of Age 65+
OCEANIA												
(continued)												
Guam	0.2	21	4	1.6	0	0.2	0.3	48	11.3	2.8	30	6
Kiribati	0.1	31	8	2.3	0	0.1	0.2	119	43	4.2	39	3
Marshall Islands	0.1	38	5	3.3	−6	0.1	0.1	60	29	4.9	42	2
Nauru	0.01	26	7	1.9	0	0.02	0.02	64	42	3.4	39	2
New Caledonia	0.2	18	5	1.3	3	0.3	0.4	49	6	2.3	28	7
New Zealand	4.2	14	7	0.7	4	4.7	5.0	21	5.1	2.0	21	13
Palau	0.02	14	7	0.7	1	0.02	0.03	30	18	2.1	24	6
Papua New Guinea	6.3	32	10	2.2	0	8.6	11.2	76	64	4.1	41	2
Samoa	0.2	29	6	2.4	−1	0.2	0.2	15	20	4.4	41	4
Solomon Islands	0.5	34	8	2.6	0	0.7	1.0	93	48	4.5	40	3
Tonga	0.1	27	6	2.1	−18	0.1	0.1	−27	12	3.6	35	6
Tuvalu	0.01	27	10	1.7	−1	0.01	0.02	83	35	3.7	36	6
Vanuatu	0.2	31	6	2.5	0	0.4	0.5	113	27	4.0	41	3

NOTES

(—) Indicates data unavailable or inapplicable.

z Rounds to zero.

a Infant deaths per 1,000 live births. Rates shown with decimals indicate national statistics reported as completely registered, while those without are estimates from the sources cited on reverse. Rates shown in italics are based upon fewer than 50 annual infant deaths and, as a result, are subject to considerable yearly variability.

b Average number of children born to a woman during her lifetime.

c Child under age 3.

d Special Administrative Region.

e The former Yugoslav Republic.

f Data are for the former Serbia and Montenegro.

* Data prior to 2001 are shown in italics.

Data prepared by PRB demographer Carl Haub

POPULATION PYRAMIDS FOR CANADA'S PROVINCES AND TERRITORIES (2006)

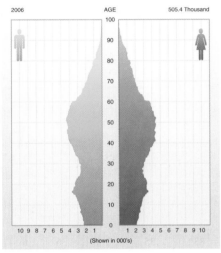

FIGURE B.1 Newfoundland and Labrador Population Pyramid 2006

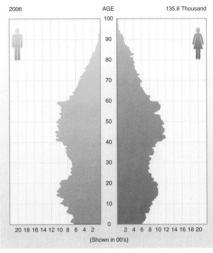

FIGURE B.2 Prince Edward Island Population Pyramid 2006

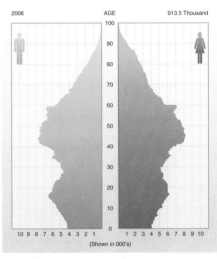

FIGURE B.3 Nova Scotia Population Pyramid 2006

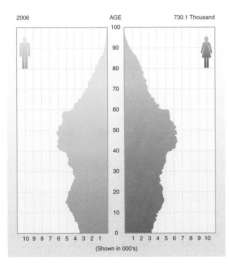

FIGURE B.4 New Brunswick Population Pyramid 2006

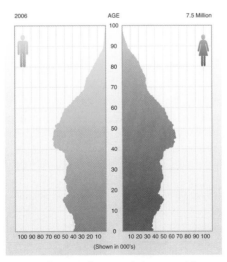

FIGURE B.5 Quebec Population Pyramid 2006

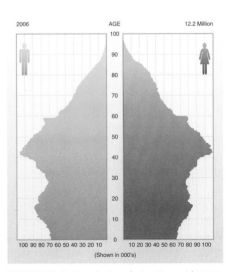

FIGURE B.6 Ontario Population Pyramid 2006

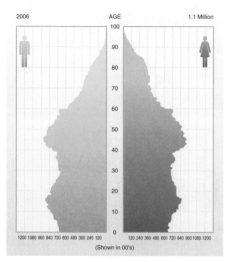

FIGURE B.7 Manitoba Population Pyramid 2006

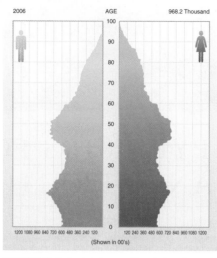

FIGURE B.8 Saskatchewan Population Pyramid 2006

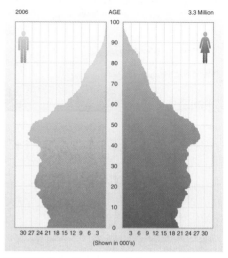

FIGURE B.9 Alberta Population Pyramid 2006

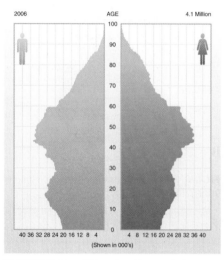

FIGURE B.10 British Columbia Population Pyramid 2006

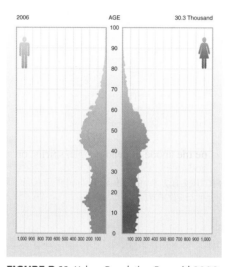

FIGURE B.11 Yukon Population Pyramid 2006

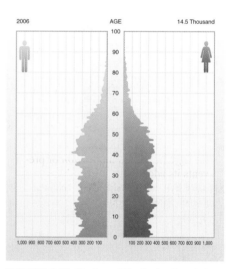

FIGURE B.12 Northwest Territories Population Pyramid 2006

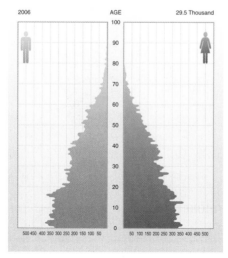

FIGURE B.13 Nunavut Population Pyramid 2006

Source of Figures B.1 to B.13: Adapted from Statistics Canada, http://www12.statcan.ca/english/census06/ analysis/agesex/tables.cfm#animations.

Glossary

Terms in *italics* identify related glossary items.

A

absolute direction Direction with respect to cardinal east, west, north, and south reference points.

absolute distance (*syn:* geodesic distance) The shortest-path separation between two places measured on a standard unit of length (miles or kilometres, usually); also called real distance.

absolute location (*syn:* mathematical location) The exact position of an object or place stated in spatial coordinates of a grid system designed for locational purposes. In geography, the reference system is the *globe grid* of parallels of *latitude* north or south of the *equator* and of meridians of *longitude* east or west of a *prime meridian*. Absolute globe locations are cited in degrees, minutes, and (for greater precision) seconds of latitude and longitude north or south and east or west of the equatorial and prime meridian base lines.

absorbing barrier A condition that blocks the *diffusion* of an *innovation* or prevents its adoption.

accessibility The relative ease with which a destination may be reached from other locations; the relative opportunity for *spatial interaction*. May be measured in geometric, social, or economic terms.

acculturation Cultural modification or change that results when one *culture* group or individual adopts traits of a dominant or *host society;* cultural development or change through "borrowing."

acid rain *Precipitation* that is unusually acidic; created when oxides of sulphur and nitrogen change chemically as they dissolve in water vapour in the *atmosphere* and return to earth as acidic rain, snow, or fog.

activity space The area within which people move freely on their rounds of regular activity.

adaptation 1: Genetic modification making a population more fit for existence under specific environmental conditions. 2: in immigration, the term summarizes how individuals, households, and communities respond and adjust to new experiences and social and cultural surroundings.

agglomeration The spatial grouping of people or activities for mutual benefit; in *economic geography,* the concentration of productive enterprises for collective or cooperative use of *infrastructure* and sharing of labour resources and market access.

agglomeration economies (*syn:* external economies) The savings to an individual enterprise derived from locational association with a cluster of other similar economic activities, such as other factories or retail stores.

agricultural density The number of rural residents per unit of agriculturally productive land; a variant of *physiological density* that excludes urban population.

agriculture The science and practice of farming, including the cultivation of the soil and the rearing of livestock.

amalgamation theory In *ethnic geography,* the concept that multiethnic societies become a merger of the *culture traits* of their member groups.

anecumene See *non-ecumene.*

animism A belief that natural objects may be the abode of dead people, spirits, or gods who occasionally give the objects the appearance of life.

antecedent boundary A *boundary* line established before the area in question is well populated.

antipode The point on the earth's surface that is diametrically opposite the observer's location.

aquaculture Production and harvesting of fish and shellfish in land-based ponds.

aquifer A porous, water-bearing layer of rock, sand, or gravel below ground level.

arable land Land that is or can be cultivated.

areal differentiation The study of the spatial distribution of physical and human elements within and between regions.

arithmetic density See *crude density.*

artifacts The material manifestations of *culture,* including tools, housing, systems of land use, clothing, and the like. Elements in the *technological subsystem* of culture.

artificial boundary See *geometric boundary.*

aspect In *map projections,* the positional relationship between the globe and the *developable surface* on which it is visually projected.

assimilation A two-part *behavioural* and *structural* process by which a minority population reduces or loses completely its identifying cultural characteristics and blends into the *host society.*

atmosphere The air or mixture of gases surrounding the earth.

autonomous nationalism Movement by a dissident minority intent to achieve partial or total independence of territory it occupies from the *state* within which it lies.

awareness space Locations or places about which an individual has knowledge even without visiting all of them; includes *activity space* and additional areas newly encountered or about which one acquires information.

azimuth Direction of a line defined at its starting point by its angle in relation to a *meridian.*

azimuthal projection See *planar projection.*

B

basic sector Those products or services of an *urban* economy that are exported outside the city itself, earning income for the community.

behavioural assimilation (*syn:* cultural assimilation) The process of integration into a common cultural life through acquisition of the sentiments, attitudes, and experiences of other groups.

behaviouralist An approach to human geography that emphasizes the psychological aspects of decision making that influence individual spatial behaviour and decision making. Examples of research include the study of attitudes, perceptions and behaviour, mental maps and the geography of place.

beneficiation The enrichment of low-grade ores through concentration and other processes to reduce their waste content and increase their *transferability.*

bilingualism Describing a society's use of two *official languages.*

biomass The total dry weight of all living organisms within a unit area; plant and animal matter that can in any way be used as a source of energy.

biome A major ecological community, including plants and animals, occupying an extensive earth area.

biosphere (*syn:* ecosphere) The thin film of air, water, and earth within which we live, including the *atmosphere,* surrounding and subsurface waters, and the upper reaches of the earth's crust.

birth rate The ratio of the number of live births during one year to the total population, usually at the midpoint of the same year, expressed as the number of births per year per 1000 population.

Boserup thesis The view that population growth independently forces a conversion from extensive to intensive *subsistence* agriculture.

boundary A line separating one political unit from another; see *international boundary.*

boundary dispute See *functional dispute.*

Brandt Report Entitled *North–South: A Program for Survival,* a report of the Independent Commission on International Development Issues, published in 1980 and named for the commission chairman, Willy Brandt.

break-of-bulk point A location where goods are transferred from one type of carrier to another (e.g., from barge to railroad).

Buddhism A *universalizing religion,* primarily of eastern and central Asia, based on teachings of Siddhartha Gautama, the Buddha, that suffering is inherent in all life but can be relieved by mental and moral self-purification.

built environment That part of the *physical landscape* that represents *material culture;* the buildings, roads, bridges, and similar structures large and small of the *cultural landscape.*

C

carrying capacity The maximum population numbers that an area can support on a continuing basis without experiencing unacceptable deterioration; for humans, the numbers supportable by an area's known and used resources—usually agricultural ones.

cartogram A map that has been simplified to present a single idea in a diagrammatic way; the base is not normally true to scale.

caste One of the hereditary social classes in *Hinduism* that determines one's occupation and position in society.

census metropolitan area (CMA) One or more adjacent municipalities situated around a major urban core with a population of at least 100,000.

central business district (CBD) The nucleus or "downtown" of a city, where retail stores, offices, and cultural activities are concentrated, mass transit systems converge, and land values and building densities are high.

central city That part of the *metropolitan area* contained within the boundaries of the main city around which suburbs have developed.

central place An *urban* or other settlement node whose primary function is to provide goods and services to the consuming population of its *hinterland, complementary region,* or trade area.

central place theory A deductive theory formulated by Walter *Christaller* (1893–1969) to explain the size and distribution of settlements through reference to competitive supply of goods and services to dispersed rural populations.

centrifugal force 1: In *urban geography,* economic and social forces pushing households and businesses outward from central and inner-city locations. **2:** In *political geography,* forces of disruption and dissolution threatening the unity of a *state.*

centripetal force 1: In *urban geography,* a force attracting establishments or activities to the city centre. **2:** In *political geography,* forces tending to bind together the citizens of a state.

chain migration The process by which *migration* movements from a common home area to a specific destination are sustained by links of friendship or kinship between first movers and later followers.

channelized migration The tendency for *migration* to flow between areas that are socially and economically allied by past migration patterns, by economic and trade connections, or by some other affinity.

charter group In plural societies, the early arriving ethnic group that created the *first effective settlement* and established the recognized cultural norms to which other, later groups are expected to conform.

chlorofluorocarbons (CFCs) A family of synthetic chemicals that has significant commercial applications but whose emissions are contributing to the depletion of the *ozone* layer.

choropleth map A *thematic map* presenting spatial data as average values per unit area.

Christaller Walter Christaller (1893–1969), German geographer credited with developing *central place theory* (1933).

Christianity A *monotheistic, universalizing religion* based on the teachings of Jesus Christ and of the Bible as sacred scripture.

circular and cumulative causation A process through which tendencies for economic growth are self-reinforcing; an expression of the *multiplier effect,* it tends to favour major cities and *core* regions over less-advantaged *peripheral* regions.

city A multifunctional nucleated settlement with a *central business district* and both residential and non-residential land uses.

class A form of social stratification and categorization based primarily upon economic position. Among the determinants of class are income—*upper, middle, or lower;* occupation—*skilled, semi-skilled, unskilled;* economic sector—*intellectual, administrative, managerial, labour;* property—*owners, users, renters;* and educational attainment—*university, college, secondary, or primary school*—among others. The opportunities and constraints resulting from class have major impacts upon the kinds of places were people live, work, and play, as well as their social status and lifestyles.

climate A summary of weather conditions in a place or region over a period of time.

cluster migration A pattern of movement and settlement resulting from the collective action of a distinctive social or *ethnic group.*

cognitive map See *mental map.*

cohort A population group unified by a specific common characteristic, such as age, and subsequently treated as a statistical unit during their lifetimes.

collective farm In the former Soviet *planned economy,* the cooperative operation of an agricultural enterprise under state control of production and market, but without full status or support as a state enterprise.

colonialism The control by one nation (i.e., extension of sovereignty) over another, dependent area.

colony In *ethnic geography,* an urban ethnic area serving as point of entry and temporary *acculturation* zone for a specific immigrant group.

commercial economy A system of production of goods and services for exchange in competitive markets where price and availability are determined by supply and demand forces.

commercial energy Commercially traded fuels, such as coal, oil, or natural gas; excluding wood, vegetable or animal wastes, or other *biomass.*

compact state A *state* whose territory is nearly circular.

comparative advantage The principle that an area produces the items for which it has the greatest ratio of advantage or the least ratio of disadvantage in comparison to other areas, assuming free trade exists.

complementarity The actual or potential relationship of two places or regions that each produce different goods or services for which the other has an effective demand, resulting in an exchange between the locales.

complementary region The area served by a *central place.*

concentration In *spatial distributions,* the clustering of a phenomenon around a central location.

concentric zone (zonal) model A model describing urban land uses as a series of circular belts or rings around a core *central business district,* each ring housing a distinct type of land use.

conformality The map property of correct angles and shapes of small areas.

conformal projection A *map projection* that retains correct shapes of small areas; lines of *latitude* and *longitude* cross at right angles and *scale* **(1)** is the same in all directions at any point on the map.

Confucianism A Chinese *value system* and *ethnic religion* emphasizing ethics, social morality, tradition, and ancestor worship.

conic projection A *map projection* employing a cone placed tangent or secant to the globe as the presumed *developable surface.*

connectivity The directness of routes linking pairs of places; an indication of the degree of internal connection in a transport *network.* More generally, all of the tangible and intangible means of connection and communication between places.

consequent boundary (*syn:* ethnographic boundary) A *boundary* line that coincides with some cultural divide, such as religion or language.

conservation The wise use or preservation of natural resources so as to maintain supplies and qualities at levels sufficient to meet present and future needs.

contagious diffusion A form of *expansion diffusion* that depends on direct contact. The process of dispersion is centrifugal, strongly influenced by distance, and dependent on interaction between actual and potential adopters of the *innovation.* Its name derives from the pattern of spread of contagious diseases.

containment A guiding principle of U.S. foreign policy during the Cold War period: to prevent or restrict the expansion of the Soviet Union's influence or control beyond its then existing limits.

continental shelf A gently sloping seaward extension of the landmass found off the coasts of many continents; its outer margin is marked by a transition to the ocean depths at about 200 metres (660 feet).

conurbation A continuous, extended *urban* area formed by the growing together of several formerly separate, expanding cities.

Convention on the Law of the Sea See *United Nations Convention on the Law of the Sea.*

core area 1: In *economic geography,* a "core region," the national or world districts of concentrated economic power, wealth, innovation, and advanced technology. **2:** In *political geography,* the heartland or nucleus of a *state,* containing its most developed area, greatest wealth, densest populations, and clearest national identity.

core-periphery model A model of the spatial structure of an economic system in which underdeveloped or declining peripheral areas are defined with respect to their dependence on a dominating developed *core region.*

core regions Highly industrialized areas that dominate trade, control the most advanced technologies, and have high levels of productivity within diversified economies. At a global scale, Western Europe, North America, and Japan are the main core regions.

counter migration (*syn:* return migration) The return of migrants to the regions from which they earlier emigrated.

country See *state.*

creole A *language* developed from a *pidgin* to become the native tongue of a society.

critical distance The distance beyond which cost, effort, and/or means play a determining role in the willingness of people to travel.

crop rotation The annual alteration of crops that make differential demands on or contributions to soil fertility.

crude birth rate (CBR) See *birth rate.*

crude death rate (CDR) See *death rate.*

crude density (*syn:* arithmetic density) The number of people per unit area of land.

culturalism Using culture to explain culture. For example, to state that an ethnic group performs a certain ceremony *because of their culture* explains nothing about culture.

cultural area A unit in space inhabited at a given period by people characterized by a shared culture.

cultural assimilation See *behavioural assimilation.*

cultural convergence The tendency for *cultures* to become more alike as they increasingly share *technology* and organizational structures in a modern world united by improved transportation and communication.

cultural divergence The likelihood or tendency for *cultures* to become increasingly dissimilar with the passage of time.

cultural ecology The study of the interactions between societies and the natural *environments* they occupy.

cultural geography A branch of *systematic geography* that focuses on culturally determined human activities, the impact of *material* and *non-material* human *culture* on the environment, and the human organization of space.

cultural history The temporal sequences in the occupation of an area or region by different cultural groups.

cultural integration The interconnectedness of all aspects of a *culture;* no part can be altered without creating an impact on other components of the culture.

cultural lag The phenomenon wherein a social group is inappropriately unresponsive—mentally, psychologically, or economically—to changing circumstances and cultural innovations.

cultural landscape The *natural landscape* as modified by human activities and bearing the imprint of a *culture* group or society; the *built environment.*

cultural politics The examination and explanation of culture as politically charged. Culture is viewed as a site of struggle over social identities and the spaces where they are created and contested by differing cultural groups. The task is to examine identities through the lens of power to see how those identities are socially and spatially constructed, negotiated, resisted, or maintained.

culture 1: A society's collective beliefs, symbols, values, forms of behaviour, and social organizations, together with its tools, structures, and artifacts created according to the group's conditions of life; transmitted as a heritage to succeeding generations and undergoing adoptions, modifications, and changes in the process. **2:** A collective term for a group displaying uniform cultural characteristics.

culture complex A related set of *culture traits* descriptive of one aspect of a society's behaviour or activity. Culture complexes may be as basic as those associated with food preparation, serving, and consumption or as involved as those associated with religious beliefs or business practices.

culture hearth A nuclear area within which an advanced and distinctive set of *culture traits,* ideas, and *technologies* develops and from which there is *diffusion* of those characteristics and the *cultural landscape* features they imply.

culture realm A collective of *culture regions* sharing related culture systems; a major world area having sufficient distinctiveness to be perceived as set apart from other realms in terms of cultural characteristics and complexes.

culture rebound The readoption by later generations of *culture traits* and identities associated with immigrant forebears or ancestral homelands.

culture region A *formal* or *functional region* within which common cultural characteristics prevail. It may be based on single *culture traits,* on *culture complexes,* or on political, social, or economic integration.

culture system A generalization suggesting shared, identifying traits uniting two or more *culture complexes.*

culture trait A single distinguishing feature of regular occurrence within a *culture,* such as the use of chopsticks or the observance of a particular caste system. A single element of learned behaviour.

cumulative causation See *circular and cumulative causation.*

custom The body of traditional practices, usages, and conventions that regulate social life.

cylindrical projection A *map projection* employing a cylinder wrapped around the globe as the presumed *developable surface.*

D

Daoism See *Taoism.*

death rate (*syn:* mortality rate) A mortality index usually calculated as the number of deaths per year per 1000 population.

deductive research Commonly referred to as the scientific approach. One starts with a model, forms a hypothesis, gathers data to test the hypothesis, performs analysis and makes a conclusion to accept the hypothesis or not. On this basis, comments about the suitability of the model to describe reality are made. Deductive reasoning works from the more general level (model) to the more specific (data). Spatial analysis

in geography often adopts this research approach.

deforestation The clearing of land through total removal of forest cover.

deglomeration The process of deconcentration; the location of industrial or other activities away from established *agglomerations* in response to growing costs of congestion, competition, and regulation.

deindustrialization The cumulative and sustained decline in the contribution of manufacturing to a national economy.

demographic equation A mathematical expression that summarizes the contribution of different demographic processes to the population change of a given area during a specified time period. $P_2 = P_1 + B_{1-2} - D_{1-2} + IM_{1-2} - OM_{1-2}$, where P_2 is population at time 2; P_1 is population at beginning date; B_{1-2} is the number of births between times 1 and 2; D_{1-2} is the number of deaths during that period; IM_{1-2} is the number of in-migrants and OM_{1-2} the number of out-migrants between times 1 and 2.

demographic momentum See *population momentum.*

demographic transition A model of the effect of economic development on population growth. A first stage involves stable numbers with both high *birth rates* and *death rates;* the second displays high birth rates, falling death rates, and population increases. Stage three shows reduction in population growth as birth rates decline to the level of death rates. The fourth and final stage again implies a population stable in size but with larger numbers than at the start of the transition process. An idealized summary of population history of industrializing Europe, its application to newly developing countries is questioned.

demography The scientific study of population, with particular emphasis upon quantitative aspects.

density The quantity of anything (people, buildings, animals, traffic, etc.) per unit area.

dependency ratio The number of dependants, old or young, that each 100 persons in the economically productive years must on average support.

dependency theory A Marxist-based theory that explains how poor nations are exploited by rich ones. The poor countries (periphery) supply primary products to the core.

desertification Extension of desertlike landscapes as a result of overgrazing, destruction of the forests, or other

human-induced changes, usually in semiarid regions.

developable surface *Projection* surface (such as a plane, cone, or cylinder) that is or can be made flat without distortion.

development The process of growth, expansion, or realization of potential; bringing regional resources into full productive use.

devolution The transfer of certain powers from the *state* central government to separate political subdivisions within the state's territory.

dialect A *language* variant marked by vocabulary, grammar, and pronunciation differences from other variants of the same common language. When those variations are spatial or regional, they are called *geographic dialects;* when they are indicative of socioeconomic or educational levels, they are called *social dialects.*

dialect geography See *linguistic geography.*

dibble Any small hand tool or stick to make a hole for planting.

diffusion The spread or movement of a phenomenon over space or through time. The dispersion of a *culture trait* or characteristic or new ideas and practices from an origin area (e.g., *language,* plant *domestication,* new industrial *technology*). Recognized types include *relocation, expansion, contagious,* and *hierarchical* diffusion.

diffusion barrier Any condition that hinders the flow of information, the movement of people, or the spread of an *innovation.*

direction bias A statement of *movement bias* observing that among all possible directions of movement or flow, one or only a very few are favoured and dominant.

dispersion In *spatial distributions,* a statement of the amount of spread of a phenomenon over area or around a central location. Dispersion in this sense represents a continuum from clustered, concentrated, or agglomerated (at one end) to dispersed or scattered (at the other).

distance bias A statement of *movement bias* observing that short journeys or interchanges are favoured over more distant ones.

distance decay The declining intensity of any activity, process, or function with increasing distance from its point of origin.

domestication The successful transformation of plant or animal species from a wild state to a condition of dependency on human management, usually with distinct physical change from wild forebears.

domino theory A *geopolitics* theory made part of American *containment* (of the former Soviet Union) policy beginning in the 1950s. The theory maintained that if a single country fell under Soviet influence or control, its neighbours would likely follow, creating a ripple effect like a line of toppling dominos.

doubling time The time period required for any beginning total experiencing a compounding growth to double in size.

E

ecology The scientific study of how living creatures affect each other and what determines their distribution and abundance.

ecological optimum The density of population which can't be supported by the area's natural resources.

economic base The manufacturing and service activities performed by the *basic sector* of a city's labour force; functions of a city performed to satisfy demands external to the city itself and, in that performance, earning income to support the urban population.

economic geography The branch of *systematic geography* concerned with how people support themselves, with the spatial patterns of production, distribution, and consumption of goods and services, and with the areal variation of economic activities over the surface of the earth.

economic imperialism The economic exploitation of one state by another through political and often military means.

ecosphere See *biosphere.*

ecosystem A population of organisms existing together in a small, relatively homogeneous area (pond, forest, small island), together with the energy, air, water, soil, and chemicals upon which it depends.

ecumene That part of the earth's surface physically suitable for permanent human settlement; the permanently inhabited areas of the earth.

edge city Distinct sizable nodal concentration of retail and office space of lower than central city densities and situated on the outer fringes of older metropolitan areas; usually localized by or near major highway intersections.

electoral geography The study of the geographical elements of the organization and results of elections.

elongated state A *state* whose territory is long and narrow.

enclave A small bit of foreign territory lying within a *state* but not under its jurisdiction.

environment Surroundings; the totality of things that in any way may affect an organism, including both physical and cultural conditions; a region characterized by a certain set of physical conditions.

environmental determinism A belief that human activities are dictated by the natural environment.

environmental perception The concept that people of different *cultures* will differently observe and interpret their *environment* and make different decisions about its nature, potentialities, and use.

environmental pollution See *pollution.*

epidemiologic transition The reduction of periodically high mortality rates from epidemic diseases as those diseases become essentially continual within a population that develops partial immunity to them.

equal-area (equivalent) projection A *map projection* designed so that a unit area drawn anywhere on the map always represents the same area on the earth's surface.

equator An imaginary east–west line that encircles the globe halfway between the North and South Poles.

equidistant projection A *map projection* showing true distances in all directions from one or two central points; all other distances are incorrect.

equivalence/equivalent projection In *map projections,* the characteristic that a unit area drawn on the map always represents the same area on the earth's surface, regardless of where drawn. See also *equal-area projection.*

erosion The wearing away and removal of rock and soil particles from exposed surfaces by agents such as moving water, wind, or ice.

ethnic enclave A small area occupied by a distinctive minority *culture.*

ethnic geography The study of spatial distributions and interactions of *ethnic groups* and of the cultural characteristics on which they are based.

ethnic group People sharing a distinctive *culture,* frequently based on common national origin, *religion, language,* or *race.*

ethnic island A small rural area settled by a single, distinctive *ethnic group* that placed its imprint on the landscape.

ethnicity Ethnic quality; affiliation with a group whose racial, cultural, religious, or linguistic characteristics or national

origins distinguish it from a larger population within which it is found.

ethnic province A large territory, urban and rural, dominated by or closely associated with a single *ethnic group.*

ethnic religion A *religion* identified with a particular *ethnic group* and largely exclusive to it. Such a religion does not seek converts.

ethnic separatism Desired *regional autonomy* expressed by a culturally distinctive group within a larger, politically dominant *culture.*

ethnocentrism Conviction of the evident superiority of one's own *ethnic group.*

ethnographic boundary See *consequent boundary.*

European Union (EU) An economic association established in 1957 by a number of Western European countries to promote free trade among members; often called the Common Market.

evapotranspiration The return of water from the land to the *atmosphere* through evaporation from the soil surface and transpiration from plants.

exclave A portion of a *state* that is separated from the main territory and surrounded by another country.

exclusion Denying an "other" individual or cultural group access to one's personal or cultural group resources and spaces of social and physical interaction.

exclusive economic zone (EEZ) As established in the *United Nations Convention on the Law of the Sea,* a zone of exploitation extending 200 nautical miles (370 km) seaward from a coastal state that has exclusive mineral and fishing rights over it.

expansion diffusion The spread of ideas, behaviours, or articles through a culture area or from one *culture* to neighbouring areas through contact and exchange of information; the dispersion leaves the phenomenon intact or intensified in its area of origin.

expulsion Forced departure of an individual or cultural group by another.

extensive agriculture A crop or livestock system characterized by low inputs of labour per unit area of land. It may be part of either a *subsistence* or a *commercial* economy.

external areas Regions of the world that were or are not part of the world-system (i.e., not involved in trade with the core).

external economies See *agglomeration economies.*

extractive industries *Primary activities* involving the mining and quarrying of *non-renewable* metallic and non-metallic mineral resources.

F

fallowing The practice of allowing plowed or cultivated land to remain (rest) uncropped or only partially cropped for one or more growing seasons.

federal state A *state* with a two-tier system of government and a clear distinction between the powers vested in the central government and those residing in the governments of the component regional subdivisions.

fertility rate The average number of live births per 1000 women of childbearing age.

feudalism The system of a political organization that prevailed in Europe between the 9th and 15th centuries. It had its basis on the relationship of lord to vassals, with all land held in fee and as chief characteristics homage, the service of tenants under arms and in court, wardship, and forfeiture.

filtering In *urban geography,* a process whereby individuals of a lower-income group replace, in a portion of an urban area, residents who are of a higher-income group.

first effective settlement The influence that the characteristics of an early dominant settlement group exert on the later *social* and *cultural geography* of an area.

fixed cost An activity cost (as of investment in land, plant, and equipment) that must be met without regard to level of output; an input cost that is spatially constant.

folk culture The body of institutions, customs, dress, *artifacts,* collective wisdoms, and traditions of a homogeneous, isolated, largely self-sufficient, and relatively static social group.

folklore Oral traditions of a *folk culture,* including tales, fables, legends, customary observations, and moral teachings.

folkway The learned manner of thinking and feeling and a prescribed mode of conduct common to a traditional social group.

footloose A descriptive term applied to manufacturing activities for which the cost of transporting material or product is not important in determining location of production; an industry or firm showing neither *market* nor *material orientation.*

Fordism The manufacturing economy and system derived from assembly-line mass production and the mass consumption of standardized goods. Named after Henry Ford, who innovated many of its production techniques.

foreign direct investment The purchase or construction of foreign factories and other fixed assets by *transnational corporations;* also the purchase of or merging with foreign companies.

formal region (*syn:* uniform region, homogeneous region, structural region) A *region* distinguished by a uniformity of one or more characteristics that can serve as the basis for areal generalization and of contrast with adjacent areas.

form utility A value-increasing change in the form—and therefore in the "utility"—of a raw material or commodity.

forward-thrust capital A capital city deliberately sited in a *state's* frontier zone.

fossil fuel (*syn:* mineral fuel) Any of the fuels derived from decayed organic material converted by earth processes; especially, coal, petroleum, and natural gas, but also including tar sands and oil shales.

fragmented state A *state* whose territory contains isolated parts, separated and discontinuous.

frame In *urban geography,* that part of the *central business district* characterized by such low-intensity uses as warehouses, wholesaling, and automobile dealers.

freight rate The charge levied by a transporter for the loading, moving, and unloading of goods; includes *line-haul costs* and *terminal costs.*

friction of distance A measure of the retarding or restricting effect of distance on *spatial interaction.* Generally, the greater the distance, the greater the "friction" and the less the interaction or exchange, or the greater the cost of achieving the exchange.

frontier That portion of a country adjacent to its boundaries and fronting another political unit.

frontier zone A belt lying between two *states* or between settled and uninhabited or sparsely settled areas.

functional dispute (*syn:* boundary dispute) In *political geography,* a disagreement between neighbouring *states* over policies to be applied to their common border; often induced by differing customs regulations, movement of nomadic groups, or illegal immigration or emigration.

functional region (*syn:* nodal region) A *region* differentiated by what occurs within it rather than by a homogeneity of physical or cultural phenomena; an earth area recognized as an operational unit based upon defined organizational criteria. The concept of unity is based on interaction and interdependence between different points within the area.

G

gated community A restricted access subdivision or neighbourhood, often surrounded by a barrier, with entry permitted only for residents and their guests; usually totally planned in land use and design, with "residents only" limitations on public streets and parks.

gathering industries *Primary activities* involving the *subsistence* or *commercial* harvesting of *renewable* natural resources of land or water. Primitive gathering involves local collection of food and other materials of nature, both plant and animal; commercial gathering usually implies forestry and fishing industries.

GDP See *gross domestic product.*

gender The socially-constructed and learned characteristics and practices attributable to femininity and masculinity.

gene flow The transfer of genes of one breeding population into the gene pool of another through interbreeding.

genetic drift A chance modification of gene composition occurring in an isolated population and becoming accentuated through inbreeding.

gentrification The movement into the inner portions of American cities of middle- and upper-income people who replace low-income populations, rehabilitate the structures they occupied, and change the social character of neighbourhoods.

geocaching An outdoor treasure-hunting game in which the participants use a Global Positioning System (GPS) to hide and seek containers (called "geocaches" or "caches") anywhere in the world. A typical cache is a small waterproof container containing a logbook and "treasure," usually toys or trinkets of little value.

geocoding The process of assigning absolute location coordinates, such as latitude and longitude, to human and physical features of the earth.

geodesic distance See *absolute distance.*

geographic dialect (*syn:* regional dialect) See *dialect.*

geographic information system (GIS) - Integrated computer programs for handling, processing, and analyzing data specifically referenced to the surface of the earth.

geographical standards The following six standards, developed in 1974 by the National Council for Geographic Education and later endorsed by the Canadian Council for Geographic

Education, identify the essential elements of geography: that are based upon six essential elements of geography: (1) the world in spatial terms (location); (2) places and regions; (3) physical systems; (4) human systems; (5) society and the environment, and (6) the uses of geography.

geometrical projection (*syn:* perspective projection; visual projection) The trace of the *graticule* shadow projected on a *developable surface* from a light source placed relative to a transparent globe.

geometric boundary (*syn:* artificial boundary) A boundary without obvious physical geographic basis; often a section of a *parallel of latitude* or a *meridian of longitude*.

geophagy The practice of eating earthy substances, usually clays.

geopolitics That branch of *political geography* treating national power, foreign policy, and international relations as influenced by geographic considerations of location, space, resources, and demography.

gerrymander To redraw voting district boundaries in such a way as to give one political party maximum electoral advantage and to reduce that of another party, to fragment voting blocks, or to achieve other non-democratic objectives.

ghetto A forced or voluntarily segregated residential area housing a racial, ethnic, or religious minority.

GIS See *geographic information system*.

global positioning system (GPS) A satellite-based navigation system, called NAVSTAR, originally developed for military purposes and maintained and controlled by the United States Department of Defence. It utilizes a set of at least 24 satellites which transmit precise microwave signals to the GPS receiver and allows it to determine its location, speed, direction, and time.

globalization The increasing level of global spatial flaws, interconnections, and the interdependence of people and places at a world scale, which is creating changes in the structures and organizations of society and places.

globe grid (*syn:* graticule) The set of imaginary lines of *latitude* and *longitude* that intersect at right angles to form a coordinate reference system for locating points on the surface of the earth.

GNI See *gross national income*.

gnomonic projection A *geometrical projection* produced with the light source at the centre of the earth.

graphic scale A graduate line included in a map legend by means of which distances on the map may be measured in terms of ground distances.

graticule The network of meridians and parallels on the globe; the *globe grid*.

gravity model A mathematical prediction of the interaction between two bodies as a function of their size and of the distance separating them. Based on Newton's *law of universal gravitation*, the model states that attraction (interaction) is proportional to the product of the masses (population sizes) of two bodies (places) and inversely proportional to the square of the distance between them. Thus, the force of attraction, *F*, between two masses M_i and M_j separated by distance, *d*, is

$$F = g \frac{M_i M_j}{d_{ij}^2}$$

where *g* is the "gravitational constant."

Henry C. Carey adapted Newton's formulation to demonstrate the theoretical interaction between two cities, noting that expected exchanges *(I)* between two places, *i* and *j*, can be calculated by equating physical mass in the Newton model with population size *(P)*, so that

$$I_{ij} = \frac{P_i P_j}{D_{ij}^2}$$

Exchanges (E) between any set of two cities, *A* and *B*, can therefore be quickly estimated:

$$E_{AB} = \frac{\text{Population of A} \times \text{Population of B}}{\text{Distance between A and B}^2}$$

great circle Line formed by the intersection with the earth's surface of a plane passing through the centre of the earth; an arc of a great circle is the shortest distance between two points on the earth's surface.

greenhouse effect Heating of the earth's surface as shortwave solar energy passes through the *atmosphere,* which is transparent to it but opaque to reradiated long-wave terrestrial energy; also, increasing the opacity of the atmosphere through addition of increased amounts of carbon dioxide and other gases that trap heat.

Green Revolution A term suggesting the great increases in food production, primarily in subtropical areas, accomplished through the introduction of very high-yielding grain crops, particularly wheat, maize, and rice.

grid system See *globe grid*.

gross domestic product (GDP) The total value of goods and services produced within the borders of a country during a specified time period, usually a calendar year.

gross national income (GNI) The total value of goods and services produced by a country per year plus net income earned abroad by its nationals; formerly called "gross national product."

gross national product (GNP) See *gross national income*.

groundwater Subsurface water that accumulates in the pores and cracks of rock and *soil*.

guest worker A foreign worker, usually male and frequently under contract, who migrates to secure permanent work in a host country without intention to settle permanently in that country; particularly, workers from North Africa and countries of eastern, southern, and southeastern Europe employed in industrialized countries of Western Europe.

H

hazardous waste Discarded solid, liquid, or gaseous material that poses a substantial threat to human health or to the *environment* when improperly disposed of or stored.

heartland theory The belief of Halford Mackinder (1861–1947) that the interior of Eurasia provided a likely base for world conquest.

hierarchical diffusion A form of *diffusion* in which spread of an *innovation* can proceed either upward or downward through a hierarchy.

hierarchical migration The tendency for individuals to move from small places to larger ones. See also *step migration*.

hierarchy of central places The steplike series of *urban* units in classes differentiated by both size and function.

high-level waste Nuclear waste with a relatively high level of radioactivity.

Hinduism An ancient and now dominant *value system* and *religion* of India, closely identified with Indian *culture* but without central creed, single doctrine, or religious organization. Dharma (customary duty and divine law) and *caste* are uniting elements.

hinterland The market area or region served by an *urban* centre.

homeostatic plateau (*syn:* carrying capacity) The application of the concept of homeostasis, or relatively stable state of equilibrium, to the balance between population numbers and areal resources; the equilibrium level of population that available resources can adequately support.

horticultural farming See *truck farming*.

host society The established and dominant society within which immigrant groups seek accommodation.

human geography One of the two major divisions (the other is *physical geography*) of *systematic geography;* the spatial analysis of human populations, their *cultures,* their activities and behaviours, and their relationship with and impact on the physical landscapes they occupy.

hunter-gatherer/hunting-gathering An economic and social system based primarily or exclusively on the hunting of wild animals and the gathering of food, fibre, and other materials from uncultivated plants.

hybridity A merging to varying degrees of cultural practices, beliefs, and/or technologies between two or more cultural groups.

hydrologic cycle The natural system by which water is continuously circulated through the *biosphere* by evaporation, condensation, and *precipitation.*

hydrosphere All water at or near the earth's surface that is not chemically bound in rocks, including the oceans, surface waters, *groundwater,* and water held in the *atmosphere.*

I

icebox effect The tendency for certain kinds of air pollutants to lower temperatures on earth by reflecting incoming sunlight back into space and thus preventing it from reaching (and heating) the earth.

iconography In *political geography,* a term denoting the study of symbols that unite a country.

identities Socially constructed markers of cultural differences. Among the major identities investigated by geographers include class, gender, ethnicity, religion, and language.

ideological subsystem The complex of ideas, beliefs, knowledge, and means of their communication that characterize a *culture.*

imperialism Relative to imperialism, refers to less formal controls one nation exerts on another. It is often in the form of economic influence or military control.

incinerator A facility designed to burn waste.

inclusion The granting of access to spaces and resources by an individual or cultural group to an "other" individual or cultural group.

independent invention (*syn:* parallel invention) *Innovations* developed in two or more unconnected locations by individuals or groups acting independently. See also *multilinear evolution.*

inductive research The opposite of deductive research. In inductive research, starts specific observations and measures (data), which can lead is to detect patterns and regularities (further observations and analysis), formulate some tentative hypotheses that we can explore, and finally end up developing some general conclusions and models. Demographic transition theory is an example of a model based on inductive reasoning.

Industrial Revolution The term applied to the rapid economic and social changes in agriculture and manufacturing that followed the introduction of the factory system to the textile industry of England in the last quarter of the 18th century.

infant mortality rate A refinement of the *death rate* to specify the ratio of deaths of infants age 1 year or less per 1000 live births.

informal economy See *informal sector.*

informal sector That part of a national economy that involves productive labour not subject to formal systems of control or payment; economic activity or individual enterprise operating without official recognition or measured by official statistics.

infrastructure The basic structure of services, installations, and facilities needed to support industrial, agricultural, and other economic development; included are transport and communications, along with water, power, and other public utilities.

innovation Introduction of new ideas, practices, or objects; usually, an alteration of *custom* or *culture* that originates within the social group itself.

insolation The solar radiation received at the earth's surface.

intensive agriculture Any agricultural system involving the application of large amounts of capital and/or labour per unit of cultivated land; this may be part of either a *subsistence* or a *commercial economy.*

interaction model See *gravity model.*

international boundary The outer limit of a *state's* claim to land or water surface, projected downward to the centre of the earth and, less certainly, upward to the height the state can effectively control.

International Date Line By international agreement, the designated line where each new day begins, generally following the 180th *meridian.* The line compensates for accumulated 1-hour time changes for each 15 degrees of longitude by adding (from east to west) or subtracting (from west to east) 24 hours for travellers crossing the line.

interrupting barrier A condition that delays the rate of *diffusion* of an *innovation* or that deflects its path.

intervening opportunity The concept that closer opportunities will materially reduce the attractiveness of interaction with more distant—even slightly better—alternatives; a closer alternative source of supply between a demand point and the original source of supply.

in-transit privilege The application of a single-haul *freight rate* from origin to destination even though the shipment is halted for processing en route, after which the journey is completed.

irredentism The policy of a *state* wishing to incorporate within itself territory inhabited by people who have ethnic or linguistic links with the country but that lies within a neighbouring state.

Islam A *monotheistic, universalizing* religion that includes belief in Allah as the sole deity and in Mohammed as his prophet completing the work of earlier prophets of *Judaism* and *Christianity.*

isochrone A line connecting points equidistant in travel time from a common origin.

isogloss A mapped boundary line marking the limits of a particular linguistic feature.

isoline A map line connecting points of equal value.

isotropic plain A hypothetical portion of the earth's surface assumed to be an unbounded, uniformly flat plain with uniform and unvarying distribution of population, purchasing power, transport costs, accessibility, and the like.

J

J-curve A curve shaped like the letter J, depicting exponential or geometric growth (1, 2, 4, 8, 16 . . .).

Judaism A *monotheistic, ethnic religion* first developed among the Hebrew people of the ancient Near East; its determining conditions include descent from Israel (Jacob), the Torah (law and scripture), and tradition.

K

krill A form of marine *plankton* composed of crustaceans and larvae.

L

landlocked Describing a *state* which lacks a sea coast.

land race A genetically diverse, naturally adapted, native food plant.

landscape By "land" is meant *that which sustains and surrounds us* and by "scape" is meant *view or representation*. A human landscape is literally a view of the arrangement in physical space of human activities and artifacts.

language The system of words, their pronunciation, and methods of combination used and mutually understood by a community of individuals.

language family A group of *languages* thought to have descended from a single, common ancestral tongue.

latitude Angular distance north or south of the *equator*, measured in degrees, minutes, and seconds. Grid lines marking latitudes are called *parallels*. The equator is 0° the North Pole is 90°N the South Pole is 90°S Low latitudes are considered to fall within the tropics (23° 30′ N and 23° 30′ S); midlatitudes extend from the tropics to the Arctic and Antarctic circles (66° 30′ N and S); high latitudes occur from those circles to the North and South poles.

law of peripheral neglect The observation that a government's awareness of or concern with regional problems decreases with the square of the distance of an outlying region from the capital city.

law of retail gravitation See *Reilly's law*.

leachate The contaminated liquid discharged from a *sanitary landfill* to either surface or subsurface land or water.

leaching The removal of soluble minerals from the upper soil horizons through the downward movement of water.

least-cost theory (*syn:* Weberian analysis) The view that the optimum location of a manufacturing establishment is at the place where the costs of transport and labour and the advantages of *agglomeration* or *deglomeration* are most favourable.

limiting factor principle The distribution of an organism or the structure of an *ecosystem* can be explained by the control exerted by the single factor (such as temperature, light, water) that is most deficient, that is, that falls below the levels required.

line-haul costs (*syn:* over-the-road costs) The costs involved in the actual physical movement of goods (or passengers); costs of haulage (including equipment and routeway costs), excluding *terminal costs*.

lingua franca Any of various auxiliary *languages* used as common tongues among people of an area where several languages are spoken; literally, "Frankish language."

linguistic geography (*syn:* dialect geography; dialectology) The study of local variations within a speech area by mapping word choices, pronunciations, or grammatical constructions.

link A transportation or communication connection or route within a *network*.

lithosphere The earth's solid crust.

locational interdependence The circumstance under which the locational decision of a particular firm is influenced by the locations chosen by competitors.

locational triangle A simple graphic model in *Weberian analysis* to illustrate the derivation of the least-transport-cost location of an industrial establishment.

longitude Angular distance of a location in degrees, minutes, and seconds measured east or west of a designated *prime meridian* given the value of 0°. By general agreement, the *globe grid* prime meridian passes through the old observatory of Greenwich, England. Distances are measured from 0° to 180° both east and west, with 180° E and W being the same line. For much of its extent, the 180° meridian also serves as the *International Date Line*. Because of the period of the earth's axial rotation, 15 degrees of longitude are equivalent to a difference of 1 hour in local time.

long lot A farm or other property consisting of a long, narrow strip of land extending back from a river or road.

long-range transboundary air pollution (LRTAP) Large quantities of human-emitted natural and synthetic chemicals into the atmosphere.

low-level waste Nuclear waste with relatively moderate levels of radioactivity.

M

malnutrition Food intake insufficient in quantity or deficient in quality to sustain life at optimal conditions of health.

Malthus Thomas R. Malthus (1766–1843). English economist, demographer, and cleric who suggested that unless self-control, war, or natural disaster checks population, it will inevitably increase faster than will the food supplies needed to sustain it. This view is known as Malthusianism. See also *neo-Malthusianism*.

map A two-dimensional spatial representation of the world (or part of the world).

map projection A systematic method of transferring the *globe grid* system from the earth's curved surface to the flat surface of a map. Projection automatically incurs error, but an attempt is usually made to preserve one or more (though never all) of the characteristics of the spherical surface: equal area, correct distance, true direction, proper shape.

map scale See *scale*.

marginal cost The additional cost of producing each successive unit of output.

mariculture Production and harvesting of fish and shellfish in fenced confinement areas along coasts and in estuaries.

market equilibrium The point of intersection of demand and supply curves of a given commodity; at equilibrium the market is cleared of the commodity.

market gardening See *truck farming*.

market orientation The tendency of an economic activity to locate close to its market; a reflection of large and variable distribution costs.

Marxism A political, economic and social philosophy whereby capitalist societies are critiqued and understood as a class struggle between workers and owners of business and industry

material culture The tangible, physical items produced and used by members of a specific *culture* group and reflective of their traditions, lifestyles, and technologies.

material orientation The tendency of an economic activity to locate near or at its source of raw material; this is experienced when material costs are highly variable spatially and/or represent a significant share of total costs.

mathematical location See *absolute location*.

mathematical projection The systematic rendering of the *globe grid* on a *developable surface* to achieve *graticule* characteristics not obtainable by visual means of *geometrical projection*.

maximum sustainable yield The maximum rate at which a *renewable resource* can be exploited without impairing its ability to be renewed or replenished.

Mediterranean agriculture An agricultural system based upon the mild, moist winters; hot, sunny summers; and rough terrain of the Mediterranean basin. It involves cereals as winter crops, summer tree and vine crops (olives, figs, dates, citrus and other tree fruits, and grapes), and animals (sheep and goats).

megalopolis 1: A large, sprawled *urban* complex with contained open, non-urban land, created through the spread and joining of separate *metropolitan areas;* **2:** When capitalized, the name applied to the continuous functionally urban area of coastal northeastern United States from Maine to Virginia.

mental map (*syn:* cognitive map) The maplike image of the world, country, region, city, or neighbourhood a person carries in mind. The representation is therefore subjective; it includes knowledge of actual locations and spatial relationships and is coloured by personal perceptions and preferences related to place.

mentifacts The central, enduring elements of a *culture* expressing its values and beliefs, including *language, religion, folklore,* artistic traditions, and the like. Elements in the *ideological subsystem* of culture.

Mercator projection A true *conformal cylindrical projection* first published in 1569, useful for navigation.

meridian A north-south line of *longitude;* on the *globe grid,* all meridians are of equal length and converge at the poles.

Mesolithic Middle Stone Age. The *culture* stage of the early postglacial period, during which earliest stages of *domestication* of animals and plants occurred, refined and specialized tools were developed, pottery was produced, and semipermanent settlements were established as climate change reduced the game-animal herds earlier followed for food.

metes-and-bounds survey A system of property description using natural features (streams, rocks, trees, etc.) to trace and define the boundaries of individual parcels.

metropolitan area In the United States, a large functionally integrated settlement area comprising one or more whole county units and usually containing several *urbanized areas;* discontinuously built up, it operates as a coherent economic whole.

microdistrict The basic neighbourhood planning unit characteristic of new urban residential construction in the planned East European city under communism.

microstate (*syn:* ministate) An imprecise term for a *state* or territory small in both population and area. An informal definition accepted by the United Nations suggests a maximum of 1 million population combined with a territory of less than 700 km^2 (270 sq mi).

migration The permanent (or relatively permanent) relocation of an individual or group to a new, usually distant, place of residence and employment.

migration field The area from which a given city or place draws the majority of its in-migrants.

millennium development goals (MDGs) Eight quantified targets to be met by 2015 to address key dimensions of poverty and basic needs that were the heart of the Brundtland Report.

mineral A natural inorganic substance that has a definite chemical composition and characteristic crystal structure, hardness, and density.

mineral fuel See *fossil fuel.*

ministate See *microstate.*

mobility The general term applied to all types of human territorial movement.

model An idealized representation, abstraction, or simulation of reality. It is designed to simplify real-world complexity and eliminate extraneous phenomena in order to isolate for detailed study causal factors and interrelationships of *spatial systems.*

modernity The term given to the last two to three hundred years of Western culture. The distinguishing feature of this period was arguably the rise of the Industrial Revolution, wherein there were immense cultural transformations in the ways good were produced, how people obtained food, shelter and clothing, and the very organization of the economy, politics, society, and space.

modernization theory Assumes that if the conditions in the first-world were replicated in the third world, development would occur.

monoculture Agricultural system dominated by a single crop.

monolingualism A society's or country's use of only one *language* of communication for all purposes.

monotheism The belief that there is but a single God.

mortality rate See *death rate.*

movement bias Any aggregate control on or regularity of movement of people, commodities, or communication. Included are *distance bias, direction bias,* and *network bias.*

multilinear evolution A concept of independent but parallel cultural development advanced by the anthropologist Julian Steward (1902–1972) to explain cultural similarities among widely separated peoples existing in similar environments but who could not have benefited from shared experiences, borrowed ideas, or diffused technologies. See *independent invention.*

multilingualism The common use of two or more *languages* in a society or country.

multinational corporation (MNC) A large business organization operating in a number of different national economies; the term implies a more extensive form of *transnational corporation.*

multiple-nuclei model The postulate that large cities develop by peripheral spread not from one *central business district*

but from several nodes of growth, each of specialized use. The separately expanding use districts eventually coalesce at their margins.

multiplier effect The direct, indirect, and induced consequences of change in an activity. **1:** In industrial *agglomerations,* the cumulative processes by which a given change (such as a new plant opening) sets in motion a sequence of further industrial employment and *infrastructure* growth. **2:** In *urban geography,* the expected addition of *non-basic* workers and dependents to a city's total employment and population that accompanies new *basic sector* employment.

N

NTS The National Topographic System provides general-purpose topographic map coverage of Canada. These maps depict ground relief (e.g., landforms and terrain), drainage patterns (e.g., lakes and water courses), forest cover, administrative areas, populated areas, transportation routes and facilities (including roads and railways), and other human-made features.

nation A culturally distinctive group of people occupying a specific territory and bound together by a sense of unity arising from shared *ethnicity,* beliefs, and *customs.*

nationalism A sense of unity binding the people of a *state* together; devotion to the interests of a particular country or *nation;* an identification with the state and an acceptance of national goals.

nation-state A *state* whose territory is identical to that occupied by a particular *ethnic group* or *nation.*

natural boundary (*syn:* physical boundary) A *boundary* line based on recognizable physiographic features, such as mountains or rivers.

natural hazard A process or event in the physical environment that has consequences harmful to humans.

natural increase The growth of a population through excess of births over deaths, excluding the effects of immigration or emigration.

natural landscape The physical *environment* unaffected by human activities. The duration and near totality of human occupation of the earth's surface assure that little or no "natural landscape" so defined remains intact. Opposed to *cultural landscape.*

natural resource A physically occurring item that a population perceives to be necessary and useful to its maintenance and well-being.

natural selection The process resulting in the reproductive success of individuals or groups best adapted to their environment, leading to the perpetuation of their genetic qualities.

natural vegetation The plant life that would exist in an area if humans did not interfere with its development.

neocolonialism A disparaging reference to economic and political policies by which major developed countries are seen to retain or extend influence over the economies of less developed countries and peoples.

neogeography People using and creating their own maps, on their own terms and by combining elements of an existing toolset.

neo-liberal Those who prefer the private sector or "free market" control the economy with very little government intervention. Policies include the elimination of subsidies, investment in education, health care, infrastructure, trade liberalization, deregulation, and privatization of state enterprises.

Neolithic New Stone Age. The *culture* (succeeding that of the *Mesolithic*) of the middle postglacial period, during which polished stone tools were perfected, the economy was solely or largely based on cultivation of crops and *domestication* of animals, and the arts of spinning, weaving, smelting and metal working were developed. More formalized societies and *culture complexes* emerged as cities developed and trade routes were established.

neo-Malthusianism The advocacy of population control programs to preserve and improve general national prosperity and well-being.

net migration The difference between in-migration and out-migration of an area.

network The areal pattern of sets of places and the routes (*links*) connecting them along which movement can take place.

network bias The view that the pattern of *links* in a *network* will affect the likelihood of flows between specific *nodes*.

network cities Two or more nearby cities, potentially or actually complementary in function, that cooperate by developing transportation links and communications infrastructure joining them.

nodal region See *functional region*.

node In *network* theory, an origin, destination, or intersection in a communication network.

nomadic herding Migratory but controlled movement of livestock solely dependent on natural forage.

non-basic sector (*syn:* service sector) Those economic activities of an urban unit that supply the resident population with goods and services and that have no "export" implication.

non-ecumene (*syn:* anecumene). That portion of the earth's surface that is uninhabited or only temporarily or intermittently inhabited. See also *ecumene*.

non-material culture The oral traditions, songs, and stories of a *culture* group along with its beliefs and customary behaviours.

non-renewable resource A *natural resource* that is not replenished or replaced by natural processes or is used at a rate that exceeds its replacement rate.

North The general term applied in the *Brandt Report* to the developed countries of the Northern Hemisphere plus Australia and New Zealand.

O

official language A governmentally designated *language* of instruction, of government, of the courts, and other official public and private communication.

offshoring Describes the relocation of business processes from one country to another. This includes any business process such as production, manufacturing, or service.

orthographic projection A *geometrical projection* that results from placing the light source at infinity.

outsourcing 1: Producing abroad parts or products for domestic use or sale; **2:** Subcontracting production or services rather than performing those activities "in house."

overpopulation A value judgment that the resources of an area are insufficient to sustain adequately its present population numbers.

over-the-road costs See *line-haul costs*.

ozone A gas molecule consisting of three atoms of oxygen (O_3) formed when diatomic oxygen (O_2) is exposed to *ultraviolet radiation*. In the upper *atmosphere* it forms a normally continuous, thin layer that blocks ultraviolet light; in the lower atmosphere it constitutes a damaging component of *photochemical smog*.

P

Paleolithic Old Stone Age. An early stage of human *culture* largely coinciding with the *Pleistocene* glacial period. Characterized by *hunting-gathering* economies and the use of fire and simple stone tools, especially those made from flint.

parallel invention See *independent invention*.

parallel of latitude An east-west line of *latitude* indicating distance north or south of the equator.

patriarchy A learned way of doing and thinking that privileges males and certain forms of masculinity over women and femininity.

pattern The design or arrangement of phenomena in earth space.

peak value intersection The most accessible and costly parcel of land in the *central business district* and, therefore, in the entire *urbanized area*.

perception The acquisition of information about a place or thing through sensory means; the subjective organization and interpretation of acquired information in light of cultural attitudes and individual preferences or experiences. See *environmental perception*.

perceptual region A *region* perceived to exist by its inhabitants or the general populace. Also known as a *vernacular region* or popular region, it has reality as an element of *popular culture* or *folk culture* represented in the *mental maps* of average people.

perforated state A *state* whose territory is interrupted ("perforated") by a separate, independent state totally contained within its borders.

periodic market A market operating at a particular location (village, city, neighbourhood) on one or more fixed days per week or month.

periphery/peripheral The outer regions or boundaries of an area. See also *core-periphery model*.

periphery regions Have underdeveloped or very specialized economies characterized by old technologies and low levels of productivity.

permeable barrier An obstacle raised by a culture group or one culture group's reluctance to accept some, but not all, innovations diffused from a related but different *culture*. Acceptance or rejection may be conditioned by religious, political, ethnic, or similar considerations of suitability or compatibility.

personal communication field An area defined by the distribution of an individual's short-range informal communications. The size and shape of the field are defined by work, recreation, school, and other regular contacts and are affected by age, sex, employment, and other personal characteristics.

personal space An invisible, usually irregular area around a person into which he or she does not willingly admit others. The sense (and extent) of personal space is a situational and cultural variable.

perspective projection See *geometrical projection.*

photochemical smog A form of polluted air produced by the interaction of hydrocarbons and oxides of nitrogen in the presence of sunlight.

physical boundary See *natural boundary.*

physical geography One of two major divisions (the other is *human geography*) of *systematic geography;* the study of the structures, processes, distributions, and change through time of the natural phenomena of the earth's surface that are significant to human life.

physical landscape The *natural landscape* plus visible elements of *material culture.*

physiological density The number of persons per unit area of cultivable land.

pidgin An auxiliary *language* derived, with reduced vocabulary and simplified structure, from other languages. Not a native tongue, it is used for limited communication among people with different languages.

placelessness The loss of locally distinctive characteristics and identity and replacement by standardized landscapes.

place perception See *perception.*

place utility **1:** In human movement and *migration* studies, a measure of an individual's perceived satisfaction or approval of a place in its social, economic, or environmental attributes. **2:** In *economic geography,* the value imparted to goods or services by *tertiary* activities that provide things needed in specific markets.

planar projection (*syn:* azimuthal projection) A *map projection* employing a plane as the presumed *developable surface.*

plankton Microscopic freely floating plant and animal organisms of lakes and oceans.

planned economy A system of production of goods and services, usually consumed or distributed by a governmental agency, in quantities, at prices, and in locations determined by governmental program.

plantation A large agricultural holding, frequently foreign owned, devoted to the production of a single export crop.

Pleistocene The geological epoch dating from 2 million to 11 thousand years ago during which four stages of continental glaciation occurred.

political ecology A set of approaches to the study of relationships between nature and society. The first studies society and land-based resources, and suggests that poverty, via poor management can induce environmental degradation (e.g., erosion), which further contributes to poverty. A second will promote the completion of regional or local research studies in order to examine how different types of decision making contribute to or reduce environmental degradation. A third will look management and the role of government and core-periphery relationships.

political geography A branch of *human geography* concerned with the spatial analysis of political phenomena.

pollution The introduction into the biosphere of materials that because of their quantity, chemical nature, or temperature have a negative impact on the *ecosystem* or that cannot be readily disposed of by natural recycling processes.

polytheism Belief in or worship of many gods.

popular culture The constantly changing mix of material and non-material elements available through mass production and the mass media to an urbanized, heterogeneous, non-traditional society.

popular region See *vernacular region.*

population density A measurement of the numbers of persons per unit area of land within predetermined limits, usually political or census boundaries. See also *physiological density.*

population geography A division of *human geography* concerned with spatial variations in distribution, composition, growth, and movements of population and the relationship of those concerns with the geographic character of areas.

population momentum (*syn:* demographic momentum) The tendency for population growth to continue despite stringent family planning programs because of a relatively high concentration of people in the chilbearing years.

population projection A statement of a population's future size, age, and sex composition based on the application of stated assumptions to current data.

population pyramid A bar graph in pyramid form showing the age and sex composition of a population, usually a national one.

positional dispute (*syn:* boundary dispute) In *political geography,* disagreement about the actual location of a *boundary.*

possibilism The philosophical viewpoint that the physical *environment* offers human beings a set of opportunities from which (within limits) people may choose according to their cultural needs and technological awareness. The emphasis is on a freedom of choice and action not allowed under *environmental determinism.*

postindustrial A stage of economic development in which service activities become relatively more important than goods production; professional and technical employment supersedes employment in agriculture and manufacturing; and level of living is defined by the quality of services and amenities rather than by the quantity of goods available.

potential model A measurement of the total interaction opportunities available under *gravity model* assumptions to a centre in a multicentre system.

power An uneven social relationship wherein a person, cultural group, institution, or country has the ability to influence, if not determine, the actions of the weaker or subordinate other.

precipitation All moisture—solid and liquid—that falls to the earth's surface from the *atmosphere.*

predevelopment annexation The inclusion within the *central city* of non-urban peripheral areas for the purpose of securing to the city itself the benefits of their eventual development.

primary activities Those parts of the economy involved in making *natural resources* available for use or further processing; included are mining, *agriculture,* forestry, fishing and hunting, and grazing.

primary data Data collected by the researchers themselves. It may be qualitative and/or quantitative data. Examples include surveys, interviews, field observations, and participant observation.

primary industries Those that make staples (or natural resources) available for use or further processing.

primate city A country's leading city, disproportionately larger and functionally more complex than any other; a city dominating an urban hierarchy composed of a base of small towns and an absence of intermediate-sized cities.

prime meridian An imaginary line passing through the Royal Observatory at Greenwich, England, serving by agreement as the 0° line of *longitude.*

private plot In the planned economies under communism, a small garden plot allotted to collective farmers and urban workers.

probabilism A view that suggest that the environment provides humans with a range of choices, with some more likely than others based on environmental characteristics. Can be perceived as being a middle ground between environmental determinism and possibilism.

projection See *map projection.*

prorupt state A *state* of basically *compact* form but with one or more narrow extensions of territory.

protolanguage An assumed, reconstructed, or recorded ancestral *language.*

proved reserves That portion of a *natural resource* that has been identified and can be extracted profitably with current technology.

psychological distance The way an individual perceives distance.

pull factors Characteristics of a locale that act as attractive forces, drawing migrants from other regions.

purchasing power parity (PPP) A monetary measurement which takes account of what money actually buys in each country.

push factors Unfavourable characteristics of a locale that contribute to the dissatisfaction of its residents and impel their emigration.

Q

qualitative data Consist of in-depth answers and responses that come from the kind of open-ended questions asked in focus groups.

quantitative data Originate from responses to structured questions (e.g., Do you agree or disagree? Circle a number from 1 to 5). Results from these types of questions can be summarized with numbers (e.g., totals, percentages, averages). They can also reflect "count data," such as those derived through the census.

quaternary activities Those parts of the economy concerned with research, with the gathering and dissemination of information, and with administration—including administration of the other economic activity levels; often considered only as a specialized subdivision of *tertiary activities.*

quinary activities A sometimes separately recognized subsection of *tertiary activity* management functions involving highest-level decision making in all types of large organizations. Also deemed the most advanced form of the *quaternary* subsector.

R

race A subset of human population whose members share certain distinctive, inherited biological characteristics.

racism An ideology whereby people are classified into distinct "races," based solely on arbitrary physical criteria. Racist actions, attitudes, and policies attribute social, cultural and cognitive characteristics to people based on "race," a socially constructed identity that lacks biological foundation.

radical geographies A term emerging in the 1970s that covered a number of philosophies that challenged dominant and generally accepted views of the world. Marism, structuralism, socialism politcal ecology andfeminism are examples of some philosophies that are considered 'radical' because they question 'coventional wisdom' and accepted norms and practices.

rank-size rule An observed regularity in the city-size distribution of some countries. In a rank-size hierarchy, the population of any given town will be inversely proportional to its rank in the hierarchy; that is, the *n*th-ranked city will be 1/*n* the size of the largest city.

rate The frequency of an event's occurrence during a specified time period.

rate of natural increase *Birth rate* minus the *death rate,* suggesting the annual rate of population growth without considering *net migration.*

reapportionment The process and outcome of a reallocation of electoral seats to defined territories, such as congressional seats to states of the United States.

recycling The reuse of disposed materials after they have passed through some form of treatment (e.g., melting down glass bottles to produce new bottles).

redistricting The drawing of new electoral district boundary lines in response to changing patterns of population or changing legal requirements.

region Any earth area with distinctive and unifying physical or cultural characteristics that set it off and make it substantially different from surrounding areas. A region may be defined on the basis of its homogeneity or its functional integration as a single organizational unit. Regions and their boundaries are devices of areal generalization, intellectual concepts rather than visible landscape entities.

regional autonomy A measure of self-governance afforded a subdivision of a *state.*

regional concept The view that physical and cultural phenomena on the surface of the earth are rationally arranged by complex, diverse, but comprehensible interrelated spatial processes.

regional dialect (*syn:* geographic dialect) See *dialect.*

regional geography The study of geographic *regions;* the study of areal differentiation.

regionalism In *political geography,* group—frequently ethnic group—identification with a particular region of a *state* rather than with the state as a whole.

Reilly's law Also known as the *law of retail gravitation;* the proposition by William J. Reilly that the breaking point or boundary marking the outer edge of either of two cities' trade areas is located by the expression

$$BP = \frac{d_{ij}}{1 + \sqrt{\dfrac{P_2}{P_1}}}$$

where

BP = distance from city 1 to the breaking point (or boundary)

d_{ij} = distance between city 1 and city 2

P_1 = population of city 1

P_2 = population of city 2

relational direction See *relative direction.*

relative direction (*syn:* relational direction) A culturally based locational reference, as the Far West, the Old South, or the Middle East.

relative distance A transformation of *absolute distance* into such relative measures as time or monetary costs. Such measures yield different explanations of human spatial behaviour than do linear distances alone. Distances between places are constant by absolute terms, but relative distances may vary with improvements in transportation or communication technology or with different psychological perceptions of space.

relative location The position of a place or activity in relation to other places or activities. Relative location implies spatial relationships and usually suggests the relative advantages or disadvantages of a location with respect to all competing locations.

relic boundary A former *boundary* line that is still discernible and marked by some *cultural landscape* feature.

religion A personal or institutionalized system of worship and of faith in the sacred and divine.

relocation diffusion The transfer of ideas, behaviours, or articles from one place to another through the *migration* of those possessing the feature transported; also, spatial relocation in which a phenomenon leaves an area of origin as it is transported to a new location.

remote sensing Any of several techniques of obtaining images of an area or object without having the sensor in direct physical contact with it, as by aerial photography or satellite sensors.

renewable resource A *natural resource* that is potentially inexhaustible either because it is constantly (as solar radiation) or periodically (as *biomass*) replenished as long as its use does not exceed its *maximum sustainable yield.*

replacement level The number of children per woman that will supply just enough births to replace parents and compensate for early deaths, with no allowance for *migration* effects; usually calculated at between 2.1 and 2.5 children.

representative fraction The *scale* of a map expressed as a ratio of a unit of distance on the map to distance measured in the same unit on the ground, e.g., 1:250,000.

reserve Land areas, both rural and urban, "reserved" for the exclusive use of First Nations peoples.

residential density The number of people living in an urban area divided by the area of the residential land.

resource See *natural resource.*

resource dispute In *political geography,* disagreement over the control or use of shared resources, such as boundary rivers or jointly claimed fishing grounds.

return migration See *counter migration.*

rhumb line A directional line that crosses each successive *meridian* at a constant angle.

rimland theory The belief of Nicholas Spykman (1894–1943) that domination of the coastal fringes of Eurasia would provide a base for world conquest.

rotation See *crop rotation.*

roundwood Timber as it is harvested, before squaring, sawing, or pulping.

S

Sahel The semiarid zone between the Sahara desert and the grassland areas to the south in West Africa; a district of recurring drought, famine, and environmental degradation and *desertification.*

salinization The process by which *soil* becomes saturated with salt, rendering the land unsuitable for *agriculture.* This occurs when land that has poor drainage is improperly irrigated.

sanitary landfill Disposal of solid wastes by spreading them in layers covered with enough soil to control odours, rodents, and flies; sited to minimize water pollution from runoff and *leachate.*

satisficing location A less-than-ideal best location, but one providing an acceptable level of utility or satisfaction.

scale 1: In cartography, the ratio between the size of area on a map and the actual size of that same area on the earth's surface. **2:** In more general terms, scale refers to the size of the area studied, from local to global.

S-curve The horizontal bending, or leveling, of an exponential or *J-curve.*

secondary activities Those parts of the economy involved in the processing of raw materials derived from *primary activities* and in altering or combining materials to produce commodities of enhanced utility and value; included are manufacturing, construction, and power generation.

secondary data Data that has not been collected directly by the researcher(s). Instead, data have been collected by individuals or public/private agencies that are not connected to the research project. Examples include surveys completed by a government/private agency. The census is an example of a secondary data source.

sector model A description of urban land uses as wedge-shaped sectors radiating outward from the *central business district* along transportation corridors. The radial access routes attract particular uses to certain sectors, with high-status residential uses occupying the most desirable wedges.

secularism A rejection of or indifference to *religion* and religious practice.

segregation A measure of the degree to which members of a minority group are not uniformly distributed among the total population.

semi-periphery regions Falling between core and peripheral regions, these areas are able to exploit nearby peripheral areas, but are themselves exploited and dominated by the core regions. They are not countries that were once peripheral, indicating that peripheral status (and possibly core status) is not permanent.

separatism See *ethnic separatism.*

service sector See *non-basic sector.*

sex ratio The ratio of males to females in a population.

sexism Actions, attitudes and policies that discriminate against people based solely on their biological sex.

shamanism A form of *tribal religion* based on belief in a hidden world of gods, ancestral spirits, and demons responsive only to a shaman or interceding priest.

shifting cultivation (*syn:* slash-and-burn agriculture; swidden agriculture) Crop production on tropical forest clearings kept in cultivation until their quickly declining fertility is lost. Cleared plots are then abandoned and new sites are prepared.

Shinto The *polytheistic, ethnic religion* of Japan that includes reverence of deities of natural forces and veneration of the emperor as descendent of the sun-goddess.

site The *absolute location* of a place or activity described by local relief, landform, and other physical (or sometimes cultural) characteristics.

situation The *relative location* of a place or activity in relation to the physical and cultural characteristics of the larger regional or *spatial system* of which it is a part. Situation implies spatial interconnection and interdependence.

slash-and-burn cultivation See *shifting cultivation.*

social area An area identified by homogeneity of the social indices (age group, socioeconomic status, *ethnicity*) of its population.

social dialect See *dialect.*

social distance A measure of the perceived degree of social separation between individuals, *ethnic groups,* neighbourhoods, or other groupings; the voluntary or enforced *segregation* of two or more distinct social groups for most activities.

social geography The branch of *cultural geography* that studies *social areas* and the social use of space, especially urban space; the study of the *spatial distribution* of social groups and of the processes underlying that distribution.

social housing Public housing and all third sector housing funded in part or in whole by the government.

social mapping Maps that tell people something about a place.

Socialism A social system based on common ownership of the means to produce and distribute products.

sociofacts The institutions and links between individuals and groups that unite a *culture,* including family structure and political, educational, and religious institutions. Components of the *sociological subsystem* of culture.

sociological subsystem The totality of expected and accepted patterns of interpersonal relations common to a *culture* or subculture.

soil The complex mixture of loose material including minerals, organic and inorganic compounds, living organisms, air, and water found at the earth's surface and capable of supporting plant life.

soil erosion See *erosion.*

solar energy Radiation from the sun, which is transformed into heat primarily at the earth's surface and secondarily in the *atmosphere.*

South The general term applied in the *Brandt Report* to the poor, developing countries of the world, generally (but not totally) located in the Southern Hemisphere.

space A theoretically dense concept which in the context of cultural geography has at least three different meanings: **(1)** space as *physical location* refers to the actual space occupied by someone or something; **(2)** space as *social status* refers to the rank or place of a person, group or institution in social space; **(3)** and spaces of *lived experience* refer to the sites, situations, and places encountered in the course of everyday life.

space–time compression/ convergence Expressions of the extent to which improvements in transportation and communication have reduced distance barriers and permitted, for example, the instantaneous *diffusion* of ideas across space.

space-time prism A diagram of the volume of space and the length of time within which our activities are confined by constraints of our bodily needs (eating, resting) and the means of mobility at our command.

spatial Of or pertaining to space on the earth's surface. Often a synonym for *geographical* and used as an adjective to describe specific geographic concepts or processes, as *spatial interaction* or *diffusion.*

spatial assimilation The overlap, intersection, and sharing of physical space between two previously separate cultural groups (e.g., immigrants and hosts).

spatial diffusion See *diffusion.*

spatial distribution The arrangement of things on the earth's surface; the descriptive elements of spatial distribution are *density, dispersion,* and *pattern.*

spatial interaction The movement (e.g., of people, goods, information) between different places; an indication of interdependence between different geographic locations or areas.

spatially fixed cost An input cost in manufacturing that remains constant wherever production is located.

spatially variable cost An input cost in manufacturing that changes significantly from place to place in its amount and its relative share of total costs.

spatial margin of profitability The set of points delimiting the area within which a firm's profitable operation is possible.

spatial search The process by which individuals evaluate the alternative locations to which they might move.

spatial system The arrangement and integrated operation of phenomena produced by or responding to spatial processes on the earth's surface.

speech community A group of people having common characteristic patterns of vocabulary, word arrangement, and pronunciation.

spine In *urban geography,* a continuation of the features of the *central business district* outward along the main wide boulevard characteristic of Latin American cities.

spread effect (*syn:* trickle-down effect) The diffusion outward of the benefits of economic growth and prosperity from the power centre or *core area* to poorer districts and people.

spring wheat Wheat sown in spring for ripening during the summer or autumn.

standard language A *language* substantially uniform with respect to spelling, grammar, pronunciation, and vocabulary and representing the approved community norm of the tongue.

standard line Line of contact between a projection surface and the globe; transformed from the sphere to the plane surface without distortion.

staples theory An unprocessed or raw commodity (good) that dominates an economy's exports. Fish, wheat and flour, timber, and furs are all considered Canadian staple products.

state (*syn:* country) An independent political unit occupying a defined, permanently populated territory and having full sovereign control over its internal and foreign affairs.

state farm In the former Soviet Union (and other planned economies), a government agricultural enterprise operated with paid employees.

step (stepwise) migration A *migration* in which an eventual long-distance relocation is undertaken in stages as, for example, from farm to village to small town to city. See also *hierarchical migration.*

stereographic projection A *geometrical projection* that results from placing the light source at the *antipode.*

stimulus diffusion A form of *expansion* diffusion in which a fundamental idea, though not the specific trait itself, stimulates imitative behaviour within a receptive population.

structural assimilation The distribution of immigrant ethnics among the groups and social strata of a *host society,* but without their full *behavioural assimilation* into it.

structuralism A philosophy that seeks to understand society and culture by revealing the larger order and forms—the structures—that major forms or structures of society and culture has order and form—a structure—and by revealing these forms we can understand meanings.

subsequent boundary A *boundary* line that is established after the area in question has been settled and that considers the cultural characteristics of the bounded area.

subsistence agriculture Any of several farm economies in which most crops are grown for food nearly exclusively for local or family consumption.

subsistence economy An economic system of relatively simple technology in which people produce most or all of the goods to satisfy their own and their family's needs; little or no exchange occurs outside of the immediate or extended family.

substitution principle In industry, the tendency to substitute one factor of production for another in order to achieve optimum plant location.

suburb A functionally specialized segment of a large *urban* complex located outside the boundaries of the *central city;* usually, a relatively homogeneous residential community, separately incorporated and administered.

superimposed boundary A *boundary* line placed over and ignoring an existing cultural pattern.

super-organic By "super" is meant *above or beyond* and "organic" in this instance refers to *human beings.* A super-organic interpretation of culture renders culture above and beyond human control. This conception is regarded as false because humans themselves create cultures.

supranationalism Term applied to associations created by three or more states for their mutual benefit and achievement of shared objectives.

sustained yield The practice of balancing harvesting with growth of new stocks so as to avoid depletion of the *resource* and ensure a perpetual supply.

swidden agriculture See *shifting cultivation.*

syncretism The development of a new form of *culture trait* by the fusion of two or more distinct parental elements.

systematic geography A division of geography that selects a particular aspect of the physical or cultural *environment* for detailed study of its areal differentiation and interrelationships. Branches of systematic geography are labelled according to the topic studied (e.g., recreational geography) or the related science with which the branch is associated (e.g., *economic geography*).

systems analysis An approach to the study of large systems through (**1**) segregation of the entire system into its component parts, (**2**) investigation of the interactions between system elements, and (**3**) study of inputs, outputs, flows, interactions, and boundaries within the system.

T

Taoism (*syn:* Daoism) A Chinese *value system* and *ethnic religion* emphasizing conformity to Tao (Way), the creative reality ordering the universe.

tapering principle A *distance decay* observation of the diminution or tapering of costs of transportation with increasing distance from the point of origin of the shipment because of the averaging of *fixed costs* over a greater number of miles of travel.

technological subsystem The complex of material objects together with the techniques of their use by means of which people carry out their productive activities.

technology The integrated system of knowledge, skills, tools, and methods developed within or used by a *culture* to successfully carry out purposeful and productive tasks.

technology gap The contrast between the *technology* available in developed *core regions* and that present in *peripheral areas* of *underdevelopment*.

technology transfer The *diffusion* to or acquisition by one *culture* or *region* of the *technology* possessed by another, usually more developed, society.

terminal costs (*syn:* fixed costs of transportation) The costs incurred, and charged, for loading and unloading freight at origin and destination points and for the paperwork involved; costs charged each shipment for terminal facility use and unrelated to distance of movement or *line-haul costs*.

terms of trade The ratio of export prices to import prices. In the context of international trade, the terms of trade for peripheral countries with core countries deteriorates when they must produce more goods (often raw materials) in order to purchase the same amount of goods (often manufactured goods) or goods protected by patents.

terracing The practice of planting crops on steep slopes that have been converted into a series of horizontal step-like level plots (terraces).

territorial dispute (*syn:* boundary dispute; functional dispute) In *political geography,* disagreement between *states* over the control of surface area.

territoriality An individual or group attempt to identify and establish control over a clearly defined territory considered partially or wholly an exclusive domain; the behaviour associated with the defense of the home territory.

territorial production complex A design in former Soviet economic planning for large regional industrial, mining, and agricultural development leading to regional self-sufficiency, diversification, and the creation of specialized production for a larger national market.

terrorism Systematic open and covert action employing fear and terror as a means of political coercion.

tertiary activities Those parts of the economy that fulfill the exchange function, that provide market availability of commodities, and that bring together consumers and providers of services; included are wholesale and retail trade, associated transportational and governmental services, and personal and professional services of all kinds.

thematic map A map depicting a specific *spatial distribution* or statistical variation of abstract objects (e.g., unemployment) in space.

Third World Originally (1950s), designating countries uncommitted to either the "First World" Western capitalist bloc or the Eastern "Second World" communist bloc; subsequently, a term applied to countries considered not yet fully developed or in a state of *underdevelopment* in economic and social terms.

threshold In *economic geography* and *central place theory,* the minimum market needed to support the supply of a product or service.

time-distance decay An influence on the rate of *expansion diffusion* of an idea, observing that the spread or acceptance of an idea is usually delayed as distance from the source of the innovation increases.

time–space convergence The concept that the world is "shrinking," as the time required to travel between locations decreases.

tipping point The degree of neighbourhood racial or ethnic mixing that induces the former majority group to move out rapidly.

toponym A place name.

toponymy The place names of a region or, especially, the study of place names.

total fertility rate (TFR) The average number of children that would be born to each woman if during her childbearing years she bore children at the current year's rate for women that age.

town A nucleated settlement that contains a *central business district* but that is small and less functionally complex than a *city*.

toxic waste Discarded chemical substances that can cause serious illness or death.

traditional religion See *tribal religion*.

tragedy of the commons The observation that in the absence of collective control over the use of a resource available to all, it is to the advantage of all users to maximize their separate shares even though their collective pressures may diminish total yield or destroy the resource altogether.

transculturation A term describing the relatively equal exchange of cultural outlooks and ways of life between two culture groups; it suggests more extensive cross-cultural influences than does *acculturation*.

transferability Acceptable costs of a spatial exchange; the cost of moving a commodity relative to the ability of the commodity to bear that cost.

transnational corporation (TNC) A large business organization operating in at least two separate national economies; a form of *multinational corporation*.

transnational migration space The network promoted through the proliferation of mobile phones and the sharp drop in calling costs have helped foreign workers maintain strong social networks with those left behind in their home countries, as well as other compatriots who may be living nearby. In this space has been enabled by advances in and relatively low cost associated with transportation and communication technologies.

tribal religion (*syn:* traditional religion) An *ethnic religion* specific to a small, localized, preindustrial culture group.

trickle-down effect See *spread effect*.

tropical rain forest Tree cover composed of tall, high-crowned evergreen deciduous species, associated with the continuously wet tropical lowlands.

truck farming (*syn:* horticultural farming; market gardening) The intensive production of fruits and vegetables for market rather than for processing or canning.

U

ubiquitous industry A *market-oriented* industry whose establishments are distributed in direct proportion to the distribution of population.

ultraviolet (UV) radiation Electromagnetic radiation from the sun with wavelengths shorter than the violet end of visible light and longer than X-rays.

underdevelopment A level of economic and social achievement below what could be reached—given the natural and human resources of an area—were necessary capital and technology available.

underpopulation A value statement reflecting the view that an area has too few people in relation to its resources and population-supporting capacity.

uniform plain See *isotropic plain.*

uniform region See *formal region.*

unitary state A *state* in which the central government dictates the degree of local or *regional autonomy* and the nature of local governmental units; a country with few cultural conflicts and with a strong sense of national identity.

United Nations Convention on the Law of the Sea (UNCLOS) A code of maritime law approved by the United Nations in 1982 that authorizes, among other provisions, territorial waters extending 12 nautical miles (22 km) from shore and 200-nautical-mile-wide (370-km-wide) *exclusive economic zones.*

universal transverse mercator (UTM) A coordinate system often incorporated into global positioning systems.

universalizing religion A *religion* that claims global truth and applicability and seeks the conversion of all humankind.

urban Characteristic of, belonging to, or related to a city or town; the opposite of rural. An agglomerated settlement whose inhabitants are primarily engaged in non-agricultural occupations.

urban density The number of people inhabiting an urban area divided by the total area of urban land.

urban geography The geographical study of cities; the branch of *human geography* concerned with the spatial aspects of **(1)** the locations, functional structures, size hierarchies, and intercity relationships of national or regional systems of cities, and **(2)** the *site,* evolution, *economic base,* internal land use, and social geographic patterns of individual cities.

urban hierarchy A ranking of cities based on their size and functional complexity.

urban influence zone An area outside of a *city* that is nevertheless affected by the city.

urban sustainability The integration of economic, social, and environmental considerations into decision making processes that will directly and indirectly influence urban quality of life over the long term.

urbanization Transformation of a population from rural to *urban* status; the process of city formation and expansion.

urbanized area A continuously built-up *urban* landscape defined by building and population densities with no reference to the political boundaries of the city; it may contain a *central city* and many contiguous towns, *suburbs,* and unincorporated areas.

usable reserves Mineral deposits that have been identified and can be recovered at current prices and with current technology.

V

value system *Mentifacts* of the *ideological subsystem* of a *culture* summarizing its common beliefs, understandings, expectations, and controls.

variable cost A cost of enterprise operation that varies either by output level or by location of the activity.

variable costs of transportation See *line-haul costs.*

verbal scale A statement of the relationship between units of measure on a map and distance on the ground, as "one inch represents one mile."

vernacular 1: The non-standard indigenous *language* or *dialect* of a locality. **2:** Of or related to indigenous arts and architecture, such as a *vernacular house.* **3:** Of or related to the perceptions and understandings of the general population, such as a *vernacular region.*

vernacular house An indigenous style of building constructed of native materials to traditional plan, without formal drawings.

vernacular region A region perceived and defined by its inhabitants, usually with a popularly given or accepted nickname.

von Thünen model Model developed by Johann Heinrich von Thünen

(1783–1850), German economist and landowner, to explain the forces that control the prices of agricultural commodities and how those variable prices affect patterns of agricultural land utilization.

von Thünen rings The concentric zonal pattern of agricultural land use around a single market centre proposed in the *von Thünen model.*

W

water table The upper limit of the saturated zone and therefore of *groundwater.*

wattle and daub A building technique featuring walls of interwoven twigs, branches, or poles (wattles) plastered (daubed) with clay and mud.

Weberian analysis See *least-cost theory.*

winter wheat Wheat sown in fall for ripening the following spring or summer.

world city One of a small number of interconnected, internationally dominant centres (e.g., New York, London, Tokyo) that together control the global systems of finance and commerce.

world-systems theory An interdependent economic system of countries, linked through trade and the flow of funds. It has both spatial and socio-economic dimensions.

X

xenophobia/ethnophobia The fear of or aversion to strangers or foreigners, often manifesting itself in the form of *ethnophobia:* fear of a particular ethnic group.

Z

zero population growth (ZPG) A term suggesting a population in equilibrium, fully stable in numbers with births (plus immigration) equaling deaths (plus emigration).

zoning Designating by ordinance areas in a municipality for particular types of land use.

zonal model See *concentric zone model.*

Abrahamson, Mark. *Global Cities.* New York: Oxford University Press, 2004.

Abramovitz, Janet N. *Imperiled Waters, Impoverished Future: The Decline of Freshwater Ecosystems.* Worldwatch Paper 128. Washington, D.C.: Worldwatch Institute, 1996.

Adams, Michael. *Unlikely Utopia: The Surprising Triumph of Canadian Pluralism.* Toronto: Viking Canada, 2007.

Agnew, John. *Geopolitics: Re-Visioning World Politics,* 2nd ed. New York: Routledge, 2003.

Agnew, John, David N. Livingstone, and Alisdair Rogers, eds. *Human Geography: An Essential Anthology.* Cambridge, Mass.: Blackwell, 1996.

Alberta Department of Energy. "Oil Sands." *Energy.* (2006): www.energy. gov.ab.ca/89.asp.

Allen, James P., and Eugene Turner. "Spatial Patterns of Immigrant Assimilation." *Professional Geography* 48, no. 2 (1996): 140–155.

Allen, James P., and Eugene Turner. *We the People: An Atlas of America's Ethnic Diversity.* New York: Macmillan, 1988.

Armstrong, R. Warwick, and Jerome D. Fellmann. "Health: One World or Two." In *The New Third World,* 2nd ed., edited by Alonso Gonzalez and Jim Norwine, pp. 75–92. Boulder: Westview Press, 1998.

Arreola, Daniel D. "Urban Ethnic Landscape Identity." *Geographical Review* 85, no. 3 (1995): 527–543.

Ashford, Lori S. "New Perspectives on Population: Lessons from Cairo." *Population Bulletin* 50, no. 1. Washington, D.C.: Population Reference Bureau, 1995.

Atkins, Peter J., and Ian Bowler. *Food in Society: Economy, Culture, Geography.* New York: Oxford University Press, 2001.

Ayres, Ed. "The Shadow Economy." *WorldWatch* 9 (1996): 10–23.

Bailey, Robert G. *Ecosystem Geography.* New York/Berlin: Springer Verlag, 1996.

Bauder, H., and Sharpe, B. "Visible Minorities in Canada's Gateway Cities." *The Canadian Geographer* 46 no. 3 2002: 204–222.

Baudrillard, J. "Modernity." *Canadian Journal of Political and Social Theory.* 11(1987): 63–72.

Beaujot, R. and D. Kerr. *Population Change in Canada,* 2nd ed. Toronto: Oxford University Press.

Beaverstock, J. V., P. J. Taylor, and R. G. Smith. "A Roster of World Cities." *Cities* 16, no. 6, 1999: 445–458.

Beaverstock, Jonathan V., Richard G. Smith, and Peter J. Taylor. "World-City Network: A New Metageography?" *Annals of the Association of American Geographers* 90, no. 1 (2000): 123–134.

Beenstock, Michael. *Health, Migration and Development.* (England: Gower Publishing Company, 1980).

Bell, Melinda. "Is Our Climate Unstable?" *Earth* 3, no. 1 (January 1994): 24–31.

Berry, Brian J. L. "An Inductive Approach to the Regionalization of Economic Development." In *Essays on Geography and Economic Development,* edited by Norton Ginsburg, pp. 78–107. Chicago: University of Chicago, Department of Geography, Research Paper No. 62, 1960.

Berry, Brian J. L., Edgar C. Conkling, and D. Michael Ray. *The Global Economy in Transition.* Upper Saddle River, N.J.: Prentice Hall, 1997.

Berry, Kate A. and Martha L. Henderson, eds. *Geographical Identities of Ethnic America.* Reno: University of Nevada Press, 2002.

Black, Jan K. *Development in Theory and Practice: Paradigms and Paradoxes.* 2nd ed. Boulder: Westview Press, 1999.

Blaikie, Piers. *The Economy of Soil Erosion.* London: Longman, 1985.

Blake, Gerald H., ed. *Maritime Boundaries.* New York: Routledge, 1994.

Blaut, James M. "Two Views of Diffusion." *Annals of the Association of American Geographers* 67, no. 3 (1977): 345–349.

Bone, R. M. *The Regional Geography of Canada.* Toronto: Oxford University Press, 2005.

Bongaarts, John. "Population Pressure and the Food Supply System in the Developing World." *Population and Development Review* 22, no. 3 (1996): 483–503.

Boserup, Ester. "Development Theory: An Analytical Framework and Selected Applications." *Population and Development Review* 22, no. 3 (1996): 505–515.

Boserup, Ester. *Woman's Role in Economic Development.* London: Allen & Unwin, 1970.

Boserup, Ester. *The Conditions of Agricultural Change: The Economics of Agrarian Change under Population Pressure.* London, England: Allyn & Unwin, 1965.

Bowen, Dawn S. "Die Auswanderung: Religion, Culture, and Migration Among Old Colony Mennonites." *The Canadian Geographer* 45 (4) (2001): 461–473.

Bowles, G. and R. Duelli-Klein. *Theories of Women's Studies.* London: Routledge and Kegan-Paul, 1983.

Boyd, Andrew. *An Atlas of World Affairs.* 10th ed. New York: Routledge, 1998.

Boyle, Paul, and Keith Halfacre, eds. *Migration and Gender in the Developed World.* New York: Routledge, 1999.

Bradley, R. "1000 Years of Climate Change." *Science* 288 (May 26, 2000): 1353–1355.

Brandes, O., K. Ferguson, M. M'Gonigle, and C. Sandborn. *At a Watershed: Ecological Governance and Sustainable Water Management in Canada.* Victoria: POLIS Project on Ecological Governance. 2005. Available at: www. waterdsm.org/PDF/atawatershed.pdf

Brewer, Cynthia, and Trudy Suchan. *Mapping Census 2000: The Geography of U.S. Diversity.* Washington, D.C.: U.S. Bureau of the Census, 2001.

Brookes, D., L. Nowlan, O. Brandes and A. Hurley. *Controlling Our Thirst: Managing Water Demands and Allocations in Canada.* Edmonton: The Walter and Duncan Gordon Foundation. 10 pp. 2004.

Brown, Lawrence A. *Innovation Diffusion: A New Perspective.* London and New York: Methuen, 1981.

Brown, Lester R. "Beyond the Oil Peak." In *Plan B 2.0: Rescuing a Planet Under Stress and a Civilization in Trouble,* pp. 21–40. New York: W. W. Norton & Co., 2006.

Brown, Lester R., et al. *State of the World.* Washington, D.C.: Worldwatch Institute. Annual.

Brown, Lester R., Gary Gardner, and Brian Halweil. *Beyond Malthus:*

Nineteen Dimensions of the Population Challenge. New York: W. W. Norton, 1999.

Brunn, Stanley, and Thomas Leinbach. *Collapsing Space and Time: Geographic Aspects of Communication and Information.* Winchester, Mass.: Unwin Hyman, 1991.

Butz, David, Steven Lonergan, and Barry Smit. "Why International Development Neglects Indigenous Social Reality." *Canadian Journal of Development Studies* 12, no. 1 (1991): 143–157.

Buzzelli, Michael. "Toronto's Postwar Little Italy: Landscape Change and Ethnic Relations." *The Canadian Geographer* 44 (3) (2000): 298–330.

Caldwell, John C., I. O. Orbulove, and Pat Caldwell. "Fertility Decline in Africa: A New Type of Transition?" *Population and Development Review* 19, no. 2 (1992): 211–242.

Calvin, William H. "The Great Climate Flip-flop." *Atlantic Monthly* 281, no. 1 (January 1998): 47–64.

Campbell, James B. *Introduction to Remote Sensing.* New York: Guilford, 2002.

Campbell, Karen. *Undermining Our Future: How Mining's Privileged Access to Land Harm's People and Environment.* West Coast Environmental Law, January 2004.

Canada's Digital History. *Moose Bay Burial Grounds.* Marieval Enterprise (2006). http://collections.ic.gc.ca/marievalhistory/Qu'Appelle%20Valley/moosebayburialgrounds.htm.

Canada's Technology Triangle: www.techtriangle.com/AboutCTT/Services.cfm##.

Canadian Council on Social Development. "Urban Poverty" in *Canada: A Statistical Profile.* Canadian Council on Social Development, 2000.

Carson, R. *Silent Spring.* New York: Houghton Mifflin Co., 1962.

Carter, Harold. *The Study of Urban Geography.* 4th ed. London: Arnold, 1995.

Cartier, Carolyn. "Cosmopolitics and the Maritime World City." *Geographical Review* 89, no. 2 (1999): 278–289.

Castles, Stephen, and Mark J. Miller. *The Age of Migration: International Population Movements in the Modern World.* 2nd ed. New York: Guilford Press, 1998.

Chang, Claudia, and Harold A. Kostner. *Pastoralists at the Periphery: Herders in a Capitalist World.* Tucson: University of Arizona Press, 1994.

Charney, Igal. "Property Developers and the Robust Downtown." *The Canadian Geographer* 49, no. 3, 2005: 301–312.

Cities Alliance. *Annual Report 2004.* Washington, D.C.: Cities Alliance, 2004.

Clark, William A. V. *The California Cauldron: Immigration and the Fortunes of Local Communities.* New York: Guilford, 1998.

Clark, William A. V. *Immigrants and the American Dream: Remaking the Middle Class.* New York: Guilford, 2003.

Cohen, Joel E. *How Many People Can the Earth Support?* New York: W. W. Norton, 1995.

Cohen, Robin, ed. *The Cambridge Survey of World Migration.* Cambridge: Cambridge University Press, 1995.

Cohen, Saul B. *Geopolitics of the World System.* Lanham, Md.: Rowman & Littlefield, 2003.

Collins, J. *Uncommon Cultures: Popular Culture and Post-Modernism.* New York: Routledge, 1989.

Condon, Patrick M. "Canadian Cities, American Cities: Our Differences are the Same." (2004): http://www.fundersnetwork.org/usr_doc/Patrick_Condon_Primer.pdf.

Conzen, Michael P. "Ethnicity on the Land." In *The Making of the American Landscape,* edited by Michael P. Conzen, pp. 221–248. Boston: Unwin Hyman, 1990.

Cowan, C. Wesley, and Patty Jo Watson, eds. *The Origins of Agriculture: An International Perspective.* Washington, D.C.: Smithsonian Institution Press, 1992.

Cowen, M.P., and R.W. Shenton. *Doctrines of Development.* New York: Routledge, 1996.

Cox, Kevin R. *Political Geography: Territory, State, and Society.* Malden, Mass.: Blackwell, 2002.

Crane, N. *Mercator: The Man Who Mapped the Planet.* London: Weidenfeld and Nicolson, 2002.

Cunningham, William P., and Barbara W. Saigo. *Environmental Science: A Global Concern.* 5th ed. Dubuque, Iowa: McGraw-Hill, 1999.

Daniels, Peter, John Bryson, and Barney Warf. *Service Industries in the New Economy.* New York: Routledge, 2003.

Daugherty, Helen Ginn, and Kenneth C.W. Kammeyer. *An Introduction to Population.* 2nd ed. New York: Guilford Publications, 1995.

Davies, W. K. D. "Globalization: A Spatial Perspective," In *Unifying Geography: Common Heritage, Shared Future.* J. A. Mathews and D. T. Herbert (eds.) New York: Routledge, 2004: 189–214.

Davis, Mike. *Planet of Slums.* New York: Verso, 2006.

Demko, George J., and William B. Wood, eds. 2d ed. *Reordering the World: Geopolitical Perspectives on the Twenty-First Century.* Boulder: Westview Press, 1999.

Demko, George J., with Jerome Agel and Eugene Boe. *Why in the World: Adventures in Geography.* New York: Anchor Books/Doubleday, 1992.

Denevan, William M. "The Pristine Myth: The Landscape of the Americas in 1492." *Annals of the Association of American Geographers* 82, no. 3 (1992): 369–385.

Dent, Borden D. *Cartography: Thematic Map Design.* 5th ed. Dubuque, Iowa: WCB/McGraw-Hill, 1999.

"Desertification after the UNCED, Rio 1992." *GeoJournal* 31, no. 1 (September 1993). Special issue.

Diamond, Jared. *Collapse: How Societies Choose to Fail or Succeed.* New York: Viking, 2005.

Diamond, Jared. *Guns, Germs and Steel: The Fates of Human Societies.* New York: Norton, 1997.

Dicken, Peter. *Global Shift: Reshaping the Global Economic Map in the 21st Century.* 4th ed. New York: Guilford Press, 2003.

Dickenson, John, ed. *Geography of the Third World.* 2d ed. New York: Routledge, 1996.

Drake, Frances. *Global Warming.* London: Arnold, 2000.

Dregne, Harold E. *Desertification of Arid Lands.* New York: Harwood Academic, 1983.

Duhaime, G., Bernard, N., and R. Comtois. "An Inventory of Abandoned Mining Exploration Sites in Nunavik, Canada.' *The Canadian Geographer,* 49, no. 3 (2005): 260–271.

Durning, Alan T. *Saving the Forests: What Will It Take?* Worldwatch Paper 117. Washington, D.C.: Worldwatch Institute, 1993.

Dutt, Ashok K., et al., eds. *The Asian City: Processes of Development, Characteristics, and Planning.* Dordrecht/Boston/London: Kluwer Academic Publishers, 1994.

Elbow, Gary S. "Regional Cooperation in the Caribbean: The Association of Caribbean States." *Journal of Geography* 96, no. 1 (1997): 13–22.

Ellis, S. "Meaningful Consideration? A Review of Traditional Knowledge in Environmental Decision Making." *Arctic* 58 (1), 2005: 66–77.

Enger, Eldon D., and Bradley F. Smith. *Environmental Science: A Study of Interrelationships.* 7th ed. Dubuque, Iowa: McGraw-Hill, 2000.

Environment Canada. *Urban Water Indicators: Municipal Water Use and Wastewater Treatment.* Ottawa. 2002. Available from: www.ec.gc.ca/soer-ree/English/Indicators/Issues/Urb_H2O/.

Evenden, L.J., and G.E. Walker. "From Periphery to Centre: The Changing Geography of the Suburbs." In *The Changing Social Geography of Canadian Cities,* edited by Larry Bourne and David Ley, pp. 234-251. McGill-Queen's University: Montreal and Kingston, 1993.

Ewing, Gordon O. "The Bases of Differences between American and Canadian Cities." *The Canadian Geographer/Le Geographie Canadien* 36, no. 3 (1992): 266–279.

Falkenmark, Malin, and Carl Widstrand. "Population and Water Resources: A Delicate Balance." *Population Bulletin* 47, no. 1. Washington, D.C.: Population Reference Bureau, 1992.

Fawcett, G. and K. Scott. *A Lost Decade: Urban Poverty in Canada, 1990 to 2000.* Ottawa: Canadian Council on Social Development, 2007.

Fernández-Armesto, Felipe, ed. *The Times Guide to the Peoples of Europe.* Boulder: Westview Press, 1995.

Feshbach, Murray, and Alfred Friendly, Jr. *Ecocide in the USSR.* New York: Basic Books, 1992.

Fisheries and Oceans Canada. *"$50 Million Action Plan."* (2003): www.dfo-mpo.gc.ca/media/backgrou/2003/cod-5_e.htm#3.

Fisheries and Oceans Canada. "Frequently Asked Questions About Canada's Seal Hunt." *Fisheries and Acquaculture Management.* (2006): www.dfo-mpo.gc.ca/seal-phoque/faq_e.htm.

Folke, C., L. Pritchard, F. Berkes, J. Colding, and U. Svedin. "The Problem of Fit Between Ecosystems and Institutions: Ten Years Later." *Ecology and Society* 12 (1), 2007: 30. [Online] URL: http://www.ecologyandsociety.org/vol12/iss1/art30/.

Food and Agriculture Organization of the United Nations. *The State of Food and Agriculture.* Rome: FAO, annual.

Ford, Larry R. *America's New Downtowns: Revitalization or Reinvention?* Baltimore: Johns Hopkins University Press, 2003.

Ford, Larry R. *Cities and Buildings: Skyscrapers, Skid Rows, and Suburbs.* Baltimore: Johns Hopkins University Press, 1994.

Foster, H. "Halting the AIDS Pandemic." In *WorldMinds: Geographical Perspectives on 100 Problems.* D. G. Janelle, B. Wharf, and K. Hansen (eds.). Boston: Kluwer, 2004: 69–73.

Frantz, Klaus, and Robert A. Sauder, eds. *Ethnic Persistence and Change in Europe and America: Traces in Landscape and Society.* Innsbruck, Austria: University of Innsbruck, 1996. Veröffentlichungen der Universität Innsbruck 213.

Galaty, John G., and Douglas L. Johnson, eds. *The World of Pastoralism: Herding Systems in Comparative Perspective.* New York: Guilford Press, 1990.

Gardner, Gary. *Shrinking Fields: Cropland Loss in a World of Eight Billion.* Worldwatch Paper 131. Washington, D.C.: Worldwatch Institute, 1996.

Gardner, Gary, and Brian Halweil. *Underfed and Overfed: The Global Epidemic of Malnutrition.* Worldwatch Paper 150. Washington, D.C.: Worldwatch Institute, 2000.

Garreau, Joel. *Edge City: Life on the New Frontier.* New York: Doubleday, 1991.

Gebauer, Anne B. and T. Douglas Price, eds. *Transitions to Agriculture in Prehistory.* Monographs in World Archeology, no. 4. Madison, Wisc.: Prehistory Press, 1992.

Gelbard, Alene, Carl Haub, and Mary M. Kent. "World Population Beyond Six Billion." *Population Bulletin* 54, no. 1. Washington, D.C.: Population Reference Bureau, 1999.

Gersmehl, Phil. *The Language of Maps.* 15th ed. Indiana, Pa.: National Council for Geographic Education, 1996.

Glassner, Martin I. *Political Geography.* 3rd ed. New York: Wiley, 2003.

Gober, Patricia. "Americans on the Move." *Population Bulletin* 48, no. 3. Washington, D.C.: Population Reference Bureau, 1993.

Goldberg, Michael A.. and John Mercer. *The Myth of the North American City.* Vancouver: University of British Columbia Press, 1986.

Golledge, Reginald G. and Robert J. Stimson. *Spatial Behavior: A Geographic Perspective.* New York: Guilford Publications, 1996.

Goudie, Andrew. *The Human Impact on the Natural Environment.* New York: Blackwell, 1999.

Goudie, Andrew. *Encyclopedia of Global Change: Environmental Change and Human Society.* New York: Oxford University Press, 2000.

Gould, Peter. *Spatial Diffusion.* Association of American Geographers, Commission on College Geography. *Resource Paper* No. 4. Washington, D.C.: Association of American Geographers, 1969.

Gould, Peter. *The Slow Plague: A Geography of the AIDS Pandemic.* Cambridge, Mass.: Blackwell, 1993.

Gould, Peter, and Rodney White. *Mental Maps.* 2nd. ed. New York: Routledge, 1986.

Government of Canada. *Climate Change Impacts and Adaptation: A Canadian Perspective* Ottawa: Government of Canada. 2004. Available at: http://adaptation.nrcan.gc.ca/perspective/toc_e.asp.

Greenhut, Melvin L. *Plant Location in Theory and in Practice.* Chapel Hill: University of North Carolina Press, 1956. Reprint. Westport, Conn.: Greenwood Press, 1982.

Greenpeace. *"Canadian Atlantic Fisheries Collapse."* (2006): http://archive.greenpeace.org/comms/cbio/cancod.html.

Grigg, David. *An Introduction to Agricultural Geography.* 2nd ed. New York: Routledge, 1995.

Gritzner, Charles F., Jr. "The Scope of Cultural Geography." *Journal of Geography* 65 (1966): 4–11.

Guibernau i Berdún, Montserrat. *Nations without States: Political Communities in a Global Age.* Malden, Mass.: Blackwell, 1999.

Guinness, Paul. *Globalisation.* Access to Geography series. London: Hodder & Stoughton, 2003.

Hägerstrand, Torsten. *Innovation Diffusion as a Spatial Process.* University of Chicago Press, 1967.

Haggett, Peter, *Geography: A Global Synthesis.* Harlow, England: Pearson Education, 2001.

Hall, Colin M., and Stephen Page. *Geography of Tourism and Recreation.* 2d ed. New York: Routledge, 2002.

Hall, Stuart, ed. *Culture, Media, Language: Working Papers in Cultural Studies.* London: University of Birmingham, 1980.

Hall, Tim. *Urban Geography.* 2nd ed. New York: Routledge, 2001.

Hamilton, Ian. *Resources and Industry.* New York: Oxford University Press, 1992.

Hanink, Dean M. *Principles and Applications of Economic Geography.* New York: Wiley, 1997.

Hanson, Susan. *Geography, Gender, and the Workaday World: Hettner-Lecture, 2002.* Stuttgart: Franz Steiner Verlag, 2003.

Hanson, Susan, and Geraldine Pratt. "Geographic Perspectives on the Occupational Segregation of Women." *National Geographic Research* 6, no. 4 (1990): 376–399.

Hanson, Victor D. *Mexifornia: A State of Becoming.* San Francisco: Encounter Books, 2003.

Hardin, Garrett. "The Tragedy of the Commons." *Science* 162 (1968): 1243–1248.

Harrington, James W., and Barney Warf. *Industrial Location: Principles and Practice.* London and New York: Routledge, 1995.

Harris, Chauncy. "New European Countries and Their Minorities." *Geographical Review* 83, no. 3 (1993): 301–320.

Harris, Cole. "French Landscapes in North America." In *The Making of the American Landscape,* edited by Michael P. Conzen, pp. 63–79. Boston: Unwin Hyman, 1990.

Harris, Richard. *Creeping Conformity: How Canada Became Suburban, 1900–1960.* Toronto: University of Toronto, 2004.

Harrison, Paul, and Fred Pearce. *AAAS Atlas of Population and Environment.* Victoria D. Markham, ed. Berkeley, Calif.: American Association for the Advancement of Science and University of California Press, 2001.

Hartshorn, Truman. *Interpreting the City.* 3rd ed. New York: Wiley, 1998.

Harvey, D. *The Condition of Postmodernity.* Cambridge, Mass.: Blackwell, 1989.

Haub, Carl. "Understanding Population Projections." *Population Bulletin* 42, no. 4. Washington, D.C.: Population Reference Bureau, 1987.

Haupt, Arthur, and Thomas Kane. *Population Handbook.* 4th ed. Washington, D.C.: Population Reference Bureau, 1997.

Hayden, Dolores. *Building Suburbia: Green Fields and Urban Growth, 1820–2000.* New York: Pantheon Books, 2003.

Hayter, Roger. *The Dynamics of Industrial Location.* New York: Wiley, 1997.

Hiebert, Daniel. "Ethnicity." In *The Dictionary of Human Geography,* 4th ed., edited by R.J. Johnston, Derek Gregory, Geraldine Pratt, and Michael Watts, pp. 235–238. Malden, Mass.: Blackwell, 2000.

Hirschman, Charles, and Philip Guest. "The Emerging Demographic Transitions of Southeast Asia." *Population and Development Review* 16, no. 1 (March 1990): 121–152.

Hodder, Rupert. *Development Geography.* New York: Routledge, 2000.

Holt-Jensen, Arild. *Geography: Its History and Concepts.* 3rd ed. Thousand Oaks, Calif.: Sage Publications, 1999.

Honari, Morteza and Thomas Boleyn, eds. *Health Ecology: Health, Culture, and Human-Environment Interaction.* (New York: Routledge, 1999).

Hornbeck, David. "Spanish Legacy in the Borderlands." In *The Making of the American Landscape,* edited by Michael P. Conzen, pp. 51–62. Boston: Unwin Hyman, 1990.

Hornby, William F., and Melvyn Jones. *An Introduction to Population Geography.* Cambridge, England: Cambridge University Press, 1993.

Houghton, John. *Global Warming: The Complete Briefing.* 2nd ed. Cambridge, England and New York: Cambridge University Press, 1997.

Howe, G.M. Man, *Environment and Disease in Britain: A Medical Geography through the Ages.* David and Charles Newton Abbot: Devon. 1972.

Hulme, Mick, and Mick Kelly. "Desertification and Climate Change." *Environment* 35, no. 6 (1993): 4–11, 39–45.

"Human-Dominated Ecosystems." A special report in *Science* 227, no. 5325 (25 July 1997): 485–525.

Humane Society of Canada. "Seal Slaughter Continues." (2006): www.humanesociety.com/newsrel/newsrel.asp?thisrel=02042006&page=1.

Huntington, Samuel P. *Who Are We? The Challenges to America's National Identity.* New York: Simon & Schuster, 2004.

Iain DeJong. Devolution Hits Housing in Canada. *Shelterforce* Sept./Oct. 2000: www.nhi.org/online/issues/113/dejong.html.

Independent Commission on International Development Issues. *North–South: A Programme for Survival.* Cambridge: MIT Press, 1980.

Inglehart, Ronald and Pippa Norris. *Rising Tide: Gender Equality and Cultural Change around the World.* New York: Cambridge University Press, 2003.

International Bank for Reconstruction and Development/The World Bank. *World Development Indicators.* Published annually for the World Bank. New York: Oxford University Press.

International Bank for Reconstruction and Development/The World Bank. *World Development Report.* Published annually for the World Bank. New York: Oxford University Press.

"International Migration and Ethnic Segregation: Impacts on Urban Areas." Special issue of *Urban Studies* 35, no. 3 (March 1998).

Isaac, Erich. *Geography of Domestication.* Englewood Cliffs, N.J.: Prentice Hall, 1970.

Jackson, Peter. *Maps of Meaning: An Introduction to Cultural Geography.* New York: Routledge, 1989.

Jackson, Richard H. *Geography of Travel and Tourism.* 3rd ed. Albany, N.Y.: Delmar Learning, 2002.

Jacobson, Jodi L. *Gender Bias: Roadblock to Sustainable Development.* Worldwatch Paper 110. Washington, D.C.: Worldwatch Institute, 1992.

Janelle, D. J. "Central Place Development in a Time-Spent Framework." *Professional Geographer* 20 (1), 1968: 5–10.

Janelle, Don G., and David C. Hodge, eds. *Information, Place, and Cyberspace: Issues in Accessibility.* Berlin: Springer Verlag, 2000.

Johnston, Ronald J., Derek Gregory, Geraldine Pratt, and Michael Watts. *The Dictionary of Human Geography.* 4th ed. Oxford, England: Blackwell Publishers, 2000.

Johnston, Ronald J. and J.D. Sidaway. *Geography and Geographers: Anglo-American Human Geography since 1945.* London: Arnold, 2004.

Johnston, Ronald. J., J. Hauer, and G. A. Koekveld, eds. *Regional Geography: Current Developments and Future Prospects.* New York: Routledge, 1990.

Johnston, Ronald J. *Geography and Geographers: Anglo-American Human Geography Since 1945.* New York: E. Arnold, 1991.

Jones, Martin, Rhys Jones, and Michael Woods. *An Introduction to Political Geography: Space, Place, and Politics.* New York: Routledge, 2004.

Kane, Hal. "Growing Fish in Fields." *WorldWatch* 6, no. 5 (September–October 1993): 20–27.

Kane, Hal. *The Hour of Departure: Forces that Create Refugees and Migrants.* Worldwatch Paper 125. Washington, D.C.: Worldwatch Institute, 1995.

Kaplan, David H., and Steven R. Holloway. *Segregation in Cities.* AAG Resource Publication 1998-1. Washington, D.C.: Association of American Geographers, 1998.

Kaplan, David H., James O. Wheeler, and Steven R. Holloway. *Urban Geography.* Hoboken, N.J.: Wiley, 2004.

Karl, T. R., et al. "The Coming Climate." *Scientific American* 276 (May 1997): 78–83.

Kearns R, Moon G. "From Medical Geography to Health Geography: Novelty, Place and Theory After a Decade of Change." *Progress in Human Geography* 2002: 26: 605–625.

Kellerman, Aharon. *Telecommunications and Geography.* New York: Halsted, 1993.

Kemp, David D. *Global Environmental Issues: A Climatological Approach.* 2nd ed. New York: Routledge, 1995.

Kent, Mary M., et al. "First Glimpses from the 2000 U.S. Census." *Population Bulletin* 56, no. 2. Washington, D.C.: Population Reference Bureau, 2001.

Keyfitz, Nathan and Wilhelm Flinger. *World Population Growth and Aging: Demographic Trends in the Late 20th Century.* Chicago: University of Chicago Press, 1991.

King, Russell, ed. *Mass Migrations in Europe: The Legacy and the Future.* London and New York: Belhaven Press and John Wiley & Sons, 1995.

Kitchin, R. "Collecting and Analysing Cognitive Mapping Data." In *Cognitive Mapping: Past, Present, and Future.* R. Kitchin and S. Freundschuh (eds.), 2000: 9–23.

Klahr, Rebecca. "Work/Workforce/Employment." In L. McDowell and J.P. Sharp (eds), *A Feminist Glossary of Human Geography.* New York: Arnold, 1999: 296–297.

Knox, Paul L., and John A. Agnew. *The Geography of the World Economy.* 3rd ed. London: Edward Arnold, 1998.

Knox, Paul, John Agnew, and Linda McCarthy. *The Geography of the World Economy.* 4th rev. ed. New York: Oxford University Press, 2003.

Knox, Paul L., and Linda M. McCarthy, *Urbanization: An Introduction to Urban Geography.* 2nd ed. Upper Saddle River, N.J.: Prentice Hall, 2005.

Knox, Paul L., and Steven Pinch. *Urban Social Geography: An Introduction.* 4th ed. Upper Saddle River, N.J.: Prentice Hall, 2000.

Knox, Paul L., and Peter J. Taylor, eds. *World Cities in a World System.* Cambridge: Cambridge University Press, 1995.

Kobayashi, A. "'Truly Our Own': Canadian Geography 50 Years After." *The Canadian Geographer.* 45 (2001): 3–13.

Kobayashi, Audrey. "Multiculturalism: Representing a Canadian Institution."

In *Place/Culture/Representation,* edited by James Duncan and David Ley, pp. 205–231. New York: Routledge, 1993.

Kobayashi, Audrey, ed. *Women, Work, and Place.* Montreal: McGill-Queen's University, 1994.

Kobayashi, Audrey. "Do Minority Judges Make a Difference?" *Canadian Journal of Women and the Law* 10, no.1 (1998): 199–212.

Kobayashi, Audrey. "'Race' and Racism in the Classroom: Some Thoughts on Unexpected Moments." *The Journal of Geography* 98 (1999): 179–182.

Kobayashi, Audrey. "Migration as a Negotiation of Gender: Recent Japanese Immigrant Women in Canada." In *New World Lives: Globalization and People of Japanese Ancestry in the Americas and from Latin America in Japan,* edited by Lane Hirabayshi, et al., pp. 205–220. Stanford: Stanford University, 2002.

Kobayashi, Audrey, and Linda Peake, Hal Beneson and Katie Pickles. "Introduction: Placing Women and Work." In Kobayashi, A. (ed.), *Women, Work, and Place.* Kingston: McGill-Queen's Press, 1994: xi–xlv.

Kotkin, Joel. *The New Geography: How the Digital Revolution Is Reshaping the American Landscape.* New York: Random House, 2000.

Kroeber, Alfred L., and Clyde Kluckhohn. "Culture: A Critical Review of Concepts and Definitions," Harvard University. *Papers of the Peabody Museum of American Archaeology and Ethnology* 47, no. 2 (1952).

Kwan, M. "Feminist Visualization: Revisioning GIS as a Method in Feminist Geographic Research." *Annals of the Association of American Geographers* 92 (4), 2002: 645–661.

Lamb, H. H. *Climate, History, and the Modern World.* New York: Routledge, 1995.

Landes, David S. *The Wealth and Poverty of Nations.* New York: Norton, 1998.

Lanegran, David A., and Risa Palm. *An Invitation to Geography.* 2nd ed. New York: McGraw-Hill, 1978.

Lee, James, and Feng Wang. *One Quarter of Humanity: Malthusian Mythology and Chinese Reality 1700–2000.* Cambridge, Mass.: Harvard University Press, 1999.

Lee, Sharon M. "Asian Americans: Diverse and Growing." *Population Bulletin* 53, no. 2. Washington, D.C.: Population Reference Bureau, 1998.

Lenssen, Nicholas. *Nuclear Waste: The Problem That Won't Go Away.* Worldwatch Paper 106. Washington, D.C.: Worldwatch Institute, 1991.

Ley, David. "Cultural/Humanistic Geography." *Progress in Human Geography* 5 (1981): 249–257; 7 (1983): 267–275.

Ley, David. "The Inner City." In *Canadian Cities in Transition: The Twenty-First Century,* edited by Trudi Bunting and Pierre Fillion, pp. 274–302. Don Mills: Oxford, 2000.

Li, X. "Development of Geography in Higher Education in China since 1980." *Journal of Geography in Higher Education* 31 (1), 2007: 19–37.

Linteau, Paul-Andre. "Canadian Suburbanization in a North American Context: Does the Border Make a Difference?" *Journal of Urban History,* 13, no. 3 (May 1987): 252–274.

Livingstone, David N. *The Geographical Tradition.* Cambridge, Mass.: Blackwell, 1992.

Lo, C. P., and Albert K. W. Yeung. *Concepts and Techniques of Geographic Information Systems.* Upper Saddle River, N.J.: Prentice Hall, 2002.

Lo, Fu-chen, and Yue-Man Yeuny, eds. *Globalization and the World of Large Cities.* New York: United Nations University Press, 1998.

Lobeck, Armin K. *Things Maps Don't Tell Us: An Adventure into Map Interpretation.* Chicago: University of Chicago Press, 1993.

Lomborg, Bjorn. *The Skeptical Environmentalist: Measuring the Real State of the World.* Cambridge: Cambridge University Press, 2001.

Lopez-Claros, Augusto, and Saadia Zahidi, *Women's Empowerment: Measuring the Global Gender Gap.* World Economic Forum, 2005. www.weforum.org.

Lynch, K. *Image of the City.* Cambridge: The Technology Press and Harvard University Press, 1960.

Macintyre, S., A. Ellaway, and S. Cummins. "Place Effects on Health: How Can We Conceptualise, Operationalise and Measure Them?" *Social Science and Medicine.* 55: 125–139, 2002.

MacNeish, Richard S. *The Origins of Agriculture and Settled Life.* Norman: University of Oklahoma Press, 1991.

Manson, Gary A., and Richard E. Groop. "U.S. Intercounty Migration in the 1990s: People and Income Move Down the Urban Hierarchy." *Professional Geographer* 52, no. 3 (2000): 493–504.

Marcuse, Peter, and Ronald van Kampen, eds. *Globalizing Cities: A New Spatial*

Order? Oxford, England: Blackwell Publishers, 2000.

Martin, Geoffrey J. *All Possible Worlds: A History of Geographical Ideas.* 4th ed. New York: Oxford University Press, 2005.

Martin, Philip, and Elizabeth Midgley. "Immigration to the United States: Journey to an Uncertain Destination." *Population Bulletin* 54, no. 2. Washington, D.C.: Population Reference Bureau, 1999.

Martin, Philip, and Jonas Widgren. "International Migration: Facing the Challenge." *Population Bulletin* 57, no. 1. Washington, D.C.: Population Reference Bureau, 2002.

Massey, Douglas S., et al. "Theories of International Migration: A Review and Appraisal." *Population and Development Review* 19, no. 3 (1993): 431–466.

Mastny, Lisa. *Traveling Light: New Paths for International Tourism.* Worldwatch Paper 159. Washington, D.C.: Worldwatch Institute, 2001.

May, Jacques. *The Ecology of Human Disease.* New York: MD Publications, 1985.

McFalls, Joseph A., Jr. "Population: A Lively Introduction." 3rd. ed. *Population Bulletin* 53, no. 3. Washington, D.C.: Population Reference Bureau, 1998.

McGuinn, Anne Platt. *Rocking the Boat: Conserving Fisheries and Protecting Jobs.* Worldwatch Paper 142. Washington, D.C.: Worldwatch Institute, 1998.

McGuinn, Anne Platt. *Safeguarding the Health of Oceans.* Worldwatch Paper 145. Washington, D.C.: Worldwatch Institute, 1999.

McKee, Jesse O., ed. *Ethnicity in Contemporary America: A Geographical Appraisal.* 2nd rev. ed. Lanham, Md.: Rowman & Littlefield, 2000.

McKenna, J., R. J. Quinn, D. J. Donnelly, and J. A. G. Cooper. "Accurate Mental Maps as an Aspect of Local Ecological Knowledge (LEK): A Case Study from Lough Neagh, Northern Ireland." *Ecology and Society* 13 (1), 2008: 13. [Online] URL: http://www.ecologyandsociety.org/vol13/iss1/art13/.

Meade, M. "Medical Geography as Human Ecology: The Dimension of Population Movement," *The Geographical Review* 67(4) 1977.

Meier, Gerald M., and James E. Rauch. *Leading Issues in Economic Development.* 7th ed. New York: Oxford University Press, 2000.

Meinig, Donald W., ed. *The Interpretation of Ordinary Landscapes: Geographical Essays.* New York: Oxford University, 1979.

Menzies, Gavin. *1421: The Year China Discovered America.* New York: William Morrow/HarperCollins, 2003.

Mercer, John, and Kim England. "Canadian Cities in Continental Context: Global and Continental Perspectives on Canadian Urban Development." In *Canadian Cities in Transition: The Twenty-First Century,* edited by Trudi Bunting and Pierre Fillion, pp. 55–75. Don Mills: Oxford, 2000.

Michalak, Wieslaw, and Richard Gibb. "Trading Blocs and Multilateralism in the World Economy." *Annals of the Association of American Geographers* 87, no. 2 (1997): 264–279.

Middleton, Nick, and David Thomas, eds. *World Atlas of Desertification.* 2nd ed. United Nations Environmental Programme. London: Edward Arnold, 1997.

Miller, Alan S. and John P. Hoffman. "Risk and Religion: An Explanation of Gender Differences in Religiosity." *Journal for the Scientific Study of Religion* 34, no. 1 (1995): 63–75.

Miller, G. Tyler, Jr. *Living in the Environment.* 11th ed. Belmont, Calif.: Wadsworth Publishing Co., 1999.

Mining Watch Canada. *Report of the Commissioner for the Environment and Sustainable Development.* (2002): www.miningwatch.ca/index.

Mitchell, B. (ed.) (2004). *Resource and Environmental Management in Canada. Addressing Conflict and Uncertainty* (3rd ed). Toronto: Oxford University Press.

Mitchell, Donald. *Cultural Geography: A Critical Introduction.* Malden, M.A.: Blackwell, 2000.

Momsen, Janet H. "Gender Bias in Development." In *The New Third World,* 2nd ed., edited by Alonso Gonzalez and Jim Norwine, pp. 93–111. Boulder: Westview Press, 1998.

Monmonier, Mark. *How to Lie with Maps.* 2nd ed. Chicago: University of Chicago Press, 1996.

Mooney, Annabelle and Betsy Evans. "Global English." In *Globalization: The Key Concepts,* edited by Annabelle Mooney and Betsy Evans, p. 106. New York: Routledge, 2007a.

Mooney, Annabelle and Betsy Evans. "Language Rights." In *Globalization: The Key Concepts,* edited by Annabelle Mooney and Betsy Evans, pp. 147–148. New York: Routledge, 2007b.

Morrill, Richard. "Gerrymandering." *Focus* 41, no. 3 (Fall 1991): 23–27.

Morrill, Richard, Gary L. Gaile, and Grant Ian Thrall. *Spatial Diffusion.* Scientific Geography Series vol. 10. Newbury Park, Calif.: SAGE Publications, 1988.

Morrill, Richard L. "The Nature, Unity and Value of Geography." *Professional Geographer* 35 (1983): 1–9.

Muehrcke, Phillip C., and Juliana O. Muehrcke. *Map Use: Reading, Analysis, and Interpretation.* 4th ed. Madison, Wis.: J.P. Publications, 1998.

Murphy, Barbara. *On The Street: How We Created Homelessness.* J. Gordon Shillingford Publishing: Winnipeg, 2000

Neuwirth, Robert. *Shadow Cities: A Billion Squatters, a New Urban World.* New York: Routledge, 2005.

Newbold, K. Bruce. "Race and Primary, Return, and Onward Interstate Migration." *Professional Geographer* 49, no. 1 (1997): 1–14.

Newhouse, John. "Europe's Rising Regionalism." *Foreign Affairs* 76 (January/February 1997): 67–84.

Noble, Allen G., ed. *To Build in a New Land: Ethnic Landscapes in North America.* Baltimore: Johns Hopkins University Press, 1992.

Nordhaus, W. D. "A Review of the Stern Review on the Economics of Climate." *Journal of Economic Literature* 45 (3), 2007: 686–702.

Nostrand, Richard L., and Lawrence Estaville, eds. *Homelands: A Geography of Culture and Place across America.* Baltimore: Johns Hopkins University Press, 2002.

O'Loughlin, John, ed. *Dictionary of Geopolitics.* Westport, Conn.: Greenwood Publishing Group, 1994.

O'Loughlin, John, Lynn Staechli, and Edward Greenberg. *Globalization and its Outcomes.* New York: Guilford, 2004.

Olshansky, S. Jay, Bruce Carnes, Richard G. Rogers, and Len Smith. "Infectious Diseases—New and Ancient Threats to World Health." *Population Bulletin* 52, no. 2. Washington, D.C.: Population Reference Bureau, 1997.

Omran, Abdel R. "The Epidemiologic Transition: A Theory of the Epidemiology of Population Change." *Milbank Memorial Fund Quarterly 49* (1971): 509–538.

Omran, Abdel R., and Farzaneh Roudi. "The Middle East Population Puzzle." *Population Bulletin* 48, no. 1. Washington, D.C.: Population Reference Bureau, 1993.

O'Neill, Brian, and Deborah Balk. "World Population Futures." *Population*

Bulletin 56, no. 3. Washington, D.C.:
Population Reference Bureau, 2001.

Pacione, Michael, ed. *Changing Cities:
International Perspectives.* Glasgow:
IGU Urban Commission and Strathclyde
University Publishing, 2004

Pacione, Michael. *Urban Geography:
A Global Perspective.* New York:
Routledge, 2001, 2005.

Palm, Risa. *Natural Hazards.* Baltimore,
Md.: Johns Hopkins University Press,
1990.

Parfit, Michael. "Hunt for the First Americans." *National Geographic* (December
2000): 41–67. "The Peopling of the
Earth." *National Geographic* (October
1988): 434–503.

Park, Chris C. *Tropical Rainforests.*
London and New York: Routledge,
1992.

Parr H. "Medical Geography: Care and
Caring." *Progress in Human Geography*
2003: 27: 212–221.

Pattison, William D. "The Four Traditions
of Geography." *Journal of Geography*
63 (1964): 211–216.

Pauly, Daniel, and Reg Watson. "The Last
Fish." *Scientific American* (July 2003):
43–47.

"The Peopling of the Earth." *National
Geographic* (October 1988): 434–503.

Peters, Gary L., and Robert P. Larkin.
*Population Geography: Problems,
Concepts, and Prospects.* Dubuque, Ia.:
Kendall/Hunt Publishing Company,
1993.

Peters, William J., and Leon
F. Neuenschwander. *Slash and Burn:
Farming in the Third World Forest.*
Moscow: University of Idaho Press,
1988.

Pickering, Kevin T., and Lewis A. Owen.
*An Introduction to Global Environ-
mental Issues.* 2nd ed. New York:
Routledge, 1997.

Pinal, Jorge del, and Audrey Singer.
"Generations of Diversity: Latinos in
the United States." *Population Bulletin*
52, no. 3. Washington, D.C.: Population
Reference Bureau, 1997.

Pinder, John. *The European Union: A Very
Short Introduction.* New York: Oxford
University Press, 2001.

Pinkey, T. (ed.). Editor's Introduction:
Modernism and Cultural Theory. In *The
Politics of Modernism,* 1–29. New York:
Verso, 1989.

Plane, David A. "Age-Composition Change
and the Geographical Dynamics of
Interregional Migration in the U.S."
*Annals of the Association of American
Geographers* 82, no. 1 (1992): 64–85.

Pooley, Colin G., and Ian D. Whyte, eds.
*Migrants, Emigrants and Immigrants: A
Social History of Migration.* New York:
Routledge, 1991.

"Population." *National Geographic*
(October 1998).

Porter, Philip W., and Eric S. Sheppard. *A
World of Difference: Society, Nature,
Development.* New York: Guilford, 1998.

Postel, Sandra. *Last Oasis: Facing Water
Scarcity.* New York: W. W. Norton, 1992.

Postel, Sandra. "When the World's Wells
Run Dry." *Worldwatch* 12, no. 5 (Sept/
Oct 1999): 30–38.

Potter, Rob, Tony Binns, Jenny Elliott,
and David W. Smith. *Geographies
of Development.* 2nd ed. London:
Longman, 2003.

Preston, P. W. *Development Theory:
An Introduction.* Cambridge, Mass.:
Blackwell, 1996.

Preston, Valerie, and Lucia Lo. "Asian
Theme Malls in Suburban Toronto:
Land Use Conflict in Richmond Hill."
The Canadian Geographer 44, no. 2
(2000): 182–190.

Price, Edward T. *Dividing the Land: Early
American Beginnings of Our Private
Property Mosaic.* Geography Research
Paper 238. Chicago: University of
Chicago Press, 1995.

Pritchett, Lant H. "Desired Fertility and the
Impact of Population Policies." *Popula-
tion and Development Review* 20, no. 1
(March 1994): 1–55.

Pritzker, Barry M. *A Native American
Encyclopedia: History, Culture, and
Peoples.* New York: Oxford University
Press, 2000.

Ravenstein, E. G. "The Laws of Migration."
Journal of the Royal Statistical Society
48 (1885): 167–227; 52 (1889): 241–301.

Reed, M. and B. Mitchell. "Gendering
Environmental Geography." *The Canadian Geographer.* 47, no. 3: 318–337, 2003.

Régie Régionale de la Santé et des Service Sociaux de Montréal-Centre
(2002). Urban Health: A Vital Factor
in Montreal's Development. Montreal,
QC.: Direction de Sante Publique Regie
Regionale de la Sante et des Services
Sociaux de Montreal Centre.

Relph, Edward. "Responsive Methods,
Geographical Imagination and the
Study of Landscapes," In Wolch, J. and
M. Dear (eds): *The Power of Geogra-
phy: How Territory Shapes Social Life.*
Great Britain: Biddles of Guildford
(1989): 49–163.

Renner, Michael. *The Anatomy of Resource
Wars.* Worldwatch Paper 162. Washington, D.C.: Worldwatch Institute, 2002.

Riche, Martha F. "America's Diversity and
Growth: Signposts for the 21st Century."
Population Bulletin 55, no. 2. Washington, D.C.: Population Reference Bureau,
2000.

Rigg, J. *Southeast Asia.* London:
Routledge. 1997.

Riley, Nancy E. "Gender, Power, and Population Change." *Population Bulletin* 52,
no. 1. Washington, D.C.: Population
Reference Bureau, 1997.

"The Rise of Europe's Little Nations." *The
Wilson Quarterly* 18, no. 1 (1994): 50–81.

Roberts, Neil. *The Changing Global Environments.* Cambridge, Mass.: Blackwell, 1994.

Robey, Bryant, Shea O. Rutstein, and
Leo Morris. "The Fertility Decline
in Developing Countries." *Scientific
American* 269 (December 1993): 30–37.

Rodrique, Christine M. "Can Religion
Account for Early Animal Domestica-
tions...?" *Professional Geographer* 44,
no. 4 (1992): 417–430.

Rodriguez-Pose, Andrés. *The European
Union: Economy, Society, and Polity.*
New York: Oxford University Press,
2002.

Rogers, Alisdair, and Heather Viles. *The
Student's Companion to Geography.* 2nd
ed. Malden, Mass.: Blackwell, 2003.

Rogers, Alisdair, ed. *Peoples and Cultures.*
The Illustrated Encyclopedia of World
Geography. New York: Oxford Univer-
sity Press, 1992.

Roodman, David Malin. *Still Waiting for
the Jubilee: Pragmatic Solutions for the
Third World Debt Crisis.* Worldwatch
Paper 155. Washington, D.C.: Worldwatch Institute, 2001.

Roseman, Curtis C. "Channelization of
Migration Flows from the Rural South
to the Industrial Midwest." *Proceedings
of the Association of American Geographers* 3 (1971): 140–146.

Roseman, Curtis C., Hans Dieter Laux,
and Gunther Thieme, eds. *EthniCity:
Geographic Perspectives on Ethnic
Change in Modern Cities.* Lanham,
Md.: Rowman & Littlefield, 1996.

Rosenberg MW. "Medical Geography or
Health Geography? Populations, Peoples
and Places." *International Journal of
Population Geography* 1998; 4: 211–226.

Ross, N.A., S. Tremblay, and K. Graham.
"Neighbourhood Influences on Health in
Montreal, Canada." *Social Science and
Medicine.* 59: 1485–1494, 2004.

Rostow, Walter W. *The Stages of Economic
Growth.* London: Cambridge University
Press, 1960, 1971.

Runnels, Curtis N. "Environmental
Degradation in Ancient Greece."

Scientific American (March 1995): 96–99.

Sachs, Jeffrey. *The End of Poverty: Economic Possibilities for Our Time.* New York: Penguin, 2005.

Sachs, Jeffrey, et al. "The Geography of Poverty and Wealth." *Scientific American* 284 (March 2001): 70–75.

Sadar, Ziauddin and Borin Van Loon. *Cultural Studies for Beginners.* Cambridge: Icon Books, 1997.

Sampat, Payal. *Deep Trouble: The Hidden Threat of Groundwater Pollution.* Worldwatch Paper 154. Washington, D.C.: Worldwatch Institute, 2000.

Sassen, Saskia, ed. *Global Networks: Linked Cities.* New York: Routledge, 2002.

Sauer, Carl, O. "The Morphology of Landscape." *University of California Publications in Geography* 2, no 2 (1925): 19–54.

Sauer, Carl. *Agricultural Origins and Dispersals.* New York: American Geographical Society, 1952.

Scientific American 261, no. 3 (September 1989). Special issue: *Managing Planet Earth.* 1989.

Seager, Joni. *The Penguin Atlas of Women in the World.* 3rd ed. New York: Penguin USA, 2003.

Servos, M., P. Chambers, R. Macdonald and G. Van Der Kraak. "Municipal Wastewater Effluents." *Threats to Sources of Drinking Water and Aquatic Ecosystem Health.* Environment Canada. Chapter 9. Ottawa: Minister of Public Works and Government Services. 2001. Available at: www.nwri.ca/threatsfull/ch9-1-e.html.

Sheehan, Molly O'Meara. *City Limits: Putting the Brakes on Urban Sprawl.* Worldwatch Paper 156. Washington, D.C.: Worldwatch Institute, 2001.

Shelley, Fred M., J. Clark Archer, Fiona M. Davidson, and Stanley D. Brunn. *Political Geography of the United States.* New York: Guilford, 1996.

Shinagawa, Larry Hajime, and Michael Jang. *Atlas of American Diversity.* Walnut Creek, Calif.: AltaMira Press/Sage Publications, 1998.

Short, John R., and Yeong-Hyun Kim. *Globalization and the City.* New York: Addison Wesley Longman, 1999.

Shumway, J. Matthew, and Richard H. Jackson. "Native American Population Patterns." *Geographical Review* 85, no. 2 (1995): 185–201.

Simmons, I. G. *Changing the Face of the Earth: Culture, Environment, History.* 2d ed. Cambridge, Mass.: Blackwell, 1996.

Simon, Julian. *The Ultimate Resource 2.* Princeton, N.J.: Princeton University Press, 1996.

Simon, Rita James and Caroline B. Brettell, eds. *International Migration: The Female Experience.* Totowa, N.J.: Rowman & Allenheld, 1986.

Sjoberg, Gideon. "The Origin and Evolution of Cities." *Scientific American* 213 (1965): 54–63.

Smil, Vaclav. *Feeding the World: A Challenge for the Twenty-First Century.* Cambridge, Mass.: MIT Press, 2000.

Smit, B. and M.W. Skinner. "Adaptation Options in Agriculture to Climate Change: A Typology." *Mitigation and Adaptation Strategies for Global Change.* 7: 85–114, 2002.

Smith, Dan. *The State of the World Atlas.* London: Earthscan, 2003.

Smith, David W. *Third World Cities.* 2nd ed. New York: Routledge, 2000.

Smith, Neil. *American Empire: Roosevelt's Geographer and the Prelude to Globalization.* Berkeley: University of California Press, 2003.

Smith, Neil. *The New Urban Frontier: Gentrification and the Revanchist City.* New York: Routledge, 1996.

Smith, Peter J. "Suburbs." In *Canadian Cities in Transition: The Twenty-First Century,* edited by Trudi Bunting and Pierre Fillion, pp. 303–332. Don Mills: Oxford, 2000.

Solow, R.M. *Growth Theory: An Exposition.* 2d ed. New York: Oxford University Press, 2000.

Statistics Canada (2005): www12.statcan.ca/english/census01/products/analytic/companion/etoimm/canada.cfm.

Statistics Canada. Canada's Ethnocultural Portrait: The Changing Mosaic, 2001: www12.statcan.ca/english/census01/products/analytic/companion/etoimm/contents.cfm.

Statistics Canada. "Canadian Industry Statistics." (2001b): http://strategis.ic.gc.ca/canadian_industry_statistics/cis.nsf/IDE/cis11gdpe.html.

Statistics Canada. "Farm Census family Size." (2001a): www40.statcan.ca/l01/cst01/agrc41a.htm.

Statistics Canada. "Francophones: Increase in Numbers Outside Quebec." (2008): http://www12.statcan.ca/english/census01/products/analytic/companion/lang/provs.cfm#francophones.

Statistics Canada. "Full-time and Part-time Employment by Sex and Age Group." (2005b): www40.statcan.ca/l01/cst01/labor12.htm.

Statistics Canada. "Gross Domestic Product at Basic Prices by Industry." (2006): www40.statcan.ca/l01/cst01/econ41.htm.

Statistics Canada. *Human Activity in the Environment.* Ottawa: Minister of Public Works and Government Services. 2002.

Statistics Canada. "Labour Survey: Distribution of Employed People, By Industry, By Province." (2005a): www40.statcan.ca/l01/cst01/labor21a.htm.

Statistics Canada. Measuring Low Income and Poverty in Canada: An Update. Ottawa, Statistics Canada. Available at: www.statcan.ca:8096/bsolc/english/bsolc?catno=75F0002M1998013.

Stern, N. *The Economics of Climate Change.* London: HM Treasury. Available at http://www.hm-treasury.gov.uk/independent_reviews/stern_review_economics_climate_change/stern_review_report.cfm.

Stevens, William K. *The Change in the Weather: People, Weather, and the Science of Climate.* New York: Delacorte Press, 1999.

Steward, Julian H. *Theory of Culture Change.* Urbana: University of Illinois Press, 1955.

Stutz, Frederick P., and Barney Warf. *The World Economy: Resources, Location, Trade, and Development.* 4th ed. Upper Saddle River, N.J.: Prentice-Hall, 2005.

Tarrant, John, ed. *Farming and Food:* New York: Oxford University Press, 1991.

Tata, Robert J., and Ronald R. Schultz. "World Variation in Human Welfare: A New Index of Development Status." *Annals of the Association of American Geographers* 78, no. 4 (1988): 580–593.

Taylor, Peter. *World City Network: A Global Urban Analysis.* London and New York: Routledge, 2004.

Taylor, Peter J. and Colin Flint. *Political Geography: World-Economy, Nation-State, and Locality.* 4th ed. Upper Saddle River, N.J.: Prentice Hall, 2000.

Thomas, Alan, et al. *Third World Atlas.* 2nd ed. Bristol, Pa.: Taylor and Francis, 1994.

Thomas, William, ed. *Man's Role in Changing the Face of the Earth.* Chicago: University of Chicago Press, 1956.

Thomas, William L., Jr., ed. *Man's Role in Changing the Face of the Earth.* Chicago: University of Chicago Press, 1956.

Thrift, N. "Space: The Fundamental Stuff of Geography." *Key Concepts in Geography.* London: Sage, 2003: 95–107.

Tuxill, John. *Nature's Cornucopia: Our Stake in Plant Diversity.* Worldwatch Paper 148. Washington, D.C.: Worldwatch Institute, 1999.

Ullman, Edward L. "The Role of Transportation and the Basis for Interaction." In *Man's Role in Changing the Face of the Earth,* edited by William E. Thomas, Jr., pp. 862–880. Chicago: University of Chicago Press, 1956.

UNAIDS. *Report on the Global AIDS Epidemic.* New York: United Nations, 2004.

UNICEF. *The State of the World's Children.* New York: United Nations, annual.

United Nations. *Population and Women.* New York: United Nations, 1996.

United Nations. *Road map towards the implementation of the United Nations Millennium Declaration.* New York: United Nations, 2001. Available at: http://daccessdds.un.org/doc/UNDOC/GEN/N01/526/07/PDF/N0152607.pdf?OpenElement.

United Nations. *Women in a Changing Global Economy: 1994 World Survey on the Role of Women in Development.* New York: United Nations, 1995.

United Nations. *World Population to 2300.* New York, United Nations, 2004.

United Nations. *The World's Women 2000: Trends and Statistics.* Social Statistics and Indicators, Series K, no. 16. New York: United Nations, 2000.

United Nations Center for Human Settlements (Habitat). *The Challenge of Slums.* London: Earthscan, 2003.

United Nations Center for Human Settlements (Habitat). *The State of the World's Cities 2004–2005.* London: Earthscan, 2004.

United Nations Conference on Trade and Development (UNCTAD). *World Investment Report.* New York and Geneva: United Nations, annual.

United Nations. Department of Economic and Social Affairs. *World Urbanization Prospects: The 2003 Revision.* New York: United Nations, 2004.

United Nations Development Programme. *Human Development Report.* New York: Oxford University Press, annual.

United Nations. High Commissioner for Refugees. *The State of the World's Refugees.* New York: Oxford University Press, annual.

United Nations Population Fund. *Food for the Future: Women, Population and Food Security.* New York: United Nations, 1996.

United Nations Population Fund. *The State of World Population.* New York: United Nations, annual.

Unwin, Tim, ed. *Atlas of World Development.* New York: John Wiley & Sons, 1994.

U.S. Global Change Research Program, National Assessment Synthesis Team. *Climate Change Impacts on the United States: The Potential Consequences of Climate Variability and Change.* New York: Cambridge University Press, 2000.

Wagner, Philip L. and Marvin W. Mikesell. "The Themes of Cultural Geography." In *Readings in Cultural Geography,* pp. 1–24. Chicago: University of Chicago, 1962.

Waldinger, Roger, ed. *Strangers at the Gates: New Immigrants in Urban America.* Berkeley: University of California Press, 2001.

Walks, Alan R. and Larry S. Bourne. "Ghettoes in Canada's Cities? Racial Segregation, Ethnic Enclaves, and Poverty Concentration in Canadian Urban Areas." *The Canadian Geographer* 50, no. 3, 2006: 273–297.

Wallach, Bret. *Understanding the Cultural Landscape.* New York: Guilford, 2005.

Wallerstein, I. *World-Systems Analysis: An Introduction.* Durham: Duke University Press, 2006.

Warf, B. "Separated at Birth? Regional Science and Social Theory." *International Regional Science Review.* 18 (1995): 185–194.

"Water: The Power, Promise, and Turmoil of North America's Fresh Water." Special edition of *National Geographic* 184, no. 5A (November 1993).

Watts, Michael. "Political Ecology." In *The Dictionary of Human Geography,* 4th ed., edited by R. J. Johnston, Derek Gregory, Geraldine Pratt, and Michael Watts, pp. 590–592. Malden, Mass.: Blackwell, 2000.

Weber, Alfred. *Theory of the Location of Industries.* Translated by Carl J. Friedrich. Chicago: University of Chicago Press, 1929. Reissue. New York: Russell & Russell, 1971.

Weber, Peter. *Abandoned Seas: Reversing the Decline of the Oceans.* Worldwatch Paper 116. Washington, D.C.: Worldwatch Institute, 1993.

Webster, Gerald R. "Representation, Geographic Districting, and Social Justice." *Journal of Geography* 103 (2004): 111–126.

Wheeler, J.O. "From Urban/Economic to Social/Cultural Geography, 1980–2001." *Urban Geography* 23 (2002): 97–102.

Wheeler, James O., Peter Muller, Grant Thrall, and Timothy Fik. *Economic Geography.* 3rd ed. New York: Wiley, 1998.

White, Gilbert F. "Geographers in a Perilously Changing World." *Annals of the Association of American Geographers* 75 (1985): 10–15.

White, Leslie A. *The Science of Culture: A Study of Man and Civilization.* New York: Farrar, Straus and Giroux, 1969.

White, Randall. *Dark Caves, Bright Visions: Life in Ice Age Europe.* New York: American Museum of Natural History in Association with W. W. Norton & Company, 1986.

Whyte, Ian D. *Climatic Change and Human Society.* New York: John Wiley & Sons, 1996.

Wilbanks, Thomas J. "'Sustainable Development' in Geographic Perspective." *Annals of the Association of American Geographers* 84, no. 4 (1994): 541–556.

Williams, Michael, ed. *Planet Management.* The Illustrated Encyclopedia of World Geography. New York: Oxford University Press, 1993.

Williams, Raymond. *Culture.* London: Fontana, 1981.

Williams, Stephen. *Tourism Geography.* New York: Routledge, 1998.

Wood, Tim F. "Thinking in Geography." *Geography* 72 (1987): 289–299.

Wood, William B. "Forced Migration: Local Conflicts and International Dilemmas." *Annals of the Association of American Geographers* 84, no. 4 (1994): 607–634.

Women and Geography Study Group. *Feminist Geographies: Explorations in Diversity and Difference.* Harlow: Longman, 1997, 109.

World Bank. *World Development Report.* New York: Oxford University Press, annual.

World Resources Institute/International Institute for Environment and Development. *World Resources.* Biennial. New York: Oxford University Press.

Yeates, Maurice. *The North American City.* 5th ed. New York: Longman, 1997.

Young, John E. *Mining the Earth.* Worldwatch Paper 109. Washington, D.C.: Worldwatch Institute, 1992.

Zohary, Daniel, and Mari Hopf. *Domestication of Plants in the Old World.* 2nd ed. Oxford: Clarendon Press, 1993.

Zook, Matthew. *The Geography of the Internet Industry.* Malden, Mass.: Blackwell, 2003.

Zelinsky, Wilbur. *The Enigma of Ethnicity: Another American Dilemma.* Iowa City: University of Iowa Press, 2001.

The authors are indebted to the following for photographs and permission to reproduce them. Copyright for each photograph belongs to the photographer or agency credited, unless specified otherwise.

Chapter 1
Opener: DAL Images; **Figure 1.3:** (a) Archives Canada, (b) Natural Resources Canada, (c) Natural Resources Canada, Canadian Forest Services (d) 1995 Canadian Space Agency. Processed by RADARSAT International Inc.; **Figure 1.4:** (a) Reuters/CORBIS, (b) © Les Stone/CORBIS, (c) Robert Wallis/CORBIS; **Figure 1.5:** Karl Weatherly/CORBIS; **Figure 1.6:** (a) Netherlands Maritime Museum, (b) *Historical Atlas of Canada: From the Beginning to 1800.* Publisher: U of T Press; **Figure 1.12:** David Greedy/Getty Images; **Figure 1.13:** NASA; **Figure 1.14:** US Geological Survey (both).

Chapter 2
Figure 2.23: 2006 Digital Globe Inc. (both); **Figure 2.25:** Courtesy of Roger Tomlinson.

Chapter 3
Opener: Photo Link/Getty Images; **Figure 3.1:** Steve Raymer/CORBIS; **Figure 3.10:** (a) McGraw-Hill Higher Education, Inc., (b) Charles Gupton; **Figure 3.20:** (a) Atlantide Phototravel/CORBIS, (b) Professor Stephen Mann.

Chapter 4
Part Opener: AP Wide World Photos; **Opener:** Rafiqur Rahman/Reuters; **Figure 4.4:** Robert Essel/CORBIS; **Figure 4.6:** William E. Ferguson; **Figure 4.20:** Library of Congress; **Figure 4.21:** Lynn Betts, USDA, Natural Resources Conservation Centre; **Figure 4.32:** Guillermo Granja/Reuters America; **Figure 4.35:** Nathan Benn/CORBIS.

Chapter 5
Opener: M.P. Kahl/DRK Photos; **Figure 5.1:** (a) Ian Murph/Getty Images, (b) Tim McCabe, U.S. Dept. of Agriculture National Resource Conservation Service; **Figure 5.2:** Kennan Ward/CORBIS; **Figure 5.3:** (a) Walter Gans/ The Image Works, (b) AP Wide World Photos; **Figure 5.4:** (a) Dave G. Houser/Hillstrom Stock Photo, (b) Scott Bauer/USDA Agriculture Research Services; **Figure 5.5:** (a) Cary Wolinsky/ Stock Boston, (b) Yigol Pardo/Hillstrom Stock Photo, (c) John Eastcott/Momatiuk/Image, (d) Stephanie Maze; **Figure 5.6:** (a) Mark Karrass/CORBIS, (b) W. Marc Bernsau/ Image Works, (c) Cory Langley/CORBIS; **Figure 5.12:** Les Stone/Sygma/CORBIS;

Figure 5.13: Tony Freeman/PhotoEdit; **Figure 5.14:** (a) Courtesy of Jean Fellmann; **Figure 5.15:** Morton Beebe/CORBIS; **Figure 5.16:** Wolfgang Kaehler/CORBIS; **Figure 5.17:** Charles O. Rear/CORBIS; **Figure 5.20:** Joyce Gregory Wyels; **Figure 5.24:** Aubrey Land/ Valan Photos; **Figure 5.27:** Susan Reisenweaver; **Figure 5.31:** (a) Photo Link/Getty Images, (b) James Darrell/Getty Images.

Chapter 6
Figure 6.1: J. Messerschmidt/Bruce Coleman; **Figure 6.3:** (a) Joseph Pierce/Valan Photos, (b) Harold E. Green/Valan Photos; **Figure 6.5:** (b) Courtesy of Nisichawayasihk Cree Nation; **Figure 6.8:** Philippe Gontier/Image Works; **Figure 6.22:** Mark Antman/The Image Works; **Figure 6.35:** David A. Burney; **Figure 6.37:** Royalty-Free Getty Images; **Figure 6.38:** Porterfield/Chickering/Photo Researchers, Inc.; **Figure 6.39:** Fred Bruemmer/Valan Photos; **Figure 6.41:** Wolfgang Kaehler; **Figure 6.42:** Kevin R. Morris/Bohemian Nomad Picture-makers/CORBIS.

Chapter 7
Opener: AP Images; **Figure 7.1:** Perry Mastrovito/CORBIS; **Figure 7.11:** Australian Information Center; **Figure 7.13:** Fred Bavendam/Peter Arnold, Inc.; **Figure 7.14:** AP Images; **Figure 7.17:** (b) San Diego Union Tribune/John Nelson; **Figure 7.20:** (b) AP Images.

Chapter 8
Part Opener: Bob Daemmrich/Image Works; **Opener:** Mike Yamashita/Woodfin Camp; **Figure 8.1:** Scott Gilchrist/Masterfile; **Figure 8.8:** (a) William E. Ferguson, (b) Courtesy of Colin Thorn, (c) Wolfgang Kaehler; **Figure 8.10:** (a) Carl Purcell/Words and Pictures, (b) Susan Reisenweaver; **Figure 8.20:** Robert Brenner/PhotoEdit; **Page 280:** Courtesy of Union Gospel Mission, Vancouver B.C.; **Figure 8.34:** (a) David Grossman/Image Works, (b) Carl Purcell/Words and Pictures; **Figure 8.35:** Robert Cameron/Getty Images; **Figure 8.36:** Thomas Kitchin/Tom Stack & Assoc.; **Figure 8.37:** Scott Gilchrist/Masterfile; **Figure 8.39:** (a) Aubrey Diem/Valan Photos, (b) Eastcott/ Momatuik/The Image Works; **Figure 8.40:** AP Images; **Figure 8.41:** (a) Julia Waterlow/ CORBIS, (b) Jose Fuste Raga/CORBIS; **Page 291:** Yann Arthus-Bertrand/CORBIS Images; **Figure 8.43:** Byron Augustin/Tom Stack & Assoc.

Chapter 9
Opener: J. Marshall/Image Works; **Figure 9.1:** John Maher/Coyote Crossing, Inc.; **Figure 9.3:**

Mark Gibson/Gibson Stock Photography; **Figure 9.9:** Wolfgang Kaehler; **Figure 9.10:** Sean Sprague; **Figure 9.13:** Bill Gillette/Stock Boston; **Figure 9.19:** Jim Pickerell/Stock Boston; **Figure 9.22:** Wolfgang Kaehler; **Figure 9.23:** Johng C. Malinowski/Human Landscape Studio; **Figure 9.24:** Jim Wark/ Lonely Planet Images; **Figure 9.27:** Cameramann International; **Figure 9.29:** Larry Tackett/ Tom Stack & Assoc.; **Figure 9.33:** Cameramann International; **Figure 9.34:** Thomas Kitchin/ Valan Photos; **Figure 9.35:** Jim Richardson/ CORBIS; **Figure 9.36:** Bruce McAlllister/Getty Images; **Figure 9.37:** UN/DPI Photo.

Chapter 10
Figure 10.6: Rick Browne/Photo Researchers, Inc.; **Figure 10.14:** Cameramann International; **Figure 10.15:** Sharon Stewart; **Figure 10.16:** (Nokia) Chris Stowers/Panos Pictures, (Ford) Steven Harris/Newsmakers/Getty Images, (IBM) Deborah Harse/Image Works, (Nestlé) Mark Henley/Panos Pictures, (Sony) Mark Henley/Panos Pictures, (British Petroleum) Caroline Penn/Panos Pictures; **Figure 10.25:** Laurence Fordyce; Eye Ubiquitous/CORBIS; **Page 369:** © Digital Vision.

Chapter 11
Opener: David Wells/Image Works; **Figure 11.1:** Dilip Mehta/Contact Press Images; **Figure 11.2:** (a) Cameramann International, (b) Jason Clay/Anthro Photo File; **Figure 11.4:** Wolfgang Kaehler; **Figure 11.5:** Rob Crandall/ The Image Works; **Page 389:** © Robert Landau/ CORBIS; **Figure 11.9:** Betty Press/Woodfin Camp; **Figure 11.10:** Bettmann/CORBIS; **Figure 11.11:** Sean Sprague/Panos Pictures; **Figure 11.14:** AP Images; **Figure 11.15:** Louise Grubb/The Image Works; **Figure 11.17:** David Hiser/Stone/Getty; **Figure 11.20:** Liba Taylor/CORBIS Images.

Chapter 12
Part Opener: Bettmann/CORBIS; **Opener:** Clive Shirley/Panos Pictures; **Page 414:** Courtesy of UBC Public Affairs; **Figure 12.2:** Rick Maiman/Stgma/CORBIS; **Figure 12.4:** (b) William E. Ferguson; **Figure 12.6:** Martin Wendler/Peter Arnold; **Figure 12.14:** J. Baylor Roberts/National Geographic Image Collection; **Figure 12.15:** San Diego Union-Tribune/Don Kohlbauer; **Figure 12.17:** Roger A. Clark/ Photo Researchers; **Figure 12.21:** D. Falconer/ Photolink/Getty Images; **Figure 12.23:** Bettmann/CORBIS; **Figure 12.24:** Sergio Moraes/Reuters.

Cassava, 310
Caste, **199**
Cathedrals, 198*f*
CBD. *See* Central business districts;
    Convention of Biological
    Diversity
CBR. *See* Crude birth rate
CCD. *See* Central Cultural District
CDR. *See* Crude death rate
Census agglomerations areas (CA), 256
Census metropolitan areas (CMA), 116,
    256
Census of Canada, 34–35
    census agglomeration (CA), 35*f*
    census consolidated subdivision, 35*f*
    census division, 35*f*
    census metropolitan area (CMA), 35*f*
    census subdivision, 35*f*
    census tracts, 35*f*
    dissemination area, 34*f*
    dissemination block, 34*f*
Central business districts (CBD), 172, 173,
    266, 268
Central cities, **256**
    See also Cities, central
Central Cultural District (CCD), 287
Centralized pattern, 22, 23*f*
Centrally planned economies, 151
Central places, **263**
    and cities, 261, 263–265
    hierarchy of, 265
    pattern of, 264*f*
Central place theory, **263**
Central planning, 360*f*
Centrifugal forces, **222**, 225–227
Centripetal forces, **222**
Certification bodies, 319
Chain migration, **112**, **174**
Champlain, Samuel de, 288*f*
Channelized migration, **113**
Charlottetown Accord, 231
Chemical industry, 151
Cheslatta Indian Band, 431
Chicago, Illinois, 172*f*, 272*f*
Childbirth, 98
Children
    child deaths, 398
    childhood diseases, 398
    child mortality, 396*t*
China
    agriculture, 307, 318–319
    Chinese ideographs, 178*f*
    culture hearths, 144
    economic competition, 233
    globalization, 67
    infrastructure, 265
    manufacturing, 361
    market system, 320*f*
    outsourcing to, 353
    population control, 94
    religion, 201
    sex ratio, 100, 101
    Shang kingdom, 145
    subsistence agriculture, 306
    urbanization, 290–291

villages, 306
    water supply, 430, 432
Cholera, 441
Choropleth map, 47, 48*f*
Christaller, Walter, **263**
Christianity, 134–135, **196**–197, 198*f*
    See also Religion
Chronic disease, **441**
Church, the, 223
CIDA. *See* Canadian International
    Development Agency
Circular and cumulative causation, 258,
    380
Circulation, 71
Cities, **256**
    Canadian, 88, 282–286
    categories of, 258, 260–261
    culture hearths, 146
    definition of, 255
    developing world, 287–293, 289*f*
    East European, 287, 288*f*
    economic base of, 258–259
    and empowerment, 283
    functions of, 258–260
    gateway cities, 174, 279
    green cities, 283
    immigration, 285
    institutional controls, 272–273
    internal characteristics of, 265–273
    Latin American, 292
    mass transit, 266
    mega-cities, 252
    nature of, 255–256
    network cities, 265
    outer cities, 274
    pedestrian cities, 21
    primate cities, 262–263
    social areas of, 270
    special-function, 261
    structure of, 269*f*
    United States, 283–286
    West European, 286–287
    and women, 279
    world cities, 261–262
Cities, central, **256**
    as centralized pattern, 23*f*
    change in, 277–278
    constriction of, 278
    expansion of, 281–282
    jurisdiction of, 275
    revitalization of, 278–281, 281*f*
Civil conflict, 140
Civilizations
    competition between, 235
    rise of, 20, 144
    See also Culture hearths
Clarity Act, 231
Class, **156**, 270–271
Cleveland, Ohio, 267–268, 268*f*
Climate, 79, 443
Climate change
    adapting to, 418–420, 418*f*
    Climate Change Science Program, 416
    and health, 443
    science of, 415

summits, 419
    See also Environment
Cluster, 271
Clustered, 22, 22*f*
Cluster village, 253*f*
CMA. *See* Census metropolitan areas
CMEA. *See* Council of Mutual Economic
    Assistance
CMHC. *See* Canadian Mortgage and
    Housing Corporation
Coal
    coal-burning power stations, 421
    and Industrial Revolution, 359
    mining of, 329
    reserves, 330*t*
    and transportation costs, 330*f*
Cod industry, 337
    See also Fishing
Cohort measures, **92**
Colonialism, **211**
    African economy, 362
    cities, 262, 264*f*, 288, 292*f*
    crop plants, 149
    cultural boundaries, 211, 212*f*
    forests, 423
    innovation, 135
    languages, 181, 184, 188
    ministates, 215
    neocolonialism, 380
    place names, 191–192
    power, 232
    states, 210, 213*f*
    superimposed boundaries, 219
    underdevelopment, 379–380
    world-systems analysis, 60
Columbus, Ohio, 267
Command centres, 262
Commercial agriculture, 311–320
    extensive commercial agriculture,
    314–316
    intensive commercial agriculture, **314**
    model of location, 312–314
    production controls, 311––312
    special crops, 316–318
Commercial economies, **299**
Commodity prices, 332
Common Market, 238, 239
Commonwealth of Nations, 211, 232, 240
Communal dwelling, 252
Communal settlements, 252
Communication
    individual communication, 75
    and industries, 279
    and information flows, 74–75
    long-distance, 74
    mass communication, 75–76
    and quaternary activities, 369
    and state cohesion, 225
Communism, 151
Commuters, 285
Comparative advantage, **351**, 352*f*, 354, 370
Competition theory, 137
Competitive equilibrium, 348*f*
Complementarity, **65**, 65*f*, 113
Complementary regions, 263–264, 264*f*

List of Maps

List of Maps